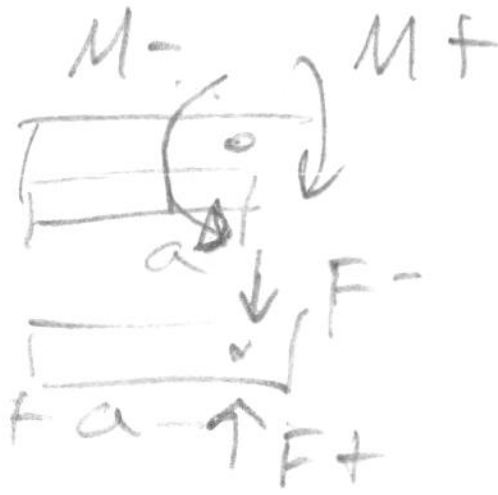

EIy'' EIy' EI

$M\langle x-a\rangle^0$ $M\langle x-a\rangle$ $\frac{1}{2}M\langle$

$F\langle x-a\rangle$ $\frac{F}{2}\langle x-a\rangle^2$ $\frac{F}{6}$

Unit Conversion Factors

Quantity	U. S. Customary	SI Equivalent
Acceleration	ft/s^2 in/s^2	$0.3048\ m/s^2$ $0.0254\ m/s^2$
Area	ft^2 in^2	$0.0929\ m^2$ $645.2\ mm^2$
Distributed Load	lb/ft lb/in.	14.59 N/m 0.1751 N/mm
Energy	ft-lb	1.356J
Force	kip = 1000 lb lb	4.448 kN 4.448N
Impulse	lb-s	4.448 N-s
Length	ft in mi	0.3048 m 25.40 mm 1.609 km
Mass	lb mass slug ton mass	0.4536 kg 14.59 kg 907.2 kg
Moments or Torque	ft-lb in-lb	1.356 N-m 0.1130 N-m
Area Moment of Inertia	in^4	$0.4162 \times 10^6\ mm^4$
Power	ft-lb/s hp	1.356 W 745.7 W
Stress and Pressure	lb/ft^2 lb/in^2 (psi) ksi = 1000 psi	47.88 Pa 6.895 kPa 6.895 MPa
Velocity	ft/s in/s mi/h (mph)	0.3048 m/s 0.0254 m/s 0.4470 m/s
Volume	ft^3 in^3 gal	$0.02832\ m^3$ $16.39\ cm^3$ 3.785 L
Work or Energy	ft-lb	1.356 J

N, m, Pa
KN, m, KPa
N, mm, MPa
KN, mm, GPa
KN·mm = N·m
KN·m ≠ N·mm
lb, in, psi
Kip, in, Ksi
1 Kip = 1000 lb
1 Ksi = 1000 psi

$\frac{KN}{m} = \frac{N}{mm}$

MECHANICS II

MECHANICS OF MATERIALS +

JAMES W. DALLY

ROBERT J. BONENBERGER, JR.

University of Maryland, College Park

College House Enterprises, LLC
Knoxville, Tennessee

The manuscript was prepared with 11 point Times New Roman font. Publishing and Printing Inc., located in Knoxville, TN, printed this textbook from pdf files.

College House Enterprises, LLC.
5713 Glen Cove Drive
Knoxville, TN 37919, U. S. A.
Phone and FAX (865) 558 6111
email jwd@www.collegehousebooks.com
Visit our web site at http://www.collegehousebooks.com

13 Digit ISBN 978-9792581-5-2
10 Digit ISBN 0-9792581-5-4

This book is for Anne
who has shared Jim's dreams for so many years

and to the memory of Ann and Bob
who had encouraged and supported Bob until they were called.

ABOUT THE AUTHORS

James W. Dally obtained a Bachelor of Science and a Master of Science degree, both in Mechanical Engineering from the Carnegie Institute of Technology. He obtained a Doctoral degree in mechanics from the Illinois Institute of Technology. He has taught at Cornell University, Illinois Institute of Technology, the U. S. Air Force Academy and served as Dean of Engineering at the University of Rhode Island. He is currently a Glenn L. Martin Institute Professor of Engineering (Emeritus) at the University of Maryland, College Park.

Dr. Dally has also held positions at the Mesta Machine Co., IIT Research Institute and IBM. He is a Fellow of the American Society for Mechanical Engineers, Society for Experimental Mechanics, and the American Academy of Mechanics. He was appointed as an honorary member of the Society for Experimental Mechanics in 1983 and elected to the National Academy of Engineering in 1984. Professor Dally was selected by his peers to receive the Senior Faculty Outstanding Teaching Award in the College of Engineering and the Distinguish Scholar Teacher Award from the University. He was also a member of the University of Maryland team receiving the 1996 Outstanding Educator Award sponsored by the Boeing Co.

Professor Dally has co-authored several other books: *Experimental Stress Analysis, Photoelastic Coatings, Instrumentation for Engineering Measurements, Packaging of Electronic Systems, Production Engineering and Manufacturing, Mechanical Design of Electronic Systems, and Introduction to Engineering Design, Books 1, 2, 3, 4, 5, 6, 7, 8 and 9.* He has authored or coauthored about 200 scientific papers and holds five patents.

Robert J. Bonenberger, Jr. obtained B.S.E., M.S. and Ph.D. degrees in Mechanical Engineering from the University of Maryland, Baltimore County and College Park campuses. He has taught undergraduate and graduate students in mechanics, strength of materials, and experimental stress analysis. Currently, he is an Assistant Research Scientist and Lecturer in the Clark School of Engineering at the University of Maryland, College Park.

Previously, Dr. Bonenberger worked in the Fracture Mechanics Section at the Naval Research Laboratory, both as a postdoctoral fellow and as a contract employee. He is a member of the American Society for Mechanical Engineers, Society for Experimental Mechanics, American Society for Materials, and American Society for Engineering Education. His research interests include material behavior at high strain rates, experimental stress analysis, and fracture mechanics. He has authored or co-authored 25 scientific papers.

PREFACE

This textbook is the second of two written to support an integrated course offering for Statics and Mechanics of Materials. Hopefully the integration of the topics of these two closely related courses will make the learning experience for the students easier and more meaningful. The Mechanics of Materials textbook is a revision of a part of the book titled Design Analysis of Structural Elements, which was too long and heavy and required a supplement for the homework exercises. The textbook for Statics published in 2009 was also drawn from part of Design Analysis of Structural Elements. Both, Statics ++ and Mechanics of Materials +, have been revised by reorganization of materials based on reactions of instructors and students. Exercises have also been added to eliminate the need for a supplementary problems book. The content of Design Analysis of Structural Elements has been divided into two volumes to reduce the size and the weight of a book covering both topics in considerable detail. The title has been changed to reflect the name of the courses at most Universities in the U. S.

The Statics course provides the first exposure of engineering students to the study of mechanics. While Statics is a relatively simple subject, many students find it difficult, and they often perform far below our expectations. In an effort to improve the curriculum, the Keystone instructors[1] at the University of Maryland have been working to enhance the student's learning experience when studying the courses in mechanics. The Statics ++ and Mechanics of Materials + textbooks indicates some of the changes in the philosophy adopted by the faculty, when presenting the subject matter traditionally offered in introductory mechanics courses.

The changes in the philosophy were based on five premises:

1. Present the fundamental concepts in a more interesting manner.
    - Change the approach to make it more realistic and less abstract.
    - Couple the mechanics content tightly to design.
2. Provide a smooth transition from the Introduction to Engineering course to Design Analysis of Structural Components that encompasses both Mechanics I: Statics and Mechanics II: Mechanics of Materials.
    - Incorporate a hands-on experience including design, construction and testing of a model of a construction project.
    - Provide the analysis methods and the scaling relations for verifying the safety of the design of this model.
3. Emphasize modeling structural components by stressing throughout the text the importance of preparing a complete free body diagram (FBD).
    - Show the method for constructing complete FBDs.
    - Integrate the FBD with the application of the equilibrium equations.
    - Approach the solution of equilibrium problems with equilibrium relations based on force and moment components.
4. Integrate the content of Statics with that of Mechanics of Materials.
    - The concepts of normal and shearing stresses are introduced early in Statics.
    - Topics associated with Statics and with Mechanics of Materials are merged in whenever possible in the Statics ++ textbook.

---

[1] The Keystone instructors have been selected from the faculty because of their recognized teaching abilities.

- The content typically found in Mechanics of Materials is presented with a heavy emphasis on design.
- Fracture mechanics, a topic new to most undergraduates, is introduced in the Mechanics of Materials + textbook.

5. Emphasize the design of structural components for safety.
   - Stress is compared to strength to give safety factors for components.
   - Behavior of engineering materials is introduced and physical properties such as strength and modulus of elasticity are described.
   - Sizing of structural components for safety and cost are demonstrated.

We began developing notes for the first edition of Design Analysis of Structural Elements with a pilot offering in the spring semester of 1998. Many revisions were made before a limited first edition of the textbook was published in the summer of 1999. The second edition was published in 2000 and was used by about a thousand students. The third edition, written in 2001, included six new chapters to expand the coverage necessary for a complete Mechanics of Materials course. The fourth edition, published in 2004, was similar to the third edition except for relatively small changes. Since that time, about 4,000 students have used the 3rd and 4th editions of Design Analysis of Structural Elements.

Errors discovered during this extensive usage have been corrected; however, errors always occur even with careful proof reading by many diligent people. We would greatly appreciate students and instructors calling any errors they find to our attention. The e-mail address of one of the authors is given on the copyright page.

ACKNOWLEDGEMENTS

As is always the case when major changes are made to the curriculum, the College administrators must lead the way. We are indeed fortunate to have several administrators who not only supported this effort, but also insisted that the mechanics offerings be markedly improved. They seek not only a much more favorable educational experience for the students, but also much better understanding and retention of the course content. We thank Dr. William L. Fourney, Chair of the Keystone Program, Dr. Avram Bar-Cohen, Chair of the Mechanical Engineering Department, and Dr. Ali Haghani, Chair of the Civil Engineering Department for their support. Particular thanks are due to Dr. Nariam Farvardin who established the Keystone Program when he was Dean of the College of Engineering and to Darrel Pines, the new Dean, who has continued the strong emphasis on continuously improving the educational experience for our engineering students..

Special thanks are due to several individuals for their significant contributions to the development of this textbook. Dr. Bill Fourney led our efforts to change the curriculum to provide a more effective approach for presenting Statics and Mechanics of Materials so students would better understand the material and retain this knowledge. Bill has stayed with the project for more than 10 years, taught sections of students every semester, and provided the leadership needed to keep others involved and interested. Dr. Hugh Bruck also made major contributions in the second edition. He also taught an early pilot section and made many excellent suggestions for changes in the sequence of the content.

Many instructors teaching the course made valuable suggestions for improvements to the textbook. These include: Dr. Mary Bowden, Dr. Hugh Bruck, Dr. James Duncan, Dr. Bongtae Han, Dr. Kwan-Nan Yeh, Mr. Christopher Baldwin, and Mr. Thomas Beigel of the University of Maryland, College

Park; Dr. Abhijit Nagchaudhuri of the University of Maryland, Eastern Shore; and Dr. Asif Shakur, of Salisbury State University.

William Rudd, former Dean of the School of Architecture at the University of Tennessee, was extremely helpful in providing several excellent photographs of bridges that were used as illustrations in Appendix F. Jim Dally took the cover photograph in the mid-1970s at Illinois Institute of Technology. It is a dark field isochromatic fringe pattern of a tube sheet, which shows the stress concentration about the holes when the sheet is loaded in uniaxial tension.

James W. Dally
Robert J. Bonenberger
College Park, MD

Summer 2010

CONTENTS

CHAPTER 8 BUCKLING OF COLUMNS

CHAPTER 9 STRESS CONCENTRATIONS

CHAPTER 10 ENERGY METHODS

CHAPTER 11 FRACTURE MECHANICS

APPENDICES

LIST OF SYMBOLS

A	area
%A	percent reduction in area
a	acceleration vector
a, b, c	dimensions
a_{CR}	critical crack length
C	constant, center dimension
D	diameter
d	diameter or distance
%e	percent elongation
E	elastic modulus or Young's modulus
E	strain energy
E	modulus scale factor
e	eccentricity
e	strain energy density
F	force magnitude
F	force as a vector
F_f	friction force or failure force
FBD	free body diagram
g	gravitational constant
G	shear modulus
GF	gage factor
H	horizontal shear force
HP	horsepower
h	height
I	moment of inertia
J	polar moment of inertia
K	stress concentration factor
K_I	stress intensity factor
K_{IC}	plane strain fracture toughness
K_c	fracture toughness
k	number, spring rate
L	length dimension
L	load scale factor
ln	natural logarithm
M	moment magnitude
M_Y	yield moment
M_L	limit moment
M	moment as a vector
M	multiplier, momentum
MA	mechanical advantage
MOS	margin of safety
m	mass, subscript for model
N	normal force, number, Newton, RPM
n	number
P	internal force
P_{CR}	critical buckling force
p	pressure, subscript for prototype
Q	first moment of the area, flow rate
q	distributed loading
r	radius, radius of gyration, distance
r	position vector
R	reaction force, radius, resistance
S	geometric scale factor
s	distance or dimension
S_{design}	design strength
S_f	fatigue strength
S_y	yield strength
S_{ys}	yield strength in shear
S_u	ultimate tensile strength
S_{us}	ultimate tensile strength in shear
SF	safety factor
SE	structural efficiency
SR	slenderness ratio
T	temperature, torque
t	time
u	unit vector
U	Distortional energy
V	shear force
v	velocity vector
V	volume
W	weight, watt
W	work
w	width dimension
x, y z	Cartesian coordinates
Z	section modulus
α	temperature coefficient of expansion
α, β, γ	direction cosines
Δ	delta
δ	deflection or displacement
ε	strain
ε_T	true strain
ϕ	angle of friction, angle of twist
γ	shear strain, density
κ	curvature
π	3.1416 radians
μ	coefficient of friction
ν	Poisson's ratio
ρ	radius of curvature
Σ	Summation sign
σ	stress
σ_a	alternating cyclic stress
σ_B	Bearing stress
σ_{design}	design stress
σ_f	failure stress
σ_m	mean cyclic stress
σ_T	true stress
σ_{fail}	stress to produce failure
σ_{yield}	stress to produce yielding
θ	angle
θ_s	angle of repose
τ	shear stress
ω	angular velocity

CHAPTER 1

REVIEW OF STATICS

1.1 INTRODUCTION

The subject of mechanics is usually divided into four different courses, which include:

Statics, Dynamics, Mechanics of Materials and Fluid Mechanics

Statics and dynamics both deal with rigid bodies that are subjected to a system of forces. The study of statics, involves the determination of either internal and/or external forces acting on a structural element that is in a state of equilibrium (usually at rest). In dynamics, the forces acting on the body produce motion and the body accelerates or decelerates. The analysis in dynamics deals with determining position, velocity (angular or linear) and acceleration as some function of time. Newton's laws guide studies of all branches of mechanics[1]. Consider Newton's second law:

$$\sum \mathbf{F} = \frac{d}{dt}(mv) \qquad (1.1)$$

where $\Sigma\mathbf{F}$ is the sum of all of the forces acting on the rigid body, m is the mass of the body, **v** is the velocity and d/dt is the derivative operator[2].

When dividing the study of mechanics into four separate subjects, educators considered the special situation where the body's velocity is either constant or zero and developed **statics** based on this simplification. In this special situation, Eq. (1.1) reduces to:

$$\sum \mathbf{F} = 0 \qquad (1.2)$$

In the study of both statics and dynamics, the material from which the body is fabricated is not a concern, providing the body remains essentially rigid when the forces are applied. However, in the

[1] Sir Isaac Newton (1642-1727) formulated three laws of motion and the law of universal gravitational attraction.

[2] Symbols in bold font indicate vector quantities.

study of mechanics of materials, the deformation of the body is an essential consideration. Two assumptions are made in studying mechanics of materials — (1) the deformations are small, and (2) plane sections remain plane. These assumptions enable the determination of the distribution of internal forces and stresses in a body. The material from which the body is fabricated is of critical importance in mechanics of materials. Also, the deformations of the body due to the forces are markedly affected by the rigidity of its material. The behavior of the body, whether it fails or not, depends on its material's strength.

1.2 STATICS AND MECHANICS OF MATERIALS

This textbook integrates two closely related subjects in mechanics, namely **statics** and **mechanics of materials**. In studying **statics**, it is assumed that the body under consideration is perfectly rigid, and does not deform when forces are applied. Solutions to statics problems involve determining **external forces** acting on some structures and the **internal forces** developed in others by using only **free body diagrams** and the **equilibrium equations**. Solutions for forces acting on bodies in equilibrium involve only three basic steps:

- Construct a complete set of free body diagrams.
- Apply the appropriate equations of equilibrium.
- Execute the mathematics required to solve one or more equilibrium equations.

Mechanics of materials is an extension of statics, which accounts for the effect of **material deformations**[3] on the **internal stresses** generated in a body. Solutions to problems that arise in mechanics of materials involve the same three basic steps, but two additional steps are required. These steps are to accommodate the effect of the deformations on the distribution of the internal stresses:

- Construct a complete set of free body diagrams.
- Apply the appropriate equations of equilibrium.
- Assume the geometry of the deformations (plane sections remain plane).
- Employ the appropriate relations between stress and strain.
- Execute the mathematics required in solving the equations.

It is evident that statics and mechanics of materials are closely related. The equilibrium equations from statics must be used to determine the internal forces before beginning to solve typical problems in mechanics of materials. In studying mechanics of materials, the concepts of stress and strain are quickly encountered. Mathematically these concepts are somewhat complex because they are tensor quantities, but physically they are simple and easily understood. Stress is a concept based on the equilibrium of a portion of a body that is produced by sectioning. The internal force acting on a section cut is developed by stresses distributed over the area exposed by that cut.

---

[3] In mechanics of materials, we assume the deformations are so small that they do not significantly affect the magnitude or the direction of the internal and external forces acting on the body.

Strain, on the other hand, is a geometric concept. Strain is determined by the change in geometry that occurs when a body deforms under load. When considered individually, both stress and strain are independent of the body's material. It is only when a relation connecting stress and strain is written that the material properties must be considered.

Materials used in constructing various structures are usually ignored in the study of statics. The equilibrium equations are identical for all materials, and the internal and external forces for statically determinant structures[4] do not depend upon the structure's material. Materials are much more important in studies of the mechanics of materials. Stress and strain are usually related in solutions, and the elastic constants that describe the rigidity of the materials must be employed. In addition, the margin of safety for a structure subjected to specific loading is often predicted. In these predictions of safety or structural failure, the appropriate **"strength"** of the material is required.

In this textbook, the physical aspects of problems solved using principles of both statics and mechanics of materials are stressed. It is essential that complete free body diagrams be constructed to model the structure and to define the unknown forces. Understanding the equations of equilibrium is as important as the use of **vector algebra** to solve them. Of course, it is essential that the equations resulting from the application of the principle of equilibrium be solved correctly.

1.3 NEWTON'S LAWS

The first of Newton's laws is derived from Eq. (1.2) and may be written as:

$$\mathbf{F_1} + \mathbf{F_2} + \ldots\ldots + \mathbf{F_n} = 0 \qquad (1.2a)$$

where n forces are acting on the body.

Equation (1.2a), in one form or the other, is used extensively in both statics and mechanics of materials, when the **equilibrium equations** are written. The vector representation of Eq. (1.2a) may be recast by writing the equivalent **scalar equations** as:

$$\Sigma F_x = 0 \qquad \Sigma F_y = 0 \qquad \text{and} \qquad \Sigma F_z = 0 \qquad (1.2b)$$

$$F_{1x} + F_{2x} + \quad + F_{nx} = 0 \quad F_{1y} + F_{2y} + \quad + F_{ny} = 0 \quad \text{and} \quad F_{1x} + F_{2x} + \ldots + F_{nx} = 0 \quad (1.2c)$$

The direction of the forces in this equation have been taken into account by considering only those forces in either the x, y or z directions. When the forces are constrained to these three directions, the **scalar form of the equilibrium equations** is employed. However, when the forces act in directions other than these directions, the vectors must first be decomposed into their **components** acting in the x, y and directions before they can be used in the scalar equations.

Newton's second law $\Sigma\ \mathbf{F} = (d/dt)(m\mathbf{v}) = m\mathbf{a}$ is the equation used most frequently in the study of **dynamics**. When the sum of the forces is not zero, the body of mass m is subjected to an acceleration **a**. The study of **dynamics** in many engineering programs is scheduled later in the curriculum.

Newton's third law is called the law of action and reaction. The concept of active and reactive forces is illustrated in Fig. 1.1. In this illustration, the sphere is in equilibrium under the

---

[4] Structures are classified as statically determinant if the reactions at their supports may be determined using only the equations of equilibrium.

action of two forces — one is the weight W due to gravity that acts downward and the other is the reaction force acting upward at its contact point. The reaction force R is equal in magnitude to the weight W, but opposite in direction. When any two bodies are in contact, the two forces that develop at the contact point are equal in magnitude and opposite in direction.

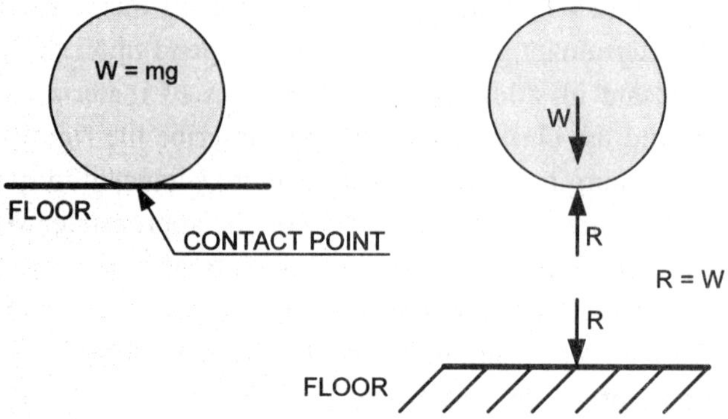

Fig. 1.1 The active force W due to gravity produces an equal and opposite reaction force R at the contact point.

1.4 FORCES

Statics involves a study of external forces that act on a body and internal forces that act within the body. In studying statics the external forces acting on a body, and the internal forces developed by stresses within the body, are determined. Some forces occurring under static (steady state) conditions include: gravitational, pressure acting over a defined area, friction, magnetic and electrostatic. In addition, forces developed under dynamic conditions are referred to as inertial forces and include: centrifugal, centripetal and Coriolis.

Let's examine the forces due to gravity because they are usually the most important forces in engineering applications. We continuously work and expend huge amounts of energy to overcome gravitational forces. Gravitational forces are the primary concern when designing building and bridge structures against failure by collapse or rupture. Even in vehicle design where dynamic forces are significant, gravitational forces are critical in the design of the vehicle's structure and its power train.

Weight is a force produced by the Earth's gravitational pull on the mass of our body as illustrated in Fig. 1.2. The force on a body due to gravity is given by:

$$F = G\, m_e\, m_b / R_e^2 \tag{1.3}$$

where m_e is the mass of the Earth, m_b is the mass of a body, R_e is the radius of the Earth, and G is the universal gravitational constant (6.673×10^{-11} $m^3/(kg\text{-}s^2)$).

In writing Eq. (1.3) it was assumed that Earth bound bodies, either those of people or objects at or near the Earth's surface, are very small compared to the radius of the Earth, which is 3,960 mi. or 6.37×10^6 m. Collecting together all of the quantities in Eq. (1.3) that are related to the Earth, and setting them equal to g_e gives:

$$g_e = Gm_e / R_e^2 \tag{1.4}$$

Note that g_e is the **gravitational constant** equal to 32.17 ft/s^2 or 9.807 m/s^2. The subscript will be dropped in subsequent discussions of the gravitational constant, with the understanding that g is to be applied to Earth bound bodies.

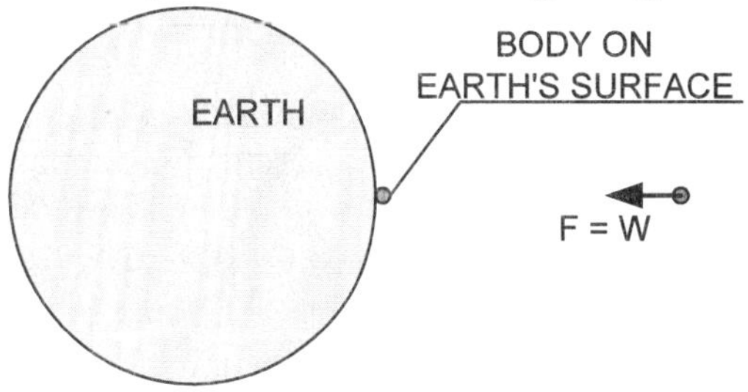

Fig. 1.2 Bodies on Earth's surface are small relative to the Earth's radius.

Combining Eq. (1.3) and Eq. (1.4) gives:

$$F = m_b\, g = W \qquad (1.5)$$

From these definitions, it is clear that the units of g are ft/s^2 or m/s^2. When the weight of an object is measured, its weight is essentially constant regardless of location if the object remains Earth bound. However, the constant quantity in Eq. (1.5) is not the weight W, but the mass m_b. To prove this statement, consider the weight of a known mass on the moon. It is known that a person weighs much less on the moon — about one sixth as much as here on Earth. Because the mass m_b is constant, the object weighs less because the gravitational constant for the moon is only about g/6. The smaller gravitational constant for the moon is due to its smaller mass when compared to the Earth's mass. The mass of a body is the same whether it is on the moon, Mars, Earth or anywhere in space.

1.5 BASIC QUANTITIES, UNITS, PREFIXES AND CONVERSIONS

In the study of mechanics, four basic quantities — length, time, force and mass — are encountered. These quantities are shown with their respective units for the SI and the U. S. Customary systems of units in the table found on the inside back cover of this book.

The basic units are not independent because they must be **dimensionally homogenous** in any equation. For example, the dimension homogeneity of Eq. (1.1), is maintained by defining the units for length, time and mass in the **SI** system, and then deriving the remaining basic unit for the force, the **newton**, in terms of length, time and mass. For the **U. S. Customary** system, the basic unit for mass, the **slug**, is derived in terms of the units for length, time, and force.

In the International System of Units (SI), length is given in meters (m), the time in seconds (s), and the mass in kilograms (kg). The unit for force is called a newton (N) in honor of Sir Isaac. The newton is derived from Eq. (1.1) so that a force of 1 N will impart an acceleration of 1 m/s^2 to a mass of 1 kg [1 N = (1 kg) (1 m/s^2)]. For dimension homogeneity, it is clear that N is equivalent to (kg-m)/s^2. In the SI system the gravitational constant g = 9.807 m/s^2. With this value of the acceleration due to gravity on Earth, the weight of a mass of 1 kg is:

$$W = mg = (1\text{kg})(9.807\ \text{m/s}^2) = 9.807\ \text{N} \qquad (a)$$

In the U. S. Customary System, length is given in feet (ft), the force in pounds (lb), and the time in seconds (s). The unit for mass is called a slug, which is derived from Eq. (1.1) so that a force of 1 lb will impart an acceleration of 1 ft/s^2 to a mass of 1 slug [1 lb = (1 slug)(1 ft/s^2)]. For dimension homogeneity, it is clear that a slug is equivalent to (lb-s^2)/ft. In the U. S. Customary System the gravitational constant g = 32.17 ft/s^2. With this value of the acceleration, the mass of a body weighing 1 lb is:

$$m = W/g = 1 \text{ lb}/(32.17 \text{ ft/s}^2) = 0.03108 \text{ slug} \qquad \text{(b)}$$

In addition to the basic quantities, several other quantities encountered in studies of statics and mechanics of materials are presented in another table shown on the inside of the back cover.

Often the metric prefixes are employed in expressing numerical results. For example, a metric prefix M with the unit for stress (Pa) is often employed. Metric prefixes are useful in dealing with either very large or very small numbers. Accordingly, it is common practice to employ them together with the symbol for the units (e.g. MPa). A table of the metric prefixes is found inside the back cover of this book.

The quantities in these tables are presented in terms of the basic units for length, time and force. However, in practice other units are often employed. For instance, moments may be expressed as in-lb instead of ft-lb, and a stress expressed as MPa instead of Pa or psi (lb/in^2) instead of (lb/ft^2). It is fortunate that strain is a dimensionless quantity and it is not necessary to convert from one system of units to another, or to convert from one unit to another within the same system. A table showing the factors used to convert from U S Customary to SI units is found inside the front cover of this book.

1.6 SIGNIFICANT FIGURES

With a hand-held calculator, numerical results with ten or more figures are common. These results are misleading because the data used to calculate them are rarely accurate to more than 0.2% or one part in 500. To avoid the implication of fictitious accuracies, it is recommended that the results from a calculator be written with four significant figures. This practice yields a computational accuracy of 1/1000 or 0.1% and is consistent with the accuracy of the physical data and the analytical model upon which the formula is based.

1.7 SCALARS, VECTORS AND TENSORS

Quantities of three types — **scalars, vectors** and **tensors** — arise in the study of Mechanics. In ordinary life it is not essential to recognize the difference among them. A person is comfortable if he or she has friends, food, shelter and some money. Incidentally, friends, food, shelter and money are all scalar quantities, because it is only necessary to count them. Other quantities encountered in engineering that are scalar include: area, energy, length, mass, moment of inertia, power, volume, work, etc.

Scalar quantities are the easiest of the three types with which to work. Simple arithmetic operations (add, subtract, multiply and divide) are sufficient in manipulating scalar quantities. However, arithmetic operations are not sufficient for manipulating vectors and tensors, because additional mathematical operations and descriptions must be introduced to manipulate equations involving these quantities.

Unfortunately, both vector and tensor quantities are found in mechanics. They are not **that difficult**, but non-scalar quantities must be recognized and treated appropriately. Mathematics beyond arithmetic is required when dealing with vectors and tensor quantities. For example, vector quantities require two descriptors — magnitude and direction. The magnitude indicates the size of the quantity, and the direction gives its orientation. Quantities that require vector representation for their complete description include: acceleration, force, impulse, momentum, moments, velocity, etc.

A typical vector quantity, such as a force, is represented with an arrow as shown in Fig. 1.3. The length of the arrow is proportional to the magnitude of the force, and its inclination relative to an x-y coordinate system gives its direction. Vectors are used extensively in statics, and it is necessary to accommodate both their magnitude and directions in the solution of many different types of equilibrium problems. Vectors are **independent** of the orientation chosen for the x-y coordinate system. However, the scalar value of the vector's direction and the magnitude of its components relative to the x and y directions are **dependent** on the orientation of the reference coordinate system. This property is important when coordinate systems are selected to solve equilibrium problems, because choices can be made that simplify a solution without changing the physical description of the problem.

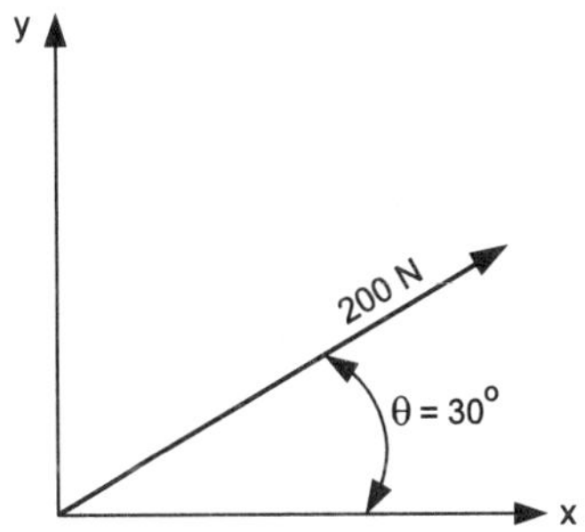

Fig. 1.3 A force vector with a magnitude of 200 N and direction of 30° relative to the x-axis.

Tensor quantities are more difficult to describe than vector quantities because their complete description requires information pertaining to three characteristics. Like vectors, the magnitude and direction of a tensor quantity must be specified. In addition, the orientation of the plane upon which a tensor quantity acts must be specified. For example, stresses σ are tensor quantities. The three characteristics — magnitude, direction, and the orientation of the plane upon which the stresses act — are illustrated in Fig. 1.4. The round bar is loaded with forces in the axial direction. A section cut exposes an internal surface (plane) of the bar normal to its axis, where stresses act in the axial direction with a magnitude of 1,000 kPa.

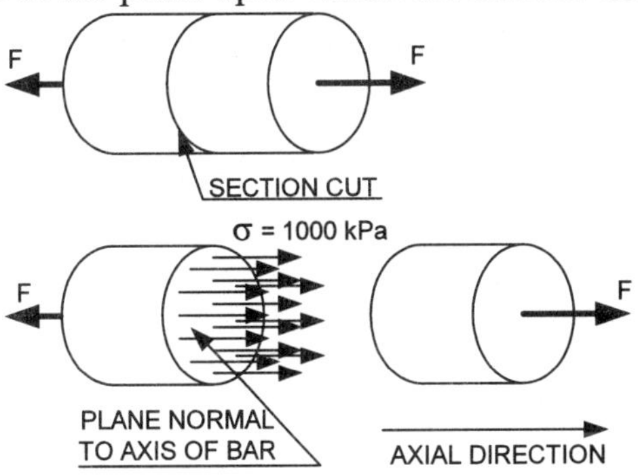

Fig. 1.4 Stresses of 1,000 kPa act in the direction of the axis of the bar. The stresses are acting on the plane normal to the bar's axis.

1.8 INTERNAL AND EXTERNAL FORCES

In dealing with forces, it is important to distinguish between those applied to a structure **(external)**, and those that develop within a structural element **(internal)**. The external forces include the active loads applied to the structure such as those shown in Fig. 1.5a-c, and the reaction forces, shown in Fig. 1.5d, that develop at the supports to maintain the structure in equilibrium.

In Fig.1.5a, a simply supported beam is loaded with a **concentrated force** F at a point near its center. The concentrated force, applied at a point, is an idealization. Forces are always distributed over some area; however, with concentrated forces, we assume that the area is so small that it approaches a point. In Fig. 1.5b, the beam is loaded with a **uniformly distributed load** q that is applied over most of its length. Uniformly distributed loads along beams are specified in terms of force/unit length (i.e. lb/ft or N/m). A distributed load that is increasing from the left end of the beam to its right end is illustrated in Fig. 1.5c. Again, the symbol q is used to designate the magnitude of the distributed forces; however, in this case q is a function of the position x along the length of the beam, and is designated by q(x).

The last example of external forces is shown in Fig. 1.5d. The beam and its loading are identical with that shown in Fig. 1.5b, but the supports have been removed. Reaction forces R developed by the supports to maintain the beam in equilibrium are shown as concentrated forces.

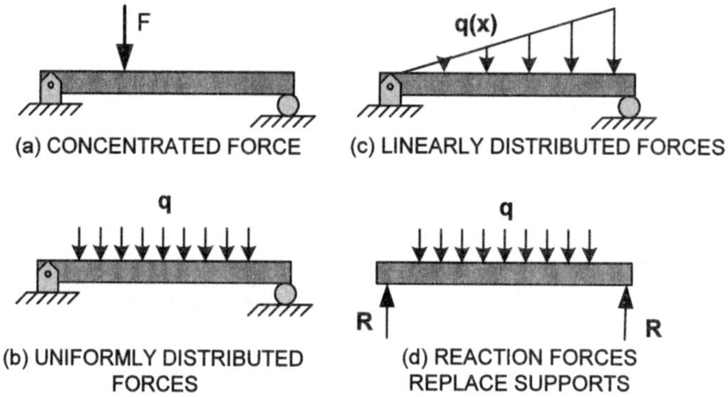

Fig. 1.5 Examples of different types of external forces applied to the structure (beam).

Internal forces develop within a structural member due to the action of applied external forces. These internal forces are not visible; they are represented by making imaginary cuts through a structural member. Examine the bar subjected to two external forces F applied at each end as shown in Fig. 1.6. A section cut is made that is perpendicular to the axis in the central region of the bar. This is an imaginary cut, not a real one, which permits visualization of either segment of the bar. Examine the segment on the left, and find a **normal stress** σ, which is uniformly distributed over the area exposed by the section cut. When this stress is integrated over the area of the bar, an internal force P is generated that acts along the axis of the bar. The magnitude of P is given by:

$$P = \int \sigma \, dA \tag{1.6}$$

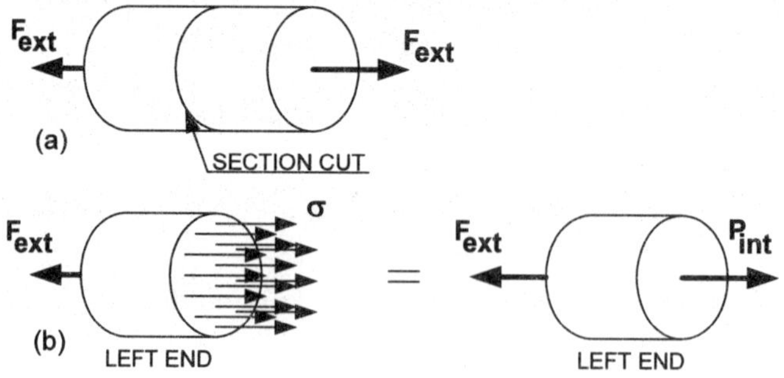

Fig. 1.6 (a) A tension bar with external loads and a section cut dividing it into two parts.
(b) Two different representations of the left side of the bar.

The left end of the bar must be in equilibrium, which implies that:

$$\Sigma F_x = 0 \tag{1.2b}$$

Summing the forces in the x direction gives:

$$P = F \tag{1.7}$$

In this elementary example of a rod in tension, the relation between the internal force P within the bar and the external force F applied to its ends has been determined. The same three-step approach will be used throughout this book in solving for the internal forces in much more complex problems.

1. Make an appropriate section cut
2. Use the equations of equilibrium
3. Solve for internal forces in structural members

1.9 MOMENTS

When using a wrench or screwdriver to tighten a bolt or screw, a moment is generated. The moment M_o is produced when a force F, as shown in Fig. 1.7, is applied in such a manner that it tends to cause a body to rotate about point O. The magnitude of a moment produced by a force is dependent on the location of the point O, and is given by:

$$M_o = (F)(d) \tag{1.8}$$

where d is the perpendicular distance from the point O to the line of action of the force F.

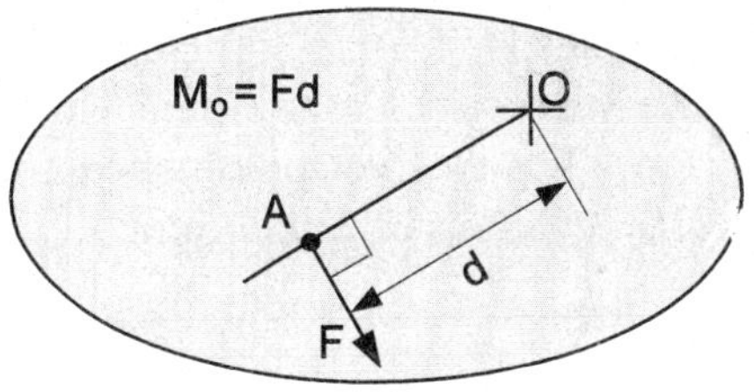

Fig. 1.7 The moment M_0 produced by a force F depends on its position relative to point O.

The units of a moment $\mathbf{M_o}$ are always (force)(length), such as N-m or ft-lb. $\mathbf{M_o}$ is a vector quantity that must be specified with both magnitude and direction. The magnitude of the vector $\mathbf{M_0}$ is given by Eq. (1.8) and its direction is perpendicular to the plane in which F and the line OA lie. As shown in Fig. 1.8, the moment $\mathbf{M_o}$ has a sense of direction. In this illustration, the moment $\mathbf{M_o}$ tends to rotate the body in a **counterclockwise** direction and is **positive**.

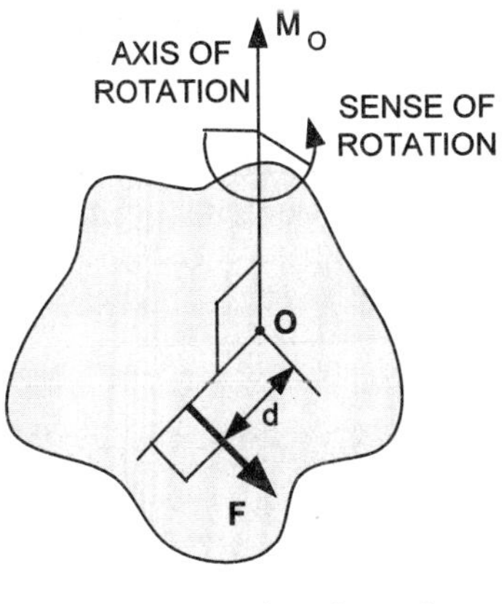

Fig. 1.8 A graphic illustration of the moment $\mathbf{M_o}$ as a vector quantity.

To determine the sign of the moment, use the **right hand rule**. In applying this rule, place the palm of your right hand along the axis of rotation and point your fingers in the direction of the force and rotate your hand. If the direction of the force causes you to rotate **counterclockwise**, with your thumb pointing up from the plane in which both F and d lie, then the moment is **positive**. However, if you must rotate your hand **clockwise**, with your thumb pointing downward, the moment is **negative**.

1.10 FREE BODY DIAGRAMS AND EQUILIBRIUM

Equilibrium is an extremely important concept because it provides an excellent approach for determining unknown forces that act on a body. It is understood that a body is in equilibrium if it is at rest or traveling at some constant velocity. For example the beam, shown in Fig. 1.9, is at rest because the loads acting downward are resisted by the two reactive forces produced by the supports. The entire assembly is fixed to bedrock.

Fig. 1.9 A simply supported beam that is at rest and in equilibrium.

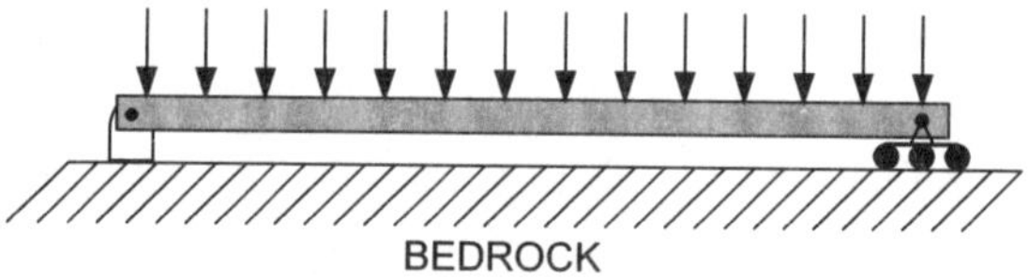

Bodies that move may or may not be in equilibrium. If a body is in equilibrium, it moves with a constant velocity and a constant **momentum**[5]. The effect of unbalanced forces ($\Sigma F \neq 0$) acting on a body is to change its momentum by altering its velocity. The rate of that change is proportional to the unbalanced force. Therefore, when a body moves at constant velocity (zero acceleration) it possesses constant momentum and is in equilibrium.

The two vector equations of equilibrium $\sum \mathbf{F} = 0$ and $\sum \mathbf{M} = 0$ are equivalent to the six scalar equations of equilibrium.

$$\Sigma F_x = 0; \qquad \Sigma F_y = 0; \qquad \Sigma F_z = 0$$
$$\Sigma M_x = 0; \qquad \Sigma M_y = 0; \qquad \Sigma M_z = 0 \qquad (1.9)$$

Solutions for many problems arising in both statics and mechanics of materials are executed by using Eqs. (1.9). The decision whether to use the vector or scalar form of the equilibrium equations is left to your discretion, although in many cases the scalar equations are easier to apply.

Although there are six scalar equations of equilibrium, it is not always necessary to employ all of them to solve an equilibrium problem. By classifying different systems of forces acting on a body, it is possible to identify only those equations that provide relevant information for solving equilibrium problems. This classification greatly simplifies the associated equilibrium problems. Four different force systems are classified as:

- Non-coplanar and non-concurrent.
- Non-coplanar and concurrent.
- Coplanar and non-concurrent.
- Coplanar and concurrent.

---

[5] Momentum, ***M*** a vector quantity, is defined as ***M*** = m**v**, where **v** is the velocity of the body.

Non-coplanar, Non-concurrent Force Systems

When a body is subjected to non-coplanar and non-concurrent forces and is in equilibrium, the directions and magnitudes of $\mathbf{F_1}$, $\mathbf{F_2}$ ..... $\mathbf{F_n}$ must satisfy the **six** Cartesian component equations of equilibrium given in Eq. (1.9).

Non-coplanar, Concurrent Force Systems

When a body is subjected to non-coplanar but concurrent forces and is in equilibrium, the directions and magnitudes of $\mathbf{F_1}$, $\mathbf{F_2}$ .... $\mathbf{F_n}$ must satisfy the **three** Cartesian component force equations, which are:

$$\Sigma F_x = 0 \qquad \Sigma F_y = 0 \qquad \Sigma F_z = 0$$

Due to concurrency, it is evident that moments do not occur about point O and the equations $\Sigma M_x = \Sigma M_y = \Sigma M_y = 0$ are satisfied regardless of the magnitude of the forces.

Coplanar, Non-concurrent Force Systems

When a body is subjected to coplanar but non-concurrent forces and is in equilibrium, the directions and magnitudes of $\mathbf{F_1}$, $\mathbf{F_2}$ .... $\mathbf{F_n}$ must satisfy **three** Cartesian component equations of equilibrium, which are:

$$\Sigma F_x = 0, \qquad \Sigma F_y = 0, \qquad \text{and} \qquad \Sigma M_z = 0$$

The remaining three equations of equilibrium are satisfied independently of the solution for the three possible unknowns.

Coplanar, Concurrent Force Systems

This category is the simplest of the four force systems because equilibrium is satisfied by using only the following **two** equations:

$$\Sigma F_x = 0 \qquad \text{and} \qquad \Sigma F_y = 0$$

The other four equilibrium relations are satisfied automatically and they do not provide useful information. Due to concurrency, it is evident that moments do not occur about point O and the equations $\Sigma M_x = \Sigma M_y = \Sigma M_y = 0$ are satisfied regardless of the magnitude of the forces. Also, because the forces are coplanar, they all lie in the x-y plane and $\Sigma F_z = 0$.

1.11 FREE BODY DIAGRAMS (FBDs)

The equations of equilibrium described in the previous section may be applied to:

- A single body or member.
- A structure made of several members.
- A portion of a multi-member structure formed by a section cut.
- A part of a body or structure that has been formed by two or more section cuts.
- An element removed from a body.

Before utilizing the equations of equilibrium, it is essential that a **free body diagram (FBD)** be constructed of the structural element being analyzed. A FBD is a model. Its purpose is to simplify the physical representation of the structure by omitting its fine details that are not necessary in solving an equilibrium problem.

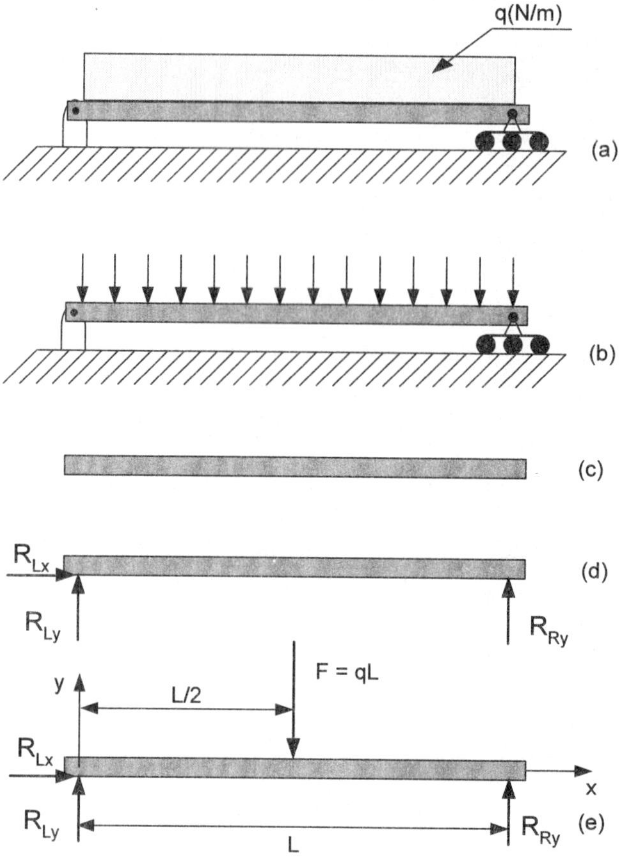

Fig. 1.10 Construction of a FBD for a simply supported uniformly loaded beam.

An example for the construction of a FBD is illustrated in Fig. 1.10. The beam is subjected to a uniformly distributed load of magnitude q (N/m), and supported near each end with simple supports. In Fig. 1.10a, a uniformly distributed load is represented with a shaded rectangle placed over the span of the beam. The uniformly distributed load may also be represented with a series of arrows as illustrated in Fig. 1.10b. Both of these techniques are used to model uniformly distributed loads. The simple supports are modeled with a pin and clevis on the left side and a roller on the right side. The pin and clevis holds the beam in a fixed position at its left end while the roller permits the beam to freely expand and/or contract with changes in temperature.

A four-step procedure is employed in drawing the free body of the beam.

1. Isolate the body (a beam in this case) by removing the supports and the uniformly distributed load. We show the isolated beam in Fig. 1.10c.
2. The supports are replaced with the **reaction loads** R_{Lx}, R_{Ly} and R_{Ry}. The pin and clevis at the left support produces reactions in both the x and y directions as shown in Fig. 1.10d. However, the roller, which is free to move horizontally, produces only a single reactive force normal to the surface of the beam (the y direction). At this stage of the analysis, the magnitude of these forces is not known.

3. The uniformly distributed load q applied over the length L of the beam is replaced with a concentrated force F located in the center of the beam. The magnitude of the force is F = (qL) and it acts downward, as shown in Fig. 1.10e.
4. Finally, dimensions are added to the FBD and a coordinate system established to facilitate the equilibrium analysis. In dimensioning the FBD, the concentrated force is placed at the centroid of the shaded rectangular area representing the uniformly distributed load (e.g. at L/2 from the left support).

1.11.1 Modeling Loads

The FBD is a model of a structure or some part of a structure. To prepare the FBD, the loads that act on the structure and its supports are modeled. First consider modeling the loads due to gravity, which is one of the most commonly encountered forces. Examine the block with a mass m as shown in Fig. 1.11a. The gravitational force due to the mass of the block is modeled with a concentrated force F = mg, which is applied at the center of the block (its centroid). Because the force is due to gravity, the direction of the force is downward (in the negative y direction).

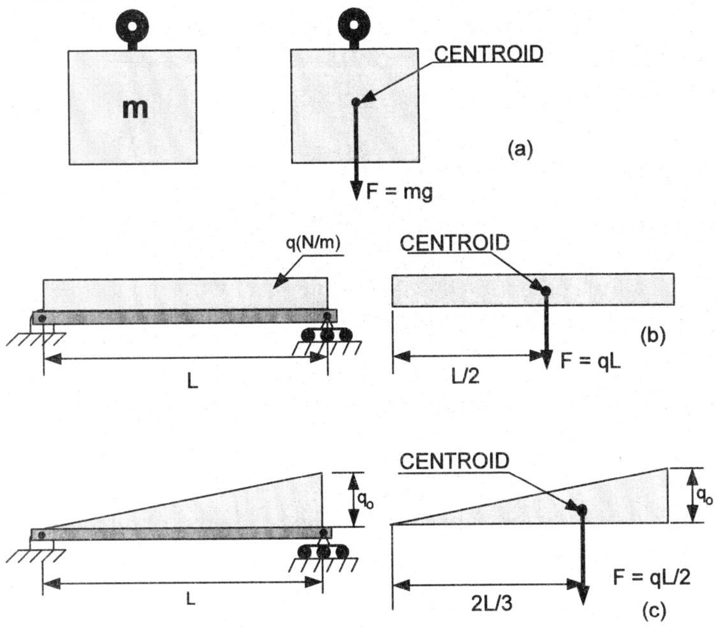

Fig. 1.11 Modeling gravitational and distributed loads.

In Fig.1.11b, a uniform load of magnitude q is distributed over the span of a beam. The magnitude q is expressed in terms of force/unit length (N/m or lb/ft). This uniformly distributed load is represented with a rectangular area of height q and length L. A concentrated force F, the static equivalent of the uniformly distributed load, is given by the area of the rectangle as F = qL. The concentrated force is applied at the centroid of the rectangular area (x = L/2) and acts downward.

In Fig. 1.11c, the load is again distributed over the length of the beam, but increases as a linear function of x (e.g. $q(x) = q_ox/L$). This load is represented with a triangular area having an altitude q_o and a base L. A concentrated force, the static equivalent of the distributed load, is given by the area of the triangle as $F = q_oL/2$, which is applied at the centroid of the triangle (x = 2L/3) acting downward.

When modeling to solve for reaction forces at structural supports, distributed loads are replaced with statically equivalent concentrated forces. However, later in Chapters 4 and 5 when dealing with internal moments and shear forces, it is not possible to use this simplified modeling technique.

1.11.2 Modeling Supports

The pin and clevis and roller are often used to support beams. The pin and clevis is stationary and does not permit the beam to move in either the x or y directions, although it does permit the beam to rotate as it deflects. On the other hand, the roller permits the beam to expand or contract with changes in temperature. When the pin and the roller are removed in the construction of a FBD, they are replaced with reaction forces shown in Fig. 1.12. For the pin and clevis, which restrains motion in the x and y directions, reaction forces R_{Ly} (perpendicular to the beam's axis) and R_{Lx} (parallel to the beam's axis) are required to represent this support. For the roller (on a frictionless surface), a single reaction force R_{Ry} perpendicular to the beam's axis is sufficient.

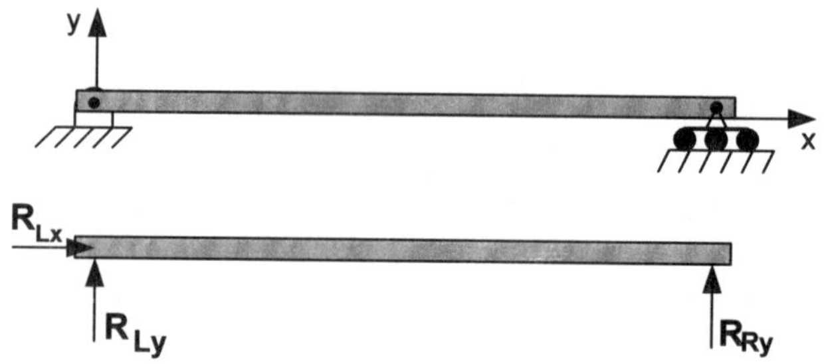

Fig. 1.12 Modeling the pivot and roller supports.

There are many support conditions and connections to structures. In constructing FBDs, the structure is modeled by removing these supports and replacing them with one or more reactive forces or reactive moments. Several different types of supports or connections and their reactive forces and moments are shown in the following table. The structure is always constrained by supports at one or more locations. These supports are modeled in FBDs with some combination of concentrated forces and moments that effectively provide the constraint the supports provide. The forces and the moments produced by common supports are listed in Table 1.1.

Table 1.1
Different types of supports or connections and their reactive forces and moments.

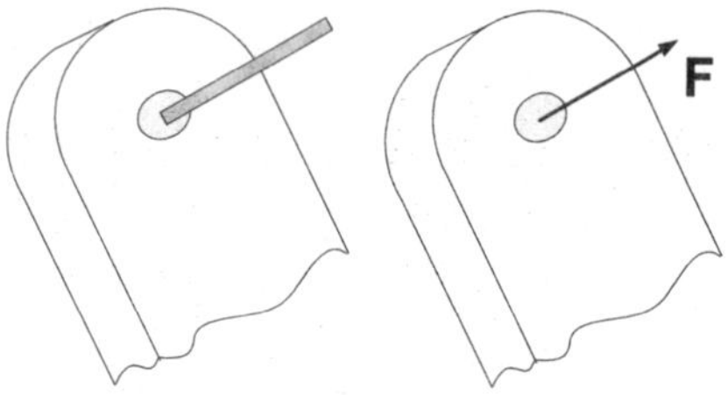

A. A cable connection is modeled with a single force acting in the direction of the cable and away from the structure.

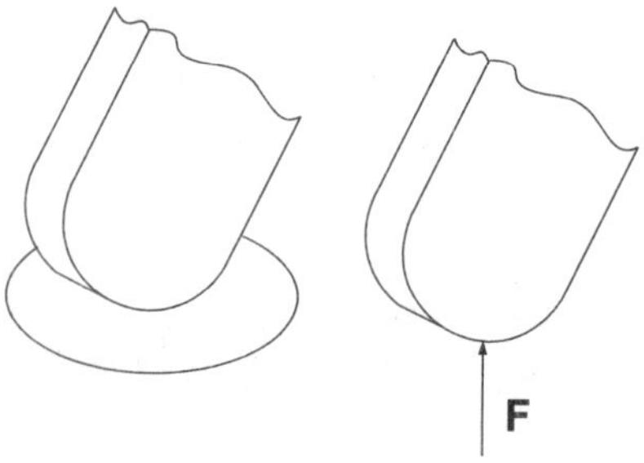

B. A rocker on a frictionless surface is modeled with a concentrated force perpendicular to the surface at the point of contact.

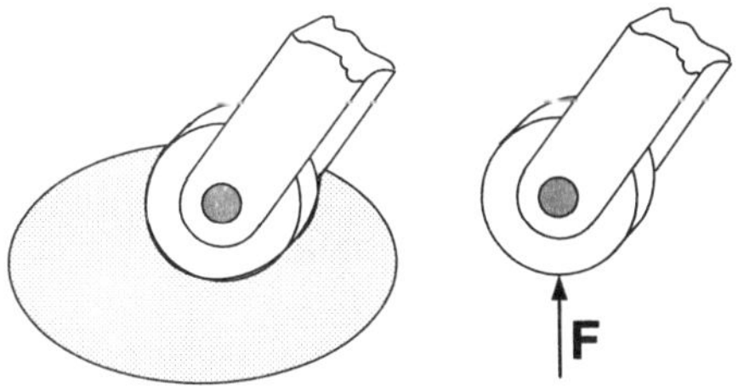

C. A roller on a flat surface is represented with a concentrated force perpendicular to the surface at the point of contact.

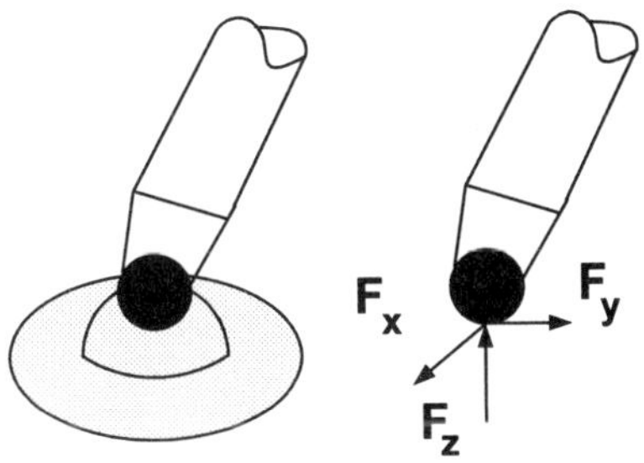

D. A ball and socket joint is modeled with three Cartesian force components.

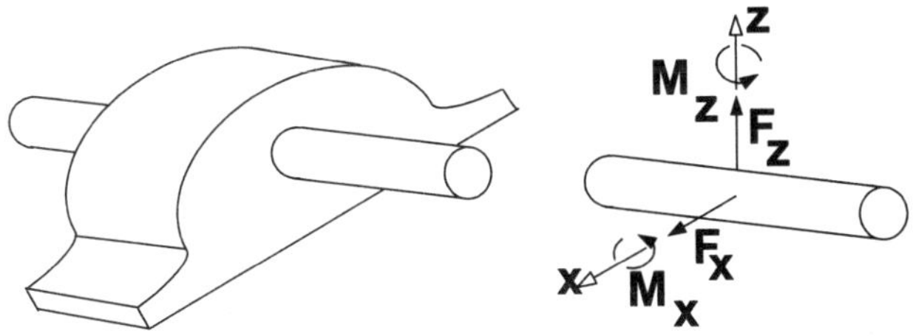

E. A journal bearing is represented with two forces perpendicular to the shaft and two moments about axes perpendicular to the shaft.

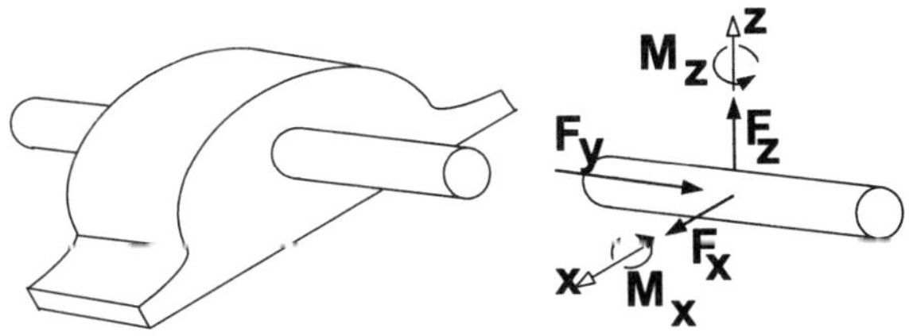

F. A thrust bearing is represented with three Cartesian forces and two moments about axes perpendicular to the shaft.

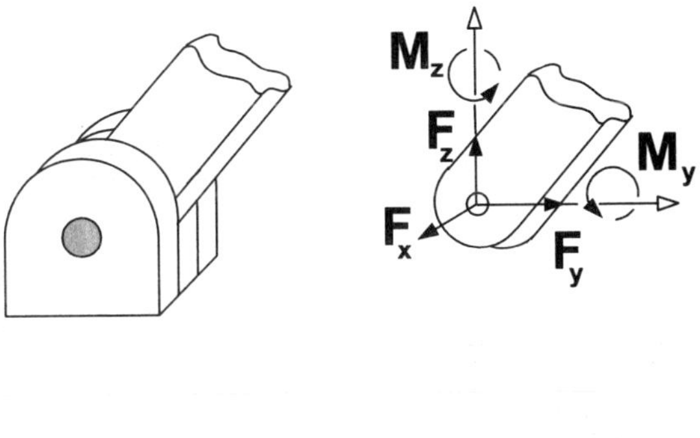

G. A pin and clevis connection is represented with three Cartesian forces and two moments about axes perpendicular to the pin.

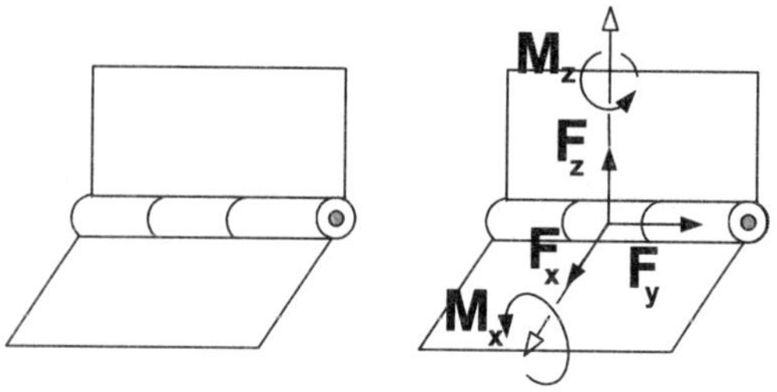

H. A hinge connection is represented with three Cartesian forces and two moments about axes perpendicular to the hinge pin.

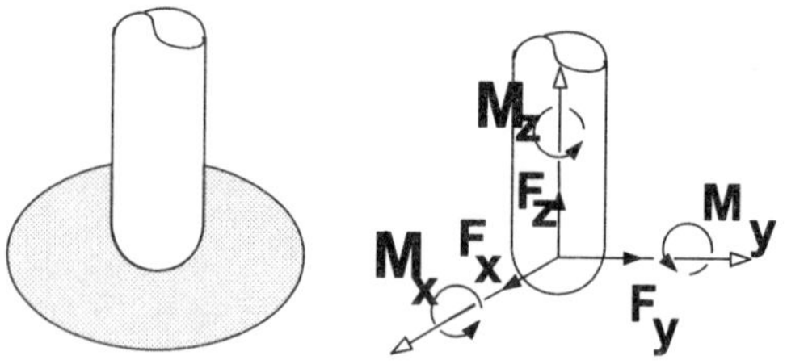

I. A fixed support is modeled with six possible reactions (three Cartesian forces and three Cartesian moments).

1.11.3 FBDs of Partial Bodies

It is very important to determine internal forces in structural members because these forces produce stresses and deflections that might cause failure of the structure. The approach followed in studying internal forces is to:

1. Make an imaginary cut through the structural member being studied.
2. Draw a FBD of one part of this member.
3. Account for the effect of the portion of the cut away member by applying internal forces and moments to the area exposed by the section cut.
4. Solve for the internal forces or moments using the appropriate equations of equilibrium.

A FBD provides a model to use in writing the equilibrium equations employed in the solution for unknown forces and reactions. The diagram indicates the known and unknown forces and their directions. It also provides the dimensions needed to compute relevant moments.

PROBLEMS

1.1 Weather satellites are often placed in geosynchronous orbit around Earth, so that they appear stationary in the sky when viewed from a point on the equator. The orbital altitude for such a satellite is 35,800 km. If a satellite weighs 1,000 N on the Earth's surface, calculate its weight in orbit. Assume Earth has a mass of 5.976×10^{24} kg and a radius of 6370 km.

1.2 An astronaut weighs 165 lb on the Earth's surface. When orbiting Earth in the space shuttle *Atlantis*, however, the astronaut's weight is measured as 140 lb. Determine the altitude of the shuttle's orbit. Assume Earth has a mass of 5.976×10^{24} kg and a radius of 6370 km.

1.3 Determine the weight of a body with the following masses in SI units:

(a) 130 kg (b) 38 kg (c) 116 kg (d) 34.6 kg (e) 69.4 kg

1.4 Determine the weight of a body with the following masses in U. S. Customary units:

(a) 9.0 slug (b) 1.2 slug (c) 55 slug (d) 41.2 slug (e) 24 slug

1.5 Determine the SI equivalent of the following forces:

(a) 2,800 lb (b) 315 lb (c) 25 tons (d) 82 kip (e) 14 kip

1.6 Determine the U. S. Customary equivalents for the following forces:

(a) 1,242 N (b) 159.6 N (c) 43.2 kN (d) 66.9 mN (e) 352.3 μN

1.7 Determine the SI equivalent of the following lengths:

(a) 16.3 ft (b) 22.3 yards (c) 4 ft - 7 in. (d) 52.5 in. (e) 6.4 miles

1.8 Determine the U. S. Customary equivalents for the following lengths:

(a) 5.8 m (b) 18.1 cm (c) 92.8 mm (d) 10.32 km (e) 26.8 μm

1.9 Determine the Cartesian components of the force vectors shown in Fig. P1.9.
(a) **A** (b) **B**

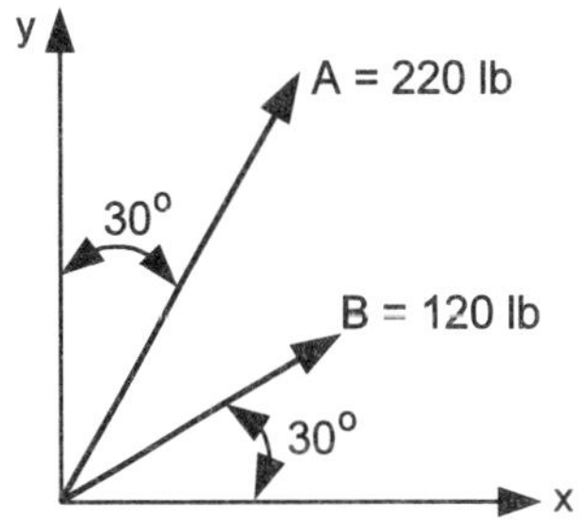

Fig. P1.9

1.10 Determine the Cartesian components of the force vectors shown in Fig. P1.10.
(a) **A** (b) **B**

Fig. P1.10

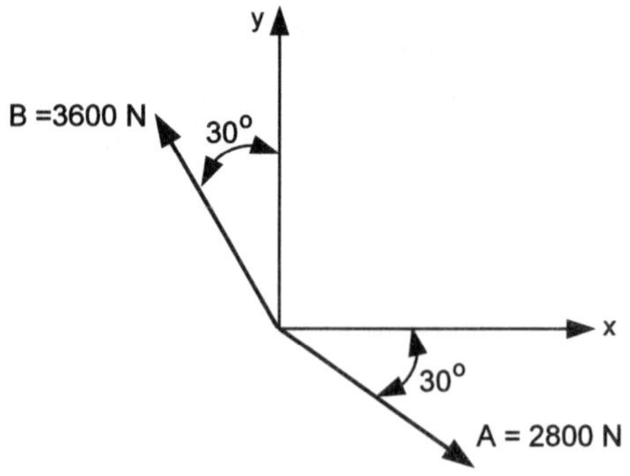

1.11 Determine the force components along the corresponding axes due to the force of 2,000 lbs that is pulling on the eyebolt shown in Fig. P1.11.
(a) x & y axes (b) x' & y' axes

Fig. P1.11

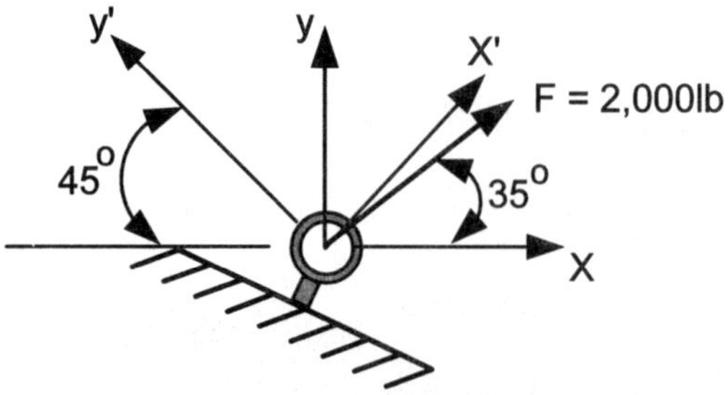

1.12 A linkage, shown in Fig. P1.12, is subjected to a force of 4,200 N. Determine the components of the force along the AB and AC directions. <u>Note</u>: This is NOT an equilibrium problem.

Fig. P1.12

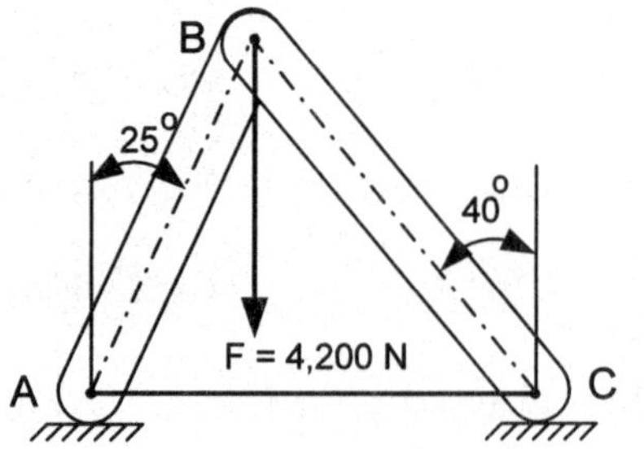

1.13 Three forces act on the bracket, illustrated in Fig. P1.13. Determine F_1 and θ if the magnitude of the Cartesian components of the vector sum are S_{vx} = 17,500 lb and $S_{vy} = 0$.

Fig. P1.13

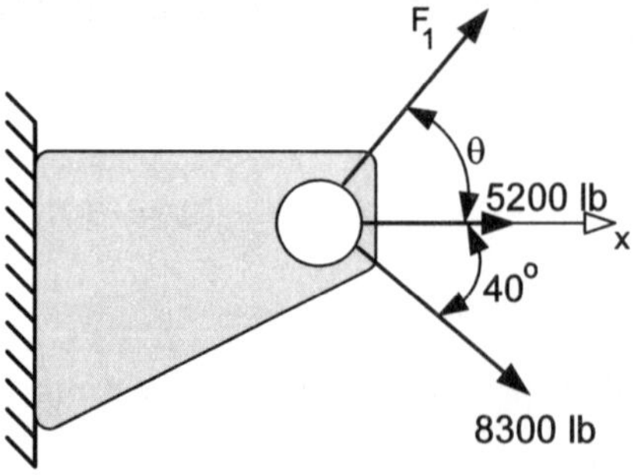

1.14 A force of 150 N is exerted on a single-ended lug wrench with a 400-mm long handle to loosen a wheel bolt. What moment (torque) is applied to the bolt?

1.15 A force of 125 N is applied to each of the handles of a double-ended lug wrench to loosen a wheel bolt. If each handle is 200 mm long, what moment (torque) is applied to the bolt?

1.16 Determine the moment about point O due to the force shown in Fig. P1.16.

Fig. P1.16

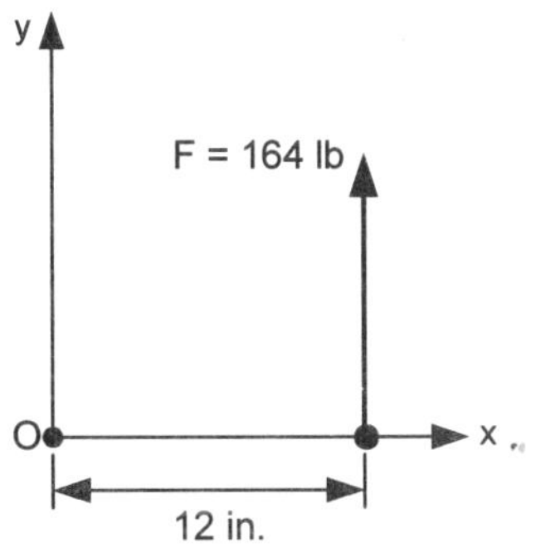

1.17 Determine the total moment about point O due to the two forces shown in Fig. P1.17.

Fig. P1.17

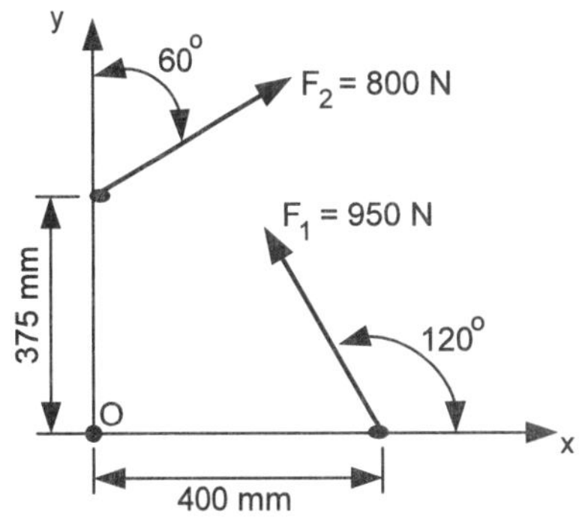

1.18 Construct a FBD for the mass and two-cable assembly shown in Fig. P1.18. Also determine the tension forces in cables AC and BC.

Fig. P1.18

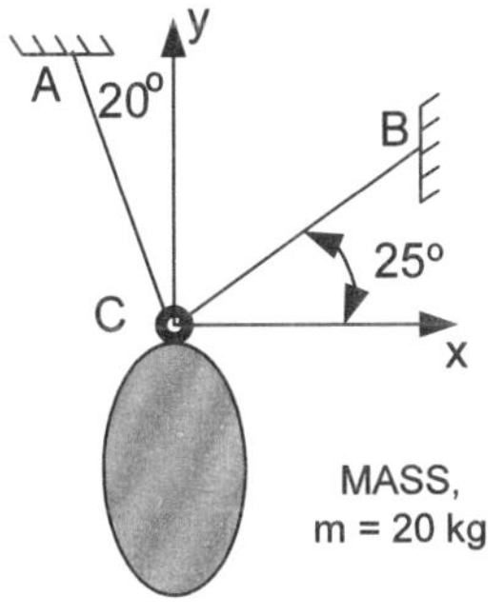

1.19 Construct a FBD for the mass and three-cable assembly shown in Fig. P1.19. Determine the tension forces in cables AC, BC and CD. Assume cable CD supports 35% of the mass.

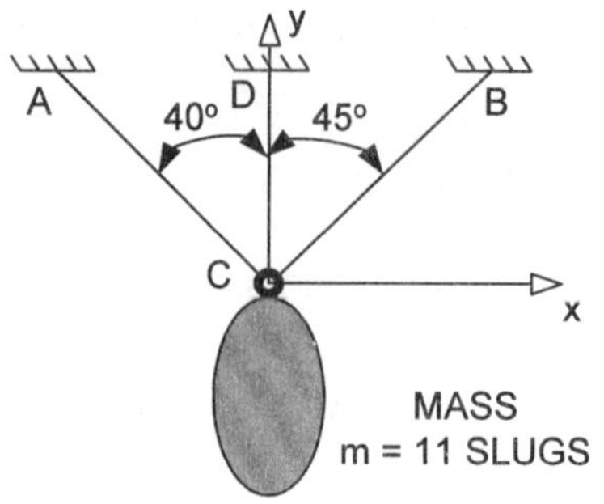

Fig. P1.19

1.20 Determine the forces in cables AC and BC that support the signal lights at a traffic intersection as illustrated in Fig. P1.20. The signal lights have a mass m = 35 kg. The dimensions for the cable arrangement are given in meters.

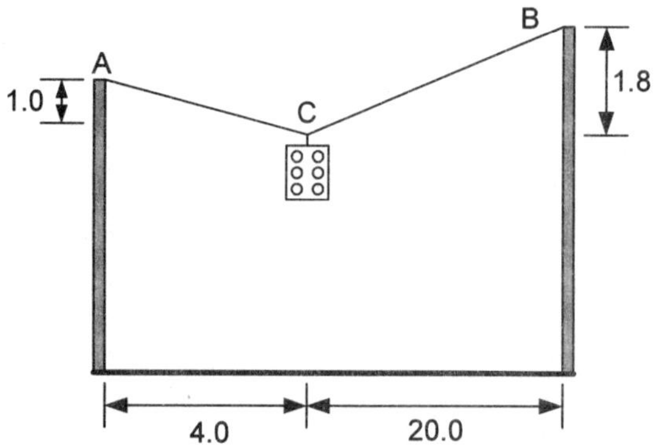

Fig. P1.20

1.21 An artist has designed a bell using a long piece of thin-wall pipe as the vibrating sound source. The pipe is to be supported using the wire ring arrangement shown in Fig. P1.21. Determine the force in each of the wires. The pipe has a mass of 14 kg.

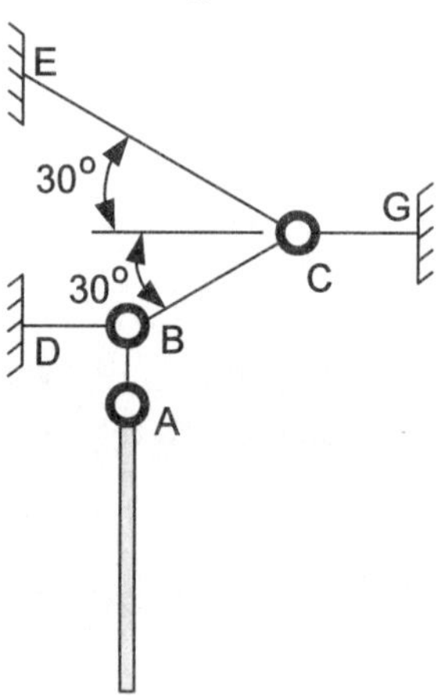

Fig. P1.21

1.22 Two masses m_B and m_C are supported by the cable arrangement shown in Fig. P1.22. Determine the mass m_C and the forces in the cables AB, BC and CD if the mass m_B = 18.0 kg.

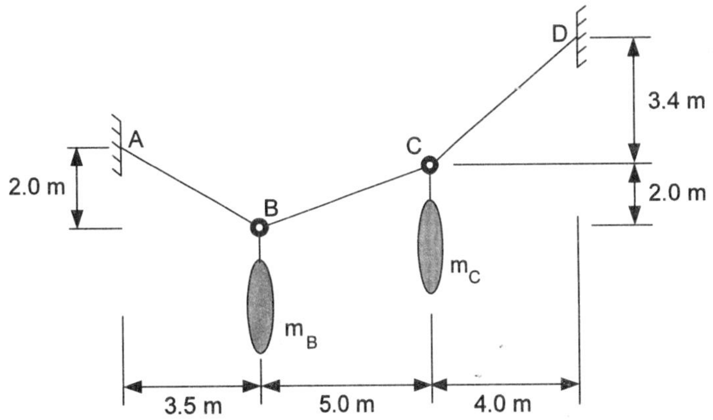

Fig. P1.22

1.23 For the beam, shown in Fig. P1.23, solve for the reactions at the pin and clevis (A) and the roller (B).

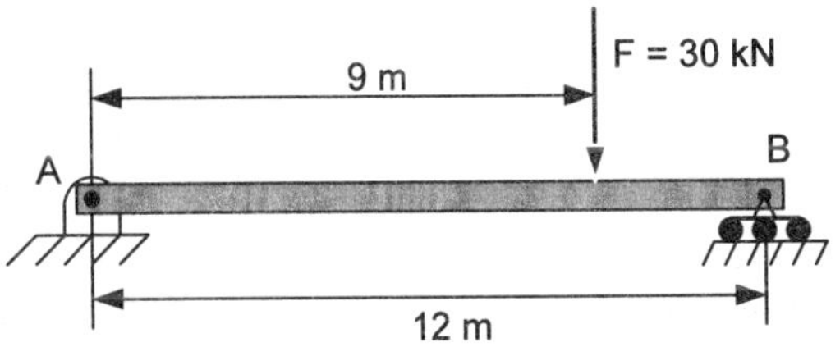

Fig. P1.23

1.24 For the beam, shown in Fig P1.24, solve for the reactions at the pin and clevis (A) and the roller (B).

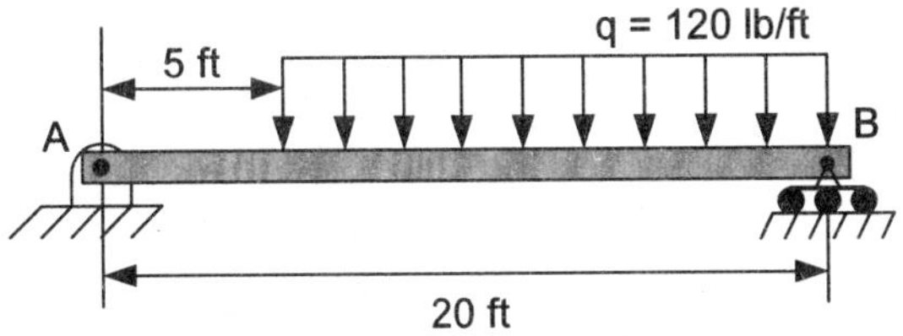

Fig. Ex 1.24

1.25 For the beam, shown in Fig. P1.25, solve for the reactions at the pin and clevis (A) and the roller (B).

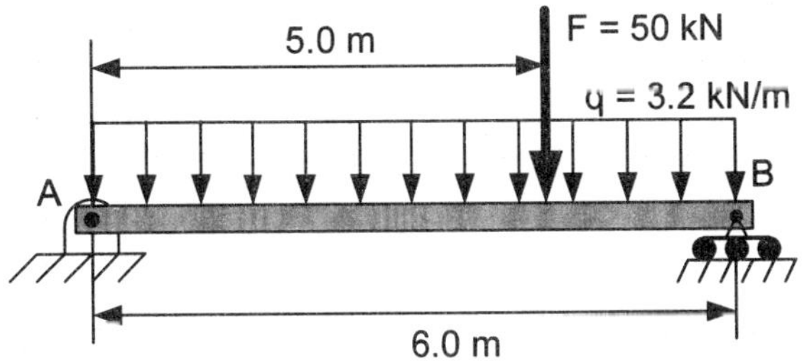

Fig. P1.25

1.26 For the beam, shown in Fig. P1.26, solve for the reactions at the built-in end of the cantilever beam (A).

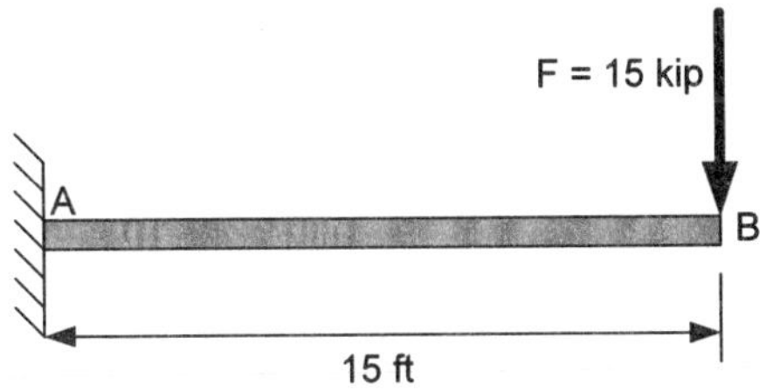

Fig. P1.26

1.27 For the cantilever beam, shown in Fig. P1.27, solve for the reactions at its built-in end (A).

Fig. P1.27

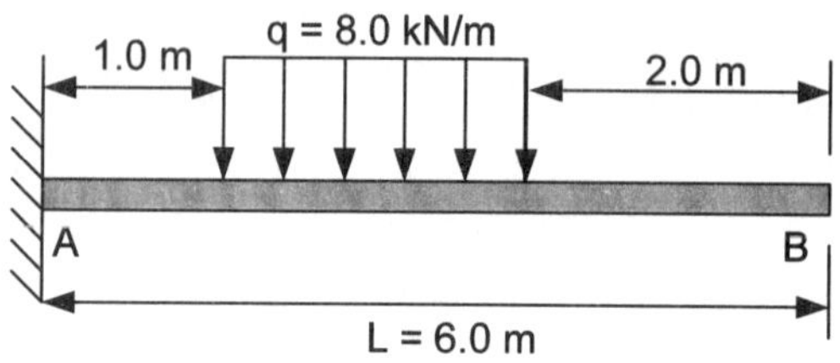

1.28 For the beam, shown in Fig. P1.28, solve for the reactions at the two supports. Note that A is a pin and B is a roller.

Fig. P1.28

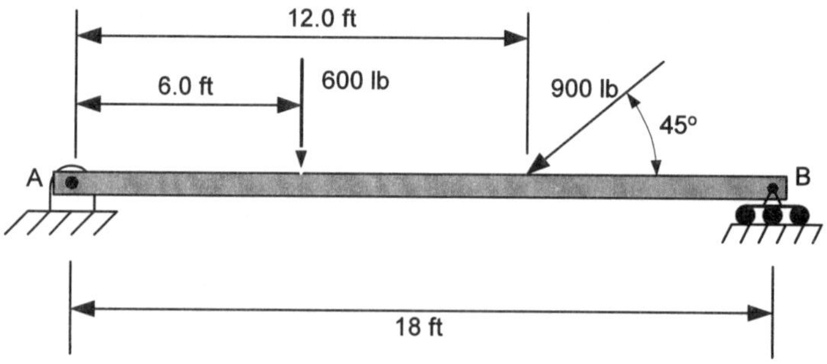

1.29 For the truss, shown in Fig. P1.29, determine the reactions at the two supports. Note that A is a pin and B is a roller.

Fig. P1.29

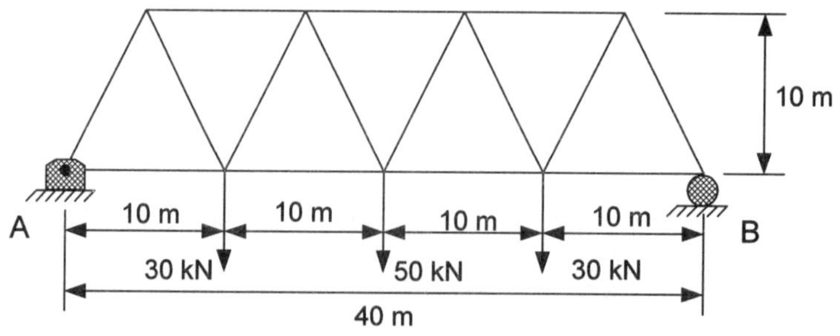

1.30 Determine the reaction forces at pins A and B that support the gusset plate shown in Fig. P1.30. Assume that the vertical components of the reaction forces at the pins are equal (i.e. $R_{Ay} = R_{By}$)

Fig. P1.30

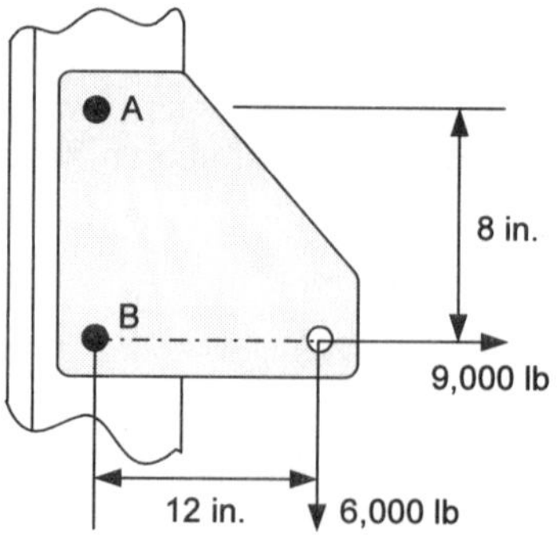

1.31 Determine the reactions at the built-in support (A) for the stadium structure shown in Fig. P1.31. Note that the 50 kN force is applied vertically to the structure.

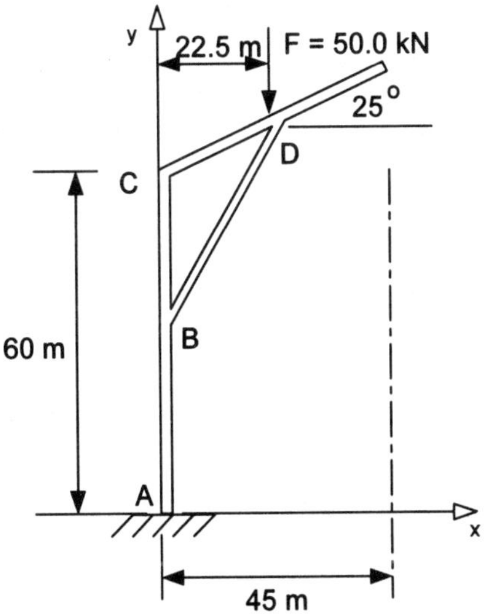

Fig. P1.31

1.32 A hanging light assembly is positioned near the corner of a gymnasium as shown in Fig. P1.32. Determine the forces in the wires AD, AC and AB, which a light assembly weighing 2,200 N. Points B and C are anchors that lie in the x-y plane and point D is an anchor that lies along the z-axis. Point A is not anchored; however it lies in the x-y plane.

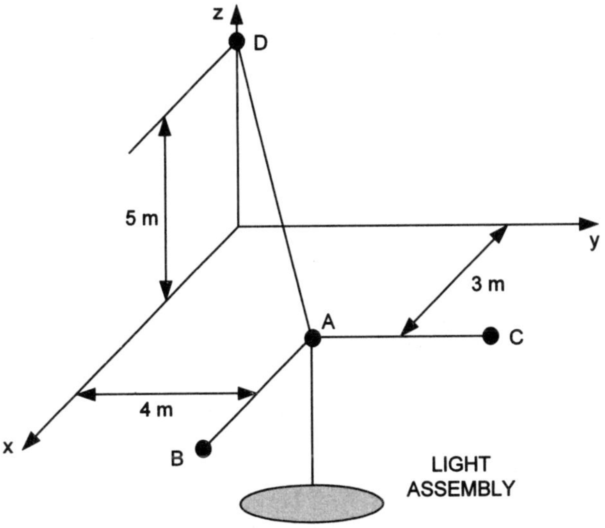

Fig. P1.32

1.33 A hot air balloon, shown in Fig. P1.33, is moored to the ground with three cables that are anchored at points A, B and C. The coordinates (x, y, z) of the anchor points on the ground and on the basket are given in the figure. Determine the force exerted by each of the cables if the upward lift of the balloon is 1,200 lb. Assume that wind forces are negligible.

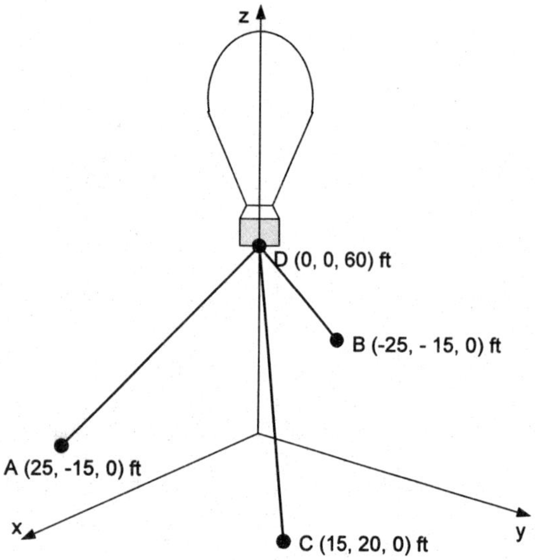

Fig. P1.33

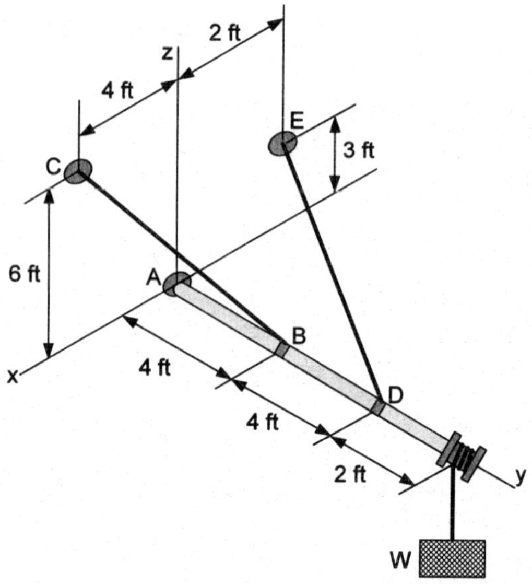

Fig. P1.34

1.34 A local firm has constructed a small crane consisting of a boom supported by two steel wires BC and DE as shown in Fig. P1.34. The boom is fixed to the supporting wall with a ball and socket joint at point A. The wires are anchored into the wall at points C and E. Determine the forces in the wires BC and DE if the mass of the weight is 10 slugs.

1.35 A hand operated lifting mechanism called a windless utilizes a crank to rotate a drum as shown in Fig. P1.35. The shaft of the mechanism is supported by a wall mounted ball and socket joint at point A and a smooth journal bearing at point B. The arm and handle of the crank in the position shown is in the y-z plane. For this position of the crank handle, determine the force F required to hold a weight of 500 kN in equilibrium. Also determine the reactions at the ball and socket joint and the journal bearing.

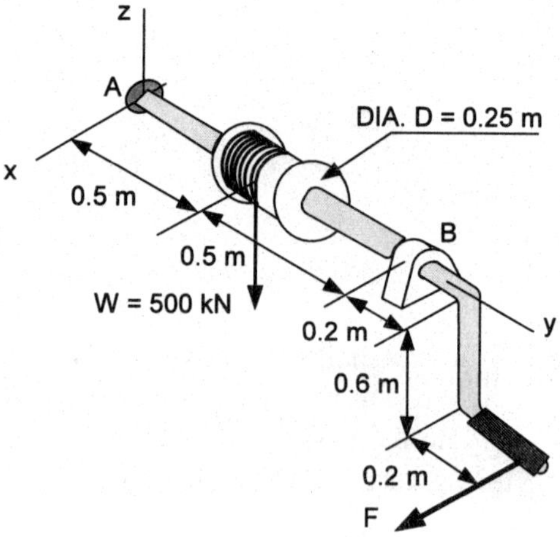

Fig. P1.35

1.36 For the tension bar, shown in Fig. P1.36, determine the internal tension force P at sections A-A and B-B.

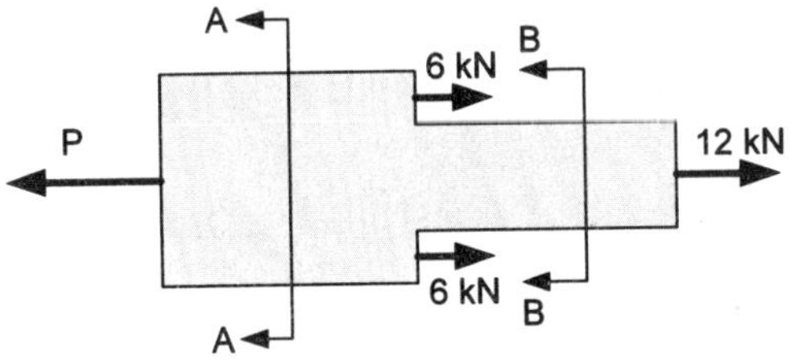

Fig. P1.36

1.37 For the beam, shown in Fig. P1.37, determine the internal shear force V and the internal moment M at the position x = 4 ft to the right of point A. Note that A is a pin and B is a roller.

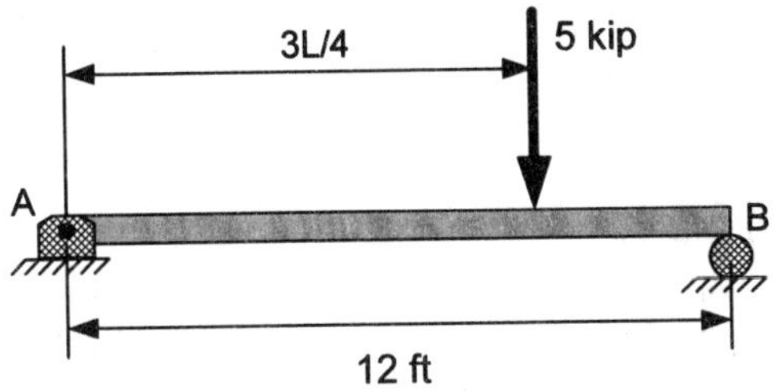

Fig. P1.37

1.38 For the beam, shown in Fig. P1.38, determine the internal shear force V and the internal moment M at the position x = 10 m to the right of point A. Note that A is a pin and B is a roller.

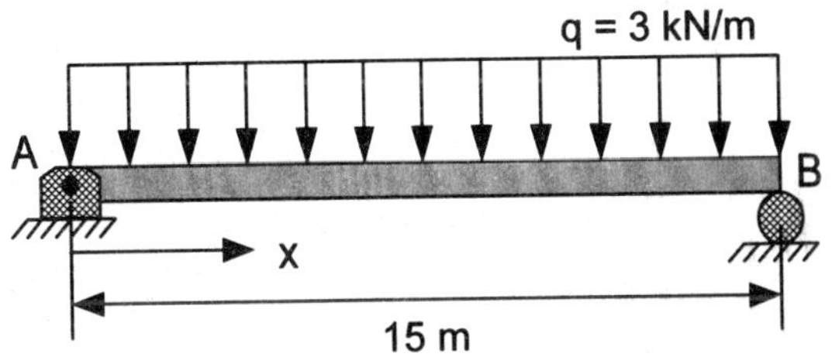

Fig. P1.38

1.39 For the beam, shown in Fig. P1.39, determine the internal shear force V and the internal moment M at position x = 15 ft to the right of point A. Note that B is a built-in support.

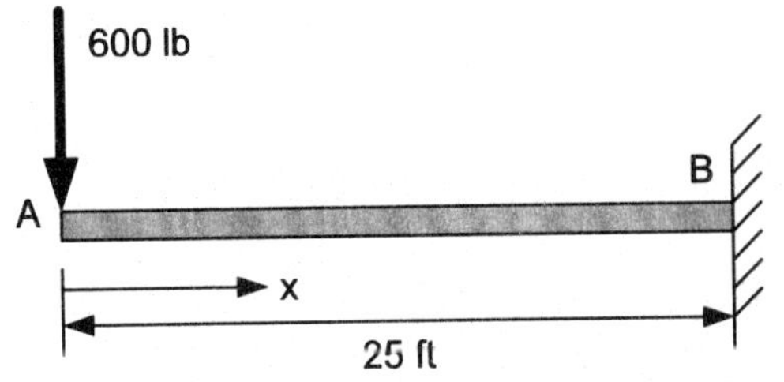

Fig. P1.39

1.40 For the beam, shown in Fig. P1.40, determine the internal shear force V and the internal moment M at the position x = 12 ft to the right of point A. Note that A is a pin and B is a roller.

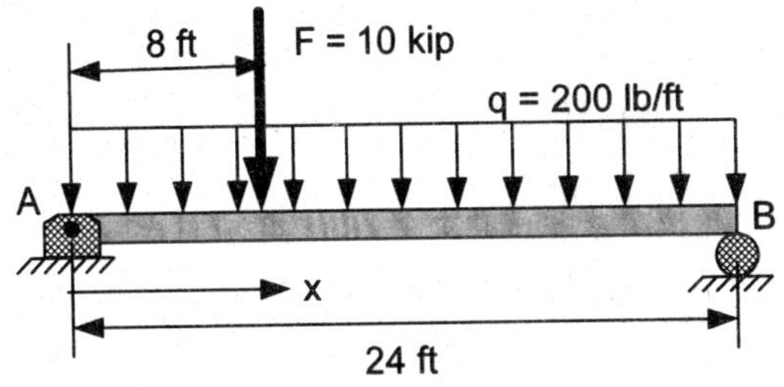

Fig. P1.40

Notes:

CHAPTER 2

AXIALLY LOADED STRUCTURAL MEMBERS

2.1 INTRODUCTION

Large structures like bridges, sports stadiums, skyscrapers, etc. are fabricated from many small structural elements. There are several reasons for constructing large structures from much smaller components. First, manufacturing facilities limit the size (width and thickness) of structural elements that are produced. The rolls used in steel and aluminum mills to produce bars, plates and sheets usually are only six to eight feet long, which limits the width of the product they produce. Even more limiting is the requirement for transport from the manufacturing facility to the construction site. If highways are used for transport, state law limits both the width and length of the structural members.

In this chapter we will consider two types of long thin structural members — flexible and stiff. Both types of these structural members will be subjected to axial loading. Wire rope or cables, which are flexible, are capable of supporting only tensile loading that tends to elongate the cable. However, rods or bars, which are stiff[1], are capable of supporting both tensile and compressive loading.

As structural elements, wire rope, cable, rods and bars subjected to axial loading have a significant advantage. They are subjected to a uniform state of stress over their cross sectional area. Also, if they are two-force members loaded only at their two ends, the stresses are uniform over their length. Thus, the entire volume of the rod or bar is subjected to the same stress, which is the optimum condition for minimum weight design.

Examples of structural applications of long thin members in bridge construction are numerous. For instance, very high-strength wire rope is used in the construction of suspension and cable stayed bridges. Also, many bridges are designed with trusses deployed on two sides of the structure. These trusses are fabricated from many bars or rods connected together at bolted or welded joints. We analyze these structural members using the same equations established for wire rope and cables. The difference is that the rods and bars are sufficiently stiff to support compressive stresses.

---

[1]Rods or bars extend or compress under the action of axial loads, but this deformation is small and is neglected in determining internal forces and stresses. However, this very small deformation is considered when determining the strain and deformation of the long thin structural members.

2.2 CHARACTERISTICS OF CABLES, RODS AND BARS

What characteristics do cables, wire ropes, rods and bars have in common and how do they differ? Cables, rods and bars exhibit lengths that are very long when compared to the dimensions of their cross section. A cable differs from a rod or a bar because it is flexible whereas rods and bars are stiff. **Cables** have a circular cross section that is uniform along its length. A cable is made from many strands of wire that are twisted together to form a larger diameter very high-strength structural member. Even though a typical cable is larger in diameter than wire, it is treated as a flexible member capable of supporting only tensile forces. We will use wire, wire rope and cable interchangeably in this text. The cross sectional area of **bars and rods**[2] may be of arbitrary shape.

Because cables are flexible, they can be wrapped about pulleys, formed into loops, and sometimes knotted. Indeed, they are so flexible that we cannot push on them because they buckle. It is possible to pull, but not push. This fact means that internal tensile forces develop within a thin flexible member but not compression forces. However, rods and bars are sufficiently stiff to support compressive forces and stresses. They are used as tie rods when loaded in tension, and as columns when loaded in compression. We will assume in this discussion that the cross section of the column is sufficiently large so that failure by buckling is not an issue.

All of the equations derived in Section 2.3 for wire and cable are also valid for rods and bars. If the external axial forces are tensile (tend to pull the bar apart), the internal forces and stresses are tensile and denoted with a positive sign. On the other hand, if the external axial forces are compressive (tend to compress the structural member), the internal forces and stresses are compressive and denoted with a minus sign.

We must qualify the capability of a rod or bar to carry compressive loads. If the rod is very long and slender and the compressive force too high, the rod may buckle. **Buckling** is an unstable condition, and if the critical load is exceeded, the rod fails suddenly and catastrophically. In this discussion, we will assume that the rods or bars loaded in compression are sized to resist buckling; consequently, they fail due to excessive compressive stresses. However, the tendency for these structures to buckle cannot always be ignored. Theories describing the failure of **columns** due to buckling will be introduced later in Chapter 8.

In this chapter, we consider the simplest structural application — the use of long thin members under axial loading. The geometry of a structural member (long length with small cross sectional dimensions) leads us to constrain the direction of the loading and to make two important assumptions about the deformation of the member that simplify the analysis.

1. The internal and external forces act along the length of the uniaxial member.
2. Plane sections before loading remain plane after loading and the subsequent deformation of the member.

Considering only loading in the axial direction is consistent with the title of the chapter. We are considering only the effects of axial loading on cables, rods and bars. Later in Chapters 4 and 5, we will consider bending of beams, which is due to loads perpendicular to the axis of the member.

The assumption that plane sections before loading remain plane after loading has also been confirmed by experiment. Suppose we draw a straight scribe line on a long thin member as shown in

---

[2]In most applications, the cross section of a rod is circular and that of a bar rectangular; however, this distinction is not always maintained and one may find cross sections of arbitrary shape for both rods and bars.

Fig. 2.1a. This line represents the edge of a plane through the cross section of the member. Now apply an axial load F to the wire as indicated in Fig. 2.1b. The wire will elongate a small amount δ, but the line remains straight and the plane through the cross section remains plane (i.e. flat). This is a very important observation because it implies that the normal stresses σ in the member are uniformly distributed across the plane.

Fig. 2.1 A section line drawn across the member remains straight after loading.

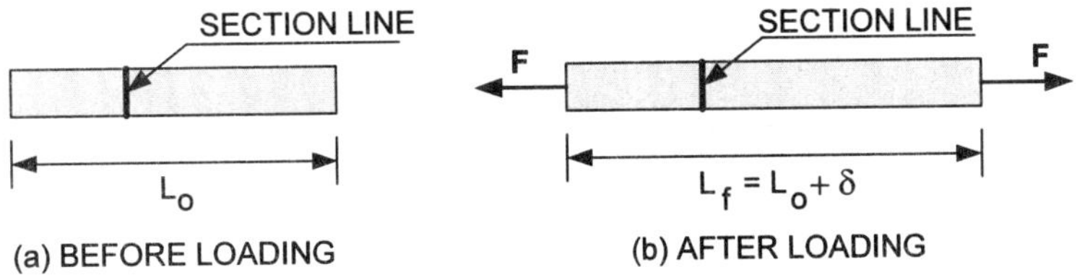

2.3 NORMAL STRESSES, STRAINS AND DEFORMATION

In a design analysis, we compute the axial forces acting on the uniaxial member, the amount it elongates under load, and the stresses developed. Next, we compare the stresses acting on the structural member with its strength to determine a safety factor. The size of the safety factor is evaluated to determine if this member is safe to be employed in a structure used by the public. This section describes methods that will enable you to size cables, rods and bars to provide structures with adequate safety margins.

We will divide the examples in this presentation into two parts; the first dealing with cables that are subjected to tensile forces, and the second involving rods and bars subjected to either tensile or compressive forces. The reason for the separation is the difference in the structural applications. The flexible cables are often used with pulleys for lifting and for high-strength tension members. Rods and bars are employed as tie rods or columns in structural applications. While the applications differ, the equations governing the behavior of the flexible and the stiff members are the same.

What happens if we pull on a wire and continue to pull with increasing force? The wire elongates, and deforms still more until it fails by breaking. Let's explore the deformation of the wire and the consequences of different types of failure of the wire in subsequent sections.

2.3.1 Deformation of Wire under Load

When we pull on a wire it elongates as shown in Fig. 2.1b. This **elongation** or **deformation** of the wire δ is defined as:

$$\delta = L_f - L_o \tag{2.1}$$

where L_f is the length of the wire under load and L_o is the original length.

A FBD of a segment of wire is shown in Fig. 2.2b. The equilibrium relation ($\Sigma F_x = 0$) indicates that the internal force P, anywhere along the length of the uniaxial member, is equal to the external force F.

Fig. 2.2 FBD of a long thin member subject to an axial load.

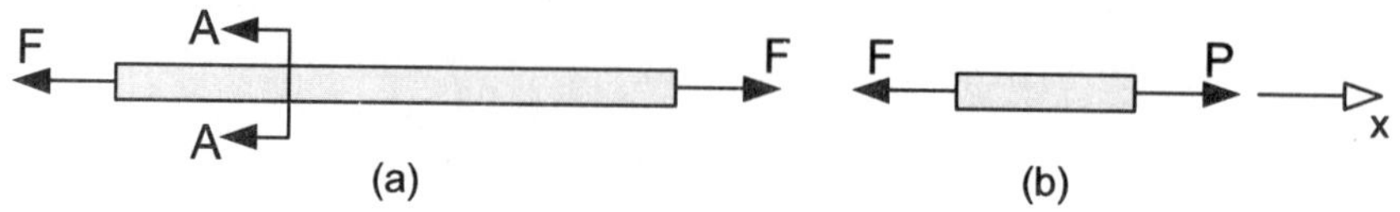

The elongation δ is determined from:

$$\delta = (PL)/(AE) \qquad (2.2)$$

where P is the internal force in the wire, in N or lb.
L is the length of the wire, in m or in.
$A = \pi r^2$ is the cross sectional area of the wire, in m^2 or in^2.
r is the radius of the wire, in m or in.
E is the **modulus of elasticity**, in GPa or psi.

We will derive Eq. (2.2) later in this section. It is important at this time to understand that the deformation of the wire δ is a very small quantity if the wire is fabricated from a metal such as steel or aluminum. To demonstrate the magnitude of the axial deformation, consider the following example.

EXAMPLE 2.1

A No. 30 gage[3] steel music wire (0.080 in. in diameter) is employed to lift a weight of 200 lb. If the wire is 6 ft. in length, determine the amount that the wire elongates under load.

Solution:

In Appendix B-1, we note that the modulus of elasticity for steel is listed as $E = 30 \times 10^6$ psi. Next, let's substitute the values for P, L, $A = \pi r^2$ and E into Eq. (2.2) to obtain:

$$\delta = (PL)/(AE) = (200\ \text{lb})(6\ \text{ft})(12\ \text{in/ft})/[\pi\ (0.040\ \text{in.})^2\ (30 \times 10^6\ \text{lb/in}^2)]$$

$$\delta = 0.09549\ \text{in.} \qquad (a)$$

Is 0.09549 in. a small deformation of the wire? Small is a relative term and must be compared to another value to be judged. Let's compare the amount of this elongation to the original length of the wire by computing the ratio:

$$\delta/L_o = 0.09549/(6)(12) = 0.001326 \text{ or } 0.1326\% \qquad (b)$$

The 200 lb load elongates the wire by slightly more than one tenth of one percent. That is a very small deformation when compared to the original length of the wire.

[3]There are several standards for gage sizes that define the diameter of wire or the thickness of sheet metal. Four of the commonly referenced standards are presented in Appendix A.

2.3.2 Strain in the Wire under Load

Let's conduct a simple experiment[4] and observe the behavior of a wire under the action of a monotonically increasing tensile load. If we measure the load F applied to the wire, the deformation δ of the wire, and equate the external force F to the internal force P, we can construct the graph shown in Fig. 2.3a.

Note a linear relationship exists between P and δ as indicated by Eq. (2.2). This P-δ curve is a straight line until the wire begins to fail by **yielding**. The linear portion of the P-δ relation is the **elastic region** of the load-deflection response. Equation (2.2) is valid only in this elastic region.

Fig. 2.3a Graph of load versus elongation and (b) stress versus strain.

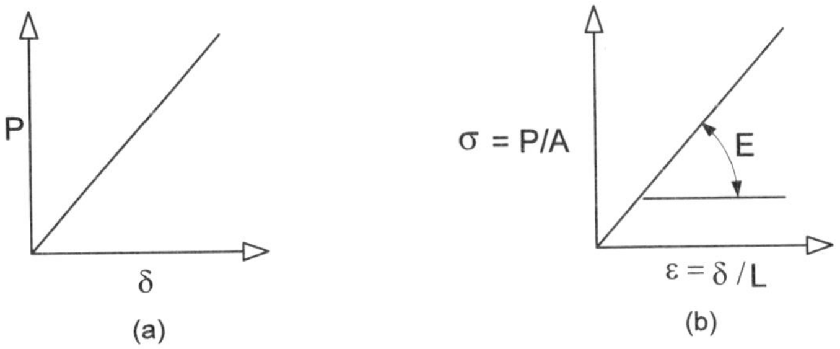

Let's modify the axes in Fig. 2.3a by dividing the force P by the area A and the deformation δ by the length L as indicated below:

$$\varepsilon = \delta/L \tag{2.3}$$

$$\sigma = P/A \tag{2.4}$$

where ε is the normal strain and σ is the normal stress in the wire, respectively.

These relations show that the **normal strain** ε is the change in length divided by the original length — a dimensionless quantity. The **normal stress** σ is the internal force P divided by the area A over which it acts. The stress is expressed in terms of Pa (Pascal) in SI units or psi (lb/in^2) in U. S. Customary units. We have shown the graph of stress versus strain in Fig. 2.3b. As expected there is a linear relation between stress and strain until the stress is sufficient to cause the wire to yield. The **slope** of the σ−ε line, in the elastic region, is the **modulus of elasticity** E of the material from which the wire is fabricated. The **modulus of elasticity** is a **material property**, which is independent of the shape of the body. More extensive descriptions of material properties and their methods of measurement are given later in Sections 2.6 and 2.7.

It is evident from the linear response in the stress-strain diagram that:

$$\sigma = E\,\varepsilon \tag{2.5}$$

This stress-strain relation is known as **Hooke's law**. It is named after Robert Hooke who is credited with the discovery of elasticity in the 17th century. A word of caution — Hooke's law is valid only for uniaxial states of stress that arise in long, thin structural members. We will introduce another

[4] Formal test procedures to determine material properties will be presented in Section 2.6.

more complex form of the stress-strain relation to accommodate multi-axial stress fields later in Chapter 7.

Let's combine Eqs. (2.3), (2.4) and (2.5) in the manner shown below:

$$\sigma = P/A = E\varepsilon = (E\delta/L) \qquad \text{(a)}$$

and solve Eq. (a) for δ to derive Eq. (2.2) as:

$$\delta = (PL)/(AE) \qquad \text{(2.2)}$$

EXAMPLE 2.2

Determine the strain that develops in a 5 m long wire, which is elongated by 8 mm.

Solution:

Using Eq. (2.3), we write:

$$\varepsilon = \delta/L = (8 \times 10^{-3}\ \text{m})/(5\ \text{m}) = 0.0016 \text{ dimensionless} \qquad \text{(a)}$$

Note that strain is dimensionless, because we divided a change in length by the original length. Also, observe that we have determined the strain without knowledge of the material used in fabricating the wire. **Strain is a geometric concept.** The strain imposed on a wire or rod may be determined without knowledge of the applied load or the material's modulus of elasticity if the amount of deformation and the original length of the member are known.

EXAMPLE 2.3

Determine the strain that develops in an 8 ft long wire that is subjected to a force of 120 lb. The wire size is Gage 10 (0.10189 in. diameter) and it is fabricated from an aluminum alloy 2024-T4.

Solution:

Using Eq. (2.3), we write:

$$\varepsilon = \delta/L \qquad \text{(a)}$$

Recall Eq. (2.2):

$$\delta = (PL)/(AE) \qquad \text{(b)}$$

Combining Eqs. (2.2) and (2.3) yields:

$$\varepsilon = P/(AE) \qquad \text{(2.6)}$$

From Appendix B-1, we find the modulus of elasticity E for aluminum alloy 2024-T4 is 10.4 × 10^6 psi. Next, we compute the cross sectional area of the wire as:

$$A = \pi r^2 = \pi d^2/4 = \pi(0.10189)^2/4 = 0.008154 \text{ in.} \qquad \text{(c)}$$

Substituting values for P, A and E into Eq. (2.6) gives:

$$\varepsilon = 120 \text{ lb}/[(0.008154 \text{ in.}^2)(10.4 \times 10^6 \text{ lb/in.}^2)] = 1.415 \times 10^{-3} \qquad \text{(d)}$$

In this example, it was necessary to use the value of the modulus of elasticity in determining the strain. Why? The modulus of elasticity was needed because the deformation (elongation) of the wire was not specified in the problem statement. It was necessary to determine the deformation of the wire from the load using Eq. (2.2). This step in the analysis required the introduction the modulus of elasticity in the calculation.

2.3.3 Internal Forces and Stresses

Internal forces that develop within a structural member when it is subjected to external loads produce stresses. In Chapter 1, we reviewed the concept of internal forces and showed that they are determined from the appropriate equations of equilibrium. We also indicated the necessity for making an imaginary section cut to expose the cross sectional area of the member over which these stresses act. In this section, we emphasize the connection between the external forces, internal forces, and the stresses that develop at any point along the length of the uniaxial member.

To illustrate these connections, examine Fig 2.4, which shows an axial member subjected to external axial forces F. To determine the internal forces and the resulting normal stresses a four step procedure is employed:

1. We identify the member of interest and the forces acting on the body in Fig. 2.4a.
2. A section cut is made at a location of interest along the length of the member. We then remove one end or the other to construct the FBD depicted in Fig. 2.4b.
3. The equilibrium relation $\Sigma F_x = 0$ is written proving that F (external) = P (internal).
4. Using Eq. (2.4) (σ = P/A), we convert the internal force P into the normal stress σ as indicated in Fig. 2.4c.

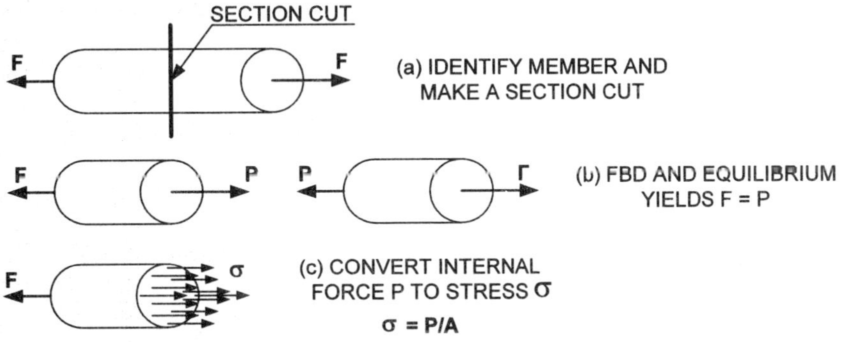

Fig. 2.4 An illustration showing the transition from external forces to internal forces to stresses.

In this illustration, the internal force P is a constant over the length of the uniaxial member and the location of the section cut is not important. However, you should be aware that in some applications the internal forces vary from one location to another. In these situations, the location of the section cut is vitally important. Also observe in Fig. 2.4c that the distribution of the stress σ is uniform over the cross sectional area exposed by the section cut. The uniform distribution is a result of two conditions:

- Plane sections remain plane for long, thin members subjected to axial loading.
- Internal moments do not develop under the applied external loading.

In the general case where the normal stresses may not be uniformly distributed, we relate the internal force and the normal stress over an area A by:

$$P = \int \sigma \, dA \qquad (2.7)$$

However, when the stress is uniformly distributed as shown in Fig. 2.4, Eq. (2.7) reduces to:

$$P = \sigma \int dA = \sigma A \qquad (2.8)$$

EXAMPLE 2.4

Determine the stress in a 2.0 mm diameter wire subjected to an axial load of 400 N.

Solution:

From Eq. (2.4), we write

$$\sigma = P/A \qquad (a)$$

From a FBD identical to the one shown in Fig. 2.4b and the equilibrium relation $\Sigma F_x = 0$, we understand that:

$$F = P = 400 \text{ N} \qquad (b)$$

The area $A = \pi d^2/4 = \pi(2.0 \text{ mm})^2/4 = 3.1416 \text{ mm}^2$. Substituting these values into Eq. (a) gives:

$$\sigma = (400 \text{ N})/(3.1416 \text{ mm}^2) = 127.3 \text{ N/mm}^2 = 127.3 \text{ MPa} \qquad (c)$$

Note that $1.0 \text{ N/mm}^2 = 1.0$ MPa. Later in this chapter, we will present an interpretation of this result after we describe in detail the strength of structural materials.

EXAMPLE 2.5

A large diameter wire rope, fabricated from steel with a cross sectional area of 12.566 in.^{2}, is to support a portion of the roadway on a suspension bridge. The highway engineers have specified that the maximum load imposed on the cable is not to exceed 200 ton. Determine the stress and strain in the wire rope when subjected to the specified load.

Solution:

Let's compute the stress from Eq. (2.4) as:

$$\sigma = P/A = (200 \text{ ton})(2{,}000 \text{ lb/ton})/(12.566 \text{ in.}^2) = 31{,}830 \text{ psi} = 31.83 \text{ ksi} \qquad (a)$$

Next, calculate the strain ε from Eq. (2.6) to obtain:

$$\varepsilon = P/(AE) = (400{,}000 \text{ lb})/[(12.566 \text{ in}^2)(30 \times 10^6 \text{ lb/in}^2)] = 1.061 \times 10^{-3} \quad \text{(b)}$$

In determining the strain, we obtained the value of $E = 30 \times 10^6$ psi for steel from Appendix B-1. We also introduced ksi, a unit in the U. S. Customary system. The conversion factor between psi and ksi is given by ⇒ 1 ksi = 1,000 psi.

EXAMPLE 2.6

Determine the stress in the bar shown in Fig. E2.6 when subjected to a compressive axial force of F that acts through the centroid of the bar. The following numerical parameters define the bar and the applied load: F = 1,000 kN, L = 600 mm, w = 150 mm and h = 100 mm.

Fig. E2.6

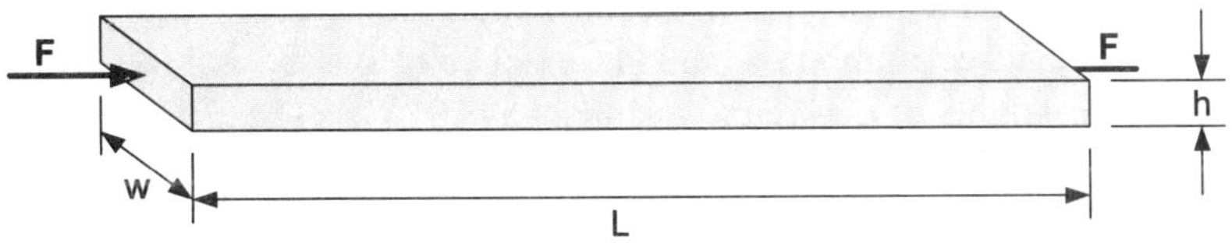

Solution:

We make a section cut near the center of the bar, and construct the free body diagram shown in Fig. E2.6a:

Fig. E2.6a

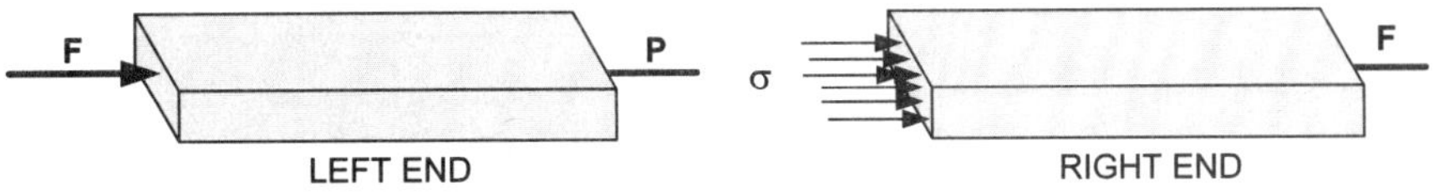

The stresses σ visible on the face exposed by the section cut are due to the internal force P. It is clear from $\Sigma F_x = 0$ that P = F; then from Eq. (2.4), we write:

$$\sigma = P/A = (-\,1{,}000 \times 10^3 \text{ N})/[(150)(100)\text{mm}^2]$$

$$\sigma = -\,66.67 \text{ N/mm}^2 = -\,66.67 \text{ MPa}$$

The axial stress is a negative number (– 66.67 MPa) indicating that a compressive stress develops in the bar due to the compressive axial loading. Also observe that the value of the stress is independent of the material used to fabricate the bar.

EXAMPLE 2.7

If the bar described in Example 2.6 is fabricated from steel, determine the length of the bar after the application of the compressive force.

Solution:

An inspection of the free body diagram shown in Fig E2.6a indicates that the internal force P is constant from one end of the bar to the other and equal to the external force F. Using Eqs. (2.1) and (2.2), we may write:

$$\delta = L_f - L_0 = (PL_0)/(AE) \qquad \text{(a)}$$

Solving Eq. (a) for L_f, gives:

$$L_f = L_0\,[1 + P/(AE)] \qquad \text{(b)}$$

Substituting numerical values for the known parameters in Eq. (b) yields:

$$L_f = 600\,[1 + (-\,1{,}000 \times 10^3)/\{(100)(150)(207 \times 10^3)\}]$$

$$L_f = 600\,[1 - 0.3221 \times 10^{-3}]\text{ m} = (600 - 0.1932)\text{ mm} = 599.807\text{ mm} \qquad \text{(c)}$$

Because the new length of the rod is 599.807 mm, it is apparent that it contracted by 0.1932 mm under the action of the compressive load. The value of P in Eq. (2.2) is treated as a negative number when the axial load on the bar is compressive. Also, the value of the modulus of elasticity was taken as 207 GPa (i.e. 207,000 MPa) from Appendix B-1.

EXAMPLE 2.8

Determine the axial deformation in a 3-foot long rod that has a diameter of 4 in. The rod is fabricated from mild steel with a yield strength S_y = 35,000 psi, and is subjected to an axial compressive load of 120,000 lb. Repeat the solution for the rod if it is fabricated from an aluminum alloy.

Solution:

Again, we begin with a drawing of the rod and a free body diagram in Fig. E2.8, which showing the forces F and P and the normal stresses σ.

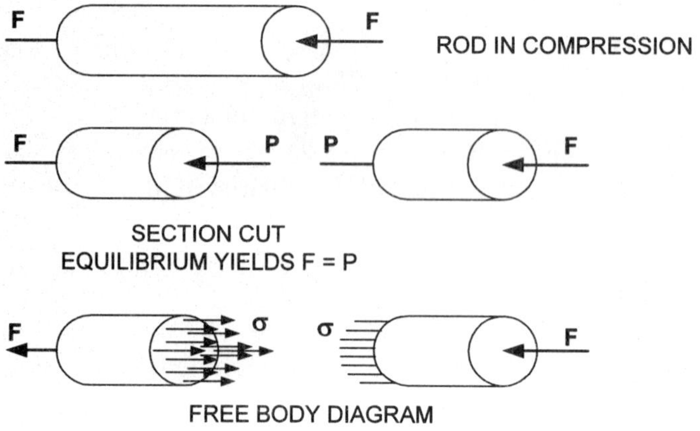

Fig. E2.8

An inspection of the free body diagram in Fig. E2.8 indicates that the internal force P is constant over the entire length of the rod. From Eq. (2.2), we write:

$$\delta = (PL)/(AE) \qquad \text{(a)}$$

Substituting the values for the known quantities for the steel rod in Eq. (a) gives:

$$\delta = -\ [(120{,}000)(3)(12)]\ /\ [(\pi)(2)^2\ (30 \times 10^6)] = -\ 0.01146 \text{ in.} \qquad \text{(b)}$$

Substituting the values for the known quantities for the aluminum rod in Eq. (a) gives:

$$\delta = -\ [(120{,}000)(3)(12)]\ /\ [(\pi)(2)^2\ (10.4 \times 10^6)] = -\ 0.03306 \text{ in.} \qquad \text{(c)}$$

Both solutions carry a negative sign indicating that the rod is compressed (shortened) by the action of the compressive force. It is interesting to observe that the rod fabricated from an aluminum alloy exhibited nearly three times the deformation of the steel rod. The reason for this difference is in the lower modulus of elasticity of aluminum relative to steel. The modulus of elasticity for aluminum and steel used in this calculation was 10.4×10^6 and 30×10^6 psi, respectively, as cited in Appendix B-1.

2.4 SHEAR STRESSES

In the preceding discussions, the stresses created by internal forces were normal to the area exposed by the section cut. To emphasize this fact, we called them **normal stresses**. A second type of stress exists—a **shear stress**. As the name implies, the shear stress lies in the plane of the area exposed by the section cut. To show shear stresses in a more graphical manner, consider the stubby block-like member loaded with the force F in Fig. 2.5.

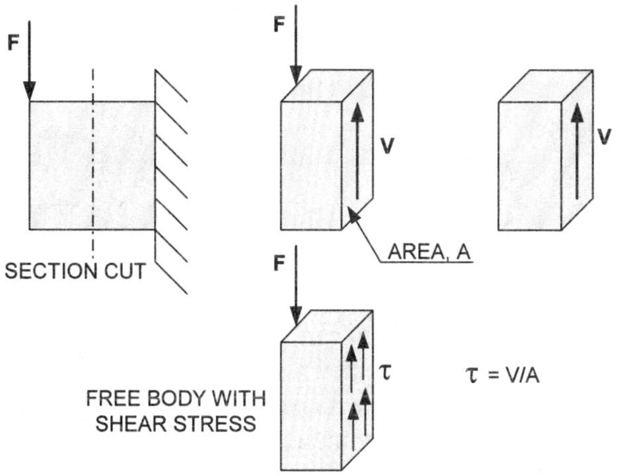

Fig. 2.5 A section cut made in a stubby block-like member produces a free body.

First, cut the stubby member to create a free body of the left end, and then apply an internal shear force V in the plane of the area exposed by the section cut[5]. From $\sum F_y = 0$, we determine that F = V. The shear force V is produced by a shear stress τ. The relation between the shear stress τ and the shear force V is:

$$\tau = V/A \qquad (2.9)$$

[5]To maintain the focus of this discussion on shear forces, we have not included the internal moment acting at the section cut on the FBD in Fig. 2.5.

We have assumed that the shear stress τ is uniformly distributed over the area of the stubby member. Later, in the discussion of beam theory found in Chapter 4, we will note that the shear stress is not uniformly distributed over the cross sectional area of a beam. However, for many short, stubby members, the assumption of a uniform distribution of shear stresses is a reasonable approximation.

EXAMPLE 2.9

A key is employed to keep a gear from slipping on a shaft when transmitting power. Forces F of 50 kN are created on the key at the locations shown in Fig. E2.9. Determine the shear stresses in the key if it is 12 mm wide, 12 mm high and 50 mm long.

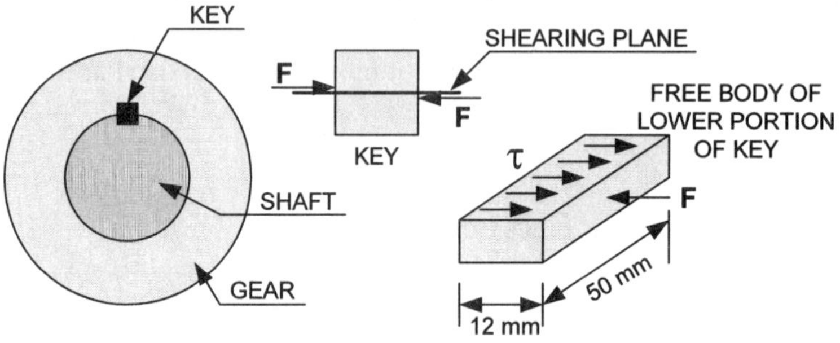

Fig. E2.9 A section cut showing shear forces acting on a key, which prevents the gear from slipping on the shaft

Solution:

We construct a FBD of the key, presented in Fig. E2.9, showing the equal and opposite forces F and the shear plane between the gear and the shaft. We section the key along the shear plane and draw another free body diagram of its lower portion. On this second free body diagram, we illustrate the shear stresses τ that occur on the shear plane.

The shear stresses on the key are given by Eq. (2.9) as:

$$\tau = V/A = (50 \times 10^3)/[(0.012)(0.050)] = 83.33 \text{ MPa} \qquad \text{(a)}$$

2.4.1 Design Analysis of Joints Fabricated with Bolts and Rivets

In the design of structures and pressure vessels joints, connecting two or more members is often required. The joints can be fabricated by welding or by bolting or riveting. Let's consider several joint designs fabricated with either bolts or rivets as shown in Fig. 2.6. The joint presented in Fig. 2.6a is an lap joint with rivets having a single shear plane. The illustration in Fig. 2.6b shows a butt joint and a single strap with rivets having a single shear plane. The joint depicted in Fig. 2.6c is a butt joint and a double strap with rivets having a double shear plane.

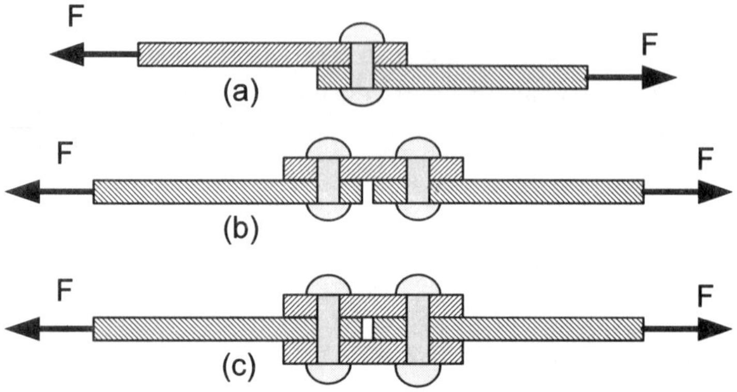

Fig. 2.6 Lap and butt joints with rivet fasteners.
(a) Overlapping joint
(b) Butt joint with single strap.
(c) Butt joint with double strap.

These joints are often used to connect wide plates[6] and the rivets or bolts are placed in single, double or triple rows depending on the forces that are transmitted across the joint. An example of a single row of rivets in a lap joint is presented in Fig. 2.7.

Fig. 2.7 A single row of rivets to fasten two overlapping plates forming a lap joint in a wide plate.

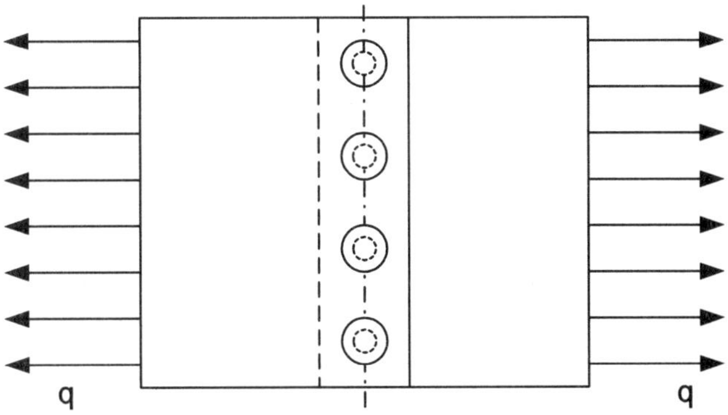

In these lap and butt joints, we are concerned with shear stresses that develop in the rivets and with the normal stresses developed along the section of the plate containing the rivet holes. Let's begin by drawing a FBD of the rivet in a single-shear-plane, lap joint, as shown in Fig. 2.8. Note that friction forces that occur between the plates that are fastened together have been neglected when preparing this FBD.

Fig. 2.8 FBD of the rivet in a single shear plane lap joint.

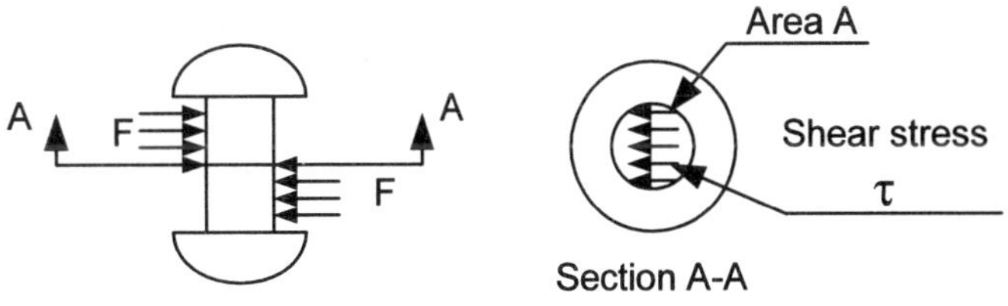

The shear stress τ developed at the shearing plane of the rivet is given by:

$$\tau = F/A \tag{2.10}$$

where A is the cross sectional area of the bolt or rivet and F is the force applied to each rivet. The force F is determined from:

$$F = qw/N \tag{2.11}$$

where q is the applied force per unit length; w is the width of the joint and N is the number of rivets.

The analysis of the butt joint that incorporates two straps (see Fig. 2.6c) is almost identical to that shown above. The FBD, presented in Fig. 2.9, shows two shearing planes, which carry the shear stresses. The shear stress on each plane is given by:

$$\tau = F/(2A) \tag{2.12}$$

[6] Aircraft structures fabricated from thin plates of aluminum employ many riveted joints to form the complex structure.

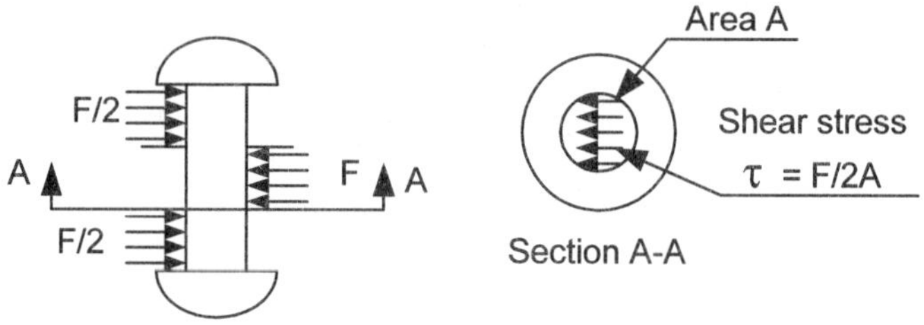

Fig. 2.9 FBD of the rivet in a butt joint with double straps.

Next consider the normal stresses σ that occur along the rivet line. Drilling holes to accommodate the rivets increases the normal stresses in the plates. To determine the elevated levels of the normal stresses along the rivet line, prepare a FBD as shown in Fig. 2.10.

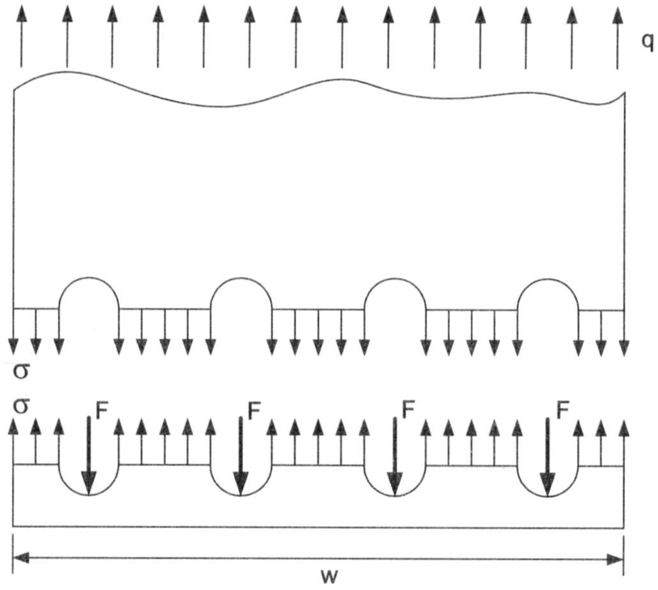

Fig. 2.10 FBD of the joint showing the normal stresses along the rivet line.

Let's consider the upper portion of the joint shown in Fig. 2.10 and write the equation of equilibrium for forces in the direction of the applied forces q to obtain:

$$\Sigma F_y = qw - \sigma t(w - Nd) = 0 \qquad \text{(a)}$$

where w is the width of the joint, d is the diameter of the rivet hole and N is the number of rivets.

Solving Eq. (a) for σ yields:

$$\sigma = qw/[t(w - Nd)] \qquad (2.13)$$

EXAMPLE 2.10

The lap joint with a single shear plane, shown in Fig. E2.10, is 400 mm wide with four bolts spaced on 100 mm centers. The two plates are each 10 mm thick and the bolts are 12 mm in diameter. Determine the shear stress in the bolts if the applied force q is uniformly distributed over the width of the joint and equal to 70 N/mm. Also determine the nominal normal stress acting along a section through the bolt line.

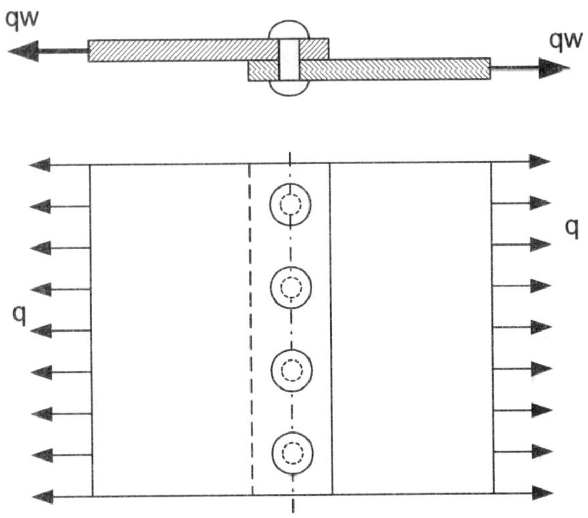

Fig. E2.10

Solution:

Substituting Eq. (2.11) into Eq. (2.10) gives:

$$\tau = qw/(NA) \qquad (a)$$

The cross sectional area of a single bolt is given by:

$$A = \pi d^2/4 = \pi\,(12)^2/4 = 113.1\ \text{mm}^2 \qquad (b)$$

Substituting Eq. (b) into Eq. (a) yields:

$$\tau = qw/(NA) = (70)(400)/(4)(113.1) = 61.89\ \text{MPa} \qquad (c)$$

The normal stresses σ in the plate along a section through the bolt line is given by Eq. (2.13) as:

$$\sigma = qw/[t(w - Nd)] = (70)(400)/[10(400 - 4 \times 12)] = 7.955\ \text{MPa} \qquad (d)$$

The determination of the shearing stress in the bolts and the normal stress along the bolt line is the first step in the analysis of a joint. We will compare these stresses to the strength of the materials from which the joint is fabricated later in this chapter.

EXAMPLE 2.11

The butt joint with double straps, shown in Fig. E2.11, is 600 mm wide with four bolts spaced on 150 mm centers on each bolt line. The four plates are each 15 mm thick and the bolts are 20 mm in diameter. Determine the shear stress in the bolts if the applied force q is uniformly distributed over the width of the joint and equal to 400 N/mm. Also determine the nominal normal stress acting along a section through the bolt line

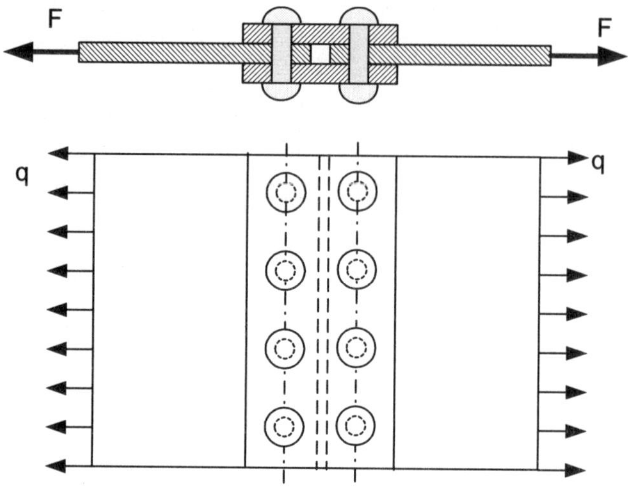

Fig. E2.11

Solution:

Substituting Eq. (2.11) into Eq. (2.12) gives:

$$\tau = qw/(2NA) \tag{2.14}$$

The cross sectional area of a single bolt is given by:

$$A = \pi d^2/4 = \pi\,(20)^2/4 = 314.2 \text{ mm}^2 \tag{a}$$

Substituting Eq. (a) into Eq. (2.14) yields:

$$\tau = qw/(2NA) = (400)(600)/(2)(4)(314.2) = 95.48 \text{ MPa} \tag{b}$$

The normal stresses σ in the plate along a section through the bolt line are given by Eq. (2.13) as:

$$\sigma = qw/[t(w - Nd)] = (400)(600)/[15(600 - 4 \times 20] = 30.77 \text{ MPa} \tag{c}$$

The determination of the shearing stress in the bolts and the normal stress along the bolt line is the first step in the analysis of a joint. We will compare these stresses to the strength of the materials from which the joint is fabricated later in this chapter.

2.4.2 Design Analysis of Pull-out in Bolted or Riveted Joints

Another mode of failure can occur with bolted or riveted joints called pullout. Pullout occurs when the distance from the bolt line to the edge of the joint is too short. Let's consider a simple joint with a single rivet, as shown in Fig. 2.11. We have represented the end of the joint with a single plate that has been sectioned along the bolt line. The load per unit length applied to the top piece is q, which is balanced by normal stresses (not shown) along the section through the bolt line. The rivet applies a force F to the bottom piece as shown in Fig 2.11. The force F is balanced by the normal stresses (not shown) along the section though the bolt line.

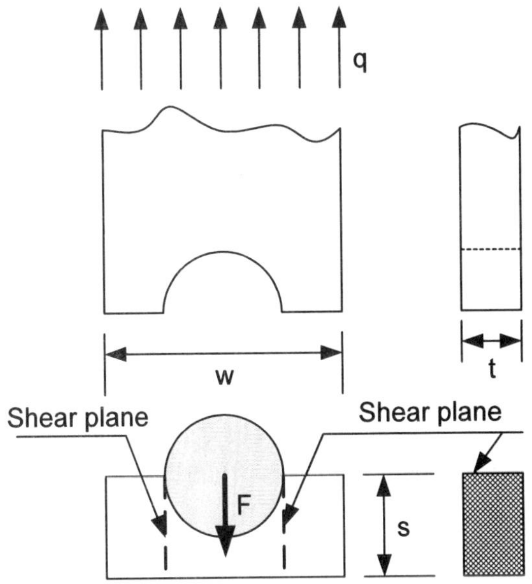

Fig. 2.11 FBD of a simple joint with a single rivet showing the shear planes associated with pullout.

Next let's remove a small region of the joint below the rivet that includes the shear planes, as shown in Fig. 2.12. There is a shear stress τ that acts on each of the two shear planes. We assume the shear stresses are uniformly distributed over the area exposed by the section cuts.

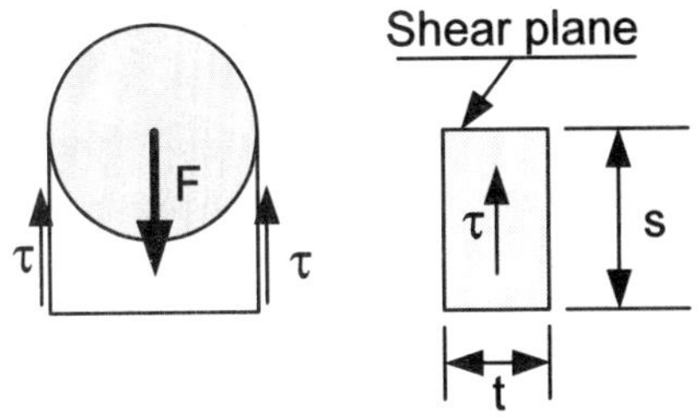

Fig. 2.12 FBD of the small region directly below the rivet that shows the shear stresses acting on the two shear planes.

The force acting on each rivet, if we consider a joint containing N rivets, is given by:

$$F = qw/N \qquad (2.11)$$

The shear stresses on each of the shearing planes is given by:

$$\tau = F/A_{Shear} = qw/[2N\,(t\,s)] = qw/[2N\,(t\,s)] \qquad (2.15)$$

EXAMPLE 2.12

For the joint described in Example 2.10, determine the shear stress associated with pullout if the distance s from the bolt centerline to the edge of the plates is 12 mm.

Solution:

The force acting on each bolt is determined from Eq. (2.11) as:

$$F = qw/N = (70)(400)/4 = 7.00 \text{ kN} \quad \text{(a)}$$

The shear stresses on each of the shearing planes determined from Eq. (2.15) as:

$$\tau = qw/[2N\ (t\ s)] = (70)(400)/[(2)(4)(10)(12)] = 29.17 \text{ MPa} \quad \text{(b)}$$

The determination of the shearing stress that lead to bolt or rivet pullout is the second step in the analysis of a joint. We will compare these shear stresses with the strengths of the plate materials from which the joint is fabricated later in this chapter.

EXAMPLE 2.13

For the joint described in Example 2.11, determine the shear stress associated with pullout if the distance s from the bolt centerline to the edge of the plates is 15 mm.

Solution:

The force acting on each bolt is determined from Eq. (2.11) as:

$$F = qw/N = (400)(600)/4 = 60.00 \text{ kN} \quad \text{(a)}$$

The shear stresses on each of the shearing planes determined from Eq. (2.15) as:

$$\tau = qw/[2N\ (ts\ )] = (400)(600)/[(2)(4)(15)(15)] = 133.3 \text{ MPa} \quad \text{(b)}$$

The determination of the shearing stress that lead to bolt or rivet pullout is the second step in the analysis of a joint. We will compare these shear stresses with the strengths of the plate materials from which the joint is fabricated later in this chapter.

2.5 BEARING STRESSES

Bearing stresses occur at the interface between two bodies on contact. Consider the case of a cylinder of diameter d in contact with a large-thick-flat plate, as shown in Fig. 2.13. A force F is applied to the cylinder, which is held in equilibrium by the reaction at the interface between the cylinder and the thick plate. The stresses that develops at the interface are called bearing stresses denoted by the symbol σ_B.

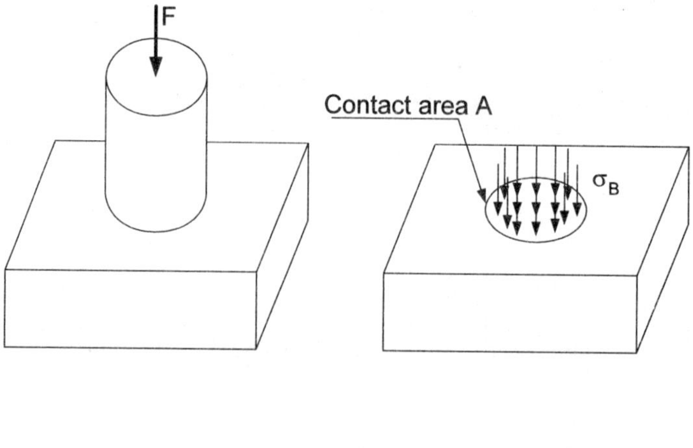

Fig. 2.13 Bearing stresses σ_B occur at the interface of two bodies in contact.

The bearing stresses are determined from:

$$\sigma_B = F/A \tag{2.16}$$

2.5.1 Bearing Stresses in Bolted or Riveted Joints

The determination of bearing stresses developed in a riveted or a bolted joint is more involved because the mating surfaces are semi-circular and not flat. Consider a rivet subjected to a force F that is supported by the plate of the joint, as shown in Fig. 2.14. In this case, the bearing stresses are distributed around the semi-circular contact region. The bearing stresses σ_B vary from zero at point A, which lies on the horizontal axis, to a maximum at point B, which is directly under the vertical centerline of the assembly.

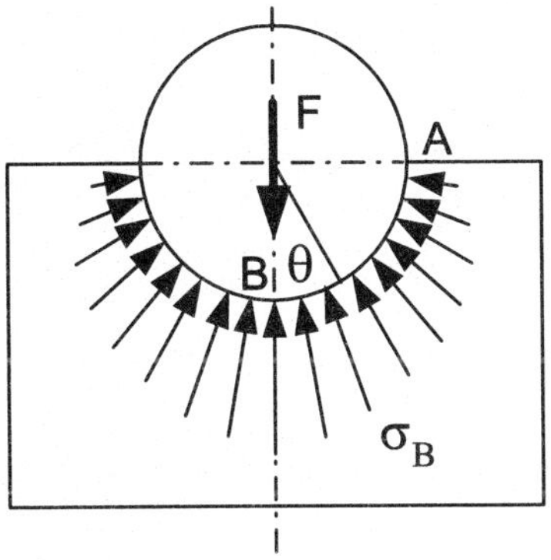

Fig. 2.14 Distribution of bearing stresses σ_B around the semi-circular contact region.

The equilibrium equation $\sum F_y = 0$ enables us to write:

$$F = 2\int_0^{\pi/2} (\sigma_B)(t)\cos\theta(r\,d\theta) \tag{2.17}$$

where t is the thickness of the plate and r is the radius of the rivet.

Next, we assume that the bearing stresses follow a cosine distribution over the contact region from $\theta = -\pi/2$ to $\theta = +\pi/2$ and write:

$$\sigma_B = (\sigma_B)_{Max} \cos\theta \tag{2.18}$$

Substituting Eq. (2.18) into Eq. (2.17) and using a trigonometric identity yields:

$$F = 2t\,r(\sigma_B)_{Max}\int_0^{\pi/2} \cos^2\theta\, d\theta = 2t\,r(\sigma_B)_{Max}\int_0^{\pi/2} \frac{1+\cos 2\theta}{2} d\theta \tag{a}$$

Integrating Eq. (a) and solving for $(\sigma_B)_{Max}$ gives:

$$(\sigma_B)_{Max} = \frac{2F}{\pi t r} = \frac{4F}{\pi t d} \tag{2.19}$$

where d is the diameter of the rivet

On the other hand, if the distribution of σ_B around the periphery of the bolt hole is assumed to be uniform, we can rewrite Eq. (2.17) as:

$$F = 2t\, r\sigma_B \int_0^{\pi/2} \cos\theta \, d\theta \qquad (2.20)$$

Integrating Eq. (2.20) and solving for (σ_B) gives:

$$(\sigma_B) = \frac{F}{2\,t\,r} = \frac{F}{t\,d} = \frac{F}{A_P} \qquad (2.21)$$

where A_P is the projected area of the semicircular region onto its horizontal axis.

Equation (2.21) is often used to estimate σ_B because it follows the classic formula for stresses — F/A; however, Eq. (2.19) provides a more accurate estimate.

EXAMPLE 2.14

The lap joint with a single shear plane, shown in Fig. E2.14, is 560 mm wide with four bolts spaced on 140 mm centers. The two plates are each 12 mm thick and the bolts are 14 mm in diameter. Determine the bearing stress on the boltholes if the applied force q is uniformly distributed over the width of the joint and equal to 100 N/mm.

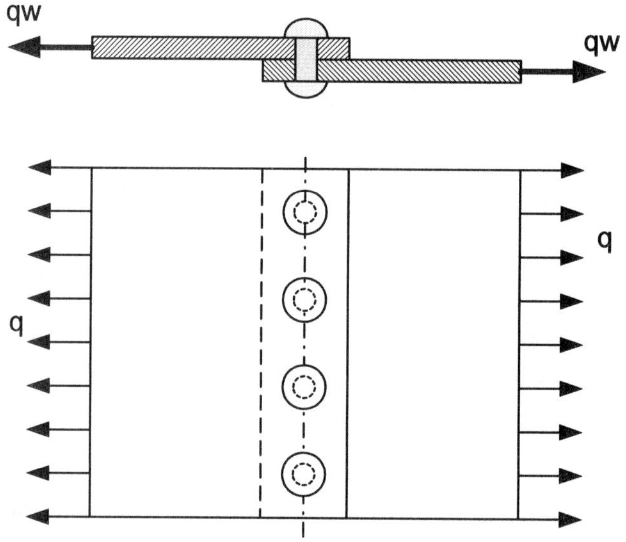

Fig. E2.14

Solution:

The force acting on a single rivet is determined from Eq. (2.11) as:

$$F = qw/N = (100)(560)/4 = 14 \text{ kN} \qquad (a)$$

If we assume the bearing stresses are distributed around the periphery of the bolthole as a cosine function, we determine σ_B using Eq. (2.19).

$$(\sigma_B)_{Max} = \frac{4F}{\pi\,t\,d} = \frac{4(14\times 10^3)}{\pi(12)(14)} = 106.1 \text{ MPa} \qquad (b)$$

If we assume the bearing stresses are uniformly distributed around the periphery of the bolthole, we determine σ_B using Eq. (2.21).

$$(\sigma_B) = \frac{F}{t\,d} = \frac{14 \times 10^3}{(12)(14)} = 83.33 \text{ MPa} \qquad \text{(c)}$$

Note that the result obtained using Eq. (2.19) is larger by a factor of $4/\pi$ or (1.273) than the result obtained with Eq. (2.21)

EXAMPLE 2.15

The butt joint with two straps, shown in Fig. E2.15, is 800 mm wide with four bolts spaced on 200 mm centers. The four plates are each 30 mm thick and the bolts are 25 mm in diameter. Determine the bearing stresses on the boltholes if the applied force q is uniformly distributed over the width of the joint and equal to 500 N/mm.

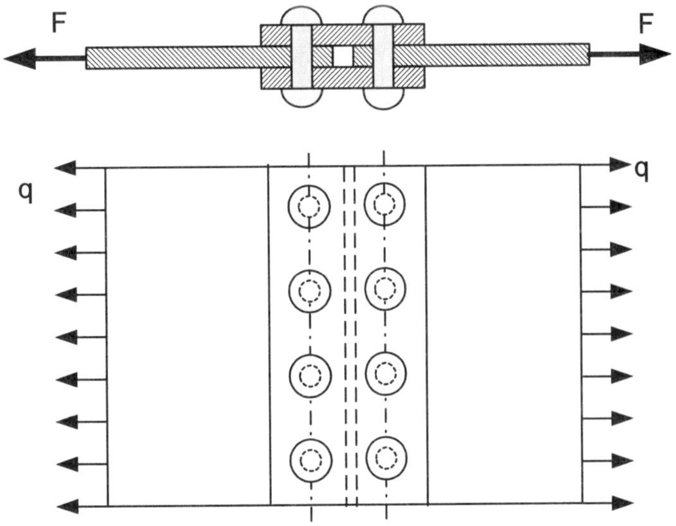

Fig. E2.15

Solution:

The force acting on a single rivet is determined from Eq. (2.11) as:

$$F = qw/N = (500)(800)/4 = 100 \text{ kN} \qquad \text{(a)}$$

If we assume the bearing stresses are distributed around the periphery of the bolthole as a cosine function, we determine σ_B using Eq. (2.19).

$$(\sigma_B)_{Max} = \frac{4F}{\pi\, t\, d} = \frac{4(100 \times 10^3)}{\pi(30)(25)} = 169.8 \text{ MPa} \qquad \text{(b)}$$

If we assume the bearing stresses are uniformly distributed around the periphery of the bolthole, we determine σ_B using Eq. (2.21).

$$(\sigma_B) = \frac{F}{t\,d} = \frac{100\times 10^3}{(30)(25)} = 133.3 \text{ MPa} \tag{c}$$

Note that the result obtained using Eq. (2.19) is larger by a factor of $4/\pi$ or (1.273) than the result obtained with Eq. (2.21)

2.6 THE TENSILE TEST

In Section 2.3 we made frequent mention of the material property known as the modulus of elasticity. In this section we will describe the methods employed to determine this property as well as the various strength of materials used in structures. Most of the material properties used in this textbook are determined by conducting standardized tensile tests[7]. For example, the yield and ultimate tensile strength are measured in this test. To begin, we prepare **tensile specimens** fabricated from the material under investigation. The standard size tensile specimen is shown in Fig. 2.15.

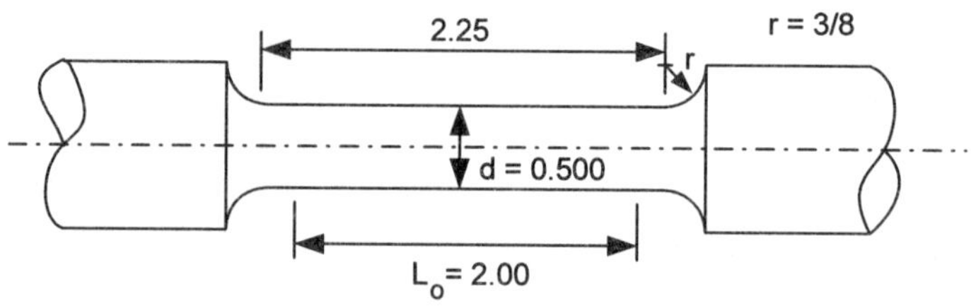

Fig. 2.15 Standard tensile test specimen (dimensions in inches).

The tensile specimen is mounted in a **universal testing machine** similar to the one illustrated in Fig. 2.16. The testing machine may be a mechanical type with one head fixed and the other driven by screws, or it may be a hydraulic machine where the movable head is driven by a hydraulic cylinder. In either instance, the testing machine applies a load F along the axis of the tensile specimen. A monotonic load is applied slowly until the specimen yields and/or fails by fracturing.

During the tension test, the applied load P and the elongation δ over the gage length L_o of the specimen are measured. A **load cell** on the universal testing machine measures the applied load and an **extensometer** mounted on the specimen, shown in Fig. 2.17, measures the elongation δ. The electrical signals from the load cell and the extensometer are recorded together on an x-y chart to provide a load-deflection (P-δ) curve that is proportional to the stress-strain (σ-ε) curve. The load-deflection curves recorded during the tension tests are converted into stress-strain curves that characterize the tensile behavior of the metallic material by utilizing:

$$\varepsilon = \delta/L_o \tag{2.3}$$

$$\sigma = P/A_o \tag{2.4}$$

where L_o and A_o are the initial gage length and cross sectional area of the tensile specimen.

[7] The American Society for Testing Materials (ASTM) publishes standards that define the test specimen and procedures for measuring the material properties described in this chapter. The standard for tension testing of metallic materials is in Section E8 of the *Annual Book of ASTM Standards*.

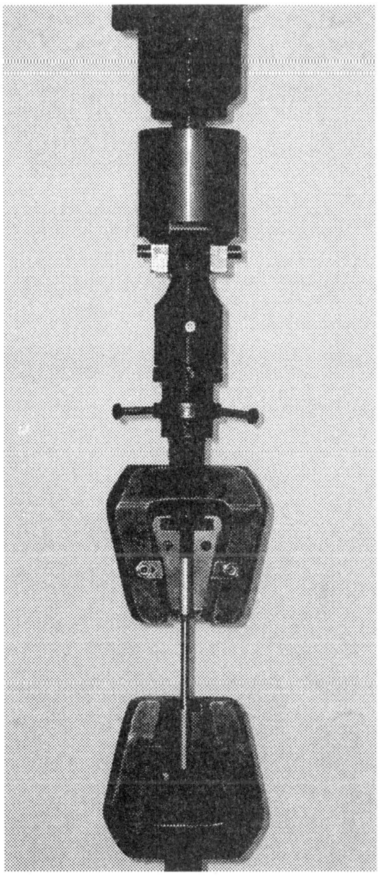

Fig. 2.16 Tensile specimen, wedge-grips, flex-joints and load cell in a testing machine.

This procedure gives the **engineering stress** and the **engineering strain,** which differ from the **true stress** and the **true strain**. In measuring the true stress and the true strain, the initial values of specimen length and area are replaced with their true values at the instant of the measurement.

For brittle materials, which do not exhibit significant plastic deformation before fracture, the stress-strain curve is nearly linear until failure, as indicated in Fig. 2.18. The stress σ_f producing the failure of the brittle specimen is recorded during the tensile test. It is this particular value of the stress that defines the material property known as the ultimate tensile strength S_u for a brittle material.

$$S_u = \sigma_f \qquad \text{for brittle materials} \qquad (2.22)$$

A photograph of a tension specimen that exhibited brittle failure is depicted in Fig. 2.19. Note the absence of any necking or extensive plastic deformation in the uniform section of the specimen. Brittle failure is dangerous because it is sudden and catastrophic. The fracture initiates without warning and the cracks propagate across the specimen (structure) in microseconds. Of course, in the selection of materials for our designs, we avoid the use of brittle materials in structures to preclude the possibility of a catastrophic failure. Brittle materials such as gray cast iron are sometimes used because of its excellent casting properties and for its ability to damp vibrations. However, when using brittle materials, care is exercised to maintain a state of compressive stress in the structure.

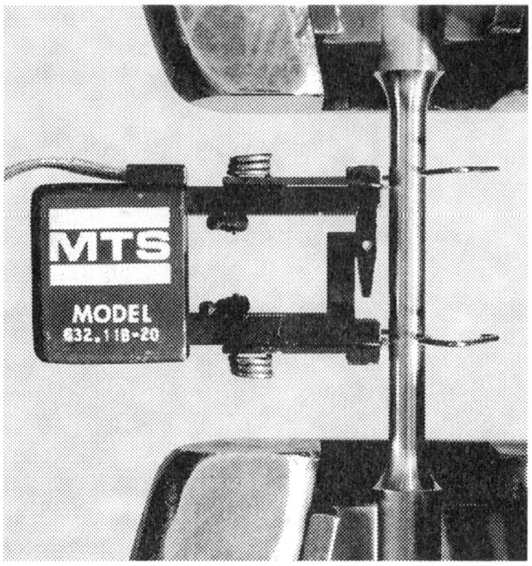

Fig. 2.17 A tension specimen with an extensometer for measuring the elongation δ.

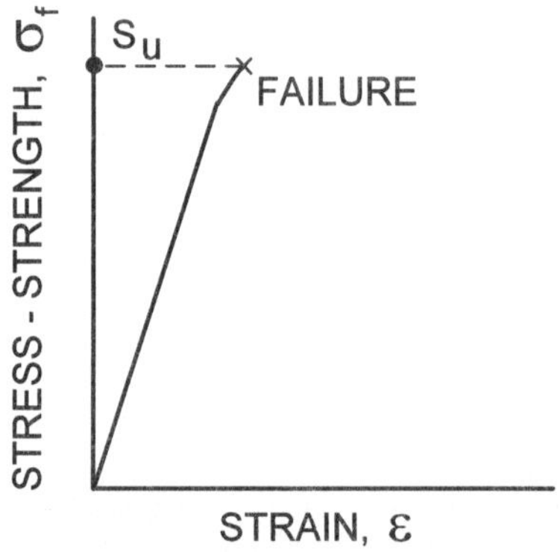

Fig. 2.18 Stress-strain curve for a brittle metallic material.

Fig. 2.19 Failure of a brittle material occurs suddenly with little plastic deformation.

Structures are designed with ductile materials, which yield and undergo extensive plastic deformation prior to rupture. A typical stress-strain curve for a ductile material (mild steel) is presented in Fig. 2.20.

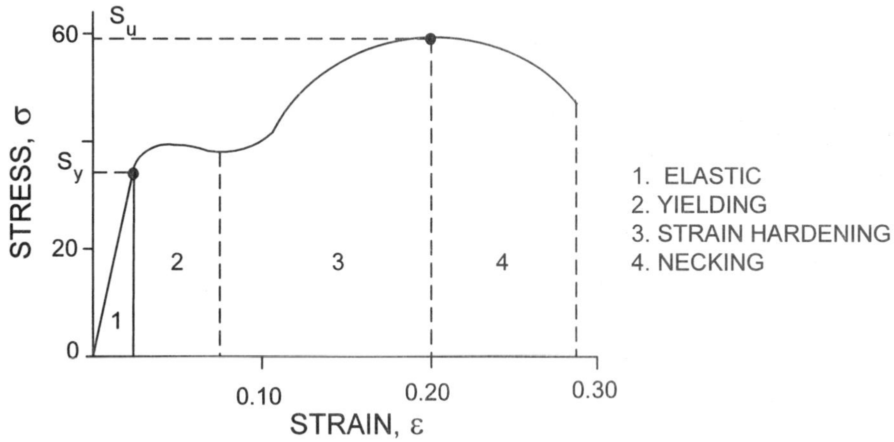

Fig. 2.20 Stress-strain diagram for low carbon steel.

An inspection of this stress-strain diagram shows that it exhibits four different regions; each region is related to a different behavior of ductile steel. The first is called the **elastic region** where the material responds in a linear manner. In this region, Hooke's law ($\sigma = E\,\varepsilon$) applies.

Hooke's law is a mathematical model of material behavior, but it is valid only in the elastic region. The elastic region extends until the low carbon steel (or some other ductile material) begins to yield. When the material yields, the linear response of the material ceases and Eq. (2.5) is no longer valid.

The second region on the stress-strain diagram depicts the initiation of yielding where the stress in the specimen exceeds the **elastic limit**. Slip planes have developed in the specimen, and deformation by slip along these planes is occurring with small or negligible increases in the stress. The stress-strain relationship is non-linear in this region. In some ductile materials, a small decrease in the applied stress is observed as the tensile specimen yields and it continues to elongate by slip.

The third region describes a material behavior known as **strain hardening**. The easy slip that occurred during the initial yielding phase becomes more difficult to induce. As a consequence, higher stresses are required to continue deforming the tensile specimen. The stresses increase with increases in the strain; however, the relationship is not linear and Eq. (2.5) is not valid in this region.

Fig. 2.21 Ductile failure of a tensile specimen.

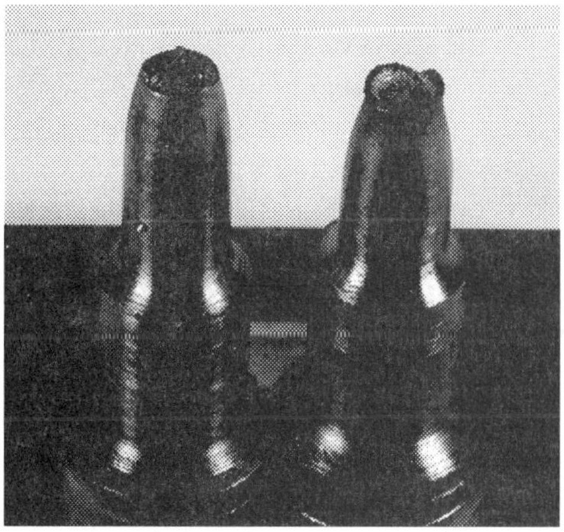

In the fourth and final region, the tensile specimen undergoes a dramatic change in appearance; it begins to **neck**. The deformation becomes localized to a small area along the length of the bar. During this phase of the deformation, the specimen resembles an hourglass. The neck decreases in diameter with increasing deformation until the specimen fails by rupturing. The axial deformation, which occurs as the tensile specimen necks, requires no increase in the applied loads. Indeed, the load may actually decrease significantly during the necking phase of the deformation processes. The appearance of a ruptured tension specimen fabricated from low carbon steel is illustrated in Fig. 2.21. Regions 2, 3 and 4, shown in Fig. 2.20, are often combined and called the **plastic regime** for a ductile material.

2.7 MATERIAL PROPERTIES

The tensile test provides several material properties that are important in the analysis of engineering components and structures. These properties include two measures of strength, two measures of ductility, and two elastic constants. Let's discuss strength first.

2.7.1 Measures of Strength

The two measures of strength determined in a tensile test of a ductile material are the yield strength and the ultimate tensile strength. The yield strength, as the name implies, is the stress required to induce yielding:

$$S_y = \sigma_y \tag{2.23}$$

To establish the yield stress σ_y, we examine the stress-strain diagram and attempt to identify the stress when yielding initiated. For some ductile materials with stress-strain diagrams similar to that shown in Fig. 2.20 the precise identification of σ_y is clear. However, the yield behavior of other materials is much less well defined. For example, suppose a material exhibits the stress-strain behavior as indicated in Fig. 2.22a. Where is the yield point?

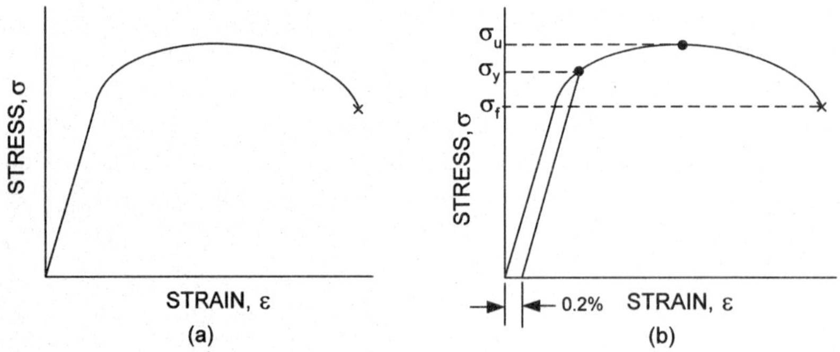

Fig. 2.22 The offset method for determining the stress σ_y for yielding.

It is evident in Fig. 2.22a that the stress-strain curve is non-linear, but we might differ in defining the point where slip and yield initiated. To eliminate the ambiguity in the definition of the yield point from a stress-strain diagram, the offset method is employed. We construct a line parallel to the linear portion of the σ-ε curve in the elastic region. This line is offset along the strain axis by 0.2% or $\varepsilon = 0.002$. The intersection of the offset line with the σ-ε curve defines the yield point as illustrated in Fig. 2.22b. With the **0.2% yield stress** σ_y defined, we use Eq. (2.23) to establish the yield strength S_y for the material.

The ultimate tensile strength is established from the maximum stress on the specimen that occurs at the onset of necking. We have defined this point on Fig. 2.22b, and have established the ultimate stress σ_u. The ultimate tensile strength S_u for a ductile material is given by:

$$S_u = \sigma_u \quad \text{for ductile materials} \qquad (2.24)$$

The stress at failure, σ_f for a ductile material, shown in Fig. 2.22b, is only of academic interest. If the structure or machine component is properly designed, the deformation state will probably be limited to the elastic region. In some instances, plastic deformations are tolerated in design, but these exceptions are limited to yielding in small local regions under conditions of constant loading. Global yielding is not tolerated, and yielding under the action of cyclic stresses is a recipe for disaster. For this reason, the stresses imposed on a structure are usually less than σ_y and certainly less than σ_u.

2.7.2 Measures of Ductility

There are two common measures of ductility for metallic materials. The first is the **percent elongation** given by:

$$\%\, e = \left(\frac{L_f - L_0}{L_0}\right) \times 100 \qquad (2.25)$$

where L_o is the gage length of the tensile specimen — usually 2.0 in. or 50 mm.
L_f is the final deformed length of the specimen between the gage length marks.

For low carbon steels, the percent elongation is usually in the range from 20 to 35%; however, the percent elongation decreases with increasing carbon content in the steel and increasing strength.

The second measure of ductility is the **percent reduction in area** that is given by:

$$\%\, A = \left(\frac{A_0 - A_f}{A_0}\right) \times 100 = \left[\left(\frac{d_0^2 - d_f^2}{d_0^2}\right)\right] \times 100 \qquad (2.26)$$

where $A_o = \pi d_o^2/4$ is the initial cross sectional area of the tensile specimen.
$A_f = \pi d_f^2/4$ is the final cross sectional area of one of the ruptured ends of the specimen.

The percent reduction in area for low carbon steel is typically in the range from 60 to 70%. As was the case with percent elongation, the percent reduction in area decreases as the carbon content of steel is increased to enhance its strength.

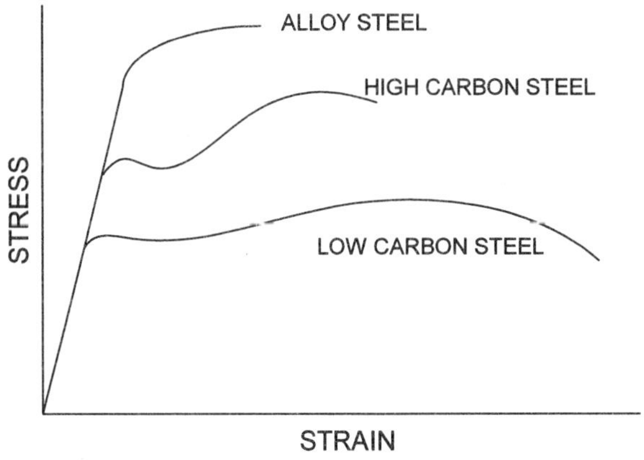

Fig. 2.23 Stress-strain curves for three different types of steels.

There is a trade-off between ductility and strength for metallic alloys. To illustrate the loss in ductility with increasing strength, let's examine typical stress-strain curves for three different types of steels that are shown in Fig. 2.23. As the strength increases, the strain to failure decreases with an accompanying decrease in the ductility. For low carbon steels, the strain to failure usually exceeds 60 to 70%. This value decreases to 30 to 40% for higher carbon steels. The very high strength steel alloys fail with strains ranging from 10 to 20%.

EXAMPLE 2.16

A steel supplier provides you with data from a recent series of tensile tests of two different steels that they sell to your corporation. Your manager questions the ductility of both materials, and asks you to determine it. An examination of the supplier's data indicates:

Lower cost steel at $18.00/100lb	Higher cost steel at $21.00/100lb
$L_f = 62$ mm and $d_f = 9.5$ mm	$L_f = 58$ mm and $d_f = 11.2$ mm

The gage length L_o and diameter d_o for both types of steel were 50 mm and 12.5 mm respectively.

Solution: For the measure of ductility known as the percent elongation, Eq. (2.25) gives:

$$\%e = [(L_f - L_o)/L_o](100) = [(62 - 50)/50](100) = 24\% \Rightarrow \text{lower cost steel.}$$

$$\%e = [(L_f - L_o)/L_o](100) = [(58 - 50)/50](100) = 16\% \Rightarrow \text{higher cost steel.} \qquad \text{(a)}$$

For the measure of ductility known as the percent reduction in area, Eq. (2.26) gives:

$$\%A = [(d_o^2 - d_f^2)/d_o^2](100) = \{[(12.5)^2 - (9.5)^2]/(12.5)^2\}(100) = 42.24\% \Rightarrow \text{lower cost steel.}$$

$$\%A = [(d_o^2 - d_f^2)/d_o^2](100) = \{[(12.5)^2 - (11.2)^2]/(12.5)^2\}(100) = 19.72\% \Rightarrow \text{higher cost steel.} \qquad \text{(b)}$$

When your manager asks which steel has the higher ductility, what is your response?

2.7.3 Elastic Constants

Modulus of Elasticity

In this discussion of the elastic constants, we limit their application to characterize deformations in the linear elastic region of the elastic-plastic regime. In this region, the material is elastic and recovers completely when the load or stress is removed from the specimen. The **slope** of the stress-strain curve is defined as the **modulus of elasticity** or Young's modulus. The slope, illustrated in Fig. 2.3b, is determined by rewriting Eq. (2.5) as:

$$\text{Slope} = E = \sigma/\varepsilon \qquad (2.5)$$

EXAMPLE 2.17

After conducting a tensile test with a mild steel specimen, you measure the slope $\Delta P/\Delta\delta$ of the linear region on the load-deflection curve (P-δ) and find:

$$\Delta P/\Delta\delta = (8{,}100 \text{ lb})/(2.75 \times 10^{-3} \text{ in.}) = 2.945 \times 10^6 \text{ lb/in.} \qquad \text{(a)}$$

If the specimen diameter is 0.504 in. and the gage length of the extensometer is 2.00 in., determine the modulus of elasticity E.

Solution:

From Eqs. (2.3), (2.4) and (2.5), we write:

$$E = \sigma/\varepsilon = (P/A)/(\delta/L) = PL/\delta A = (\Delta P)L/(\Delta\delta)A \qquad \text{(b)}$$

$$E = [(8{,}100 lb)(2 \text{ in.})]/[(2.75 \times 10^{-3} \text{ in.})(\pi\ (0.2520)^2 \text{ in.}^2)] = 29.53 \times 10^6 \text{ psi} \qquad \text{(c)}$$

Poisson's Ratio

Another elastic constant, **Poisson's ratio**, may be determined in a tensile test; however, strain gages must be attached to the specimen to measure the strain in both the axial and the transverse directions. Poisson's ratio is defined as:

$$\nu = -\varepsilon_t/\varepsilon_a \qquad (2.27)$$

where ε_t and ε_a are the strains in the transverse and axial directions, respectively. Please note that ε_a and ε_t are both normal strains determined from Eq. (2.3).

When a specimen is subjected to a tensile force, its length extends and its diameter contracts. This contraction is usually ¼ to ½ of the amount of the specimen's axial elongation. The extension of the specimen in the elastic region produces a contraction that is usually too small to be observed during a tensile test. Although too small to be observed, the Poisson effect is a very important phenomenon, because it significantly affects the analysis of structures subjected to multiaxial states of stress, where stresses are imposed in more than one direction.

To describe the Poisson contraction in more detail, consider the rectangular bar of an elastic material with dimensions L, W, and D as shown in Fig. 2.24a. Next, apply an axial strain ε_a and write:

$$\varepsilon_a = \Delta L/L \qquad \text{(a)}$$

In the deformed state, the dimensions of the bar change to L + ΔL, W + ΔW, and D + ΔD as shown in Fig. 2.24b. The strains ε_t in the x and y directions (both x and y are transverse directions) are both due to the Poisson effect and are equal. They are given by:

$$\varepsilon_{tx} = \Delta W/W = -\nu\varepsilon_a \qquad \varepsilon_{ty} = \Delta D/D = -\nu\varepsilon_a \qquad \text{(b)}$$

If we substitute Eq. (2.27) and Eq. (a) into Eq. (b), we obtain:

$$\varepsilon_t = -\nu\varepsilon_a = -\nu\Delta L/L = \Delta W/W = \Delta D/D \qquad (2.28)$$

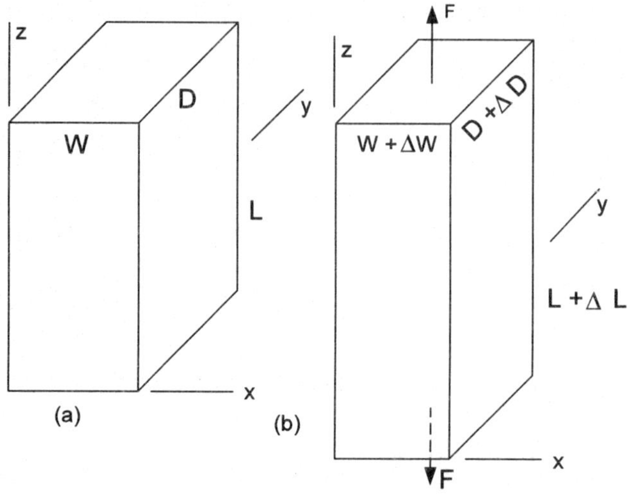

Fig. 2.24a A rectangular bar before imposing an axial deformation (b) after deformation.

From Eq. (2.28) it is clear that the changes in the transverse dimensions of the bar due to the Poisson effect are given by:

$$\Delta W = -(\nu W \Delta L)/L; \qquad \Delta D = -(\nu W \Delta L)/L \qquad \text{(c)}$$

From this elementary analysis of the deformed geometry of a rectangular bar, we note that the material property **Poisson's ratio, ν** enables the transverse deformation to be determined in terms of the axial deformation when a structural member is subjected to a uniaxial loading. The quantities ΔW and ΔD are negative when ΔL is positive because the Poisson effect produces a contraction in the transverse (x and y) directions when the body is extended in the axial (z) direction.

EXAMPLE 2.18

Suppose you cut a 100-mm diameter circular hole in a large sheet of dental dam (very thin rubber sheet). If the sheet, originally 1,000 mm long by 500 mm wide, is extended until it is 1,400 mm long, determine the new width of the sheet and the dimensions of the deformed hole. Assume that the rubber is perfectly elastic with a Poisson's ratio, ν = 0.5.

Solution:

Recall Eq. (2.28) and write:

$$\varepsilon_t = -\nu\varepsilon_a = -\nu\, \Delta L/L_o = -0.5\,(1{,}400 - 1{,}000)/1{,}000 = -0.200$$

$$\varepsilon_a = \Delta L/L_o = (1{,}400 - 1{,}000)/1{,}000 = 0.400 \qquad \text{(a)}$$

Because these strains are imposed over the entire sheet, determine the deformed width W_{NEW} from:

$$W_{NEW} = W_o + \Delta W = W_o + \varepsilon_t\, W_o = (1 + \varepsilon_t)W_o = (1 - 0.200)500 = 400 \text{ mm} \qquad \text{(b)}$$

The dimensions of the deformed hole are given by:

$$D_a = D_o + \Delta D_a = D_o + \varepsilon_a D_o = (1 + \varepsilon_a)D_o = (1 + 0.400)100 = 140 \text{ mm}$$
$$D_t = D_o + \Delta D_t = D_o + \varepsilon_t D_o = (1 + \varepsilon_t)D_o = (1 - 0.200)100 = 80 \text{ mm} \quad \text{(c)}$$

where D_a and D_t are the axial and transverse diameters of the hole after deformation.

EXAMPLE 2.19

Determine the change in volume of a rectangular bar subjected to an axial strain of $\varepsilon_a = 2 \times 10^{-3}$. The dimensions of the bar before deformation were L = 4W = 3D = 16 in. The material from which the bar is fabricated has a Poisson's ratio of $\nu = 0.25$.

Solution:

The original volume, $\boldsymbol{V}$ of the bar is given by:

$$\boldsymbol{V} = L \times W \times D = L^3/12 = (16)^3/12 = 341.33 \text{ in}^3 \quad \text{(a)}$$

From Eq. (2.28), we determine the new dimensions of the bar as:

$$W_{NEW} = (1 - \nu\varepsilon_a)W; \qquad D_{NEW} = (1 - \nu\varepsilon_a)D,; \qquad L_{NEW} = (1 + \varepsilon_a)L \quad \text{(b)}$$

We rewrite Eq. (b) as:

$$W_{NEW} = (1 - \nu\varepsilon_a)(L/4); \qquad D_{NEW} = (1 - \nu\varepsilon_a)(L/3); \qquad L_{NEW} = (1 + \varepsilon_a)L \quad \text{(c)}$$

The new volume is given by:

$$\boldsymbol{V}_{NEW} = L_{NEW} \times W_{NEW} \times D_{NEW} = (1 + \varepsilon_a)(1 - \nu\varepsilon_a)(1 - \nu\varepsilon_a)(L^3/12) \quad \text{(d)}$$

From Eqs. (a) and (d), it is evident that:

$$\Delta\boldsymbol{V} = [(1 + \varepsilon_a)(1 - \nu\varepsilon_a)^2 - 1](L^3/12) \quad \text{(e)}$$

Substituting $\varepsilon_a = 2 \times 10^{-3}$ and $\nu = 0.25$ into Eq. (e) yields:

$$\Delta\boldsymbol{V} = \{(1 + 2 \times 10^{-3})[1 - (0.25)(2 \times 10^{-3})]^2 - 1\}\,\boldsymbol{V} \quad \text{(f)}$$

Performing the calculation gives:

$$\Delta\boldsymbol{V} = 9.9825 \times 10^{-4}\,\boldsymbol{V} = (9.9825)\times 10^{-4}(341.33) = 0.3407 \text{ in}^3 \quad \text{(g)}$$

The percentage change in the volume is given by:

$$\Delta\boldsymbol{V}/\boldsymbol{V} = [(1 + \varepsilon_a)(1 - \nu\varepsilon_a)^2 - 1] = 9.9825 \times 10^{-4} = 0.099825\% \quad \text{(h)}$$

From these results, it is evident that the change in the volume is extremely small for strains in the elastic region.

Shear Modulus

Another elastic constant that we often use in the analysis of structures subjected to shear stress is the **shear modulus**, G. The shear modulus relates the shear stress to the shear strain by:

$$\tau = G\,\gamma \qquad (2.29)$$

where τ is the shear stress and γ is the shear strain.

The shear strain γ is defined as the change in angle of two perpendicular lines when a body is deformed. For instance, suppose we have a Cartesian coordinate system scribed on a body with the x and y axes serving as the two perpendicular lines. When the body deforms under the action of a shear stress τ, these two lines rotate, and the angle at their intersection changes from 90° to some other angle 90° $\pm\,\gamma$ as illustrated in Fig. 2.25.

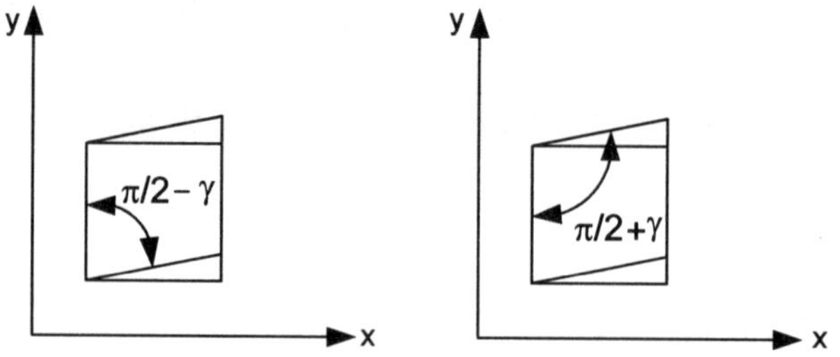

Fig. 2.25 Shear strain is the change in a right angle when a body deforms.

The shear modulus G is related to the modulus of elasticity and Poisson's ratio by:

$$G = \frac{E}{2(1 + \nu)} \qquad (2.30)$$

EXAMPLE 2.20

Determine the shear modulus G for:

(a) Steel with the modulus of elasticity $E = 30 \times 10^6$ psi and Poisson's ratio $\nu = 0.30$.
(b) An aluminum alloy with E = 73 GPa and Poisson's ratio $\nu = 0.33$.

Solution:

From Eq. (2.30) we write for steel the following relation:

$$G = (30 \times 10^6) / [2(1 + 0.30)] = 11.54 \times 10^6 \text{ psi for steel.} \qquad (a)$$

For the aluminum alloy, the shear modulus is given by:

$$G = (73) / [2(1 + 0.33)] = 27.44 \text{ GPa for an aluminum alloy.} \qquad (b)$$

2.8 DESIGN ANALYSIS OF WIRE, RODS AND BARS

We have defined two different strengths (i.e. yield and ultimate tensile) in Section 2.7. Because a structural member may fail by excessive deformation, we may choose to limit the stress applied to the structure so that it is less than the yield strength S_y. On the other hand in some structures, we can tolerate plastic deformation in one or more members without compromising the structure's function. In these cases, we can tolerate stresses exceeding the yield strength, S_y but they must be less than the ultimate strength, S_u. For example, when designing a bridge, it is important that its shape remain fixed under normal service loads. In this case, the yield strength is specified as the maximum limit for the design stress for the bridge to prevent post-yield deformations. However, in designing a bridge to remain standing during a collision with a tugboat or during an earthquake, the ultimate strength of the structural members is sometimes the design criterion.

When designing a structural member to carry a specified load, we always size the member so that the **design stress**, σ_{design}, is less than the strength based on either the yield or failure criteria. It would not be prudent to permit the design stress to equal the strength of the member. To size structural members so they are safe, a **factor of safety, SF** is employed in the analysis. The safety factor is defined as the ratio of a strength divided by the design stress. This definition leads to the relations given below:

$$\mathbf{SF_u} = S_u / \sigma_{design} \tag{2.31}$$

$$\mathbf{SF_y} = S_y / \sigma_{design} \tag{2.32}$$

$$\sigma_{design} = P_{design}/A \tag{2.33}$$

where S_u and S_y are the ultimate strength and yield strength of the material, respectively.
σ_{design} and P_{design} are the design stress and the design load, respectively.

The value for the factor of safety depends upon the application. Ideally, you would like the factor of safety to be as large as possible. However, excessive safety factors must be balanced by practical considerations such as economics, aesthetics, functionality and ease of assembly. In designing a structure, you will be concerned with the cost and weight of its components in addition to safety. The factor of safety specified for a structure or machine component should reflect these concerns.

2.8.1 Design Analysis of Wire and Cables

In most of the previous examples, solutions were limited to the determination of the stresses developed under specified loading condition. Determining the stress is the first step in the design process; however, it is necessary to extend the analysis to determine if these stress levels are safe or if the structural element may fail in service. Safety factors, defined in Eqs. (2.31) and (2.32), are used when designing a structural element to insure that the stresses developed under the specified loads are less that the strength of the material from which the element is fabricated. Other design analyses are employed to select the materials from which the structural element is fabricated. To illustrate the design procedure, a number of examples will be presented for uniaxial members subjected to axial loading. We begin with examples for design analyses involving wire and cables, which can carry tensile stresses but not compressive stresses. Later in this section we will provide examples of design analyses for bars and rods that are capable of carrying both tensile and compressive stresses.

EXAMPLE 2.21

A hoisting cable with a diameter of ½ in. is fabricated from many strands of an improved plow steel wire. The manufacturer of the cable certifies its breaking load as 16,500 lb. Determine the strength of the wire used in the manufacture of the cable. Also discuss the assumption pertaining to the cable made in the analysis and its implication on the strength of the strands of wire.

Solution:

Recall Eq. (2.22), which gives:

$$S_u = \sigma_f \quad \text{(a)}$$

From Eqs. (a) and (2.4), it is evident that:

$$S_u = \sigma_f = P_{fail}/A \quad (2.34)$$

The cross sectional area of the cable will be less than $A = \pi d^2/4 = 0.1963\ \text{in}^2$. Substituting this value for the area A into Eq. (2.34) yields:

$$S_u = 16{,}500\ \text{lb}/\ 0.1963\ \text{in.}^2 = 84.06\ \text{ksi} \quad \text{(b)}$$

We have assumed the cross sectional area of the wire rope to be equivalent to that of a solid wire with a diameter of ½ in. Wire rope is made of many very small diameter wires that are twisted together to form strands. The strands in turn are formed in a helix about a fiber core. The wire rope in this example has a designation of 6 × 19 (6 strands with 19 small wires in each strand). The cross section of this 6 by 19-wire rope is illustrated in Fig. 2.26.

The assumption of a solid cross sectional area overestimates the cross sectional area, A by a factor of more than two. The ultimate tensile strength of the small diameter wire used to form the strands of wire for a typical cable is usually in excess of 200 ksi.

Fig. 2.26 A wire rope is fabricated from many strands of small-diameter high-strength wire.

EXAMPLE 2.22

A solid hard drawn copper wire exhibits an ultimate tensile strength of 400 MPa. If the diameter of the wire is 2.0 mm, determine the load required to break the wire.

Solution:

Recall Eq. (2.34), which gives:

$$S_u = \sigma_f = P_{fail}\ /A \quad \text{(a)}$$

Rearrange this relation and substitute known quantities to give:

$$P_{fail} = S_u\, A = (400)(\pi/4)(2.0)^2 = 1.257 \text{ kN} \qquad \text{(b)}$$

An axial load in excess of 1.20 kN is required to rupture the hard drawn copper wire.

EXAMPLE 2.23

A monofilament, nylon fishing line is rated at 12-lb test. If the line is 0.014 inch in diameter, determine the strength of the nylon in the form of a small diameter line. Comment on the effect that the filament geometry has on the strength of a polymer like nylon-6/6.

Solution:

Recall Eq. (2.34), which gives:

$$S_u = \sigma_f = P_{fail}/A \qquad \text{(a)}$$

$$S_u = (4)(12)/[\pi\,(0.014)^2] = 77{,}950 \text{ psi} \qquad \text{(b)}$$

Monofilaments of polymers like nylon-6/6 are drawn from a melt into thin fibers or lines. In this process, the long molecules of the polymer are aligned with the axis of the filament thus enhancing its strength.

EXAMPLE 2.24

A No. 14 gage (0.080 in. diameter) black annealed steel wire is listed in a materials handbook with a yield strength of 220 MPa and an ultimate tensile strength of 340 MPa. Determine the axial load that will cause the wire to yield.

Solution:

Recall Eqs. (2.4) and (2.23), and rearrange them to give:

$$S_y = \sigma_y = P_{yield} / A \qquad (2.35)$$

$$P_{yield} = S_y\, A \qquad \text{(a)}$$

Because we have mixed units in the problem statement, let's convert the units for the diameter of the wire to the SI system and determine the cross sectional area A in mm^2.

$$A = \pi d^2/4 = \pi\,(0.080 \text{ in.})^2\,(25.4 \text{ mm/in.})^2/4 = 3.243 \text{ mm}^2 \qquad \text{(b)}$$

Next, substitute Eq. (b) into Eq. (a) to obtain:

$$P_{yield} = S_y\, A = (220 \text{ MPa})(3.243 \text{ mm}^2) = 713.5 \text{ N} \qquad \text{(c)}$$

EXAMPLE 2.25

A single #20 gage steel wire with a solid cross section is 0.0348 in. in diameter is intended to carry a load of 120 N with a safety factor of 3.0. Specify the steel alloy from which the wire should be manufactured to avoid failure by rupture.

Solution:

Recall Eqs. (2.31) and solve it to obtain an expression for S_u:

$$\mathbf{SF_u} = AS_u / P_{design} \quad \text{(a)}$$

$$S_u = (P_{design})\mathbf{SF_u}/A = 4(120\text{ N})(3.0)/[\pi\ (0.0348\text{ in.})^2(25.4\text{ mm/in.})^2] = 586.7\text{ MPa} \quad \text{(b)}$$

It is necessary to refer to a materials handbook to select a suitable material for this application. Reference to Appendix B-2 indicates three steel alloys and three stainless steel alloys with ultimate tensile strengths exceeding the requirement for S_u in this example.

EXAMPLE 2.26

A cold drawn alloy steel wire, with a yield strength of 120,000 psi, is to carry a load of 500 lb while incorporating a safety factor of 2.50. You are to inform the purchasing representative regarding the size of the wire to be ordered.

Solution:

To determine the size of the wire in this application, recall Eq. (2.32).

$$\mathbf{SF_y} = S_y / \sigma_{design} = AS_y / P_{design} \quad \text{(a)}$$

Solve Eq. (a) for the area to obtain:

$$A = \mathbf{SF_y}\ (P_{design})/S_y = \pi d^2/4 \quad \text{(b)}$$

$$A = (2.5)(500)/120{,}000 = 0.01042\text{ in}^2 = \pi d^2/4 \quad \text{(c)}$$

$$d = 0.1152\text{ in.} \quad \text{(d)}$$

Do you call the purchasing representative and order a cold drawn alloy steel wire with a diameter of 0.1152 in? **No!!!** If you make this mistake, you will soon learn that steel wire is available only with a standard diameter. Economic laws dictate that the most cost effective way to mass-produce materials is by limiting inventories to only those sizes and geometries that satisfy most customers. In Appendix A standard wire sizes and their corresponding gage numbers are listed. For this example, four entries from the listings in Appendix A for standard steel wire are presented below:

Gage No.[8]	Diameter (in.)	Area (in^2)
10	0.1350	0.01431
11	0.1205	0.01140
12	0.1055	0.00874
13	0.0915	0.00658

The response to the purchasing representative is to procure Gage No. 11 wire. It is important for you to specify a standard size in ordering structural members. Standard sizes are available with minimum delay at the lowest cost. Numerical results rarely yield dimensions for structural members that correspond to the available standard sizes. The usual practice is to increase the size determined in the analysis to the next larger dimension available as a standard. This approach enhances safety while minimizing cost and delivery time.

2.8.2 Design Analysis of Rods and Bars

All of the equations derived in for wire and cable, are also valid for rods and bars. If the external axial forces are tensile (tend to pull the bar apart), the internal forces and stresses are tensile and denoted with a positive sign. On the other hand, if the external axial forces are compressive (tend to press on the bar), the internal forces and stresses are compressive and denoted with a minus sign.

As indicated in Section 2.2, we must qualify the capability of a rod or bar to carry compressive loads. If the rod is very long and slender and the compressive force too high, the rod may buckle. **Buckling** is an unstable condition, and if the critical load is exceeded, the rod fails suddenly and catastrophically. In this chapter, we will assume that the rods or bars loaded in compression are sized to resist buckling; consequently, they fail due to excessive compressive stresses. However, the tendency for these structures to buckle cannot always be ignored. Theories describing the failure of **columns** due to buckling will be introduced later in the Chapter 8.

The procedure for determining the normal stresses σ is the same in bars or rods as described previously for wires and cables except for the fact that the internal forces may be compressive as well as tensile. We begin by constructing a FBD to show the point of application and the directions of the internal and external forces. From the equilibrium relations, the internal forces and their sign are determined. Finally, Eq. (2.4) is employed to determine the normal stresses σ. This procedure is demonstrated in two example problems presented below.

EXAMPLE 2.27

Let's reconsider Example 2.6 where we determined the stress in the bar shown in Fig. E2.6. We made a section cut near the center of the bar, constructed the free body diagram and determined the normal stress due to the 1,000 kN axial load as:

---

[8] There are several different standards that refer to gage numbers for wire and steel sheet. In this example, we list the American Steel and Wire Co. standard that is commonly used for steel wire.

$$\sigma = P/A = -\ 1{,}000 \times 10^3\ N/(150)(100)mm^2 = -\ 66.67\ N/mm^2 = -\ 66.67\ MPa$$

If the bar is fabricated from 1212 HR steel, determine the safety factor based on the yielding criterion.

Solution:

From Tablc B-2, the yield strength S_y is given as 193 MPa.

The safety factor is determined from Eq. (2.32) as:

$$SF_y = S_y/\sigma_{Design} = 193/66.67 = 2.895 \qquad (a)$$

Note that the sign of the stress, a negative number, was ignored in this determination. We have assumed that the compressive and tensile strengths are the same for this material, which is true for most steels. However, this in not the case for very brittle materials such as gray cast iron.

EXAMPLE 2.28

Determine the stress in a three-foot long rod that has a diameter of 4 in. The bar is fabricated from mild steel with a yield strength S_y = 35,000 psi, and is subjected to an axial compressive load of 120,000 lb. Also, compute the safety factor of the bar against failure by yielding.

Solution:

Again, we begin with a drawing of the rod and a free body diagram in Fig. E2.28, showing the forces F and P and the normal stresses σ.

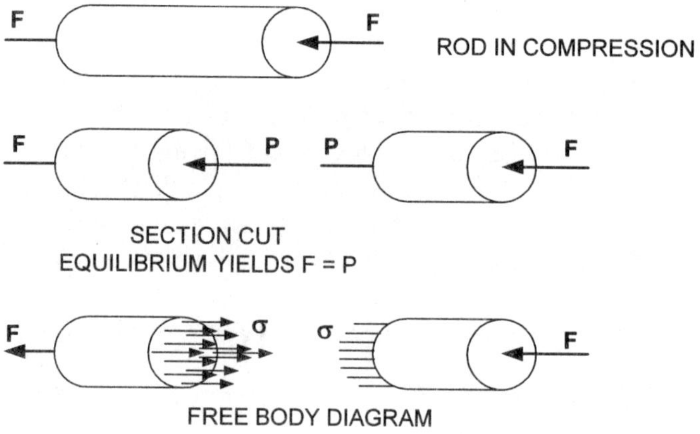

Fig. E2.28

From Eq. (2.4), we write:

$$\sigma = P/A = -\ 120{,}000\ lb/[\pi \times (2)^2] = -\ 9{,}549\ psi \qquad (a)$$

We determine the safety factor against yielding from Eq. (2.32).

$$\mathbf{SF}_y = S_y/S_{design} = -\,35{,}000/-\,9{,}549 = 3.665 \qquad \text{(b)}$$

Note, the safety factor is always a positive quantity. In this problem, we compared a compressive strength of – 35,000 psi (taken as a negative quantity) with the design stress of –9,549 psi.

EXAMPLE 2.29

In Example 2.9, we determined the shear stresses in a key that was employed to keep a gear from slipping on a shaft when transmitting power. The solution, which involved two FBDs and Eq. (2.9), gave the shear stresses on the key as:

$$\tau = V/A = (50 \times 10^3)/(0.012)(0.050) = 83.33 \text{ MPa}$$

If the yield strength, S_y of the steel used in manufacturing the key was 250 MPa, determine the yield strength in shear and the safety factor for the key.

Solution:

The average shear stress acting on the key is 83.33 MPa. To analyze the impact of this solution on the design of a structure, it is necessary to compare the imposed stress with the shear strength of the material from which the key is fabricated. The shear strength is usually lower than the yield or ultimate tensile strength of a material. A common practice is to consider either the yield or tensile strength of a material and multiply that value by $\sqrt{3}/3$ = 0.5774 to estimate the shear strength. Because the tensile yield strength, S_y of the steel used in manufacturing the key was 250 MPa, the yield strength in shear S_{ys} is estimated as:

$$S_{ys} = 0.5774\, S_y \qquad (2.36)$$

$$S_{ys} = (0.5774)(250) = 144.35 \text{ MPa} \qquad \text{(a)}$$

The safety factor for the key is determined from:

$$\mathbf{SF}_{ys} = S_{ys}/\tau \qquad (2.37)$$

$$\mathbf{SF}_{ys} = 144.35/125 = 1.155 \qquad \text{(b)}$$

In interpreting the results for normal stresses, we recognize the difference between tensile (+) and compressive (–) values for the results. The reason for the careful distinction is the fact that the strength of material subjected to tensile or compressive stresses is often different. However, shear strength is not sensitive to the sign of the shear stress τ. The strength of a material to an imposed shear stress is not dependent on the direction of the imposed shear force. For this reason, we usually neglect the sign of the shear force in our analysis of stress on machine components.

2.9 STRESSES ON OBLIQUE PLANES

In making section cuts on bars and rods, we have limited our choices to sections perpendicular to the axis of the bar. This restriction was helpful because it simplified the state of stress that was examined. With these perpendicular section cuts, we considered only the normal stresses acting on the area exposed by the cut.

We showed that shear stresses exist in Section 2.4 and computed their magnitude in Example 2.9. In this case, we restricted the section cut to one parallel to the imposed system of equal and opposite forces. With this restriction on the section cut, only shear forces are developed. By restricting the section cut, we develop special cases where normal stresses exist in the absence of shear stresses and vice versa.

Let's treat the more general case with the bar cut at an arbitrary angle as shown in Fig 2.27.

Fig. 2.27 Axially loaded bar with a section cut at an arbitrary angle.

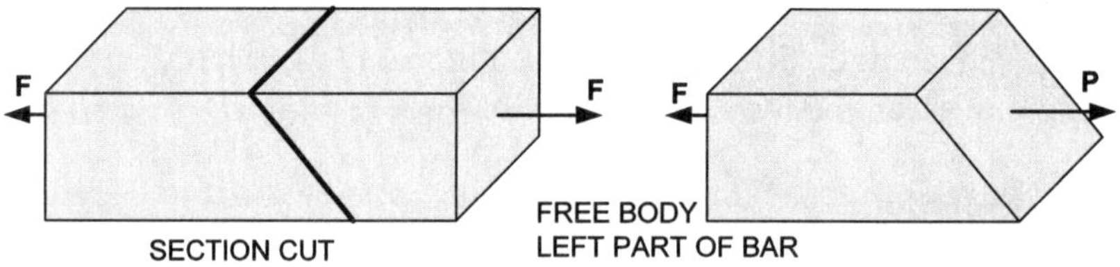

Let's cut the free body of Fig. 2.27 with still another section to produce a triangular shape as shown in Fig. 2.28a. The triangular shape in Fig. 2.28b is defined with the angle θ. The left side of this triangle has an area A; therefore, the hypotenuse of the triangle has an area = A/cos θ. Note, the x-axis is coincident with the axis of the bar; the n axis is coincident with the outer normal to the inclined cut; the t axis is tangential to the inclined cut.

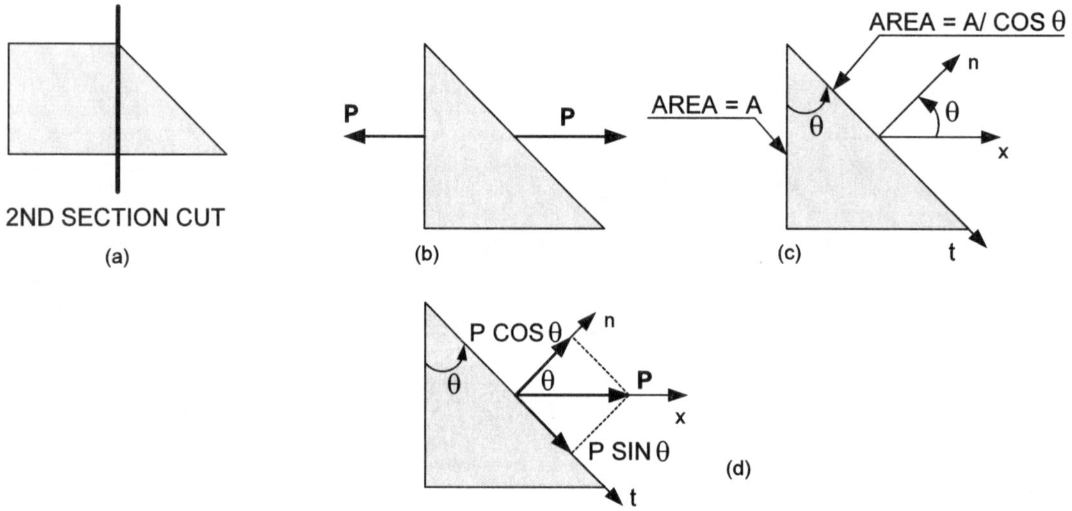

Fig. 2.28 Free body diagrams of the bar with an inclined cut: (a) The section cut is perpendicular to the axis of the bar to produce a triangle; (b) Internal forces acting on both faces of the element are shown; (c) The areas of the left side and the hypotenuse are illustrated; (d) The force P on the surface of the inclined cut is resolved into components along the n and t axes.

As shown in Fig. 2.28c, the internal force P has been resolved into components along the n and t axes to yield:

$$P_n = P \cos\theta \qquad \text{(a)}$$

$$V_t = P \sin\theta \qquad \text{(b)}$$

To ascertain the stresses on the inclined surface, we simply divide either P_n or V_t by the area formed with the inclined section cut in accordance with Eq. (2.4) or Eq. (2.9). The stress σ_θ in the normal direction (n) is determined from Eq. (2.4) as:

$$\sigma_\theta = (P \cos\theta)/(A/\cos\theta) = (P/A)\cos^2\theta \qquad \text{(c)}$$

If we define the axial stress $\sigma_x = P/A$, then we may write:

$$\sigma_\theta = (\sigma_x)\cos^2\theta \qquad (2.38)$$

The shear stress τ_θ that acts along the face of the inclined surface is given by Eq. (2.9) as:

$$\tau_\theta = (P \sin\theta)/(A/\cos\theta) = (P/A)\sin\theta\cos\theta \qquad \text{(d)}$$

This relation is rewritten as:

$$\tau_\theta = (\sigma_x/2)\sin 2\theta \qquad (2.39)$$

Numerical results are presented in Fig. 2.29 for both σ_θ and τ_θ, as the angle of the inclined section varies from zero (a perpendicular cut) to 90° (a parallel cut). In this figure, the axial stress $\sigma_x = 100$ units. From Fig. 2.29 it is evident that the normal stress σ is a maximum when $\theta = 0°$ and the section cut is perpendicular to the axis of the bar. For this angle of the cut, $\sigma_\theta = \sigma_x = P/A$. Thus, when employing Eq. (2.4) to compute the normal stress, we determine the maximum possible value of σ_θ. The shear stress is zero on the plane defined by $\theta = 0°$ where the normal stress is a maximum.

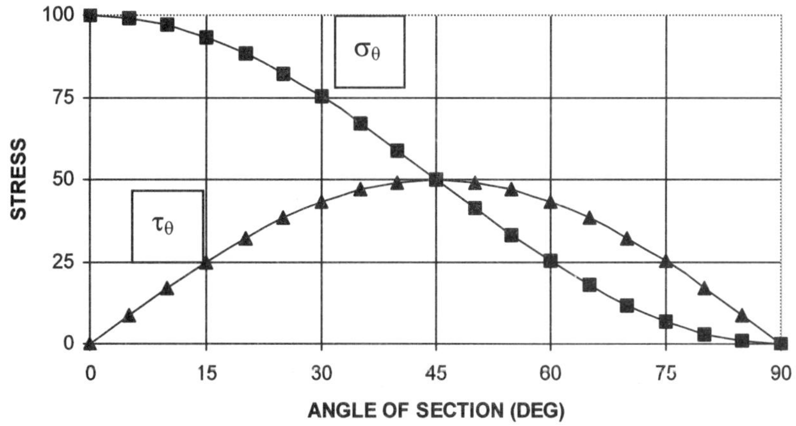

Fig. 2.29 Variation in σ_θ and τ_θ with the angle of the inclined section.

Both the normal and shear stress vanish when the section cut is made at 90°. The shear stress is a maximum when the section cut is defined by $\theta = 45°$. When $\theta = 45°$, the normal and shear stresses are equal to each other $\sigma_{45} = \tau_{45} = \sigma_x/2$.

The example of the axially loaded bar, with an inclined section cut, illustrates why stresses must be treated as tensor quantities. As we vary the angle of inclination of the section cut, two parameters are changing relative to either the normal or the shear stresses. First, the magnitude of the force components in the n and t direction changes with the angle θ because forces are vector quantities. Second, the area of the inclined surface exposed by the section cut increases with θ. Both of these parameters affect the magnitude of the normal and shear stresses; therefore stresses must be treated as tensor quantities — not vectors.

EXAMPLE 2.30

A circular rod 40 mm in diameter and 2 m long is subjected to an axial load of 100 kN. Determine:

- The maximum normal stress and the plane upon which it acts.
- The maximum shear stress and the plane upon which it acts.
- Draw a FBD of the section for the maximum normal stress.
- Draw a FBD of the section for the maximum shear stress.

Solution:

The maximum normal stress occurs on a plane perpendicular to the axis of the rod where $\theta = 0°$. Equation (2.38) applies.

$$\sigma_{\theta=0} = (\sigma_x)\cos^2\theta = (P/A)\cos^2\theta = (100 \times 10^3)/[\pi\,(0.020)^2]\cos^2(0°) = 79.58 \text{ MPa} \qquad \text{(a)}$$

The maximum shear stress occurs when $\theta = 45°$ as indicated by the results depicted in Fig. 2.29. From Eq. (2.39), we write:

$$\tau_{\theta=45} = (\sigma_x/2)\sin 2\theta = (79.58/2)\sin[2(45°)] = 39.79 \text{ MPa} \qquad \text{(b)}$$

The FBDs for the right portion of the bar showing the maximum normal and shear stresses are shown in Fig. 2.30:

Fig. 2.30 Section cuts for (a) maximum normal stress (b) maximum shear stress.

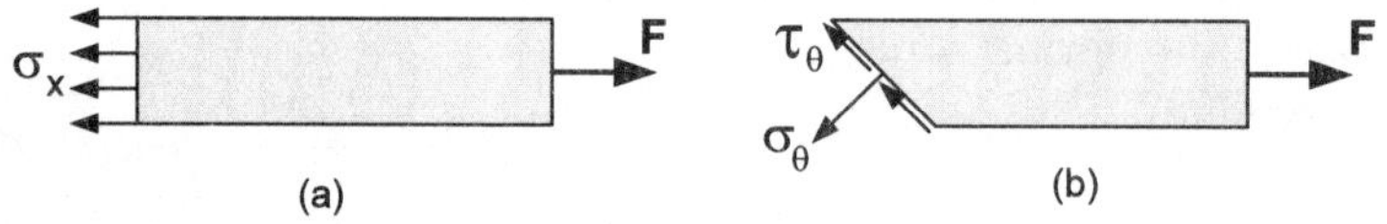

The FBD in Fig. 2.30a shows the normal stresses σ acting on a plane area perpendicular to the axis of the rod. The shear stresses are shown in Fig. 2.30b where they act on a surface inclined at a 45° angle to the axis of the rod.

2.10 AXIAL LOADING OF A TAPERED BAR

The discussion of stress and deformation of a rod or bar has been limited to those members with a uniform cross sectional area. Of course, uniform bars and rods are most commonly employed in building structures because they are readily available and less expensive to manufacture; however, in some instances it may be more desirable to use members that are not uniform. In these cases, we must accommodate the effect of the changing cross sectional area over the length of the bar on both the stresses and deformation.

2.10.1 Normal Stresses in Tapered Bars

The normal stresses that occur in a tapered bar or rod are determined using Eq. (2.4). The only consideration made to account for the taper in the bar is to adjust the area A to correspond with its position along the length of the bar. Let's consider the tapered bar presented in Fig. 2.31. The thickness of the bar b is constant along its entire length. The height, h_x, of the bar varies with position x according to the relation:

$$h_x = h_1 + (h_2 - h_1)(x/L) \qquad \text{(a)}$$

The area, A_x, at any position x along the length of the bar is then:

$$A_x = bh_x = b[h_1 + (h_2 - h_1)(x/L)] \qquad (2.40)$$

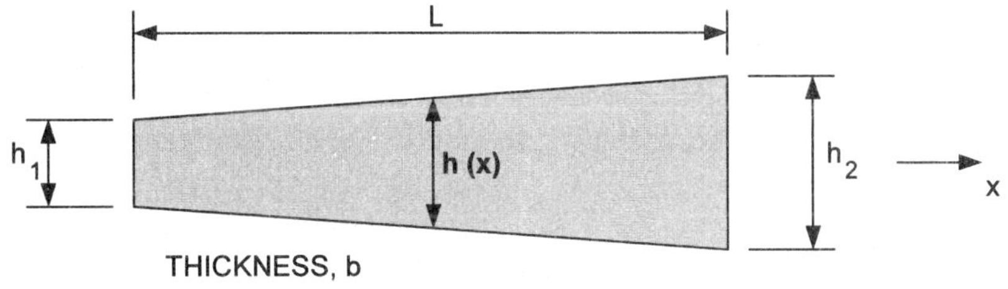

Fig. 2.31 Geometry of a tapered bar with a uniform thickness.

The normal stresses σ_x due to an axial force are determined by substituting Eq. (2.40) into Eq. (2.4) to obtain:

$$\sigma_x = P/A_x = P/\{b[h_1 + (h_2 - h_1)(x/L)]\} \qquad (2.41)$$

where L is the length of the tapered bar and b is its thickness.

EXAMPLE 2.31

For a tapered bar similar to the one shown in Fig. 2.31, determine the normal stress as a function of position x along the length of the bar. The geometry of the bar is given by h_1 = 2 in., h_2 = 6 in., b = 3 in. and L = 36 in. The axial load imposed on the tapered bar is 50,000 lb.

Solution:

We employ Eq. (2.41) and write:

$$\sigma_x = P/\{b[h_1 + (h_2 - h_1)(x/L)]\} = (50{,}000)/\{3[2 + (6 - 2)(x/36)]\}$$

$$\sigma_x = (150{,}000)/(18 + x) \qquad \text{(a)}$$

The stress σ_x = 8,333 psi is a maximum at x = 0, and decreases to a minimum value of σ_x = 2,778 psi when x = 36 in. Note that the stress will **always** be largest where the cross sectional area of the bar is smallest, which is at the left end of the bar in this example.

2.10.2 Deformation of Tapered Bars

The deformation of a tapered bar may be determined from Eq. (2.2) although we must again modify the approach to accommodate for the changing cross sectional area over the length of the bar. To determine the axial deformation, this accommodation is more difficult because the total deformation of the bar is the sum of the incremental deformations at each position x along the length of the bar. We begin by considering an incremental length dx at some position x as shown in Fig. 2.32.

Fig. 2.32 An incremental length (slice) dx at position x along the length of the tapered bar.

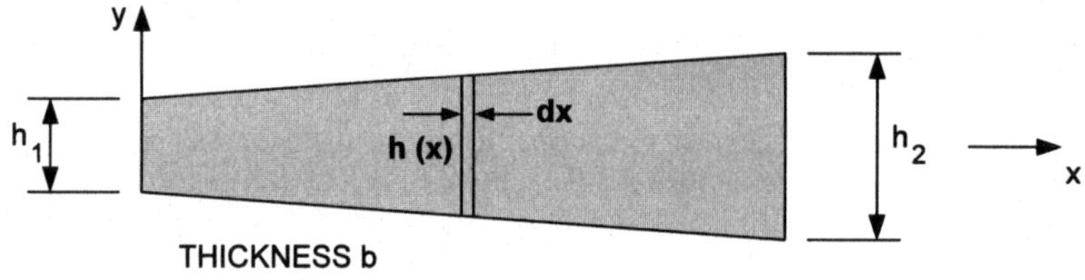

To accommodate for the taper in the bar, we determine the incremental deformation dδ of a bar of length dx. Because dx approaches zero, we treat the cross sectional area as a constant over the incremental length. Accordingly, we modify Eq. (2.2) to read:

$$d\delta = (P\,dx)/(A_x\,E) \tag{2.42}$$

where A_x is the cross sectional area of the bar as a function of x, that is given by Eq. (2.40).

Substitute Eq. (2.40) into Eq. (2.42), simplify, and integrate to obtain:

$$\delta = \frac{PL}{Eb}\int_0^L \frac{dx}{h_1L + (h_2 - h_1)x} \tag{a}$$

$$\delta = \frac{PL}{Eb}\left(\frac{1}{h_2 - h_1}\right)\ln\left(\frac{h_2}{h_1}\right) \tag{2.43}$$

EXAMPLE 2.32

Determine the deformation of the tapered bar described in Example 2.31 if the bar is fabricated from an aluminum alloy with a modulus of elasticity $E = 10.4 \times 10^6$ psi.

Solution:

Let's solve this example problem by recalling Eq. (2.43).

$$\delta = \frac{PL}{Eb}\left(\frac{1}{h_2 - h_1}\right)\ln\left(\frac{h_2}{h_1}\right) \tag{a}$$

Substituting the parameters describing the geometry and the material constant for the bar into this relation yields:

$$\delta = \frac{P(50{,}000)(36)}{(30\times 10^6)(3)}\left(\frac{1}{6-2}\right)\ln\left(\frac{6}{2}\right) = 0.01585 \text{ in.} \qquad \text{(b)}$$

Examine the magnitude of the deformation of the tapered bar. Is the deformation large or small? What reference do you use to judge? Clearly, the axial extension of the bar is small. For small quantities, we sometimes use the human hair as a reference. The diameter of a single strand of hair is slightly more than 2×10^{-3} in.; hence, the extension is about eight times the diameter of a human hair.

2.11 AXIAL LOADING OF A STEPPED BAR

In some structures, bars of different cross sectional areas are employed where the area changes abruptly at some position along the length of the bar. An illustration of a stepped bar where the cross section undergoes an abrupt change is presented in Fig. 2.33.

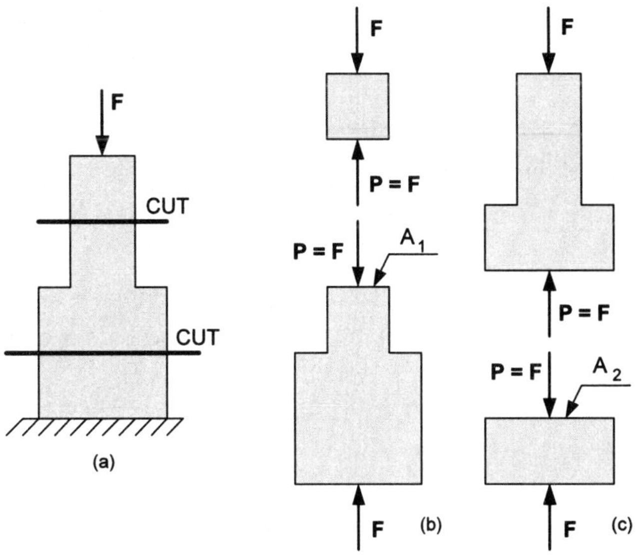

Fig. 2.33 A stepped bar with free body diagrams for each section of the bar.

The procedure for determining the normal stresses and deformation remains the same as for a bar with a uniform cross sectional area:

1. Draw a free body diagram of each section of the bar.
2. Use the equilibrium relations to establish the internal axial forces acting on each section.
3. Determine the stresses from Eq. (2.4) using the area of the section of interest.
4. Solve for the deformation of each segment of the bar from Eq. (2.2) and then add them to obtain the total deformation.

After drawing the free body diagrams of the stepped bar and determining the internal forces at each section of the bar, a force position diagram can be constructed to show the distribution of the forces over the entire length of the stepped bar. An example of two different stepped bars with their force distribution is presented in Fig. 2.34.

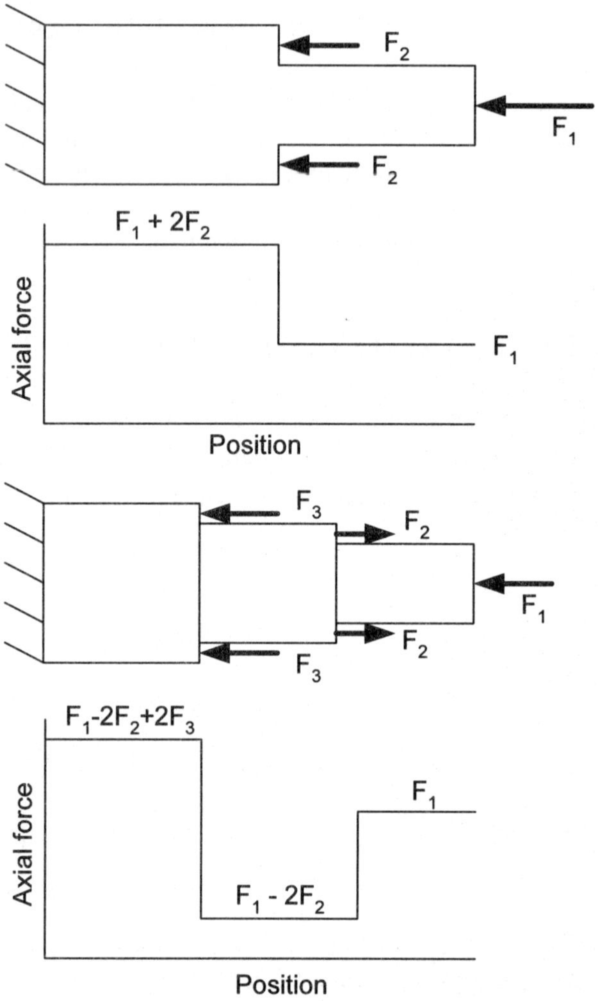

Fig. 2.34 Force position diagrams that are useful in analyzing step bars. The forces shown here are compressive.

2.11.1 Normal Stresses in Stepped Bars

The normal stress varies with the cross sectional area of the bar. For example, the illustration in Fig 2.33, shows the normal stress in the larger section of the bar, which is given by $\sigma = P/A_2$. The stress in the smaller section of the bar is $\sigma = P/A_1$.

EXAMPLE 2.33

For the stepped bar shown in Fig. E2.33, determine the normal stress in each of the two sections of the bar if $F_1 = 80$ kN; $F_2 = 40$ kN; $w_1 = 50$ mm; $b_1 = 60$ mm; $w_2 = 90$ mm; $b_2 = 60$ mm; $L_1 = 200$ mm and $L_2 = 300$ mm

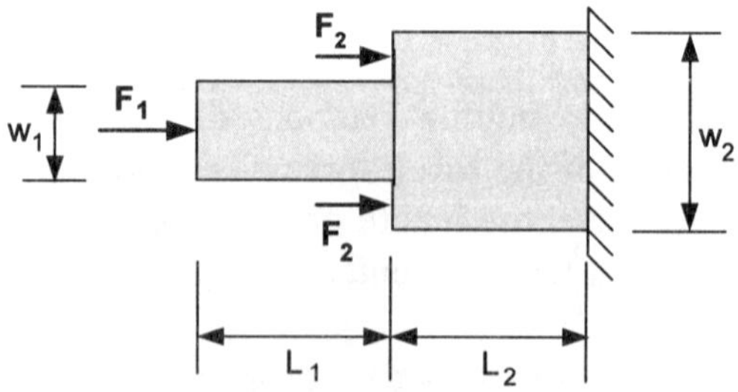

Fig. E2.33 The thickness of the bar is given by b_1 and b_2.

Solution:

Let's begin the solution by drawing free bodies of both sections of the bar. We make two section cuts A and B as illustrated in Fig. E2.33a. Then draw free bodies associated with the portion of the bar to the left side of the section cut as shown in Figs. E2.33b and E2.33c:

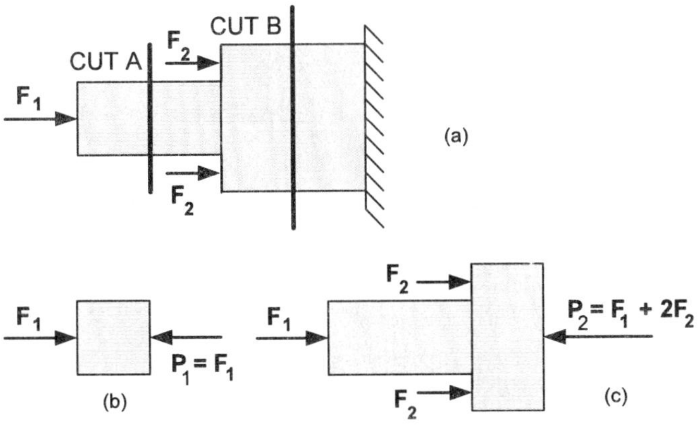

Fig. E2.33a-c FBDs of stepped sections.

From the equilibrium relations, it is clear that the internal force $P_1 = F_1$ in the smaller section of the stepped bar. Also, for the larger section of the bar, the internal force $P_2 = F_1 + 2F_2$.

Finally, from Eq. (2.4) for the smaller section of the bar, we write:

$$\sigma_1 = P_1/A_1 = -(80 \times 10^3)/[(50)(60)] = -26.67 \text{ N/mm}^2 = -26.67 \text{ MPa} \quad \text{(a)}$$

For the larger section of the bar, we write:

$$\sigma_2 = P_2/A_2 = -\{[80 + (2)(40)] \times 10^3\}/[(90)(60)] = -29.63 \text{ N/mm}^2 = -29.63 \text{ MPa} \quad \text{(b)}$$

Note, the minus sign indicates the stresses in the bar are compressive.

2.11.2 Deformation of Stepped Bars

To compute the axial extension or compression of the stepped bar, we consider each uniform section of the bar separately. Equation (2.2) is valid for each section because each has a uniform cross sectional area. For a stepped bar comprised of n uniform sections, we superimpose the individual deformations δ to obtain:

$$\delta_{total} = \delta_1 + \delta_2 + \delta_3 + \ldots.. + \delta_n \quad (2.44)$$

EXAMPLE 2.34

If the stepped bar defined in Example 2.33 is fabricated from a titanium alloy with a modulus of elasticity E = 114 GPa, determine the total deformation of the bar.

Solution:

We recognize that the deformation of the stepped bar is determined from Eq. (2.44) and Eq. (2.2) as:

$$\delta_{total} = \delta_1 + \delta_2 = (P_1 L_1)/(A_1 E) + (P_2 L_2)/(A_2 E) \qquad (a)$$

Because the modulus of elasticity is constant for both sections of the bar, Eq. (a) reduces to:

$$\delta_{total} = \delta_1 + \delta_2 = \frac{1}{E}\left[\frac{P_1 L_1}{A_1} + \frac{P_2 L_2}{A_2}\right] \qquad (b)$$

Substituting the numerical parameters for the unknown quantities in this relation yields:

$$\delta_{total} = \delta_1 + \delta_2 = \frac{1}{114 \times 10^9}\left[\frac{(-80 \times 10^3)(0.2)}{(0.05)(0.06)} + \frac{(-160 \times 10^3)(0.3)}{(0.09)(0.06)}\right] = -0.1248 \times 10^{-3} \text{m}$$

$$\delta_{total} = -\ 0.1248 \text{ mm} \qquad (c)$$

Let's interpret this solution. The negative sign indicates the bar was compressed and the deformations reduced its length. The original length of the bar was $L_1 + L_2 = 500$ mm. When the total deformation of the bar is compared to this length, we find the deformation is very small — only 0.025%. This example again emphasizes that deformations of metallic members are usually very small. For this reason, we neglect these deformations and use the original lengths of structural members when employing the equilibrium equations.

2.12 SCALE MODELS

We have described methods for determining the stresses, strains and deformation of bars and rods subjected to axial tension or compression forces. The analysis required to determine these quantities is relatively simple when the bar can be isolated and the forces acting on it are known. However, if the bar is part of a complex structure, determining the forces acting on the bar may prove to be more difficult. In some cases, scale models of the structure under consideration are constructed and then subjected to various loads to verify structural integrity.

2.12.1 Geometric Scaling Factors

Scale models of structures are usually much smaller than the real thing. Let's call the real structure — a bridge, building or stadium — the prototype, and consider a scale model that is 100 times smaller than the prototype. In this case, the geometric scale factor $\boldsymbol{S} = 1/100$. If the same scale factor $\boldsymbol{S}$, is used for all three dimensions (i.e., length, width and thickness), we may write:

$$L_m = \boldsymbol{S}\, L_p$$

$$w_m = \boldsymbol{S}\, w_p \qquad (2.45)$$

$$b_m = \boldsymbol{S}\, b_p$$

where L, w and b represent length, width and thickness and subscripts m and p refer to the model and the prototype, respectively.

We note from Eq. (2.45), that the scale model is exactly the same shape as the prototype except for its size. It is geometrically proportional.

2.12.2 Scaling Factor for Stresses

Let's continue with the concept of scaling and consider the stresses occurring in both the model and the prototype. The stress σ in a bar subjected to axial loading is given by Eq. (2.4) as:

$$\sigma = P/A = P/(w\ b) \qquad \text{(a)}$$

where P is the axial load applied to the bar and A = (w b) is the cross sectional area of a bar of width w and depth b.

If the left side of Eq. (a) is divided by its right side, a unit dimensionless ratio involving the stress and its controlling parameters is formed:

$$\sigma(w\ b)/P = 1 \qquad \text{(b)}$$

Let's designate a model and a prototype in Eq. (b) by writing:

$$\sigma_m\ (w_m\ b_m)/P_m = \sigma_p\ (w_p\ b_p)/P_p \qquad \text{(c)}$$

Rearranging the terms in Eq. (c) gives:

$$\sigma_m = (P_m / P_p)(w_p / w_m)(b_p / b_m)\sigma_p \qquad \text{(d)}$$

Substituting Eq. (2.45) into Eq. (d) yields:

$$\sigma_m = (P_m / P_p)(1/\boldsymbol{S}^2)\sigma_p \qquad \text{(e)}$$

Examining Eq. (e) shows that the stresses in the model and the prototype are related by the geometric scale factor ***S*** and load scale factor ***L***, which is defined by:

$$\boldsymbol{L} = (P_m / P_p) \qquad (2.46)$$

Finally, we substitute Eq. (2.45) into Eq. (e) and obtain:

$$\sigma_m = (\boldsymbol{L}/\boldsymbol{S}^2)\ \sigma_p \qquad (2.47)$$

Clearly, the stresses produced in the model are related to the scale factors for the load and the geometry. It is also important to recognize that the geometric scale factor usually differs significantly from the load scale factor.

EXAMPLE 2.35

Suppose we construct a scale model of the Golden Gate Bridge using a scale factor ***S*** of 1/400. Determine the size of the model if:

- Total bridge length ⇒ 8,981 feet
- Length of suspended structure ⇒ 6,450
- Length of main span ⇒ 4,200 feet
- Length of each side span ⇒ 1,125 feet
- Width of bridge ⇒ 90 feet
- Diameter of main cable ⇒ 36-3/8 inch
- Width of roadway between curbs ⇒ 60 feet
- Lanes of vehicular traffic ⇒ 6
- Weight of main span per lineal foot ⇒ 21,300 lb
- Live load capacity per lineal foot ⇒ 4,000 lb

Solution:

The model bridge is constructed in three parts including the main span and the two side spans. The length of the main span of the model is given by Eq. (2.45) as:

$$L_m = \boldsymbol{S}\, L_p = (1/400)(4{,}200) = 10.5 \text{ ft} = 126 \text{ in.} \qquad \text{(a)}$$

The width of the model bridge is determined in the same manner as:

$$w_m = \boldsymbol{S}\, w_p = (1/400)(90) = 0.225 \text{ ft} = 2.7 \text{ in.} \qquad \text{(b)}$$

The diameter, D of the main cable on the model is:

$$D_m = \boldsymbol{S}\, D_p = (1/400)(36.375) = 0.09094 \text{ in.} \qquad \text{(c)}$$

All geometric features of the model of the bridge are determined in this manner.

EXAMPLE 2.36

Let's suppose a strain gage is installed on a steel bar of a model used to simulate a critical structural member in a prototype. The gage provides a measurement of the strain equal to $3{,}000 \times 10^{-6}$ when the model bridge was fully loaded. If the scaling factors for the load and geometry are $\boldsymbol{L}$ = 1/100,000 and $\boldsymbol{S}$ = 1/500, determine the stress in the main cable of the prototype.

Solution:

The stress acting on the bar in the model is given by Hooke's law as:

$$\sigma = E\, \varepsilon \qquad (2.5)$$

Substituting numerical values for the modulus of elasticity and the strain into Eq. (2.5) gives the stress in the main cable of the model as:

$$\sigma_m = E_m\, \varepsilon_m = (30 \times 10^6)(3{,}000 \times 10^{-6}) = 90{,}000 \text{ psi} \qquad \text{(a)}$$

where the modulus of elasticity $E = 30 \times 10^6$ psi for steel.

Solving Eq. (2.47) for the stress on the prototype gives:

$$\sigma_p = (\boldsymbol{S}^2/\boldsymbol{L})\,\sigma_m \qquad (2.48)$$

Substituting the scale factors for $\boldsymbol{S}$ and $\boldsymbol{L}$ into Eq. (2.47) yields:

$$\sigma_p = (\boldsymbol{S}^2/\boldsymbol{L})\,\sigma_m = [(1/500)^2/(1/100{,}000)][90{,}000] = (0.4)(90{,}000) = 36{,}000 \text{ psi} \qquad (b)$$

This example illustrates that the scale factors for the load and the geometry of the structure should be selected to limit the stresses induced in the model. In most instances, the scale factor for the load is much smaller than the scale factor for the geometry.

2.12.3 Scaling Factor for Displacements

A model of the structure may also provide displacement measurements that may be used to predict displacements in the prototype. To develop the displacement relation between the model and the prototype, we again seek a unit dimensionless quantity that includes the variables controlling the displacement. Recalling Eq. (2.2), it may be shown that the displacement δ of a rod of length L subjected to an axial load P is given by:

$$\delta = PL/AE = PL/[(w\,b)E] \qquad (a)$$

If the left side of Eq. (a) is divided by its right side, a unit dimensionless ratio is formed:

$$[\delta(w\,b)E]/(PL) = 1 \qquad (b)$$

Let's identify the model and the prototype with appropriate subscripts in Eq. (b) and write:

$$[\delta_m\,(w_m\,b_m)\,E_m\,]/(P_m\,L_m\,) = [\delta_p\,(w_p\,b_p)\,E_p\,]/(P_p\,L_p\,) \qquad (c)$$

Solving Eq. (c) for δ_p and substituting Eq. (2.45) and (2.46) into the result, yields:

$$\delta_p = [(\boldsymbol{S}\,\boldsymbol{E})/\boldsymbol{L}]\,\delta_m \qquad (2.49)$$

where $\boldsymbol{E} = E_m/E_p$ is the modulus scale factor between the model and the prototype.

If the same materials are employed in the manufacture of both the model and the prototype the modulus scale factor is one. However, selection of the model materials is not restricted. We may use a wide variety of materials to fabricate the model providing they respond in a linear elastic manner.

EXAMPLE 2.37

Suppose that a model of a truss type bridge structure is fabricated from members formed from sheet aluminum with $E = 10.4 \times 10^6$ psi. The prototype structure is to be fabricated from steel with a span of 1,000 feet. The model is geometrically scaled so that its span is 10 feet. The capacity of the live load on the prototype is 20,000 lb/ft, and the model is loaded with 50 lb/ft. If the model deflects a distance of 1.5 inches under full load at the center of the span, determine the deflection of the prototype under the design load.

Solution:

From Eq. (2.49), we write:

$$\delta_p = [(\boldsymbol{S}\ \boldsymbol{E}) / \boldsymbol{L}]\ \delta_m \qquad \text{(a)}$$

Note the scale factors are given by:

$$\boldsymbol{S} = 10/1{,}000 = 1/100$$

$$\boldsymbol{L} = 50/20{,}000 = 2.5 \times 10^{-3}$$

$$\boldsymbol{E} = (10.4 \times 10^6)/(30 \times 10^6) = 0.3467$$

Substituting the scale factors into Eq. (2.49) yields:

$$\delta_p = [(\boldsymbol{S}\ \boldsymbol{E})/\boldsymbol{L}]\ \delta_m = [(1/100)(0.3467)/(2.5 \times 10^{-3})](1.5) = 2.0802 \text{ in.}$$

In this instance, the deflection of the prototype is slightly (25%) larger than the deflection of the model. The choice of materials for the model and the scaling factors for both the load and geometry influence the differences in the stress, and deflection between the model and the prototype.

2.13 SUMMARY

This chapter treats structural members that are long and thin. Flexible members, such as wire and cable, only support axial tensile loads. They cannot support compressive forces because they buckle under very low loads. In addition, they cannot support transverse loads with out large deflections, because their transverse stiffness is also negligible. Under increasing tension forces applied along the axis of these long, thin, and flexible members, they elongate, yield and finally rupture.

Rods and bars are sufficiently stiff to carry compressive forces. In this chapter, we consider only axial loading of the bars and rods. The case of transverse loading is deferred until Chapters 4 and 5. The equations derived for stresses and deformations in wire and cable are also applicable to bars and rods. When dealing with compressive forces and stresses, a minus sign is used to indicate the direction of the loading. We also assume compressively loaded bars and rods are sized so they will not fail by buckling. Examples are presented for determining stresses and deformations of uniform axial bars.

Relations have been derived to determine the axial deformation. Stress and strain have been defined and the stress-strain relation (Hooke's law) has been discussed. Several examples have been provided to guide you in determining, stress, strain and axial deformation.

We have shown that the internal force P is equal to the external force F for these uniaxial members. The internal force is produced by normal stresses that are uniformly distributed over the cross section of the uniaxial member. Several examples are present to demonstrate methods for solving for axial (normal) stresses in wire, bars and rods under axial loading.

Shear stresses are then introduced and applications involving keys and joints are presented. The analysis of bolted or riveted joints was treated in some detail as methods for determining shear stresses in the rivets, normal stresses along the rivet line and shear stresses involved in pullout were described. Examples demonstrating these methods were presented. Bearing stresses were defined and two methods for determining their magnitude in bolted or riveted joints were presented. Examples demonstrating these methods were presented.

The standard ASTM tensile test is introduced in Section 2.6. Using a standard tensile specimen and standard test procedures a force-deflection curve is generated. We convert this force-deflection data to a stress-strain curve, and then interpret the curve to give the strength, ductility and the elastic constants. Care is exercised in the interpretation to distinguish between "brittle" and "ductile" materials because the yield strength cannot be measured for brittle materials. For ductile materials, procedures are described for measuring both the yield strength and the ultimate tensile strength.

The ductility of a material is indicated by two measurements — the percent elongation and the percent reduction in area. Methods for determining both of these quantities have been given. We noted that for most types of steel the ductility decreased with increasing carbon content used for strength enhancement.

Two elastic constants, the modulus of elasticity E and Poisson's ratio ν, are measured in a tensile test. The modulus of elasticity is determined from the slope of the stress-strain curve in the elastic region. Poisson's ratio is determined from the ratio of strain in both the axial and transverse directions measured during a uniaxial tension test. The shear modulus, another elastic constant often used in analysis of shear stresses and torsion loading of circular shafts, is introduced.

We describe failure by yielding and rupture and introduce the stress-strain curve for different types of materials. Ultimate tensile strength and yield strength are defined. Safe design philosophy is discussed together with the use of factors of safety in design. Examples are provided to demonstrate problem-solving techniques dealing with strength and safety factors. The importance of specifying standard sizes of structural members in design is illustrated in one of the examples.

Stresses that occur on oblique planes were introduced by making a section cut at some angle θ along an axially loaded bar. The normal stress σ and the shear stress τ both vary with the angle of the section cut. The normal stress σ is a maximum when θ = 0° and the shear stress τ is a maximum when θ = 45°.

Methods of analysis of the stress σ and deformation δ in tapered and stepped bars were described. Equations for the deformation in tapered bars involved integrating incremental deformations over the length of the bar. The analysis for step bars involved summing the deformations from each segment of the bar.

The concept of models that are geometrically similar to actual structures is introduced. The stresses and displacements produced by loading or deforming a model are related to those developed in the prototype (structure). Relations involving scaling factors are employed to determine the stresses and displacements in the structure based on measurements made on a geometrically scaled model.

The equations developed in this chapter for uniaxial members subjected to axial forces are summarized below:

$$\delta = L_f - L_o \tag{2.1}$$

$$\delta = (PL)/(AE) \tag{2.2}$$

$$\varepsilon = \delta/L \tag{2.3}$$

$$\sigma = P/A \tag{2.4}$$

$$\sigma = E\varepsilon \tag{2.5}$$

$$\varepsilon = P/(AE) \tag{2.6}$$

$$P = \int \sigma \, dA \tag{2.7}$$

$$P = \sigma \int dA = \sigma A \tag{2.8}$$

$$\tau = V/A \tag{2.9}$$

$$\tau = F/A \tag{2.10}$$

$$\sigma = qw/[t(w - Nd)] \tag{2.13}$$

$$\tau = qw/[2N(t\,s)] \tag{2.15}$$

$$(\sigma_B)_{Max} = \frac{2F}{\pi t r} = \frac{4F}{\pi t d} \tag{2.19}$$

$$(\sigma_B) = \frac{F}{2tr} = \frac{F}{td} = \frac{F}{A_P} \tag{2.21}$$

$$S_y = \sigma_y \tag{2.23}$$

$$S_u = \sigma_u \tag{2.24}$$

$$\%\, e = \left(\frac{L_f - L_0}{L_0} \right) \times 100 \tag{2.25}$$

$$\%\, A = \left(\frac{A_0 - A_f}{A_0} \right) \times 100 \tag{2.26}$$

$$\nu = -\varepsilon_t/\varepsilon_a \tag{2.27}$$

$$\tau = G\gamma \tag{2.29}$$

$$G = \frac{E}{2(1 + \nu)} \quad (2.30)$$

$$\mathbf{SF_u} = S_u / \sigma_{design} \quad (2.31)$$

$$\mathbf{SF_y} = S_y / \sigma_{design} \quad (2.32)$$

$$\sigma_{design} = P_{design}/A \quad (2.33)$$

$$S_u = \sigma_f = P_{fail} /A \quad (2.34)$$

$$S_y = \sigma_y = P_{yield} /A \quad (2.35)$$

$$S_{ys} = 0.5774\ S_y \quad (2.36)$$

$$\mathbf{SF_{ys}} = S_{ys} / \tau \quad (2.37)$$

$$\sigma_\theta = (\sigma_x)\cos^2 \theta \quad (2.38)$$

$$\tau_\theta = (\sigma_x/2) \sin 2\theta \quad (2.39)$$

$$\sigma_x = P/A_x = P/\{b[h_1 + (h_2 - h_1)(x/L)]\} \quad (2.41)$$

$$\delta = \frac{PL}{Eb}\left(\frac{1}{h_2 - h_1}\right)\ln\left(\frac{h_2}{h_1}\right) \quad (2.43)$$

$$\delta_{total} = \delta_1 + \delta_2 + \delta_3 + \ldots.. + \delta_n \quad (2.44)$$

$$\sigma_m = (\boldsymbol{L}/\boldsymbol{S}^2)\ \sigma_p \quad (2.47)$$

$$\delta_p = [(\boldsymbol{SE})/\boldsymbol{L}]\ \delta_m \quad (2.49)$$

PROBLEMS

2.1 A steel music wire (Gage No. 10 with a diameter of 0.024 in.) is employed to support an axial load P of 9.40 lb. If the wire was initially 20 ft in length, determine its final length and the stress and strain in the wire.

2.2 A steel music wire is tightened on a guitar by rotating the wire supporting post through an angle of 10°. If the post has a diameter d = 8.0 mm and the length of the wire is 900 mm, determine the added strain induced in the guitar string assuming it was tight before the post was turned.

2.3 Referring to Problem 2.2, determine the additional stress induced in the guitar string as it is tightened.

2.4 A hemp rope 18 m long and 45 mm in diameter is supported from one of the roof beams in a gymnasium. Three gymnasts climb this rope together. The lead gymnast has a mass of 60 kg, the next is 64 kg, and the trailing gymnast is 56 kg.
   (a) Determine the maximum stress in this rope.
   (b) Determine the stress in the rope at a location between the lead and middle gymnasts.
   (c) Determine the stress in the rope at a location between the middle and trailing gymnasts.

2.5 A suspension bridge is to carry a roadway and traffic that may weigh up to 10,000 ton. If the safe load that can be imposed on the wire rope to be used in the construction is 125 ton, specify the number of cables to be employed. Justify your answer.

2.6 For the cable-pulley-mass arrangement shown in Fig. P2.6, determine the stresses in the cable. The effective cable diameter is 10 mm.

Fig. P2.6

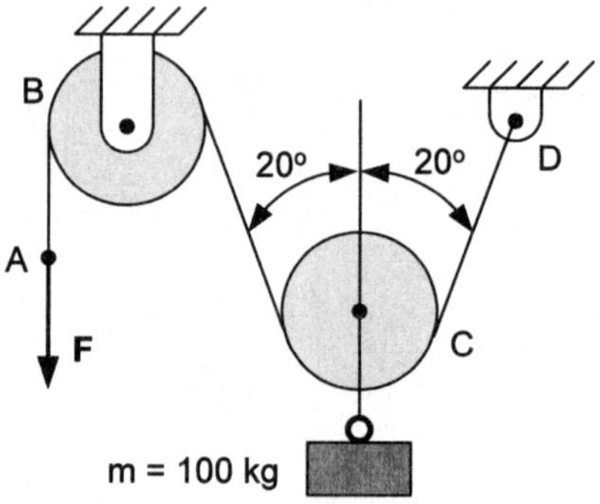

2.7 Determine the mass m, shown in Fig. P2.6, that is required to yield the cable CD if the cables are each 25 ft long, exhibit a yield strength of 80ksi and have an effective cross sectional area of 0.020 in.^{2} Assume that the forces in the horizontal wires are equal in magnitude and opposite in direction (F_{CB} = – F_{CA}). Also assume F_{CB} = (0.25)F_{CD}. Is the cable-weight arrangement stable after yield? Why?

2.8 Determine the stress in the bar shown in Fig. P2.8 when subjected to a compressive axial force of F that acts through the centroid of the bar. The following numerical parameters define the bar and the applied load: F = 1,200 kN, L = 500 mm, w = 120 mm and h = 90 mm.

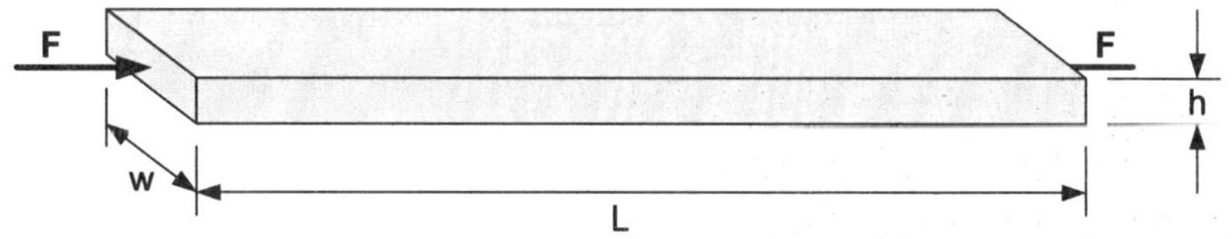

Fig. P2.8

2.9 Determine the stress in the bar shown in Fig. P2.9 when subjected to a tensile axial force of F that acts through the centroid of the bar. The following numerical parameters define the bar and the applied load: F = 1,500 kN, L = 750 mm, w = 125 mm and h = 75 mm.

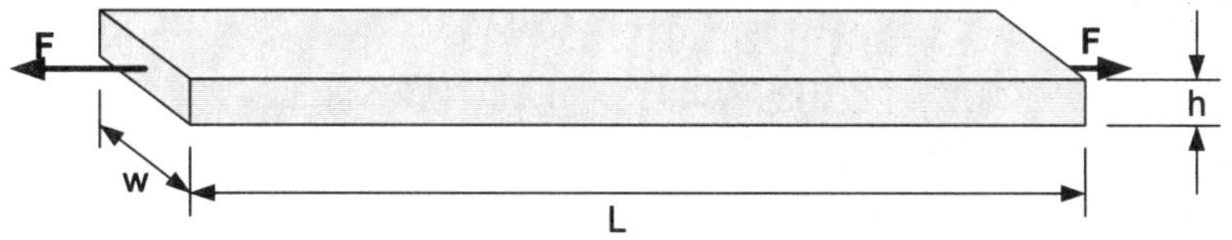

Fig. P2.9

2.10 If the bar described in Problem 2.8 is fabricated from steel, determine the length of the bar after the application of the compressive force.

2.11 If the bar described in Problem 2.9 is fabricated from steel, determine the length of the bar after the application of the tensile force.

2.12 Determine the axial deformation in a 4-foot long rod that has a diameter of 3.5 in. The rod is fabricated from mild steel with a yield strength S_y = 37,000 psi, and is subjected to an axial compressive load of 110,000 lb. Repeat the solution for the rod if it is fabricated from an aluminum alloy.

2.13 A key is employed to keep a gear from slipping on a shaft when transmitting power. Forces F of 60 kN are created on the key at the locations shown in Fig. P2.13. Determine the shear stresses in the key if it is 15 mm wide, 15 mm high and 60 mm long.

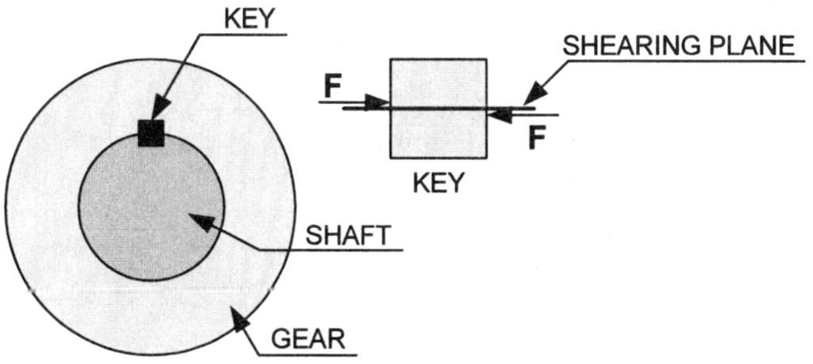

Fig. P2.13

2.14 The lap joint with a single shear plane, shown in Fig. P2.14, is 500 mm wide with four bolts spaced on 125 mm centers. The two plates are each 12 mm thick and the bolts are 15 mm in diameter. Determine the shear stress in the bolts if the applied force q is uniformly distributed over the width of the joint and equal to 100 N/mm. Also determine the nominal normal stress acting along a section through the bolt line.

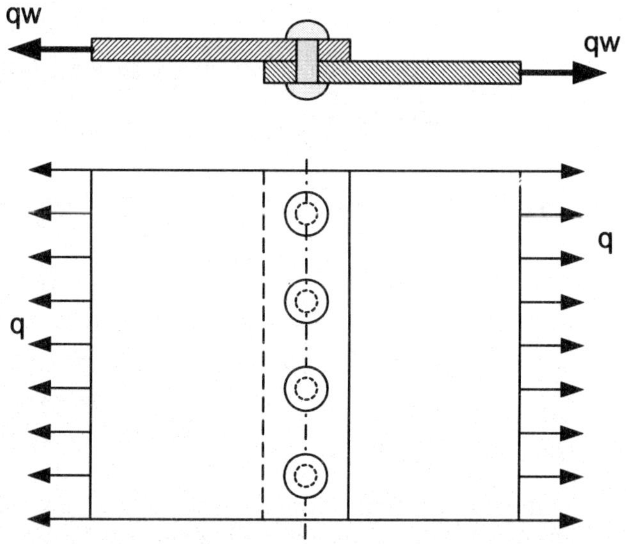

Fig. P2.14

2.15 The lap joint with a single shear plane, shown in Fig. P2.14, is 300 mm wide with four rivets spaced on 75 mm centers. The two plates are each 8 mm thick and the rivets are 9 mm in diameter. Determine the shear stress in the bolts if the applied force q is uniformly distributed over the width of the joint and equal to 30 N/mm. Also determine the nominal normal stress acting along a section through the bolt line.

2.16 The butt joint with double straps, shown in Fig. P2.16, is 800 mm wide with four bolts spaced on 200 mm centers on each bolt line. The four plates are each 18 mm thick and the bolts are 20 mm in diameter. Determine the shear stress in the bolts if the applied force q is uniformly distributed over the width of the joint and equal to 350 N/mm. Also determine the nominal normal stress acting along a section through the bolt line

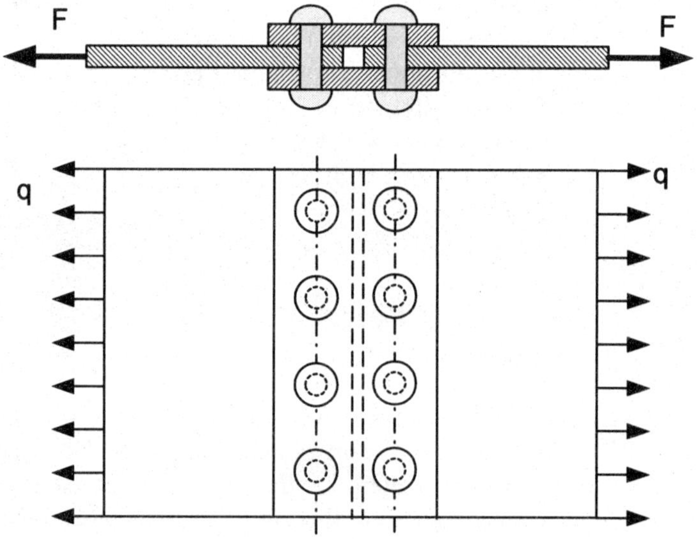

Fig. P2.16

2.17 The butt joint with double straps, shown in Fig. P2.16, is 400 mm wide with four bolts spaced on 100 mm centers on each bolt line. The four plates are each 10 mm thick and the bolts are 14 mm in diameter. Determine the shear stress in the bolts if the applied force q is uniformly distributed over the width of the joint and equal to 250 N/mm. Also determine the nominal normal stress acting along a section through the bolt line

2.18 The butt joint with double straps and two rows of rivets, shown in Fig. P2.18, is 800 mm wide with rivets spaced on 200 mm centers on each rivet line. The four plates are each 18 mm thick and the rivets are 14 mm in diameter. Determine the shear stress in the rivets if the applied force q is uniformly distributed over the width of the joint and equal to 500 N/mm. Also determine the nominal normal stress acting along a section through the bolt line. Assume the loads are uniformly distributed over the rivets.

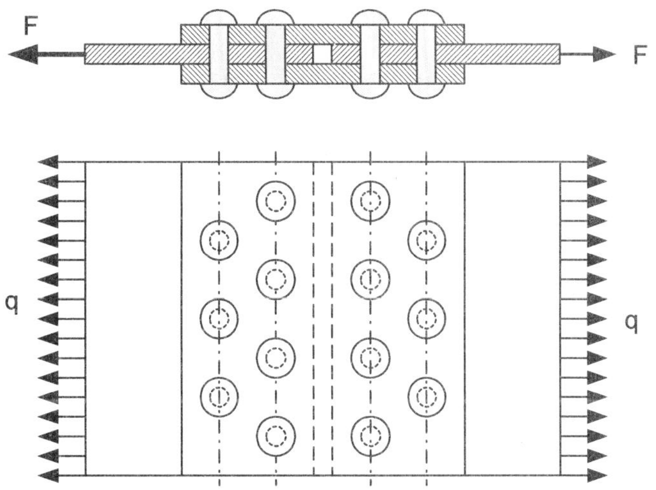

Fig. P2.18

2.19 The butt joint with double straps and two rows of rivets, shown in Fig. P2.18, is 1.00 m wide with rivets spaced on 250 mm centers on each rivet line. The four plates are each 20 mm thick and the rivets are 18 mm in diameter. Determine the shear stress in the rivets if the applied force q is uniformly distributed over the width of the joint and equal to 400 kN/m. Also determine the nominal normal stress acting along a section through the bolt line

2.20 For the joint described in Problem 2.14, determine the shear stress associated with pullout if the distance s from the bolt centerline to the edge of the plates is 18 mm.

2.21 For the joint described in Problem 2.16, determine the shear stress associated with pullout if the distance s from the bolt centerline to the edge of the plates is 16 mm.

2.22 For the joint described in Problem 2.14, determine the average bearing stress on the bolts.

2.23 For the joint described in Problem 2.14, determine the maximum bearing stress on the bolts.

2.24 For the joint described in Problem 2.16, determine the average bearing stress on the bolts.

2.25 For the joint described in Problem 2.16, determine the maximum bearing stress on the bolts.

2.26 For the joint described in Problem 2.18, determine the average bearing stress on the rivets.

2.27 For the joint described in Problem 2.18, determine the maximum bearing stress on the rivets.

2.28 Sketch a stress-strain diagram for a relatively brittle material and identify the ultimate tensile strength on the diagram.

2.29 Sketch a stress-strain diagram for a relatively ductile material and identify the yield strength and ultimate tensile strength on the diagram.

2.30 Sketch a stress-strain diagram for a ductile material that does not exhibit a well defined yield point. Identify on the diagram the yield strength and the ultimate tensile strength.

2.31 Determine the yield strength and the ultimate tensile strength for the material represented by the stress-strain diagram shown in Fig. P2.31.

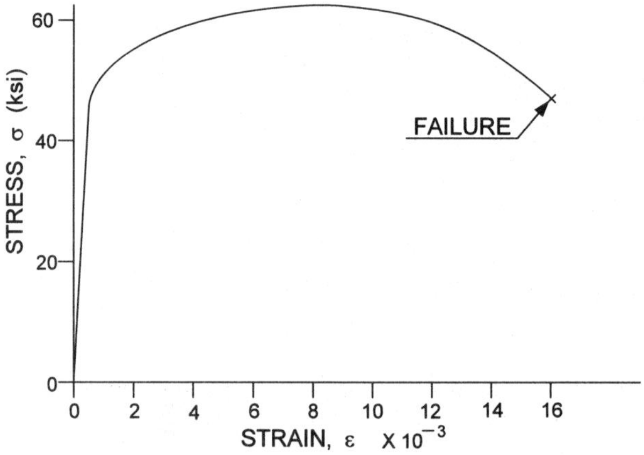

Fig. P2.31

2.32 Determine the percent elongation and the percent reduction in area if measurements of L_f = 63.2 mm and d_f = 10.78 mm were made during a standard tensile test. The initial length and diameter of the standard tensile specimen is L_o = 50 mm and d_o = 12.7 mm.

2.33 Determine the yield strength and the ultimate tensile strength for the material represented by the stress-strain diagram shown in Fig. P2.33.

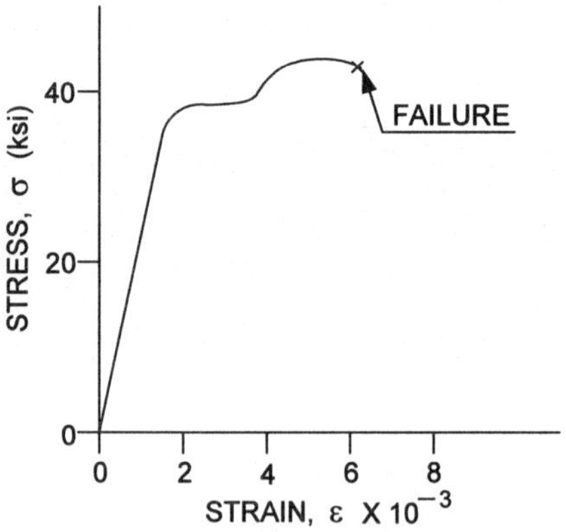

Fig. P2.33

2.34 In conducting a tensile test of an aluminum alloy, you adjust the signals from the load cell and the extensometer to zero and then load the specimen. You dwell at several loads in the elastic region of the stress-strain response, and record readings of the load F and the elongation δ. The values of F and δ are plotted on an F-δ diagram to obtain the slope $\Delta F/\Delta\delta$ = (180 × 10^{-3} N/mm). Determine the elastic modulus of the aluminum alloy if the initial length and diameter of the tensile specimen is L_o = 50 mm and d_o = 12.7 mm.

2.35 If a steel alloy exhibits a Poisson's ratio of $\nu = 0.30$, determine the diameter of a tensile specimen when it is subjected to an elastic stress of $\sigma = 60.0$ ksi. The dimensions L_o and d_o for the specimen are 2.00 in. and 0.500 in., respectively.

2.36 A long (3 m) sheet of an aluminum alloy is elongated in a manufacturing process until it is 3.30 m in length. If the sheet was initially 0.5 m wide and 2 mm thick, determine its new width and thickness. In the plastic regime, Poisson's ratio is 0.5 for all metallic materials because volume is conserved in the plastic deformation process.

2.37 A long (4.0 m) sheet of an aluminum alloy is elongated in a manufacturing process until it is 4.5 m in length. If a central hole initially 80 mm in diameter was drilled in the sheet prior to elongating, determine its new dimensions. In the plastic regime, Poisson's ratio is 0.5 for all metallic materials because volume is conserved in the plastic deformation process.

2.38 Prove that volume of an object is conserved in a uniaxial stress state if $\nu = 0.5$.

2.39 If a steel alloy is linearly elastic until the applied axial stress equals the yield strength, determine the strain at yield for a structural steel with a yield strength of 42 ksi and a modulus of elasticity of 30×10^6 psi.

2.40 A long, thin, aluminum-alloy bar is subjected to an axial stress of 205 MPa. Determine the strain in the axial and transverse directions of the bar.

2.41 A rod with a diameter of 1.00 in. and length of 4.0 ft undergoes a deformation of 0.100 in. when subjected to an axial force of 52.0 kip. The diameter of the rod decreases by 0.0007 in. at this load. Determine the modulus of elasticity, Poisson's ratio and the shear modulus for the rod's material.

2.42 A standard tensile specimen, having a diameter of 0.5 in, was fitted with an extensometer with a 2.00-inch gage length and tested until failure. The force and deformation measured during the test is presented in the table below. The diameter of the specimen at the fracture neck was 0.406 in. Analyze the data using a spreadsheet to plot a stress-strain curve, and then determine the following quantities.

a. Modulus of elasticity
b. Yield strength (0.2% offset)
c. Ultimate strength
d. Fracture stress
e. Strain at fracture
f. Percent elongation
g. Percent reduction in area

Load (kip)	Deformation (in.)	Load (kip)	Deformation (in.)
0	0	10.8	0.255
2.0	0.0021	11.2	0.279
4.0	0.0040	11.6	0.307
6.0	0.0061	11.6	0.320
7.0	0.0071	11.5	0.329
7.8	0.0082	11.2	0.348
8.3	0.0270	10.8	0.364
8.7	0.0525	10.1	0.390
9.2	0.0840	9.7	0.405
9.8	0.1480	9.6	0.431
10.4	0.2240		

2.43 A standard tensile specimen 12.7 mm in diameter was fitted with an extensometer with a 50 mm gage length and tested until failure. The force and deformation measured during the test is presented in the table below. The diameter of the specimen at the fracture neck was 9.0 mm. Analyze the data using a spreadsheet to plot a stress-strain curve, and then determine the following quantities.

a. Modulus of elasticity
b. Yield strength (0.2% offset)
c. Ultimate strength
d. Fracture stress
e. Strain at fracture
f. Percent elongation
g. Percent reduction in area

Load (kN)	**Deformation (mm.)**	**Load (kN)**	**Deformation (mm)**
0	0	35.0	3.41
5.0	0.010	37.0	4.35
10.0	0.019	38.0	5.48
15.0	0.031	38.0	6.05
20.0	0.041	36.0	6.51
25.0	0.049	33.0	7.22
26.0	0.520	30.0	7.64
27.0	1.00	27.0	8.31
29.0	1.45	23.0	8.67
31.5	2.10	19.0	9.20

2.44 A long thin steel bar with a length of 2.0 m, a width of 50 mm, and a thickness of 30 mm is subjected to an axial force of 30 kN. Determine the tensile stress and the axial deformation of the bar.

2.45 Determine the design load that can be specified for Gage No. 00 steel wire with a yield strength of 500 MPa, if the design specification calls for the safety factor of 3.2.

2.46 Cold drawn steel alloy wire exhibits an ultimate tensile strength of 600 MPa and a yield strength of 500 MPa. If this alloy is employed, specify the gage of the wire if it is to support a design load of 9.0 kN with a safety factor of 3.4. Specify the gage number for the wire required based on both yielding and rupturing as modes of failure.

2.47 Determine the safety factor for the wire CD in the cable-weight arrangement shown in Fig. P2.47 The steel cables are each 10 m long, exhibit a yield strength of 500 MPa and have an effective cross sectional area of 10 mm^2. Assume that the forces in the horizontal wires are equal in magnitude and opposite in direction ($F_{CB} = -F_{CA}$). Also assume $F_{CB} = (0.18)F_{CD}$.

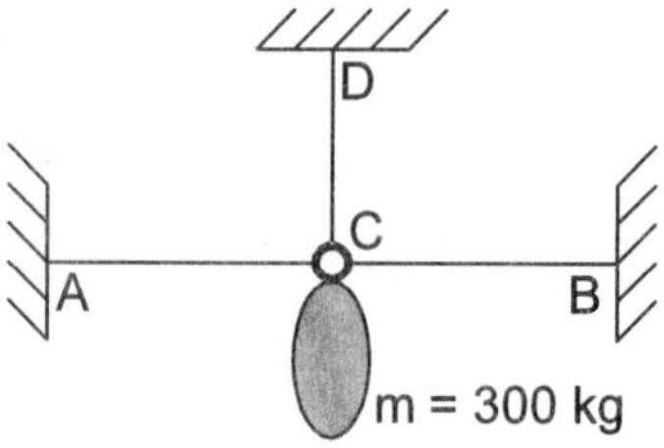

Fig. P2.47

2.48 The wire-mass system, shown in Fig. P2.48, is constructed using steel wire. Specify a suitable alloy and the gage number for the wires if the criterion for failure is based on yielding. Use the same diameter for both wires. The safety factor imposed on the design is 3.2.

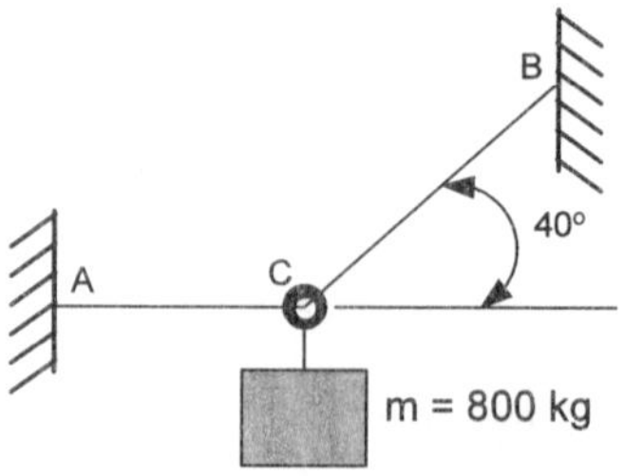

Fig. P2.48

2.49 The wire-mass system, shown in Fig. P2.49, is constructed using aluminum wire. Specify a suitable alloy and the gage number for the wires if the criterion for failure is based on ultimate tensile strength. Use the same diameter for both wires. The safety factor imposed on the design is 2.4.

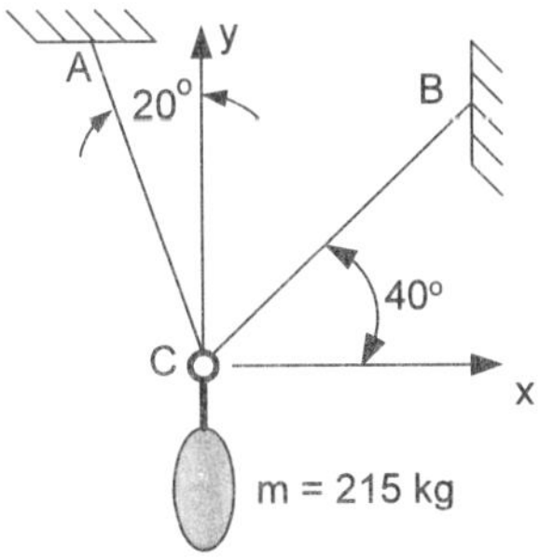

Fig. P2.49

2.50 The wire-mass system, shown in Fig. P2.50, is constructed using steel wire fabricated from 1010 A. A safety factor of 2.6, based on the ultimate tensile strength, is to be employed for both wires. Find the maximum weight that can be lifted (in pounds) and specify the required gage numbers for each wire.

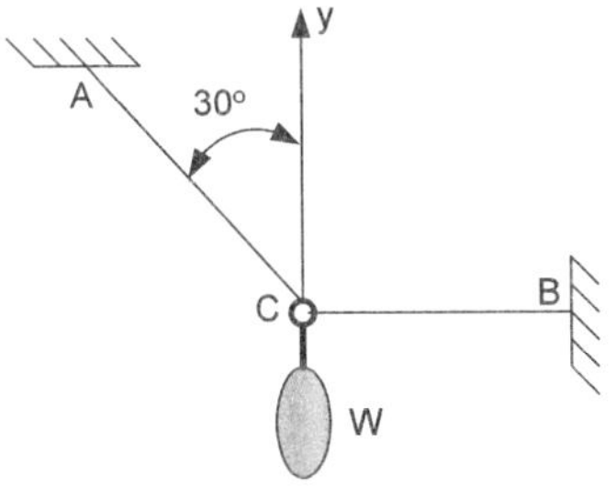

Fig. P2.50

2.51 A bar fabricated from steel with a tensile strength of 50.0 ksi is subjected to an axial tensile force of 25 kip. The bar is designed with a safety factor of 3.0. Determine the design stress for the bar and the required cross sectional area.

2.52 A bar fabricated from an aluminum alloy with a tensile strength of 400 MPa is subjected to an axial tensile force of 80 kN. The bar is designed with a safety factor of 2.75. Determine the design stress for the bar and the required cross sectional area.

2.53 A bar fabricated from brass with a tensile strength of 247 MPa is subjected to an axial compressive force of 85 kN. The bar is designed with a safety factor of 3.2. Determine the design stress for the bar and the required cross sectional area. Assume the tensile and compressive stresses are equal.

2.54 A structural member is fabricated from a solid round bar of steel with a diameter $d = 50$ mm. If the member is 6.0 m long, determine the maximum axial force that can be applied if the axial stress is not to exceed 175 MPa and the total elongation is not to exceed 0.14% of its length.

2.55 A key used to lock a gear onto a shaft is subjected to a shear force of 20.0 kip. If the key is 0.50 in. wide by 0.50 in. high by 2.0 in. long, determine the shear stress acting on the key. Draw a free body diagram showing this shear stress.

2.56 If the key in Problem 2.55 is machined from a steel alloy with a tensile yield strength of 54,000 psi, determine the safety factor for the key.

2.57 A rectangular bar, shown in Fig. P2.57, is subjected to an axial tensile force $F = 25$ kN. Determine the normal stress and the shear stress on an inclined plane if the angle of the section cut is $\theta = 30°$.

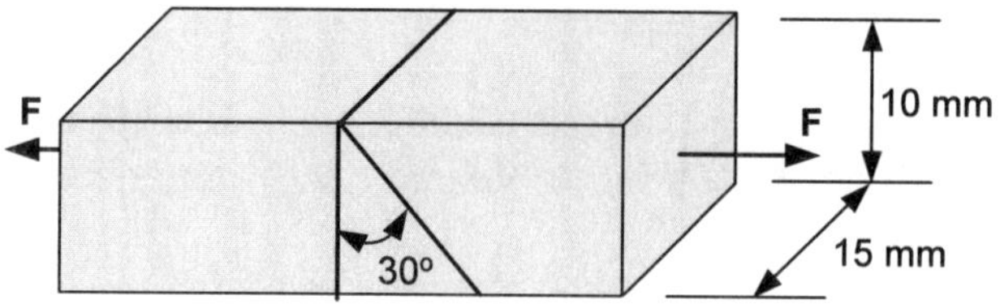

Fig. P2.57

2.58 A rectangular bar, similar to the one shown in Fig. P2.57, is adhesively bonded along a 40° section cut. The normal stress in the bond line is limited to 2.5 ksi and the shear stress to 1.5 ksi. If the bar has a cross sectional area A = 2.00 in.^{2} and a safety factor of 2.5 is specified, determine the largest axial force that can be applied to the bar.

2.59 A rod with a circular cross section with a diameter d is fabricated from two pieces as illustrated in Fig. P2.59. If a force F is applied to the bar, derive the expression for the normal and shear stress acting in the plane of the adhesive joint as a function of angle ϕ. Note that $\phi \neq \theta$.

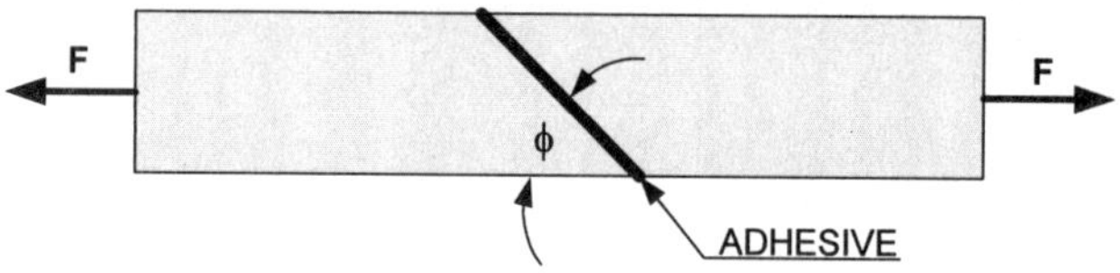

Fig. P2.59

2.60 For the bar illustrated in Fig. P2.59, determine the shear stresses in the adhesive joint if the angle ϕ is varied from 0° to 90°. The axial force applied to the bar is 4.0 kN and its diameter is 30 mm. Also compute the normal stresses acting on the adhesive joint. Note that $\phi \neq \theta$. Hint: Use a spreadsheet to determine the shear and tensile stresses in the adhesive joint for the range of ϕ specified.

2.61 A tensile bar, defined in Fig. P2.61, has a cross sectional area of 200 mm^2 and is subjected to a tensile force F. The stresses on the inclined plane A—B are σ_θ = 81 MPa and τ_θ = 27 MPa. Determine the stress σ_x, the angle θ and the force F.

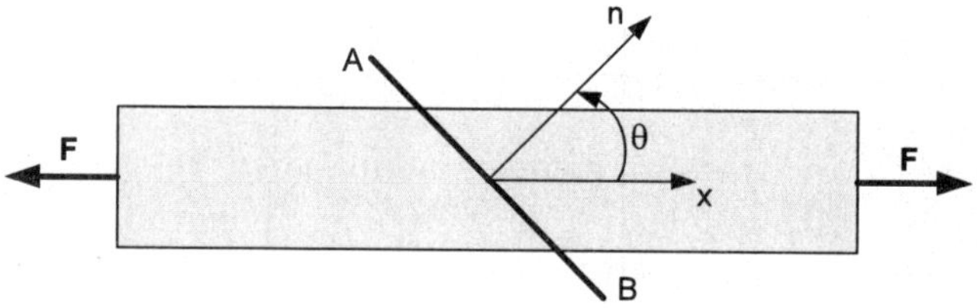

Fig. P2.61

2.62 The tensile bar, defined in Fig. P2.61, has a cross sectional area of 200 mm^2 and is subjected to a tensile force F. The stresses on the inclined plane A—B are σ_θ = 81 MPa and τ_θ = −27 MPa. Determine the shear and normal stresses acting on an inclined plane with θ = 45°.

2.63 For the tensile bar in Problem 2.61, prepare a graph that shows the stresses σ_θ and τ_θ as a function of the angle of the inclined cut as θ varies from 0 to 90°.

2.64 The tensile bar, presented in Fig. P2.64, is fabricated with an adhesive joint inclined at an angle ϕ to the axis of the bar. Determine the optimum angle ϕ for the inclined plane if the stresses in the adhesive are not to exceed either 2.5 ksi in tension or 1.4 ksi in shear. Also determine the maximum force that can be applied to the member without exceeding the stresses in the adhesive joint.

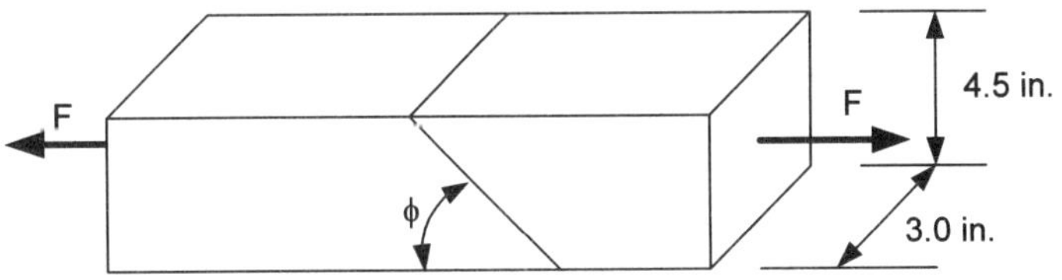

Fig. P2.64

2.65 Consider the tapered bar presented in Fig. P2.65. The tapered bar is subjected to an axial force of 1,000 kN. Prepare a graph of the axial stress σ_x as a function of x as it varies from 0 to 4 m.

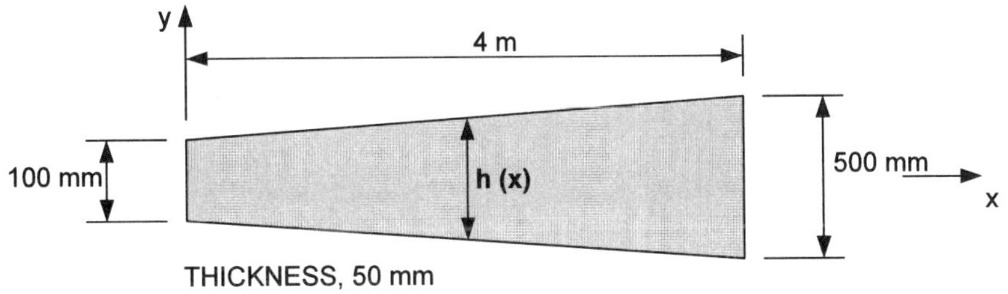

Fig. P2.65

2.66 Consider the tapered bar presented in Problem 2.65. If the bar is fabricated from an aluminum alloy, determine the deformation of the bar when it is subjected to an axial tensile force of 800 kN.

2.67 Consider the tapered bar presented in Fig. P2.67. If the bar is fabricated from an aluminum alloy, determine the deformation of the bar when it is subjected to a tensile force of 100 kN. In this solution, do not employ Eq. (2.43). Instead, use Eq. (2.42) and perform a numerical integration on a spreadsheet.

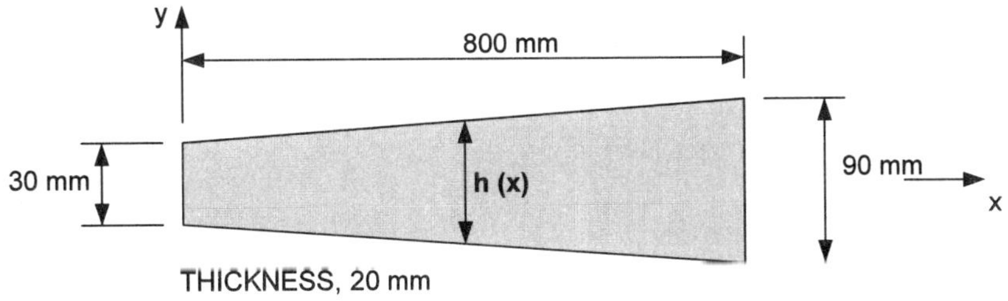

Fig. P2.67

2.68 For the stepped bar, illustrated in Fig. P2.68, determine the stresses in both portions of the bar and its total deformation. The bar is fabricated from steel.

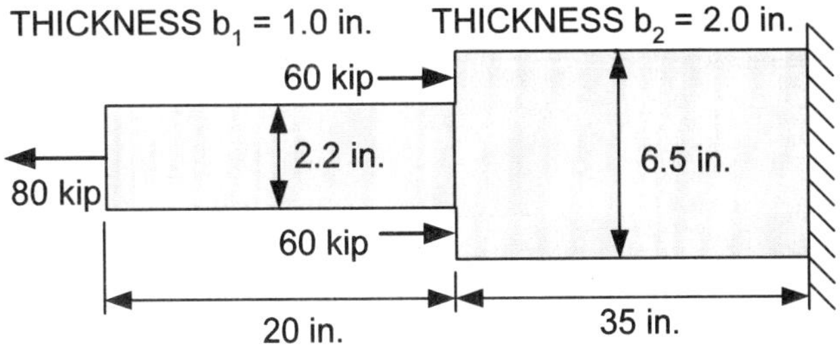

Fig. P2.68

2.69 A steel tie rod with a diameter of 1.0 in. and length of 30.0 in. is employed to compress a brass bushing with an outer diameter of 3.0 in., an unknown inner diameter of d_i, and a length of 20.0 in. as shown in Fig. P2.69. Determine the minimum wall thickness t of the bushing if the deflection of the tie rod is limited to δ = 0.018 in. Note that F = 12 kip.

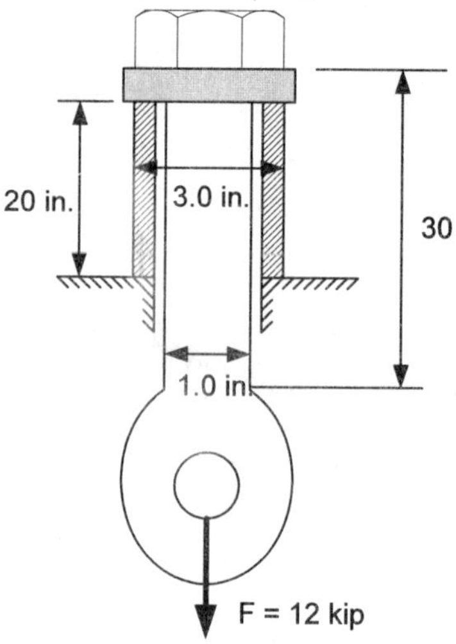

Fig. P2.69

2.70 A scale model of a large structure has been fabricated from steel and tested. A strain gage on one member of the structure indicated an axial strain of ε = 1,600 μm/m. Determine the stress in the corresponding member of the prototype. The numerical parameters defining the scaling factors for the loads and the size of the structural member are: w_m = 1.6 mm, w_p = 80 mm, b_m = 3.0 mm, b_p = 120 mm, L_m = 140 mm and L_p = 5.6 m. The load scaling factor $\boldsymbol{L}$ = 1/10,000.

2.71 Suppose that a model of a structure is fabricated from members formed from sheet aluminum. The prototype structure is to be fabricated from steel with an open span of 200 feet. The model is geometrically scaled so that its span is four feet. The capacity of the live load on the prototype is 200 lb/ft, and the model is loaded with 2.0 lb/ft. If the model deflects a distance of 0.180 in. under full load at the center of the span, determine the deflection of the prototype under the design load.

CHAPTER 3

TORSION OF STRUCTURAL ELEMENTS

3.1 TORSION LOADING

Circular shafts are commonly employed to transmit power from a motor or engine to some appliance. For example, when a power drill is used to drive a screw into a sheet of metal, a short circular shaft transmits the power from the electric motor to the chuck holding the screwdriver. When you operate a car, two shafts transmit power from the gearbox to the drive wheels. You may recall the relation between the power P transmitted and the torque T applied to the shaft as:

$$P = T\omega \tag{3.1}$$

where ω is the angular velocity of the shaft in radian/s.
P is the power in watts W, where 1W = 1 N-m/s.
T is the torque in N-m.

If Eq. (3.1) is employed, the power and torque are expressed in SI units. In U. S. Customary units, the power is expressed in horsepower HP and the torque in terms of ft-lb. The definition of horsepower[1] is given by:

$$1 \text{ HP} = 33{,}000 \text{ ft-lb/min} = 550 \text{ ft-lb/s} \tag{3.2}$$

We are particularly interested in the torsion load (torque) produced when a shaft transmits power. The torque produces stresses and angular deformations in the shaft. If either of these two quantities becomes excessive, the shaft will fail in service.

As a motor or engine turns, it acts on the shaft producing a torque T. We illustrate this action in Fig. 3.1 where two circular disks are connected by a circular shaft. A couple with forces F_1 act on the larger diameter disk producing a torque $T_1 = F_1\, d_1$. Another couple with forces F_2 act on the smaller diameter disk producing a torque $T_2 = F_2\, d_2$. If the shaft is either stationary or rotating at a constant angular velocity, it is in equilibrium and the torques T_1 and T_2 are equal in magnitude and opposite in direction (sign). The shaft transmits the torque from one disk to the other.

---

[1] James Watt conducted experiments in 1782 to determine that a "brewery horse" was able to produce power equivalent to 32,400 ft-lb per minute. He standardized the conversion factor at 33,000 ft-lb per minute to classify the Boulton and Watt steam engine that his company was manufacturing at the time.

In subsequent sections of this chapter, the relations for determining the stresses and strains produced in the shaft by this torque are shown. We will also demonstrate the methods for calculating the stresses, strains and deformations when designing a shaft for an infinite service life.

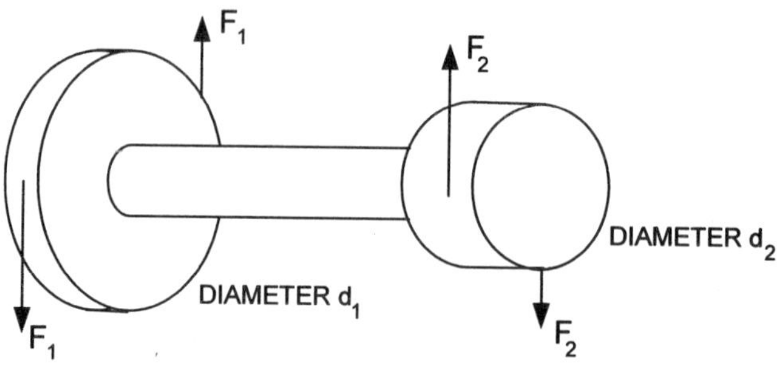

Fig. 3.1 A circular shaft transmitting torque $T_1 = F_1\ d_1 = T_2 = F_2\ d_2$.

EXAMPLE 3.1

A small gasoline engine powers a string type trimmer used to cut grass and weeds. If the maximum power generated by the engine is 900 W, determine the torque imposed on the shaft from the engine to its string disk, if it is rotating at 500 RPM.

Solution:

Using Eq. (3.1), we write:

$$T = P/\omega = 900/\ [2\pi\ (500/60)] = 17.19\ \text{N-m} \qquad \text{(a)}$$

Note that the angular velocity of the shaft was converted from RPM to radians per second by employing the conversion shown below:

$$\omega\ (\text{radian/s}) = 2\pi\ n/60 \qquad \text{(b)}$$

where n is the angular velocity in RPM.

We will return to this example later in this chapter and determine the stress in the shaft under these operating conditions.

EXAMPLE 3.2

The output shaft from an electric motor drives a compressor on a household refrigerator. If the motor operates at 1,780 RPM and is rated at 0.80 HP determine the torque on the shaft.

Solution:

Substituting conversion factors into Eq. (3.1) and solving for the torque on the motor-compressor shaft gives:

$$T = 33{,}000\ HP/(2\pi n) \qquad (3.3)$$

where HP is the power transmitted by the shaft in horsepower and n is the angular velocity in RPM.

$$T = (33{,}000)(0.80)/[2\pi\ (1{,}780)] = 2.360 \text{ ft-lb} \qquad \text{(a)}$$

The torque applied to a shaft is a twisting moment. This moment (torque) acts about the centerline of the shaft and tends to twist it. Plane sections (disks), perpendicular to the axis of the circular shaft, remain plane as the shaft is twisted. This fact is extremely important, because it enables us to determine the stresses and deformation from relatively elementary equations for shafting with circular cross sections. In the next section, we will show how the strains are produced by this twisting action on the shaft.

3.2 DEFORMATION OF A CIRCULAR SHAFT DUE TO TORSION

Let's consider a circular shaft of length L with one end built-in (fixed) and the other end free. A twisting moment (torque) is applied to its free end as illustrated in Fig. 3.2. A straight line A-B is scribed on the outside surface of the shaft prior to the application of the torque T. Upon the application of the torque, the shaft deforms, the scribe line rotates through an angle γ and point B moves to a new location given by point C.

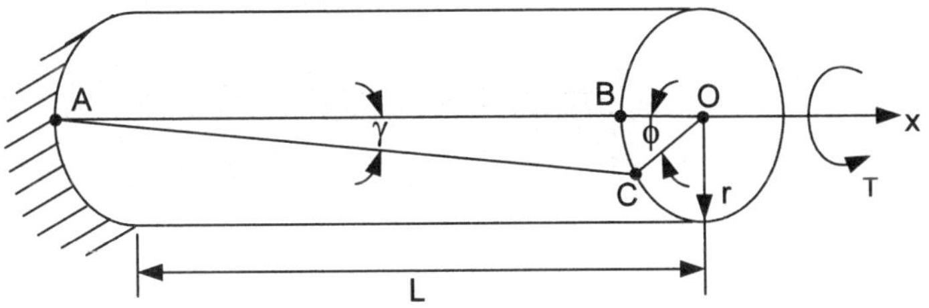

Fig. 3.2 Deformation of a circular shaft due to the application of a torque T at its free end.

The length of the arc B-C is given by:

$$BC = \gamma L \qquad (3.4)$$

The angle ϕ, defined in Fig. 3.2, is known as the angle of twist for the shaft. Let's examine the deformation of the circular shaft more closely by considering a square scribed on its surface at some arbitrary position along line A-B as shown on Fig. 3.3.

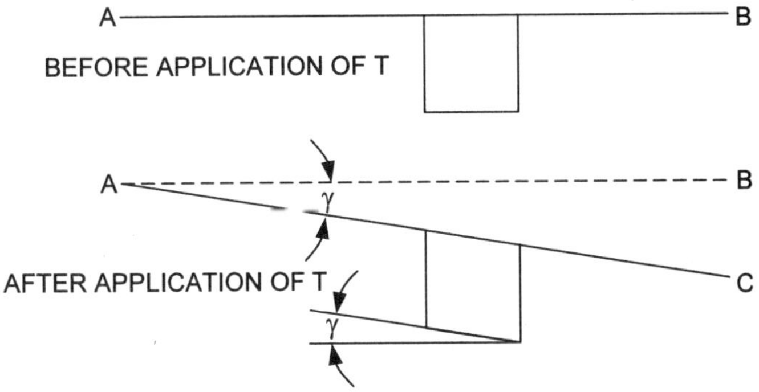

Fig. 3.3 Deformation of a small square scribed on the surface of the shaft before and after application of the torque.

When the shaft deforms under the action of the torque, the line A-B rotates, remains straight, and assumes the orientation of line A-C. The two sides of the inscribed square that are perpendicular to the axis of the shaft do not rotate. However, both of the sides of the square that are parallel to the axis of the shaft rotate through the angle γ. Clearly, the element is distorted as indicated in Fig. 3.3. The included angles of the square have changed $90° \pm \gamma$. Therefore, it is clear that a shearing strain γ occurs on the external surface of the circular shaft.

3.2.1 Shear Strain Due to Torque Applied to a Circular Shaft

To determine a relation for the magnitude of the shearing strain γ, let's consider the free end of a circular shaft subjected to an applied torque T, as indicated in Fig. 3.4. The line OB rotates through an angle ϕ sweeping through an arc BC. The length of the arc B-C is given by:

$$BC = r\phi \tag{3.5}$$

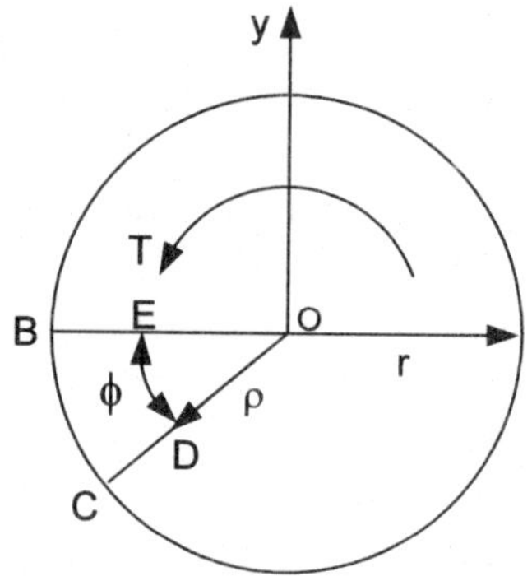

Fig. 3.4 Rotation of line OB on the free end of a circular shaft subjected to a torque T.

Substituting Eq. (3.4) into Eq. (3.5) yields:

$$\gamma_{\rho=r} = r\phi/L \tag{3.6}$$

The shear strain on the surface of the shaft, where $\rho = r$, is given by Eq. (3.6). The shear strain at some point D on the interior of the shaft is less because the arc length D-E is decreased. Following the same procedure, we write the shearing strain γ for an arbitrary point defined by the position radius ρ as:

$$\gamma_\rho = \rho\phi/L \tag{3.7}$$

Examination of Eq. (3.7) shows that the shearing strain varies from zero at the centerline of the shaft to a maximum value at the surface that is given by:

$$\gamma_{Max} = r\phi/L \tag{3.8}$$

Because the applied torque is constant along the length of the shaft, the strain is also constant along its length.

3.3 STRESSES PRODUCED BY TORSION

To determine the shear stresses acting on the circular shaft, we employ the relation between shear stress and shear strain.

$$\tau = G\,\gamma \tag{3.9}$$

where G is the shear modulus of the shaft material given by:

$$G = \frac{E}{2(1+\nu)} \tag{3.9a}$$

Substituting Eq. (3.7) into Eq. (3.9) yields:

$$\tau_\rho = G\phi\rho/L \tag{3.10}$$

Again, we observe that the shear stress τ increases linearly with the position radius ρ from zero at the centerline to a maximum value at the surface of the shaft. This linear distribution of shear stress is illustrated in Fig. 3.5 a.

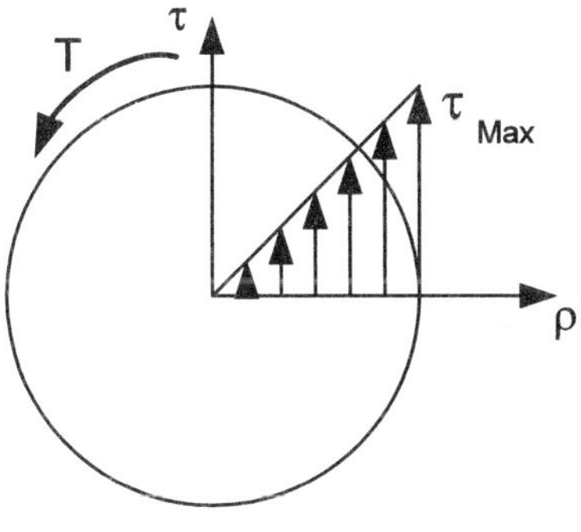

Fig. 3.5a Linear distribution of shear stress τ.

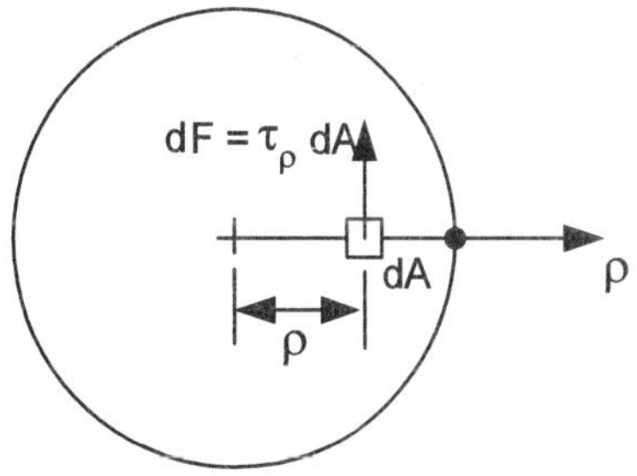

Fig. 3.5b The incremental force dF = τdA.

Next, let's consider the equilibrium of the shaft with an applied torque. The shear stress produces an equal and opposite moment to the applied torque at the far end of the shaft. We write the equilibrium equation $\Sigma M_x = 0$ as:

$$\Sigma M_x = T - \int \rho\tau_\rho \, dA = 0 \tag{3.11}$$

where the x-axis coincides with the axis of the shaft.

The sum of all the incremental forces ($dF = \tau_\rho \, dA$) produce the moment M_x about the centerline of the shaft as presented in Fig. 3.5b. Substituting Eq. (3.10) into Eq. (3.11) gives:

$$T = (G\phi \int \rho^2 \, dA)/L \tag{3.12}$$

The term $\int \rho^2 \, dA$ is the polar moment of inertia J of a circular area about its center. Hence, we can rewrite Eq. (3.12) as:

$$T = G\phi J/L \tag{3.13}$$

Finally, we note from Eq. (3.10) that $(G\phi/L) = \tau_\rho/\rho$. Accordingly, we can write:

$$\tau_\rho = T\rho/J \tag{3.14}$$

Equation (3.14) is employed to determine the shear stresses in circular shafts when the applied torque is known. Clearly, the maximum shear stress occurs when $\rho = r$. In this instance:

$$\tau_{Max} = Tr/J = Td/(2J) \qquad (3.15)$$

Because $J = \pi r^4/2 = \pi d^4/32$ for solid circular shafts, we may express Eq. (3.15) as:

$$\tau_{Max} = 2\ T/(\pi r^3) = 16\ T/(\pi d^3) \qquad (3.16)$$

To demonstrate the method for determining stresses in circular shafts, let's consider two examples.

EXAMPLE 3.3

A solid circular shaft with a diameter d is fabricated from 1020 HR steel and subjected to a torque T = 5,000 in-lb. Determine the shear stress τ as a function of the diameter of the shaft.

Solution:

To determine the shear stresses in the circular shaft, substitute the numerical parameters describing the shaft and the applied torsion into Eq. (3.16) to obtain:

$$\tau_{Max} = 16\ T/(\pi d^3) = (16)(5{,}000)/(\pi d^3) = 80 \times 10^3 \text{ in-lb}/(\pi d^3) \qquad \text{(a)}$$

We now have an equation relating the shear stress on the surface to the shaft diameter. Let's study several cases by permitting the diameter of the shaft to vary from 0.25 to 2.00 in. Using a spreadsheet in performing the calculations, we obtain the results shown below:

d (in.)	d^3 (in.^{3})	Stress, τ (ksi)
0.250	0.0156	1,630
0.375	0.0527	482.9
0.500	0.1250	203.7
0.625	0.2441	104.3
0.750	0.4219	60.36
0.875	0.6699	38.02
1.000	1.0000	25.46
1.250	1.9531	13.04
1.500	3.3750	7.54
1.750	5.3594	4.76
2.000	8.0000	3.18

The numerical values for the shear stress vary from 1,630 ksi for a shaft with a diameter of 0.25 in. to only 3.18 ksi for a 2.0 in. diameter shaft. Obviously, a large range in the results is evident. The very large variations in τ, with small changes in d, are due to the fact that the diameter occurs as a cube in the denominator of Eq. (3.16).

To determine a suitable diameter of the shaft, we must compare the stresses to the strength of the 1020 HR steel. This task raises a question — is it possible to compare shear stress with yield strength or ultimate tensile strength? The answer is **no**. Yield and ultimate tensile strength for materials are measured in a tensile test and cannot be directly compared to shear strength. Let's consider another example to introduce an accepted technique for approximating the shear strengths of most metals.

EXAMPLE 3.4

A shaft diameter of 1.25 in. is selected for the shaft described in Example 3.3. Determine the safety factor for this shaft if the applied torque is 5,000 in.-lb.

Solution:

To account for the effects of shear stress on failure, we determine yield S_{ys} and ultimate S_{us} strengths in terms of shear by multiplying the yield and ultimate tensile strengths, S_y and S_u, by a constant = $\sqrt{3}/3 = 0.5774$:

$$S_{ys} = 0.5774\ S_y \tag{3.17a}$$

$$S_{us} = 0.5774\ S_u \tag{3.17b}$$

Reference to Appendix B-2 indicates that $S_y = 42$ ksi and $S_u = 66$ ksi for 1020 HR steel.

Substituting numerical values into Eq. (3.17) gives the yield and ultimate shear strength for 1020 HR steel as:

$$S_{ys} = 0.5774\ S_y = (0.5774)(42) = 24.25 \text{ ksi} \qquad \text{(a)}$$

$$S_{us} = 0.5774\ S_u = (0.5774)(66) = 38.11 \text{ ksi} \qquad \text{(b)}$$

The safety factor is determined by computing the ratio of strength to the stress according to:

$$SF = S_{ys}/\tau_{Max} \tag{3.18}$$

Substituting the results from Eq. (a) and from the table for Example 3.3 into Eq. (3.18) gives:

$$SF = 24.25/13.04 = 1.860 \qquad \text{(c)}$$

We have used the yield strength in shear for the 1020 HR steel in determining the safety factor. Reference to Eq. (c) shows a safety factor of nearly 2, which should be adequate if the applied torque is specified accurately.

EXAMPLE 3.5

A shaft, fabricated from 302 A stainless steel, is to transmit 1,000 W of power while rotating at 1,190 RPM. Specify the diameter of the shaft in millimeters if the safety factor is to be in the range of 2.75 to 3.50.

Solution:

Let's substitute Eq. (3.17 a) into Eq. (3.18) and rearrange terms to obtain:

$$\tau_{Max} = S_{ys}/SF = 0.5774\ S_y / SF \qquad \text{(a)}$$

Reference to Appendix B-2 indicates that $S_y = 234$ MPa for 302 A stainless steel.

Consider the lowest safety factor SF = 2.75; for this choice, determine τ_{Max} from Eq. (a).

$$\tau_{Max} = S_{ys}/SF = (0.5774)(234)/2.75 = 49.13 \text{ MPa} \qquad \text{(b)}$$

Then using Eq. (3.16) we write:

$$d^3 = (16T)/(\pi\tau_{Max}) \qquad \text{(c)}$$

To compute the required diameter d, it is necessary to determine the applied torque from Eq. (3.1).

$$T = P/\omega = [(1{,}000)(60)]/[(1{,}190)(2\pi)] = 8.025 \text{ N-m} = 8{,}025 \text{ N-mm} \qquad \text{(d)}$$

Substituting Eq. (d) into Eq. (c) gives:

$$d^3 = (16)(8{,}025)/[\pi(49.13)] = 831.9 \text{ mm}^3 \qquad \text{(e)}$$

Consider d = 10 mm and note that $d^3 = 1{,}000$ mm^3. This choice is a standard size round bar in the SI system that is somewhat larger in diameter than that necessary to achieve a value of $d^3 = 831.9$ mm^3. Let's check to determine if this 10 mm diameter bar is sufficient to provide a safety factor of 3.5 or less.

From Eq. (3.16), we write:

$$\tau_{Max} = (16T)/(\pi d^3) = (16)(8{,}025)/[\pi\,(1{,}000)] = 40.87 \text{ MPa} \qquad \text{(f)}$$

Next, substitute the results from Eq. (f) into Eq. (a) to obtain:

$$SF = 0.5774 S_y/\tau_{Max} = (0.5774)(234)/40.87 = 3.31 \qquad \text{(g)}$$

This result indicates that the diameter of 10 mm is sufficient to provide a safety factor that lies within the range specified for this application.

3.3.1 Hollow Circular Shafts

In many engineering applications, weight is an important consideration, because it often detrimentally affects performance and usually increases cost. It is possible to reduce the weight of shafting by using tubes instead of solid rounds. The weight penalty associated with solid round bars is due to the reduced stresses in central regions of the bar, which are much smaller than the maximum shear stress that occurs on the outer diameter of the shaft. With a tube, the central region of the shaft is removed and the resulting structure is more uniformly stressed and structurally more efficient.

Equation (3.14), derived for a solid circular shaft, is also valid for a hollow circular shaft. The only difference that arises is in the expression for the polar moment of inertia J. For a solid shaft $J = \pi d^4/32$; however, for a hollow circular shaft, the polar moment of inertia is given by:

$$J = (\pi/32)(d_o^4 - d_i^4) \qquad (3.19)$$

where d_i and d_o represent the inside and outside diameters, respectively.

Substituting the results for Eq. (3.19) into Eq. (3.14) yields:

$$\tau_\rho = 32T\rho/[\pi(d_o^4 - d_i^4)] \qquad (3.20)$$

The maximum shear stress occurs when $\rho = d_o/2$; hence Eq. (3.20) may be rewritten as:

$$\tau_{Max} = 16\ Td_o/[\pi(d_o^4 - d_i^4)] \qquad (3.21)$$

EXAMPLE 3.6

A hollow circular shaft is fabricated from a seamless tube of 1018 HR steel. It is subjected to a torque T = 4,000 in-lb. If the outside diameter of the tube is fixed at 2.00 in., determine the shear stress τ_{Max} as a function of the inside diameter of the shaft.

Solution:

Let's employ Eq. (3.21) and substitute numerical values for the known quantities in this relation.

$$\tau_{Max} = (16)(4{,}000)(2.00)/\{\pi[(2.00)^4 - d_i^4)]\} = 40{,}744/[(16) - d_i^4)] \qquad (a)$$

Using a spreadsheet to evaluate Eq. (a) gives:

d_i (in.)	d_i^4 (in.)^4	Stress, τ (ksi)
0.000	0	2.546
0.250	0.0039	2.547
0.500	0.0625	2.556
0.750	0.3164	2.598
1.000	1.0000	2.716
1.250	2.4414	3.005
1.500	5.0625	3.725
1.750	9.3789	6.154
1.875	12.360	11.19
2.000	16.000	∞

Examination of these results shows that the maximum shear stress increases very slowly as the inside diameter of the tube increases. This fact indicates that the material removed from the shaft with increasing diameter of d_i carries very little shear stress. Compared to the shear strength of the 1018 HR steel, which is $S_{ys} = 0.5774$ (32 ksi) = 18.48 ksi, the maximum shear stresses are lower than this value for every inside diameter considered if $d_i \leq 1.875$ in. However, the safety factor is only 1.65 when $d_i = 1.875$in.

3.3.2 Section Modulus in Torsion

When considering beams in bending, we will introduce the concept of section modulus that defines the influence of the shape of the beam's cross-section on the flexural stress. Let's adapt the same concept to circular shafts in torsion by rewriting Eq. (3.21) as:

$$\tau_{Max} = 16\, Td_o/[\pi(d_o^4 - d_i^4)] = T/Z_T \tag{3.22}$$

$$Z_T = \pi(d_o^4 - d_i^4)/(16d_o) \tag{3.23}$$

Clearly, to reduce the maximum shear stress it is necessary to increase the section modulus Z_T. In a hollow shaft, Eq. (3.23) indicates that both the internal and external diameters of the shaft influence the section modulus. To limit the shear stress, we seek to increase Z_T, but without the penalty of a large increase in the weight of the shaft. To establish the most suitable approach to achieve large Z_T values without incurring weight penalties, let's first consider q that is defined as the weight W per unit length L of the shaft.

$$q = W/L = \gamma(\pi/4)(d_o^2 - d_i^2) \tag{3.24}$$

where γ is the weight per unit volume of the shaft.

Because it is good design practice to increase the section modulus while limiting the increase in q, it is useful to examine the ratio Z_T/q. Dividing Eq. (3.23) by Eq. (3.24) yields:

$$(Z_T/q)_{Hollow} = [\pi(d_o^4 - d_i^4)/(16d_o)]/\,[\gamma(\pi/4)(d_o^2 - d_i^2)] \tag{a}$$

$$(Z_T/q)_{Hollow} = (d_o^2 + d_i^2)/(4\gamma d_o) \tag{3.25}$$

For a solid shaft, $d_i = 0$ and Eq. (3.25) reduces to:

$$(Z_T/q)_{Solid} = d_o/4\gamma \tag{3.26}$$

Comparing the ratio Z_T/q for the hollow and solid shafts provides a method for assessing the improvement in the design by employing hollow shafting. Accordingly, we form the ratio shown below:

$$\frac{\left[\dfrac{Z_T}{q}\right]_{Hollow}}{\left[\dfrac{Z_T}{q}\right]_{Solid}} = 1 + \left(\frac{d_i}{d_o}\right)^2 \tag{3.27}$$

As d_i becomes large and approaches d_o, the ratio in Eq. (3.27) approaches 2, indicating a hollow shaft with a very thin wall has nearly twice the section modulus per unit weight when compared to a solid shaft. Of course, there is a limit selected for the diameter d_i. When the wall thickness of a hollow shaft becomes too small, the shaft will fail by buckling under torsion.

The disadvantage of using hollow shafts in the design of power transmission shafts is cost and availability. It is more expensive to manufacture a tube than it is to manufacture a solid shaft. Sometimes the manufacturing costs are larger than the savings achieved by reducing the weight of the shaft. Also for equal values of Z_T, hollow shafts are larger in outside diameter than solid shafts; hence, larger diameter and more costly bearings are necessary to support hollow tubular shafts.

EXAMPLE 3.7

A 16 in. long shaft, fabricated from cold rolled alloy steel, exhibits a yield strength of 60 ksi and is to support a torque of 500 in.-lb. If a safety factor of at least 3.0 is employed, determine the weight of a solid shaft for this application. Also, determine the weight of a hollow shaft for this same application if $d_i = 0.8\ d_o$.

Solution:

The design stress τ_{Design} is given by Eq. (3.17a) and Eq. (3.18) as:

$$\tau_{Design} = (0.5774)S_y/SF \qquad \text{(a)}$$

Substituting numerical parameters into Eq. (a) gives:

$$\tau_{Design} = (0.5774)(60)/(3.0) = 11.55 \text{ ksi} \qquad \text{(b)}$$

The diameter is determined from Eq. (3.16) as:

$$d^3 = (16T)/(\pi\tau_{Design}) = (16)(500)/[\pi(11{,}550)] = 0.2205 \text{ in.}^3 \qquad \text{(c)}$$

Solving Eq. (c) gives d = 0.6041 in. Selecting a commercially available standard size round bar gives:

$$d = 5/8 = 0.625 \text{ in.} \qquad \text{(d)}$$

The weight W of the shaft is given by Eq. (3.24) as:

$$W = \gamma(\pi/4)d^2\,L = 0.283(\pi/4)(0.625)^2\,(16) = 1.389 \text{ lb} \qquad \text{(e)}$$

where the weight density of steel is $\gamma = 0.283$ lb/in.^{3}

For the hollow shaft, the diameter is determined from Eq. (3.21) as:

$$[(d_o^4 - d_i^4)]/d_o = (16T)/\pi\tau_{Design} \qquad \text{(f)}$$

Substitute $d_i = 0.8\ d_o$ into Eq. (f) and simplify to obtain:

$$d_o^3 = (16)(500)/[(0.5904)(\pi)(11{,}550)] = 0.3734 \text{ in.}^3 \qquad \text{(g)}$$

Solving Eq. (g) for the outside diameter gives d_o = 0.7201 in. Selecting the next larger standard size tube gives:

$$d_o = 3/4 = 0.750 \text{ in. and } d_i = (0.8)(0.750) = 0.600 \text{ in.} \qquad \text{(h)}$$

The weight is determined as:

$$W = \gamma(\pi/4)(d_o^2 - d_i^2)\,L = (0.283)(\pi/4)[(0.750)^2 - (0.600)^2](16) = 0.7201 \text{ lb} \qquad \text{(i)}$$

The results show that the use of a hollow shaft in this application reduces the weight of the shaft from 1.389 lb to 0.7201 lb. This savings in shaft weight of 0.669 lb (48.16%) reduces the overall weight of the product; however, the costs may increase because of the need to procure tubing instead of solid rod and to employ larger diameter bearings that are more expensive.

3.3.3 Structural Efficiency of Circular Shafts

The term structural efficiency ***SE*** is defined as the section modulus of the shaft divided by its cross sectional area. Adapting this definition to torsion of both solid and hollow circular shafts gives:

$$\boldsymbol{SE} = Z_T/A \qquad (3.28)$$

Substituting Eq. (3.23) into Eq. (3.28) and simplifying yields:

$$\boldsymbol{SE} = \frac{d_o^2 + d_i^2}{4d_o} \qquad (3.29)$$

As d_i increases from zero towards the value of d_o, the structural efficiency increases from 0.250 d_o to 0.500 d_o. Of course, d_i must always be less than d_o. In fact, the tubular shaft will buckle in torsion if the wall thickness becomes too small.

3.4 SHEAR STRESSES ON DIFFERENT PLANES

3.4.1 Shear Stresses on Orthogonal Planes

Let's consider an elemental area ΔA scribed on the surface of a circular shaft as shown in Fig. 3.6. The x-axis is parallel to the shaft's longitudinal axis and the y-axis is perpendicular to it. With the x and y axes defined in this manner, the shear stress $\tau_{xy} = \tau_{Max} = 16T/\pi d^3$. Let's remove this elemental area and draw a FBD of the element as shown in Fig. 3.7.

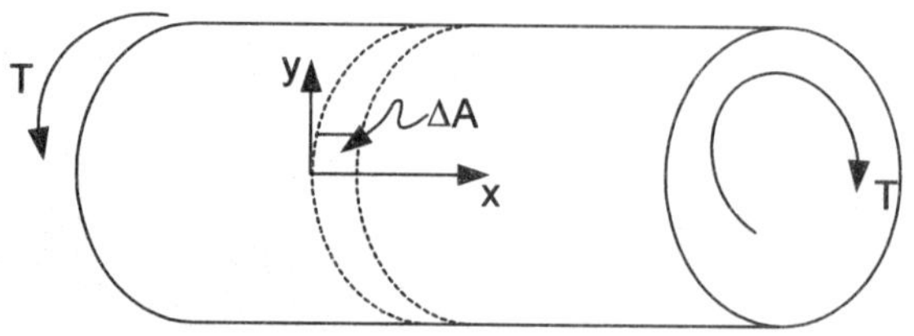

Fig. 3.6 An elemental area ΔA on the surface of a circular shaft subjected to torque T.

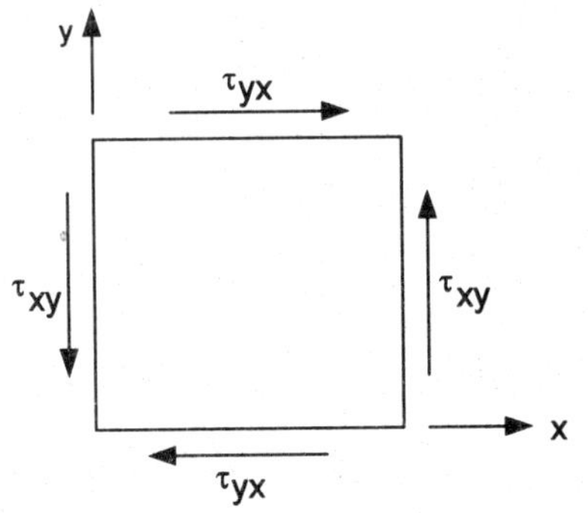

Fig. 3.7 A FBD of an elemental area ΔA from the surface of the shaft. All of the shear stresses shown on the element are considered positive.

In drawing the FBD of the elemental area, we note that both of the edges of the element that are perpendicular to the x-axis are subjected to the shear stress $\tau_{xy} = \tau_{Max}$. The convention for the double subscript placed on τ is:

- The first subscript identifies the outer normal to the surface upon which the stress acts.
- The second subscript shows the direction in which the stress acts.
- The stress is considered positive if the outer normal is positive and its direction is positive.
- The stress is considered positive if the outer normal is negative and its direction is negative.

Let's convert the shear stresses acting on the elemental area to shear forces and then write the equilibrium equations. The element has dimensions Δx, Δy and Δz; hence, the shear forces acting on the sides perpendicular to the x-axis are given by:

$$V_y = \tau_{xy}\, \Delta y \Delta z \qquad (3.30\text{ a})$$

Similarly, the shear forces acting on the sides perpendicular to the y-axis are:

$$V_x = \tau_{yx}\, \Delta x \Delta z \qquad (3.30\text{ b})$$

Next, consider the equilibrium equation $\Sigma F_y = 0$. This relation shows that the shear force V_y acting on the right side of the element in the positive y direction must be balanced by an equal and opposite force acting on the left side of the element. Similarly the equation $\Sigma F_x = 0$ indicates that the shear force V_x acting on the top side of the element must be balanced by an equal and opposite force acting on the bottom side of the element. We have shown these shear stresses in Fig. 3.7 with the correct directions, and have satisfied these two of the three applicable equilibrium relations.

Finally, apply the equilibrium equation $\Sigma M_z = 0$ about the origin and write:

$$(\tau_{yx}\, \Delta x \Delta z)\Delta y/2 = (\tau_{xy}\, \Delta y \Delta z)\Delta x/2 \qquad (a)$$

This relation reduces to:

$$\tau_{xy} = \tau_{yx} \qquad (3.31)$$

To satisfy the equilibrium equations, the shear stresses acting on orthogonal planes must be equal in magnitude.

3.4.2 Shear Stresses on Oblique Planes

To examine the shear stress acting on planes that are oblique relative to the shaft's axis, let's slice a corner from this elemental area as shown in Fig. 3.8. If the inclined side of the triangular element has an area ΔA, the vertical and horizontal sides have areas of ΔA cos θ and ΔA sin θ respectively. Two stress components act on the inclined plane — one perpendicular to the surface (σ_n) and one along the surface (τ_{nt}). Applying the equations of equilibrium to the small triangular element gives:

$$\Sigma F_t = 0 \tag{a}$$

$$\tau_{nt}\,\Delta A - [\tau_{xy}\,(\Delta A\cos\theta)]\cos\theta + [\tau_{yx}\,(\Delta A\sin\theta)]\sin\theta = 0 \tag{b}$$

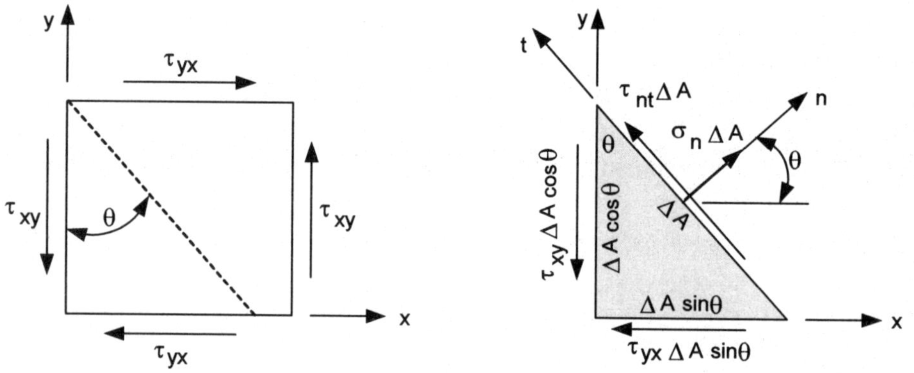

Fig. 3.8 Forces acting on a triangular element cut from the square element.

Solving Eq. (b) and recalling the results of Eq. (3.31) yields:

$$\tau_{nt} = \tau_{xy}\,(\cos^2\theta - \sin^2\theta) = \tau_{xy}\cos 2\theta \tag{3.32}$$

$$\Sigma F_n = 0 \tag{c}$$

$$\sigma_n\,\Delta A - [\tau_{xy}\,(\Delta A\cos\theta)]\sin\theta - [\tau_{yx}\,(\Delta A\sin\theta)]\cos\theta = 0 \tag{d}$$

Solving Eq. (d) and using Eq. (3.31) yields:

$$\sigma_n = 2\,\tau_{xy}\cos\theta\sin\theta = \tau_{xy}\sin 2\theta \tag{3.33}$$

Equation (3.33) shows that a normal stress σ_n occurs on all planes except those perpendicular or parallel to the axis of the shaft. Let's take τ_{xy} = 1 unit and evaluate Eq. (3.33) by permitting θ to vary from 0 to 360°. The results obtained for the normal stress σ_n, which acts on the oblique plane, are presented in Fig. 3.9.

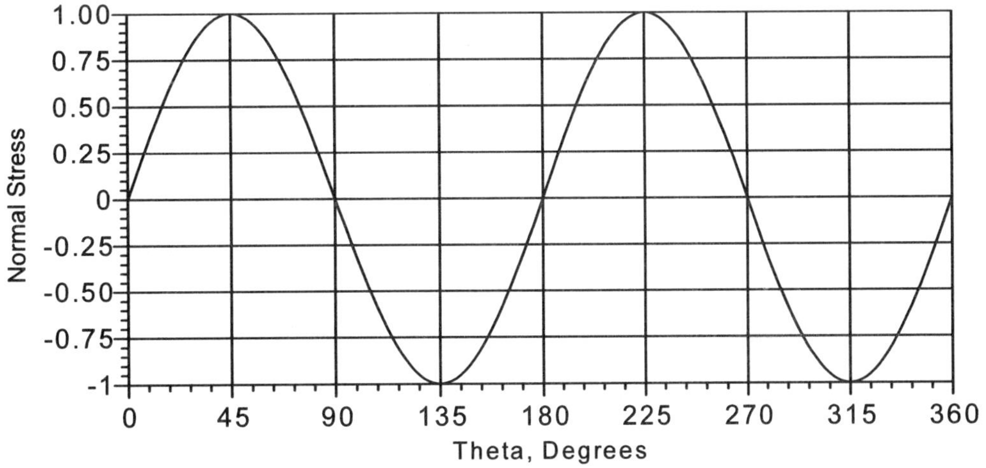

Fig. 3.9 The distribution of σ_n as a function of the orientation of the plane defined by θ.

The interpretation of the result shown in this graph will be deferred until Section 3.9.

EXAMPLE 3.8

If the shear stress $\tau_{xy} = 1$ unit, determine the shear stress τ_{nt} as a function of the orientation of the n-t plane defined by θ.

Solution:

Let's employ $\tau_{nt} = \tau_{xy} \cos 2\theta$ and solve for τ_{nt} as a function of θ. We will make use of a spreadsheet and vary θ from 0 to 360° in steps of 5° in this evaluation. The results are shown in Fig. E3.8. Also it is clear that $\tau_{Max} = \tau_{xy} = 1$ unit when $\theta = 0°$ and 180° and $\tau_{Min} = -\tau_{xy} = -1$ unit when $\theta = 90°$ and 270°. The shear stress vanishes on planes defined by $\theta =$ 45°, 135°, 225°, 315°, etc.

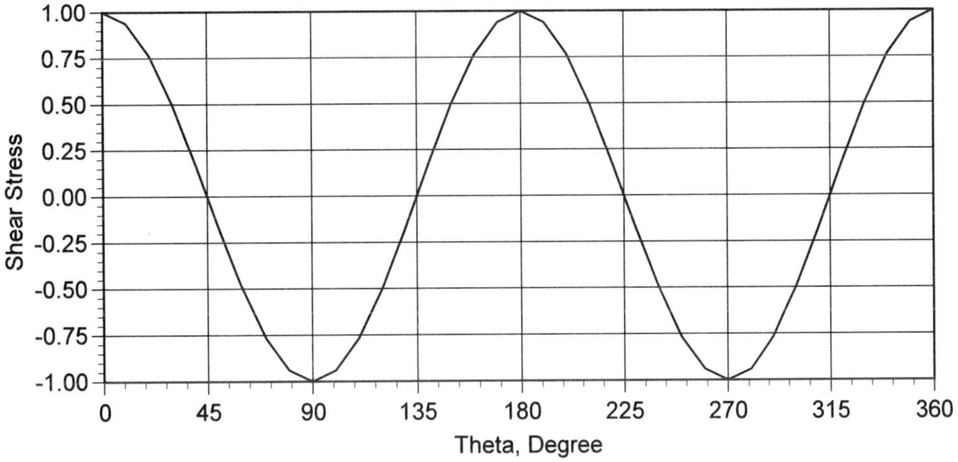

Fig. E3.8 Shear stress τ_{nt} as a function of the inclination angle θ.

3.5 PRINCIPAL STRESSES IN SHAFTS

It is evident from Fig. 3.9 that the normal stress is a maximum ($\sigma_n = \sigma_{Max} = \tau_{xy} = \tau_{Max}$) when $\theta = 45°$ and 225° and a minimum ($\sigma_n = \sigma_{Min} = -\tau_{xy} = -\tau_{Max}$) when $\theta = 135°$ and 315°. Also the shear stress on these four planes is given by Eq. (3.32) as:

$$\tau_{nt} = \tau_{xy} \cos 2\theta = 0 \qquad \text{when } \theta = (1 + 2n)\pi/4 \text{ and } n = 0, 1, 2, \text{etc.} \tag{3.32a}$$

When the normal stress is a maximum or a minimum acting on a plane with zero shear stress, a principal state of stress exists. The planes upon which the normal stress acts are called principal planes. We usually attempt to determine the direction of the principal planes and the magnitude of the principal stresses, because failure often occurs along these planes when the stresses become excessive.

For a circular bar subjected to a torque T, the principal plane makes an angle of 45° with the bar's axis as shown in Fig. 3.10. The principal plane spirals like a helix along the length of the bar. If this bar is made of a brittle material such as gray cast iron or chalk, its failure surface forms a helix as illustrated in Fig. 3.11.

Fig. 3.10 The principal planes for a circular shaft subjected to torque T form a helix about its surface.

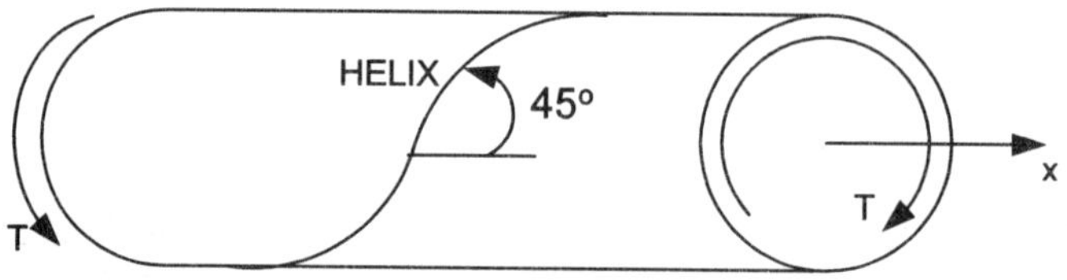

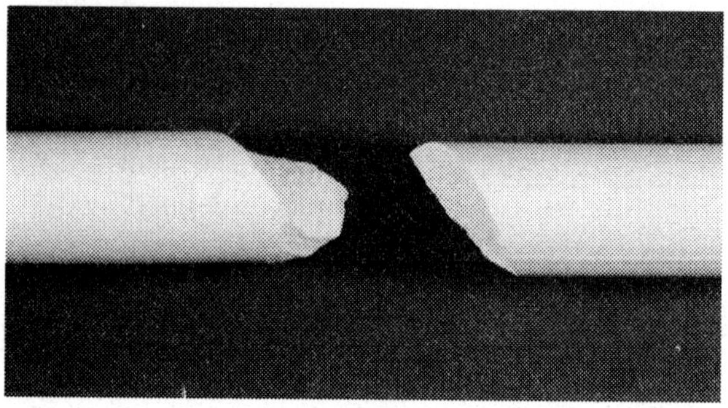

Fig. 3.11 Twisting a piece of chalk produces a helical failure making a 45° angle with its axis.

EXAMPLE 3.9

A circular shaft 12 mm in diameter is transmitting 5 kW from an electric motor to an air compressor. If the motor is operating at 1,200 RPM, determine the maximum normal stress acting on the shaft. Also determine the plane upon which this maximum normal stress acts.

Solution

We solve for the torque acting on the shaft by using Eq. (3.1) to obtain:

$$T = P/\omega = (5{,}000)(60)/(1{,}200)(2\pi) = 39.79 \text{ N-m} \tag{a}$$

The maximum shear stress may be determined from Eq. (3.16) as:

$\tau_{Max} = \tau_{xy} = 16T/(\pi d^3) = (16)(39.79)(1{,}000)/[\pi(12)^3] = 117.3\ N/mm^2 = 117.3\ MPa$(b)

The relation between the shear stress and the normal stress is given by Eq. (3.33) as:

$$\sigma_n = \tau_{xy} \sin 2\theta \quad \text{(c)}$$

The normal stress is a maximum when $2\theta = \pi/2$ or $\theta = \pi/4$. This result for the principal angle is consistent with the helix presented in Figs. 3.10 and 3.11.

In this example, the maximum normal stress $(\sigma_n)_{Max}$ is the principal stress σ_1 given by:

$$(\sigma_n)_{Max} = \sigma_1 = \tau_{xy} \quad (3.34)$$

$$(\sigma_n)_{Max} = \sigma_1 = \tau_{xy} = 117.3\ MPa \quad \text{(d)}$$

3.6 ANGLE OF TWIST

When torque is applied to a shaft, it twists through some angle ϕ about its longitudinal axis. This angle of twist of a circular shaft, illustrated in Fig. 3.2, is analogous to the elongation in a tension rod under the action of an axial force. To derive the expression for the angle of twist, rewrite Eq. (3.8) as:

$$\phi = \gamma_{Max}\, L/r \quad \text{(a)}$$

Substituting Eq. (3.9) into Eq. (a) yields:

$$\phi = (\tau_{Max}\, L)/(G\, r) \quad \text{(b)}$$

Finally, substituting Eq. (3.15) into Eq. (b) gives:

$$\phi = (T\, L)/(G\, J) \quad (3.35a)$$

Noting that the polar moment of inertia $J = \pi d^4/32$, we may rewrite Eq. (3.35 a) as:

$$\phi = (32\, T\, L)/(\pi d^4\, G) \quad (3.35b)$$

where is the shear modulus defined in Eq. (3.9a).

If T, G or J are not constant along the length of the shaft, then Eq. (3.35a) must be modified to accommodate the different shaft sizes by writing:

$$\phi_{Total} = \sum_{i=1}^{n} \frac{T_i L_i}{G_i J_i} \quad (3.35c)$$

In this instance, the shaft must be divided into several sections and Eq. (3.35a) used to determine ϕ for each section. The total angle of twist, ϕ_{Total} is calculated by summing the ϕ from each section.

Let's consider two examples to demonstrate the application of Eq. (3.35).

EXAMPLE 3.10

A solid steel shaft is 120 mm long and is subjected to a torque T of 300 N-m. If the shaft is 30 mm in diameter, determine the shear stress τ_{Max} and the angle of twist ϕ.

Solution

Let's employ Eq. (3.16) to solve for the maximum shear stress as:

$$\tau_{Max} = (16T)/(\pi d^3) = (16)(300)(1000)/[\pi(30)^3] = 56.59 \text{ MPa} \qquad \text{(a)}$$

The angle of twist is given by Eq. (3.35b) as:

$$\phi = (32\ TL)/(\pi d^4\ G) = (32)(300)(0.120)/[\pi(0.03)^4\ (79 \times 10^9)]$$

$$\phi = 0.005730 \text{ radian} = 0.3283° \qquad \text{(b)}$$

Inspection of Eq. (b) shows that the angle of twist is given in radians. The result is converted to degrees by multiplying by the conversion factor 180°/π.

EXAMPLE 3.11

A line shaft, shown in Fig. E3.11, fabricated from high-strength steel incorporates five spur gears. Gear A provides the input torque T_A and gears B, C, D and E each remove torque from the shaft. Determine the angle of twist for the entire shaft AE and between gears at A and C. The shaft diameters and lengths are $d_{A\text{-}B}$ = 2.00 in., $d_{B\text{-}C}$ = 1.75 in., $d_{C\text{-}D}$ = 1.50 in. and $d_{D\text{-}E}$ = 1.25 in., $L_{A\text{-}B}$ = 30 in., $L_{B\text{-}C}$ = 24 in., $L_{C\text{-}D}$ = 36 in. and $L_{D\text{-}E}$ = 48 in. The applied torques are T_A = 1,200 ft-lb, T_B = 300 ft-lb, T_C = 400 ft-lb, T_D = 350 ft-lb and T_E = 150 ft-lb. Neglect the effect of gear deformations.

Fig. E3.11

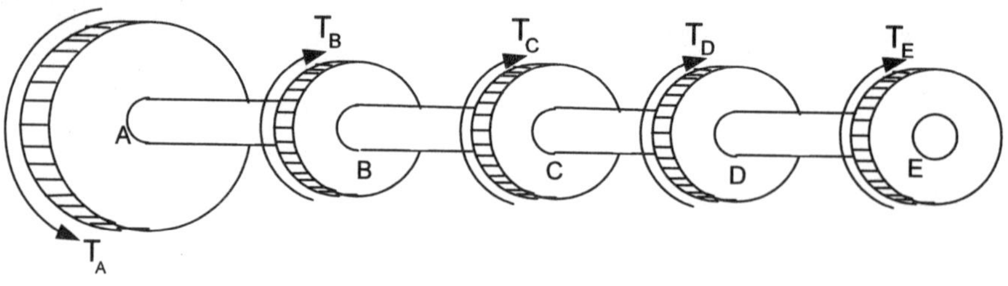

Solution:

First, prepare a series of FBDs at each section of the shaft and determine the torque acting on the shaft segments between the gears. Then construct a torque-position diagram that shows the distribution of torque along the line shaft as shown in Fig. E3.11a.

Fig. E3.11a

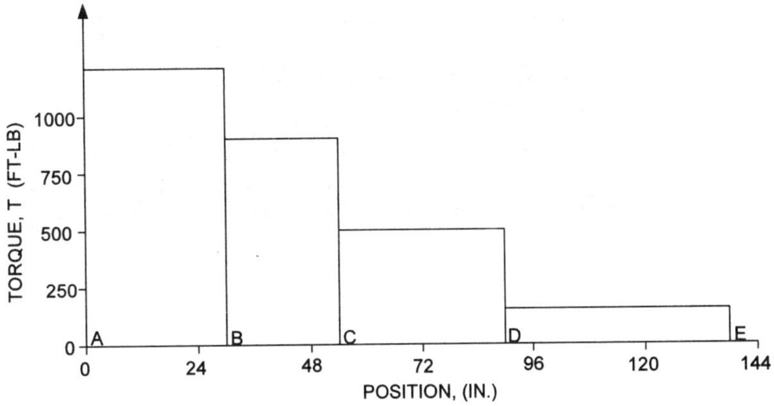

Next, write Eq. (3.35b) to determine the angle of twist for each segment of the line-shaft.

$$\phi_{A\text{-}B} = \frac{32TL}{\pi d^4 G} = \frac{32(-1{,}200)(12)(30)}{\pi (2)^4 (11.5\times 10^6)} = -0.02391 \text{ radians} = -1.370^\circ$$

$$\phi_{B\text{-}C} = \frac{32TL}{\pi d^4 G} = \frac{32(-900)(12)(24)}{\pi (1.75)^4 (11.5\times 10^6)} = -0.02448 \text{ radians} = -1.403^\circ$$

$$\phi_{C\text{-}D} = \frac{32TL}{\pi d^4 G} = \frac{32(-500)(12)(36)}{\pi (1.5)^4 (11.5\times 10^6)} = 0.03779 \text{ radians} = -2.165^\circ$$

$$\phi_{D\text{-}E} = \frac{32TL}{\pi d^4 G} = \frac{32(-150)(12)(48)}{\pi (1.25)^4 (11.5\times 10^6)} = 0.03135 \text{ radians} = -1.796^\circ$$

The angle of twist for the entire shaft AE is given by Eq. (3.35c) as:

$\phi_{A\text{-}E} = \phi_{A\text{-}B} + \phi_{B\text{-}C} + \phi_{C\text{-}D} + \phi_{D\text{-}E} = -\ 1.370^\circ - 1.403^\circ - 2.165^\circ - 1.796^\circ = -\ 6.734^\circ$

The angle of twist between gears A and C can be determined from Eq. (3.35c) as:

$$\phi_{A\text{-}C} = \phi_{A\text{-}B} + \phi_{B\text{-}C} = -\ 1.370 - 1.403^\circ = -\ 2.773^\circ$$

The negative signs describe the sense of rotation (clockwise).

3.6.1 Torsion Bar Springs

When torque is applied to a shaft, it twists through an angle ϕ and strain energy is stored in the shaft. The strain energy ***E*** is equal to the work ***W*** input to the shaft as it twists. We depict this work as the shaded triangular area in Fig. 3.12.

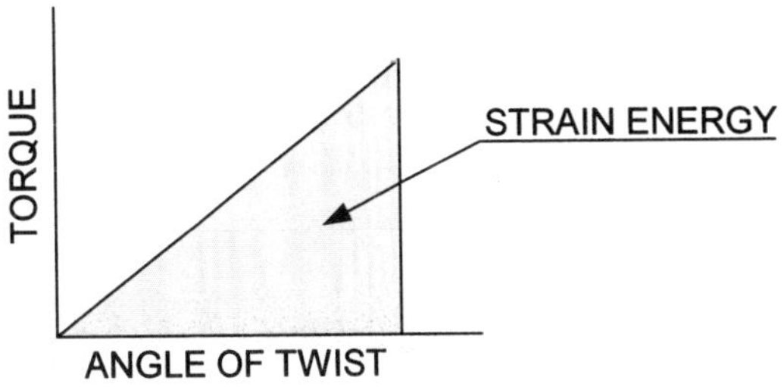

Fig. 3.12 The area under the torque-angle of twist curve is equal to the strain energy stored in a shaft.

The strain energy $\boldsymbol{E}$ is given by:

$$\boldsymbol{E} = (1/2)\, T\phi \tag{3.36}$$

Substituting Eq. (3.35a) into Eq. (3.36) gives:

$$\boldsymbol{E} = (T^2 L)/(2GJ) \tag{3.37}$$

$$\boldsymbol{E} = (\phi^2 GJ)/(2L) \tag{3.38}$$

The shaft acts as a torsion spring with the applied torque linearly proportional to the angle of twist.

$$T = k_T\, \phi \tag{3.39}$$

where k_T is the spring rate given by:

$$k_T = GJ/L \tag{3.40}$$

EXAMPLE 3.12

A steel torsion bar is incorporated into the chassis of an automobile to serve as a suspension spring. If the bar is fabricated from a steel rod 16 mm in diameter and 1.0 m long, determine its spring rate. Also determine its angle of twist if it stores strain energy $\boldsymbol{E}$ = 4.0 N-m as the automobile traverses a bump.

Solution:

We apply Eq. (3.40) to obtain:

$$k_T = GJ/L = [(79)(10^9)\,\pi\,(0.016)^4]/[(1.0)(32)] = 508.3 \text{ N-m} \tag{a}$$

From Eq. (3.38) and Eq. (a), it is evident that:

$$\phi = [2\boldsymbol{E}/k_T\,]^{1/2} = [(2)(4)/\,508.3]^{1/2} = 0.1255 \text{ radians} = 7.188° \tag{b}$$

The result shows that the torsion spring undergoes a relatively large angle of twist. Will it survive over the service life of the automobile?

3.7 DESIGN OF POWER TRANSMISSION SHAFTING

Power transmission shafts connect a power source such as an electric motor or an internal combustion engine to industrial equipment such as a compressor or a machine tool. Shafts are circular in cross section because they rotate (often at very high speed) and are supported by bearings. Shafting is usually fabricated from alloy steel because of its superior strength. Because the shafting rotates and the stresses imposed are usually cyclical, the design is based on the fatigue strength of the steels. Also, stress concentrations[2] are taken into account in a typical design analysis.

---

[2] Methods for designing to accommodate stress concentrations and fatigue loading will be described later in Chapter 9.

The relations for determining the shearing stress in shafting were introduced in a previous section of this chapter. The purpose of this section is to demonstrate the application of these relations in a design analysis of two challenging problems.

EXAMPLE 3.13

The electric motor shown in Fig. E3.13 is rated at 300 kW and operates at 1,180 RPM. It powers a gear drive with a variable load, which at times requires the motor to operate at its maximum rating. The shaft is supported by four bearings — one on each side of the gear drive, shown in Fig. E3.13, and two bearings within the motor to support the armature. The shaft has a diameter D. Select a material for the shaft and determine its diameter, if the maximum shear stress in the material is not to exceed 1/2 the yield strength of the material in shear. Another constraint on the design is the angle of twist ϕ, which is not to exceed 2.0° measured from the motor to the gear drive.

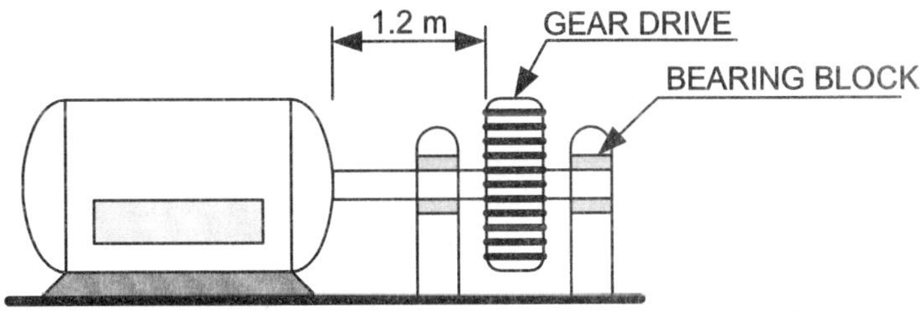

Fig. E3.13

Solution:

A step-by step approach will be used in the solution of this example.

Step 1: We begin by selecting the material for the shaft. Alloy steel, 4340 HR, is specified because it exhibits a very high strength. The high strength is important because it will reduce the diameter of the shaft and hence the diameter of the bearings and the size of the armature in the electric motor. The cost savings in the bearings and armature will offset the added cost of the alloy steel.

From Appendix B-1 and B-2, we determine the material's strength and shear modulus as:

$$G = 79 \text{ GPa} \qquad S_u = 1041 \text{ MPa} \qquad S_y = 910 \text{ MPa} \qquad \text{(a)}$$

Next we use Eq. (3.17a) to determine the yield strength of the 4340 HR alloy steel in shear.

$$S_{ys} = 0.5774\, S_y = (0.5774)(910) = 525.4 \text{ MPa} \qquad \text{(b)}$$

Step 2: Determine the maximum shear stress that can be imposed on the shaft from the problem statement and Eq. (b) as:

$$\tau_{Max} = S_{ys}/2 = 525.4/2 = 262.7 \text{ MPa} \qquad \text{(c)}$$

Step 3: Determine the torque applied to the shaft when the electric motor is operating at its rated capacity by using Eq. (3.1):

$$T = P/\omega = [(300 \times 10^3)(60)]/[(1{,}180)(2\pi)] = 2{,}428 \text{ N-m} \qquad \text{(d)}$$

Step 4: If we employ a solid steel shaft, which is the most cost effective choice, Eq. (3.16) can be used together with Eq. (c) and Eq. (d) to determine the diameter D of the shaft as:

$$D^3 = (16\ T)/(\pi\tau_{Max}) = (16)(2{,}428)/[\pi(262.7 \times 10^6)] = 47.07 \times 10^{-6}\ m^3$$

$$D = 0.0361\ m = 36.1\ mm \qquad (e)$$

Select a standard size available in metric diameters, which is 37 mm.

Step 5: Check to determine if the angle of twist ϕ is within the specified limit of 2.0° by employing Eq. (3.35b).

$$\phi = (32TL)/(\pi D^4 G) = [(32)(2{,}428)(1.2)]/[\pi(0.037)^4\ (79 \times 10^9)]$$

$$\phi = 0.2004\ radians = 11.48° \qquad (f)$$

This angle of twist is outside the specifications outlined in the problem statement. It is clear that the angle of twist is the controlling parameter in the design of this shaft and not the maximum shear stress.

Step 6: To determine the shaft diameter limiting the angle of twist to 2° (0.03491 radians), we rearrange Eq. (3.35b) to give:

$$D^4 = 32\ TL/\pi\phi G = [(32)(2{,}428)(1.2)]/[\pi(0.03491)\ (79 \times 10^9)] = 10.76 \times 10^{-6}\ m^4$$

$$D = 0.05727\ m = 57.27\ mm \qquad (g)$$

Metric dimensioned shafts are available with a diameter of 60 mm.

EXAMPLE 3.14

The electric motor shown in Fig. E3.14 is rated at 250 HP and operates at 1,780 RPM. It powers a drive shaft with three output gears. When the motor is operating at rated capacity, gear A removes 1/2 the power developed by the motor, while gear B and gear C remove 1/3 and 1/6, respectively. The shaft is supported by the bearings shown in Fig. E3.14. The shaft from the motor has a diameter D. If an alloy steel with a yield strength in shear of 125 ksi is used to fabricate the shaft, determine the diameter of the shaft, if the maximum shear stress in the material is not to exceed 1/3 the yield strength of the material in shear. Another constraint on the design is the angle of twist ϕ, which is not to exceed 3.2° measured from the motor to the gear C.

Fig. E3.14

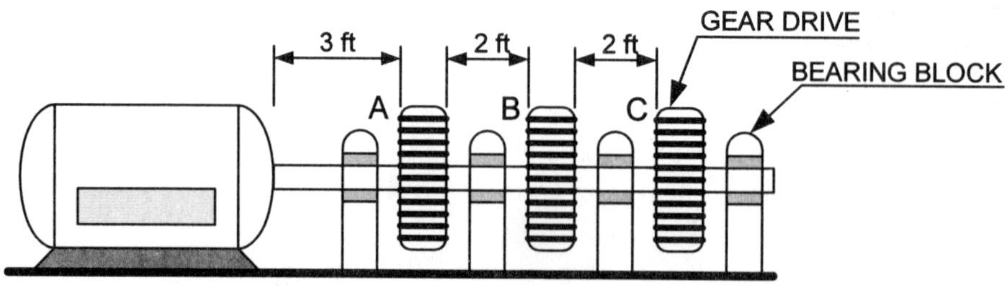

Solution:

The shaft is of uniform diameter from the motor to the free end of the shaft. A step-by-step solution is given below:

Step 1: Determine the torque exerted on the shaft when the motor is operated at its rated capacity from Eq. (3.3).

$$T = 33{,}000\ HP/2\pi n = (33{,}000)(250)/(2\pi)(1{,}780) = 737.7 \text{ ft-lb} \qquad \text{(a)}$$

Step 2: Compute the torque removed at each gear by using the fractions listed in the problem statement and construct a torque position diagram as shown in Fig. E3.14a:

$T_A = 737.7\ (1/2) = 368.8$ ft-lb, $T_B = 737.7\ (1/3) = 245.9$ ft-lb, $T_C = 737.7\ (1/6) = 123.0$ ft-lb

Fig. E3.14a

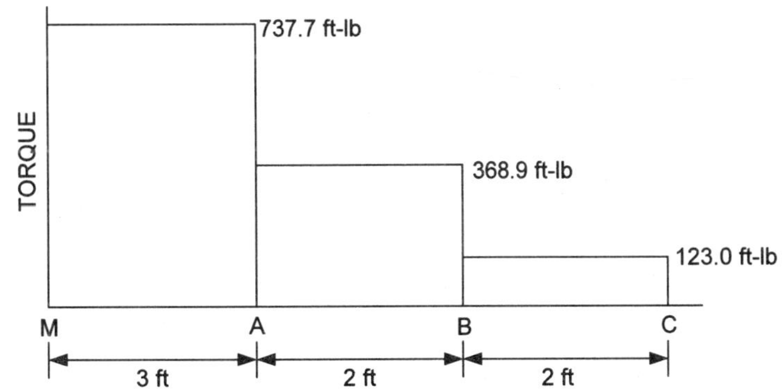

Step 3: Determine the maximum shear stress that is allowable for the shaft from:

$$\tau_{Max} = 125/3 = 41.67 \text{ ksi} \qquad \text{(b)}$$

Step 4: If a solid steel shaft is employed, Eq. (3.16) can be used together with Eq. (a) and Eq. (b) to determine the diameter D of the shaft as:

$$D^3 = (16\ T)/(\pi\tau_{Max}) = (16)(737.7)(12)/[\pi(41.67 \times 10^3)] = 1.082 \text{ in.}^3$$

$$D = 1.027 \text{ in.} \qquad \text{(c)}$$

Select a standard size diameter as D = 1 - 1/16 = 1.0625 in.

Step 5: Determine the total angle of twist by summing the twist of the shaft between each of the gears. We will assume that the twist due to the deflection of the gear teeth is sufficiently small to neglect. From Eqs. (3.35b) and (3.35c), we write:

$$\phi_{M\text{-}C} = \phi_{M\text{-}A} + \phi_{A\text{-}B} + \phi_{B\text{-}C} = [(32)/(\pi D^4 G)][T_{M\text{-}A}\ L_{M\text{-}A} + T_{A\text{-}B}\ L_{A\text{-}B} + T_{B\text{-}C}\ L_{B\text{-}C}]$$

$$\phi_{M\text{-}C} = \{32/[\pi(1.0625)^4\ (11.5 \times 10^6)]\}\{(737.7)(12)(36) + (368.9)(12)(24) + (123.0)(12)(24)\}$$

$$\phi_{M\text{-}C} = 0.3199 \text{ radians} = 18.33° \qquad \text{(d)}$$

Clearly this angle of twist exceeds the allowable twist of 3.2°, which is specified, by a factor of nearly six. It is necessary to increase the shaft diameter to reduce ϕ. If we recognize that the angle of twist decreases as the fourth power of the shaft diameter, it is easy to compute the required diameter from:

$$(d_{2nd}/d_{1st})^4 = 6 \quad \text{or} \quad d_{2nd} = (6)^{1/4} d_{1st} = (1.565)(1.0625) = 1.663 \text{ in.} \qquad \text{(e)}$$

Selecting the next larger standard size gives D = 1.75 in.

3.8 TORSION OF NON-CIRCULAR SHAFTS

The discussion of torsion thus far has focused on rotating shafts with circular cross sections, because most applications involve transmitting power from a motor or engine to an appliance. However, structural engineers sometimes load members such as angle and channel sections with transverse forces that induce torque. The derivations of the equations for the maximum shear stress and the angle of twist in shafts with non-circular cross sections are beyond the scope of this text. For this reason, this section is limited to the definition of the cross section geometry and the presentation of the equations for τ_{Max} and ϕ.

Elliptical Cross Section

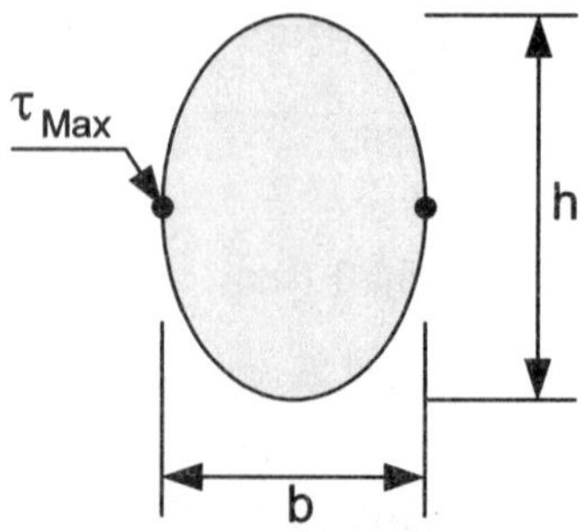

$$\tau_{Max} = 16T/\pi b^2 h$$
$$\phi = (4\pi^2 TLJ)/(A^4 G) \qquad (3.41)$$
$$J = (\pi/64)(b h^3 + b^3 h)$$
$$A = \pi bh/4$$

Equilateral Triangle

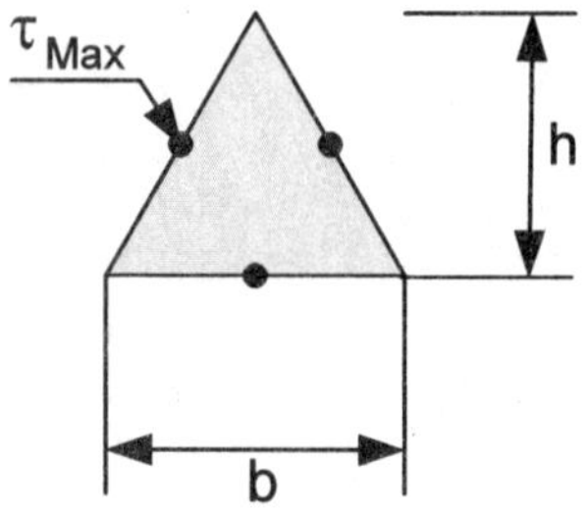

$$\tau_{Max} = 20T/b^3$$
$$\phi = (TL)/(0.6\ GJ) = 46.2TL/b^4 G \qquad (3.42)$$

Hexagon

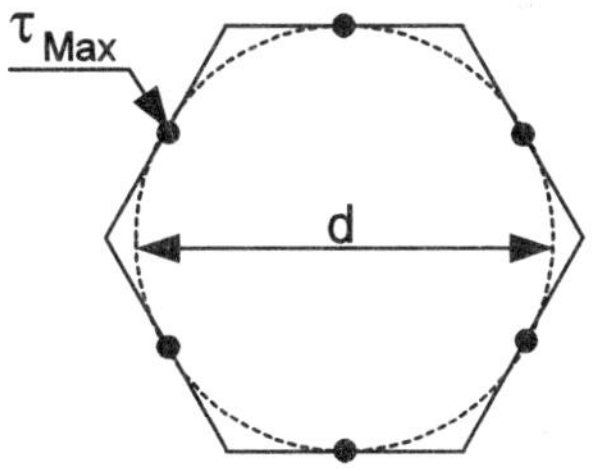

$\tau_{Max} = T/[0.217\ Ad]$
$\phi = (TL)/(0.133\ Ad^2\ G)$ (3.43)
$A\ 0.866d^2$

Rectangle

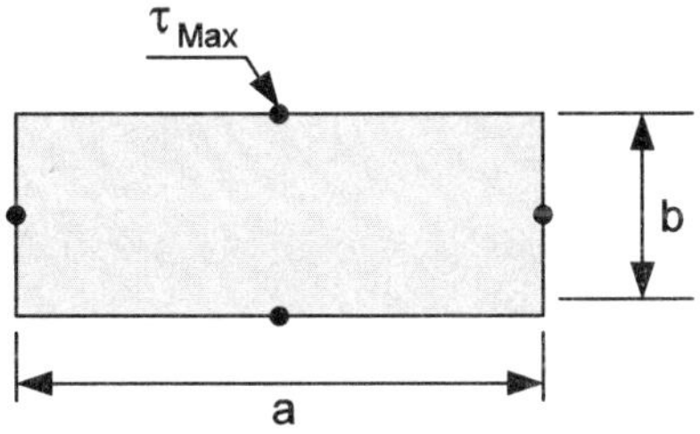

$\tau_{Max} = T/(\alpha ab^2)$ for $a \geq b$
$\phi = (TL)/(\beta ab^3\ G)$ (3.44)

$\alpha = 0.3334 - 0.1904(b/a) - 0.2574(b/a)^2 + 1.0255(b/a)^3$
$\quad - 1.0946(b/a)^4 + 0.3916(b/a)^5$
$\beta = 0.3333 - 0.1997(b/a) - 0.0790(b/a)^2$
$\quad + 0.1892(b/a)^3 - 0.1766(b/a)^4 + 0.0739(b/a)^5$

Thin Rectangle

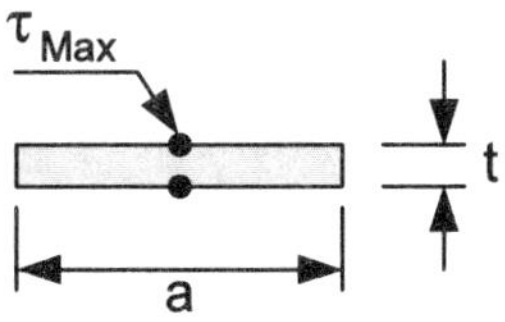

$\tau_{Max} = 3.0\ T/at^2$
$\phi = (3TL)/(a\ t^3\ G)$ (3.45)

Angle Section

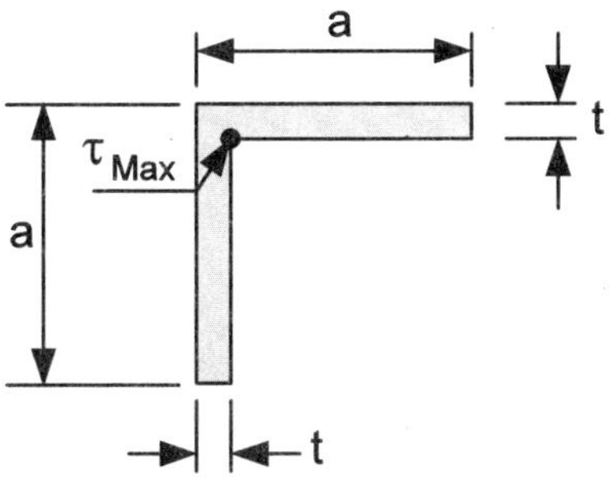

$\tau_{Nom} = 3.0\ T/2at^2$
$\phi = (3TL)/(2a\ t^3\ G)$ (3.46)
for $t \ll a$

The maximum shear stress occurs at the reentrant corner of the angle, channel and I sections. The stress concentration associated with the reentrant corner is usually neglected, if the section is fabricated from a ductile material and is not subjected to cyclic loading.

Channel Section

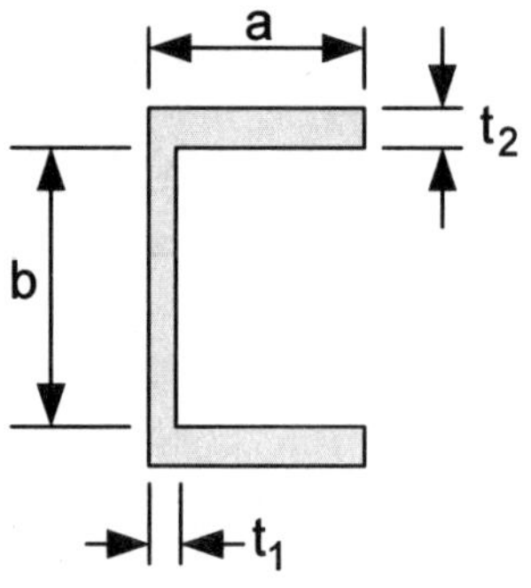

$$\tau_{Nom} = 3.0\, Tt_2 /(bt_1^3 + 2at_2^3)$$
$$\phi = (3TL)/[(bt_1^3 + 2at_2^3)G] \quad (3.47)$$

I Section

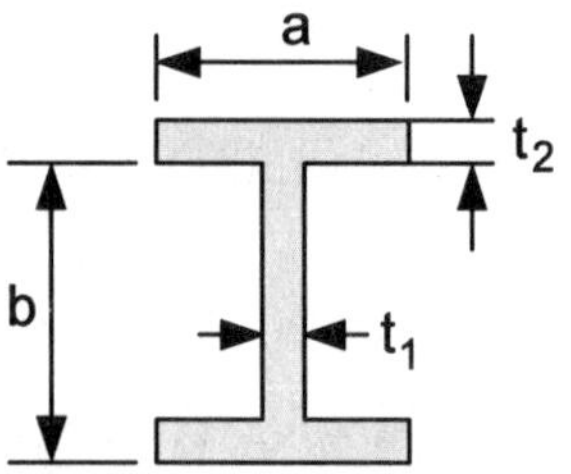

$$\tau_{Nom} = 3.0\, Tt_2 /(bt_1^3 + 2at_2^3)$$
$$\phi = (3TL)/[(bt_1^3 + 2at_2^3)\, G] \quad (3.48)$$

EXAMPLE 3.15

A torque T = 600 N-m is applied to a structural member with a square cross section. If the square section is 40 mm on a side and is 3 m long, determine the maximum stress and the angle of twist. Will the structural member yield if it is fabricated from 1010 A carbon steel?

Solution:

First calculate the numerical factors α and β from Eq. (3.44):

For $(b/a) = 1.0$ $\Rightarrow\Rightarrow \alpha = 0.2081$; $\beta = 0.1411$

Reference Eq. (3.44) and write:

$$\tau_{MAX} = T/(\alpha ab^2) = (600)/[(0.2081)(0.04)^3] = 45.05 \text{ MPa} \quad \text{(a)}$$

Next use Eq. (3.17a) to determine the yield strength of the 1010A carbon steel in shear.

$$S_{ys} = 0.5774S_y = (0.5774)(200) = 115.5 \text{ MPa} \quad \text{(b)}$$

It is clear that the structural member will not yield because S_{ys} exceeds τ_{Max} by a factor of more than 2.5.

The angle of twist for the square cross section is given by:

$$\phi = (TL)/(\beta ab^3\ G) = (600)(3)/[(0.1411)(.04)^4\ (79 \times 10^9)] = 0.06308 \text{ radians}$$

$$\phi = 3.614° \qquad \text{(c)}$$

3.9 SHEAR CENTER

The topic of shear center combines the concept of shear stresses induced by transverse forces applied to beams and the angle of twist in torsion. Twisting of beams in bending does not arise for beams with symmetric cross sections. If the cross section of the beam is symmetric about its vertical axis, the shear stresses, which exist, do not produce a twisting moment. However, if the beam's cross-section is not symmetric, transverse loads will cause twisting to occur. To illustrate this point, consider a cantilever beam loaded at its free end with a concentrated force F. The concentrated load is applied through the center of gravity of the channel section as shown in Fig. 3.13. When the load is applied, the beam will twist about its longitudinal axis through an angle ϕ.

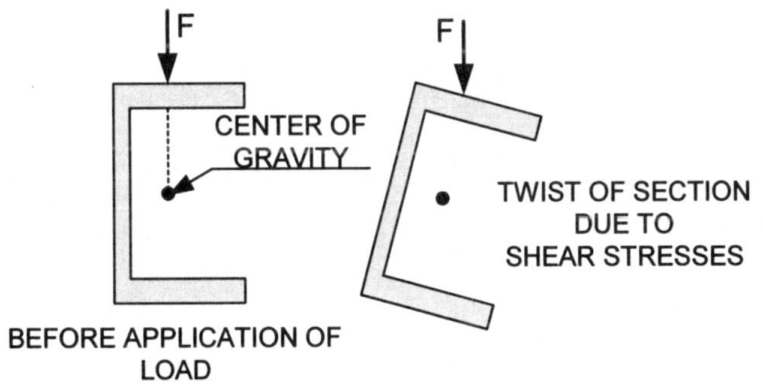

Fig. 3.13 Twisting of unsymmetrical beam section induced by shear stresses.

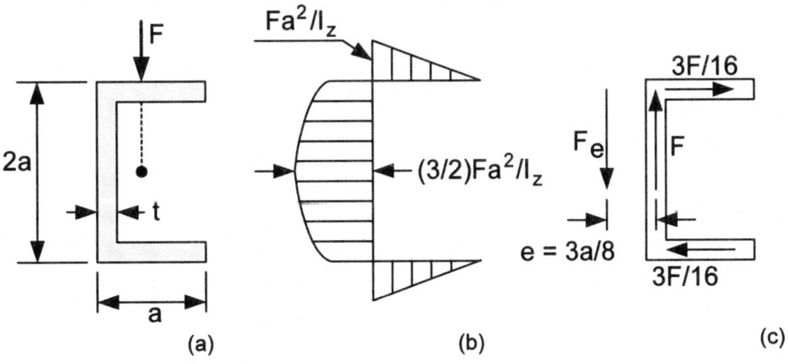

Fig. 3.14 Shear stress distribution in a channel section subjected to shearing forces V = F.

Let's consider a cantilever beam fabricated from a channel section with the force F applied at its free end through its center of gravity as illustrated in Fig. 3.14a. A constant shear force V = F occurs over the length L of the beam. This shear force produces shear stresses in both the web and the flanges of the channel section that are given by Eq. (3.49) as[3]:

$$\tau = \tau_V = \tau_H = VQ_1/(bI_z) \qquad (3.49)$$

[3] Equation (3.49) will be derived later in Chapter 4.

where $$Q_1 = \int_{y_1}^{c} y dA \qquad (3.50)$$

where Q_1 is the first moment of the area from the section cut at position y to the location of the top fiber of the beam at y = c.
V is the internal shear force
I_z is the moment of inertia about the neutral axis of the beam.
b is the width of the beam

If the shear stresses in the channel section are determined from Eq. (3.49), the distribution of τ_V and τ_H are shown in Fig. 3.14b. In this solution of Eq. (3.49) higher powers of the dimension ratio (t/a) have been disregarded, because they are small in relation to the other terms. Integrating the shear stress distribution over the three rectangular areas comprising the channel section and substituting:

$$I_z = 8a^3t/3 \qquad (a)$$

Into Eq. (3.49) yields the three shear forces shown in Fig. 3.14c.

Examination of Fig. 3.14c shows that the shear force V in the vertical portion of the channel is equal to the applied force F as expected. The two horizontal forces 3F/16 are equal and opposite and cancel satisfying $\Sigma F_z = 0$. However, these two forces produce a couple, a torque T = (3/8)Fa, which tends to twist the channel section (in a clockwise direction) producing the twisted shape presented in Fig. 3.13.

The shear center is established from this twisting moment. If a transverse force $F_e = F$ is applied at an eccentric position, e = (3/8)a, from the centerline of the vertical segment of the channel, as shown in Fig. 3.14c, it produces a couple with T = (3/8)Fa in the counter clockwise direction. Thus, the couples cancel and the channel section will not twist, when the transverse force is applied at the eccentric position. When loading unsymmetrical sections, the transverse force must be applied through the shear center instead of the center of gravity to avoid twisting deformations.

Channel sections and other unsymmetrical sections are often employed in structural applications. In these cases, attachments are welded to the main beams to allow for the eccentric placement of the applied forces as indicated in Fig. 3.15.

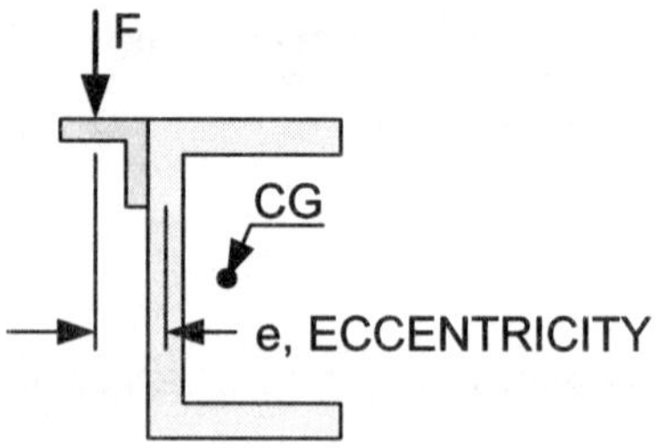

Fig. 3.15 Eccentric placement of the applied force to suppress twisting due to shear stresses.

EXAMPLE 3.16

The channel section presented in Fig. E3.16 is to be employed in fabricating a cantilever beam. Determine the eccentricity e of the transverse force F if the beam is to deflect without twisting.

Fig. E3.16

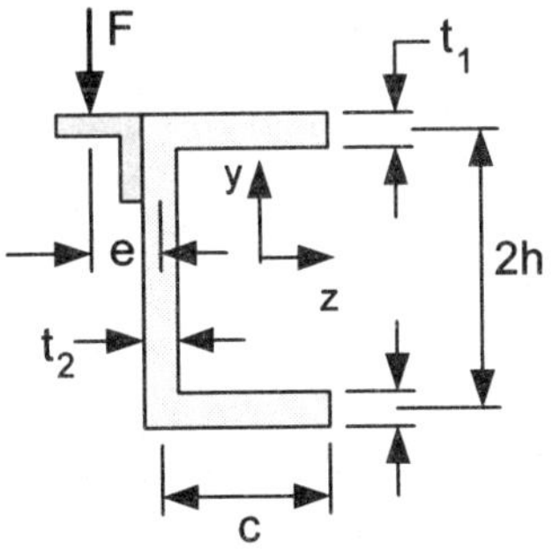

Solution:

Step 1: Prepare FBDs showing the shear stresses introduced by the shear force V = F. Section the top flange of the channel section a distance d from its edge as shown in Fig. E3.16a.

Fig. E3.16a

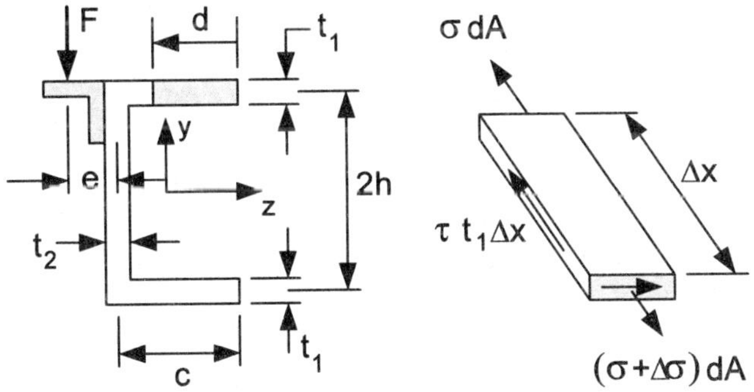

Step 2: The shear stress τ in the top flange is determined from Eq. (3.49) as:

$$\tau = VQ_1/I_z\, b = (F\ h\ d/I_z) \qquad (a)$$

where V = F, $b = t_1$ and $Q_1 = h\ d\ t_1$

The shear stress in the flange is a linear function of d increasing from zero at the edge of the flange to a maximum value where the flange intersects the web of the channel and d = c. Clearly τ_{Max} is given by:

$$(\tau_{Max})_{Flange} = F\ h\ c/I_z \qquad (b)$$

Step 3: The shear stress at the top of the web is also determined from Eq. (3.49) as:

$$\tau = VQ_1\ /I_z\, b = [(F\ h\ c\ t_1)/(t_2\ I_z)] \qquad (c)$$

where V = F, $b = t_2$ and $Q_1 = h\ c\ t_1$

Step 4: The shear stress is a maximum at the center of the web where y = 0. From Eq. (3.49), we write:

$$\tau = VQ_1 / I_z b = Fh[c(t_1/t_2) + (h/2)]/I_z \qquad \text{(d)}$$

where $V = F$, $b = t_2$ and $Q_1 = h\,[c\,t_1 + t_2\,(h/2)]$

The shear stress exhibits a parabolic distribution over the height of the web. If this shear stress is integrated over the area of the web, we find:

$$\int \tau \, dA_{Web} \approx F = V \qquad \text{(e)}$$

Step 5: The shear stress in the flanges varies linearly from zero to a maximum at the junction of the web and the flange. Integrating the shear stresses, given in Eq. (a), over the area of the top flange yields the shear force H_1 as:

$$H_1 = \int \tau \, dA_{Flange} = (1/2)(ct_1)(Fhc/I_z) = (Fhc^2t_1)/(2I_z) = -H_2 \qquad \text{(f)}$$

A second shear force H_2, equal in magnitude and opposite in direction, is induced in the lower flange as shown in Fig E3.16b.

Fig. E3.16b

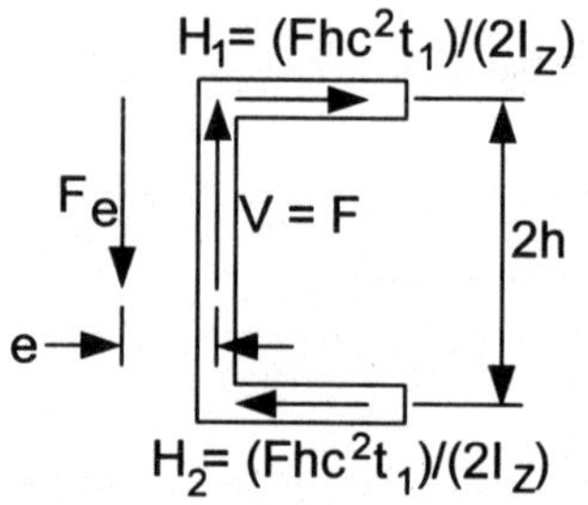

Step 6: The two equal and opposite shear forces, H_1 and H_2, produce a clockwise couple T equal to:

$$T = (2h)H_1 = (Fh^2 c^2 t_1)/(I_z) \qquad \text{(g)}$$

Step 7: An equal and opposite moment (torque) is produced by applying the force F with an eccentricity e as shown in Fig. E3.16b. The eccentricity is given by $e = T/F$ as:

$$e = T/F = (h^2 c^2 t_1)/(I_z) \qquad \text{(h)}$$

The moment of inertia I_z of the channel section is given by:

$$I_z = (2/3)t_2 h^3 + 2t_1 ch^2 \qquad \text{(i)}$$

Step 8: Substituting Eq. (i) into Eq. (h) gives the eccentricity necessary in locating the point of application of the transverse force F to avoid twisting the channel section beam:

$$e = \left(\frac{3}{2}\right)\left[\frac{c^2 t_1}{t_2 h + 3t_1 c}\right] \qquad \text{(j)}$$

3.10 THIN WALLED TUBE WITH ARBITRARY SHAPE

In Section 3.3.1, we determined the shear stress and the angle of twist in circular, thin-walled tubes subjected to torsion loading. We noted that the shear stresses were linearly distributed with only small differences across the thickness of the wall, as shown in Fig. 3.16. It is evident from this illustration that the average shear stress τ_{ave} is a close approximation of τ_{Max} for very thin walled tubes. We will make use of this fact in developing the expression for shear stresses in thin-walled tubes with arbitrary cross sections.

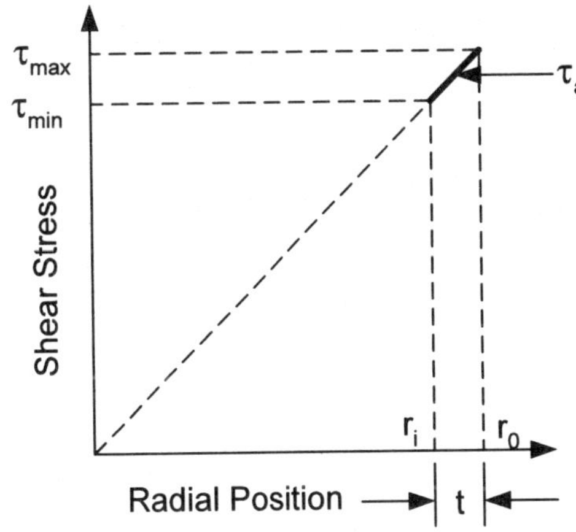

Fig. 3.16 Shear stress distribution across the wall of a thin-walled circular tube.

Consider the thin walled tube, shown in Fig. 3.17, subjected to a torque T. The shape of the cross section is not circular, nor is the wall thickness uniform; however, the thickness of the wall is small relative to the other dimensions of the tube.

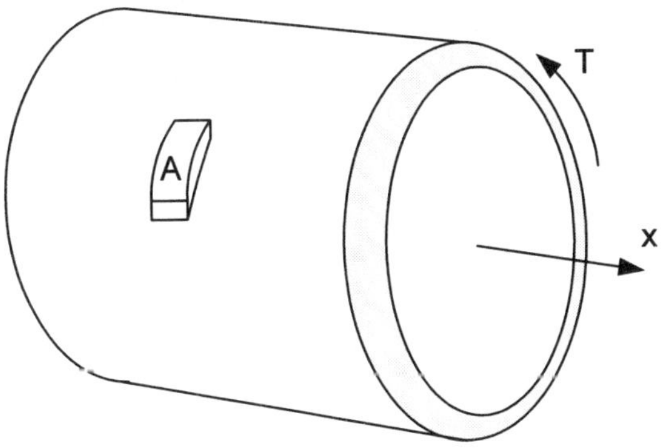

Fig. 3.17 A thin-walled tube with an arbitrary shape.

Next, let's remove element A from the wall of the tube and note the forces F_1 and F_2 acting on the elements longitudinal faces, as shown in Fig. 3.18. These forces are due to the shear stresses τ_{yx} distributed over the longitudinal faces of the element A. The shear stresses in the vertical direction τ_{xz} and τ_{yz} on all four faces vanish due to the proximity of the free boundaries formed by the inside and outside surfaces of the tube.

Considering equilibrium of the element A in the x direction enables us to write:

$$\Sigma F = F_1 - F_2 = 0 \tag{3.51}$$

The forces F_1 and F_2, due to the average shear stresses τ_{1Ave} and τ_{2Ave} acting on the element faces, can be expressed as:

$$F_1 = \tau_{1Ave}\, t_1\, dx \qquad \text{and} \qquad F_2 = \tau_{2Ave}\, t_2\, dx \qquad (3.52)$$

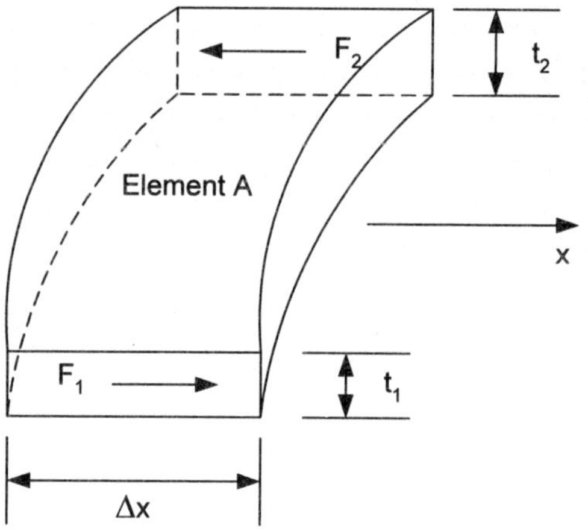

Fig. 3.18 Forces acting on the longitudinal faces of element A.

Substituting Eq. (3.52) into Eq. (3.51) yields:

$$\tau_{1Ave}\, t_1\, dx - \tau_{2Ave}\, t_2\, dx = 0 \qquad (a)$$

or

$$\tau_{1Ave}\, t_1 = \tau_{1Ave}\, t_2 \qquad (b)$$

If we define the product in Eq. (b) as the shear flow rate q, we may write:

$$q = \tau_{ave}\, t = C \qquad (3.53)$$

where C is a constant.

Because the element A can be selected anywhere on the tube, it is evident that the shear flow rate q is constant and independent of the tube's thickness and position of element A.

Next consider a sub-element cut from element A as indicated in Fig. 3.19.

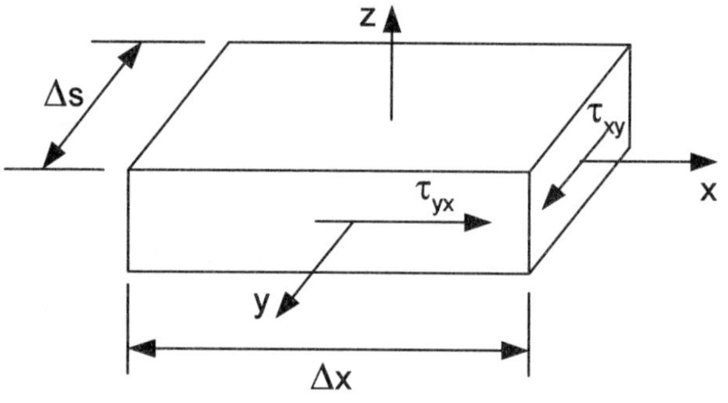

Fig. 3.19 Sub-element showing shear stresses on the longitudinal and transverse faces.

Note that:

$$\tau_{xy} = \tau_{yx} = \tau_{1Ave} \qquad (3.54)$$

Also it is evident that $\tau_{xz} = \tau_{yz} = 0$, because of the thin wall and the proximity of the two free boundaries.

It is useful at this stage of the derivation to introduce an analogy involving steady state fluid flow in a closed-rectangular channel with a unit depth but a variable width w. The flow rate $\boldsymbol{Q}$ in this channel is given by:

$$\boldsymbol{Q} = v_{Ave}\, w = \text{Constant} \tag{3.55}$$

where v_{Ave} is the average flow velocity.

It is clear that the average velocity of the flow will increase or decrease as the width of the channel decreases or increases. This analogy has lead the engineering community to define $q = \tau_{Ave}\, t$ as the shear flow rate, where $\boldsymbol{Q}$ is analogous to q, v_{Ave} is analogous to τ_{Ave}, and w is analogous to t.

Next let's determine the relation between the shear flow rate q and the applied torque by considering an element on the cross section of the tube as shown in Fig. 3.20.

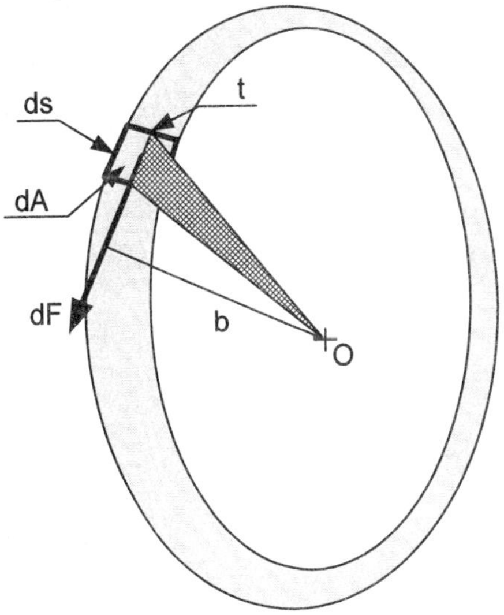

Fig. 3.20 A element on the cross section of the tube showing the incremental force dF.

Using Eq. (3.53) we can write the following relation for the force dF:

$$dF = \tau_{Ave}\, dA = \tau_{Ave}\, t\, ds = q\, ds \tag{3.56}$$

From Fig. 3.20 and Eq. (3.56), the incremental moment dM_0 produced by dF can be written as:

$$dM_0 = bdF = q(bds) \tag{3.57}$$

The determine the quantity (b ds), let's consider the two triangles shown in Fig. 3.20. For clarity these triangles have been redrawn as indicated in Fig. 3.21.

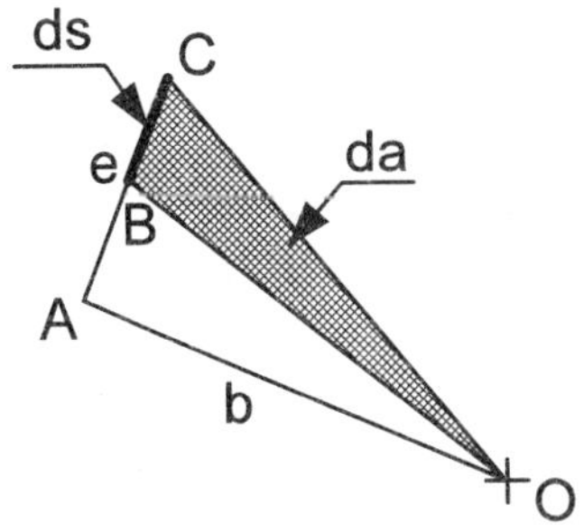

Fig. 3.21 Redrawn triangles from Fig. 3.20 showing the cross hatched area da.

The area of the triangle AOC is $A_2 = ½\ be$ and the area of the triangle AOB is $A_1 = ½\ b(e - ds)$. The area da of the cross hatched triangle is given by:

$$da = A_2 - A_1 = ½\ b\ ds \tag{3.58}$$

Substituting Eq. (3.58) into Eq. (3.57) yields:

$$dM_0 = 2q\ da \tag{3.59}$$

The torque T is obtained by integrating da as the element in Fig. 3.20 is swept around the perimeter of the tube. The integration involves a line integral as indicated below:

$$T = \oint dM_0 = 2q \oint da \tag{3.60}$$

Integration of Eq. (3.60) gives:

$$T = 2qA_i \tag{3.61}$$

where A_i is the area of the interior of the tube measured to the mid point of the thickness of the wall.

Substituting Eq. (3.53) into Eq. (3.61) yields:

$$T = 2\ \tau_{ave}\ t\ A_i \tag{3.62}$$

or

$$\tau_{Ave} = T/(2tA_i) \tag{3.63}$$

The angle of twist ϕ of the tube is obtained using energy methods that are beyond the scope of this book. For a tube of length L, the elastic deformation ϕ due to the torque T is given by:

$$\phi = \frac{TL}{4A_i^2 G} \oint \frac{ds}{t} \tag{3.64}$$

This shear stress flow approach provides a method for determining the average shear stress about the perimeter of a tube with an arbitrary shape. The shear stress is an average across the thickness of the tube's wall. If the wall is thin, a requirement to apply this method, the average stress is a close approximation of the maximum shear stress. When the wall thickness varies around the perimeter of the tube, the maximum average shear stress occurs where the wall is the thinnest, as indicated in Eq. (3.63).

EXAMPLE 3.17

A square hollow tube with the dimensions shown in Fig. E3.17 is subjected to a torque of 20,000 in.-lb. If the tube is fabricated from steel with a uniform wall thickness and is 4.0 ft long, determine the average shear stress and the angle of twist.

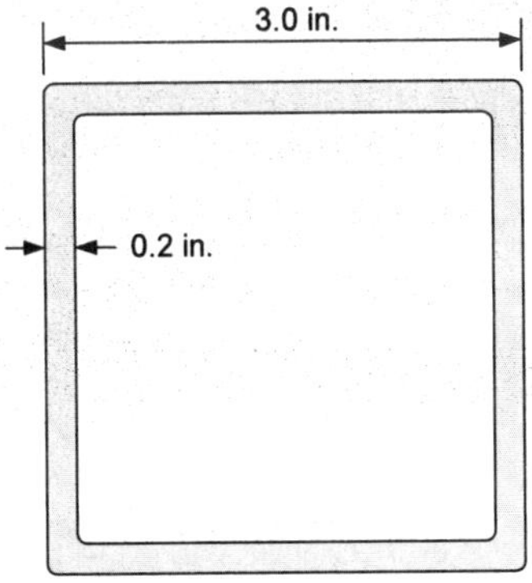

Fig. E3.17

Solution:

The average shear stress in the wall of the tube is given by Eq. (3.63) as:

$$\tau_{Ave} = T/(2tA_i) \qquad \text{where } A_i = (2.8)^2 = 7.84 \text{ in.}^2 \tag{a}$$

Then:

$$\tau_{Ave} = 20{,}000/[(2)(0.2)(7.84) = 6{,}378 \text{ psi} \tag{b}$$

Next calculate the angle of twist ϕ using Eq. (3.64):

$$\phi = \frac{TL}{4A_i^2G}\oint\frac{ds}{t} \tag{c}$$

Note that:

$$\oint\frac{ds}{t} = \frac{(4)(2.8)}{0.2} = 56 \tag{d}$$

Then from Eqs. (c) and (d), we obtain:

$$\phi = \frac{20\times 10^3(4)(12)}{4(7.84)^2(11.5\ \times 10^6)}(56) = 0.01901 \text{ radians} = \ 1.089 \text{ degrees} \tag{e}$$

EXAMPLE 3.18

A rectangular hollow tube, with the dimensions shown in Fig. E3.18, is subjected to a torque of 1,200 N-m. If the tube is fabricated from aluminum and is 3.0 m long, determine the maximum value of the average shear stress and the angle of twist.
Note that the wall thickness is not uniform.

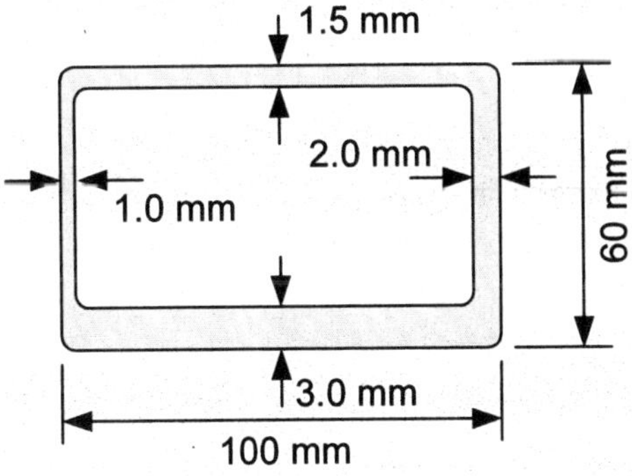

Fig. E3.18

Solution:

The maximum value of the average shear stress in the wall of the tube is given by Eq. (3.63) as:

$$(\tau_{Ave})_{Max} = T/(2t_{Min}\,A_i) \qquad \text{(a)}$$

where $A_i = (100 - 1.5)(60 - 2.25) = 5{,}688\ \text{mm}^2$ (b)

Then:

$$(\tau_{Ave})_{Max} = 1.2 \times 10^6 /[(2)(1.0)(5{,}688) = 105.5\ \text{N/mm}^2 = 105.5\ \text{MPa} \qquad \text{(c)}$$

Next calculate the angle of twist ϕ using Eq. (3.64):

$$\phi = \frac{TL}{4A_i^2 G}\oint \frac{ds}{t} \qquad \text{(d)}$$

Note that:

$$\oint \frac{ds}{t} = \frac{98.5}{1.5} + \frac{57.75}{2} + \frac{98.5}{3} + \frac{57.75}{1} = 185.1 \qquad \text{(e)}$$

Then from Eqs. (d) and (e), we obtain:

$$\phi = \frac{1.2\times 10^6 (3\times 10^3)}{4(5{,}688)^2 (27\ \times 10^3)}(185.1) = 0.1907\ \text{radians} = \ 10.93\ \text{degrees} \qquad \text{(f)}$$

The angle of twist is significant but the member is highly stressed and relatively long.

EXAMPLE 3.19

An irregular shaped hollow tube, with the dimensions shown in Fig. E3.19, is subjected to a torque of 22,000 in-lb. If the tube is fabricated from aluminum and is 5.0 ft long, determine the maximum value of the average shear stress and the angle of twist. Note that the wall thickness of the vertical sides is 1/4 in. and the thickness of the horizontal sides is 1/8 in.

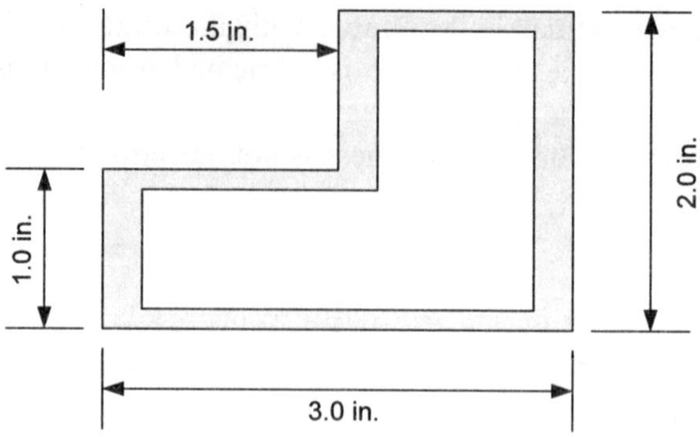

Fig. E3.19

Solution:

The maximum value of the average shear stress in the wall of the tube is given by Eq. (3.63) as:

$$(\tau_{Ave})_{Max} = T/(2t_{Min}\ A_i) \quad \text{(a)}$$

where $A_i = (2.75)(0.875) + (1.25)(0.875) = 3.50\ in^2$ (b)

Then from Eq. (3.63) we write:

$$(\tau_{Ave})_{Max} = 22 \times 10^3 /[(2)(0.125)(3.50) = 25{,}140 \text{ psi} \quad \text{(c)}$$

Next calculate the angle of twist ϕ using Eq. (3.64):

$$\phi = \frac{TL}{4A_i^2 G} \oint \frac{ds}{t} \quad \text{(d)}$$

Note that:

$$\oint \frac{ds}{t} = (2.75)(8) + (1.875)(4) + (2)(1.25)(8) + (2)(0.875)(4) = 56.5 \quad \text{(e)}$$

Then from Eq. (d) and (e), we obtain:

$$\phi = \frac{(22 \times 10^3)(5)(12)}{4(3.50)^2(3.9 \times 10^6)}(56.5) = 0.3903 \text{ radians} = 22.36 \text{ degrees} \quad \text{(f)}$$

The angle of twist is significant but the member is highly stressed and relatively long.

3.11 SUMMARY

The emphasis in this chapter was on the design of shafting fabricated from circular rods. Shafts are commonly employed to transmit power from an electric motor or an internal combustion engine to some appliance. In transmitting power, the shaft is subjected to a torque and it may fail due to shear stresses that produce yielding or due to an excessive angle of twist ϕ. The relation between power transmitted and the torque developed in the shaft was given as:

$$P = T\omega \quad (3.1)$$

When a shaft is subjected to a torque T, it twisted through an angle ϕ. This deformation in turn produces a shearing strain γ given by:

$$\gamma_\rho = \rho\phi/L \quad (3.7)$$

The shearing stress τ in the shaft is determined from the stress-strain relation for shearing deformation, which is given by:

$$\tau = G\gamma \quad (3.9)$$

where the shear modulus is related to the elastic modulus by:

$$G = \frac{E}{2(1+\nu)} \qquad (3.9a)$$

The shear stress in terms of the torque and radial position ρ is:

$$\tau_\rho = T\rho/J \qquad (3.14)$$

The shear stress τ_ρ is a maximum on the outside surface of the shaft where $\rho = r = d/2$.

$$\tau_{Max} = 2\ T/(\pi r^3) = 16\ T/(\pi d^3) \qquad (3.16)$$

The yield strength in shear is much lower than the yield strength in either tension or compression. We approximate the yield and ultimate strength in shear as:

$$S_{ys} = 0.5774\ S_y \qquad (3.17a)$$

$$S_{us} = 0.5774\ S_u \qquad (3.17b)$$

We introduced the concept of section modulus in torsion Z_T for a hollow circular shaft by defining τ_{Max} as:

$$\tau_{Max} = 16\ Td_o/[\pi(d_o^4 - d_i^4)] = T/Z_T \qquad (3.22)$$

$$\text{where } Z_T = \pi(d_o^4 - d_i^4)/(16d_o) \qquad (3.23)$$

Using the section modulus in torsion, we introduced the concept of structural efficiency ***SE*** of a shaft in torsion following the same approach that we employed in the discussion of beams in bending.

$$\boldsymbol{SE} = Z_T/A \qquad (3.28)$$

$$\boldsymbol{SE} = \frac{d_o^2 + d_i^2}{4d_o} \qquad (3.29)$$

We considered shear stress acting on orthogonal planes and established that they are equal in magnitude and opposite in direction.

$$\tau_{xy} = \tau_{yx} \qquad (3.31)$$

We examined the shear stresses on oblique planes and found that the shear and normal stresses on the oblique planes oscillate as sinusoids:

$$\tau_{nt} = \tau_{xy}\ (\cos^2\theta - \sin^2\theta) = \tau_{xy} \cos 2\theta \qquad (3.32)$$

$$\sigma_n = 2\ \tau_{xy} \cos\theta \sin\theta = \tau_{xy} \sin 2\theta \qquad (3.33)$$

We found that the normal stresses are a maximum on planes where the shear stress vanishes. This fact enabled us to define principal planes and leads to the relation for the principal stress σ_1:

$$(\sigma_n)_{Max} = \sigma_1 = \tau_{xy} \tag{3.34}$$

We considered the deformation of the shaft due to torsion and established the expression for the angle of twist as:

$$\phi = (TL)/(GJ) \tag{3.35 a}$$

$$\phi = (32\ TL)/(\pi d^4\ G) \tag{3.35 b}$$

Torsion rods are often employed as springs in suspension systems or to store strain energy. We derived the relation between the torsion and the angle of twist in terms of the spring rate k_T as:

$$T = k_T\,\phi \tag{3.39}$$

$$k_T = GJ/L \tag{3.40}$$

Torsion of non-circular sections was introduced. When the section is non-circular, the plane sections do not remain plane when the bar is subjected to torsion. Instead the plane sections warp. This distortion complicates the derivation of the relations for the maximum shear stress and the angle of twist. We have provided these equations without derivation for the following cross sections: elliptical, equilateral triangle, hexagon, rectangle, thin rectangle and angle, channel and I sections.

We introduced the concept of shear stresses produced as a beam bends under the action of transverse forces. If the cross section of the beam is not symmetric about a vertical axis, the beam will twist due to the effect of these shear stresses. The twisting couple produced by bending a cantilever beam fabricated from a channel section was discussed. The twisting of the beam can be avoided if the transverse force is applied through the shear center of the section. Example 3.16 demonstrated the analysis used to determine the location of the shear center.

Finally we introduced a method to approximate the shearing stresses and the angle of twist in tubes with an arbitrary shape and a varying wall thickness. We established that the shear flow rate q was a constant independent of the wall thickness of the tube.

$$q = \tau_{ave}\, t = C \tag{3.53}$$

Integration of the incremental moments produced by the shear stresses enabled us to write the relation for the average shear stresses in the tube produced by the torque T as:

$$\tau_{Ave} = T/(2tA_i) \tag{3.63}$$

The angle of twist is determined by using a relation involving the line integral as shown below:

$$\phi = \frac{TL}{4A_i^2 G}\oint \frac{ds}{t} \tag{3.64}$$

PROBLEMS

3.1 A shaft is employed to transmit 850 W of power from an electric motor to an appliance. Determine the torque imposed on the shaft if the motor is operated at the angular velocity of 3,600 RPM.

3.2 A shaft with a circular cross section is twisted through an angle $\phi = 2.4°$. If the diameter of the shaft is 18 mm and its length is 1.5 m, determine the maximum shearing strain γ.

3.3 Determine the maximum shearing stress τ_{Max} for the conditions described in Problem 3.2 if the shaft is fabricated from steel.

3.4 A shaft with a circular cross section is subjected to a torque of 180 ft-lb. If the shaft's diameter is 1.00 in. and its length is 18 in., determine the maximum shearing stress τ_{Max}.

3.5 A shaft fabricated from 302 A stainless steel transmits 3.2 kW of power while rotating at an angular velocity of 1,180 RPM. Specify a standard size round for the diameter of the shaft, if a safety factor of 3.2 with respect to yielding is specified.

3.6 A hollow tube is employed in the design of a shaft to transmit 2.5 kW of power at 1,180 RPM with a safety factor of 3.0 with respect to yielding. Determine the outside diameter d_o of the tube if its wall thickness is 0.08 d_o. The tube is fabricated from 1020 HR steel.

3.7 Clearly a hollow tube is structurally more efficient than a solid rod as a shaft for transmitting power. Cite several reasons for the limited usage of tubes to transmit power in actual practice.

3.8 Determine the section modulus of a circular tube with an outside diameter of 100 mm and an inside diameter of 80 mm.

3.9 Determine the structural efficiency ***SE*** of the shaft described in Problem 3.8.

3.10 For the inclined surface, defined in the Fig. P3.10, determine the stresses τ_{nt} and σ_n on the inclined plane. The shear stress $\tau_{xy} = 9.3$ ksi and the angle $\theta = 32°$.

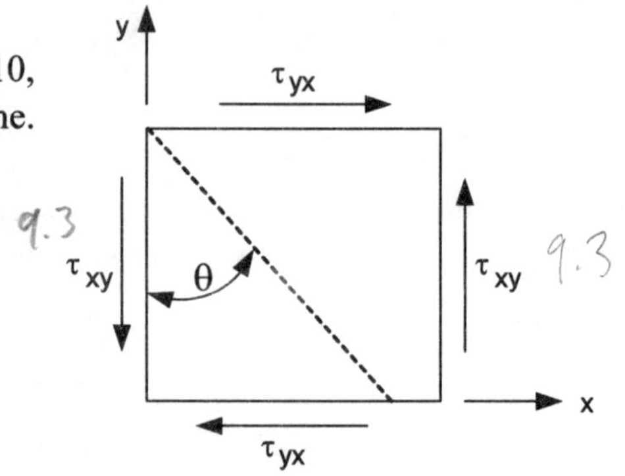

Fig. P3.10

3.11 For a stress $\tau_{xy} = 100$ MPa specified in Fig. P3.10, prepare a graph of τ_{nt} and σ_n as θ varies from zero to 360°. Define the principal planes and the planes on which the shear stress is a maximum.

3.12 A solid circular shaft with a diameter of 0.875 in. is transmitting 5.0 HP from an electric motor to an air compressor. If the motor is operating at 1,800 RPM, determine the maximum normal stress acting on the shaft. Also determine the plane upon which this maximum normal stress acts.

3.13 A steel shaft with a circular cross section is subjected to a torque of 240 ft-lb. If the shaft's diameter is 1.25 in. and its length is 11.0 in., determine its angle of twist ϕ.

3.14 A line shaft, shown in the Fig. P3.14, is fabricated from high-strength steel and incorporates five spur gears. The gear A provides the input torque T_A and gears B, C, D and E each remove torque from the shaft. Determine the angle of twist for the entire shaft AE and between gears at A and C. The shaft diameters and lengths are given in the table below. The torque at each gear is also listed in this table. Neglect the effect of gear deformation on the angle of twist. Also determine the maximum shear stress in the shaft. Where does this shear stress occur?

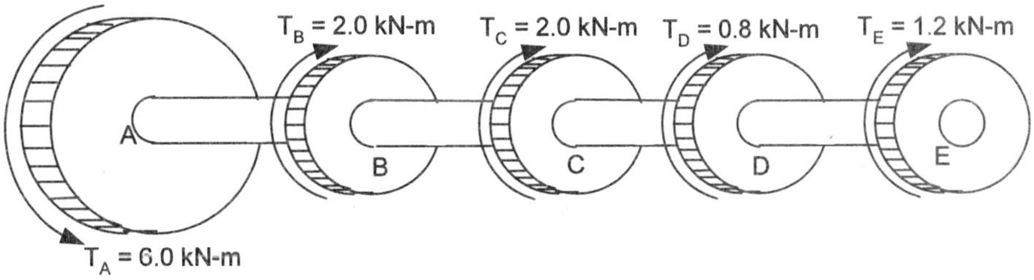

Fig. P3.14

Prob. No.	d_{A-B}	d_{B-C}	d_{C-D}	d_{D-E}	L_{A-B}	L_{B-C}	L_{C-D}	L_{D-E}
3.14	50 mm	40 mm	35 mm	32 mm	0.4 m	0.4 m	0.5 m	0.7 m

3.15 A line shaft, shown in Fig. P3.15, is fabricated from high-strength steel and incorporates five spur gears. The gears A and E provide input torques T_A and T_E. Gears B, C, and D each remove torque from the shaft. Determine the angle of twist for the entire shaft AE and between gears at A and C. The shaft diameters and lengths are given in the table below. The torque at each gear is also listed in this table. Neglect the effect of gear deformation on the angle of twist. Also determine the maximum shear stress in the shaft. Where does this shear stress occur?

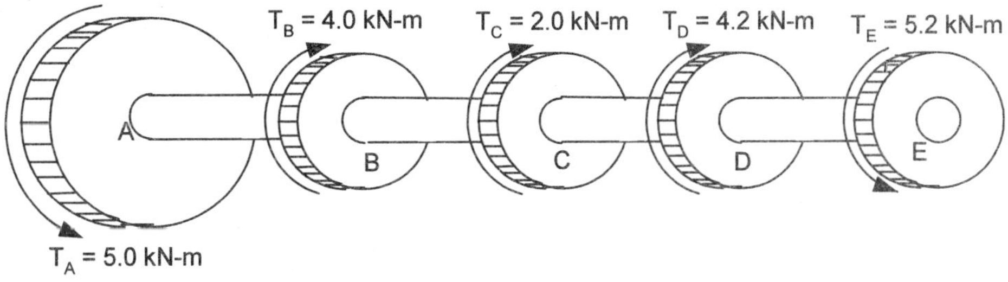

Fig. P3.15

Prob. No.	d_{A-B}	d_{B-C}	d_{C-D}	d_{D-E}	L_{A-B}	L_{B-C}	L_{C-D}	L_{D-E}
3.15	50 mm	40 mm	35 mm	30 mm	0.4 m	0.4 m	0.5 m	0.7 m

3.16 A steel torsion bar is incorporated into the chassis of an automobile to serve as a suspension spring. If the bar is fabricated from steel rod with a diameter of 14 mm and a length of 1.3 m, determine its spring rate. Also determine its angle of twist if it stores a strain energy of $\boldsymbol{E}$ = 5.0 N-m as the automobile traverses a bump.

3.17 The electric motor shown in Fig. P3.17 has a power rating of 5.0 kW and operates at 1,180 RPM. It powers a gear drive with a variable load, which sometimes requires the motor to operate at its maximum rating. The shaft is supported by two bearings — one on each side of the gear drive. The shaft from the motor has a diameter D. Select a material for the shaft and determine its diameter, if the maximum shear stress in the material is not to exceed 1/4 of the yield strength of the material in shear. Another constraint on the design is the angle of twist ϕ, which is not to exceed 3.0° measured from the motor to the gear drive.

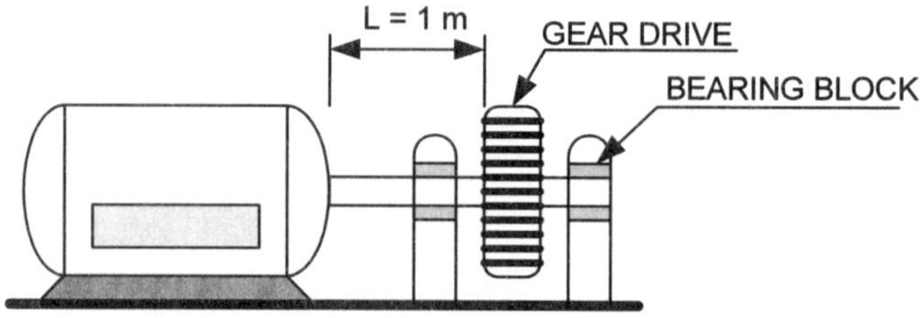

Fig. P3.17

3.18 The electric motor, shown in Fig. P3.18, has a power rating of 20.0 HP and operates at 1,780 RPM. It powers a drive shaft with three gears. When the motor is operating at rated capacity, gear A removes 1/2 of the power developed by the motor, while gear B and gear C remove 1/3 and 1/6 of the power, respectively. The shaft is supported by four bearings as shown in the figure. The shaft from the motor has a diameter D. If an alloy steel with a yield strength in shear of 150 ksi is used to fabricate the shaft, determine its diameter, if the maximum shear stress in the material is not to exceed 1/3 of the yield strength of the material in shear. Another constraint on the design is the angle of twist ϕ, which is not to exceed 4.4° measured from the motor to the gear C.

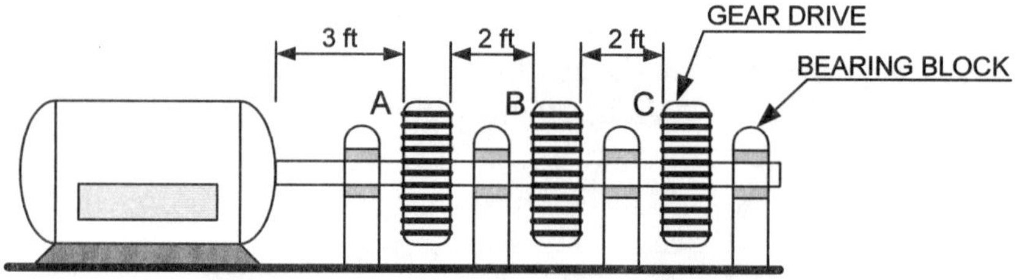

Fig. P3.18

3.19 A torque of 30 ft-lb is applied to a structural member with an elliptical cross section that is fabricated from steel. The length of the structural member is 6.2 ft. The height h of the ellipse is 1.5 in. and its depth b is 0.50 in. Determine the maximum shear stress and the angle of twist for this structural member.

3.20 A torque of 20 N-m is applied to a steel structural member with an equilateral triangle for its cross section. The length of the structural member is 750 mm. The equilateral triangle has a base b = 25 mm. Determine the maximum shear stress and the angle of twist for this structural member.

3.21 A torque of 45 ft-lb is applied to a steel structural member with a hexagon for its cross section. The length of the structural member is 5 ft. The inscribed diameter within the hexagon has a diameter of 1.00 in. Determine the maximum shear stress and the angle of twist for this structural member.

3.22 A torque of 1.2 kN-m is applied to a steel structural member with a square cross section. The length of the structural member is 2.0 m. The side of the square section measures 55 mm. Determine the maximum shear stress and the angle of twist for this structural member.

3.23 A torque of 120 ft-lb is applied to a steel structural member with an angle cross section. The length of the structural member is 7.5 ft. The sides of the angle are ¼ in. thick and 2.0 in. long. Determine the maximum shear stress and the angle of twist for this structural member.

3.24 A torque of 1.4 kN-m is applied to a steel structural member with a channel cross section. The length of the structural member is 3.5 m. The channel flange dimensions are 35 mm long by 6 mm thick and the channel web dimensions are 100 mm high by 4 mm thick. Determine the maximum shear stress and the angle of twist for this structural member.

3.25 Prove that the shear stress τ is zero at all four corners of a shaft with a square cross section that is subjected to a torque T.

3.26 Determine the eccentricity e locating the shear center for a beam fabricated from the channel section as shown in Fig. P3.26.

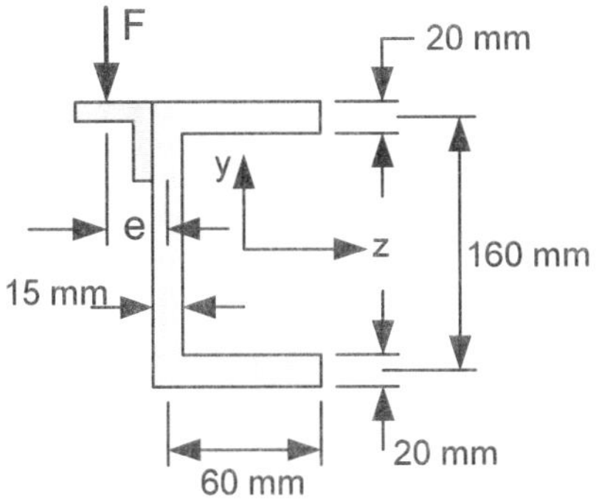

Fig. P3.26

3.27 For the channel section, illustrated in Fig. P3.26, show that integrating the parabolic distribution of shear stresses over the area of the web yields a shear force V equal to:

$$V = F\left[\frac{2ct_1 + (3/5)ht_2}{2ct_1 + (2/3)ht_2}\right]$$

Explain why V is slightly less than F. Hint: the shear stress at the top of the web is given by:

$$\tau = F\left[\frac{ct_1 h}{t_2 I_z}\right]$$

3.28 A square hollow tube with the dimensions shown in Fig. P3.28 is subjected to a torque of 4 kN-m. If the tube is fabricated from steel with a uniform wall thickness and is 1.25 m long, determine the average shear stress and the angle of twist.

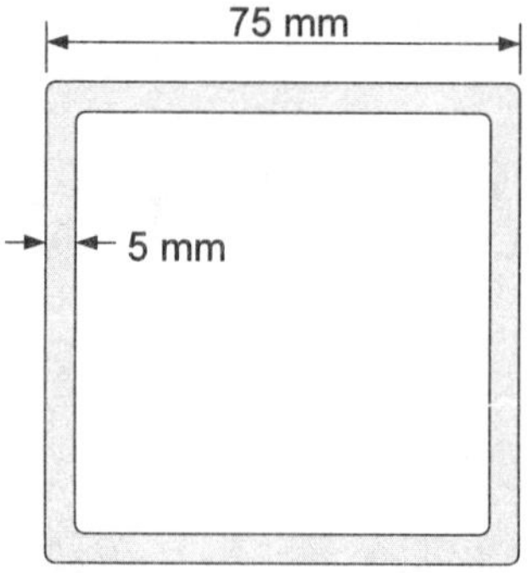

Fig. P3.28

3.29 A rectangular hollow tube, with the dimensions shown in Fig. P3.29, is subjected to a torque of 12,000 in.-lb. If the tube is fabricated from steel and is 10 ft long, determine the maximum value of the average shear stress and the angle of twist. Note that the wall thickness is not uniform.

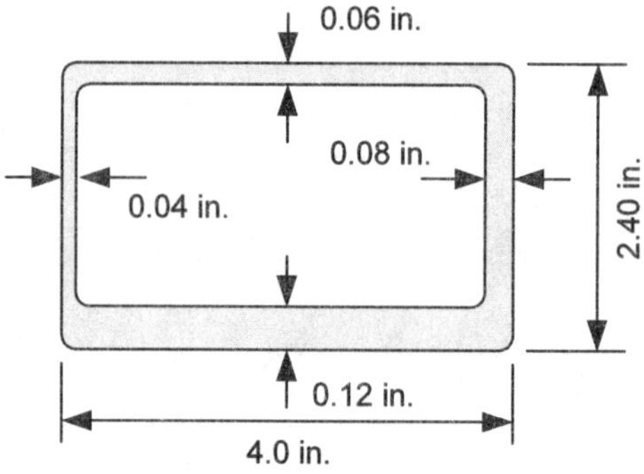

Fig. P3.29

3.30 An irregular shaped hollow tube, with the dimensions shown in Fig. P3.30, is subjected to a torque of 2.5 kN-m. If the tube is fabricated from steel and is 3 m long, determine the maximum value of the average shear stress and the angle of twist. Note that the wall thickness of the vertical sides is 6.0 mm and the thickness of the horizontal sides is 4.0 mm.

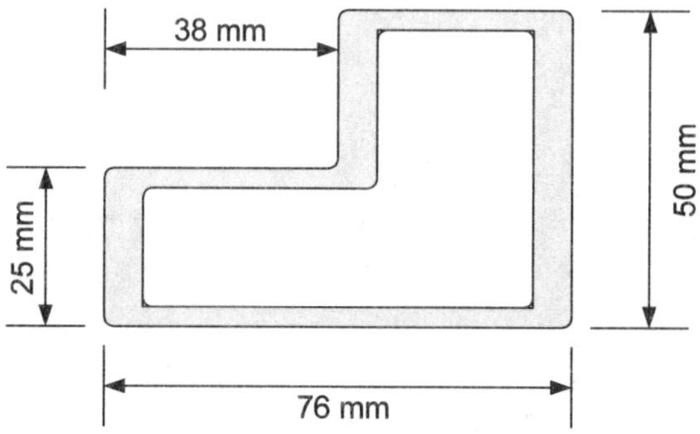

Fig. P3.30

3.31 An hollow tube extruded with the shape of an equilateral triangle is shown in Fig. P3.31. Its base is 2.0 in. long and its wall thickness is 0.125 in. The tube is subjected to a torque of 8,000 in.-lb. If the tube is fabricated from aluminum and is 52 in. long, determine the maximum value of the average shear stress and the angle of twist.

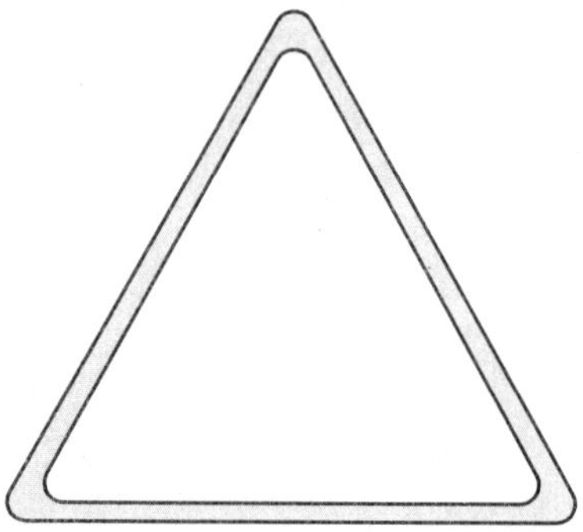

Fig. P3.31

CHAPTER 4

STRESSES IN BEAMS

4.1 INTRODUCTION

A beam is similar to a rod because both have the same geometry — long and slender. However, the beam is loaded differently. A rod is subjected to tensile or compressive forces applied in its axial direction. A beam is subjected to transverse forces applied in a perpendicular direction to its longitudinal axis. The difference in the loading is depicted in Fig. 4.1.

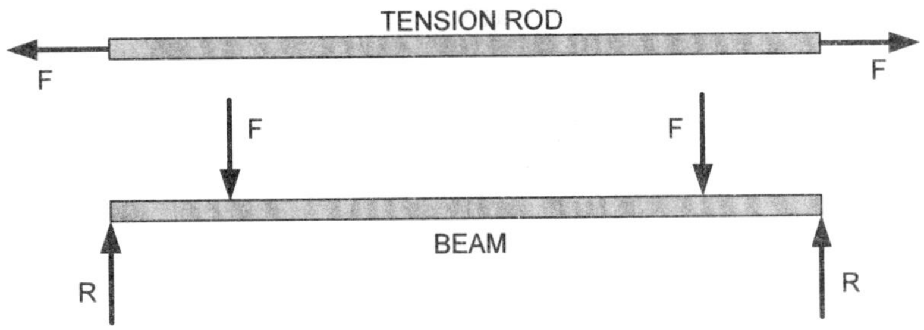

Fig. 4.1 Both the rod and beam are fabricated from long, thin members, but the direction of the applied external loads is different.

Beams are common elements that appear in many engineering designs. Examples of structures that contain beams are floor and roof supports in buildings, decks in highway bridges, frames in automobiles, and wings on airplanes. In each application, engineers must be certain that the stresses and deformations are kept below critical limits to prevent failure and ensure safety for occupants. The loads that produce these stresses and deformations can be broadly classified into two categories: (1) pure bending, and (2) transverse bending. Both of these loading cases will be addressed in this chapter.

4.2 INTERNAL LOADS IN BEAMS

Before considering stresses and deformations, we must first understand the internal loads that exist inside beams. Bending moments and shear forces are induced in beams when they are subjected to transverse forces. In structures, the most significant loads are usually due to gravitational forces although in machine components the loading is due to a number of different effects and gravitational forces are often negligible. It is important, when modeling a beam, to consider both the various types of loading and supports for the beam. Typical examples of different loads and supports for the beams are illustrated in Fig. 4.2.

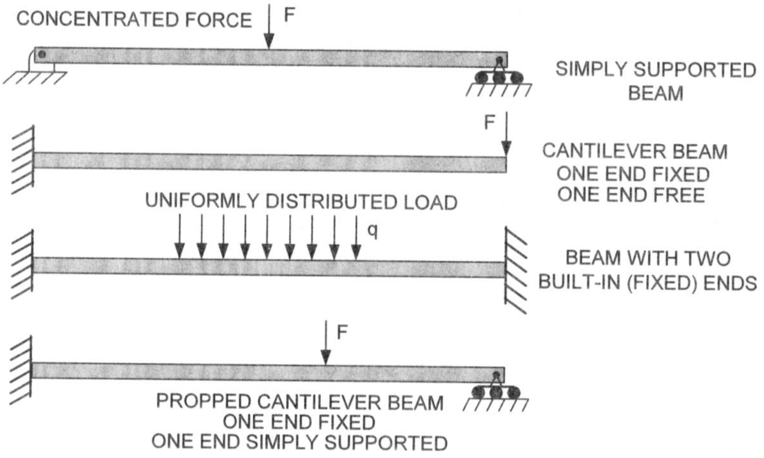

Fig. 4.2 Various types of transverse loading and supports for beams.

4.2.1 Shear and Bending Moments in Beams

Let's begin by considering the simply supported beam with a single concentrated force F as illustrated in Fig. 4.2. How does a concentrated force develop a moment? Where is the moment arm? We answer these questions by drawing several FBDs of the beam as shown in Fig. 4.3. In Fig. 4.3a, a simply supported beam of length L with a concentrated force F applied a distance, a, from the left end is shown. A FBD of the entire beam, in Fig. 4.3b, shows the supports replaced with reaction forces R_L and R_R. When the beam deforms, its ends are free to rotate over the simple supports (the pin at A or the rollers at B); consequently the moment M = 0 at both ends of the beam.

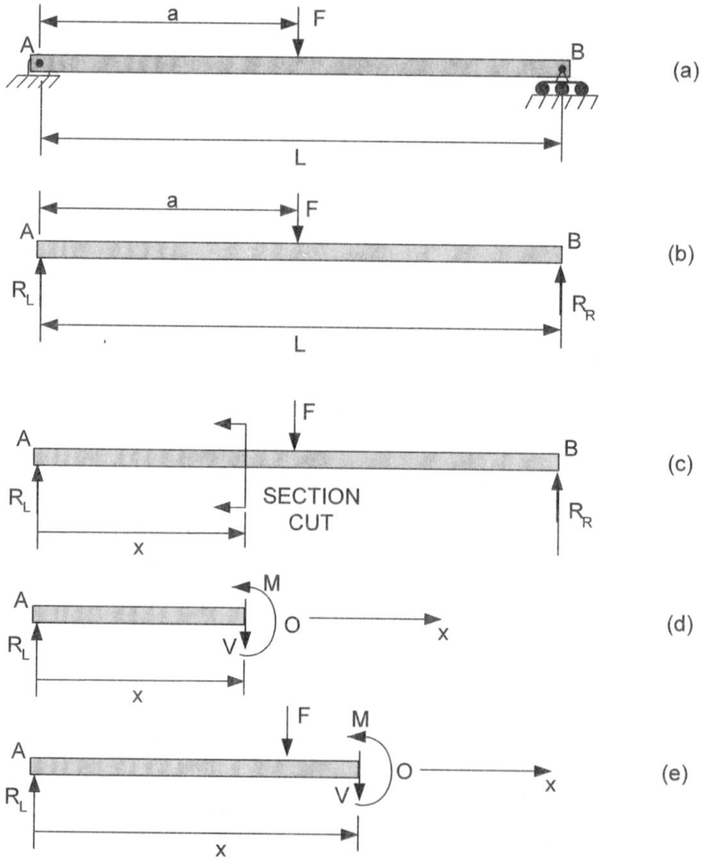

Fig. 4.3 FBDs of a simply supported beam with a concentrated load F.

We use the equilibrium equations to solve for the reaction forces R_L and R_R.

$$\Sigma M_A = R_R\, L - F\, a = 0$$

$$R_R = F\, a/L \qquad \text{(a)}$$

$$\Sigma F_y = R_L + R_R - F = 0 \qquad \text{(b)}$$

Substituting Eq. (a) into Eq. (b) gives:

$$R_L = F - R_R = F - F\, a/L = F[(L - a)/L] = F\, c/L \qquad \text{(c)}$$

where $c = L - a$

Next, we make a section cut a distance x from the left end of the beam where $0 < x < a$ as shown in Fig. 4.3c. The left side of the beam is removed as a free body. We apply a positive[1] internal shear force V and a positive internal moment M to the surface exposed by the section cut as indicated in Fig. 4.3d.

From the equilibrium equations, we write:

$$\Sigma F_y = R_L - V = Fc/L - V = 0$$

$$V = F\, c/L \quad \Rightarrow \quad 0 < x < a \qquad \text{(d)}$$

$$\Sigma M_O = M - R_L\, x = M - F\, x\, c/L = 0$$

$$M = F\, x\, c/L \quad \Rightarrow \quad 0 < x < a \qquad \text{(e)}$$

To determine the relations for the shear force V and the internal moment M for the remaining part of the beam, we consider the FBD shown in Fig. 4.3e and repeat the equilibrium analysis.

$$\Sigma F_y = R_L - F - V = F(L - a)/L - F - V = 0$$

$$V = -F\, a/L \quad \Rightarrow \quad a < x < L \qquad \text{(f)}$$

$$\Sigma M_O = M - R_L\, x + F(x - a) = M - F\, x(L - a)/L + F(x - a) = 0$$

$$M = F\, a(L - x)/L \quad \Rightarrow \quad a < x < L \qquad \text{(g)}$$

Note, Eqs. (f) and (g) are only valid for $a < x < L$, and Eqs. (d) and (e) only apply for $0 < x < a$.

[1] We consider the internal shear force to be positive when it acts downward in the negative y direction on the FBD of the left end of the beam.

Equations (d) and (f) give the shear force V and Eqs. (e) and (g) give the internal moment M as a function of position x along the length of the beam. Examination of Eqs (e) and (g) shows that the maximum moment occurs at the load point x = a. Accordingly, we write:

$$M_{Max} = F\,a\,c/L \tag{4.1}$$

where c = L – a.

4.2.2 Shear and Bending Moment Diagrams

The equations for the shear force V and the bending moment M are often represented with diagrams that show the distribution of both of these quantities over the length of the beam. The diagrams are simply graphs of the equations developed by an analysis of the appropriate free bodies. An example of the shear and bending moment diagrams for the beam loaded with a single concentrated force F is presented Fig. 4.4.

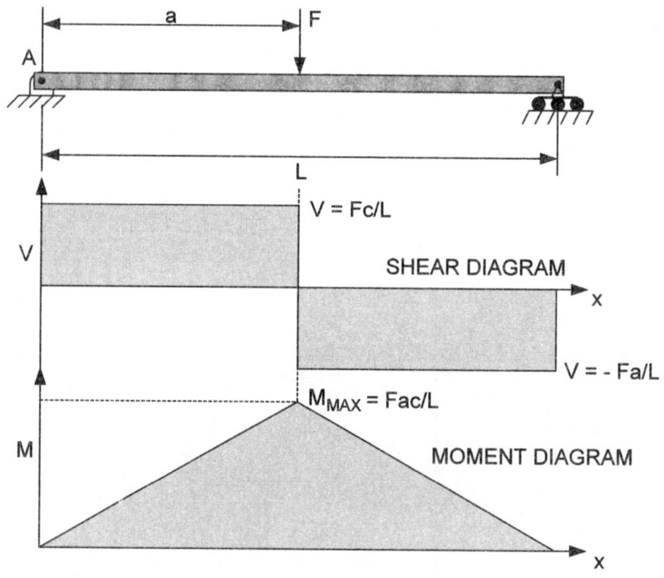

Fig. 4.4 Shear and bending moment diagrams show the distribution of V and M with x.

Shear and bending moment diagrams are useful for two reasons. First, they aid in the visualization of the distribution of the shear force V and the bending moment M inside beams. Second, we employ these diagrams to graphically determine the maximum moment and shear force, which are then used to calculate the maximum normal and shear stresses in the beam. Table 4.1 below shows the relationship among the loading condition and the lines or curves used in representing the shear and bending moment diagrams.

Let's consider several examples demonstrating graphical and analytical methods for determining the shear and moment diagrams.

Table 4.1
Relationships among the loading conditions and the shear and bending moment diagrams

TYPE OF LOAD	SHEAR DIAGRAM	MOMENT DIAGRAM
NO LOAD	HORIZONTAL	OR RAMP
CONCENTRATED LOAD	OR VERTICAL JUMP	OR SLOPE CHANGE
UNIFORMLY DISTRIBUTED LOAD	OR RAMP	OR PARABOLA
LINEARLY DISTRIBUTED LOAD	OR 2nd DEGREE CURVE	OR 3rd DEGREE CURVE
CONCENTRATED MOMENT	HORIZONTAL	CCW OR CW VERTICAL JUMP

EXAMPLE 4.1

For the simply supported beam loaded as indicated in Fig. E4.1, construct the shear and bending moment diagrams using the graphical approach.

Fig. E4.1

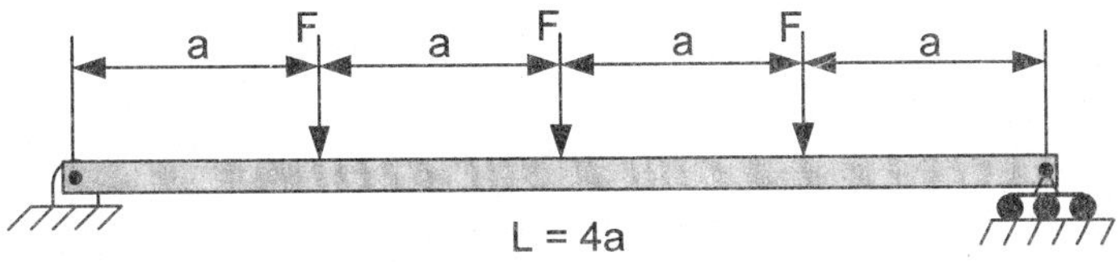

Solution:

The simply supported beam is symmetric; hence it is evident by inspection that:

$$R_L = R_R = 3F/2 \qquad (a)$$

We construct the FBD of the beam and then draw the shear diagram as shown in Fig. E4.1a:

Fig. E4.1a

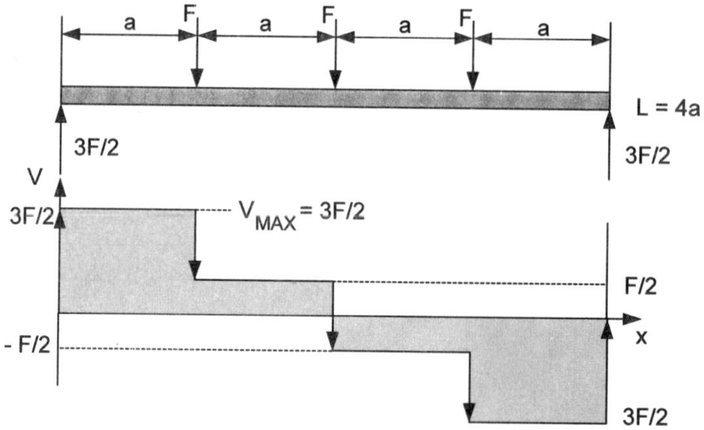

To construct the shear diagram, begin at the left end of the beam at the origin of the V – x axes. Because the left hand reaction is upward and equal to 3F/2, we draw a line along the positive V axis (upward) scaled to a length proportional to 3F/2. Move to the right on the beam (the positive x direction) and observe the beam is free of loads until x = a. This observation means the shear force is constant from $0 < x < a$. At x = a, we encounter a concentrated force F which is directed downward. Because F is downward, we decrease the shear force by $\Delta V = -F$ so that $V = 3F/2 - F = F/2$, as shown in the shear diagram.

We proceed without change in the shear force until x = 2a where we again encounter another concentrated force of magnitude F. As before, we decrease V by this amount so that $V = F/2 - F = -F/2$. We continue to increase x without change in the shear force until x = 3a where another concentrated force of magnitude F is encountered. As before, we decrease V by this amount so that $V = -F/2 - F = -3F/2$.

We continue to increase x without change in the shear force until x = 4a = L where we encounter the right hand reaction $R_R = 3F/2$ that is directed upward. Because the force is directed upward, we increase V by this amount so that $V = -3F/2 + 3F/2 = 0$. It is evident by the construction demonstrated that concentrated forces produce step changes in the shear diagram. Constructing the shear diagram in this example consists of drawing straight-line segments and adding or subtracting the concentrated forces to or from the shear force.

To construct the moment diagram, we make use of a relation between the shear forces and bending moments[2], namely:

$$dM/dx = V \tag{4.2}$$

From Eq. (4.2), it is clear that the slope of the moment diagram at any position x is equal to the value of the shear force V at that same position. Integrating Eq. (4.2), we obtain:

$$M_{x_2} - M_{x_1} = \int_{x_1}^{x_2} V dx \tag{4.3}$$

Equation (4.3) shows that $\Delta M_{x1 \text{ to } x2}$ is equal to the area under the V–x diagram from x_1 to x_2. For the shear diagram in this example, the areas under the V – x diagram are simple

[2] We will defer the derivation of Eq. (4.2) until Section 4.6.1.

rectangles; hence, the integral $\int V dx$ between x_2 and x_1 is $V(x_2 - x_1)$. It is easy to draw the moment diagram shown in Fig. E4.1b using the shear diagram as a guide.

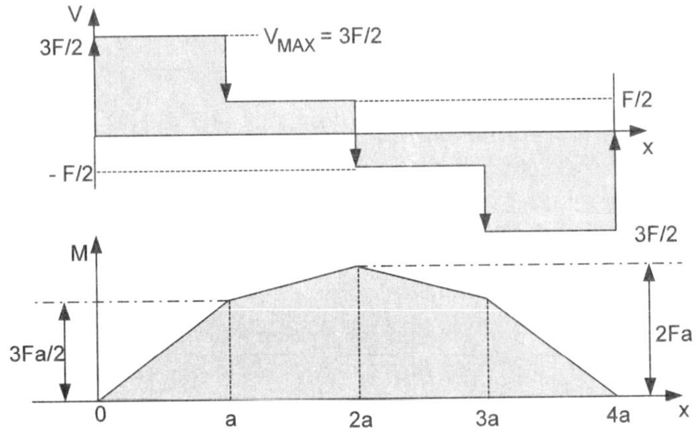

Fig. E4.1b

The area of the first rectangle between x = 0 and x = a is 3Fa/2. Because the area of the rectangle increases linearly with position x, we draw a straight line on the M – x diagram from the origin to the point with coordinates x = a, M = 3Fa/2. The area of the next rectangle from a < x < 2a is Fa/2. We add this area to the existing moment to obtain 3Fa/2 + Fa/2 = 2Fa. Again we draw a straight line on the M – x diagram from the point (a, 3Fa/2) to the next point with coordinates x = 2a, M = 2Fa. We may construct the remainder of the moment diagram by repeating the procedure. Note that the next two areas on the V-x diagram lie below the axis and are negative. These areas cause the M-x diagram to decrease and return to zero at x = 4a. The beam is symmetric; consequently, the moment diagram is also symmetric[3].

EXAMPLE 4.2

For the simply supported beam with a uniformly distributed load of magnitude q, shown in Fig. E4.2, write the equations for the internal shear force V and the moment M as functions of position x. Also construct the shear and bending moment diagrams.

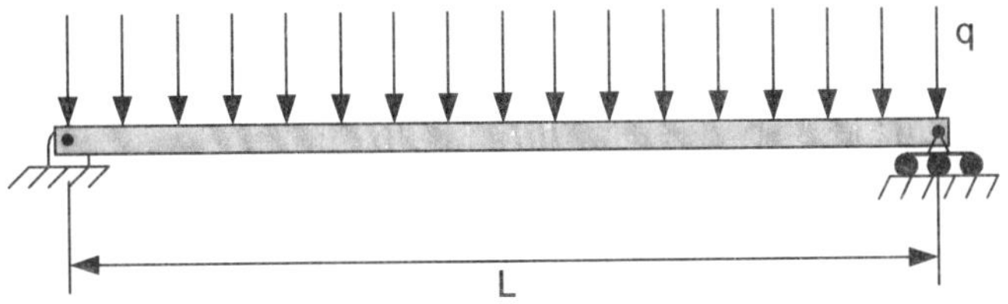

Fig. E4.2

Solution:

The beam is symmetric so that the reactions R_L and R_R are equal. In addition, the total force in the negative y direction is F = qL; therefore, it is evident that

[3] The shear diagram is also symmetric with respect to the magnitude of V, but the signs of the shear forces are not symmetric.

$$R_L = R_R = qL/2 \qquad \text{(a)}$$

Let's make a section cut at some arbitrary position x and construct a FBD of the left side of the beam as shown in Fig. E4.2a and b.

Fig. E4.2a-c

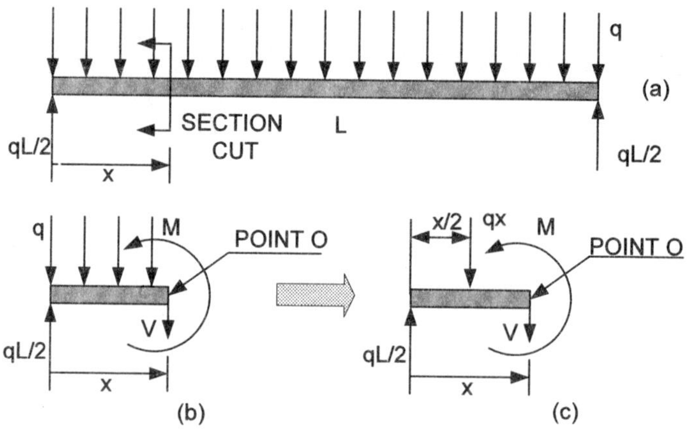

The FBD of the left side of the beam is shown with a uniformly distributed load acting over a length x of the beam segment. We replace this uniformly distributed load with an equivalent concentrated force $F_{eq} = qx$ located at the center of the segment as shown in Fig. E4.2c. Next, we apply the equilibrium equations and write:

$$\Sigma F_y = qL/2 - qx - V = 0$$

$$V = (q/2)(L - 2x) \quad \Rightarrow \quad 0 < x < L \qquad \text{(b)}$$

$$\Sigma M_O = M + qx(x/2) - (qL/2)x = 0$$

$$M_x = (qx/2)(L - x) \quad \Rightarrow \quad 0 < x < L \qquad \text{(c)}$$

Inspection of Eq. (b) shows that V = 0 at x = L/2. This zero crossing of the shear force on the V – x diagram locates the position of the maximum moment. Solving for M_{Max} at x = L/2 using Eq. (c) gives:

$$M_{Max} = qL^2/8 \qquad \text{(d)}$$

We may construct graphs of Eqs. (b) and (c) showing V and M as a function of position along the length of the beam to produce the shear and moment diagrams. Alternatively we may construct them directly from the transverse forces applied to the beam as shown below.

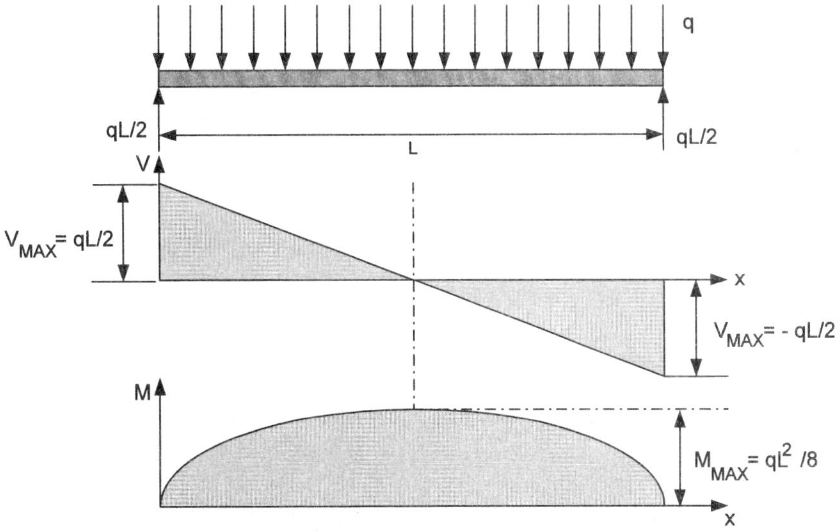

Fig. E4.2d

EXAMPLE 4.3

For the cantilever beam with a concentrated force F at its free end, shown in Fig. E4.3, write the equations for the internal shear force V and the moment M, and construct the shear and bending moment diagrams.

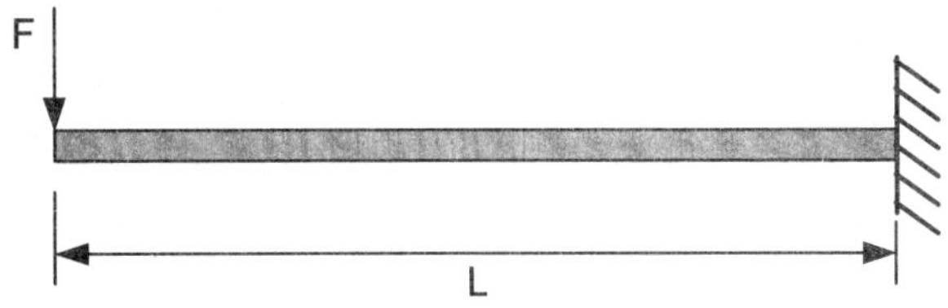

Fig. E4.3

Solution:

Let's begin by removing the built-in end and replacing it with a shear force V_{FE} and a moment M_{FE} when constructing the FBD of the cantilever beam as shown in Fig. E4.3a:

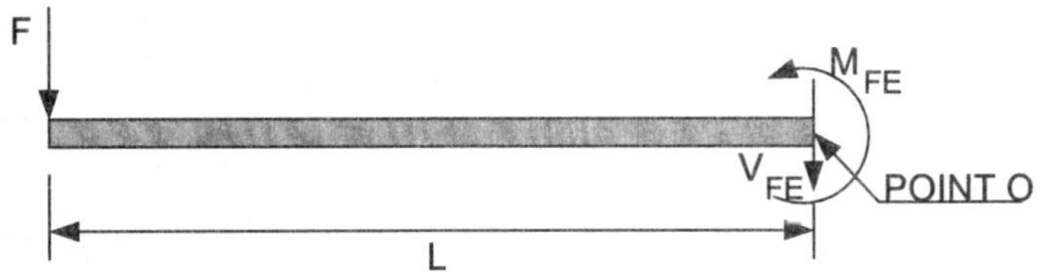

Fig. E4.3a

From the equilibrium equations, we write:

$$\Sigma F_y = -F - V_{FE} = 0$$

$$V_{FE} = -F \qquad \text{(a)}$$

$$\Sigma M_O = M_{FE} + FL = 0$$

$$M_{FE} = -FL \qquad \text{(b)}$$

The negative signs for V_{FE} and M_{FE} imply that the directions shown in the FBD are not correct. We change the directions in the FBD shown in Fig. E4.3b.

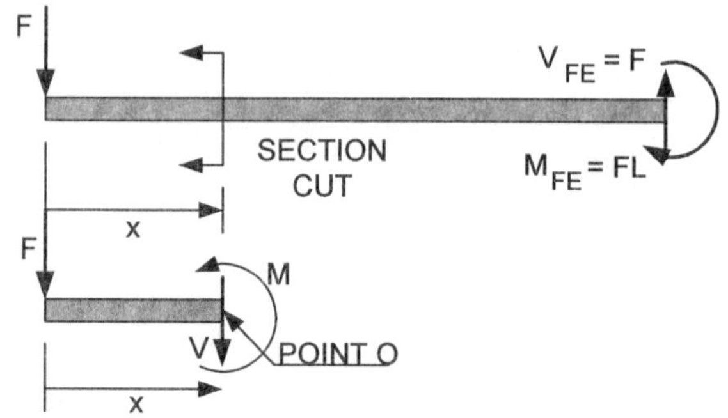

Fig. E4.3b

Next, we make a section cut at position x and remove the left side of the cantilever beam as a free body. Again, we write the equilibrium equations to obtain.

$$\Sigma F_y = -F - V = 0; \quad \Rightarrow \quad V = -F \qquad \text{(c)}$$

$$\Sigma M = M + Fx = 0; \quad \Rightarrow \quad M = -Fx \qquad \text{(d)}$$

The shear and moment diagrams are constructed by using Eq. (c) and Eq. (d) or by drawing the diagrams directly from the knowledge of the distribution of forces over the length of the beam as indicated in Fig. E4.3c. The shear force, V is a constant along the entire length of the beam. The bending moment M increases linearly in x, starting at zero at the free end and reaching a maximum $M_{Max} = -FL$ at the fixed end.

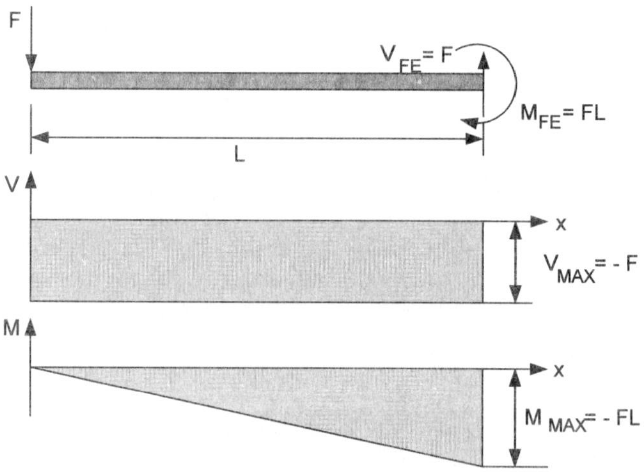

Fig. E4.3c

4.3 PURE BENDING OF SYMMETRIC BEAMS

Now that we understand the geometry and the loading of a beam, let's consider what the expression "pure" bending implies. A beam is in "pure" bending if it is subjected to a constant moment over its length. When a straight beam is subject to a constant moment, as illustrated in Fig. 4.5, it deforms into a circular arc with a radius of curvature ρ.

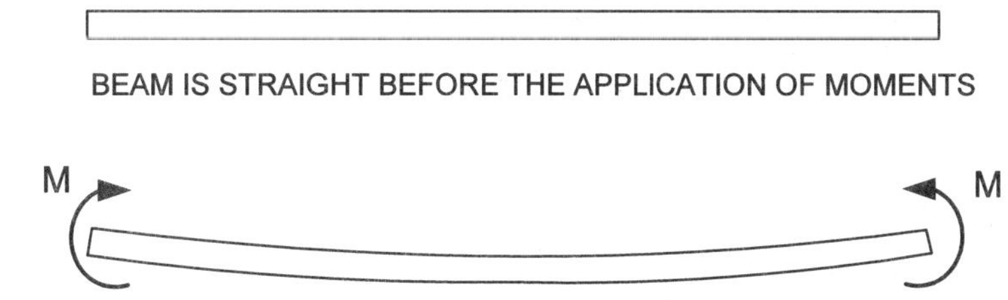

Fig. 4.5 A beam subjected to external moments M deforms into a circular arc with a radius ρ.

We limit our analysis to beams with symmetric cross sections. Several examples of symmetric cross sections are shown in Fig. 4.6. Clearly, the symmetry is only about the vertical direction (y-axis). The theory for beams in bending accommodates the lack of symmetry with respect to the horizontal direction (z-axis).

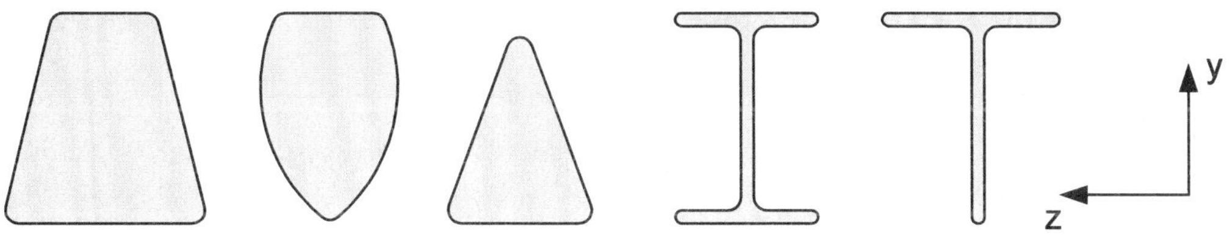

Fig. 4.6 Cross sectional areas of beams exhibiting symmetry about the vertical y-axis.

4.3.1 External Moments Produced by Internal Forces

Suppose we consider a beam with moments applied at its ends as shown in Fig. 4.5. Clearly, the entire beam is in equilibrium because the equilibrium equation $\Sigma M = 0$ is satisfied. The clockwise moment acting on the left end of the beam is equilibrated by the counterclockwise moment on the right end. Next, let's make a section cut at some position x along the length of the beam, as indicated in Fig. 4.7, and consider the left portion of the beam. In constructing this FBD, we must apply internal forces that will maintain equilibrium of this portion of the beam. Equilibrium is achieved by placing two equal and opposite internal forces P that act normal to the surface of the cross sectional area exposed by the section cut. Because the internal forces are equal and opposite, the equilibrium equation $\Sigma F_x = 0$ is satisfied. The equation of equilibrium for the moments is satisfied if:

$$\Sigma M = M - P\,d = 0$$

$$M = P\,d \qquad \text{(a)}$$

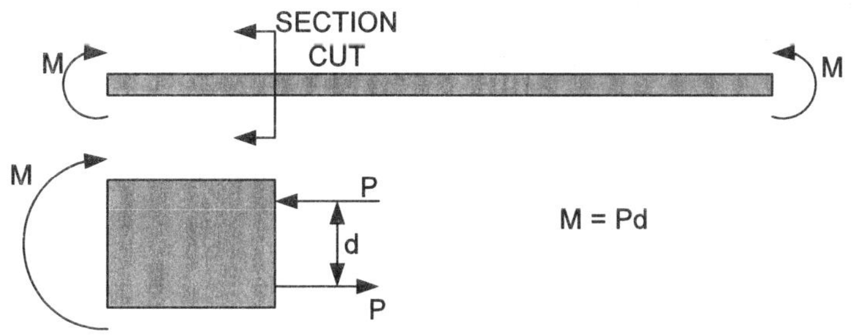

Fig. 4.7 The left-hand portion of the beam showing a couple M = (P)(d) acting on the area exposed by a section cut.

EXAMPLE 4.4

The concept of a pure moment acting on a beam may be difficult to comprehend. How can a pure moment be generated in a beam?

Solution:

We produce moments by applying forces to a member or component in such a way that the forces create a moment. For instance, we pull with a force F on a wrench with a length d to create a moment (torque) on a bolt to screw it into a joint by overcoming resistance to the bolt's rotational motion. A method for producing a pure moment on a beam is to apply two forces to a simply supported beam in what is referred to as a **four-point bend configuration**, as illustrated in Fig. E4.4.

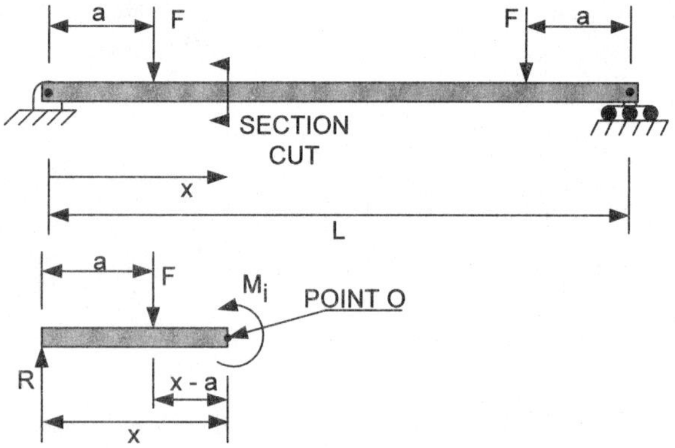

Fig. E4.4

To show that this arrangement of externally applied forces produce a pure moment, we make a section cut at position x, remove the left end of the beam, and construct a FBD. Let's apply the equilibrium equations to this FBD and write:

$$\Sigma F_y = R - F = 0, \qquad \Rightarrow \qquad R = F \qquad \text{(a)}$$

Next, consider moments about point O, and write:

$$\Sigma M_O = -Rx + F(x - a) + M_i = 0 \qquad \text{for } a < x < (L - a)$$

$$M_i = Fa \qquad \text{(b)}$$

where the subscript i refers to an internal moment produced by internal forces.

It is evident that only the moment M_i acts anywhere along the central segment of the beam. For the segment of the beam defined by $a < x < (L - a)$, we have a state of pure bending. No shear force V exists on this section and the net normal force in the x direction is zero.

4.3.2 Stress Distributions

We have used the concept of equilibrium to establish that equal and opposite internal forces P act on the surface exposed by the section cut. The forces produce an internal couple, M_i = (P)(d) that counteracts the externally applied moment M. However, at this stage in the analysis, we cannot determine the individual values of either P or d, although we know the direction of the forces. We need to introduce the concept of **stress distributions** to continue the analysis.

The internal forces P are due to normal stresses σ_x, which act over the surface of the exposed cross sectional area. Clearly, the upper most force in Fig. 4.7 is compressive because it presses against the surface exposed by the section cut. Similarly, the lower force is tensile. We are concerned with the distribution of the normal stresses that produce these two forces. Several possible stress distributions are suggested in Fig. 4.8.

The distributions of normal stresses presented in Fig. 4.8 produce equal and opposite internal forces P separated by some distance d. Accordingly, each distribution satisfies the equilibrium equations. However, which (if any) of the three possibilities is correct? We have exhausted the equilibrium principle, and to continue it is necessary to consider the deformation of the beam when it bends. To begin this second phase of the analysis, let's make an assumption about the geometry of the beam in its deformed state.

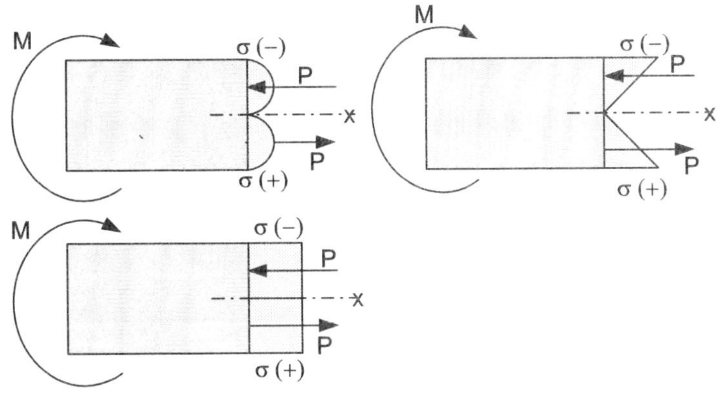

Fig. 4.8 Possible distributions of stress σ_x acting on an internal surface producing the couple M = P d.

4.4 DEFORMATION OF A BEAM IN PURE BENDING

When a beam is subjected to a moment as shown in Fig. 4.5, it bends into a circular arc. Parallel vertical lines scribed on the sides of the beam remain straight after the beam undergoes deformation from a straight member to one with curvature. We show a segment of the beam before and after deformation into a circular arc in Fig. 4.9.

The geometry of the deformed segment of the beam is extremely important. The circular arc is centered at point O. The lines A – A and B – B are straight and radial. They have each rotated about axes perpendicular to the plane of bending, and their extensions intersect at the center of curvature to form an angle θ. In addition to the lines A – A and B – B remaining straight, the transverse sections of the beam, originally plane, remain plane after bending.

The dotted line C – D is exactly the same length as it was before deformation. This line defines what is known as the **neutral axis**. The radius of curvature ρ of the circular arc is the distance from the center of curvature O to the neutral axis (the arc C – D). Lines (arcs) above the neutral axis, become shorter after deformation and lines (arcs) below the neutral axis, such as E – F, become longer. These changes in the length of lines (arcs) above and below the neutral axis result in longitudinal strain. The strains are compressive (negative) above the neutral axis when the beam has a positive curvature[4] as illustrated in Fig. 4.9. Similarly, the strains are tensile (positive) below the neutral axis when the beam has a positive curvature.

---

[4] We define positive curvature of the beam in two ways. The curvature is positive if the beam bends so it will hold water (concave upward). The curvature is positive if the internal moment acting on the section under consideration is positive.

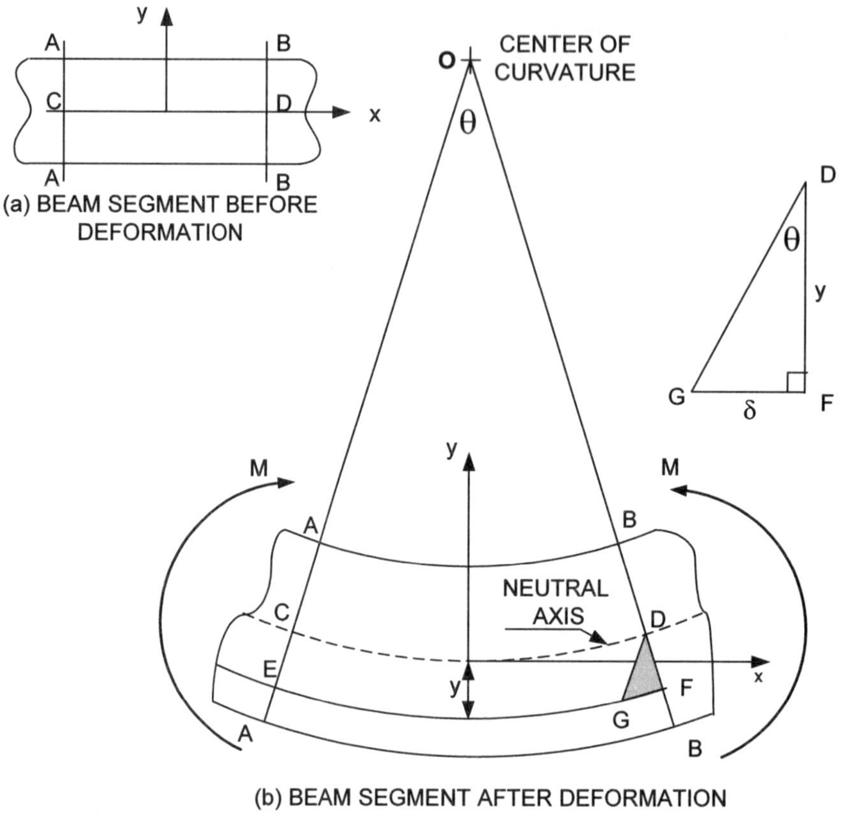

Fig. 4.9 Plane sections A – A and B – B of the beam remain plane after deformation. Note the line D-G is parallel to the line A-A.

4.4.1 Strains in Beams with a Constant Radius of Curvature

Let's determine the magnitude of the strains by examining the changes in the length of line E – F in Fig. 4.9. Clearly, the line E - F is lengthened in the deformation process. The distance GF in Fig. 4.9b shows the increase in the length, δ, of line E - F. Note that we constructed line D - G parallel to line A – A to produce the shaded triangle in Fig. 4.9b. Recall Eq. (2.3) and write:

$$\varepsilon = \delta/L = GF/EG \qquad \text{(a)}$$

The similarity of triangle COD and the triangle GDF, shown in the inset of Fig. 4.9b, enables us to write:

$$CD = EG = \rho\theta; \qquad GF = -\,y\theta \qquad \text{(b)}$$

$$GF/EG = -\,y\theta/\rho\theta = -\,y/\rho \qquad \text{(c)}$$

Combining Eqs. (a) and (c) yields:

$$\varepsilon = -\,y/\rho \qquad (4.4)$$

where y is the distance from the neutral axis (CD) to the fiber in question (EF).

Note, the strain ε is a **linear function** of the position y. The strain is a minimum (zero) at the neutral axis and a maximum when y locates either the top or bottom fiber of the beam. If we consider a beam with a rectangular cross section and define its height as h, then $y_{max} = -h/2$ and from Eq. (4.4), it is evident that:

$$\varepsilon_{Max} = h/(2\rho) \qquad (4.5)$$

The sign of the maximum strain is positive (tensile) for fibers along the bottom surface of the beam if the curvature is positive.

EXAMPLE 4.5

A thin strip of metal 1.50 mm thick and 12.0 mm wide is wrapped about a mandrel with a radius of 250 mm. Determine the maximum bending strain produced in the strip. Assume that the neutral axis is in the center of the cross sectional area as shown below:

Fig. E4.5

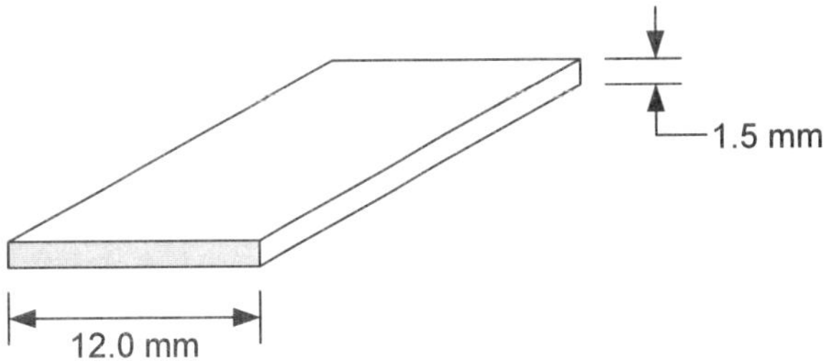

Solution:

From Eq. (4.5), we write:

$$\varepsilon_{Max} = y_{max}/\rho = h/(2\rho) = 1.5/[(2)(250.75)] = 0.002991$$

While this is a very simple example, you should note that we have determined a strain for a beam in bending without employing the elastic constants for the material. Indeed, we did not even specify the metal employed in fabricating the strip in the problem statement. Strain is a geometric quantity (a change in length over original length). If we know the geometry before and after deformation, strain can be determined without knowledge of either the loads or the material properties.

4.4.2 Stresses in Beams

It is easy to convert the strains in the beam to stresses if we recall Hooke's Law — Eq. (2.5). The longitudinal fibers in the beam are subjected to a uniaxial state of stress with fibers on the convex side of the neutral axis in tension and those on the concave side in compression. By combining Eqs. (4.4) and (2.5), we obtain:

$$\sigma = E\varepsilon = -yE/\rho \qquad (4.6)$$

Examination of Eq. (4.6) indicates that the normal stress σ is **linearly distributed** with respect to y, exhibits a minimum of zero at the neutral axis where y = 0, and a reaches maximum at the outer fibers in the beam where y is a maximum.

The fact that the stresses are not uniformly distributed has significant implications regarding the design of the cross section of the beam. We will discuss this important design consideration in much more detail in Section 4.5.

4.4.3 Locating the Neutral Axis

The results in Eq. (4.6) may be used to calculate the stress on a beam if we know the material from which it is fabricated, the location of its neutral axis and its radius of curvature. However, in most cases we have knowledge of the applied external forces — not the radius of curvature. Also, we have not yet established the location of the neutral axis relative to the cross section of the beam.

To establish the position of the neutral axis of the beam, let's consider the portion of the beam shown in Fig. 4.10 as a free body. Writing the equilibrium relation $\Sigma F_x = 0$ and using Eq. (4.6) gives:

$$\Sigma F_x = \int \sigma \, dA = -\int (Ey/\rho) \, dA = -(E/\rho) \int y \, dA = 0 \qquad \text{(a)}$$

where A is the cross sectional area over which the stress σ is distributed.

Fig. 4.10 The normal stresses σ are linear in y for a beam in bending.

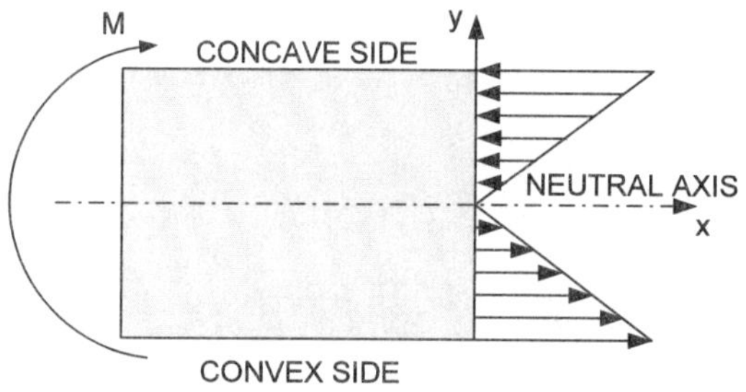

Because (E/ρ) cannot be zero when the beam is deformed, it is evident that:

$$\int y \, dA = Q_z = 0 \qquad (4.7)$$

where Q_z is the first moment of the area A of the cross section of the beam.

For equilibrium of the beam in the x direction to be satisfied, it is necessary that the position of the neutral axis be adjusted so that $Q_z = 0$. If the neutral axis passes through the centroid of the area of the transverse section of the beam, Eq. (4.7) is satisfied. For common cross section shapes such as circular, rectangular, I, H, wide-flange, etc., the location of the centroid is at the intersection of the two axes of symmetry.

4.4.4 The Relationship between Moment and Curvature

Now that a procedure has been presented for locating the neutral axis, it is necessary to develop an approach for determining the radius of curvature. The stresses σ are distributed, as shown in Fig. 4.10, so as to produce a moment M. We will use this fact in the following derivation. The moment produced by the force acting on an element dA, shown in Fig. 4.11, with respect to the neutral axis is:

$$dM = -\sigma\, dA\,(y) = -(-Ey/\rho)(dA)(y) = +(Ey/\rho)(dA)(y) \qquad (a)$$

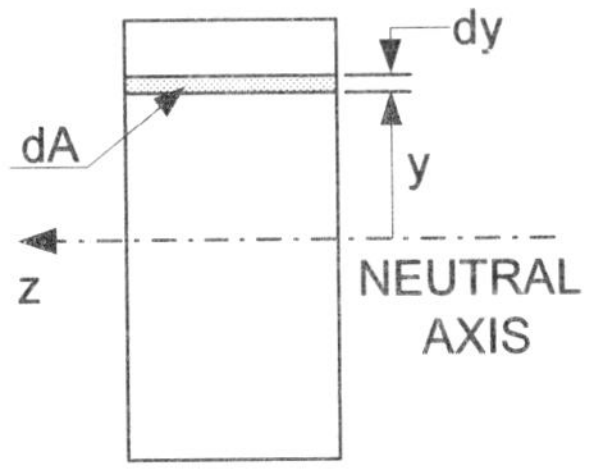

Fig. 4.11 Cross sectional area of a rectangular beam with elemental area dA.

Integrate Eq. (a) to obtain the internal moment M_i:

$$M_i = \int (Ey^2/\rho)\, dA = (E/\rho)\int y^2\, dA \qquad (b)$$

Recall that the second moment of the area A relative to the neutral axis I_z is given by:

$$I_z = \int y^2\, dA \qquad (c)$$

Combining Eqs. (b) and (c), and using the equilibrium relation $\Sigma M = 0$ gives:

$$M_i = (EI_z/\rho) = M \qquad (4.8)$$

$$\kappa = 1/\rho = M/(EI_z) \qquad (4.9)$$

where $\kappa = 1/\rho$ is the curvature of the beam and M is the moment.

From Eq. (4.9), it is evident that the curvature κ is directly proportional to the moment M and inversely proportional with the flexural rigidity (EI_z) of the beam. We have dropped the subscripts on the moments because it is understood that the internal moment produces the stress σ.

Finally, by substituting Eq. (4.9) into Eq. (4.6), the relationship between the applied moment and the internal stress distribution can be obtained:

$$\sigma = -My/I_z \qquad (4.10)$$

In Eq. (4.10), M is positive when the beam is deflected so that the convex side is on the bottom and y is positive in the upward direction. Equation (4.10) is considered to be one of the most important of the many equations employed by engineers when designing structures that contain beams, and as such it will become essential to you in the design of the structure involved in your design project.

4.4.5 Stresses in Beams with Rectangular Cross Sections

Consider a beam with a rectangular cross section as defined in Fig. 4.12. For a rectangular cross section, the neutral axis coincides with the horizontal axis of symmetry:

$$y_{Top} = h/2; \qquad y_{Bottom} = -h/2 \qquad (a)$$

Substituting Eq. (a) into Eq. (4.10) yields:

$$\sigma_{Max} = Mh/(2I_z) \quad \text{and} \quad \sigma_{Min} = -Mh/(2I_z) \qquad (4.11)$$

The tensile stress is a maximum when y is equal to – h/2, and the compressive stress is a maximum when y is equal to h/2. The tensile and compressive stresses are equal because the neutral axis for the rectangular section divides the section into two equal parts.

Fig. 4.12 Rectangular cross section of a beam with height h and width b.

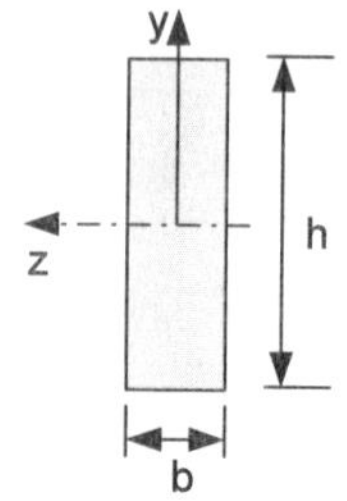

Let's define the **section modulus**, Z, for a symmetric cross section of arbitrary geometry as:

$$Z = I_z / c \tag{4.12a}$$

where c is the distance from the centroid to an outer fiber of the beam. For a rectangular cross section, c = h/2 and Eq. (4.12a) becomes:

$$Z = 2I_z/h \tag{4.12b}$$

Then, we may express the maximum and minimum normal stress σ as:

$$\sigma_{Max} = M/Z \qquad \text{and} \qquad \sigma_{Min} = -\,M/Z \tag{4.13}$$

For a rectangular cross section, the second moment of the area I_z and the section modulus are given by:

$$I_z = bh^3/12 \qquad \text{and} \qquad Z = bh^2/6 \tag{4.14}$$

We now have the relations necessary to determine the stresses in a beam subjected to internal moments that are constant along its length. Let's consider two examples to illustrate the procedure for determining the stresses in beams with rectangular cross sections.

EXAMPLE 4.6

Consider a beam with a rectangular section with h = 5.0 in. and b = 1.0 in. Determine the margin of safety for the beam if it is loaded with a moment of 9,000 ft-lb and fabricated from steel with a yield strength of 42,000 psi.

Solution:

Let's substitute Eq. (4.14) into Eq. (4.11) to determine the maximum stress.

$$\sigma_{Max} = Mh/(2I_z) = 12\ Mh/(2bh^3) = 6M/(bh^2) \tag{4.15}$$

$$\sigma_{Max} = [(6)(9{,}000)(12)]/[(1.0)(5.0)^2] = 25{,}920 \text{ psi} = \sigma_{Design}$$

Finally, the safety factor and the margin of safety are given by:

$$SF = S_y/\sigma_{Design} = 42{,}000/25{,}920 = 1.620; \qquad MOS = SF - 1 = 62.0\%$$

The margin of safety for this beam is relatively small and careful consideration should be given to reducing either the applied moment or to increasing the size of its cross section.

EXAMPLE 4.7

Consider a beam with a rectangular section with h = 400 mm and b = 100 mm. Determine the largest moment that can be applied to the beam if it is fabricated from steel with a yield strength of 300 MPa. The beam is to have a safety factor of 2.75.

Solution:

Determine the allowable design stress by considering the safety factor and the yield strength:

$$\sigma_{Design} = S_y/SF = (300)/(2.75) = 109.1 \text{ MPa} = \sigma_{Max} \qquad \text{(a)}$$

Rearrange Eq. (4.15) to solve for the moment as:

$$M = \sigma_{Max}(bh^2)/6 = (109.1)(100)(400)^2/(6) = 290.9 \times 10^6 \text{ N-mm} = 290.9 \text{ kN-m} \qquad \text{(b)}$$

In this solution, we used the fact that 1MPa = 1 N/mm^2. Alternatively, we could have obtained the same result by expressing the stress in Pa and all lengths in m.

4.5 PROPERTIES OF CROSS SECTIONS

If we examine the stress distribution shown in Fig. 4.10, it is clear that the beam is not an efficient structural component. Only the top and the bottom fibers of the beam are stressed to the maximum. The interior region of the beam is under utilized. Indeed, near the neutral axis the stresses approach zero. A beam with a rectangular cross section is extremely inefficient because the average magnitude of stress over the section is only $\sigma_{Max}/2$. The closer the average magnitude of stress is to the maximum stress, the more efficient will be the use of the cross sectional area of the beam.

To improve the effectiveness of beams, the under-stressed, central-region of the cross section, is removed to produce I beams and WF (wide-flange) shapes. A typical example of a more efficient section is shown in Fig. 4.13.

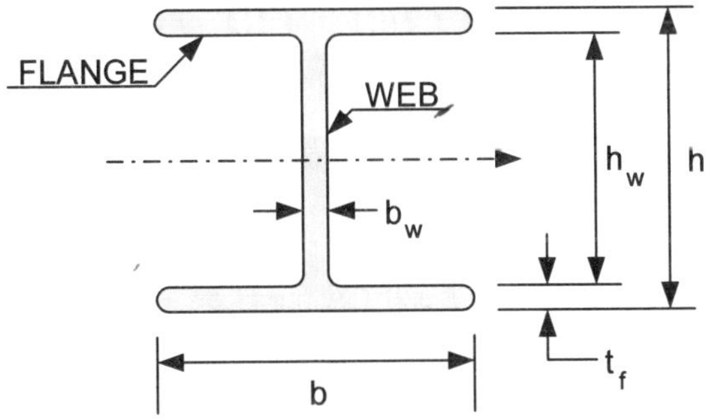

Fig. 4.13 Removing a large part of the under stressed material in a section of a beam increases its structural effectiveness.

For a beam section with a specified height h, we judge its structural effectiveness ***SE*** by the ratio of its section modulus to its cross sectional area.

$$\boldsymbol{SE} = Z/A \qquad (4.16)$$

The effectiveness of a beam with a rectangular cross section is determined by combining Eqs. (4.14) and (4.16):

$$\boldsymbol{SE} = bh^2/(6bh) = h/6 = 0.1667\ h \qquad (4.17)$$

For the wide flange section illustrated in Fig. 4.13, the relation for the effectiveness depends on several variables including b, h, b_w and h_w. To derive the relation for ***SE***, we begin by determining I_z as:

$$I_z = I_{web} + I_{flange} \qquad (a)$$

$$I_{web} = b_w\, h_w^{\,3}/12 \qquad (b)$$

$$I_{flange} = 2\left[\frac{1}{12}bt_f^3 + bt_f\left(\frac{h_w + t_f}{2}\right)^2\right] \qquad (c)$$

Using Eqs. (a), (b), (c) and (4.12b) to solve for Z gives:

$$Z = \frac{2I_z}{h} = \frac{1}{h}\left[\frac{b_w h_w^3}{6} + \frac{bt_f^3}{3} + bt_f(h_w + t_f)^2\right] \qquad (d)$$

The area of the wide flange section is given by:

$$A = 2bt_f + b_w h_w \qquad (e)$$

Substituting (d) and (e) into Eq. (4.16) yields:

$$\boldsymbol{SE} = \frac{1}{h(2bt_f + b_w h_w)}\left\{\frac{b_w h_w^3}{6} + \frac{bt_f^3}{3} + bt_f(h_w + t_f)^2\right\} \qquad (4.18)$$

The result in Eq. (4.18) involves many terms and the improvement in the effectiveness of the section is not apparent simply by inspecting this relation. To ascertain the benefits of removing the under-stressed material, let's consider Example 4.8.

EXAMPLE 4.8

If the wide flanged section is fabricated with the following geometry, determine the effectiveness of the section and compare it with the effectiveness of a rectangular section.

$b_w = 0.08\ b$; $\quad h_w = 0.76\ h$; $\quad$ then $\quad t_f = (1 - 0.76)(h/2) = 0.12\ h$

Solution:

Substituting these quantities into Eq. (4.18) yields:

$$\boldsymbol{SE} = \frac{1}{h[0.24bh + (0.08b)(0.76h)]}\left\{\frac{(0.08b)(0.76h)^3}{6} + \frac{b(0.12h)^3}{3} + b(0.12h)[0.76h + 0.12h]^2\right\}$$

Reducing this expression gives:

$$\boldsymbol{SE} = 0.3303\ h \qquad \text{(a)}$$

A comparison of this result with Eq. (4.17) indicates that the wide flanged section defined in this example with $\boldsymbol{SE}$ = 0.3303 h is about twice as efficient as the rectangular cross section with $\boldsymbol{SE}$ = 0.1667 h.

Determining I_z and Z for the various non-rectangular cross sections is a time consuming task. Fortunately, others have resolved this problem for us. The American Institute of Steel Construction (AISC) has prepared tables showing the properties of the commercially available sections. An abridged version of these tables is presented in Appendix D.

EXAMPLE 4.9

For the simply supported beam described in Fig. 4.4, determine the margin of safety if the beam and its loading are specified as:

- A wide flanged (WF) shape W 10 × 60
- F = 22 kip
- L = 20 ft
- a = 8 ft.
- The yield strength of the hot rolled steel beam is 42 ksi.

Solution:

The properties of the WF section are given in Appendix D as:

$$I_z = 341 \text{ in.}^4 \qquad Z = 66.7 \text{ in.}^3 \qquad \text{(a)}$$

The maximum moment occurs at x = a = 8 ft and is given by Eq. (4.1) as:

$$M_{Max} = F\ a\ c/L = (22 \times 10^3)(8)(20 - 8)/(20) = 105.6 \times 10^3 \text{ ft-lb} \qquad \text{(b)}$$

The maximum stress is given by Eq. (4.13) as:

$$\sigma_{Max} = M_{Max}/Z = [(105.6 \times 10^3)(12)]/(66.7) = 19.0 \text{ ksi} \qquad \text{(c)}$$

Finally, the margin of safety is given by:

$$MOS = SF - 1 = S_y/\sigma_{Max} - 1 = (42.0)/(19.0) - 1 = 1.21 \Rightarrow 121\% \qquad \text{(d)}$$

The margin of safety is probably adequate at 121% unless there is considerable uncertainty about the loading. The beam is hot rolled to a standard section shape — its geometry is well-established and not subject to significant error in fabrication. The yield strength is typical of low alloy steel and it will not usually vary by more than ± 10% from one shipment of steel to another.

EXAMPLE 4.10

For the simply supported beam with a uniformly distributed load described in Example 4.2, determine the margin of safety if the beam and its loading are specified as:

- A S8 × 23 American Standard shape
- $q = 1.2$ kip/ft
- $L = 15$ ft
- The yield strength of the steel from which the beam is hot rolled is 38 ksi.

Solution:

The properties of the American Standard section are given in Appendix D as:

$$I_z = 64.9 \text{ in.}^4 \qquad Z = 16.2 \text{ in.}^3 \tag{a}$$

The maximum moment occurs at $x = L/2 = (15)/2 = 7.5$ ft and is given by:

$$M_{Max} = qL^2/8 = (1.2 \times 10^3)(15)^2/(8) = 33{,}750 \text{ ft-lb} \tag{b}$$

The maximum stress is given by Eq. (4.13) as:

$$\sigma_{Max} = M_{Max}/Z = (33{,}750)(12)/(16.2) = 25.0 \text{ ksi} \tag{c}$$

Finally, the margin of safety is given by:

$$MOS = SF - 1 = S_y/\sigma_{Max} - 1 = (38.0)/(25.0) - 1 = 0.52 \Rightarrow 52\% \tag{d}$$

The margin of safety is probably somewhat low at about 52%. While the beam is hot rolled to a standard section shape (its geometry is well-established and not subject to error in fabrication), any significant over loading can endanger the stability of the structure. Consideration should be given to increasing the section size to an American Standard S10 × 25.4.

EXAMPLE 4.11

For the cantilever beam with a concentrated force F applied at its free end described in Example 4.3, determine the margin of safety if the beam and its loading are specified as:

- A WT 5 × 30 structural tee
- $F = 500$ lb
- $L = 12$ ft
- The yield strength of the steel is 44 ksi.

Solution:

The properties of the structural tee are given in Appendix D as:

$$I_z = 12.9 \text{ in.}^4 \qquad Z = 3.04 \text{ in.}^3 \qquad \text{(a)}$$

The maximum moment occurs at x = L = 12 ft and is given by:

$$M_{Max} = FL = (500)(12) = 6{,}000 \text{ ft-lb} \qquad \text{(b)}$$

The maximum stress is given by Eq. (4.13) as:

$$\sigma_{Max} = M_{Max}/Z = (6{,}000)(12)/(3.04) = 23.68 \text{ ksi} \qquad \text{(c)}$$

Finally, the margin of safety is given by:

$$MOS = SF - 1 = S_y/\sigma_{Max} - 1 = (44.0)/(23.68) - 1 = 0.8581 \Rightarrow 85.81\% \qquad \text{(d)}$$

It appears that the margin of safety is marginal given the specification for the beam and the loading. Consideration should be given to selection of a larger or heavier beam with a larger section modulus, such as WT5 × 44 or WT6 × 25.

4.6 TRANSVERSE BENDING OF SYMMETRIC BEAMS

In the previous two sections, we considered the case of pure bending and learned that a normal stress σ occurs in beams due to the internal bending moment, M. For the more general case of transverse bending, both a shear force (V) and bending moment (M) exist at each cross section along the beam. A normal stress σ again develops due to the bending moment, M, and a shear stress τ also develops due to the shear force, V. For long thin beams, the shear stress τ is generally small when compared to the normal stress σ and is usually ignored without compromising the safety of the structure. However, for short beams with significant height, shear stresses must be considered. Shear stresses are also important when the beams are fabricated from fibrous materials like wood, because the shear strength in the direction of the fibers is very low.

4.6.1 Shear Stresses in Beams

The transverse forces applied to beams produce internal shear forces in both horizontal and vertical directions (H and V respectively). These shear forces give rise to shear stresses τ_H and τ_V. Let's first establish the relationship between the internal bending moment M and the internal vertical shear force V. Consider a simply supported beam with a uniformly distributed load q as illustrated in Fig. 4.14a. We make two section cuts and remove the segment of the beam between these section cuts with a length Δx. The FBD of this beam segment is presented in Fig. 4.14b. Writing the equilibrium equations yields:

$$\Sigma F_y = V - q\Delta x - (V + \Delta V) = 0$$

$$\Delta V/\Delta x = dV/dx = -q \qquad (4.19)$$

$$\Sigma M_O = (M + \Delta M) - M + (q\Delta x)(\Delta x/2) - V\Delta x = 0$$

$$\Delta M/\Delta x = dM/dx = V \qquad (4.2)$$

Note that $q\Delta x^2/2$ is a second order term and can be neglected because it is small when compared to the other terms in the equation. Next, let's sub-section this small beam segment with a horizontal cut some distance y_1 above the neutral axis as shown in Fig. 4.14c. The FBD of this subsection of the beam segment is illustrated in Fig. 4.14d.

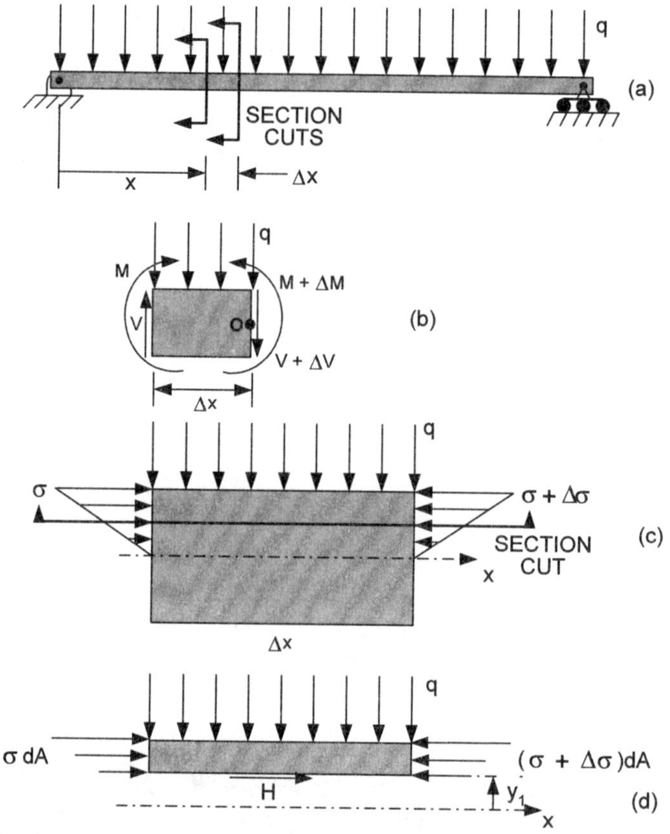

Fig. 4.14 Several FBDs that show the relation between M and V.

We write the equilibrium equation $\Sigma F_x = 0$ for this free body to obtain:

$$\Sigma F_x = -\int(\sigma + \Delta\sigma)dA + \int\sigma dA + H = 0$$

$$H = \int\Delta\sigma\, dA \qquad (a)$$

where H is a horizontal shear force.
From Eq. (4.10), we may write:

$$\Delta\sigma = -\Delta M y/I_z \qquad (b)$$

Substituting Eq. (4.2) and Eq. (b) into Eq. (a) gives:

$$H = -(V\Delta x/I_z)\int y dA = -(V\Delta x/I_z)Q_1 \qquad (4.20)$$

where Q_1 is defined by:

$$Q_1 = \int_{y_1}^{c} y\,dA \qquad (4.21)$$

Q_1 is the first moment of the area from the section cut at position y_1 to the location of the outer fiber on the top surface of the beam at y = c. The horizontal shear stress τ_H acting on the surface exposed by the section cut is given by:

$$\tau_H = H/A_H = - VQ_1/(bI_z) \qquad (c)$$

where $A_H = b\Delta x$ and b is the beam thickness.

We are not usually concerned with the sign in determining the shear stress. Failure of the material, from which structural components are fabricated, is independent of the direction of the shear stress. Finally, we show that the horizontal and vertical shear stresses[5] are equal.

$$\tau = \tau_V = \tau_H = VQ_1/(bI_z) \qquad (4.22)$$

The equality of the shear stresses ($\tau = \tau_V = \tau_H$) is established by taking moments about the point O for the element Δx by Δy shown in Fig. 4.15. This element may be removed from any plane body such as a beam. Also the location of point O is arbitrary.

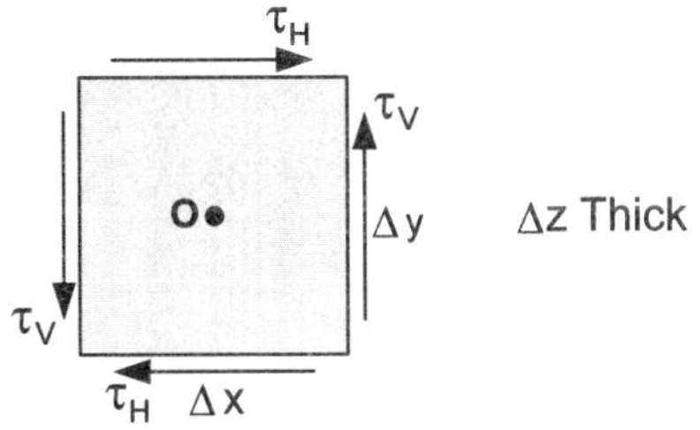

Fig. 4.15 An element Δx by Δy by Δz with shear stresses τ_V and τ_H acting on its faces.

$$\Sigma M_O = (\tau_V\,\Delta y\,\Delta z)\,\Delta x - (\tau_H\,\Delta x\,\Delta z)\,\Delta y = 0$$

$$\tau_V = \tau_H \qquad (4.23)$$

Examination of Eq. (4.22) indicates that the shear stress τ_V is a maximum when Q_1 is a maximum. It is evident from Eq. (4.21) that Q_1 is a maximum for any given section when $y_1 = 0$. Therefore, the shear stress τ is a maximum at the neutral axis. As y_1 approaches the outer fiber at $y_1 = c$, Q_1 approaches zero. For this reason, the shear stresses τ are zero on the top and bottom surfaces of the beam where the normal stresses σ are a maximum. We will demonstrate the method for solving for the shear stresses in a beam with rectangular and circular cross sections in the following examples.

EXAMPLE 4.12

Consider a simply supported beam of length L with a concentrated force F of 20 kN applied at the center of the span. The beam cross section is rectangular with b = 50 mm and h = 150 mm and the beam length L = 5 m. Determine the maximum normal stress σ and the maximum shear stress τ.

---

[5] The vertical shear stresses τ_V and vertical shear force V act on the surface exposed by a vertical section cut.

Solution:

Because the simply supported beam is symmetric, it is clear that the reactions are equal to:

$$R_L = R_R = F/2 = (20)/2 = 10.0 \text{ kN} \qquad \text{(a)}$$

Next, we construct the shear and moment diagrams as shown in Fig. E4.12.

From the shear and bending moment diagrams, we determine that:

$$V_{Max} = 10 \text{ kN} \quad \text{and} \quad M_{Max} = 25 \text{ kN-m} \qquad \text{(b)}$$

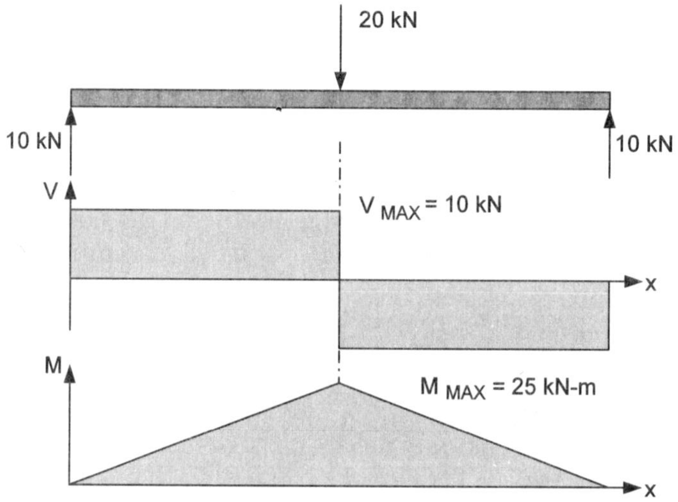

Fig. E4.12

The maximum normal stress is determined from Eq. (4.15) as:

$$\sigma_{Max} = 6M_{Max}/(bh^2) = [(6)(25 \times 10^6)]/[(50)(150)^2] = 133.3 \text{ MPa} \qquad \text{(c)}$$

The maximum shear stress is given by Eq. (4.22) as:

$$\tau_{Max} = V(Q_1)_{Max}/(bI_z) \qquad \text{(d)}$$

To evaluate Eq. (d), let's first determine $(Q_1)_{Max}$ using Eq. (4.21):

$$Q_1 = \int_{y_1}^{y_2} y\,dA = b\int_0^{h/2} y\,dy = \frac{b}{2}\left[y^2\right]_0^{h/2} = \frac{bh^2}{8} \qquad \text{(e)}$$

We may also determine Q_1 without integrating by recalling that the first moment of the area A_1 shown in Fig. E4.12a is given by:

$$Q_1 = A_1\bar{y} \qquad \text{(f)}$$

where A_1 is the area of the cross section above the section cut and $\overline{y}$ is the distance from the neutral axis to the centroid of the area A_1.

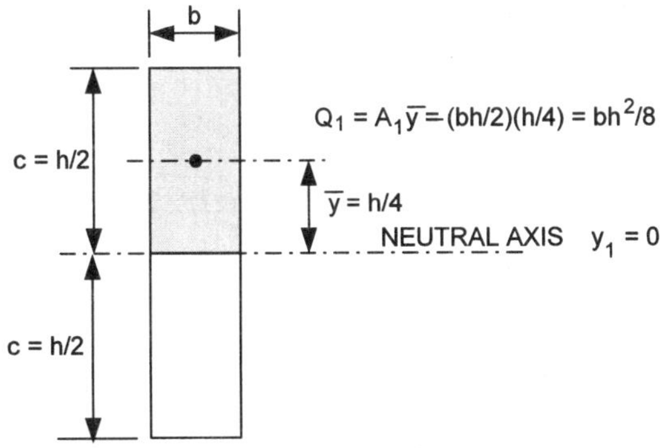

Fig. E4.12a

For a rectangular cross section the moment of inertia is:

$$I_z = bh^3/12 \tag{g}$$

Substituting Eq. (e) and Eq. (g) into Eq. (d) yields:

$$\tau_{Max} = (3/2)(V/bh) = (3/2)(V/A) \tag{4.24}$$

$$\tau_{Max} = (1.5)(10 \times 10^3) /[(50)(150)] = 2.0 \text{ MPa} \tag{h}$$

Comparison of the maximum normal stress and the maximum shear stress for this example shows that the shear stress is very small (1.5% of the maximum normal stress). For long thin beams, the shear stresses are usually small enough to be neglected[6].

Equation (4.24) indicates that the maximum shear stress is 1.5 times the average shear stress. The shear stress is not distributed uniformly over the cross sectional area, but varies as a parabolic function; the maximum occurs at the neutral axis as shown in Fig. E4.12b.

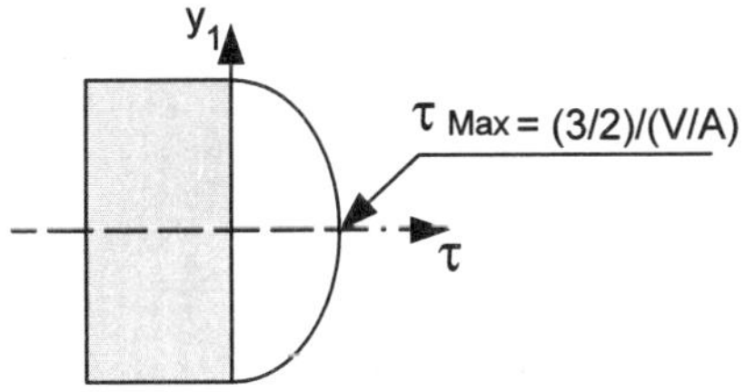

Fig. E4.12b

EXAMPLE 4.13

Let's again consider a simply supported beam of length L = 6 m with a concentrated force F = 15 kN applied at the center of the span. The beam cross section is circular with a diameter d = 120 mm. Determine the maximum normal stress σ and the maximum shear stress τ.

---

[6] The exception is when wood is used to fabricate the beam. The shear strength of wood is very low and even small shear stresses may be sufficient to split the wooden beam along its neutral axis.

Solution:

The beam in this example is similar to the one in the previous example except for its cross section. The reactions, shear and bending moment diagrams, maximum shear force, and maximum bending moment are determined in the same manner:

$$R_L = R_R = F/2 = (15)/2 = 7.5 \text{ kN} \quad \text{(a)}$$

$$V_{Max} = 7.5 \text{ kN} \quad \text{and} \quad M_{Max} = 22.5 \text{ kN-m} \quad \text{(b)}$$

Because the moment of inertia I_z for a circular area about its centerline is given by:

$$I_z = \pi d^4/64 = \pi r^4/4 \quad \text{(c)}$$

The maximum normal stress is given by:

$$\sigma_{Max} = M_{Max} d/(2I_z) = 64\ M_{Max} d/(2\pi d^4) = 32\ M_{Max}/(\pi d^3) \quad (4.25)$$

$$\sigma_{Max} = (32)(22.5 \times 10^6)/[(\pi)(120)^3] = 132.6 \text{ MPa} \quad \text{(d)}$$

The maximum shear stress is given by Eq. (4.22) as:

$$\tau_{Max} = V(Q_1)_{Max}/(bI_z) \quad \text{(e)}$$

We will determine Q_1 using the procedure described below. For the circular bar, the parameter $b = 2r$ at the neutral axis, and $Q_1 = 2r^3/3$ as indicated in Fig. E4.13.

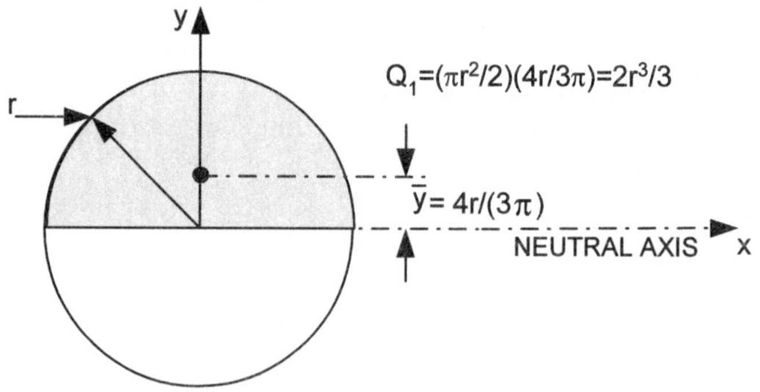

Fig. E4.13

Substituting these results for $(Q_1)_{Max}$ and I_z into Eq. (e) gives:

$$\tau_{Max} = (4/3)(V/\pi r^2) = (4/3)(V/A) \quad (4.26)$$

$$\tau_{Max} = (4/3)(7.5 \times 10^3)/[\pi\ (60)^2] = 0.8842 \text{ MPa}$$

Again, it is evident that the maximum shear stress is very small (less than 1%) when compared to the normal stress.

4.6.2 Shear Flow in Built-Up Beams

In constructing homes and commercial buildings, beams may be fabricated from several simple members to provide a complex structure that is efficient and cost effective. Common examples are built-up beams fabricated from wooden planks as shown in Fig. 4.16.

Fig. 4.16 Wide flange and box beams fabricated from wooden planks with rectangular cross sections.

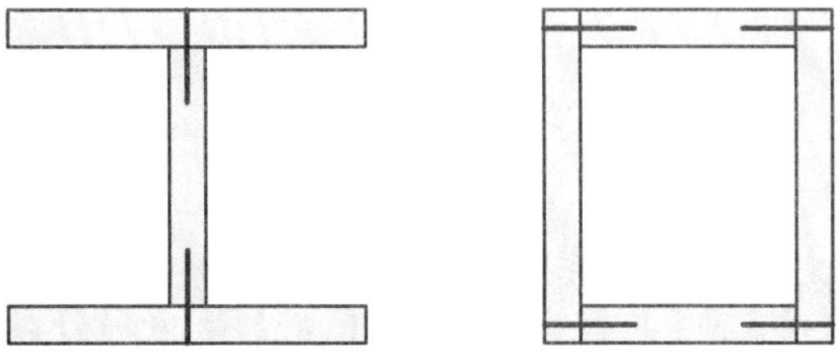

The planks used in the beams shown in Fig. 4.16 are fastened together with a row of nails periodically spaced along the length of the beam. Alternatively an adhesive may be used to fasten the members together. For built-up beams fabricated from metal, the members are usually welded or bolted together.

In designing these built-up beams, it is necessary to specify the number and size of the fasteners and their spacing. If adhesive bonding is used to fabricate the beam, the strength of the adhesive in the joint must be specified. If the beams are produced from steel members with welds, it is necessary for the designer to specify the size of the weld and the strength of the weld metal. This task requires us to determine the shear stress at the joints, where the individual pieces are bonded together. One approach is to determine the shear flow[7] q at the joint, which is the shear force H per unit length.

Refer to Fig. 4.14 and note Eq. (4.20), which gives:

$$H = -(V\Delta x/I_z)\int y\,dA = -(V\Delta x/I_z)Q_1 \qquad (4.20)$$

Rearranging Eq. (4.20) it is clear that:

$$q = H/\Delta x = VQ_1/I_z \qquad (4.27)$$

where q is the shear flow, which is equal to the shear force H per unit length. Note that Q_1 is defined in Eq. (4.21). Also as in the derivation for shear stresses in Eq. (4.22), the negative sign in the above expression was dropped.

Let's consider two examples to demonstrate the method for designing a built-up beam using two types of fasteners.

EXAMPLE 4.14

A wide-flange, cantilevered beam is fabricated from three wooden planks each 1.5 in. thick by 8 in. wide, as shown in Fig. E4.14. The beam is 16 ft. long and is subjected to a concentrated force of 800 lb applied at its free end. If each nail used in fastening the flanges can accommodate a shear force of 410 lbs, determine the number of nails required and specify their spacing.

---

[7] The shear flow q is similar to the concept introduced in Section 3.9, which pertained to the shear stress developed in thin-wall tubes with arbitrary shape subjected to torsion loading.

Fig. E4.14

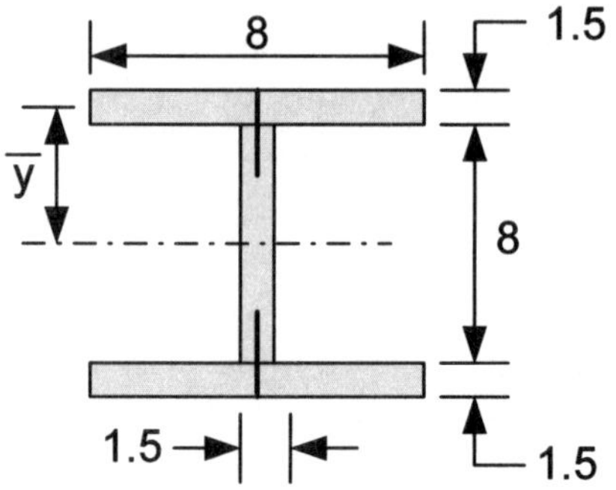

Solution:

Determine Q_1 for the top flange from $Q_1 = A_1\bar{y}$ to obtain:

$$Q_1 = A_1\bar{y} = (8)(1.5)(4.75) = 57 \text{ in.}^3 \quad \text{(a)}$$

Determine I_z from the composite areas as:

$$I_z = (b_w h_w^3)/12 + 2[(b_f h_f^3)/12 + Ad^2]$$

$$= (1.5)(8)^3/12 + 2[(8)(1.5)^3/12 + (8)(1.5)(4.75)^2] = 610 \text{ in}^4. \quad \text{(b)}$$

We note that the shear force V = 800 lb is constant along the entire length of the beam. Then by substituting Eqs. (a) and (b) into Eq. (4.27), we obtain:

$$q = VQ_1/I_z = (800)(57)/(610) = 74.75 \text{ lb/in.}$$

The spacing of the nails is given by:

$$s = F_s/q \quad (4.28)$$

where F_s is the allowable shear force resisted by the nail.

Using Eq. (4.28), we obtain the nail spacing as:

$$s = F_s/q = (410)/(74.75) = 5.485 \text{ in.} \quad \text{(c)}$$

The total number of nails for each joint is given by:

$$N = L/s = (16)(12)/(5.485) = 35 \text{ nails} \quad \text{(d)}$$

The normal stress on the beam is a maximum at its built-in end and is given by Eq. (4.10) as:

$$\sigma = Mc/I_z = [(800)(16)(12)](5.5)/(610) = 1{,}385 \text{ psi} \quad \text{(e)}$$

EXAMPLE 4.15

A box beam is formed by adhesively bonding together four planks, as shown in Fig. E4.15. The planks are each 1.25 in. thick. The shear strength of the adhesive is S_{ys} = 600 psi. If the beam is subjected to a maximum shear force V = 8,400 lb, determine the safety factor for the adhesive joints.

Fig. E4.15

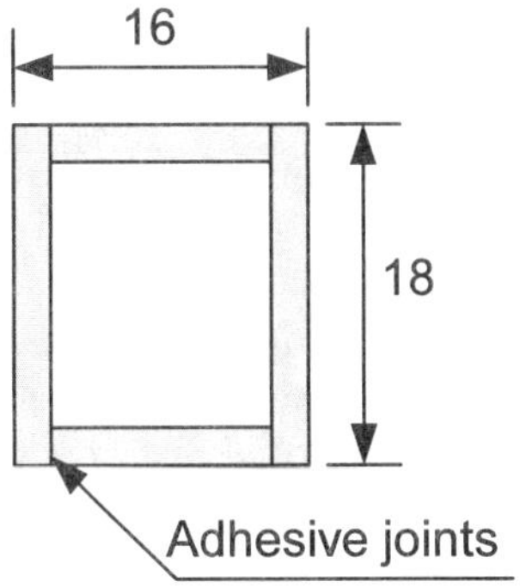

Solution:

Determine Q_1 for the top most horizontal plank from $Q_1 = A_1\bar{y}$ to obtain:

$$Q_1 = A_1\bar{y} = (1.25)[16 - (2)(1.25)][9 - 0.625] = 141.3 \text{ in.}^3 \quad \text{(a)}$$

Determine I_z from the composite areas as:

$$I_z = [(b_1 h_1^3) - (b_2)(h_2^3)]/12 = [(16)(18)^3 - (13.5)(15.5)^3]/12 = 3{,}587 \text{ in.}^4 \quad \text{(b)}$$

From Eq. (4.27) we can compute the shear flow q as:

$$q = VQ_1/I_z = (8{,}400)(141.3)/(3{,}587) = 330.9 \text{ lb/in.} \quad \text{(c)}$$

The shear stress is determined from Eqs. (4.22) and (4.27) as:

$$\tau_H = q/w \quad (4.29)$$

where w is the thickness of the joint or joints.

In this case we have two joints resisting the shear flow generated by the top most plank; hence:

$$\tau_H = q/w = (330.9)/[(2)(1.25)] = 132.4 \text{ psi} \quad \text{(d)}$$

From Eq. (d), we determine the safety factor for the adhesive joints as:

$$SF = S_{ys}/\tau_H = (600)/(132.4) = 4.532 \quad \text{(e)}$$

It appears that the specified box beam is sufficiently strong to resist the imposed shear force at any location along the length of the beam with a generous safety factor.

4.7 BENDING OF COMPOSITE BEAMS

In our discussions of beams, we have considered only those fabricated from a single material such as steel, aluminum or wood. However, in engineering design there is an increasing trend to employ beams fabricated from two or more materials. These are called **composite beams**; they offer the opportunity of using each of the materials employed in their construction to advantage. You may want to consider using them in the design of your project structure.

4.7.1 Foam Core with Metal Cover Plates

Let's consider a composite beam fabricated with thin metal cover plates on the top and bottom with a plastic foam core as shown by the cross sectional area depicted in Fig. 4.17.

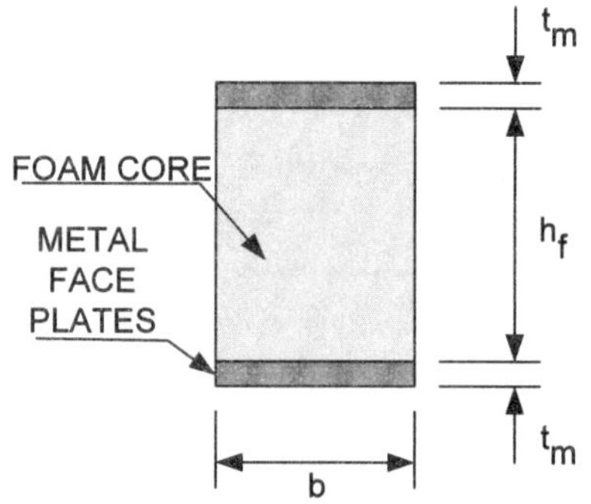

Fig. 4.17 Cross section of a composite beam with a foam core and metal cover plates.

The design concept for the foam core beam is to use light, low-strength foam to support the load-bearing metal plates positioned at the top and bottom, where they are the most efficient. To analyze the composite beam, we again assume that plane sections remain plane before and after loading so the strain is linearly distributed as shown in Fig. 4.18. Note that the strain is continuous across the interface between the foam and the cover plates.

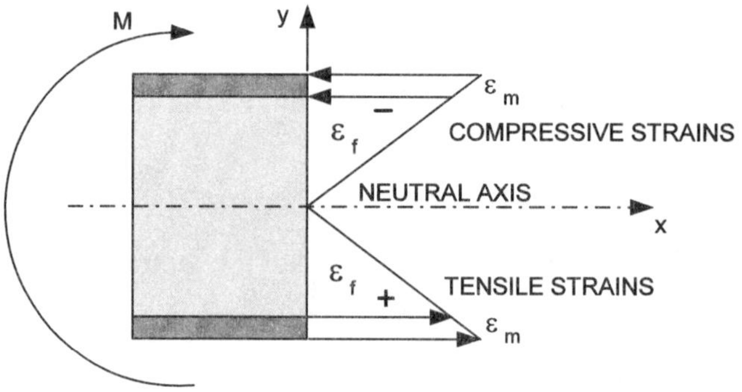

Fig. 4.18 The strain distribution is continuous across the foam-metal interface.

The stress in the foam is given by:

$$\sigma_f = E_f \varepsilon \approx 0 \qquad \text{(a)}$$

We set the stress in the foam equal to zero because its modulus of elasticity E_f is very small when compared to the modulus of elasticity of the metal.

Of course, the stress in the metal of the cover plates, σ_m, is described by Hooke's law as:

$$\sigma_m = E_m \varepsilon = - E_m y/\rho \qquad \text{(b)}$$

We substitute Eq. (4.9) into Eq. (b) to obtain:

$$\sigma_m = -M\,y/I_z \qquad (4.10)$$

The relation for the stress is the same as that established previously in Section 4.4; however, the foam does not directly contribute to the load carrying capacity of the beam because its modulus of elasticity is negligible. For this reason, we do not consider the foam in determining I_z. Instead, we consider only the metal plates when writing the relation for I_z as:

$$I_z \cong 2Ad^2 = 2\left[bt_m\left(\frac{h_f + t_m}{2}\right)^2\right] = \frac{bt_m}{2}(h_f + t_m)^2 \qquad (4.30)$$

Combining Eqs. (4.10) and (4.30) gives the maximum stress in the metal plates as:

$$\sigma_{Max} = \frac{M(h_f + 2t_m)}{bt_m(h_f + t_m)^2} \qquad (4.31)$$

Let's utilize this result to determine the effectiveness of foam core-metal plate composite beams.

EXAMPLE 4.16

Consider a simply supported, foam core, metal cover plate composite beam with a uniformly distributed load of magnitude q. Aluminum cover plates 0.063 in. thick, 8 in. wide and 8 ft long are adhesively bonded to a polystyrene foam core. The foam is 8 in. wide, 6 in. high and 8 ft long. If the yield strength of the aluminum cover plates is 32 ksi, determine the distributed load q_y that produces yielding.

Solution:

From Example 4.2, we note the maximum moment at x = L/2 as:

$$M_{Max} = qL^2/8 = q[(8)(12)]^2/8 = 1{,}152\ q \qquad (a)$$

where q is in units of lb/in.

When the composite beam yields, the stresses in the cover plates are:

$$\sigma_{Max} = S_y = 32{,}000 \text{ psi.} \qquad (b)$$

Substituting Eqs. (a) and (b) into Eq. (4.31) gives:

$$\sigma_{Max} = \frac{M(h_f + 2t_m)}{bt_m(h_f + t_m)^2} = S_y \quad \Rightarrow \quad 32{,}000 = \frac{(1{,}152q_y)[6 + 2(0.063)]}{(8)(0.063)(6.063)^2} = 380.9\ q_y \qquad (c)$$

Solving Eq. (c) for q_Y gives:

$$q_Y = 84.0 \text{ lb/in.} = 1{,}008 \text{ lb/ft} \qquad (d)$$

The effectiveness of this beam may be judged by the ratio of its load carrying capacity to its weight per unit length. Its weight w per unit length is:

$$w = 2bt_m\,\gamma_m + bh_f\,\gamma_f \tag{e}$$

where γ_m = 0.10 lb/in.^{3} and γ_f = 0.001 lb/in.^{3} are the densities of the aluminum and foam respectively.

Substituting these quantities into Eq. (e) yields:

$$w = (2)(8)(0.063)(0.10) + (8)(6)(0.001) = 0.1008 + 0.048 = 0.1488 \text{ lb/in.}$$

The ratio of $q_y/w = 84.0/0.1488 = 564.5$

With the composite beam described, we can support a uniformly distributed load that is 564.5 times larger than the weight of the beam. That is a very good ratio. Composite structures with foam cores are used in aircraft structures where minimizing structural weight is a critical design criterion.

EXAMPLE 4.17

A cantilever beam 4 m long is subjected to a concentrated force of 1.25 kN applied at its free end. The beam has a rectangular cross section with b = 75 mm. Determine the height of the foam and the thickness of the aluminum cover plates if the maximum stress is limited to 200 MPa. In this determination, please note that the standard thickness of stock aluminum sheet from which the cover plates are cut is 0.016, 0.020, 0.025, 0.032, 0.040, 0.050, 0.063, and 0.090 in.

Solution:

For a cantilever beam, the maximum moment is given by:

$$M_{Max} = FL = (1.25 \times 10^3)(4) = 5.0 \times 10^3 \text{ N-m} = 5.0 \times 10^6 \text{ N-mm} \tag{a}$$

Because the maximum stress is limited to 200 MPa, we may write:

$$\sigma_{Max} = \frac{M(h_f + 2t_m)}{bt_m(h_f + t_m)^2} = 200\text{N/mm}^2 \tag{b}$$

In composite beam construction, we often find that:

$$t_m << h_f \qquad \text{hence,} \qquad h_f + 2t_m \approx h_f + t_m. \tag{c}$$

This approximation simplifies Eq. (b):

$$\sigma_{Max} \approx \frac{M}{bt_m(h_f + t_m)} \tag{d}$$

Substituting known quantities into Eq. (d) and solving for h_f leads to:

$$h_f = \frac{M}{bt_m\sigma_{Max}} - t_m = \frac{(5.0\times10^6)}{(75)t_m(200)} - t_m = \frac{333.3\ \text{mm}^2}{t_m} - t_m \qquad \text{(e)}$$

In Eq. (e) we have expressed one unknown h_f in terms of another unknown t_m. However, the thickness of the metal cover plates is restricted to standard sizes. Let's evaluate Eq. (e) for all possible choices of t_m and then select the most suitable combination for the design of the beam. The computation was performed with the aid of a spreadsheet and the results are shown in Table 4.2.

Examination of this table shows that we have many different solutions to consider in designing a beam; however, not all of them are realistic. If we use very thin cover plates (0.406 mm), the height of the foam is excessive (819.7 mm). If we use thick cover plates (2.29 mm), the height of the foam core (143.5 mm) is only about twice the width of the beam (75 mm). There is no unique solution, but the cross section with h_f = 327 mm and t_m = 1.016 mm gives a h/b ratio of about 4/1 that appears reasonable.

Table 4.2
Height of foam as a function of cover plate thickness

COVER PLATE THICKNESS	COVER PLATE THICKNESS	HEIGHT OF FOAM
t_m (in.)	t_m (mm)	h_f (mm)
0.016	0.4064	819.7
0.020	0.5080	655.6
0.025	0.6350	524.2
0.032	0.8128	409.3
0.040	**1.0160**	**327.0**
0.050	1.2700	261.2
0.063	1.6002	206.7
0.090	2.2860	143.5

4.7.2 General Case of Beams with Two Materials

In Section 4.7.1, we studied the case of a composite beam fabricated with thin metal cover plates on the top and bottom and a plastic foam core in the center. We ignored the effect of the foam because its elastic modulus E_f was several orders of magnitude less than the elastic modulus of the metal cover plates E_m. This fact allowed us to assume that the cover plates carried the entire load in the beam. However, what would happen if the core were wood instead of foam? Wood is stronger than foam, and its stiffness is closer to that of structural metals. It seems reasonable to expect that the wood would carry a portion of the load in the beam. In this section, we will study the case of composite beams fabricated from two materials that both share the load applied to the beam.

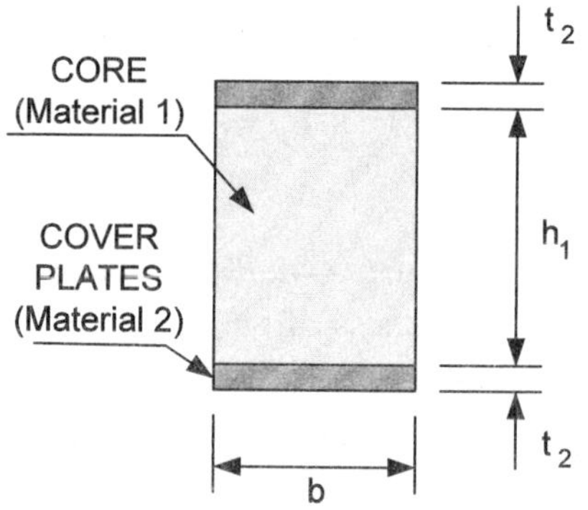

Fig. 4.19 Cross section of a composite "sandwich" beam with a core and cover plates.

Let's begin with a composite "sandwich" beam composed of two materials having a cross section shown in Fig. 4.19. The core is made of one material (with E_1) and the cover plates are made of a second material (with E_2). To analyze the beam, we again assume that plane sections remain plane before and after loading so the strain is linearly distributed as shown in Fig. 4.20. Note that the strain is continuous across the material interface between the core and the cover plates.

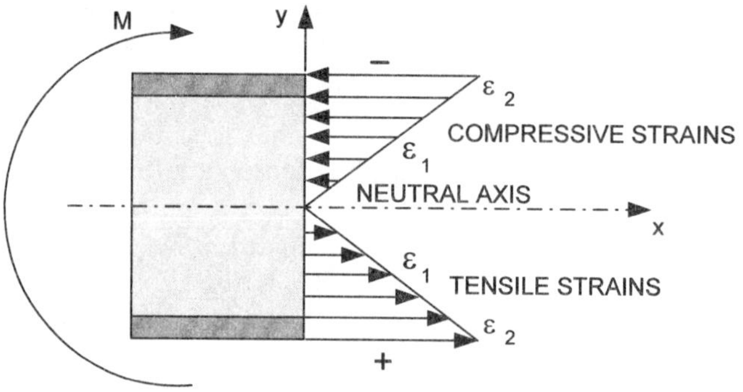

Fig. 4.20 The strain distribution **is continuous** across the material interface.

The stresses in the core and cover plate materials are given by:

$$\sigma_1 = E_1\, \varepsilon_1 \qquad \text{(a)}$$

$$\sigma_2 = E_2\, \varepsilon_2 \qquad \text{(b)}$$

where the strains ε_1 and ε_2 depend on the distance from the neutral axis.

At the interface between the core and the cover plate, the strains are equal in both materials ($\varepsilon_1 = \varepsilon_2$) because the distance from the neutral axis to the bond line is identical. However, Eq. (a) and Eq. (b) indicate that the stresses are not equal ($\sigma_1 \neq \sigma_2$) because the elastic moduli E_1 and E_2 of the materials are different. The stress distribution across the cross section is shown in Fig. 4.21 and, unlike the strain distribution, is not continuous across the material interface.

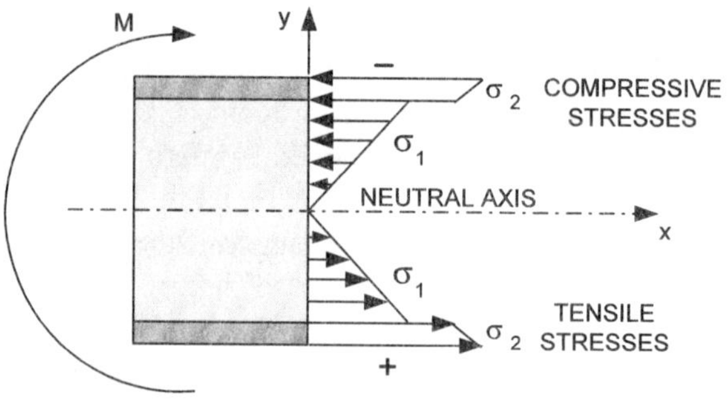

Fig. 4.21 The stress distribution **is not continuous** across the material interface.

To continue the analysis, we convert the composite (heterogeneous) beam into a homogeneous beam by transforming the cross sectional area. First, we establish the transformation factor k as the ratio of the elastic moduli of the two materials:

$$k = E_1/E_2 \quad (4.32)$$

The material in the core (E_1) will be changed into a modified material with a stiffness equivalent to the cover plate material (E_2). Let's assume that $E_2 > E_1$, so that the transformation factor k is less than 1. Next, we transform the cross section by adjusting the width of the modified material by the transformation factor:

$$b_{1T} = k\, b_1 \quad (4.33)$$

The transformed cross section, composed of only the cover plate material (2), is depicted in Fig. 4.22.

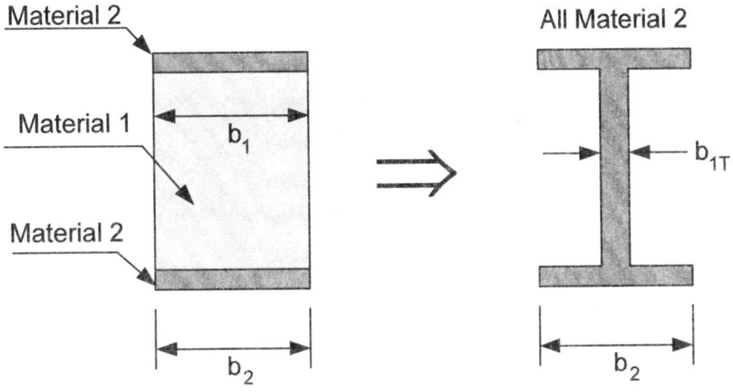

Fig. 4.22 Transformed cross section of a composite beam.

From this figure, we note that the width of the core material (1) has changed to the value given by Eq. (4.33). Because the transformation factor is less than 1, the new width is smaller than the original width. The transformed cross section appears as an I-beam composed entirely of the cover plate material (2). Notice that the cover plate material (2) remains unchanged after transformation. Also, the vertical dimensions in both materials are not changed, preserving the linearity of strain across the section. In fact, the stress distribution also varies linearly across the transformed section. The transformed section is completely equivalent to the original cross section in terms of beam stiffness.

After transforming the cross section into a single material, we can now solve for stresses at any point along the new cross section by using the elastic flexure formula from Eq. (4.10):

$$\sigma_T = -M\, y/I_{Tz} \quad (4.10)$$

In this equation, the moment of inertia I_{Tz} refers to the transformed section shown in Fig. 4.22. We can readily determine the moment of inertia for this new cross section. Also, remember that stresses calculated from Eq. (4.10) are for the transformed section. We must use the following equations to determine stresses in the actual beam:

$$\sigma_1 = -k\, M\, y/I_{Tz} \quad (4.34a)$$

$$\sigma_2 = -M\, y/I_{Tz} \quad (4.34b)$$

Eqs. (4.34) show that the transformation factor is required to determine stresses in the modified core material (1) but not for the cover plate material (2), which was not transformed. The maximum stress in each material occurs at the farthest point from the neutral axis. This point occurs at the top and bottom edges of the beam for the cover plates. However, the maximum stress for the core material is located at the interface between the core and cover plates.

EXAMPLE 4.18

A composite "sandwich" beam is fabricated by adhesively bonding steel strips to the top and bottom faces of a western white pine beam. The cross section of the wood is 200 × 200 mm square, and the steel strips each have a 200 × 20 mm rectangular cross section. The beam is subjected to a maximum bending moment of 25 kN-m. Determine the maximum stress in the wood and in the steel. Assume the modulus of elasticity for the wood is 10 GPa and for the steel is 200 GPa.

Solution:

Start by transforming the beam into one equivalent material — steel. The appropriate transformation factor is given by Eq. (4.32) as:

$$k = E_w/E_s = (10)/(200) = 0.05 \qquad \text{(a)}$$

The thickness of the wood in the transformed section is determined from Eq. (4.33):

$$b_{1T} = k\, b_1 = (0.05)(200) = 10.0 \text{ mm} \qquad \text{(b)}$$

A diagram of the original and transformed cross sections is shown in Fig. E4.18.

Fig. E4.18

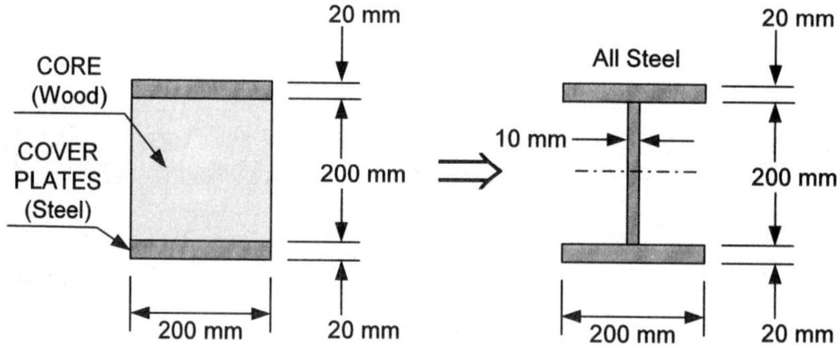

The transformed cross section becomes an I-beam composed entirely of steel. Because this beam has vertical symmetry, the neutral axis is located at the centerline of the section, which is 120 mm from its bottom edge. Next, the transformed moment of inertia I_{Tz} must be determined. One method is to divide the section into three rectangles, a vertical one for the web and two horizontal ones for the flanges, and find the moment of inertia of each rectangle about the neutral axis. The moment of inertia of the web is:

$$I_{wz} = (1/12)\, b_w\, (h_w)^3 = (1/12)(10)(200)^3 = 6.667 \times 10^6 \text{ mm}^4 \qquad \text{(c)}$$

The moment of inertia for each flange is more complex because the parallel axis theorem is involved:

$$I_{fz} = (1/12)\, b_f\, (h_f)^3 + A_f\, (d_f)^2 = (1/12)(200)(20)^3 + (200)(20)(120 - 10)^2$$

$$I_{fz} = 48.53 \times 10^6 \text{ mm}^4 \qquad \text{(d)}$$

Finally, the total moment of inertia for the cross section is determined from Eqs. (c) and (d) as:

$$I_{Tz} = I_{wz} + 2\, I_{fz} = (6.667 \times 10^6) + 2(48.53 \times 10^6) = 103.7 \times 10^6 \text{ mm}^4 \qquad \text{(e)}$$

The maximum stress in the steel occurs at the top and bottom surface of the beam where y = c = 120 mm. The maximum stress in the wood occurs at the interface between the core and the cover plates where y = 100 mm. Substituting these values, the bending moment, and I_{Tz} into Eqs. (4.34) gives the two stresses as:

$$\sigma_w = k\, M\, y/I_{Tz} = (0.05)(25 \times 10^6)(100)/(103.7 \times 10^6) = 1.205 \text{ MPa} \qquad \text{(f)}$$

$$\sigma_s = M\, y/I_{Tz} = (25 \times 10^6)(120)/(103.7 \times 10^6) = 28.93 \text{ MPa} \qquad \text{(g)}$$

Note that the moment terms appearing in (f) and (g) have been converted to N-mm to maintain consistent units. Also, the negative signs from Eqs. (4.34) have been dropped for convenience. The answers show that the maximum stress in the steel is over 24 times greater than the largest stress in the wood. Clearly the steel carries a much larger portion of the load applied to the beam than the wooden core. It is interesting to compare these results with the results for the beam with a foam core and metal cover plate described in Section 4.7.1. Recall in that earlier case, the contribution of the foam core was ignored and all of the beam's load carrying capacity was attributed to the cover plates. Using Eq. (4.31) from Section 4.7.1 in solving Example 4.18 gives a maximum stress in the steel of 30.99 MPa. Thus, by ignoring the wood completely, the stress in the steel is over-estimated by only about 7%.

4.7.3 Reinforced Concrete

Another method of producing composite beams combines steel and concrete that utilizes both materials to advantage. **Concrete** is a mixture of sand, aggregate and cement that is mixed with water, poured into a mold and cured into the shape of some structural member. Concrete is a durable material that has replaced stone in many structural applications. Like stone, it exhibits a satisfactory compressive strength, but it fails when subjected to relatively low tensile stresses. Its compressive strength ranges from 2,500 to 10,000 psi depending on the constituents used in the mix. However, its tensile strength is only 50 to 100 psi. It is so weak in tension that it cannot be employed to fabricate beams without reinforcement.

To reinforce concrete so that it may be used in beams, steel rods are embedded in the concrete when it is cast into forms that define the shape of the beam. The concrete solidifies about the reinforcing steel rods, called **rebar**, producing a composite beam. A typical cross section of a concrete beam reinforced with steel rebar is illustrated in Fig. 4.23.

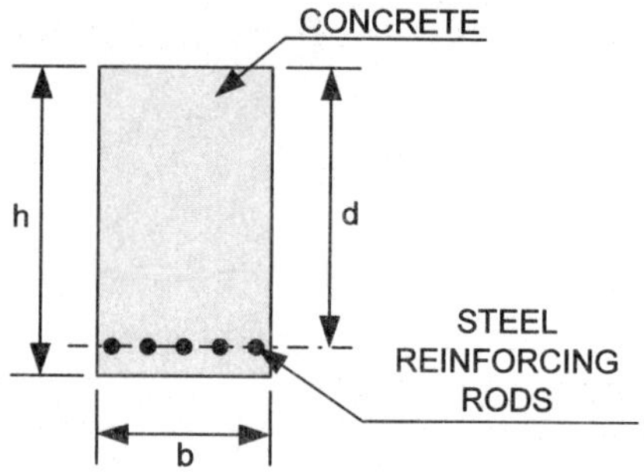

Fig. 4.23 Typical cross section of a reinforced concrete beam. Steel reinforcing rods are placed a short distance above the beam's bottom surface.

In preparing the drawing for Fig. 4.23, we assumed the beam was subjected to positive moments that produce tension in regions below the neutral axis. The positive bending moment produces tensile strains in both the concrete and the steel reinforcing rods because plane sections before deformation remain plane after loading for composite beams as well as homogenous beams. These tensile strains produce tensile stresses that are sufficient to fail the concrete. When the concrete fails, micro-cracks initiate and grow into the tension region of the cross section. However, these cracks arrest near the neutral axis. The steel does not fail and the beam remains intact and rigid. However, the concrete on the tension side of the section does not contribute to the strength and rigidity of the beam except to position the reinforcing rods some distance from its neutral axis. To accommodate for the lack of tensile strength of the concrete, we model the cross section of the beam as shown in Fig. 4.24.

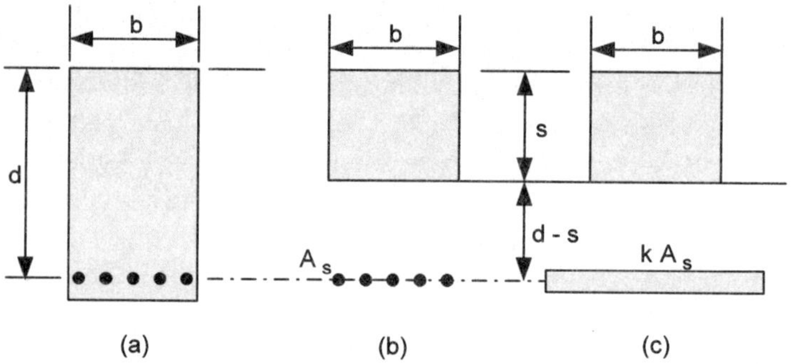

Fig. 4.24 Modeling a steel-bar reinforced concrete beam.

The original cross section of the beam is shown in Fig. 4.24a. All of the concrete located below the neutral axis is removed from the model to account for the micro-cracking in Fig. 4.24b. The remaining rectangular section of concrete, s high by b wide, resists the compressive forces acting above the neutral axis. We also indicate the total area A_s of the steel reinforcing rods that carry the tensile forces. The model in Fig. 4.24b is difficult to analyze because it involves two different materials, both of which contribute to the load carrying capacity of the beam.

To facilitate the analysis, we convert the composite (heterogeneous) model into a homogenous model by representing the steel area with an equivalent concrete area, as shown in Fig. 4.24c. The equivalent concrete area A_{eq} for the steel rods is:

$$A_{Eq} = kA_s \tag{4.35}$$

where

$$k = E_s / E_c \tag{4.36}$$

Note that E_s and E_c are the elastic moduli of the steel and concrete, respectively.

The analysis of the model shown in Fig. 4.24 requires that we first determine the position of the neutral axis. Recall that the neutral axis is coincident with the centroid of the section so that $\int y dA = 0$; hence, we may write:

$$(s)(b)(s/2) - kA_s(d - s) = 0$$

$$(b/2)s^2 + kA_s s - kA_s d = 0 \qquad (4.37)$$

Solution of this quadratic equation gives the dimensions locating the neutral axis and establishing the amount of concrete above the neutral axis.

The maximum stress σ_{Con} in the concrete portion of the beam is given by:

$$\sigma_{Con} = Ms/I_z \qquad (4.38)$$

The stress in the steel reinforcing rods is given by:

$$\sigma_{Steel} = kM(d - s)/I_z \qquad (4.39)$$

Note in Eq. (4.39), we have incorporated the multiplier k in the relation to convert the results from an equivalent concrete beam to a real beam containing steel reinforcing rods.

Finally, the second moment of the area illustrated in Fig. 4.24c is given by:

$$I_z = bs^3/3 + kA_s(d - s)^2 \qquad (4.40)$$

The first term in Eq. (4.40) refers to the concrete above the neutral axis, and the second term is from the parallel axis theorem (Ad^2) for the steel rods. We have neglected the moment of inertia of the rods about their centroidal axis. This term is usually very small (much less than 1%) for reinforced concrete beams so it can be omitted without impairing the safety of the reinforced concrete beam.

EXAMPLE 4.19

A concrete floor slab is reinforced with five 0.75-in. diameter steel bars placed on 8 in. centers. The slab is 44 in. wide and 6 in. thick, and the centerline of the steel rebar is 1 in. above the bottom surface of the slab. The slab is 24 ft. long and is simply supported when installed. If a uniformly distributed load q is applied to the floor, determine the largest magnitude of q if the stress in the steel is limited to 20,000 psi and in the concrete to 1,500 psi. The modulus of elasticity of the steel and the concrete is 30×10^6 psi and 2.5×10^6 psi respectively.

Solution:

Let's first determine the equivalent area of the model produced by the five steel rebars. From Eqs. (4.35) and (4.36), we write:

$$A_{Eq} = kA_s = (E_s / E_c)(\pi d^2/4)N \qquad (a)$$

where N is the number of rebars.

$$A_{Eq} = (30/2.5)[\pi(0.75)^2/4](5) = (12)(9\pi/64)(5) = 26.51 \text{ in}^2 \qquad (b)$$

Next, let's use Eq. (4.37) to locate the position of the neutral axis

$$(b/2)\ s^2 + kA_s s - kA_s d = (b/2)\ s^2 + A_{Eq}s - A_{Eq}d = 0 \qquad \text{(c)}$$

$$(44/2)s^2 + 26.51\ s - 26.51(6 - 1) = 0$$

Solving this quadratic equation gives:

$$s = 1.925 \text{ in.} \qquad \text{and } s = -3.130 \text{ in.} \qquad \text{(d)}$$

We select the positive value because the negative result has no physical meaning.

Having established the position of the neutral axis we may determine I_z from Eq. (4.40) as:

$$I_z = bs^3/3 + kA_s(d - s)^2 = (44)(1.925)^3/3 + (26.51)(5 - 1.925)^2 = 355.3 \text{ in}^4. \qquad \text{(e)}$$

The maximum stress σ_{Con} in the concrete portion of the beam is given by Eq. (4.38) as:

$$\sigma_{Con} = Ms/I_z \quad \Rightarrow \quad 1{,}500 = M(1.925)/(355.3) \qquad \text{(f)}$$

Solving this relation for M yields:

$$M_{Max} = 276{,}900 \text{ in-lb} \qquad \text{(g)}$$

For a uniformly loaded beam, the maximum moment is:

$$M_{Max} = qL^2/8 = 276{,}900 \qquad \text{(h)}$$

$$q_{Max} = (8)(276{,}900)/[(24)(12)]^2 = 26.71 \text{ lb/in.} = 320.5 \text{ lb/ft} \qquad \text{(i)}$$

We reach the limit of the stress in the concrete when the uniformly distributed load q is 320.5 lb/ft. However, it is necessary to determine if the limiting stress in the steel rebar is achieved with a higher or lower value of q. The stress in the steel reinforcing rods is given by Eq. (4.39) as:

$$\sigma_{Steel} = kM(d - s)/I_z \quad \Rightarrow \quad 20{,}000 = (30/2.5)M(5 - 1.925)/(355.3) \qquad \text{(j)}$$

Solving this relation for M yields:

$$M_{Max} = 192{,}600 \text{ in-lb} \qquad \text{(k)}$$

And in a similar manner, we solve for the limiting value of q as:

$$q_{Max} = 8\ M_{Max}/L^2 = (8)(192{,}600)/[(24)(12)]^2 = 18.58 \text{ lb/in.} = 223.0 \text{ lb/ft} \qquad \text{(l)}$$

Compare Eqs. (i) and (l) and select the smaller value to give q_{Max} = 223.0 lb/ft.

An examination of the results in Eq. (i) and Eq. (l) indicates that the design of the reinforced slab is not balanced. The steel meets the limiting stress of 20,000 psi at loads less than that required for the concrete to reach its design stress. To improve the design of the slab the amount of steel should be increased to better balance the load carrying capacity of the reinforced concrete slab. A problem at the end of the chapter provides you with the opportunity to increase the size or number of the rebars to increase the amount of steel and better balance the design of this reinforced concrete slab.

EXAMPLE 4.20

A concrete beam is reinforced with three 1 in. diameter steel bars placed on 6 in. centers. The section of the beam is rectangular — 16 in. wide and 32 in. high with the centerline of the steel rebar 1.5 in. above the bottom surface of the beam. The beam is 20 ft. long and simply supported. If it supports three concentrated loads F = 10 kip, as shown in Fig. E4.20, determine the margin of safety for the beam. The yield strength of the steel is 42 ksi and the compressive strength of the concrete is 3,000 psi. The modulus of elasticity of the steel and the concrete is 30×10^6 psi and 3.0×10^6 psi respectively.

Fig. E4.20

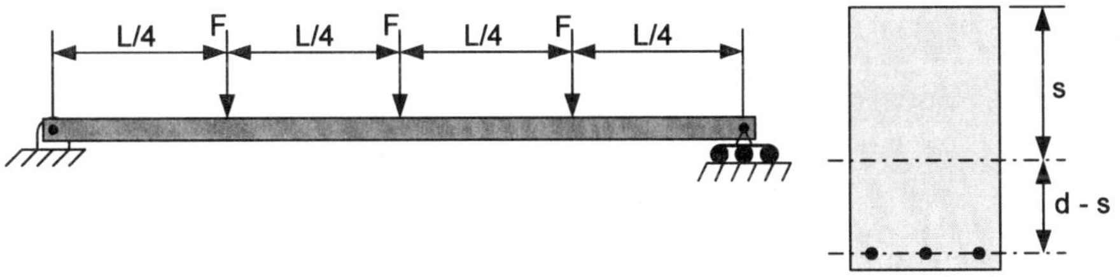

Solution:

The reactions for the symmetrically loaded beam are:

$$R = R_L = R_R = 3F/2 = (3)(10)/2 = 15 \text{ kip} \qquad (a)$$

The bending moment is a maximum at the center of the beam where x = L/2 and is:

$$M_{Max} = R_L(L/2) - F(L/4) = FL/2 = (10{,}000)(20)(12)/(2) = 1.20 \times 10^6 \text{ in-lb} \qquad (b)$$

After the point of failure and the maximum bending moment for the composite beam have been determined, the location of the neutral axis is ascertained from Eq. (4.37).

$$(b/2)s^2 + kA_s s - kA_s d = 0 \qquad (c)$$

$$(8)s^2 + (10)(3\pi/4)s - (10)(3\pi/4)(30.5) = 0 \qquad (d)$$

From the quadratic formula, we calculate that:

$$s = 8.119 \text{ in.} \quad \text{and } s = -11.064 \text{ in.} \qquad (e)$$

Again, ignore the negative root and select s = 8.119 in.

From Eq. (4.40), we establish that I_z is:

$$I_z = bs^3/3 + kA_s(d - s)^2 \qquad (f)$$

$$I_z = (16)(8.119)^3/3 + (10)(3\pi/4)(30.5 - 8.119)^2 = 14{,}657 \text{ in}^4. \quad \text{(g)}$$

The maximum stress σ_{Con} in the concrete portion of the beam is given by Eq. (4.38) as:

$$\sigma_{Con} = Ms/I_z = (1.2 \times 10^6)(8.119)/(14{,}657) = 664.7 \text{ psi} \quad \text{(h)}$$

The maximum stress in the steel reinforcing rods is given by Eq. (4.39) as:

$$\sigma_{Steel} = kM(d - s)/I_z = (10)(1.2 \times 10^6)(30.5 - 8.119)/(14{,}657) = 18.324 \text{ ksi} \quad \text{(i)}$$

The safety factors and the margins of safety are given by:

$$SF_{Con} = S_{Con}/\sigma_{Con} = 3{,}000/664.7 = 4.51 \qquad MOS = SF_{Con} - 1 = 4.51 - 1 = 351\%$$

$$SF_{Steel} = S_{Steel}/\sigma_{Steel} = 42.0/18.324 = 2.29 \qquad MOS = SF_{Steel} - 1 = 2.29 - 1 = 129\%$$

A review of these results indicates that the margin of safety for the steel is much lower than the margin of safety for the concrete, which is more than adequate. Clearly, the design of the composite beam is deficient. The fact that one safety factor is high while the other is low indicates that the amount of steel relative to the size of section is not properly balanced. In this example, the amount of steel is inadequate. Adding more steel (increasing A_s) increases s, decreases (d – s), and increases I_z. All of these changes decrease the stresses in the steel rebar. A problem at the end of the chapter is provided to enable you to redesign this beam with a margin of safety for the steel that is more comparable with the margin of safety for the concrete.

4.8 PLASTIC BENDING

In this discussion of beams, we have considered only their elastic response and have limited our interest to situations where the stresses were lower than the yield strength. This approach insures an adequate margin of safety based on the elastic behavior of the beam's material. However, it is important to realize that beams do not suddenly collapse when the applied bending moment exceeds that required to produce stresses equal to the yield strength.

The behavior of a beam subjected to moments larger than the yield moment depends on the post-yield response of the beam material. In this discussion, we consider a well-known class of materials: **elastic, perfectly-plastic**. The stress-strain diagram for elastic, perfectly-plastic material is shown in Fig. 4.25. The material responds elastically until it yields, and then additional strain is imposed at constant stress $\sigma = S_y$.

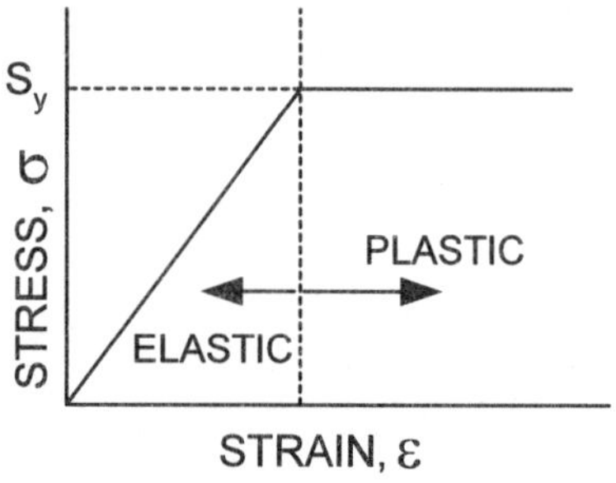

Fig. 4.25 The stress-strain diagram for an elastic perfectly-plastic material.

As we increase the moment applied to a beam, both the stress and the strain at the outer fibers of the beam increase linearly with the moment until $\sigma = S_y$ as illustrated in Fig. 4.26a. When the moment is increased by an additional increment, the strain continues to increase, and the distribution of strain from the neutral axis to the outside fibers remains linear with respect to the position y. As indicated in Fig. 4.26b, no discontinuity occurs at the elastic-plastic interface, as the curvature κ of the beam becomes larger.

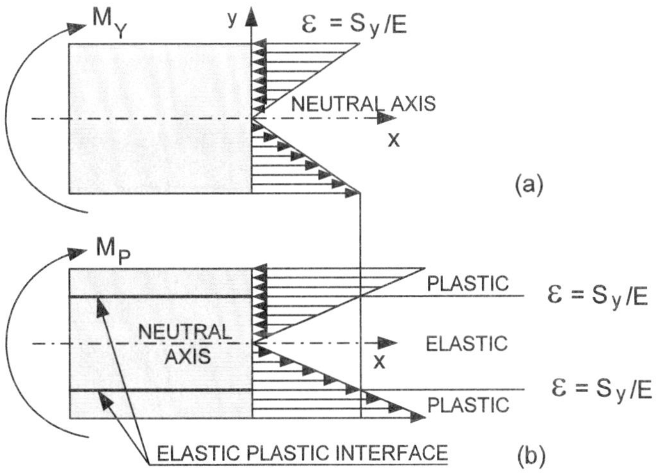

Fig. 4.26 Strain distribution due to pure bending: (a) at yield (b) beyond yield.

The distribution of stress with position y across the section exhibits a discontinuity at the elastic-plastic interface, as shown in Fig. 4.27b. The maximum stress $\sigma_{Max} = S_y$ is achieved at the outside fibers when M equals the yield moment M_Y. As the moment is increased beyond M_Y, the outer fibers yield, the stress in the plastic region remains constant at $\sigma = S_y$, and an elastic-plastic interface develops. This elastic-plastic interface separates the cross section into two regions — an elastic core near the neutral axis and plastic zones adjacent to the top and bottom surfaces.

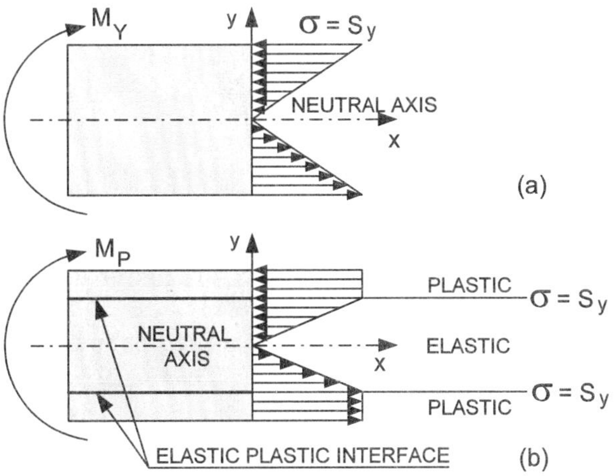

Fig. 4.27 Stress distributions: (a) $M = M_Y$; (b) $M_Y < M < M_L$.

The moment M_Y required to produce a stress $\sigma = S_y$ on the outside fibers of a beam with a rectangular cross section is given by:

$$M_Y = \frac{\sigma(2I_z)}{h} = \frac{S_y}{h}(2)\frac{1}{12}\left(bh^3\right) = S_y\frac{bh^2}{6} \tag{4.41}$$

The moment M_P that is required to drive the elastic-plastic interface to some position y_p is determined from Fig. 4.28. The equal and opposite forces F_e and F_p form two couples — one associated with the elastic region ($F_e\, d_e$) and the other with the plastic region ($F_p\, d_p$).

The forces, due to the stress σ, are given by:

$$F_p = (b/2)(h - 2y_p)S_y \qquad \text{and} \qquad F_e = (by_p/2)S_y \qquad \text{(a)}$$

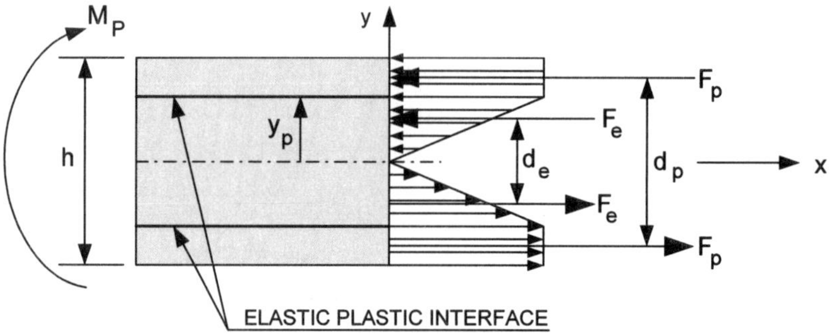

Fig. 4.28 Couples developed in the elastic and plastic regions of the cross section.

And the distances d_p and d_e are given by:

$$d_p = (1/2)(h + 2y_p) \qquad \text{and} \qquad d_e = (4/3)y_p \qquad \text{(b)}$$

Summing moments about the origin of the x-y coordinate system gives:

$$\Sigma M_O = F_p\, d_p + F_e\, d_e - M_P = 0 \qquad \text{(c)}$$

Substituting Eq. (a) and Eq. (b) into Eq. (c) and solving for M_P yields:

$$M_P = S_y b\left(\frac{1}{2}(h - 2y_p)\frac{1}{2}(h + 2y_p) + \frac{y_p}{2}\frac{4y_p}{3}\right) = \frac{S_y b}{12}\left(3h^2 - 4y_p^2\right) \qquad (4.42)$$

Equation (4.42) indicates that beams are capable of supporting moments larger than the yield moment M_Y. The beam will be damaged in the process because it will be permanently deformed; however, it will not collapse. The question then arises as to how large of an overload that can be placed on a beam before it collapses.

To answer this question, consider the behavior of a beam when the elastic-plastic interface is driven into the neutral axis. The elastic core disappears and the entire cross section of the beam is in the plastic regime. At this point, the beam has become **fully plastic** reaching its **limit moment** where additional moments cannot be supported.

It is easy to determine the limit moment, M_L from Eq. (4.42) if we set $y_p = 0$, thereby moving the position of the elastic-plastic interface to the neutral axis. Then, Eq. (4.42) reduces to:

$$M_L = S_y\, bh^2/4 \qquad (4.43)$$

A comparison of the yield moment and the limit moment is possible from Eq. (4.41) and Eq. (4.43). The ratio M_L/M_Y is given by:

$$\frac{M_L}{M_Y} = \left(\frac{S_y bh^2}{4}\right)\left(\frac{6}{S_y bh^2}\right) = \frac{3}{2} \tag{4.44}$$

For the rectangular cross section, the limit moment is 150% of the yield moment. This is a comfortable margin that adds to the safety factor if collapse is an important criterion for design. However, the ratio of M_L/M_Y is a function of the shape of the cross section. For WF and standard I beam shapes, the ratio M_L/M_Y is usually only about 1.10 to 1.15.

EXAMPLE 4.21

Consider the simply supported beam of length L = 10 m with a concentrated force **F** located 4 m from the left end as shown in Fig. E4.21. Determine the force required to produce the yield moment and the force required for the beam to collapse. The cross section of the beam is rectangular with a height h = 120 mm and a width b = 60mm. The beam is fabricated from steel with a yield strength of 300 MPa. We will assume that the steel responds as an elastic, perfectly-plastic material.

Fig. E4.21

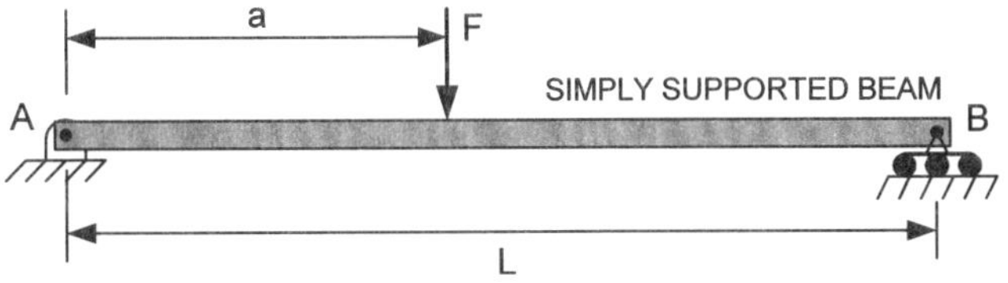

Solution:

Recall from Section 4.2.1 that the reaction forces R_R and R_L for this loading are given by:

$$R_R = Fa/L \qquad \text{and} \qquad R_L = Fc/L \tag{a}$$

where c = L – a.

In Eq. (4.1), we showed that the moment was a maximum at x = a (under the load point):

$$M_{Max} = Fac/L \tag{b}$$

Combining Eqs. (4.41) and (b) while setting $F = F_Y$ and $M_{Max} = M_Y$ yields:

$$F_Y ac/L = S_y\, bh^2/6$$

$$F_Y = S_y\, bh^2L/(6ac) \tag{c}$$

Substituting the parameters describing the beam and the material into Eq. (c) yields:

$$F_Y = \frac{S_y bh^2 L}{6ac} = \frac{(300\times 10^6)(0.06)(0.12)^2(10)}{(6)(4)(10-4)} = 18.0 \text{ kN} \tag{d}$$

The force associated with the limit load is determined by substituting Eq. (4.43) into Eq. (b) or by recognizing that $M_L = 3M_Y/2$ as indicated in Eq. (4.44). Accordingly, we find that:

$$F_L = 3F_Y/2 = (3)(18)/(2) = 27 \text{ kN} \qquad \text{(e)}$$

When F_L produces the moment M_L, a **plastic hinge** forms under the load point and the beam collapses as indicated with the schematic illustration presented in Fig. E4.21a.

Fig. E4.21a

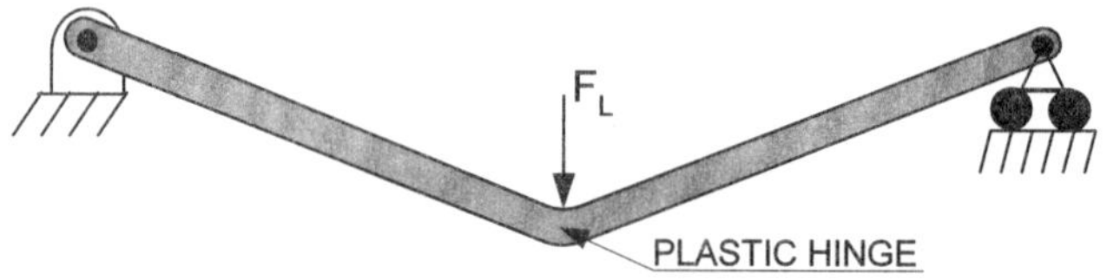

A plastic hinge has formed under the load when $M = M_L$ with both sides of the beam rotating about this point. The hinge is not frictionless; hence, the force F_L performs work ($M_L \times \theta$) as it deflects the beam and rotates the plastic hinge.

EXAMPLE 4.22

Consider a simply supported beam of length L = 8 m with a uniformly distributed load q acting over its entire the length, as shown in Fig. E4.22. Determine the magnitude of the uniformly distributed load required to produce the yield and limit moments. The cross section of the beam is rectangular with h = 150 mm and b = 50 mm. The beam is fabricated from steel with a yield strength of 320 MPa. We will assume that the steel acts like an elastic, perfectly-plastic material.

Fig. E4.22

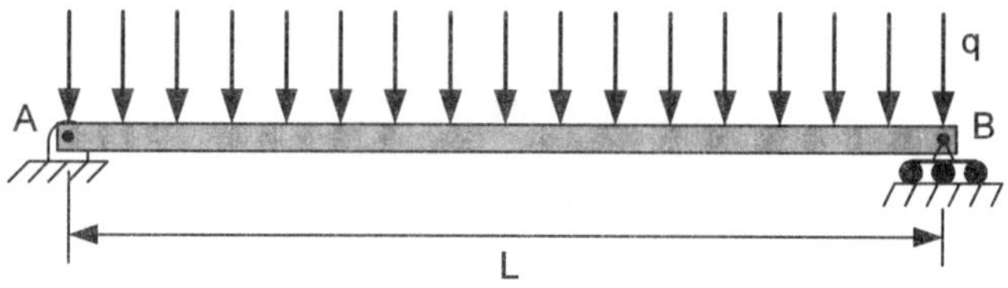

Solution:

Recall from Example 4.2 that the reaction forces R_R and R_L are given by:

$$R_R = R_L = qL/2 \qquad \text{(a)}$$

Also in Example 4.2, we showed that the moment was a maximum at x = L/2:

$$M_{Max} = qL^2/8 \qquad \text{(b)}$$

Combining Eqs. (4.41) and (b) while setting $M_{Max} = M_Y$ yields:

$$q_Y L^2/8 = S_y\, bh^2/6$$

$$q_Y = (4/3)S_y b(h/L)^2 \qquad \text{(c)}$$

Substituting the parameters describing the beam and its material into Eq. (c) yields:

$$q_Y = \frac{4S_y bh^2}{3L^2} = \frac{(4)(320\times 10^6)(0.05)(0.15)^2}{3(8)^2} = 7.50\ \text{kN/m} \qquad \text{(d)}$$

The distributed load associated with the limit load is determined by substituting Eq. (4.43) into Eq. (b).

$$q_L = \frac{2S_y bh^2}{L^2} = \frac{(2)(320\times 10^6)(0.05)(0.15)^2}{(8)^2} = 11.25\ \text{kN/m} \qquad \text{(e)}$$

When the distributed load $q = q_L$ a plastic hinge forms at the beam's center point and the beam collapses.

4.9 SHEAR CENTER

The topic of shear center[8] combines the concept of shear stresses induced by transverse forces applied to beams and the angle of twist in torsion. Twisting of beams in bending does not arise for beams with symmetric cross sections. If the cross section of the beam is symmetric about its vertical axis, the shear stresses, which exist, do not produce a twisting moment. However, if the beam's cross-section is not symmetric, transverse loads will cause twisting to occur. To illustrate this point consider a cantilever beam loaded at its free end with a concentrated force F. The concentrated load is applied through the center of gravity of the channel section as shown in Fig. 4.29. When the load is applied, the beam will twist about its longitudinal axis through an angle ϕ.

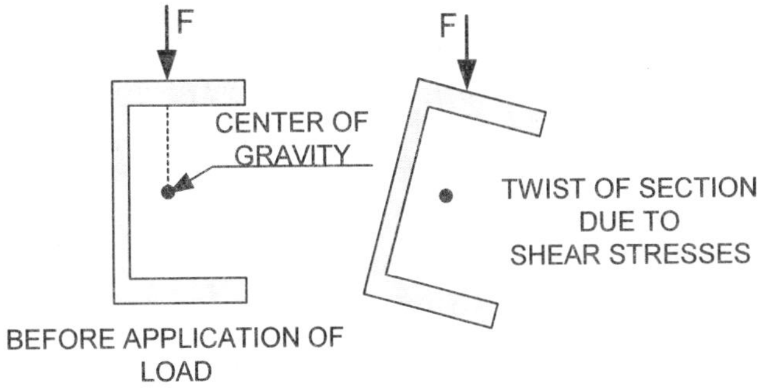

Fig. 4.29 Twisting of unsymmetrical beam sections induced by shear stresses.

Let's consider a cantilever beam fabricated from a channel section with the force F applied at its free end through its center of gravity as illustrated in Fig. 4.30a. A constant shear force V = F occurs over the length L of the beam. This shear force produces shear stresses in both the web and the flanges of the channel section that are given by Eq. (4.22) as:

$$\tau = \tau_V = \tau_H = VQ_1/(bI_z) \qquad (4.22)$$

where

$$Q_1 = \int_{y_1}^{c} y\,dA \qquad (4.21)$$

In the above equations, recall that Q_1 is the first moment of the area from the section cut at position y to the location of the top fiber of the beam at y = c, V is the internal shear force, I_z is the moment of inertia about the neutral axis of the beam, and b is the width of the beam.

[8] This topic has been described in Section 3.9 in Chapter 3 on Torsion of Structural Elements. It is repeated here because some instructors prefer to cover this topic as part of beam theory.

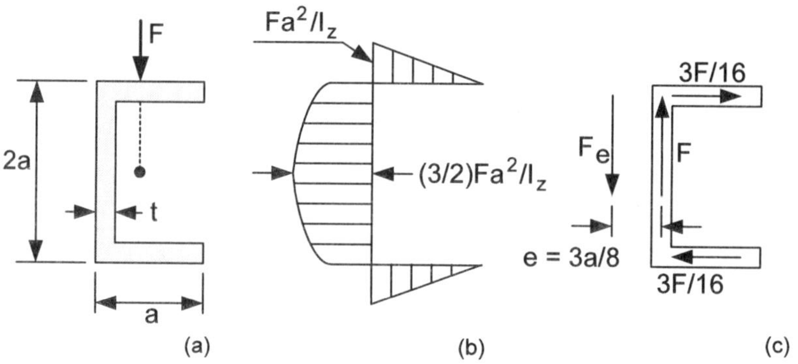

Fig. 4.30 Shear stress distribution in a channel section subjected to shearing forces V = F.

If the shear stresses in the channel section are determined from Eq. (4.22), the distribution of τ_V and τ_H are shown in Fig. 4.30b. In this solution of Eq. (4.22) higher powers of the dimension ratio (t/a) have been disregarded because they are small in relation to the other terms. Integrating the shear stress distribution over the three rectangular areas comprising the channel section and substituting:

$$I_z \approx 8a^3t/3 \qquad \text{(a)}$$

yields the three shear forces shown in Fig. 4.30c.

Examination of Fig. 4.30c shows that the shear force V in the vertical portion of the channel is equal to the applied force F as expected. The two horizontal forces 3F/16 are equal and opposite and cancel satisfying $\Sigma F_z = 0$. However, these two forces produce a couple, a torque T = (3/8)Fa, which tends to twist the channel section (in a clockwise direction) producing the twisted shape presented in Fig. 4.29.

The shear center is established from this twisting moment. If the transverse force $F_e = F$ is applied at an eccentric position, e = (3/8)a, from the centerline of the vertical segment of the channel as shown in Fig. 4.30c, it produces a couple with T = (3/8)Fa in the counter clockwise direction. Thus, the couples cancel and the channel section will not twist when the transverse force is applied. When loading unsymmetrical sections, the transverse force must be applied through the shear center instead of the center of gravity to avoid twisting deformations.

Channel sections and other unsymmetrical sections are often employed in structural applications. In these cases, attachments are welded to the main beams to allow for the eccentric placement of the applied forces as indicated in Fig. 4.31.

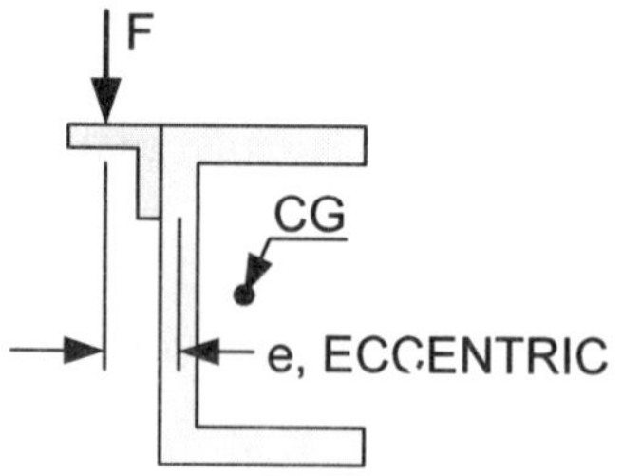

Fig. 4.31 Eccentric placement of the applied force to suppress twisting due to shear stresses.

EXAMPLE 4.23

The channel section presented in Fig. E4.23 is to be employed in fabricating a cantilever beam. Determine the eccentricity e of the transverse force F if the beam is to deflect without twisting.

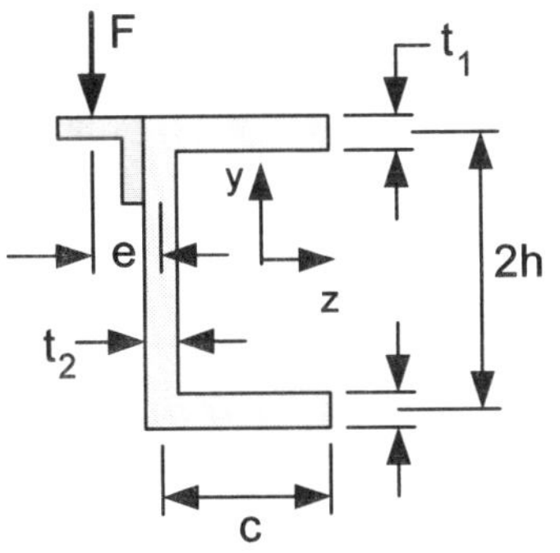

Fig. E4.23

Solution:

Step 1: Prepare FBDs to show the shear stresses introduced by the shear force V = F. Section the top flange of the channel section a distance d from its edge as shown in Fig. E4.23a.

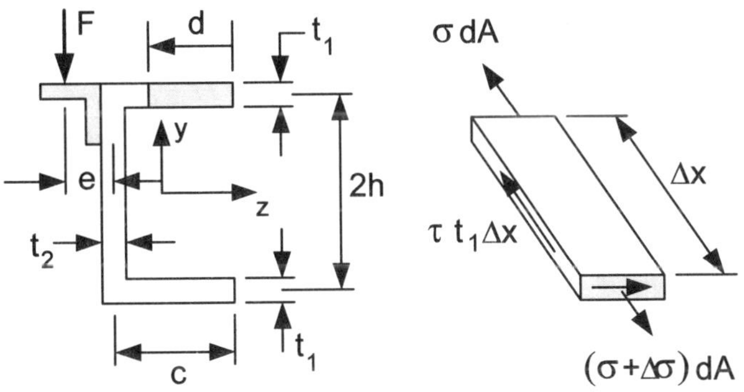

Fig. E4.23a

Step 2: The shear stress τ in the top flange is determined from Eq. (4.22) as:

$$\tau = VQ_1/(I_z\ b) = (F\ h\ d/I_z) \qquad \text{(a)}$$

where V = F, b = t_1 and $Q_1 = h\ d\ t_1$

The shear stress in the flange is a linear function of d increasing from zero at the edge of the flange to a maximum value where the flange intersects the web of the channel and d = c. Clearly τ_{MAX} is given by:

$$(\tau_{MAX})_{Flange} = F\ h\ c/I_z \qquad \text{(b)}$$

Step 3: The shear stress at the top of the web is also determined from Eq. (4.22) as:

$$\tau = VQ_1\ /(I_z\ b) = [(F\ h\ c\ t_1)/(t_2\ I_z)] \qquad \text{(c)}$$

where V = F, b = t_2 and $Q_1 = h\ c\ t_1$

Step 4: The shear stress is a maximum at the center of the web where y = 0. From Eq. (4.22), we write:

$$\tau = VQ_1\ /I_z\ b = Fh[c(t_1/t_2) + (h/2)]/I_z \qquad \text{(d)}$$

The shear stress exhibits a parabolic distribution over the height of the web. If this shear stress is integrated over the area of the web, we find:

$$\int \tau dA_{Web} \approx F = V \tag{e}$$

Step 5: The shear stress in the flanges varies linearly from zero to a maximum at the junction of the web and the flange. Integrating the shear stress over the area of the top flange gives the shear force H_1 as:

$$H_1 = \int \tau dA_{Flange} = (1/2)(ct_1)(Fhc/I_z) = (Fhc^2t_1)/(2I_z) = -H_2 \tag{f}$$

A second shear force H_2, equal in magnitude and opposite in direction, is induced in the lower flange as shown in Fig E4.23b.

Fig. E4.23b

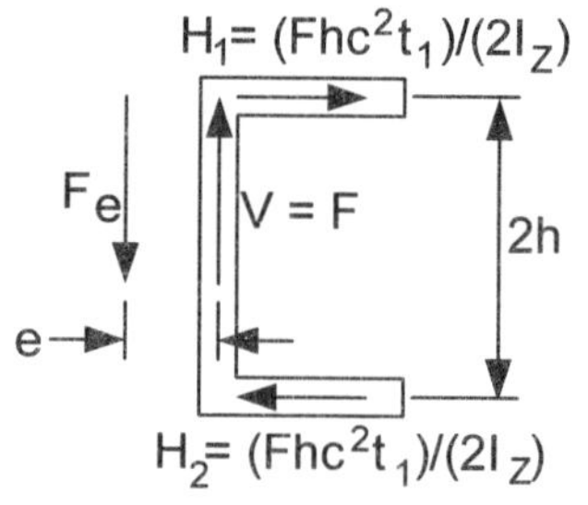

Step 6: The two equal and opposite shear forces, H_1 and H_2, produce a clockwise couple T equal to:

$$T = (2h)H_1 = (Fh^2 c^2t_1)/(I_z) \tag{g}$$

Step 7: An equal and opposite moment (torque) is produced by applying the force F with an eccentricity e as shown in Fig. E4.23b. The eccentricity is given by e = T/F as:

$$e = T/F = (h^2 c^2t_1)/(I_z) \tag{h}$$

The moment of inertia I_z is given by:

$$I_z = (2/3)t_2 h^3 + 2t_1 ch^2 \tag{i}$$

Step 8: Substituting Eq. (i) into Eq. (h) gives the eccentricity necessary in locating the point of application of the transverse force F to avoid twisting the channel section beam.

$$e = \left(\frac{3}{2}\right)\left[\frac{c^2t_1}{t_2h + 3t_1c}\right] \tag{j}$$

4.10 SUMMARY

Beams are long thin members subjected to transverse forces—either reactionary or applied. These transverse forces produce internal moments in the beam, which bend it into a circular arc. The curvature of the arc depends on the internal moment and may vary along the length of the beam.

In most cases, the moment varies along the length of the beam and it is necessary to determine the shear forces and bending moments as a function of position. We introduced methods for constructing free bodies of the beam to determine the reactions, shear forces and bending moments. Also, the method for constructing shear and bending moment diagrams was introduced. It is important to recall the relations between loads, shear force and bending moment, as indicated below, in constructing the shear and bending moment diagrams.

$$dM/dx = V \qquad (4.2)$$

$$M_{x_2} - M_{x_1} = \int_{x_1}^{x_2} V dx \qquad (4.3)$$

In bending, we assume that plane sections of the beam remain plane as the beam deforms. This assumption permits us to determine the longitudinal strain in the beam if we know its radius of curvature, ρ.

$$\varepsilon = -\, y/\rho \qquad (4.4)$$

The equations of equilibrium are employed to establish the position of the neutral axis of the beam at the centroid of its cross sectional area. We also showed the relation between the internal moment M and the radius of curvature as:

$$M = (EI_z/\rho) \qquad (4.8)$$

With a knowledge of the relation between curvature and the moment, we were able to establish the important relationship between the internal moment and normal stress:

$$\sigma = -\, My/I_z \qquad (4.10)$$

Using Eq. (4.10), we consider beams with rectangular cross sections and showed that they were not efficient structural members because they have extensive regions near their neutral axis that are subjected to relatively small stresses.

We introduced more efficient designs of cross sections by considering American Standard I and WF shapes. An effectiveness factor ***SE*** = Z/A was introduced to judge the adequacy of the design of various cross sections for beams.

$$\boldsymbol{SE} = \frac{1}{h(2bt_f + b_w h_w)} \left\{ \frac{b_w h_w^3}{6} + \frac{bt_f^3}{3} + bt_f (h_w + t_f)^2 \right\} \qquad (4.18)$$

Several examples are presented to demonstrate methods for calculating stresses, safety factors, and margins of safety for beams with various types of supports subjected to both concentrated forces and uniformly distributed forces.

We have briefly introduced the topic of shear stress in beams, and showed that:

$$Q_1 = \int_{y_1}^{c} y\,dA \qquad (4.21)$$

$$\tau = \tau_V = \tau_H = VQ_1/(bI_z) \qquad (4.22)$$

The shear stresses are not uniformly distributed over the cross section of the beam; they are a maximum at the neutral axis and zero at the top and bottom surfaces of the beam. In most cases, the shear stresses are small when compared to the normal stresses and they are often ignored. The exception is when the beams are fabricated from wood. The shear strength of wood is so small that even the low shear stresses may be sufficient to split wooden beams at their neutral axis.

To determine the shear stress at the joints of built-up beams, we developed the relation for the shear flow q at the interface between the two materials and showed that:

$$q = H/\Delta x = VQ_1/I_z \qquad (4.27)$$

Using the shear flow concept, we presented equations that assess the ability of fasteners or glue to resist these shear stresses:

$$s = F_s/q \qquad (4.28)$$

$$\tau_H = q/w \qquad (4.29)$$

The bending of composite beams fabricated from two materials was discussed. The first composite section described consisted of a foam core with adhesively bonded metal cover plates. The maximum stress in the metal cover plates is given by:

$$\sigma_{Max} = \frac{M(h_f + 2t_m)}{bt_m(h_f + t_m)^2} \qquad (4.31)$$

We also developed methods for determining stresses in a composite beam fabricated with a stiff core and cover plates and for a concrete beam reinforced with steel rods. These methods involved the development of an equivalent section where one of the materials was transformed into a modified material with the same stiffness of the other material. The composite beam fabricated with a stiff core and cover plates was analyzed using the equations listed below:

$$k = E_1/E_2 \qquad (4.32)$$

$$b_{1T} = k\,b_1 \qquad (4.33)$$

$$\sigma_1 = -\,k\,M\,y/I_{Tz} \qquad (4.34a)$$

$$\sigma_2 = -\,M\,y/I_{Tz} \qquad (4.34b)$$

The reinforced concrete beam was then analyzed using the equations listed below:

$$A_{Eq} = kA_s \qquad (4.35)$$

$$k = E_s/E_c \qquad (4.36)$$

$$(b/2)s^2 + kA_s s - kA_s d = 0 \qquad (4.37)$$

$$\sigma_{Con} = Ms/I_z \qquad (4.38)$$

$$\sigma_{Steel} = kM(d - s)/I_z \qquad (4.39)$$

$$I_z = bs^3/3 + kA_s(d - s)^2 \qquad (4.40)$$

Examples were presented to demonstrate the analytical procedure and to introduce the concept of balanced design of composite beams.

The plastic response of beams was introduced for an elastic, perfectly-plastic material. We showed that the strain increased linearly with increasing moment even in the plastic regime. However, the stresses were limited to the yield strength of the beam's material. As a consequence, a discontinuity formed in the distribution of the stresses across the section. This discontinuity defines the elastic-plastic interface. As the moment increases the elastic-plastic interface is driven toward the neutral axis, a plastic hinge forms, and a simply supported beam collapses. Concepts of the yield moment, M_Y and the limit moment, M_L were introduced and equations were developed for computing these quantities for beams with rectangular cross sections.

$$M_Y = S_y \frac{bh^2}{6} \qquad (4.41)$$

$$M_L = S_y\, bh^2/4 \qquad (4.43)$$

Note that M_L is 1.5 times higher than M_Y for beams with rectangular cross sections, but only 1.10 to 1.15 times higher for wide flange and standard I-beams.

If the cross section of a beam is not symmetric about a vertical axis, the beam will bend and twist under the action of transverse forces. The twisting couple produced by bending a cantilever beam fabricated from a channel section was discussed. The twisting of the beam can be avoided if the transverse force is applied through the shear center of the section. Example 4.23 demonstrated the analysis used to determine the location of the shear center.

PROBLEMS

4.1 Four different beams with various end conditions are shown Fig. P4.1. Construct FBDs of each beam showing the forces and/or moments at each support.

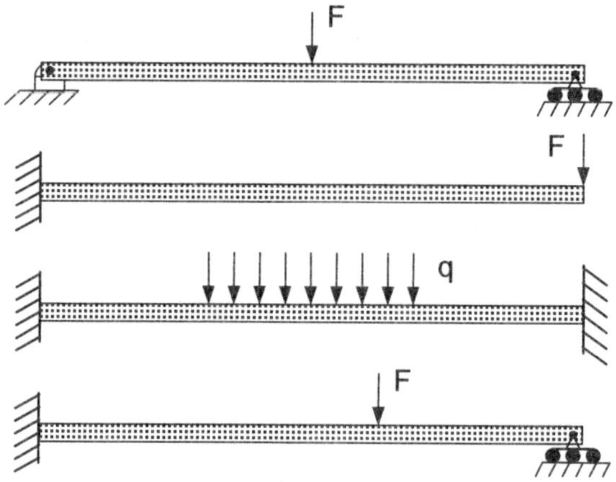

Fig. P4.1

4.2 Construct the shear and bending moment diagrams for the simply-supported beam shown in Fig. P4.2 by using:
(a) the equation approach.
(b) the graphical approach.

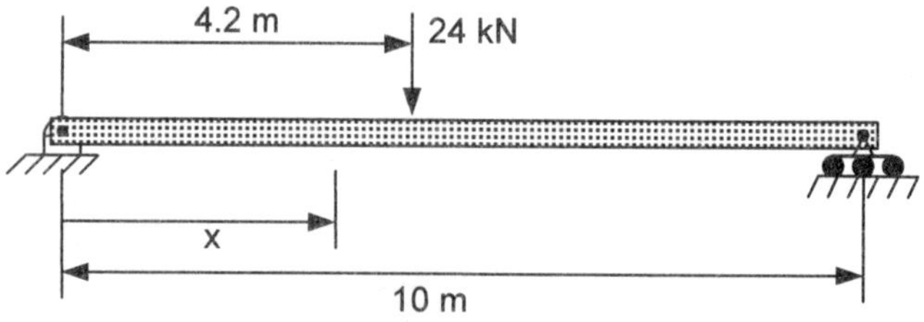

Fig. P4.2

4.3 Construct the shear and bending moment diagrams for the simply-supported beam shown in Fig. P4.3 by using:
(a) the equation approach.
(b) the graphical approach.

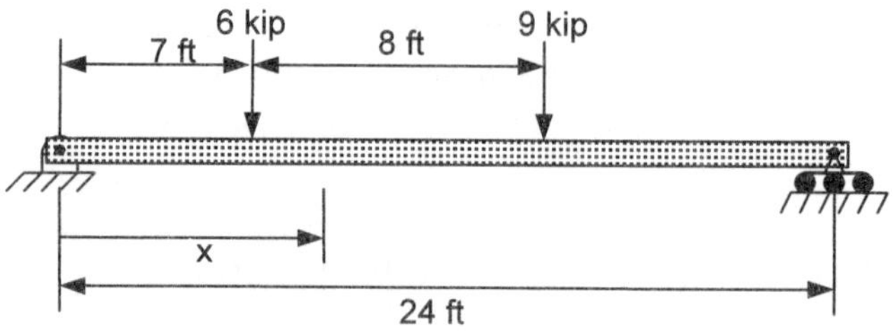

Fig. P4.3

4.4 Construct the shear and bending moment diagrams for the cantilever beam shown in Fig. P4.4 by using:
(a) the equation approach.
(b) the graphical approach.

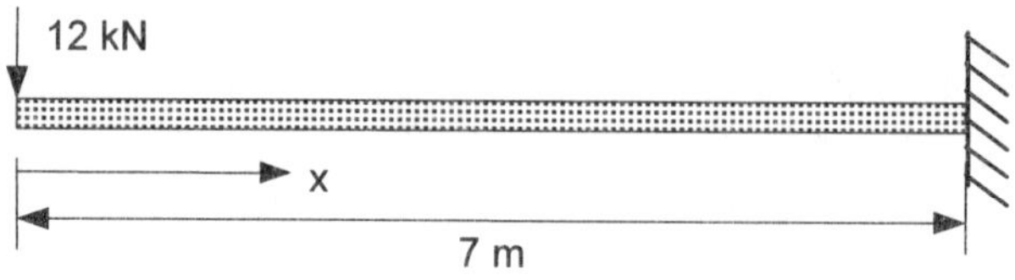

Fig. P4.4

4.5 Construct the shear and bending moment diagrams for the cantilever beam shown in Fig. P4.5 by using:
(a) the equation approach.
(b) the graphical approach.

Fig. P4.5

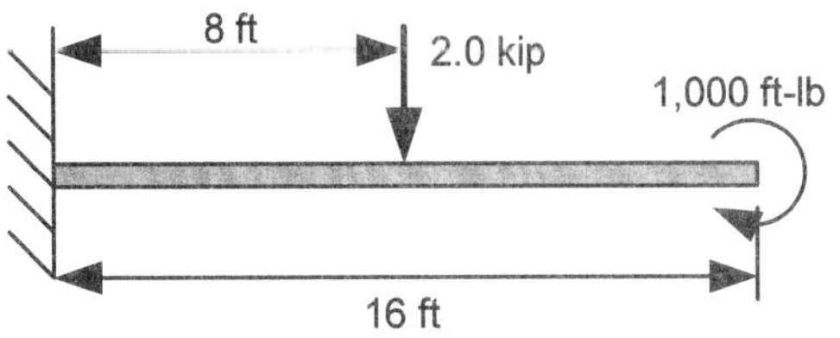

4.6 Construct the shear and bending moment diagrams for the simply-supported beam shown in Fig. P4.6 by using:
(a) the equation approach.
(b) the graphical approach.

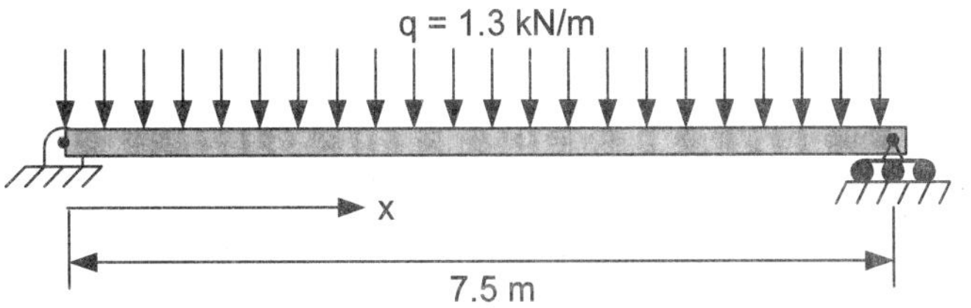

Fig. P4.6

4.7 Construct the shear and bending moment diagrams for the simply-supported beam shown in Fig. P4.7 by using:
(a) the equation approach.
(b) the graphical approach.

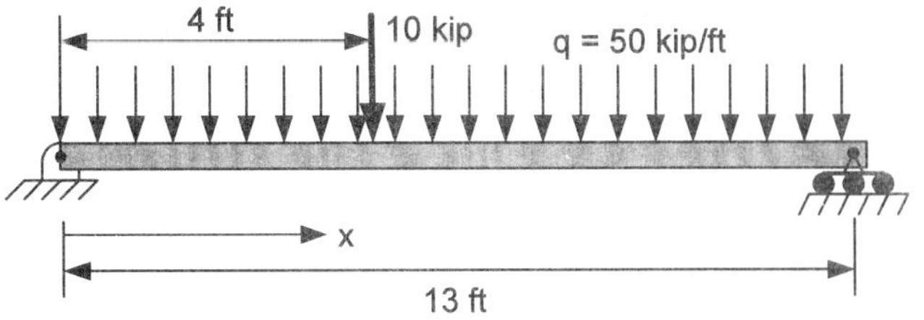

Fig. P4.7

4.8 Construct the shear and bending moment diagrams for the cantilever beam shown in Fig. P4.8 by using:
(a) the equation approach.
(b) the graphical approach.

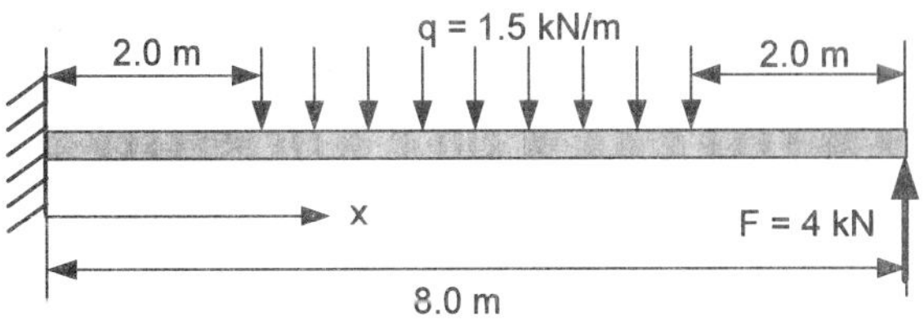

Fig. P4.8

4.9 Construct the shear and bending moment diagrams for the cantilever beam shown in Fig. P4.9 by using:
(a) the equation approach.
(b) the graphical approach.

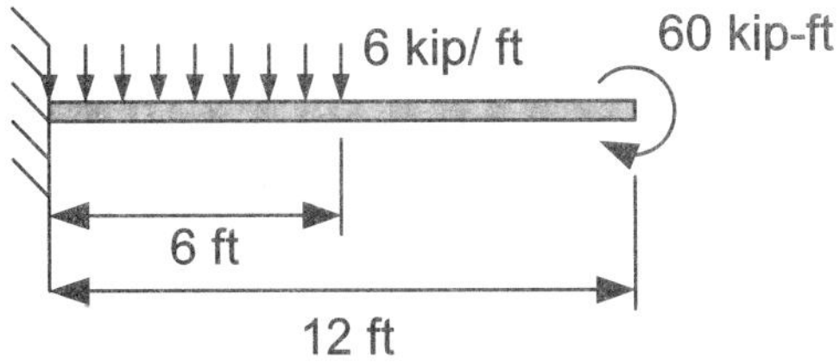

Fig. P4.9

4.10 Draw three different shapes of cross sectional areas that exhibit symmetry about the vertical or y axis.

4.11 In a manufacturing process, an aluminum sheet with a thickness of 1.0 mm is passed around a roller with a 500 mm diameter. Determine (a) the maximum strain and (b) the maximum stress in the sheet when it is bent around the roller.

4.12 A steel sheet with a thickness of 1/32 in. is passed around a roller during a metalworking process. The roller has a diameter of 20 in. Determine (a) the maximum strain and (b) the maximum stress in the sheet when it is bent around the roller.

4.13 A beam with a rectangular cross section has a thickness b = 90 mm and a height h = 800 mm. If the yield strength of the beam's material is 220MPa, determine the maximum moment that the beam can support before it yields if the margin of safety is 100%.

4.14 A beam with a rectangular cross section has a thickness b = 4 in. and a height h = 12 in. The beam is fabricated from 1045 HR steel and supports a maximum moment of 200 kip-ft. Determine the margin of safety of the beam with respect to yielding.

4.15 A beam with a rectangular cross section supports a maximum moment of 50 kN-m with a margin of safety of 150% with respect to yielding. If the beam is fabricated from 2024-T4 aluminum and has a thickness b = 65 mm, determine the required height h for the beam.

4.16 Three planks with dimensions of 2.0 by 8.0 inches are adhesively bonded together to form a timber I beam as shown in Fig. P4.16. Determine the stresses due to bending at points A, B, C and D if the bending moment applied to the beam is (a) +25,000 ft-lb, and (b) −15,000 ft-lb. Indicate whether each stress is tensile or compressive.

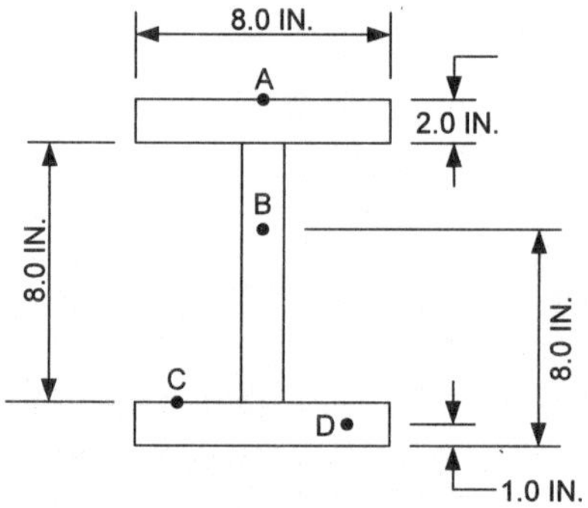

Fig. P4.16

4.17 Consider the flange and web section, defined in Fig. P4.17. If b_w = (A)(b) and h_w = (C)(h), determine the effectiveness ***SE*** as A varies from 0.05 to 0.25 and C varies from 0.7 to 0.95. It is suggested that you perform these calculations on a spreadsheet and prepare a graph displaying your results.

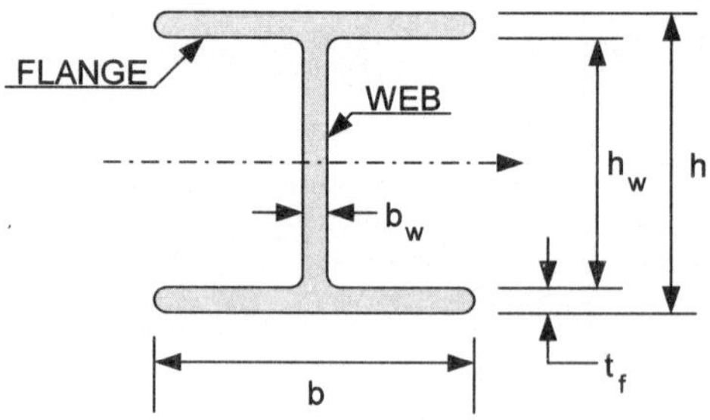

Fig. P4.17

4.18 Calculate values of I_Z and Z relative to the Z-Z axis using the method described in Appendix C for the following beam sections: (a) W406 × 100, (b) S203 × 34, and (c) WT5 × 30. Compare your values with those listed in Appendix D.

4.19 Two steel plates 10.0 in. by 1.0 in. are welded to the flanges of an S18 × 70 American Standard I-beam as shown in Fig. P4.19. Calculate the moment of inertia about each of the axes of symmetry (Y-Y and Z-Z).

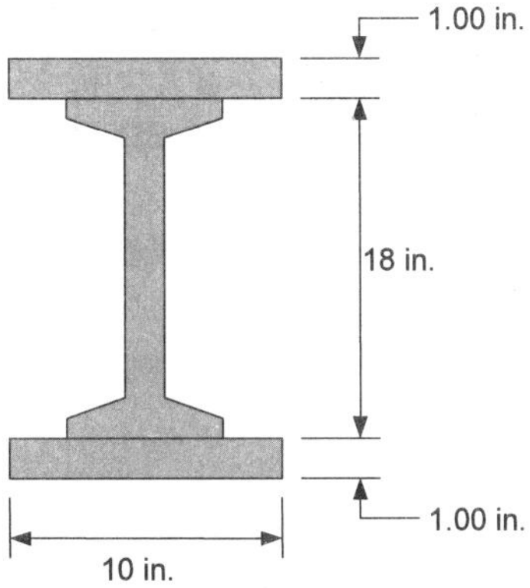

Fig. P4.19

4.20 If the thickness of the two plates were increased from 1.0 in. to 1.25 in. for the modified I-beam shown in Fig. P4.19, determine the moment of inertia about each of the axes of symmetry (Y-Y and Z-Z).

4.21 For the modified I-beam in Fig. P4.19 with the 1.0 in. thick plates, determine the added capacity of the beam in supporting bending moments about the horizontal axis of symmetry.

4.22 A WT6 × 60 structural T section is employed as a cantilever beam. The beam is fabricated from steel that has a yield strength of 52 ksi in tension and 88 ksi in compression. Bending occurs about the z-axis and a safety factor of at least 2.6 is required. Determine the maximum (a) positive bending moment, and (b) negative bending moment that the beam can withstand if all of the requirements are satisfied.

4.23 A WT203 × 30 structural T section is employed as a cantilever beam. The beam is fabricated from steel that has a yield strength of 400 MPa in tension and 800 MPa in compression. Bending occurs about the z-axis and a safety factor of at least 2.0 is required. Determine the maximum (a) positive bending moment, and (b) negative bending moment that the beam can withstand if all of the requirements are satisfied.

4.24 Select a wide-flange (W) section for the steel beam shown in Fig. P4.24. The margin of safety (MOS) is 180% and the yield strength of the material is 280 MPa.

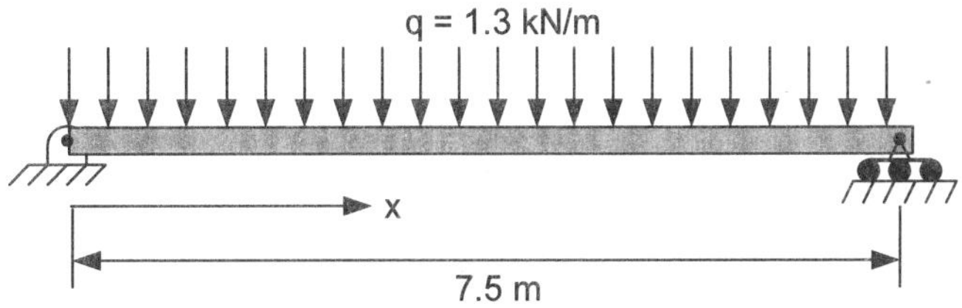

Fig. P4.24

4.25 Select an American Standard (S) section for the steel beam described in Problem 4.2. The margin of safety (MOS) is 200% is and the yield strength of the material is 310 MPa.

4.26 Select a structural tee (WT) section for the steel beam shown in Fig. P4.26. The margin of safety (MOS) is 200% and the yield strength of the material is 300MPa.

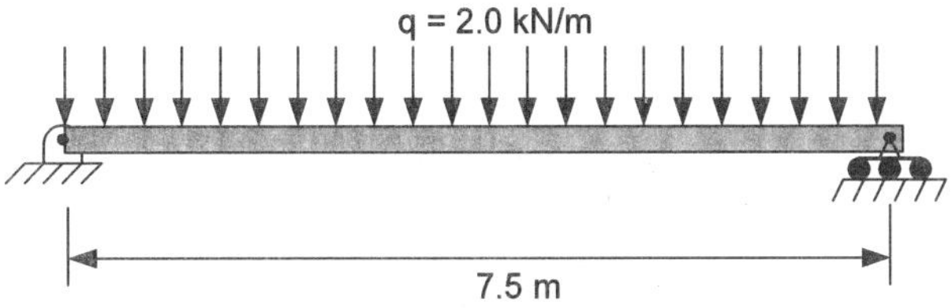

Fig. P4.26

4.27 Select a wide-flange (W) section for the steel beam described in Problem 4.3. The margin of safety (MOS) is 150% and the yield strength of the material is 40 ksi.

4.28 Select an American Standard (S) section for the steel beam shown in Fig. P4.28. The margin of safety (MOS) is 100% is and the yield strength of the material is 310 MPa.

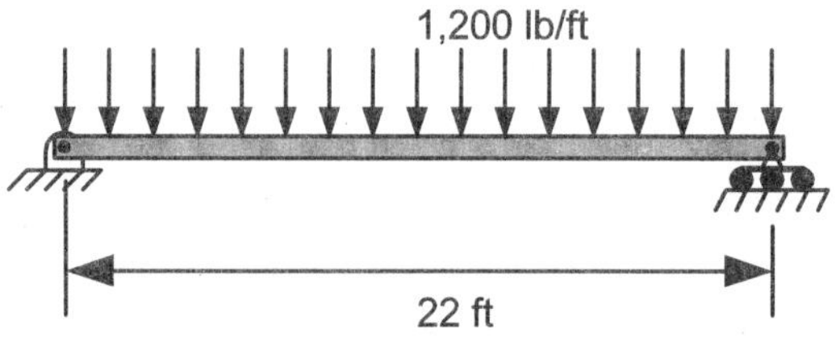

Fig. P4.28

4.29 Select a structural tee (WT) section for the steel beam described in Problem 4.5. The margin of safety (MOS) is 200% and the yield strength of the material is 60 ksi.

4.30 For the beam described in Fig. P4.30, determine the maximum (a) shear stress and (b) normal stress if the cross section of the beam is rectangular with a height h = 6.0 in. and a thickness b = 1.25 in.

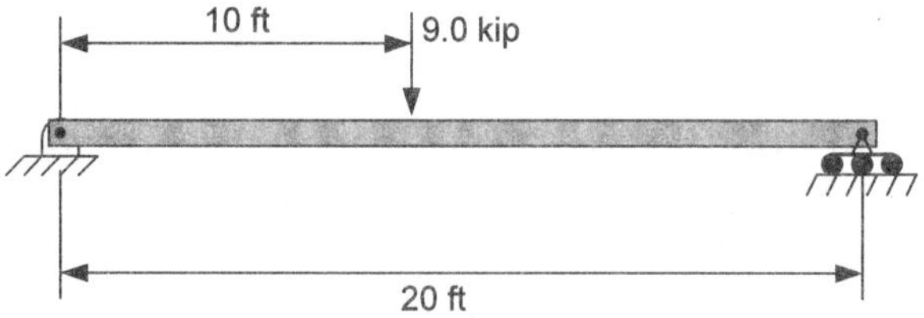

Fig. P4.30

4.31 Repeat Problem 4.30 if the cross section is changed to a rectangular tube (i.e. box beam) with a height h = 6.0 in., a thickness b = 1.25 in., and a wall thickness t = 0.25 in.

4.32 A circular shaft with a diameter of 60 mm is subjected to transverse loading from a gear set. The shaft is simply-supported with a concentrated force of 70 kN at the center of a 600 mm span. Determine the maximum (a) shear stress and (b) normal stress in the shaft.

4.33 Repeat Problem 4.32 if the cross section is changed to a circular tube with an outer diameter of 60 mm and an inner diameter of 50 mm.

4.34 Calculate the largest vertical shear force V that can be supported by a W305 × 45 wide-flange beam if the shear stress is limited to 120 MPa.

4.35 Calculate the largest vertical shear force V that can be supported by a WT7 × 60 structural tee beam if the shear stress is limited to 20 ksi.

4.36 Calculate the largest vertical shear force V that can be supported by a S8 × 23 American standard beam if the shear stress is limited to 100 MPa.

4.37 A cantilever beam supports a vertical load of 30 kips at the free end. The beam is composed of a W10 × 60 wide-flange section and is 4 ft. long. Calculate (a) the maximum normal stress, (b) the maximum shear stress, and (c) the shear stress at the junction between the web and the flange.

4.38 A simply-supported beam supports a uniform distributed load of 40 kN/m across the entire span. The beam is composed of an S305 × 74 American standard section and is 5 m long. Calculate (a) the maximum normal stress, (b) the maximum shear stress, and (c) the shear stress at the junction between the web and the flange.

4.39 A simply-supported beam supports a vertical load of 15 kips at the center of a 30 ft. span. The beam is composed of a WT5 × 30 structural tee section. Calculate (a) the maximum normal stress, (b) the maximum shear stress, and (c) the shear stress at the junction between the web and the flange.

4.40 The maximum shear stress for an I-beam is often approximated as $\tau \approx V/A_{web}$. Calculate the error between this approximation and the actual shear stress determined from Eq. (4.22) for the following beams: (a) W24 × 104, (b) W10 × 60, (c) S15 × 50, and (d) S8 × 23. Assume each beam is subjected to a shear load of 10 kips.

4.41 A timber company has designed a series of box beams with the geometry presented in the Fig. P4.41. The beams are constructed by bonding the top and bottom boards to the edges of the vertical members at the four interfaces. Determine the maximum shear stress τ_{Max} and the shear stress at the adhesive joints. The vertical shear force V is 8.0 kN.

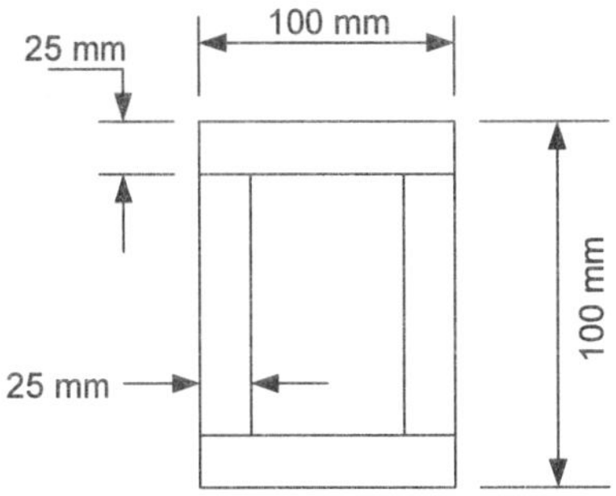

Fig. P4.41

4.42 Repeat Problem 4.41 if the beam height is increased to 400 mm. All other dimensions remain the same.

4.43 A timber company has designed a series of unsymmetrical T-sections to serve as beams as indicated in Fig. P4.43. The beams are constructed by bonding the top and bottom flanges to the edges of the vertical web at the two interfaces. Determine the maximum shear stress τ_{Max} and the shear stress at each of the adhesive joints. The vertical shear force V is 4,000 lb.

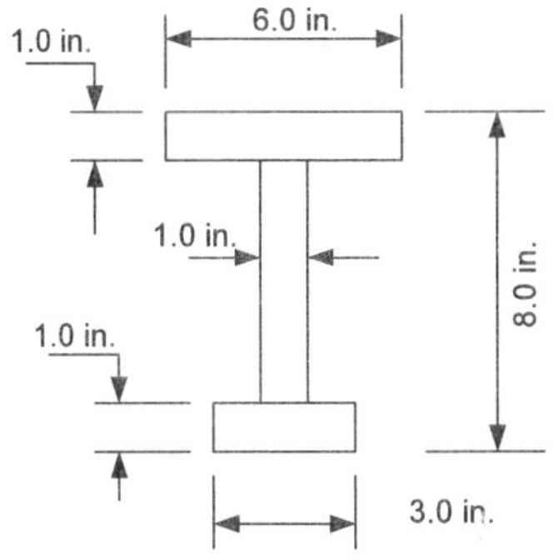

Fig. P4.43

4.44 Repeat Problem 4.43 if the width of the bottom flange is increased to 9.0 in. All other dimensions remain the same.

4.45 A box beam is formed by adhesively bonding together four planks, as shown in Fig. P4.45. The planks are each 2 in. thick. The shear strength of the adhesive is S_{ys} = 500 psi. If the beam is subjected to a maximum shear force V = 12 kip, determine the safety factor for the adhesive joints.

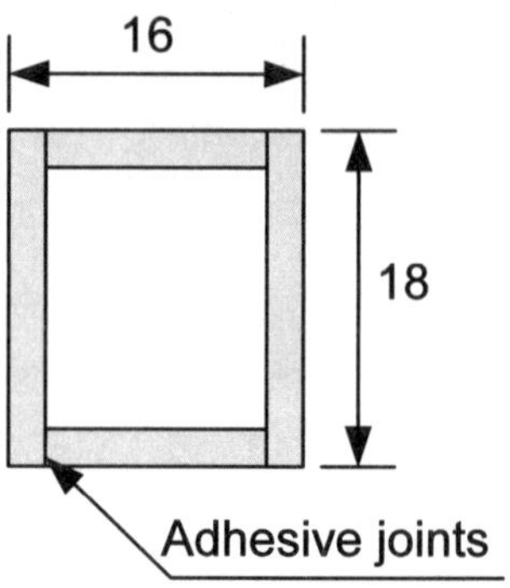

Fig. P4.45

4.46 Repeat Problem 4.45 if the plank thickness is increased to 4 in. All other dimensions remain the same.

4.47 A timber company produces a series of I-beams fabricated from three pieces of timber as shown in Fig. P4.47. The flange of the I-beam is fastened to the web with spikes that are each capable of resisting a shear force of 960 lb. The beams are 16 ft long and are simply supported. They carry a concentrated force of 2,800 lb at mid-span. Determine the maximum spacing of the spikes needed to transmit the shear from the web to the flange of the beam.

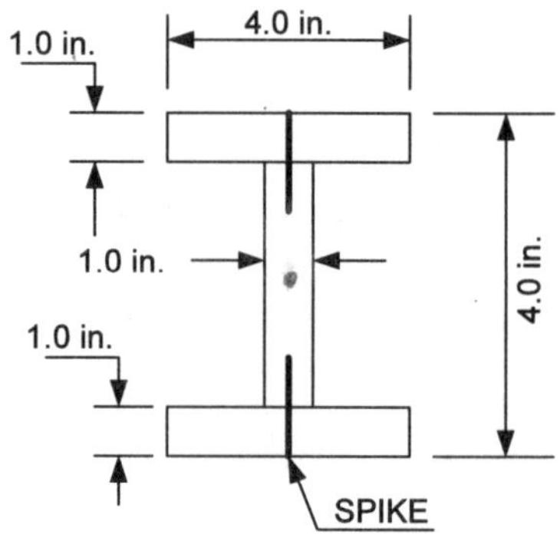

Fig. P4.47

4.48 Repeat Problem 4.47 if the height of the beam is increased to 8 in. All other dimensions remain the same.

4.49 An S18 × 70 American Standard I-beam is reinforced by bolting steel plates to the top and bottom flanges, as shown in Fig. P4.49. Each steel plate is 10 in. wide by 1 in. high and is attached to the flange by two steel bolts (not shown). Each bolt can withstand a shear force of 25 kips. If the beam is subjected to a vertical shear force V = 100 kips, find the maximum longitudinal spacing of the bolts.

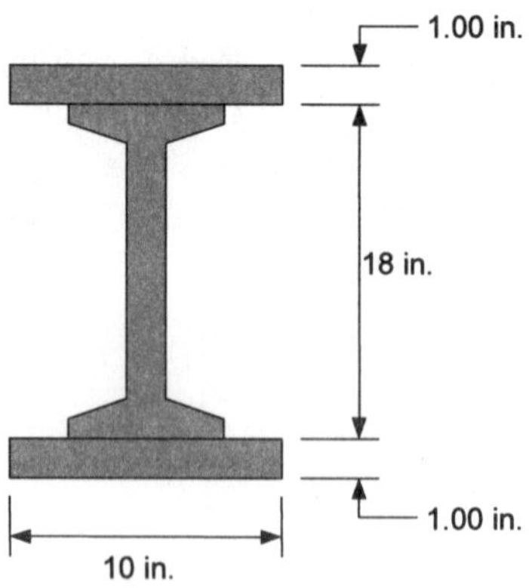

Fig. P4.49

4.50 Repeat Problem 4.48 if the bottom plate is removed and the height of the top plate in increased to 2 in. All other information remains the same.

4.51 Consider a simply-supported, foam core, metal cover plate composite beam as illustrated in Fig. P4.51. If the beam is loaded with a uniformly distributed load, determine the magnitude of q_Y that produces yielding. Aluminum cover plates are adhesively bonded to a polystyrene foam core. The beam is 3.2 m long and the yield strength of the aluminum is 280 MPa.

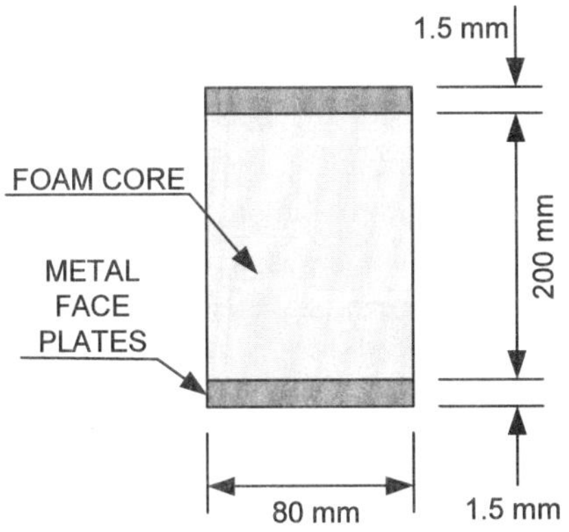

Fig. P4.51

4.52 Design a portable, one-way, bridge beam with a single structural member consisting of metal cover plates and foam core. The bridge is to support the weight of six people uniformly distributed over the span of the bridge beam. Assume that the average weight of a typical person is 650 N. The bridge beam spans a ravine 9 m wide.

4.53 A cantilever beam 2.5m long is subjected to a concentrated force of 1,200 N applied at its free end. The beam has a rectangular cross section with a width of 120 mm. Determine the height of the foam h_f and the thickness of the cover plate t_m if the design stress in each plate is limited to 160 MPa. In this determination, recall that the standard thickness of aluminum sheet stock from which the cover plates are cut is 0.016, 0.020, 0.025, 0.032, 0.040, 0.050, 0.063, and 0.090 in.

4.54 A beam fabricated from western white pine, with dimensions shown in Fig. P4.54, has been reinforced by bonding steel strips on its top and bottom surfaces. If the design stress is limited to 1.5 ksi in the wood and 35 ksi in the steel, determine the maximum bending moment if the beam bends about its horizontal axis of symmetry.

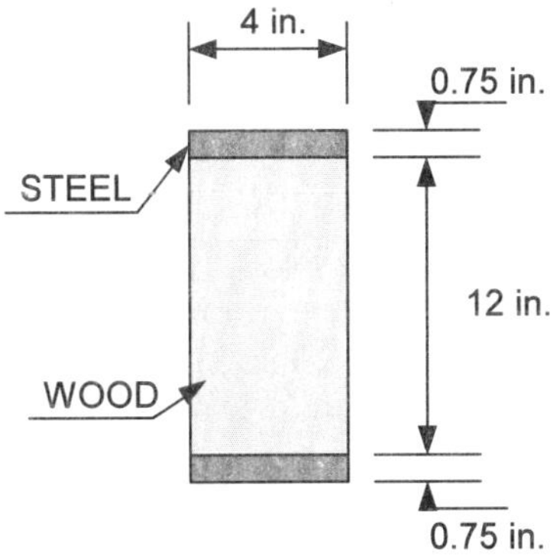

Fig. P4.54

4.55 For the wood and steel composite beam described in Problem 4.54, determine the maximum bending moment if the beam is bent about its vertical axis of symmetry.

4.56 Repeat Problem 4.54 if aluminum strips are used instead of steel strips. All other information remains the same.

4.57 For the wood and aluminum composite beam described in Problem 4.56, determine the maximum bending moment if the beam is bent about its vertical axis of symmetry.

4.58 Repeat Problem 4.54 if the top steel strip is removed. All other information remains the same.

4.59 Repeat Problem 4.55 if the top steel strip is removed. All other information remains the same.

4.60 A composite beam consists of an aluminum core reinforced with steel strips bonded to the top and bottom surfaces, as shown in Fig. P4.60. The aluminum has a width of 100 mm and a height of 200 mm. Each steel strip has a width of 100 mm and a thickness of 20 mm. If the beam is bent around a horizontal axis with a moment M = 50 kN-m, determine the maximum stresses in the steel and in the aluminum.

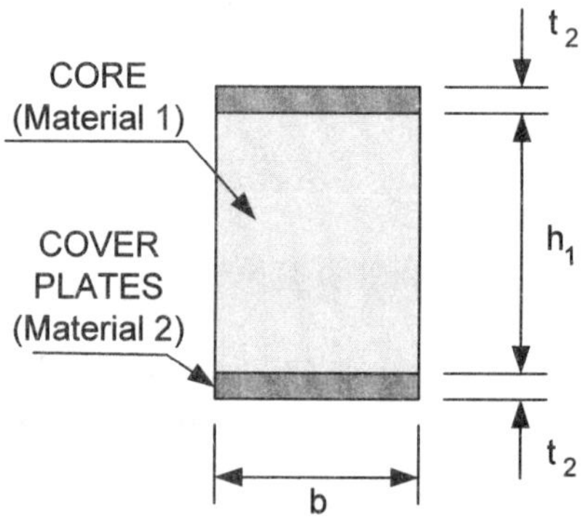

Fig. P4.60

4.61 Repeat Problem 4.60 for a composite beam with a steel core reinforced with brass strips bonded to the top and bottom surfaces. The beam dimensions and loading remain unchanged.

4.62 Repeat Problem 4.60 for a composite beam with a brass core reinforced with aluminum strips bonded to the top and bottom surfaces. The beam dimensions and loading remain unchanged.

4.63 Repeat Problem 4.60 if the top steel strip is removed. All other information remains the same.

4.64 Repeat Problem 4.61 if the top brass strip is removed. All other information remains the same.

4.65 Repeat Problem 4.62 if the top aluminum strip is removed. All other information remains the same.

4.66 Derive Eq. (4.37) and Eq. (4.40).

4.67 A concrete floor slab is reinforced with 10 steel rebars each with a diameter of ¾ in. as illustrated in Fig. P4.67. The slab is 24 ft long and is simply supported when installed. If a uniformly distributed load q is applied to the floor, determine its maximum magnitude if the stress in the steel is limited to 25 ksi and in the concrete to 2,500 psi. Note the modulus of elasticity of the steel and the concrete is 30×10^6 and 2.8×10^6 psi, respectively. Comment on the balance of the design of this reinforced concrete slab.

Fig. P4.67

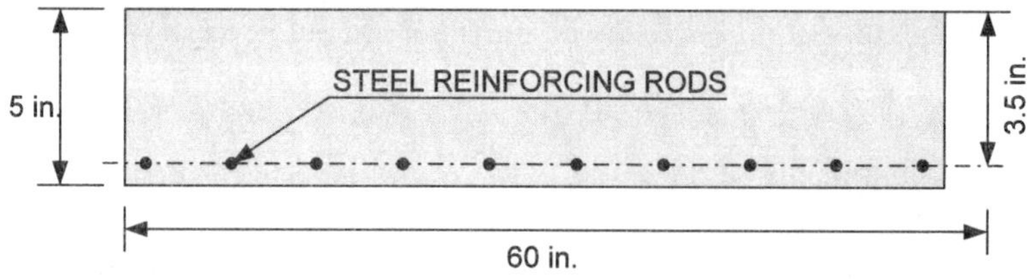

4.68 Repeat Problem 4.67 if high strength concrete is used, with an elastic modulus of 4.5×10^6 psi and a maximum stress limit of 4,000 psi. All other information remains the same.

4.69 A concrete beam is reinforced with 5 steel rebars each with a ¾ in. diameter as shown in Fig. P4.69. The beam is 20 ft long and simply supported. If it supports three concentrated forces each 10.0 kip positioned at L/4, L/2 and 3L/4, determine the margin of safety for the beam. The yield strength of the rebar is 36 ksi and the compressive strength of concrete is 3.0 ksi. The modulus of elasticity of the steel and the concrete is 30×10^6 and 2.8×10^6 psi, respectively.

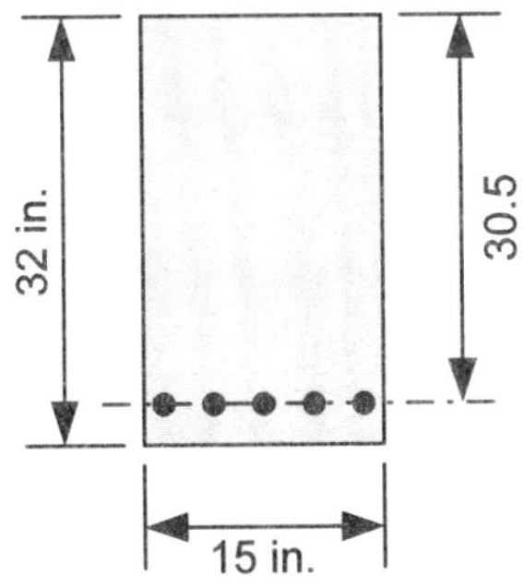

Fig. P4.69

4.70 Repeat Problem 4.69 if high strength concrete is used, with an elastic modulus of 4.5×10^6 psi and a maximum compressive strength of 6 ksi. All other information remains the same.

4.71 A high strength concrete beam is reinforced with 3 steel rods each with an area of 300 mm² located at positions shown in Fig. P4.71. For an applied bending moment of M = 12 kN-m, determine the maximum stress in the steel rebars and the concrete.

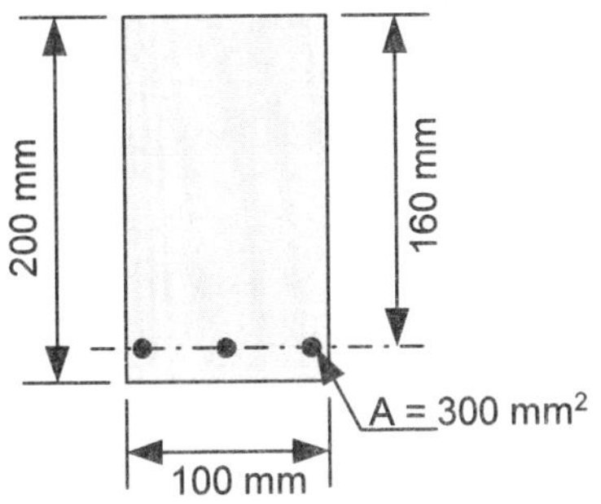

Fig. P4.71

4.72 Repeat Problem 4.71 if 4 steel rods are used rather than 3. All other information remains the same.

4.73 Discuss the advantage of using steel reinforced concrete beams as structural components in a building in the event of a severe fire. In your discussion, discuss the effect of prolonged exposure to flames on the strength of steel.

4.74 Redesign the steel reinforced concrete floor slab in Example 4.19 to improve the balance between the stresses in the steel and concrete.

4.75 Redesign the steel reinforced concrete beam in Example 4.20 to improve the balance in the margin of safety between the steel and concrete.

4.76 A beam with a rectangular cross section, defined in Fig. P4.76, is fabricated from steel with S_y = 280 MPa. Determine the yield moment M_Y.

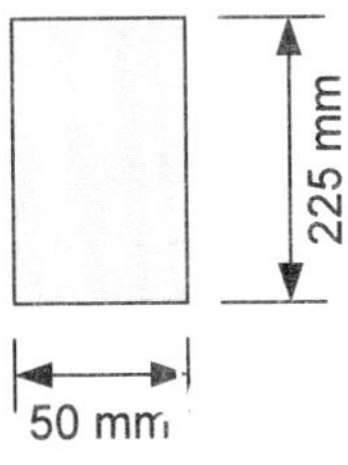

Fig. P4.76

4.77 A beam with a rectangular cross section, defined in the Problem 4.76, is fabricated from steel with $S_y = 300$ MPa. Determine the moment M_p required to drive the elastic-plastic interface to the position $y_p = h/4$.

4.78 For a beam with a rectangular cross section, show that $M_P = M_Y$ when $y_p = h/2$. You may wish to examine Eq. (4.42) in developing this solution.

4.79 Determine the ratio of M_L/M_Y for the web and flange section, defined in Fig. P4.79, if $b_w = (A)(b)$ and $h_w = (C)(h)$. Let A vary from 0.05 to 0.25 and C vary from 0.75 to 0.95. It is suggested that you perform these calculations on a spreadsheet and prepare a graph displaying your results.

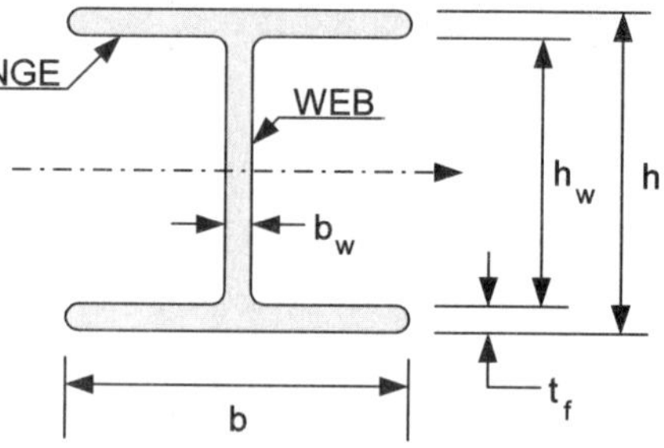

Fig. P4.79

4.80 Determine the eccentricity e locating the shear center for a beam fabricated from the channel section as shown in Fig. P4.80.

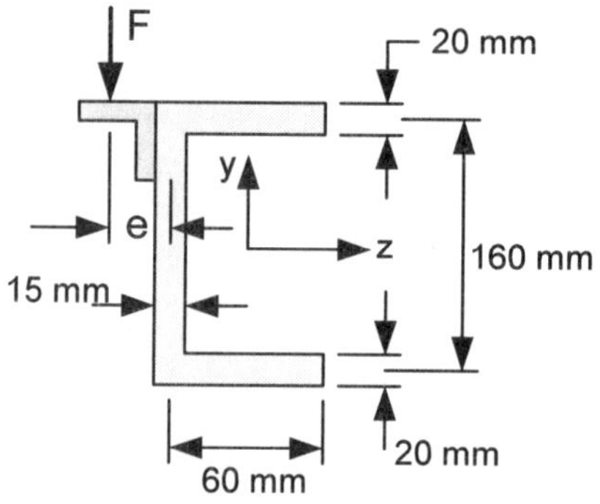

Fig. P4.80

4.81 For the channel section, illustrated in Fig. P4.80, show that integrating the parabolic distribution of shear stresses over the area of the web yields a shear force V equal to:

$$V = F\left[\frac{2ct_1 + (3/5)ht_2}{2ct_1 + (2/3)ht_2}\right]$$

Explain why V is slightly less than F. Hint: the shear stress at the top of the web is given by:

$$\tau = F\left[\frac{ct_1h}{t_2I_z}\right]$$

CHAPTER 5

DEFLECTION OF BEAMS

5.1 INTRODUCTION

In Chapter 4, we studied the bending stresses produced in beams subjected to transverse loading. These uniaxial stresses σ_x were generated by the bending moments M(x) produced by the transverse loads. When a beam is subjected to a moment as shown in Fig. 5.1, it bends into a circular arc and deflects. As the beam deforms, the neutral axis becomes a circular arc and plane sections remain plane.

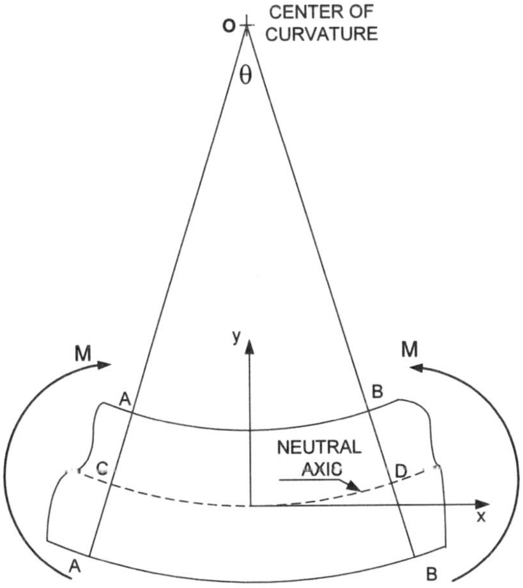

Fig. 5.1 A bending moment M causes the neutral axis of the beam to form a circular arc and deflect.

In Section 4.4, we used the geometry of the beam's deformation and equilibrium relations to position the neutral axis and to establish a relation between the bending moment and the radius of curvature ρ as:

$$M(x) = (EI_z/\rho) \tag{4.8}$$

$$\kappa = 1/\rho = M(x)/[EI_z] \tag{4.9}$$

where $\kappa = 1/\rho$ is the curvature of the beam and M(x) is a moment that varies with x.

5.2 THE ELASTIC CURVE FOR A BEAM

When a beam deflects under the action of a bending moment, the neutral axis becomes curved. Locally it is a circular arc with a radius of curvature ρ that depends on the bending moment M(x). As the local curvature varies with the bending moment, the neutral axis generates an elastic curve over the length of the beam. If we can write an equation for the elastic curve (the deformed shape of the neutral axis), the deflection of the beam will be apparent.

Let's rewrite Eq. (4.8) as:

$$1/\rho = (M/EI_z) \tag{5.1}$$

A well-known relation from calculus gives the curvature κ of any curve as a function of the derivatives of y as:

$$\kappa = \frac{1}{\rho} = \frac{\dfrac{d^2y}{dx^2}}{\left[1+\left(\dfrac{dy}{dx}\right)^2\right]^{3/2}} \tag{5.2}$$

Well-designed beams are stiff and consequently the deflections are very small compared to the length of the beam. Because of this fact, the slope of the elastic curve (dy/dx) is small when compared to 1 and $(dy/dx)^2$ is extremely small compared to 1. Hence, Eq. (5.2) can be closely approximated with:

$$\kappa = \frac{1}{\rho} = \frac{d^2y}{dx^2} \tag{5.3}$$

Substituting Eq. (5.1) into (5.3) yields:

$$\frac{d^2y}{dx^2} = \frac{M(x)}{EI_z} \tag{5.4}$$

If we recall Eq. (4.2), which states that shear force V(x) = dM(x)/dx, and substitute this relation into Eq. (5.4), we obtain:

$$\frac{d^3y}{dx^3} = \frac{V(x)}{EI_z} \tag{5.5}$$

Similarly note that the load q(x) = – dV(x)/dx and substitute this relation into Eq. (5.5) to obtain:

$$\frac{d^4y}{dx^4} = \frac{-q(x)}{EI_z} \tag{5.6}$$

Clearly the elastic curve y(x) can be determined by integrating any one of the three equations given above. We usually employ Eq. (5.4) because only two integrations are necessary to obtain the results for the elastic curve y(x) for the beam.

5.3 ESTABLISHING THE ELASTIC CURVE BY INTEGRATION

There are three different approaches for determining the equation describing the elastic curve which include:

1. Integrating the equation for the bending moment M(x) with respect to x
2. Integrating the equation for the shear force V(x) with respect to x
3. Integrating the equation for the transverse loading q(x) with respect to x

We usually integrate Eq. (5.4), which involves M(x) because only two integrations are needed to convert d^2y/dx^2 into y(x). The mathematics give rise to two integration constants that are determined so as to satisfy constraints to the beam by its supports. In most examples, the integration is not difficult because M(x) is usually a polynomial in x. The difficulty arises in the form of the moment equation. In many instances, a single equation cannot be written that expresses M(x) over the entire length L of the beam. Instead, it is often necessary to write two or more different equations for M(x), each valid over a segment of the beam. Each of these moment equations must be integrated twice and the two constants of integration must be determined for each beam segment. The result is a time-consuming and tedious approach in which there are many opportunities for mathematical errors.

It is possible to integrate Eq. (5.5) to obtain the equation for the elastic curve y(x). In this case, we integrate the function for the shear force V(x) with respect to x. Because the unknown y occurs as the third derivative in Eq. (5.5), it is clear that the solution for the differential equation requires three integrations giving rise to three constants of integration. Because all of the mathematical difficulties mentioned in the previous paragraph occur with this approach, there is little merit in pursuing the topic.

It is also possible to integrate Eq. (5.6) to obtain the equation for the elastic curve y(x). In this case, we integrate the function for the load q(x) with respect to x. As the unknown y occurs as the fourth derivative in Eq. (5.6), it is clear that the solution for the differential equation requires four integrations giving rise to four constants of integration. Because all of the mathematical difficulties mentioned in the previous two paragraphs become more severe with this approach, there is very little merit in pursuing the topic.

Regardless of the approach employed to determine the equation of the elastic curve by integration we make several assumptions, which include:

- The deflections are small compared to the length of the beam so that the slope (dy/dx) is small and the square of the slope $(dy/dx)^2$ is negligible when compared to unity.
- The stresses in the beam are lower than the yield strength so that the modulus of elasticity E can be treated as a constant.
- The beam's cross-section does not change along the length of the beam so that the second moment of inertia I_z is a constant with respect to x.
- The distortion due to the shearing stress τ_{xy} is sufficiently small that the out of plane deformations of the beam's section can be ignored. (Plane sections remain plane.)

Let's consider six examples that demonstrate the integration method, describe the effect of beam constraints (boundary conditions), and make use of compatibility and symmetry conditions. We will test the small slope approximation and illustrate some of the difficulties encountered with this approach.

EXAMPLE 5.1

Determine the elastic curve for the simply supported beam subjected to a uniformly distributed load q as shown in Fig. E5.1.

Fig. E5.1

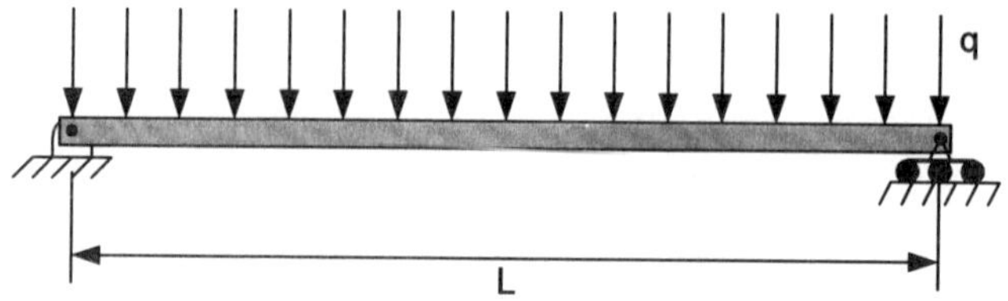

Solution:

Step 1: Prepare a FBD of the entire beam and employ the equilibrium relations to determine the reactions at the beam's simple supports. We have performed this task in Example 4.2 and obtained the results shown below for the reaction forces R_L and R_R as:

$$R_L = R_R = qL/2 \tag{a}$$

Step 2: Prepare a FBD of a segment removed from the left side of the beam, and solve for the internal shear force V(x) and the internal moment M(x). See Fig. E4.2a.

$$V(x) = (q/2)(L - 2x) \quad \Rightarrow \quad 0 < x < L \tag{b}$$

$$M(x) = (qx/2)(L - x) \quad \Rightarrow \quad 0 < x < L \tag{c}$$

Step 3: Write the differential equation for the elastic curve by substituting Eq. (c) into Eq. (5.4) to obtain:

$$EI_Z \frac{d^2y}{dx^2} = \frac{qx}{2}(L - x) \tag{d}$$

Step 4: Integrate both sides of Eq. (d) and simplify to obtain:

$$EI_Z \frac{dy}{dx} = \frac{q}{2}\left(\frac{x^2L}{2} - \frac{x^3}{3}\right) + C_1 = \frac{qx^2}{12}(3L - 2x) + C_1 \tag{e}$$

$$EI_Z y = \frac{q}{12}\left(x^3L - \frac{x^4}{2}\right) + C_1x + C_2 = \frac{qx^3}{24}(2L - x) + C_1x + C_2 \tag{f}$$

Step 5: The integration process has generated two constants of integration — C_1 and C_2. To determine these constants, we examine the constraints placed on the beam because these constraints control the shape of the elastic curve. The beam is constrained at its supports. On the left end, where x = 0, the beam is constrained by a pin and clevis arrangement which provides the following constraint:

$$y(0) = 0 \tag{g}$$

At the right end, where x = L, the beam is constrained by a set of rollers, which provides the following constraint:

$$y(L) = 0 \tag{h}$$

Step 6: The relations presented in Eqs. (g) and (h) are known as boundary conditions. Let's substitute the boundary requirement of Eq. (g) into Eq. (f) to obtain:

$$y(0) = 0 \qquad \Rightarrow \qquad C_2 = 0 \tag{i}$$

Now substitute Eq. (h) into Eq. (f) to obtain:

$$EI_Z y = \frac{qL^3}{24}(2L - L) + C_1 L = 0 \tag{j}$$

Solving for C_1 yields:

$$C_1 = -\frac{qL^3}{24} \tag{k}$$

Substituting Eq. (k) into Eq. (f) gives the relation for the elastic curve from $0 < x < L$ as:

$$y = \frac{qx}{24EI_Z}\left[x^2(2L - x) - L^3\right] \tag{5.7}$$

Following a similar process, we can write the expression for the slope (dy/dx) as:

$$\frac{dy}{dx} = \frac{q}{24EI_Z}\left(6x^2L - 4x^3 - L^3\right) \tag{5.8}$$

We have evaluated Eq. (5.7) to determine $24EI_Zy/q$ as a function of x where x varied from 0 to L with L = 1.0 units. The result is shown in Fig. E5.1a.

Fig. E5.1a

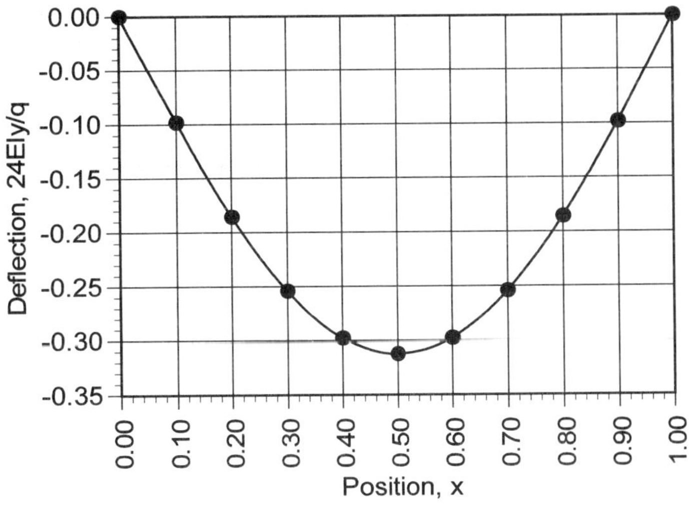

The normalized value of y associated with the elastic curve is a negative quantity because we defined y positive upward previously in Chapter 4. The elastic curve presented in Fig. E5.1a indicates that the deflection y is zero at x = 0 and x = L as required by the constraints of the simply supported beam. The deflection is a maximum at the center of the span of the beam.

EXAMPLE 5.2

The simply supported beam in Example 5.1 is fabricated from a wide flange rolled steel shape. The architect designing the building has indicated a W8 × 40 beam from 1020 HR steel. The beam is 24 ft long and the uniformly distributed load q = 600 lb/ft. Determine the maximum stresses in the beam and the safety factor against failure by yielding, the maximum deflection and the maximum slope. Interpret the results.

Solution:

Step 1: The maximum bending stress σ_{Max} in the beam is calculated from Eq. (4.13) as:

$$\sigma_{Max} = M_{Max}/Z = qL^2/(8Z) \qquad \text{(a)}$$

where $M_{Max} = qL^2/8$ and Z is the section modulus

Reference to Appendix D indicates that the section modulus Z and moment of inertia I_z for a W8 × 40 beam are:

$$Z = 35.5 \text{ in.}^3 \qquad I_z = 146 \text{ in.}^4 \qquad \text{(b)}$$

From Eq. (a) and (b), we write:

$$\sigma_{Max} = qL^2/(8Z) = (600)(24)^2(12)/[(8)(35.5)] = 14.60 \text{ ksi} \qquad \text{(c)}$$

From Appendix B-2, we find S_y = 42 ksi for 1020 HR steel. Then we can determine the safety factor as:

$$SF = S_y/\sigma_{Max} = 42/14.60 = 2.88 \qquad \text{(d)}$$

This is a reasonable safety factor considering that the loads in a building are well known and not subject to significant changes over the anticipated service life of the structure.

Step 2: The maximum deflection y is calculated by setting x = L/2 in Eq. (5.7) to obtain:

$$y_{Max} = -\frac{5qL^4}{384EI_Z} \qquad (5.9)$$

Substituting numerical parameters into Eq. (5.9) gives:

$$y_{Max} = -\frac{5qL^4}{384EI_Z} = -\frac{(5)(600)(24)^4(12)^4}{(384)(12)(30\times 10^6)(146)} = -1.023 \text{ in.} \qquad \text{(e)}$$

While this deflection is small compared to the length of the beam it is relatively large compared to the 8.25 in. height of the beam. A suggestion to the architect to consider a W16 × 40 section is in order. This beam has the same weight of 40 lb/ft, but much higher values for Z and I_z. The increase in cost would be modest for significant improvements in both strength and rigidity. The only disadvantage is the increased height of the structure that would be required to accommodate the increased height of the beam.

Step 3: It is evident from an examination of Fig. E5.1a that the maximum slope occurs at the supports for the beam where x = 0 and L. At x = 0, Eq. (5.8) reduces to:

$$\left(\frac{dy}{dx}\right)_{Max} = -\frac{qL^3}{24EI_Z} = -\frac{(600)(24)^3(12)^3}{(24)(12)(30\times 10^6)(146)} = -11.36\times 10^{-3} \qquad \text{(f)}$$

The negative sign in Eq. (f) indicates that the deflection y is becoming more negative as x is increasing. Let's square Eq. (f) and compare the result to unity.

$$\left(\frac{dy}{dx}\right)^2_{Max} = \left(-11.362\times 10^{-3}\right)^2 = 1.290\times 10^{-4} \qquad \text{(g)}$$

Clearly, the square of the maximum slope for this practical example is extremely small when compared with unity. This fact verifies the assumption made in reducing the form of Eq. (5.2) to the much simpler version presented in Eq. (5.3).

EXAMPLE 5.3

Derive the equation for the elastic curve for the simply supported beam loaded with a single concentrated force F, as shown in Fig. E5.3.

Fig. E5.3

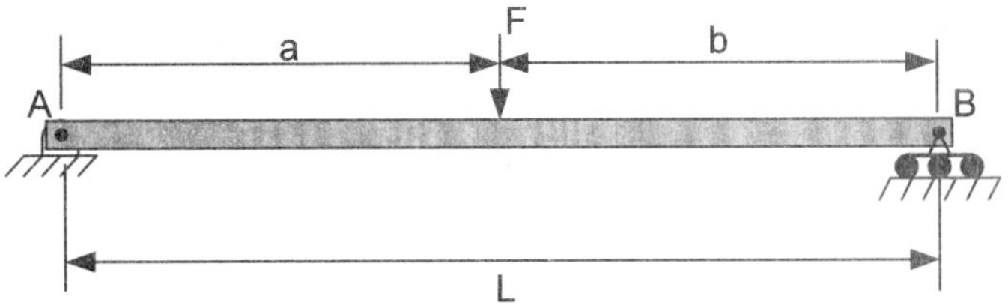

Solution:

Step 1: Determine the reaction forces at the simple supports. Reference to Section 4.2.1 shows the approach and gives the results as:

$$R_L = Fb/L \qquad R_R = Fa/L \qquad \text{(a)}$$

Step 2: Write equations for the bending moment M as a function of x covering the range in x from zero to L. The procedure followed is illustrated in Section 4.2.1.

$$M(x) = Fbx/L \qquad 0 \le x < a \qquad \text{(b)}$$

$$M(x) = Fbx/L - F(x - a) \qquad a \le x \le L \qquad \text{(c)}$$

These results differ from those presented in Example 5.1 where a single relation was written to describe the distribution of the bending moments over the entire length of the beam. The fact that it is necessary to write two equations to express M(x) complicates the solution.

Step 3: Write the differential equations for the elastic curve by substituting Eqs. (b) and (c) into Eq. (5.4) to obtain:

$$EI_z \frac{d^2y_1}{dx^2} = M(x) = \frac{Fbx}{L} \qquad 0 \le x \le a \qquad \text{(d)}$$

$$EI_z \frac{d^2y_2}{dx^2} = M(x) = \frac{Fbx}{L} - F(x-a) \qquad a \le x \le L \qquad \text{(e)}$$

Step 4: Integrate these second order differential equations once to obtain the equation for the slopes of the elastic curve as:

$$EI_z \frac{dy_1}{dx} = \frac{Fbx^2}{2L} + C_1 \qquad 0 \le x \le a \qquad \text{(f)}$$

$$EI_z \frac{dy_2}{dx} = \frac{Fbx^2}{2L} - \frac{F(x-a)^2}{2} + C_2 \qquad a \le x \le L \qquad \text{(g)}$$

Step 5: Before proceeding, let's use one of the compatibility conditions to evaluate the constants of integration in Eqs. (f) and (g). The elastic curve is continuous at the point of load application. Hence, the slope of the elastic curve dy_1/dx is the same as the slope dy_2/dx at x = a where we transition from one solution for the slope to another. Accordingly, we equate Eq. (f) and Eq. (g) and set x = a to obtain:

$$\frac{Fba^2}{2L} + C_1 = \frac{Fba^2}{2L} - 0 + C_2 \qquad \text{at } x = a$$

$$C_1 = C_2 \qquad \text{(h)}$$

Step 6: Integrate Eqs. (f) and (g) to obtain the equations for the elastic curve as:

$$EI_z y_1 = \frac{Fbx^3}{6L} + C_1x + C_3 \qquad 0 \le x \le a \qquad \text{(i)}$$

$$EI_z y_2 = \frac{Fbx^3}{6L} - \frac{F(x-a)^3}{6} + C_1x + C_4 \qquad a \le x \le L \qquad \text{(j)}$$

Step 7: Let's again recognize the compatibility conditions that exist at x = a. Because the elastic curve is continuous, it is clear that $y_1 = y_2$ at x = a. Hence, we can equate Eq. (i) and Eq. (j) and set x = a to obtain:

$$\frac{Fba^3}{6L} + C_1 a + C_3 = \frac{Fba^3}{6L} - \frac{F(a-a)^3}{6} + C_1 a + C_4 \qquad \text{at } x = a$$

$$C_3 = C_4 \tag{k}$$

We have used the two compatibility conditions to establish that $C_1 = C_2$ and $C_3 = C_4$, which reduces the four constants of integration to two.

Step 8: Let's consider the constraints placed on the elastic curve by the simple supports at each end of the beam. Clearly, the simple supports constrain the deflection at both ends of the beam to zero. Hence, we can write:

$$y_1(0) = 0 \tag{l}$$

$$y_2(L) = 0 \tag{m}$$

Substituting Eq. (l) into Eq. (i) and recalling Eq. (k) gives:

$$C_3 = 0 = C_4 \tag{n}$$

Substituting Eq. (m) into Eq. (j) gives:

$$0 = \frac{FbL^3}{6L} - \frac{F(L-a)^3}{6} + C_1 L + 0$$

$$C_1 = -\frac{Fb}{6L}(L^2 - b^2) \tag{o}$$

Step 9: With the four constants of integration established, we write the solutions for the elastic curve as:

$$EI_z y_1 = -\frac{Fbx}{6L}(L^2 - x^2 - b^2) \qquad 0 \le x \le a \tag{5.10}$$

$$EI_z y_2 = -\frac{Fbx}{6L}(L^2 - x^2 - b^2) - \frac{F(x-a)^3}{6} \qquad a \le x \le L \tag{5.11}$$

We will determine the maximum deflection of a simply supported beam with a concentrated load in the next example. However, you should be aware that the double integration method often gives rise to four or even six constants of integration. As such, it is tedious and time consuming to execute solutions to even simple problems. We will introduce a method involving singularity functions in Section 5.4 that involves the determination of only two constants of integration.

EXAMPLE 5.4

For the simply supported beam described in Example 5.3, determine the maximum deflection y_{Max}. The beam spans 7 m and is made from an American Standard shape with a designation of S203 × 34. The beam is fabricated from 1020 HR steel. A concentrated force of F = 8 kN is applied at a = 4 m.

Solution:

Step 1: Let's begin by deriving the equation for the maximum deflection by considering the slope dy_1/dx. At the position x where the deflection is a maximum[1], $dy_1/dx = 0$. Differentiating Eq. (5.10) and setting the result to zero gives the location of the maximum deflection as:

$$EI_z \frac{dy_1}{dx} = -\frac{Fb}{6L}(L^2 - 3x^2 - b^2) = 0$$
$$x = \sqrt{\frac{L^2 - b^2}{3}} \qquad \text{(a)}$$

Evaluating Eq. (a) gives:

$$x = \sqrt{\frac{L^2 - b^2}{3}} = \sqrt{\frac{49 - 9}{3}} = 3.651 \text{ m} \qquad \text{(b)}$$

Step 2: Determine the bending stresses in the beam to insure that the beam is elastic. The moment is a maximum at x = a = 4.0 m. Hence, we write:

$$M_{Max} = Fba/L = (8 \times 10^3)(3.0)(4.0)/7.0 = 13.71 \text{ kN-m} \qquad \text{(c)}$$

And the bending stress is given by:

$$\sigma_{Max} = M_{Max}/Z = [13.714 \times 10^3 \text{ (N-m)}(10^3 \text{ mm/m})/(265 \times 10^3 \text{ mm}^3) = 51.85 \text{ MPa}$$

where the section modulus $Z = 265 \times 10^3 \text{ mm}^3$ is listed in Appendix D.

Because σ_{Max} is less than the yield strength of 1020 HR steel (290 MPa), we conclude that the beam under load is elastic and Eq. (5.10) is valid.

Step 3: To determine the expression for the maximum deflection, substitute the results for x from Eq. (a) into Eq. (5.10) gives the expression for y_{Max} as:

$$y_{Max} = -\frac{Fb}{9\sqrt{3}LEI_z}\left(L^2 - b^2\right)^{3/2} \qquad (5.12)$$

Evaluating Eq. (5.12) with the numerical parameters listed in the problem statement and in Appendices B and D gives:

---

[1] Because a > b the maximum deflection will occur on the left portion of the beam where x < a.

$$y_{Max} = -\frac{(8\times 10^3)(3{,}000)}{9\sqrt{3}(7{,}000)(207\times 10^3)(27\times 10^6)}\left[(7{,}000)^2-(3{,}000)^2\right]^{3/2}$$

$$y_{Max} = -9.956 \text{ mm} \qquad \text{(d)}$$

Again we note that the deflection is small compared to both the length and the height of the beam.

EXAMPLE 5.5

Determine the equation for the elastic curve for the cantilever beam presented in Fig. E5.5. Also write the equation for the maximum deflection and the maximum slope.

Fig. E5.5

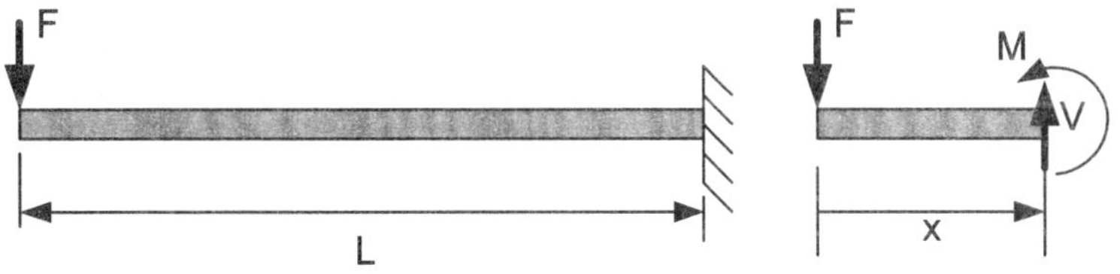

Solution:

Step 1: Prepare a FBD of a segment of the beam where $0 \leq x \leq L$ and write an equation for M(x) as:

$$M(x) = -Fx \qquad \text{(a)}$$

Step 3: Write the differential equation for the elastic curve by substituting Eq. (a) into Eq. (5.4) to obtain:

$$EI_z\frac{d^2y}{dx^2} = M(x) = -Fx \qquad 0 \leq x \leq L \qquad \text{(b)}$$

In this problem a single moment equation is valid over the entire length of the beam indicating that only two constants of integration will be required in the integration process.

Step 4: Integrating Eq. (b), we obtain:

$$EI_z\frac{dy}{dx} = -\frac{Fx^2}{2} + C_1 \qquad 0 \leq x \leq L \qquad \text{(c)}$$

Step 5: The constraint condition (a built-in end) at the right support of the beam, where x = L, forces the slope at the wall to be zero. Hence, Eq. (c) evaluated at x = L reduces to:

$$EI_z\frac{dy}{dx} = 0 = -\frac{FL^2}{2} + C_1 \qquad \Rightarrow \qquad C_1 = FL^2/2 \qquad \text{(d)}$$

Substituting the value for C_1 into Eq. (c) gives the equation for the slope of the elastic curve at any location along its length as:

$$\frac{dy}{dx} = \frac{F(L^2 - x^2)}{2EI_z} \qquad 0 \leq x \leq L \qquad (5.13)$$

Step 6: Integrate Eq. (c) to obtain the expression for the elastic curve as:

$$EI_z y = -\frac{Fx^3}{6} + \frac{FL^2 x}{2} + C_2 \qquad (e)$$

Step 7: The constraint condition on the right end of the beam due to the built-in support is that the deflection at the wall is zero. Evaluating Eq. (e) with y = 0 at x = L gives:

$$EI_z y = 0 = -\frac{FL^3}{6} + \frac{FL^3}{2} + C_2 \quad \Rightarrow \quad C_2 = -\frac{FL^3}{3} \qquad (f)$$

Substituting for the constant C_2 into Eq. (e) gives:

$$EI_z y = -\frac{Fx^3}{6} + \frac{FL^2 x}{2} - \frac{FL^3}{3} = -\frac{F}{6}\left[x^3 - 3L^2 x + 2L^3\right] \qquad (5.14)$$

Step 8: Inspection of Eq. (5.14) shows that the deflection is a maximum at the free end where x = 0.

$$y_{Max} = -\frac{FL^3}{3EI_z} \qquad (5.15)$$

The maximum slope also occurs at the free end. Setting x = 0 in Eq. (5.13) gives the relation for the maximum slope as:

$$\left(\frac{dy}{dx}\right)_{Max} = \frac{FL^2}{2EI_z} \qquad (5.16)$$

EXAMPLE 5.6

For the simply supported beam shown in Fig. E5.6, determine the equation for the elastic curve. Also determine the maximum deflection and the maximum slope of the beam.

Fig. E5.6

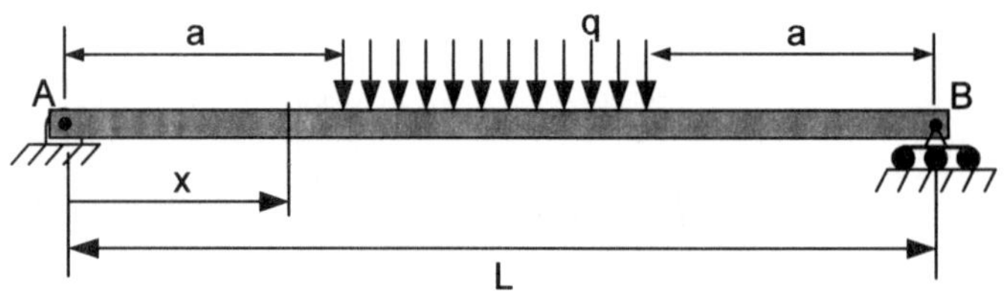

Solution:

Step 1: Write the equations for the reaction forces at the beam's supports and the moments as a function of position x. FBDs of the entire beam and segments of the beam and the application of the equations of equilibrium lead to:

$$R_L = R_R = qb/2 \qquad \text{with } b = (L - 2a) \qquad (a)$$

$$M(x) = qbx/2 \qquad 0 \le x \le a \qquad \text{(b)}$$

$$M(x) = qbx/2 - q(x-a)^2/2 \qquad a \le x \le a+b \qquad \text{(c)}$$

$$M(x) = qbx/2 - qb(2x-L)/2 \qquad a+b \le x \le L \qquad \text{(d)}$$

We note that three different equations are necessary for describing the bending moments over the entire length of this beam. If we double integrate all of these equations, six constants of integration will be generated. Clearly, this approach will be long and tedious and should be avoided if possible. Fortunately, we recognize that the loading and the supports of the beam are symmetric. Symmetry enables us to solve for the equation of the elastic curve for the left half of the beam and to infer the solution for the right half of the beam. With this approach, we will integrate only the first two of the three moment equations.

Step 2: Substituting Eqs (b) and (c) into Eq. (5.4) gives a second order differential equation for the elastic curve as:

$$EI_z \frac{d^2y_1}{dx^2} = M(x) = \frac{qbx}{2} \qquad 0 \le x \le a \qquad \text{(e)}$$

$$EI_z \frac{d^2y_2}{dx^2} = M(x) = \frac{qbx}{2} - \frac{q(x-a)^2}{2} \qquad a \le x \le a+b \qquad \text{(f)}$$

Step 3: Integrating Eq. (e) twice gives:

$$EI_z \frac{dy_1}{dx} = \frac{qbx^2}{4} + C_1 \qquad 0 \le x \le a \qquad \text{(g)}$$

and

$$EI_z y_1 = \frac{qbx^3}{12} + C_1 x + C_2 \qquad 0 \le x \le a \qquad \text{(h)}$$

To satisfy the boundary condition at the left support where $y = 0$ at $x = 0$, it is evident that:

$$C_2 = 0 \qquad \text{(i)}$$

Step 4: Integrating Eq. (f) twice gives:

$$EI_z \frac{dy_2}{dx} = \frac{qbx^2}{4} - \frac{q(x-a)^3}{6} + C_3 \qquad a \le x \le a+b \qquad \text{(j)}$$

$$EI_z y_2 = \frac{qbx^3}{12} - \frac{q(x-a)^4}{24} + C_3 x + C_4 \qquad a \le x \le a+b \qquad \text{(k)}$$

Step 5: Determine C_3 by noting that the beam is symmetric; hence, $(dy_2/dx) = 0$ at $x = L/2$. Substituting this information into Eq. (j) and simplifying the result yields:

$$C_3 = -\frac{qb(3L^2 - b^2)}{48} \qquad (l)$$

To evaluate the remaining two constants of integration, we use the compatibility conditions which indicate that $(dy_1/dx) = (dy_2/dx)$ and $y_1 = y_2$ at $x = a$. From Eqs. (g) and (j) and the compatibility condition $(dy_1/dx) = (dy_2/dx)$ at $x = a$, it is apparent that:

$$C_1 = C_3 = -\frac{qb(3L^2 - b^2)}{48} \qquad (m)$$

From Eqs. (h) and (k) and the compatibility condition $y_1 = y_2$ at $x = a$, we find that:

$$C_2 = C_4 = 0 \qquad (n)$$

Step 6: Substituting the results for the four constants into Eqs. (h) and (k) yields:

$$y_1 = \frac{qbx}{48EI_z}\left[4x^2 - 3L^2 + b^2\right] \qquad 0 \le x \le a \qquad (5.17)$$

$$y_2 = \frac{q}{48EI_z}\left[4bx^3 - 2(x-a)^4 - bx(3L^2 - b^2)\right] \qquad a \le x \le a+b \qquad (5.18)$$

Step 7: We write the relation for the maximum deflection by observing that $y_{Max} = y_2$ at $x = L/2$. Substituting $x = L/2$ into Eq. (5.18) gives:

$$y_{Max} = -\frac{qb}{384EI_z}\left[8L^3 + b^3 - 4b^2L\right] \qquad (5.19)$$

Substituting the results for the constants C_1 and C_3 into Eqs. (g) and (j) gives the equations for the slopes of the elastic curve as:

$$\frac{dy_1}{dx} = \frac{qb}{48EI_z}\left[12x^2 - 3L^2 + b^2\right] \qquad 0 \le x \le a \qquad (5.20)$$

$$\frac{dy_2}{dx} = \frac{q}{48EI_z}\left[12bx^2 - 8(x-a)^3 - 3bL^2 + b^3\right] \qquad a \le x \le a+b \qquad (5.21)$$

The maximum slope occurs at the supports. We write the relation for the maximum slope by setting $x = 0$ in Eq. (5.20) to obtain:

$$\left(\frac{dy_1}{dx}\right)_{Max} = -\frac{qb}{48EI_z}\left[3L^2 - b^2\right] \qquad (5.22)$$

These six examples have shown that the double integration of the moment equation enables one to establish the equation of the elastic curve and the equation for the slope over the entire length of the beam. The difficulty that often arises is in determining the constants of integration, which are generated during the integration process. When several different moment equations must be written to cover the span of the beam, the number of constants of integration increases and the work involved in the solution becomes excessive. We will introduce an approach in Section 5.4 that avoids this difficulty.

5.3.1 Boundary and Compatibility Conditions

In the solutions to the previous examples, we used information describing the beam's constraints in deriving the equation for the elastic curve of a beam in bending. Beams are supported (constrained) by simple supports or by built-in supports. If simple supports are used, a minimum of two supports is necessary for stability. Usually the supports are placed at the ends of the beam, but this is not required if overhangs provide some design advantage. If the beam has a built-in support at one end, the other end may be free. Fixed and simple supports may both be employed in constraining the deformation of a beam. However, this practice produces a statically indeterminate beam.

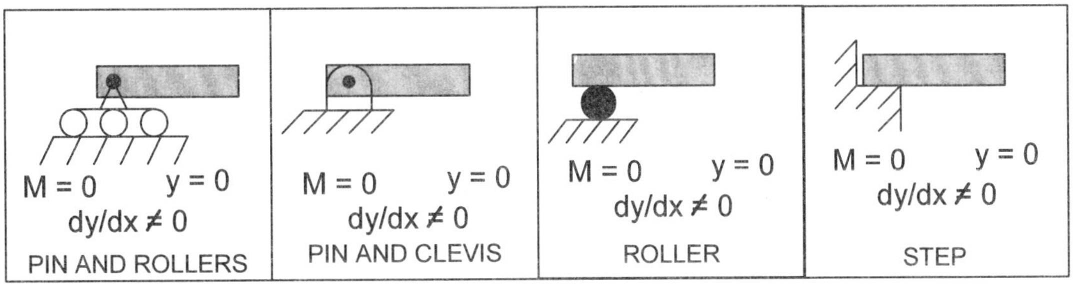

Fig. 5.2 Different simple supports for a beam that yield the same boundary conditions.

Simple supports are designed with several different arrangements that permit free rotation of the beam over the support (M = 0) while constraining the deflection so that y = 0. Several of the designs for simple supports are illustrated in Fig. 5.2. The roller and the step configurations are the most common because they are less expensive to implement in construction.

Fixed or built-in supports are more difficult to achieve in practice. Two methods are illustrated in Fig. 5.3 together with the boundary conditions. Both the slope and the deflection are constrained so that (dy/dx) = 0 and y = 0. However, the moment at the support is not equal to zero.

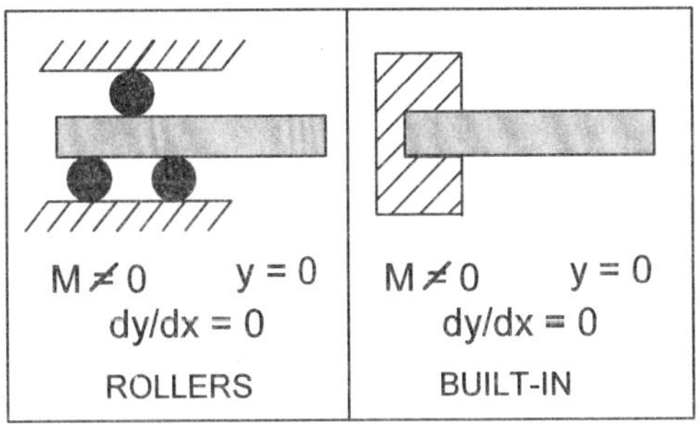

Fig. 5.3 Illustration of fixed or built-in supports for a beam.

With a built-in or fixed support at one end of a beam, the other end may be free as is the case for a cantilever beam. The free end will deflect and rotate so that (dy/dx) ≠ 0 and y ≠ 0. However the moment M and the shear force V both are zero at the free end of the beam.

Compatibility and Symmetry Conditions

When it is necessary to write two or more moment equations to describe M(x) over the entire length of the beam, the integration method produces two or more equations for the elastic curve. Each of these equations is valid over some segment of the beam. For instance in Example 5.3, the expression for y_1 was valid for $0 \le x \le a$, and the relation for y_2 was valid for $a \le x \le L$. However at x = a, the results for both y_1 and y_2 must be identical. In addition the slopes dy_1/dx and dy_2/dx must also be identical at x = a. The deflection given by both solutions must be continuous as we transition from one solution to another. We illustrate the concept of continuity of the slope and the deflection by observing the elastic curve in Fig. 5.4

Fig. 5.4 For the elastic curve to be continuous, $y_1 = y_2$ and $(dy_1/dx) = (dy_2/dx)$ at x = a.

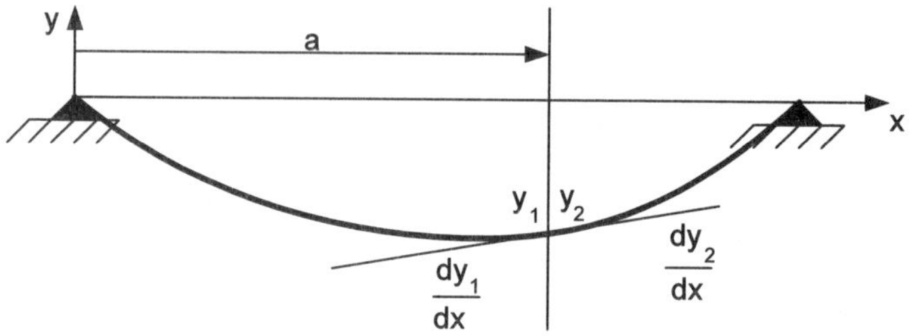

When the loading on a uniform beam is symmetric, the elastic curve is also symmetric as illustrated in Fig. 5.5. Because of this symmetry, the slope at the center of the beam where x = L/2 is zero. We will employ boundary conditions, compatibility conditions and symmetry to establish constants of integration when establishing the equations for the elastic curve.

Fig. 5.5 The slope is zero at the mid point of a symmetrically loaded beam.

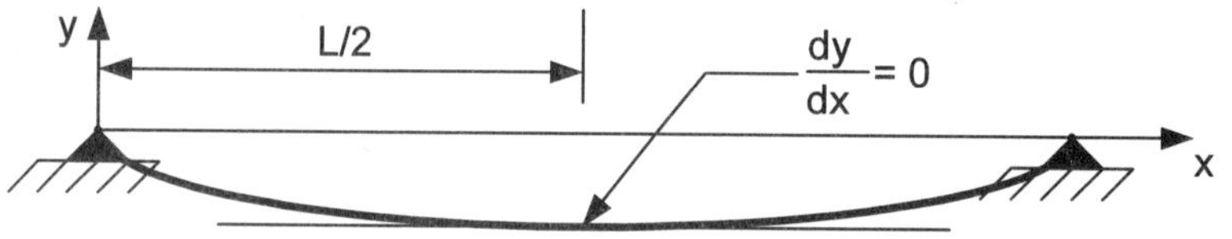

5.3.2 Integrating the Shear Force Relation and the Load Relation

It is possible to write one or more equations describing the variation of the shear force V as a function of position x over the span of the beam. Substituting V(x) into Eq. (5.5) yields a third order differential equation in terms of the deflection y. By integrating this differential equation three times, we can obtain the equation for the elastic curve. The difficulty with this approach is the number of constants of integration that are generated during the integration process. For a simply supported beam with a single concentrated force, two equations are needed to express the shear force over the length of the beam. Integrating these equations three times produces six constants of integration that can be determined from boundary and compatibility conditions. However, the time and effort required is excessive.

Similarly it is possible to write equations describing the forces q applied to the beam as a function of x. Substituting q(x) into Eq. (5.6) yields a fourth order differential equation in terms of the deflection y. By integrating this differential equation four times, we can obtain the equation for the elastic curve. We encounter the same difficulty with this approach — the number of constants of integration that are generated require an excessive effort to determine. A much better approach for determining the equation for the elastic curve is presented in the next section.

5.4 DEFLECTIONS AND SLOPES WITH SINGULARITY FUNCTIONS

5.4.1 Singularity Functions

In Section 5.3, we found that the integration method was tedious and time consuming when two or more equations were required to express the bending moment over the entire length of the beam. To avoid this difficulty, we will consider a family of singularity functions that will enable us to express the moment over the length of the beam in a single equation regardless of the complexity of the loading. Macauley first introduced singularity functions in 191; however, the mechanics community adapted singularity functions much later in the decade 1960-70.

To begin, consider a family of singularity functions given by:

$$f_n(x) = <x - a>^n \tag{5.23}$$

When $n \geq 0$ the function f_n is evaluated using the following rule:

$$\begin{aligned} f_n(x) &= 0 && \text{if } x < a \\ f_n(x) &= (x - a)^n && \text{if } x \geq a \end{aligned} \tag{5.24}$$

Clearly, the pointed brackets are identical to ordinary brackets if the quantity within the pointed brackets is zero or positive. However, if the quantity within the pointed brackets is negative, we set f_n equal to zero. Think of the pointed brackets as a switch that turns off a term when the quantity within the pointed brackets is negative.

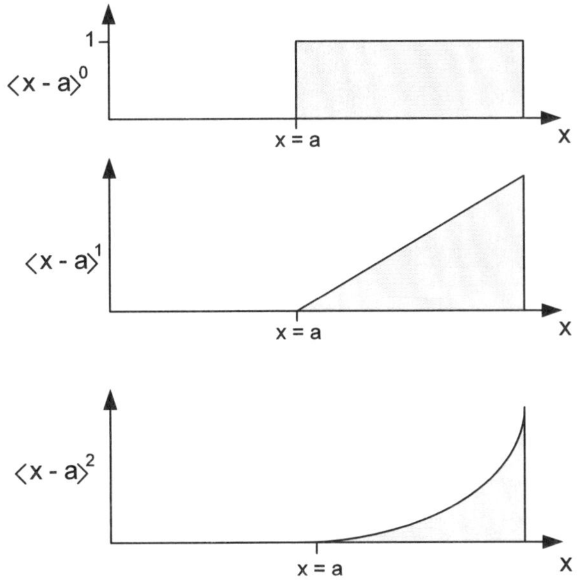

Fig. 5.6 Singularity functions for n = 0, 1 and 2.

Let's determine $f_n(x)$ as a function of x if n = 0, 1 and 2. These three results are presented as graphs in Fig. 5.6. The function $<x - a>^0 = 1$ when $x \geq a$ is called the unit step function, and $<x - a>^1$ is called the ramp function, which begins at x = a. We integrate these functions using the following rule:

$$\int_{-\infty}^{x} < x - a >^n dx = \frac{< x - a >^{n+1}}{n+1} \qquad n \geq 0 \tag{5.25}$$

Different rules apply for $f_n(x)$ when n is either –1 or – 2.

$$f_n(x) = 0 \qquad \text{if } x < a$$

$$f_n(x) = 0 \qquad \text{if } x > a \tag{5.26}$$

$$f_n(x) \Rightarrow \infty \qquad \text{if } x = a$$

The singularity in f_n at x = a does not lead to mathematical difficulty because when $<x - a>^{-1}$ and $<x - a>^{-2}$ are integrated, the result is finite as indicated below:

$$\int_{-\infty}^{x} < x - a >^{-2} dx = < x - a >^{-1} \tag{5.27}$$

$$\int_{-\infty}^{x} < x - a >^{-1} dx = < x - a >^{0} \tag{5.28}$$

The function $<x - a>^{-1}$ gives rise to a concentrated load and the function $<x - a>^{-2}$ produces a concentrated moment at x = a, as shown in Fig. 5.7.

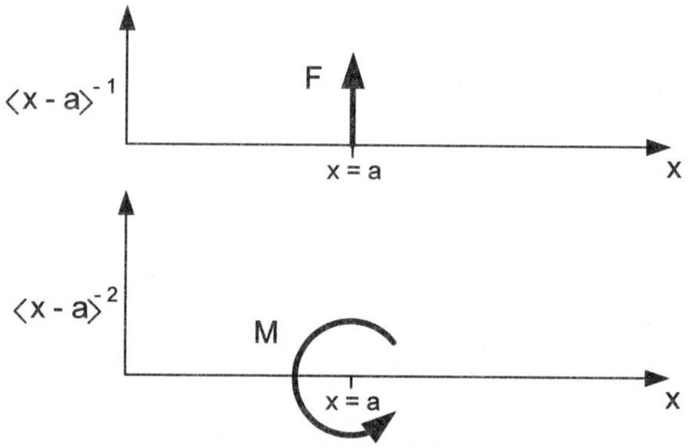

Fig. 5.7 Singularities produced by the function $<x - a>^{-1}$ and $<x - a>^{-2}$ at x = a.

Next, let's show the application of the new singularity function to writing equations for the load, shear force and bending moments as a function of position over the entire length of a beam.

5.4.2 Writing Equations with Singularity Functions

Typical loading q(x) applied to beams includes the four cases listed below. The equation for the load q(x) for each of these different loads can be written using singularity functions as:

1. A concentrated moment at some location x = a.

$$q(x) = M_o<x - a>^{-2} \tag{5.29}$$

2. A concentrated force F at some location x = a.

$$q(x) = F\langle x - a\rangle^{-1} \tag{5.30}$$

3. A uniformly distributed load q_o beginning at x = a.

$$q(x) = q_o\langle x - a\rangle^{0} \tag{5.31}$$

4. A linearly increasing (ramp) load q(x) beginning at x = a.

$$q(x) = (q_o/b)\langle x - a\rangle^{1} \tag{5.32}$$

where q_o/b is the slope of the ramp function.

A summary of results for q(x) for different loading conditions is shown in Fig. 5.8.

BEAM LOADING	LOAD EQUATION	SHEAR FORCE EQ.	MOMENT EQUATION
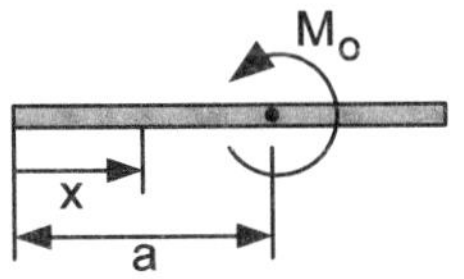	$q(x) = M_o\langle x-a\rangle^{-2}$	$V(x) = -M_o\langle x-a\rangle^{-1}$	$M(x) = -M_o\langle x-a\rangle^{0}$
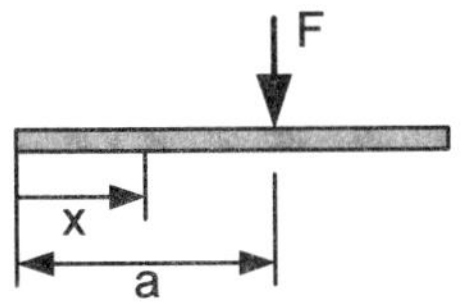	$q(x) = F\langle x-a\rangle^{-1}$	$V(x) = -F\langle x-a\rangle^{0}$	$M(x) = -F\langle x-a\rangle^{1}$
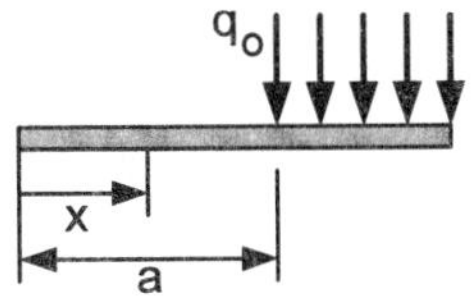	$q(x) = q_o\langle x-a\rangle^{0}$	$V(x) = -q_o\langle x-a\rangle^{1}$	$M(x) = -\frac{q_o}{2}\langle x-a\rangle^{2}$
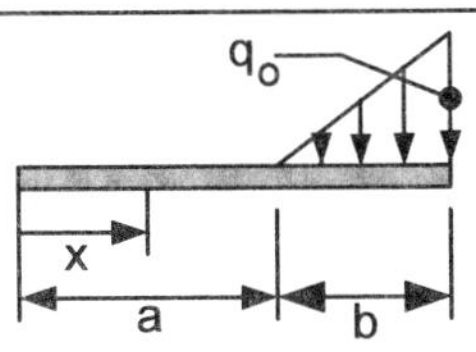	$q(x) = \frac{q_o}{b}\langle x-a\rangle^{1}$	$V(x) = -\frac{q_o}{2b}\langle x-a\rangle^{2}$	$M(x) = -\frac{q_o}{6b}\langle x-a\rangle^{3}$

Fig. 5.8 Equations for q(x), V(x) and M(x) for four different types of beam loading.

Equations for the shear force V(x) can be written by substituting Eq. (5.29) into q(x) = – dV(x)/dx and integrating using Eq. (5.27) to obtain:

$$V(x) = -\int_{-\infty}^{x} q(x)dx = -M_o\int_{-\infty}^{x} \langle x-a\rangle^{-2}\,dx = -M_o\langle x-a\rangle^{-1} \tag{5.33}$$

Similarly, equations for the bending moment can be obtained by substituting V(x) into Eq. (4.2) and integrating using Eq. (5.28) to obtain:

$$M(x) = \int_{-\infty}^{x} V(x)dx = -M_o \int_{-\infty}^{x} < x - a >^{-1} dx = -M_o < x - a >^{0} \qquad (5.34)$$

Using this same procedure, the equations for V(x) and M(x) were derived for each of the four types of beam loading functions. The summary of the results obtained is presented in Fig. 5.8.

5.4.3 Applying Singularity Functions to Beams

Let's consider five examples to demonstrate the economy of effort in solving for the equation of the elastic curve of a beam when using singularity functions. The examples will illustrate several concepts including:

1. Writing shear and bending moment equations for different beam loadings using singularity functions.
2. Writing the equations for the elastic curve and its slope for different beam loadings using singularity functions.
3. Solving for constants of integration that are generated in the integration process.
4. Integrating the pointed brackets that arise when using singularity functions.

EXAMPLE 5.7

For the simply supported beam shown in Fig. E5.7, write the equation for the loading function q(x). Then integrate this function to determine V(x) and M(x). Solve for the integration constants that arise in the integration process.

Fig. E5.7

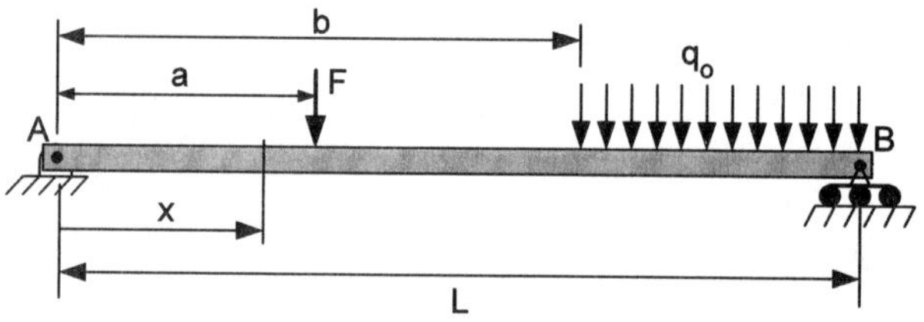

Solution:

Replace the pin and clevis support with a concentrated force R_L directed in the positive y direction. Beginning at x = 0, we must accommodate three loadings in writing q(x) — R_L, F and q_o. Using the results from Fig. 5.8, we write:

$$q(x) = -R_L<x - 0>^{-1} + F<x - a>^{-1} + q_o<x - b>^{0} \qquad (a)$$

where the sign of the term containing R_L is negative because it is in the positive y direction.

Integrate Eq. (a) using q(x) = – dV(x)/dx and the integration rules for pointed brackets to obtain the shear force V(x) as:

$$V(x) = R_L\langle x - 0\rangle^0 - F\langle x - a\rangle^0 - q_o\langle x - b\rangle^1 + C_1 \quad \text{(b)}$$

Integrate Eq. (b) using Eq. (4.2) and the integration rules to obtain the bending moment M(x) as:

$$M(x) = R_L\langle x - 0\rangle^1 - F\langle x - a\rangle^1 - (q_o/2)\langle x - b\rangle^2 + C_1x + C_2 \quad \text{(c)}$$

The constants of integration C_1 and C_2 both are zero because M(0) = 0 and V(0) = R_L. In addition, because R_L occurs at the left end of the beam where x = 0, the pointed brackets for the first term in Eq. (b) and Eq. (c) are equal to 1.0 and x, respectively. Hence, we write:

$$V(x) = R_L - F\langle x - a\rangle^0 - q_o\langle x - b\rangle^1 \quad \text{(d)}$$

$$M(x) = R_Lx - F\langle x - a\rangle^1 - (q_o/2)\langle x - b\rangle^2 \quad \text{(e)}$$

EXAMPLE 5.8

For the simply supported beam shown in Fig. E5.7, write the equation for the elastic curve and the slope of this curve as a function of x. Locate the position of the maximum deflection and determine y_{Max}. Assume EI_z is a constant with respect to x and the dimensions in Fig. E5.7 are a = 2 m, b = 4 m and L = 6m. The force F = 25 kN and the distributed load q_o = 14 kN/m. The beam is fabricated from a steel American Standard S381×64 section.

Solution:

Prepare a FBD of the entire beam and solve for the reaction load R_L at x = 0 by writing a moment equation to obtain:

$$R_L = 2F/3 + q_o/3 = (2)(25)/3 + 14/3 = 21.33 \text{ kN} \quad \text{(a)}$$

Substitute the result for M(x) from Example 5.7 into Eq. (5.4) and integrate to obtain:

$$EI_z\frac{d^2y}{dx^2} = 21.33x - 25\langle x-2\rangle^1 - 7\langle x-4\rangle^2 \quad \text{(b)}$$

$$EI_z\frac{dy}{dx} = 10.667x^2 - 12.5\langle x-2\rangle^2 - 2.333\langle x-4\rangle^3 + C_3 \quad \text{(c)}$$

$$EI_z y = 3.556x^3 - 4.167\langle x-2\rangle^3 - 0.5833\langle x-4\rangle^4 + C_3x + C_4 \quad \text{(d)}$$

The constants of integration are determined from the boundary conditions, which are:

$$y(0) = 0 \qquad y(6) = 0 \quad \text{(e)}$$

From the boundary condition y(0) = 0 it is evident that $C_4 = 0$. From the boundary condition y(6) = 0, we determine C_3 from Eq. (d) as:

$$EI_z y = 3.556(6)^3 - 4.167(4)^3 - 0.5833(2)^4 + C_3(6) = 0 \quad \Rightarrow \quad C_3 = -82.00 \text{ kN-m}^2 \quad \text{(f)}$$

We can then substitute Eq. (f) into Eqs. (c) and (d) and write the equations for the elastic curve and the slope of the elastic curve as:

$$EI_z \frac{dy}{dx} = 10.667x^2 - 12.5 < x - 2 >^2 - 2.333 < x - 4 >^3 - 82.00 \qquad \text{(g)}$$

$$EI_z y = 3.556x^3 - 4.167 < x - 2 >^3 - 0.5833 < x - 4 >^4 - 82.00x \qquad \text{(h)}$$

To locate the position of the maximum deflection we use the fact that (dy/dx) = 0 when y is a maximum. Also, the position of the force F and its magnitude compared to q_o leads us to conclude that the maximum deflection will occur in the region 2 m < x < 4 m. Substituting this information into Eq. (g), we obtain:

$$EI_z \frac{dy}{dx} = 10.67x^2 - 12.5(x - 2)^2 - 82.00 = 0 \qquad \text{(i)}$$

Note that the term $<x - 4>^3 = 0$ for $x \leq 4$ m.

Solving the quadratic equation gives the position for the maximum deflection as:

$$x = 2.962 \text{ m} \qquad \text{(j)}$$

This result verifies the conclusion that the maximum location[2] would occur from 2 m < x < 4 m. The other root of Eq. (i) — x = 24.32 m — is disregarded because it not realistic because the beam is only 6 m long.

Substituting Eq. (j) into Eq. (h) gives $EI_z\, y_{Max}$ as:

$$EI_z y_{Max} = 3.556(2.962)^3 - 4.167(0.962)^3 - 0 - (82.00)(2.962) = -154.2 \text{ kN-m}^3 \quad \text{(k)}$$

The negative sign is to be expected because the beam deflects downward while the y-axis is upward. Let E = 207 GPa for steel and reference Appendix D to find $I_z = 186 \times 10^6$ mm^4. Substituting these values into Eq. (k) yields:

$$y_{Max} = \frac{-(154.2 \times 10^3)(10^9)}{(207 \times 10^3)(186 \times 10^6)} = -4.005 \text{ mm} \qquad \text{(l)}$$

This deflection is very small compared to the dimensions of the beam (height h = 381 mm and length L = 6,000mm.

---

[2] The maximum deflection is usually near the center of the span of the beam even when the loading is not symmetric.

EXAMPLE 5.9

A simply supported beam with a constant cross sectional area over its entire length is subjected to loads F and q as shown in Fig. E5.9. Determine the equation for the elastic curve and its slope. Also determine the maximum deflection y_{Max}. The dimensions in Fig. E5.9 are a = 5 ft and L = 20 ft. The loads are F = 24 kip and q_o = 4 kip/ft. Assume the beam is fabricated from a steel wide flange W16×67 section.

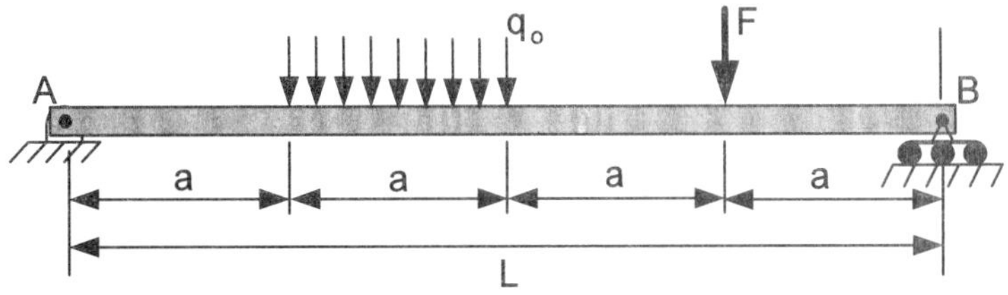

Fig. E5.9

Solution:

As we examine the uniformly distributed load in Fig. E5.9, we are faced with a problem. We can use a singularity function to activate q_o at x = a, but how do we turn it off at x = 2a? The answer is to introduce a new loading, shown in Fig. E5.9a, that is more amendable to using singularity functions. This new loading involves a downward acting q_o from $a \leq x \leq L$ and an upward acting q_o from $2a \leq x \leq L$. The two distributed loads cancel each other for $x \geq 2a$ producing the loading shown in Fig. E5.9.

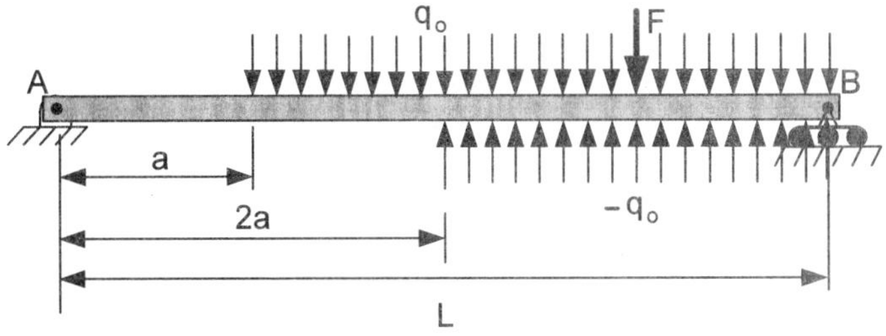

Fig. E5.9a

Let's write the equation for the loading function q(x) by using the results in Fig. 5.8 as:

$$q(x) = -R_L <x-0>^{-1} + q_o <x-a>^0 - q_o <x-2a>^0 + F <x-3a>^{-1} \quad \text{(a)}$$

where the sign of the term containing R_L is negative because R_L is in the positive y direction.

Integrate Eq. (a) using $q(x) = -\, dV(x)/dx$ and the integration rules for pointed brackets to obtain the shear force V(x) as:

$$V(x) = R_L - q_o <x-a>^1 + q_o <x-2a>^1 - F <x-3a>^0 + C_1 \quad \text{(b)}$$

Integrate Eq. (b) using Eq. (4.2) and the integration rules to obtain the bending moment M(x) as:

$$M(x) = R_L x - (q_o/2) <x-a>^2 + (q_o/2) <x-2a>^2 - F <x-3a>^1 + C_1 x + C_2 \quad \text{(c)}$$

The constants of integration C_1 and C_2 both are zero because V(0) = R_L and M(0) = 0. Hence, we write:

$$V(x) = R_L - 4 <x - 5>^1 + 4 <x - 10>^1 - 24 <x - 15>^0 \tag{d}$$

$$M(x) = R_L x - 2 <x - 5>^2 + 2 <x - 10>^2 - 24 <x - 15>^1 \tag{e}$$

Prepare a FBD of the entire beam and solve for the reaction load R_L at x = 0 by writing a moment equation to obtain:

$$R_L = (5/2)(a^2 q_o/L) + aF/L = [(2.5)(25)(4) + (5)(24)]/20 = 18.5 \text{ kip} \tag{f}$$

Substitute the result for M(x) from Eq. (e) into Eq. (5.4) and integrate to obtain:

$$EI_z \frac{d^2y}{dx^2} = 18.5x - 2 < x - 5 >^2 + 2 < x - 10 >^2 - 24 < x - 15 >^1 \tag{g}$$

$$EI_z \frac{dy}{dx} = 9.25x^2 - \frac{2}{3} < x - 5 >^3 + \frac{2}{3} < x - 10 >^3 - 12 < x - 15 >^2 + C_3 \tag{h}$$

$$EI_z y = 3.083x^3 - 0.1667 < x - 5 >^4 + 0.1667 < x - 10 >^4 - 4.0 < x - 15 >^3 + C_3 x + C_4 \tag{i}$$

The constants of integration are determined from the boundary conditions, which are:

$$y(0) = 0 \qquad\qquad y(20) = 0 \tag{j}$$

From the boundary condition y(0) = 0 it is evident that C_4 = 0. From the boundary condition y(20) = 0, we determine C_3 as:

$$C_3 = -\ 869.6 \text{ kip-ft}^2 \tag{k}$$

We can then substitute Eq. (k) into Eqs. (h) and (i) and write the equations for the elastic curve and the slope of the elastic curve as:

$$EI_z \frac{dy}{dx} = 9.25x^2 - \frac{2}{3} < x - 5 >^3 + \frac{2}{3} < x - 10 >^3 - 12 < x - 15 >^2 - 869.6 \tag{l}$$

$$EI_z y = 3.083x^3 - 0.1667 < x - 5 >^4 + 0.1667 < x - 10 >^4 - 4.0 < x - 15 >^3 - 869.6x \tag{m}$$

To locate the position of the maximum deflection we use the fact that (dy/dx) = 0 when y is a maximum. Also, the position of the force F and its magnitude compared to q_o leads us to conclude that the maximum deflection will occur in the region 5 ft < x < 15 ft. Substituting this information into Eq. (l), we obtain:

$$EI_z \frac{dy}{dx} = 9.25(x)^2 - \frac{2}{3}(x - 5)^3 + \frac{2}{3}(x - 10)^3 - 869.6 = 0 \tag{n}$$

Note the term <x – 15>^{2} goes to zero for $x \leq 15$ ft.

Solving the cubic equation obtained by expanding Eq. (n) gives the position for the maximum deflection as:

$$x = 10.21 \text{ ft} \qquad (o)$$

The two other roots are impossible because they do not lie on the beam. This result verifies the conclusion that the maximum location would occur slightly to the right of the center of the beam where 5 ft < x < 15 ft.

Substituting Eq. (o) into Eq. (m) gives $EI_z\, y_{Max}$ as:

$$EI_z\, y_{Max} = 3.083(10.21)^3 - 0.1667(10.21-5)^4 + 0.1667(10.21 - 10)^4$$

$$- (869.6)(10.21) = - 5{,}720.1 \text{ kip-ft}^3 \qquad (p)$$

The negative sign is to be expected because the beam deflects downward while the y-axis is upward. Let $E = 30 \times 10^6$ psi for steel and reference Appendix D to find $I_z = 954$ in.^{4} for the wide flange section. Substituting these values into Eq. (p) yields:

$$y_{Max} = \frac{-(5{,}720.1)(12)^3}{(30 \times 10^3)(954)} = -0.3454 \text{ in.} \qquad (q)$$

Again it is noted that the magnitude of the deflection of the beam is small compared to its height.

EXAMPLE 5.10

A cantilever beam with a constant cross sectional area over its entire length is subjected to a concentrated force F and a ramp load with a maximum distributed force of q_o as shown in Fig. E5.10. Determine the equation for the elastic curve and its slope. Also determine the maximum deflection y_{Max}. The dimensions are a = 3 m and L = 9 m and the loads are F = 30 kN and q_0 = 9 kN/m. Assume the beam is aluminum with a W686 × 217 wide flange section.

Fig. E5.10

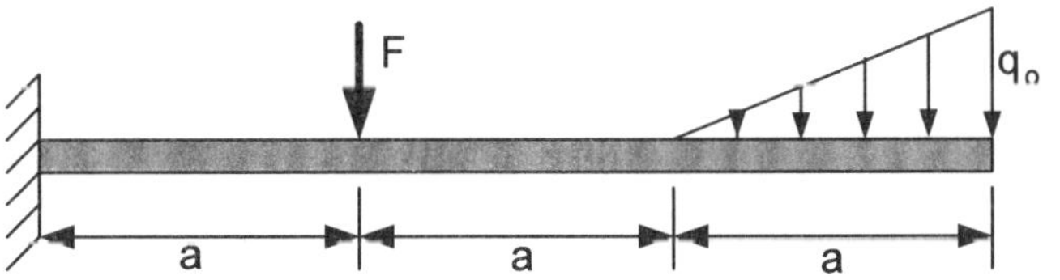

Solution:

Let's begin by drawing a FBD of the entire beam to show the moment and shear force at the built-in support as shown in Fig. E5.10a.

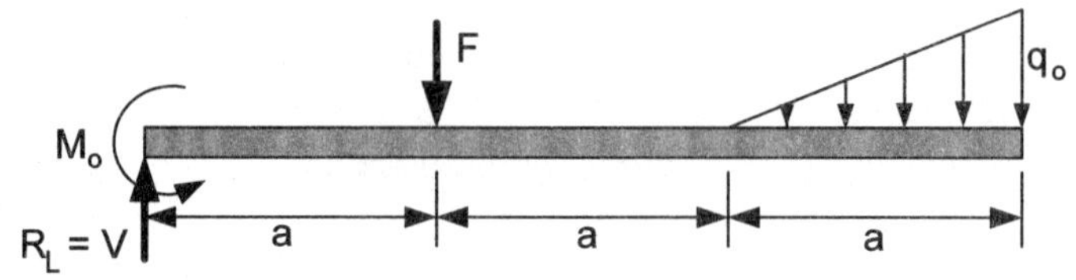

Fig. E5.10a

At the support on the left side of the beam ΣF = 0 and ΣM = 0 yields:

$$R_L = V(0) = F + q_o a/2 \quad \text{(a)}$$

$$M_o = Fa + (4q_o a^2)/3 \quad \text{(b)}$$

Let's write the equation for the loading function q(x) by using the results in Fig. 5.4 as:

$$q(x) = M_o <x - 0>^{-2} - R_L <x - 0>^{-1} + F <x - a>^{-1} + (q_o/a) <x - 2a>^1 \quad \text{(c)}$$

Integrate Eq. (c) using $q(x) = -\,dV(x)/dx$ and the integration rules for pointed brackets to obtain the shear force V(x) as:

$$V(x) = - M_o <x - 0>^{-1} + R_L <x - 0>^0 - F <x - a>^0 - (q_o/2a) <x - 2a>^2 + C_1 \quad \text{(d)}$$

Integrate Eq. (b) using Eq. (4.2) and the integration rules to obtain the bending moment M(x) as:

$$M(x) = - M_o <x - 0>^0 + R_L <x - 0>^1 - F <x - a>^1 - (q_o/6a) <x - 2a>^3 + C_1 x + C_2 \quad \text{(e)}$$

The constants of integration C_1 and C_2 both are zero because $M(0) = - M_o$ and $V(0) = R_L$. Hence, we write:

$$V(x) = - M_o /x + R_L - F <x - a>^0 - (q_o/2a) <x - 2a>^2 \quad \text{(f)}$$

$$M(x) = - M_o + R_L x - F <x - a>^1 - (q_o/6a) <x - 2a>^3 \quad \text{(g)}$$

Substitute numerical values for F and q_o in Eqs. (a) and (b) to obtain:

$$R_L = V(0) = F + q_o a/2 = 30 + (9)(3)/2 = 43.5 \text{ kN} \quad \text{(h)}$$

$$M_o = Fa + (4q_o a^2)/3 = (30)(3) + (4)(9)(3)^2/3 = 198 \text{ kN-m} \quad \text{(i)}$$

Substitute the result for M(x) from Eq. (g) into Eq. (5.4) and simplify using Eqs. (h) and (i). Then integrate the result to obtain:

$$EI_z \frac{d^2y}{dx^2} = -198 + 43.5x - 30 < x - 3 >^1 - \frac{1}{2} < x - 6 >^3 \quad \text{(j)}$$

$$EI_z \frac{dy}{dx} = -198x + 21.75x^2 - 15 < x - 3 >^2 - \frac{1}{8} < x - 6 >^4 + C_3 \quad \text{(k)}$$

$$EI_z y = -99x^2 + 7.25x^3 - 5 < x-3 >^3 - \frac{1}{40} < x-6 >^5 + C_3 x + C_4 \qquad (l)$$

The constants of integration are determined from the boundary conditions, which are:

$$y(0) = 0 \qquad (dy/dx)(0) = 0 \qquad (m)$$

From the boundary condition y(0) = 0 it is evident that $C_4 = 0$, and from the boundary condition (dy/dx)(0) = 0, we determine $C_3 = 0$.

We set $C_3 = C_4 = 0$ in Eqs. (k) and (l) and write the equations for the elastic curve and the slope of the elastic curve as:

$$EI_z \frac{dy}{dx} = -198x + 21.75x^2 - 15 < x-3 >^2 - \frac{1}{8} < x-6 >^4 \qquad (n)$$

$$EI_z y = -99x^2 + 7.25x^3 - 5 < x-3 >^3 - \frac{1}{40} < x-6 >^5 \qquad (o)$$

It is evident from inspection that the maximum deflection of the cantilever beam is at its free end where x = L = 9 m. Accordingly, we write:

$$EI_z y_{Max} = -99(9)^2 + 7.25(9)^3 - 5(6)^3 - \frac{1}{40}(3)^5 = -3{,}820 \text{ kN-m}^3 \qquad (p)$$

Let E = 72 GPa for aluminum and reference Appendix D to find $I_z = 2{,}345 \times 10^6$ mm^4 for the wide flange section. Substituting these values into Eq. (p) yields:

$$y_{Max} = \frac{-(3{,}820 \times 10^3)(10^3)^3}{(72 \times 10^3)(2{,}345 \times 10^6)} = -22.62 \text{ mm} \qquad (q)$$

EXAMPLE 5.11

A simply supported beam with a constant cross sectional area over its entire length is designed with an overhang as shown in Fig. E5.11. The beam carries a uniformly distributed load q_o and a concentrated force F. Determine the equation for the elastic curve and its slope. Also determine the maximum deflection y_{Max}. The dimensions are a = 6 ft and L = 24 ft and the loads are F = 12 kip and q_q = 1.0 kip/ft. Assume an aluminum beam fabricated from a 12 × 52 structural tee section.

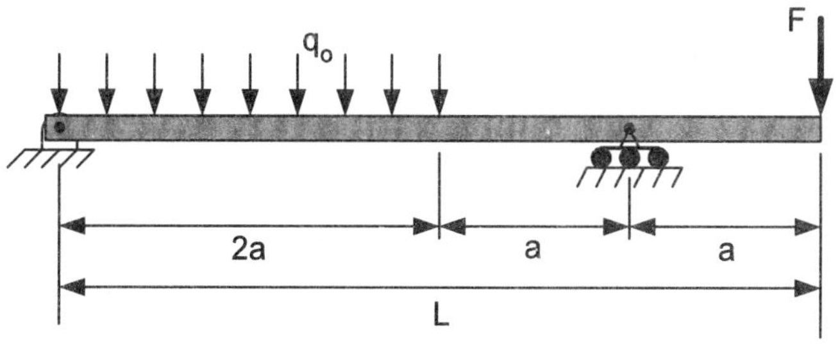

Fig. E5.11

Solution:

Let's begin by determining the reactions R_L and R_R at the two supports. Prepare a FBD and take moments about the right hand support to obtain:

$$R_L = [4aq_o - F]/3 = [(4)(6)(1.0) - 12]/3 = 4 \text{ kip} \qquad \text{(a)}$$

$$R_R = 2aq_o + F - R_L = 12 + 12 - 4 = 20 \text{ kip} \qquad \text{(b)}$$

When we attempt to write the equation for the loading function q(x) by using the results in Fig. 5.4, we note a difficulty. If we accommodate the uniform load with the singularity term $q_o \langle x - 0\rangle^0$, it applies that loading occurs over the entire length of the beam. To remove the uniform loading from the right half of the beam, we must introduce an equal and opposite loading that begins at x = 2a and continues to the right side of the beam, as shown in Fig. E5.11a.

Fig. E5.11a

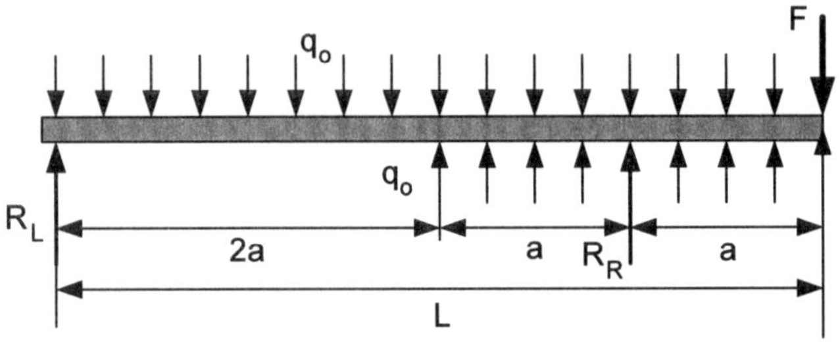

Writing the relation for the loading shown in Fig. E5.11a yields:

$$q(x) = -R_L \langle x - 0\rangle^{-1} + q_o \langle x - 0\rangle^0 - q_o \langle x - 2a\rangle^0 - R_R \langle x - 3a\rangle^{-1} \qquad \text{(c)}$$

Integrate Eq. (c) using q(x) = dV(x)/dx and the integration rules for pointed brackets, to obtain the shear force V(x). Also substitute numerical values for a, F, q_o, R_L and R_R into Eq. (c).

$$V(x) = +4 \langle x - 0\rangle^0 - 1.0 \langle x - 0\rangle^1 + 1.0 \langle x - 12\rangle^1 + 20 \langle x - 18\rangle^0 + C_1 \qquad \text{(d)}$$

Integrate Eq. (d) using Eqs. (4.2) and the integration rules to obtain the bending moment M(x) as:

$$M(x) = +4 \langle x - 0\rangle^1 - \tfrac{1}{2} \langle x - 0\rangle^2 + \tfrac{1}{2} \langle x - 12\rangle^2 + 20 \langle x - 18\rangle^1 + C_1 x + C_2 \qquad \text{(e)}$$

The constants of integration C_1 and C_2 both are zero because M(0) = 0 and V(0) = R_L. Hence, we write:

$$V(x) = +4 - 1.0x + 1.0 \langle x - 12\rangle^1 + 20 \langle x - 18\rangle^0 \qquad \text{(f)}$$

$$M(x) = +4x - \tfrac{1}{2} x^2 + \tfrac{1}{2} \langle x - 12\rangle^2 + 20 \langle x - 18\rangle^1 \qquad \text{(g)}$$

Substitute the result for M(x) from Eq. (g) into Eq. (5.4) and then integrate to obtain:

$$EI_z \frac{d^2y}{dx^2} = 4x - \frac{1}{2}x^2 + \frac{1}{2} < x-12 >^2 + 20 < x-18 >^1 \qquad \text{(h)}$$

$$EI_z \frac{dy}{dx} = 2.0x^2 - \frac{1}{6}x^3 + \frac{1}{6} < x-12 >^3 + 10 < x-18 >^2 + C_3 \qquad \text{(i)}$$

$$EI_z y = \frac{2}{3}x^3 - \frac{1}{24}x^4 + \frac{1}{24} < x-12 >^4 + \frac{10}{3} < x-18 >^3 + C_3 x + C_4 \qquad \text{(j)}$$

To solve for C_3 and C_4, we use the boundary conditions that y(0) = 0 and y(18) = 0. The first of these boundary conditions yields $C_4 = 0$. The second boundary condition gives:

$$0 = \frac{2}{3}(18)^3 - \frac{1}{24}(18)^4 + \frac{1}{24}(6)^4 + \frac{10}{3}(0) + C_3(18) \Rightarrow C_3 = 24.0 \text{ kip-ft}^2 \qquad \text{(k)}$$

We can then substitute Eq. (k) into Eqs. (i) and (j) and write the equations for the elastic curve and the slope of the elastic curve as:

$$EI_z \frac{dy}{dx} = 2.0x^2 - \frac{1}{6}x^3 + \frac{1}{6} < x-12 >^3 + 10 < x-18 >^2 + 24.0 \qquad \text{(l)}$$

$$EI_z y = \frac{2}{3}x^3 - \frac{1}{24}x^4 + \frac{1}{24} < x-12 >^4 + \frac{10}{3} < x-18 >^3 + 24.0x \qquad \text{(m)}$$

There are two possibilities for the location of the maximum deflection of the beam — between the supports or at the free end of the overhanging beam. If y_{Max} occurs between the supports, then (dy/dx) = 0 when y is a maximum. Let's initially assume that the maximum will be near the center of the beam with $12 \le x \le 15$ so that we can write Eq. (l) as:

$$EI_z \frac{dy}{dx} = 2.0x^2 - \frac{1}{6}x^3 + \frac{1}{6}(x-12)^3 + (0) + 24.0 = 0 \qquad \text{(n)}$$

Expanding and solving the cubic Eq. (n) gives the location of y_{Max} as:

$$x = 12.873 \text{ ft} \qquad \text{(o)}$$

Substituting Eq. (o) into Eq. (m) gives $EI_z\, y_{Max}$ as:

$$EI_z y_{Max} = \frac{2}{3}(12.873)^3 - \frac{1}{24}(12.873)^4 + \frac{1}{24}(0.873)^4 + 0 + 24(12.873) = 586.9 \text{ kip-ft}^3 \qquad \text{(p)}$$

In this problem, the maximum deflection is positive indicating the beam deflects in the positive y direction with a deflection curve of the shape shown in Fig. E5.11b. The result given by Eq. (p) is the maximum deflection between the supports, but it may not be the maximum for the beam. It is necessary to check the deflection at the free end of the beam.

Fig. E5.11b

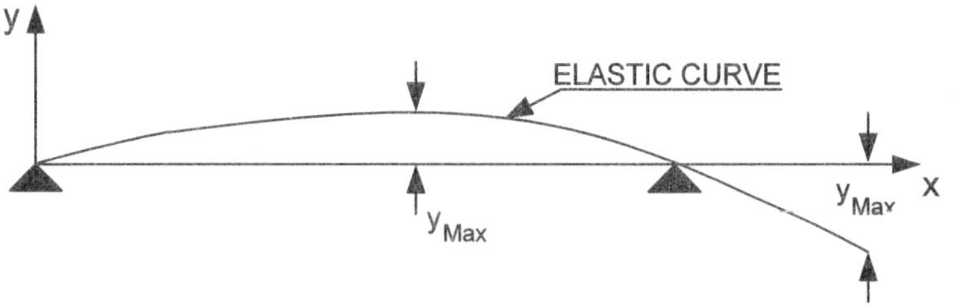

To determine the deflection at the end of the beam, we employ Eq. (m), set x = 24 ft and write:

$$EI_z y_{Max} = \frac{2}{3}(24)^3 - \frac{1}{24}(24)^4 + \frac{1}{24}(12)^4 + \frac{10}{3}(6)^3 + 24(24) = -2{,}448 \text{ kip-ft}^3 \quad \text{(r)}$$

Comparing the results from Eq. (p) and (r) indicates that the maximum deflection occurs at the free end of the overhanging beam and is given by Eq. (r). Let E = 10.4 × 10^3 ksi for aluminum and reference Appendix D to find I_z = 189 in.^{4} for the structural tee section. Substituting these values into Eq. (r) yields:

$$y_{Max} = \frac{-(2{,}448)(12)^3}{(10.4 \times 10^3)(189)} = -2.152 \text{ in.} \quad \text{(s)}$$

5.5 SUPERPOSITION CONCEPTS

The principle of superposition is useful in solving for the deflection of beams that are loaded with two or more forcing functions. We have presented the integration method that is effective when the bending moment equation M(x) is valid from $0 \leq x \leq L$. This method becomes cumbersome when two or more bending moment equations are necessary to describe M(x) over the entire length of the beam. We introduced singularity functions that were employed with the integration method to significantly reduce the mathematical complexities involved in solving for constants of integration. Superposition represents a third method for determining the equation of the elastic curve.

Superposition involves combining together the results of the deflection from two or more separate solutions to yield a new solution containing all of the loading functions involved in the separate solutions. This concept of superposition of displacement functions is demonstrated better by the graphic shown in Fig. 5.9. Three concentrated forces — F_1, F_2 and F_3 — load the beam on the left in Fig. 5.9. These forces are located a distance a, b and c from the left side of the beam, respectively. If the solution is known for the elastic curve for a beam loaded with a single concentrated force, we can use superposition to add together the solutions for the displacement y(x) associated with the three separate forces.

One of the advantages of the method of superposition is that we make use of the many solutions that already exist. Mechanics of materials is a subject with a long history, and the classic problems of bending of beams were solved many years ago. We have provided a catalog of several of these solutions for your convenience in Appendix E.

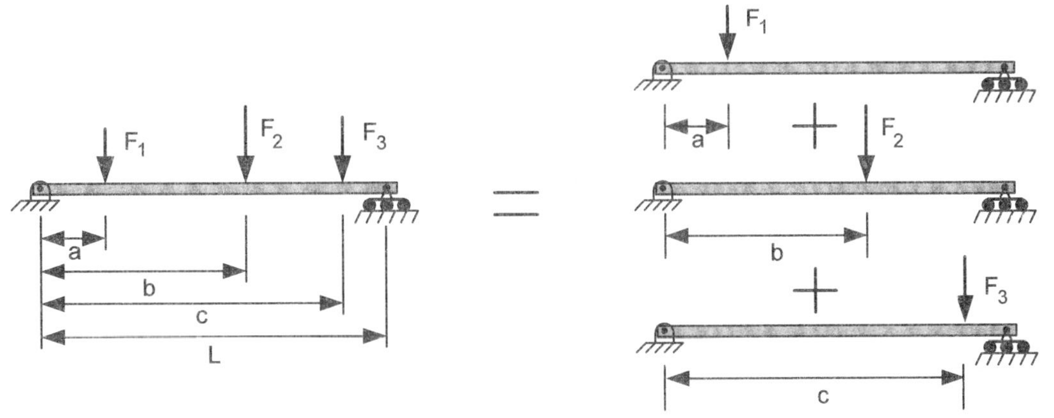

Fig. 5.9 Superposition is adding solutions for y(x) for a single loading function to obtain solutions for two or more loading functions.

There are two requirements that must be satisfied before using the principle of superposition. The first is the linearity requirement. The solution for y(x) must be linear with respect to the loading functions. We have solved several different problems determining y(x) for several different loading functions including concentrated forces, concentrated moments, uniformly distributed loads and ramp functions. In all cases we found that y(x) was linear with respect to the loading function. The second requirement pertains to the integrity of the geometry of the beam during the loading. Does the beam change its dimensions? The beam on the left in Fig. 5.9 must have essentially the same geometry as each of the three beams on the right of Fig. 5.9. If the beam deformations are small, we can conclude that the geometry does not change significantly as the beam is loaded. We have solved for the maximum deflection in several problems and noted that the deflection of the beam was always small when compared to its length. Hence, we conclude that the principle of superposition is valid and can be employed as another method for determining the deflection of a beam in bending.

We will demonstrate the methods of superposition with several examples that show combinations of different loading functions applied to beams supported in different ways.

EXAMPLE 5.12

Consider the simply supported beam subjected to a uniformly distributed load and a concentrated force as illustrated in Fig. E5.12. Determine the deflection at mid span and the slope at x = L. The beam is fabricated from a steel wide flange section W203×60 with a length L = 6 m. The force F = 40 kN is applied at a = 4 m and q_o = 12 kN/m = 12 N/mm.

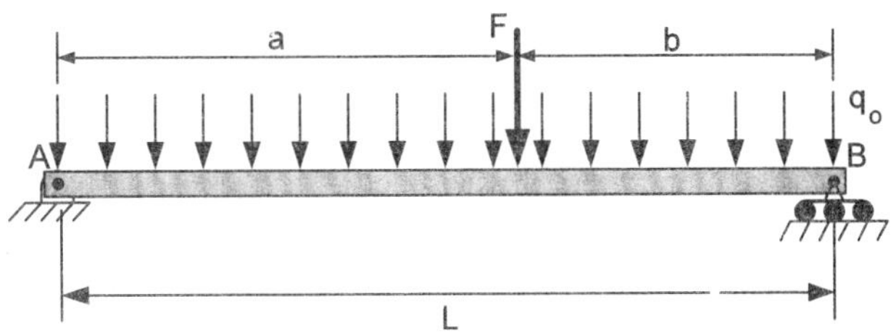

Fig. E5.12

Solution:

Let's employ the principle of superposition to solve this problem. Two identical simply supported beams each with a single load as illustrated in Fig. E5.12a represent the simply supported beam with the two different loadings.

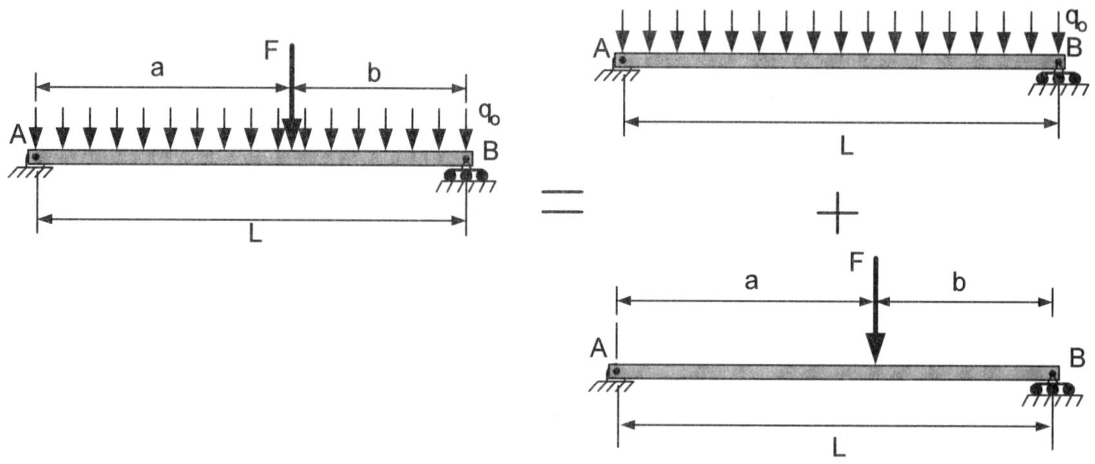

Fig. E5.12a

Consider first the simply supported beam with the uniformly distributed load. Reference to the solutions presented in Appendix E gives the equations for the deflection and slope as:

$$y = -\frac{q_0 x}{24EI_z}\left(x^3 - 2Lx^2 + L^3\right) \qquad \text{(a)}$$

$$\left(\frac{dy}{dx}\right)_{x=0,L} = \pm\frac{q_0 L^3}{24EI_z} \qquad \text{(b)}$$

Note that $I_z = 60.8 \times 10^6$ mm^4 is given in Appendix D for the specified wide flange section. Substituting numerical parameters into Eq. (a) and Eq. (b) gives

$$y_{x=L/2} = -\frac{q_0 L}{48EI_z}\left(\frac{L^3}{8} - \frac{L^3}{2} + L^3\right) = -\frac{5q_0 L^4}{384EI_z} \qquad \text{(c)}$$

$$y_{x=L/2} = -\frac{5q_0 L^4}{384EI_z} = -\frac{(5)(12)(6\times 10^3)^4}{(384)(207\times 10^3)(60.8\times 10^6)} = -16.09 \text{ mm} \qquad \text{(d)}$$

$$\left(\frac{dy}{dx}\right)_{x=L} = \frac{q_0 L^3}{24EI_z} = \frac{(12)(6\times 10^3)^3}{(24)(207\times 10^3)(60.8\times 10^6)} = 8.581\times 10^{-3} \text{ Radians} \qquad \text{(e)}$$

Next, reference the solution for the simply supported beam subjected to a concentrated load at position x = a in Appendix E and write the relations for the displacement and the slope as:

$$y = -\frac{Fbx}{6EI_zL}\left(L^2 - b^2 - x^2\right) \tag{f}$$

$$\left(\frac{dy}{dx}\right)_{x=L} = +\frac{Fab(L+a)}{6EI_zL} \tag{g}$$

Substituting x = L/2 and numerical parameters into Eq. (f) and solving gives:

$$y_{X=L/2} = -\frac{Fb}{48EI_z}\left(3L^2 - 4b^2\right) = -\frac{(40\times 10^3)(2\times 10^3)}{(48)(207\times 10^3)(60.8\times 10^6)}[3(36) - 4(4)]\times 10^6 = -12.18 \text{ mm} \tag{h}$$

Substituting numerical parameters into Eq. (g) gives:

$$\left(\frac{dy}{dx}\right)_{x=L} = \frac{Fab(L+a)}{6EI_zL} = \frac{(40\times 10^3)(4\times 10^3)(2\times 10^3)(10\times 10^3)}{6(207\times 10^3)(60.8\times 10^6)(6\times 10^3)} = 7.063\times 10^{-3} \text{ Radians} \tag{i}$$

The final step in this process is to superimpose the results from the two solutions. Adding the results from Eqs. (d) and (h) gives the total displacement at mid span as:

$$y_{x=L/2} = -(16.09 + 12.18) = -28.27 \text{ mm} \tag{j}$$

Similarly, the slope at x = L is given by adding the results from Eqs. (e) and (i) to obtain:

$$(dy/dx)_{x=L} = (8.581 + 7.063)\times 10^{-3} = 0.01564 \text{ Radians} = 0.8963° \tag{k}$$

The use of the superposition principle enables one to solve for deflections in beams subjected to multiple loads by considering identical beams subjected to a single load function. The solutions for the beams with single loadings are then added to obtain the results for the beam with multiple loads. It is a simple technique that makes use of the existing solutions that are tabulated in Appendix E.

EXAMPLE 5.13

Consider the simply supported beam subjected to a ramp type distributed load and a concentrated moment as illustrated in Fig. E5.13. Determine the deflection at midspan and the slope at both ends of the beam. The steel beam is fabricated from an American Standard flange section S10×35 with a length L = 20 ft. The concentrated moment M_o = 2,000 ft-lb is applied at x = 0. The ramp load is specified with q_o = 1.80 kip/ft = 150 lb/in.

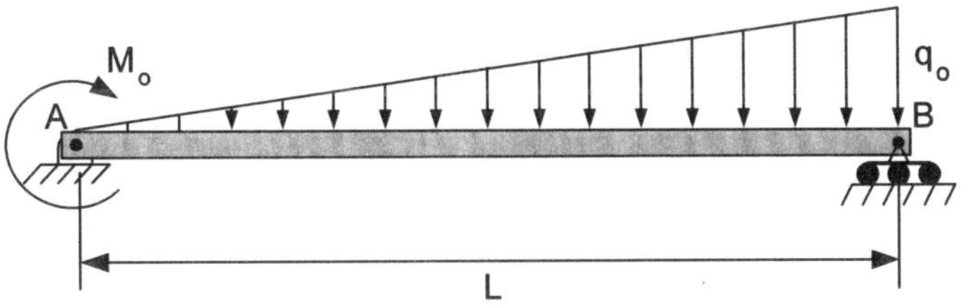

Fig. E5.13

Solution:

We again use the principle of superposition in solving this problem. Two identical simply supported beams each with a single load, as illustrated in Fig. E5.13a, represent the simply supported beam with the ramp distribution and the concentrated moment loads.

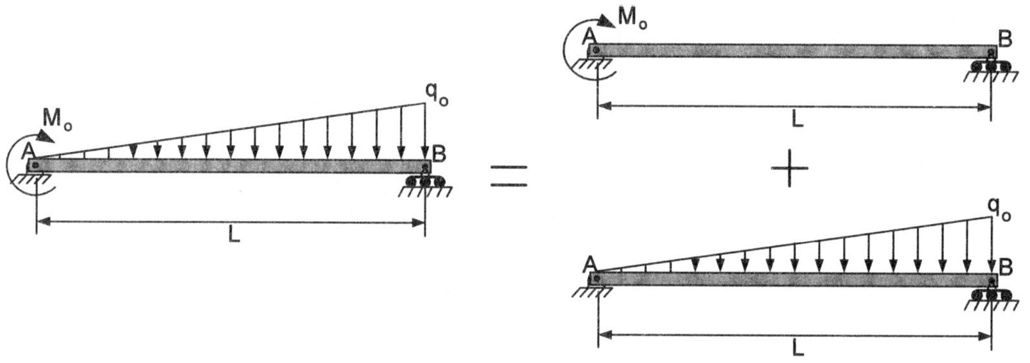

Fig. E5.13a

First, consider the solution for the simply supported beam subjected to a concentrated moment at x = 0 that is given in Appendix E. Write the relations for the displacement and the slope as:

$$y = -\frac{M_0 x}{6EI_z L}\left(x^2 - 3Lx + 2L^2\right) \quad \text{(a)}$$

$$\left(\frac{dy}{dx}\right)_{x=0} = -\frac{ML}{3EI_z} \quad \text{(b)}$$

$$\left(\frac{dy}{dx}\right)_{x=L} = \frac{ML}{6EI_z} \quad \text{(c)}$$

At midspan x = L/2 and Eq. (a) reduces to:

$$y = -\frac{3M_0L^2}{48EI_z} \quad \text{(d)}$$

Note that I_z = 147 in.^{4} is given in Appendix D for the specified American Standard section. Substituting numerical parameters into Eqs. (b), (c) and (d) gives:

$$y = -\frac{3M_0L^2}{48EI_z} = -\frac{3(2{,}000)(12)(20)^2(12)^2}{48(30\times 10^6)(147)} = -0.01959 \text{ in.} \quad \text{(e)}$$

$$\left(\frac{dy}{dx}\right)_{x=0} = -\frac{ML}{3EI_z} = -\frac{(2{,}000)(12)(20)(12)}{3(30\times 10^6)(147)} = -4.354\times 10^{-4} \text{ Radians} \quad \text{(f)}$$

$$\left(\frac{dy}{dx}\right)_{x=L} = \frac{ML}{6EI_z} = 2.177 \times 10^{-4} \text{ Radians} \qquad (g)$$

Consider next the simply supported beam with the ramp type distributed load. Reference to the solutions presented in Appendix E gives the equations for the deflection and slope as:

$$y = -\frac{q_0 x}{360EI_z L}\left(3x^4 - 10L^2x^2 + 7L^4\right) \qquad (h)$$

$$\left(\frac{dy}{dx}\right)_{x=0} = -\frac{7q_0L^3}{360EI_z} \qquad (i)$$

$$\left(\frac{dy}{dx}\right)_{x=L} = \frac{q_0L^3}{45EI_z} \qquad (j)$$

Substitute x = L/2 into Eq. (h) to obtain:

$$y_{x=L/2} = -\frac{q_0}{(2)(360)EI_z}\left(\frac{3L^4}{16} - \frac{10L^4}{4} + 7L^4\right) = -\frac{75q_0L^4}{11{,}520EI_z} \qquad (k)$$

Substituting numerical parameters into Eqs. (i), (j) and (k) gives:

$$y_{x=L/2} = -\frac{75q_0L^4}{11{,}520EI_z} = -\frac{(75)(150)(20)^4(12)^4}{11{,}520(30\times 10^6)(147)} = -0.7347 \text{ in.} \qquad (l)$$

$$\left(\frac{dy}{dx}\right)_{x=0} = -\frac{7q_0L^3}{360EI_z} = -\frac{7(150)(20)^3(12)^3}{360(30\times 10^6)(147)} = -0.009143 \text{ Radians} \qquad (m)$$

$$\left(\frac{dy}{dx}\right)_{x=L} = \frac{q_0L^3}{45EI_z} = \frac{(150)(20)^3(12)^3}{45(30\times 10^6)(147)} = 0.01045 \text{ Radians} \qquad (n)$$

The final step in this process is to superimpose the results from the two solutions. Adding the results from Eqs. (e) and (l) gives the total displacement at mid span as:

$$y_{x=L/2} = -(0.01959 + 0.7347) = -\,0.7543 \text{ in.} \qquad (o)$$

Similarly the slope at x = 0 and x = L is obtained by adding the results to obtain:

$$(dy/dx)_{x=0} = -(4.354 + 91.43) \times 10^{-4} = -\,0.009578 \text{ Radian} = 0.5488° \qquad (p)$$

$$(dy/dx)_{x=L} = (2.172 + 104.5) \times 10^{-4} = 0.01067 \text{ Radian} = 0.6113° \qquad (q)$$

The use of the superposition principle enables one to solve for deflections in beams subjected to multiple loads by considering identical beams subjected to a single load function. The solutions for the beams with single loadings are then added to obtain the results for the beam with multiple loads.

EXAMPLE 5.14

Consider the cantilever beam subjected to a concentrated force applied at its free end and a uniformly distributed load over the left half of the beam as shown in Fig. E5.14. Determine the deflection and the slope at the free end of the beam. The steel beam is fabricated from a structural tee section WT178 × 61 with a length L = 6.0 m. The concentrated force is F = 1.5 kN and the uniformly distributed load is specified with q_o = 3.0 kN/m = 3.0 N/mm.

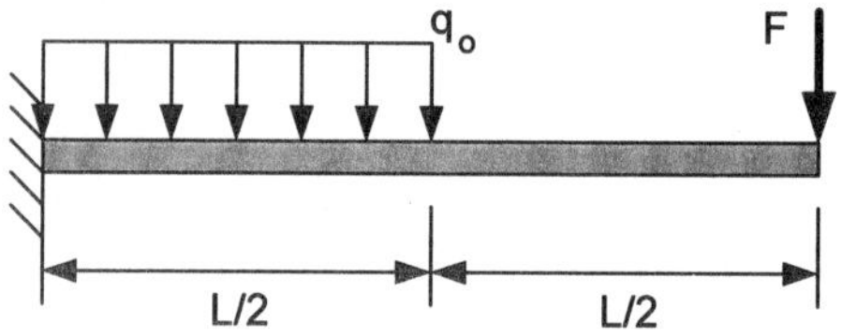

Fig. E5.14

Solution:

Apply the principle of superposition by dividing the loading into two separate parts as shown in Fig. E5.14a.

Fig. E5.14a

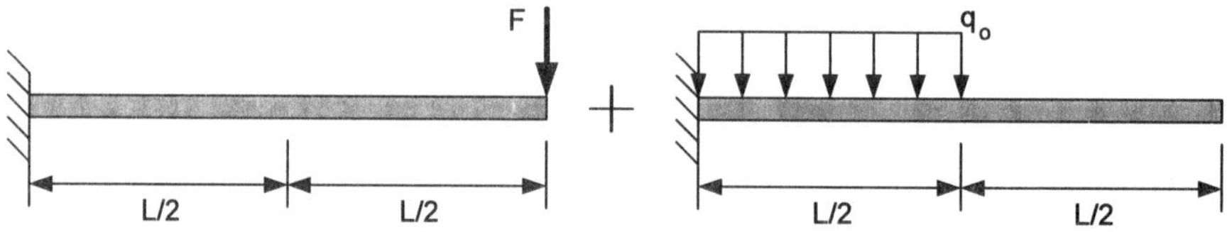

Consider first the solution for the cantilever beam with a concentrated load applied at its free end that is presented in Appendix E. We write the expressions for the deflection and the slope at the free end and substitute numerical parameters to obtain:

$$y_{x=L} = -\frac{FL^3}{3EI_z} = -\frac{1{,}500(6{,}000)^3}{3(207\times 10^3)(17.1\times 10^6)} = -30.51 \text{ mm} \qquad \text{(a)}$$

$$\left(\frac{dy}{dx}\right)_{x=L} = -\frac{FL^2}{2EI_z} = -\frac{1{,}500(6{,}000)^2}{2(207\times 10^3)(17.1\times 10^6)} = -7.628\times 10^{-3} \text{ Radians} \qquad \text{(b)}$$

The value of $I_z = 17.1 \times 10^6$ mm^4 was determined from Appendix D.

Next consider the solution for the cantilever beam with a uniformly distributed load applied over its left half. Using the solution presented in Appendix E, we write the expressions for the deflection and the slope at the free end and substitute numerical parameters to obtain:

$$y_{x=L} = -\frac{7q_0L^4}{384EI_z} = -\frac{7(3)(6{,}000)^4}{384(207\times 10^3)(17.1\times 10^6)} = -20.02 \text{ mm} \qquad \text{(c)}$$

$$\left(\frac{dy}{dx}\right)_{x=L} = -\frac{q_0L^3}{48EI_z} = -\frac{3(6{,}000)^3}{48(207\times 10^3)(17.1\times 10^6)} = -3.814\times 10^{-3} \text{ Radians} \qquad \text{(d)}$$

Finally we add the results for the deflections and the slopes to obtain:

$$y_{x=L} = -(30.51 + 20.02) = -\ 50.53\ \text{mm} \qquad \text{(e)}$$

$$\left(\frac{dy}{dx}\right)_{x=L} = -\ (7.628 + 3.814)\times 10^{-3} = 0.01144\ \text{Radian} = 0.6555° \qquad \text{(f)}$$

5.6 SUMMARY

In this chapter, we returned to study beams subjected to transverse forces with an emphasis on the deflection. The geometry of the deformation of the beam (plane sections remain plane) enabled writing an expression relating curvature κ to the bending moment.

$$\kappa = 1/\rho = M(x)/[EI_z] \qquad (4.9)$$

We referred to an equation derived in analytical geometry that gives the curvature as a function of the derivatives of the elastic curve and simplified this equation by assuming the square of the slope of the beam was small compared to unity.

$$\kappa = \frac{1}{\rho} = \frac{\dfrac{d^2y}{dx^2}}{\left[1+\left(\dfrac{dy}{dx}\right)^2\right]^{3/2}} \cong \frac{d^2y}{dx^2} \qquad (5.2)$$

We showed that derivatives of the elastic curve y(x) were related to M(x), V(x) and q(x) as:

$$\frac{d^2y}{dx^2} = \frac{M(x)}{EI_z} \qquad (5.4)$$

$$\frac{d^3y}{dx^3} = \frac{V(x)}{EI_z} \qquad (5.5)$$

$$\frac{d^4y}{dx^4} = -\frac{q(x)}{EI_z} \qquad (5.6)$$

There are three different approaches for determining the equation for the elastic curve y(x) which include:

1. Integrating Eq. (5.4) with the moment M(x) with respect to x
2. Integrating Eq. (5.5) with the shear force V(x) with respect to x
3. Integrating Eq. (5.6) with the transverse loading q(x) with respect to x

Several examples were presented to show the application of Eq. (5.4) to determine the equation of the elastic curve. To determine the constants of integration, we made use of boundary conditions, symmetry and compatibility conditions. It was clear for beams with multiple loadings that the double integration method was time consuming and tedious because of the large number of constants of integration that developed during the integration process. To reduce the number of constants of integration, we introduced the concept of singularity functions $f_n(x)$ given by:

$$f_n(x) = <x - a>^n \qquad (5.23)$$

When the exponent $n \geq 0$, the pointed brackets were interpreted either as zero or as regular brackets depending upon the value of the constant a as indicated below:

$$f_n(x) = 0 \qquad \text{if } x < a$$
$$(5.24)$$
$$f_n(x) = (x - a)^n \qquad \text{if } x \leq a$$

When integrating pointed brackets with $n \geq 0$, the integration rule is:

$$\int_{-\infty}^{x} <x - a>^n \, dx = \frac{<x - a>^{n+1}}{n+1} \qquad n \geq 0 \qquad (5.25)$$

However, when n is negative (– 1 or –2) a singularity exists and we define $f_n(x)$ as:

$$f_n(x) = 0 \qquad \text{if } x < a$$
$$f_n(x) = 0 \qquad \text{if } x > a \qquad (5.26)$$
$$f_n(x) \Rightarrow \propto \qquad \text{if } x = a$$

The singularity in f_n at $x = a$ does not lead to mathematical difficulty because when $f_n(x) =<x - a>^{-1}$ and $f_n(x) = <x - a>^{-2}$ are integrated, the result is finite as indicated below:

$$\int_{-\infty}^{x} <x - a>^{-2} \, dx = <x - a>^{-1} \qquad (5.27)$$

$$\int_{-\infty}^{x} <x - a>^{-1} \, dx = <x - a>^{0} \qquad (5.28)$$

We then described the use of singularity functions for writing the expression for four common loading functions as:

1. A concentrated moment at $x = a$: $\Rightarrow q(x) = M_o<x - a>^{-2}$ (5.29)

2. A concentrated force F at $x = a$: $\Rightarrow q(x) = F<x - a>^{-1}$ (5.30)

3. A uniformly distributed load q_o beginning at x = a: $\Rightarrow q(x) = q_o<x - a>^0$ (5.31)

4. A linearly increasing (ramp) load q(x) beginning at x = a:

$$q(x) = (q_o/b)<x - a>^1 \quad \text{where } q_o/b \text{ is the slope of the ramp.} \tag{5.32}$$

A graphic in Fig. 5.8 is presented to aid you in writing expressions for loads, shear forces and moments in terms of singularity functions. Several examples are presented to demonstrate the techniques used in applying singularity methods to solve for beam deflections.

We introduced another technique for solving for beam deflections called superposition. Superposition involves combining together the results of the deflection from two or more separate solutions to yield a new solution containing all of the loading functions involved in the separate solutions. One of the advantages of the method of superposition is that we make use of the many solutions that already exist. Mechanics of materials is a subject with a long history, and the classic problems in bending of beams were solved many years ago. We have provided a catalog of several of these solutions for your convenience in Appendix E.

PROBLEMS

5.1 For the cantilever beams shown in Fig. P5.1, write the equation for the elastic curves. Also determine the deflection and slope at the free end.

Fig. P5.1

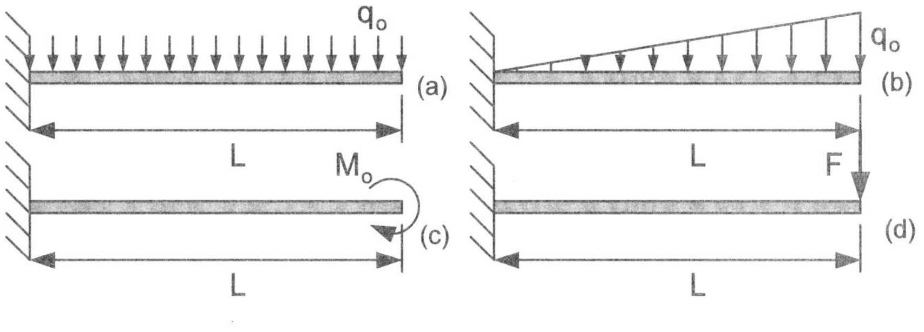

5.2 For the steel cantilever beam, shown in Fig. P5.2, determine the deflection and slope at the free end if the beam is fabricated from a W305 × 74 wide flange section.

Fig. P5.2

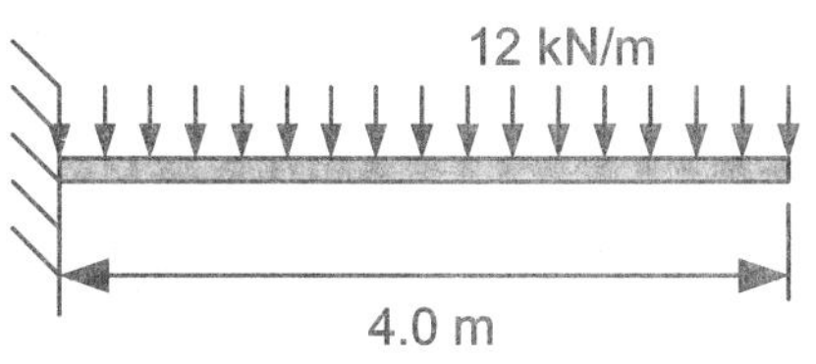

5.3 Repeat Problem 5.2 if the uniformly distributed load q_0 = 15 kN/m and the length of the cantilever beam is 3.4 m.

5.4 For the steel cantilever beam, shown in Fig. P5.4, determine the deflection and slope at the free end if the beam is fabricated from an American Standard section S254 × 38.

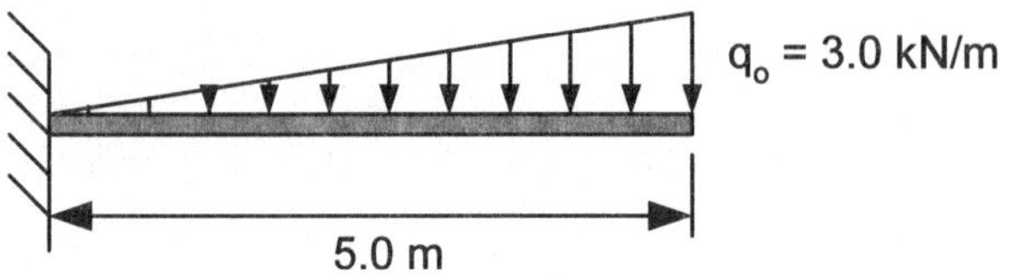

Fig. P5.4

5.5 Repeat Problem 5.4 if the ramp load q_0 is increased to 4.0 kN/m and if the beam is fabricated from a W254 × 45 wide flange section.

5.6 For the steel cantilever beam, shown in Fig. P5.6, determine the deflection and slope at the free end if the beam is fabricated from a W18 × 60 wide flange section.

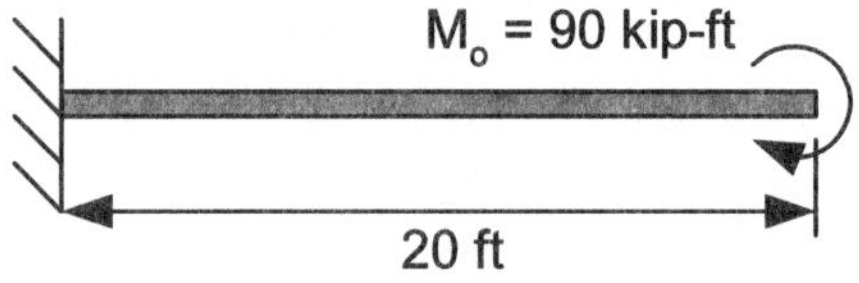

Fig. P5.6

5.7 Repeat Problem 5.6 if the moment M_0 is increased to 120 kip-ft and the length of the beam is decreased to 18 ft.

5.8 For the steel cantilever beam, shown in Fig. P5.8, determine the deflection and slope at the free end if the beam is fabricated from an American Standard section S381 × 64.

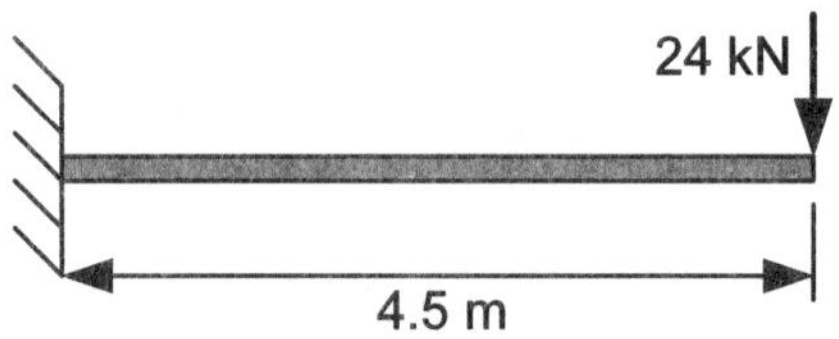

Fig. P5.8

5.9 Repeat Problem 5.8 if the force F is increased to 30 kN and the length of the beam is decreased to 4.0 m and the beam is fabricated from American Standard section S381 × 74.

5.10 For the simply supported beams, shown Fig. P5.10, write the equation for the elastic curves. Also determine the deflection at mid-span and the slope at both ends.

Fig. P5.10

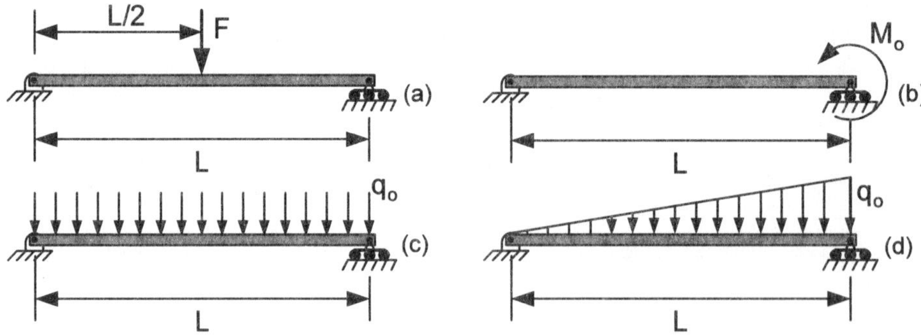

5.11 For the steel simply supported beam shown Fig. P5.11, determine the mid-span deflection and slope at both ends if the beam is fabricated from a S203 × 27 American Standard section.

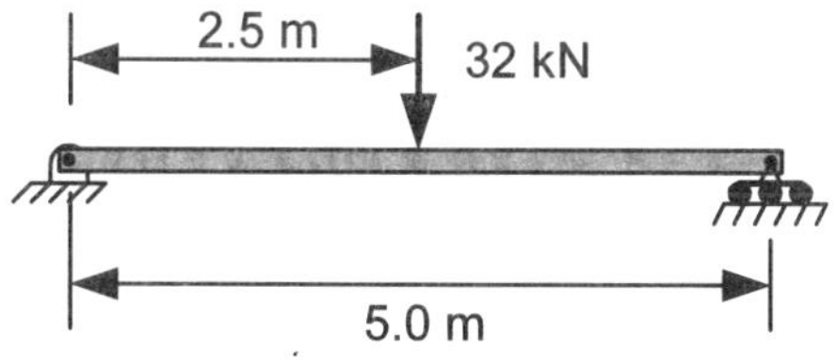

Fig. P5.11

5.12 Repeat Problem 5.11 if the load is increased from 32 kN to 40 kN and the American Standard section is changed to S203 × 34.

5.13 For the steel simply supported beam, shown in Fig. P5.13, determine the mid-span deflection and slope at both ends if the beam is fabricated from a W152 × 37 wide flange section.

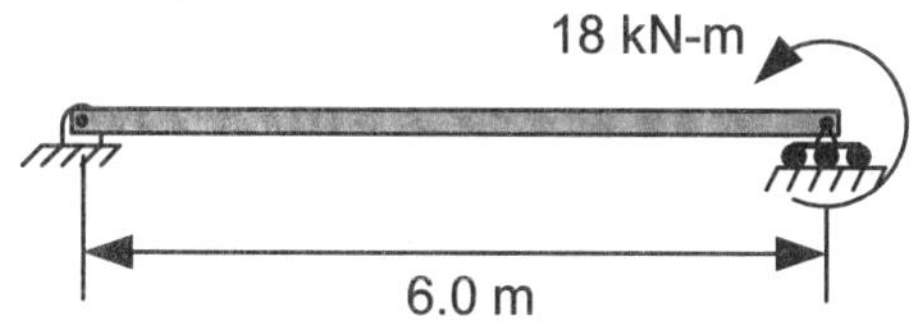

Fig. P5.13

5.14 Repeat Problem 5.13 if the applied moment M is increased from 18 kN-m to 24 kN-m and the wide flange section is changed from W152 × 37 to W203 × 36.

5.15 For the steel simply supported beam, shown in Fig. P5.15, determine the mid-span deflection and slope at both ends if the beam is fabricated from a W10 × 60 wide flange section.

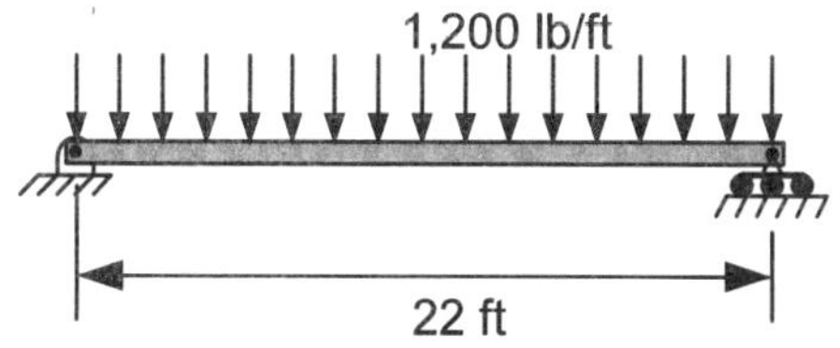

Fig. P5.15

5.16 For the beam in Problem 5.15 determine the deflection and slope at $x = 9$ ft.

5.17 For the steel simply supported beam, shown in Fig. P5.17, determine the mid-span deflection and slope at both ends if the beam is fabricated from a S254 × 38 American Standard section.

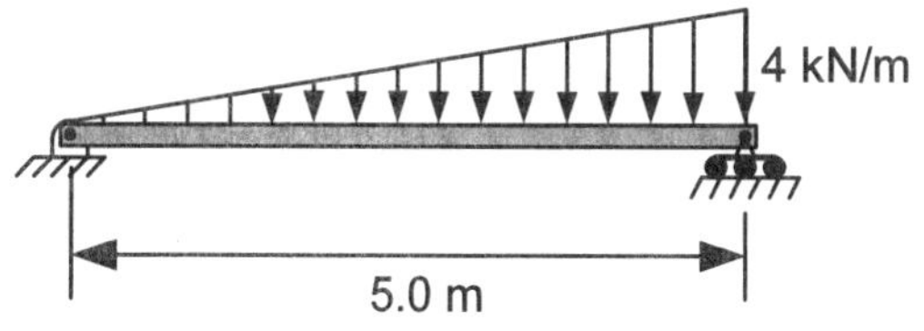

Fig. P5.17

5.18 For the beam in Problem 5.17 determine the deflection and slope at $x = 3.5$ m.

5.19 For the simply supported beam, shown in Fig. P5.19, determine the equation of the elastic curve and the slope at both ends.

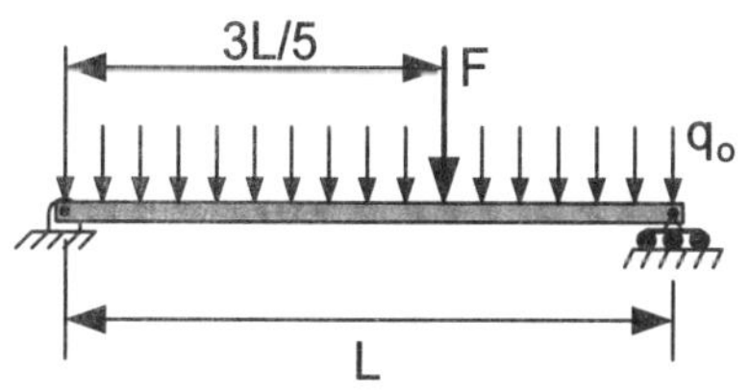

Fig. P5.19

5.20 For the steel simply supported beam, shown in Fig. P5.20, determine the mid-span deflection and the slope at both ends if the beam is fabricated from a W10 × 60 wide flange section.

Fig. P5.20

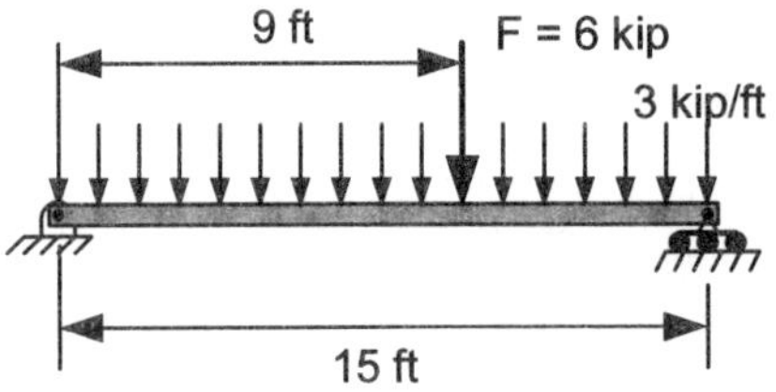

5.21 For the beam in Problem 5.20 determine the deflection and slope at x = 9.0 ft.

5.22 For the simply supported beam, shown in Fig. P5.22, determine the equation of the elastic curve and the slope at both ends.

Fig. P5.22

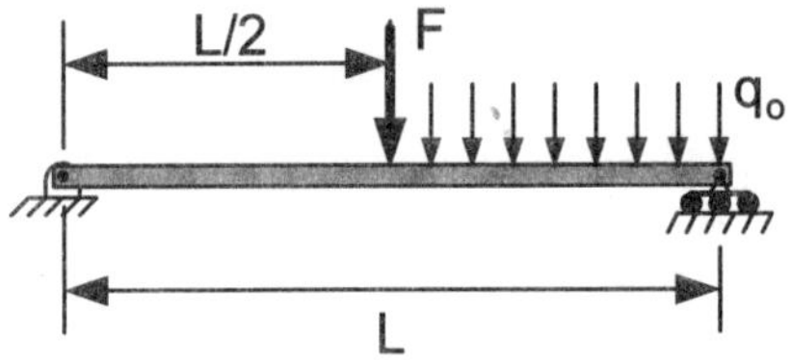

5.23 For the steel simply supported beam, shown in Fig. P5.23, determine the mid-span deflection and the slope at both ends if the beam is fabricated from a S18 × 70 American Standard section.

Fig. P5.23

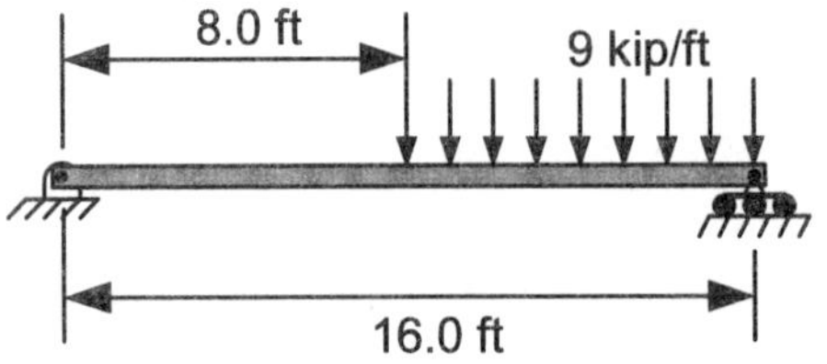

5.24 For the beam in Problem 5.23 determine the deflection and slope at x = 10.0 ft.

5.25 For the simply supported beam, shown Fig. P5.25, determine the equation of the elastic curve and the slope at both ends.

Fig. P5.25

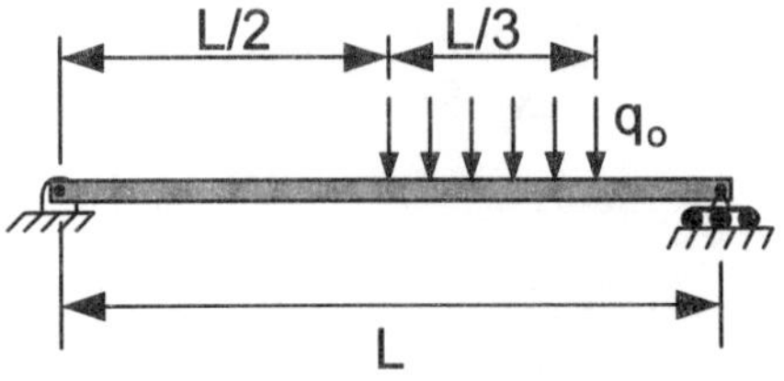

5.26 For the aluminum simply supported beam, shown in Fig. P5.26, determine the mid-span deflection and the slope at both ends if the beam is fabricated from a W457 × 89 wide flange section.

Fig. P5.26

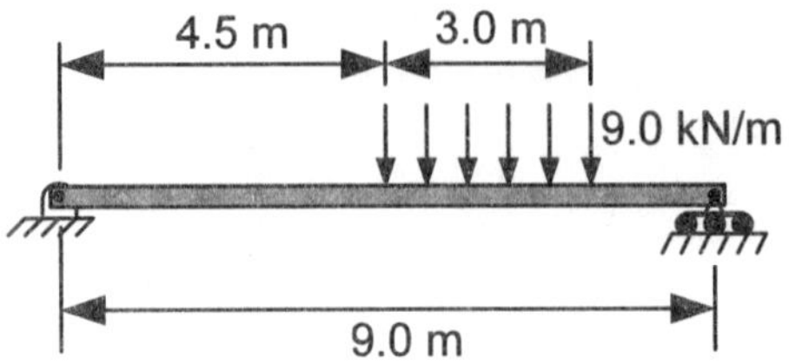

5.27 Repeat Problem 5.26 if the loading is increased from 9.0 kN/m to 11.0 kN/m and the wide flange section is changed to W457 × 113.

5.28 For the simply supported beam, shown in Fig. P5.28, determine the equation of the elastic curve and the slope at both ends.

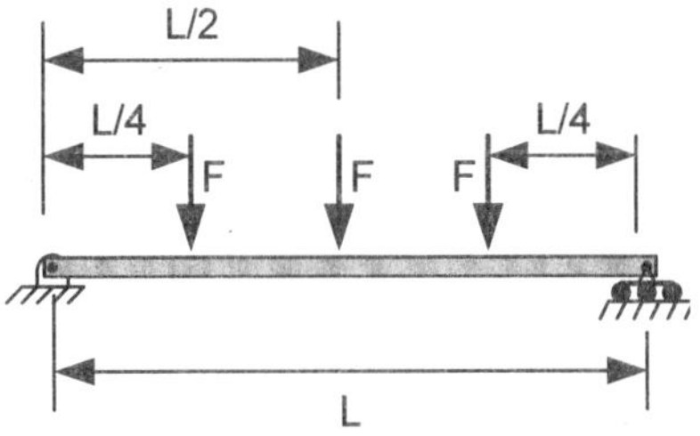

Fig. P5.28

5.29 For the steel simply supported beam, shown in Fig. P5.29, determine the mid-span deflection and the slope at both ends if the beam is fabricated from a W203 × 46 wide flange section.

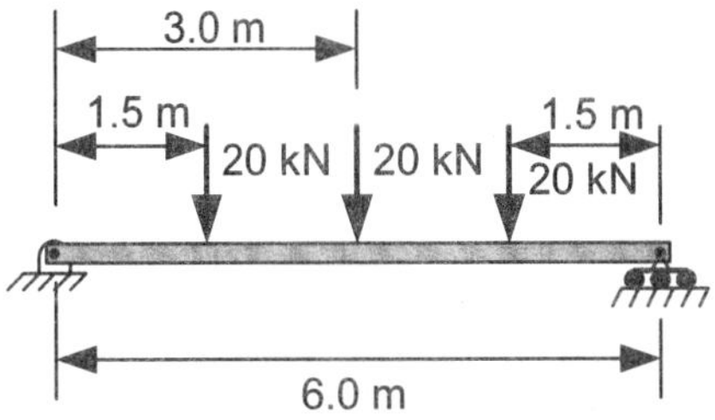

Fig. P5.29

5.30 For the beam described in Problem 5.29 determine the deflection at x = 1.5 and x = 4.5 m.

5.31 For the simply supported beam, shown in Fig. P5.31, determine the equation of the elastic curve and the slope at both ends.

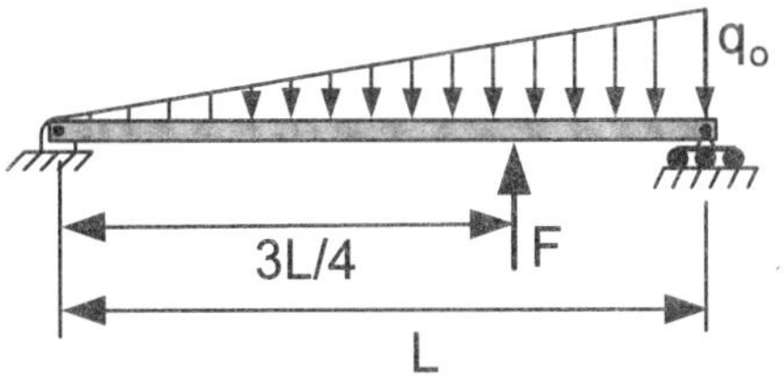

Fig. P5.31

5.32 For the steel simply supported beam, shown in Fig. P5.32, determine the mid-span deflection and the slope at both ends if the beam is fabricated from a W533 × 92 wide flange section.

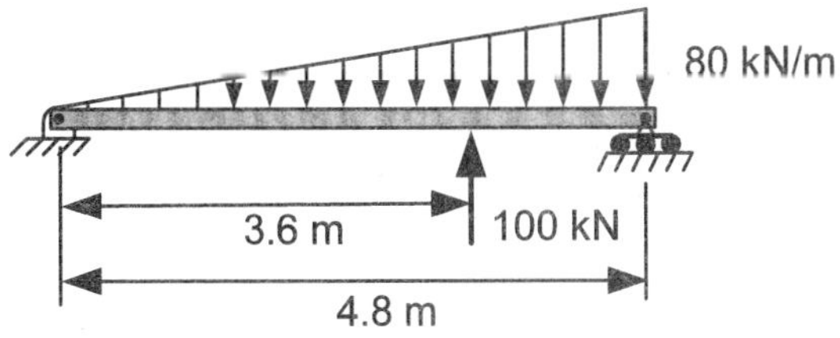

Fig. P5.32

5.33 For the beam described in Problem 5.32 determine the deflection and the slope at x = 3.6m.

5.34 For the cantilever beam, shown in Fig. P5.34, write the equation for the elastic curve. Also determine the equations for deflection and slope at the free end.

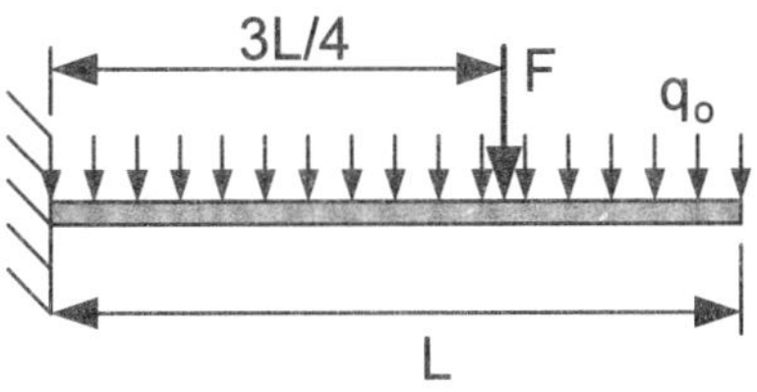

Fig. P5.34

5.35 For the steel cantilever beam, shown in Fig. P5.35, determine the deflection and the slope at the free end if the beam is fabricated from a S305 × 74 American Standard section.

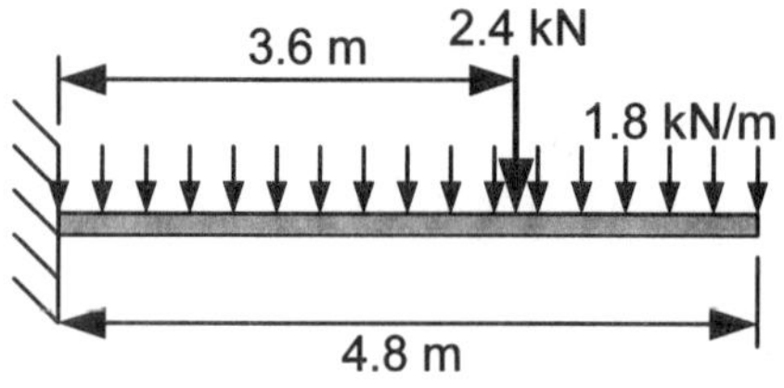

Fig. P5.35

5.36 For the beam described in Problem 5.35 determine the deflection and slope at mid span.

5.37 For the cantilever beam, shown in Fig. P5.37, write the equation for the elastic curve. Also determine the equations for the deflection and slope at the free end.

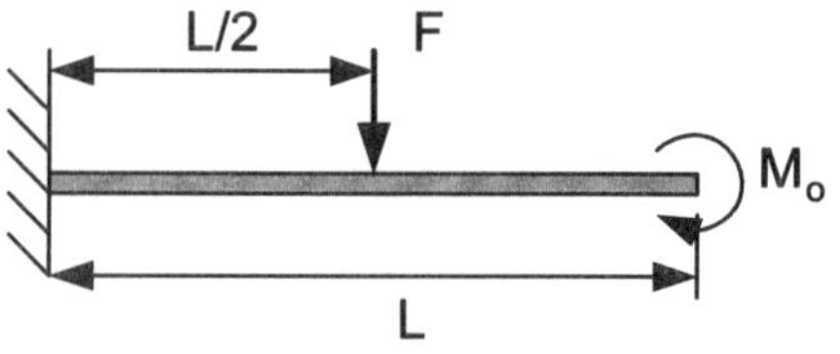

Fig. P5.37

5.38 For the steel cantilever beam, shown in Fig. P5.38 determine the minimum weight wide flange section if the deflection at the free end is limited to 1.4 in.

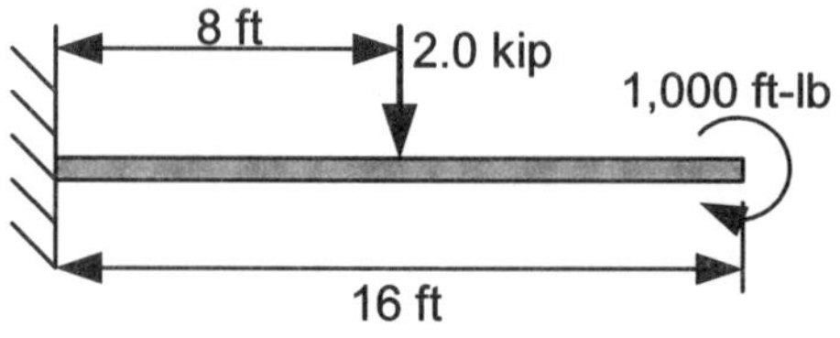

Fig. P5.38

5.39 For the beam described in Problem 5.38 determine the minimum weight American Standard section if the deflection is limited to 1.0 in.

5.40 For the cantilever beam, shown in Fig. P5.40, write the equation for the elastic curve. Also determine the equations for the deflection and slope at the free end.

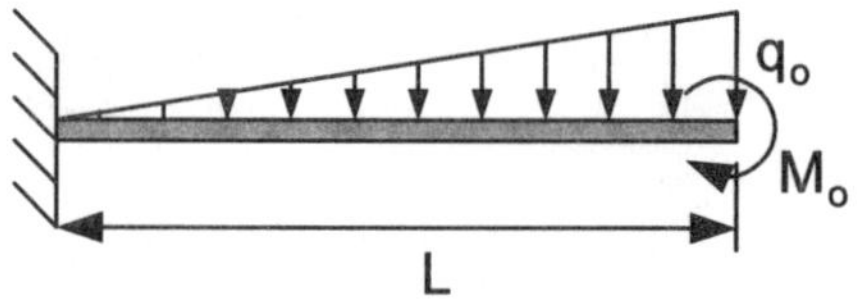

Fig. P5.40

5.41 For the steel cantilever beam, shown in Fig. P5.41, determine the minimum weight American Standard section if the deflection at the free end is limited to 26 mm.

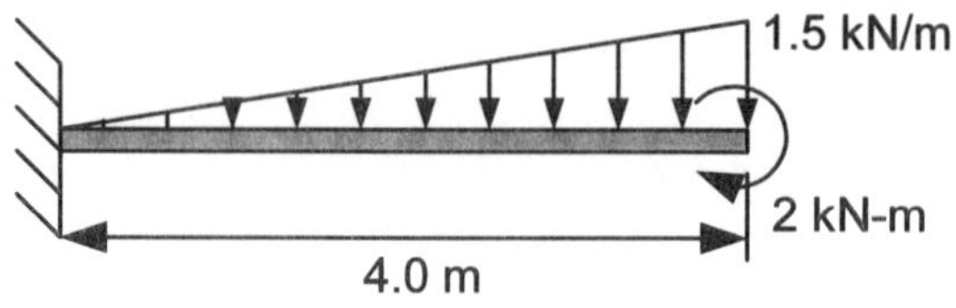

Fig. P5.41

5.42 For the beam described in Problem 5.41 determine the minimum weight wide flange section if the deflection is limited to 20 mm.

5.43 For the cantilever beam, shown in Fig. P5.43, write the equation for the elastic curve. Also determine the deflection and slope at the free end.

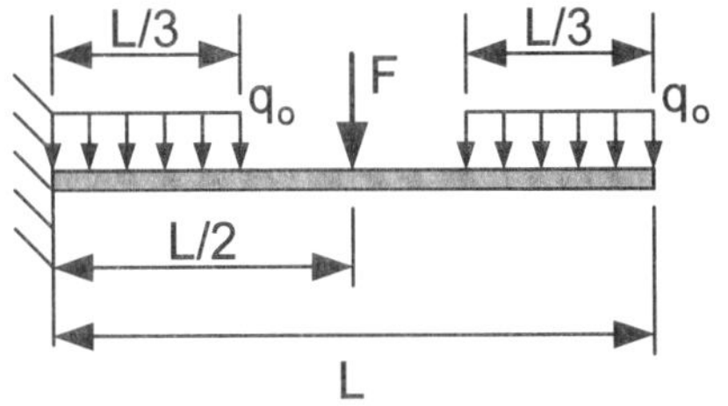

Fig. P5.43

5.44 For the steel cantilever beam, shown in Fig. P5.44, determine the minimum weight structural tee section if the deflection at the free end is limited to 1.1 in.

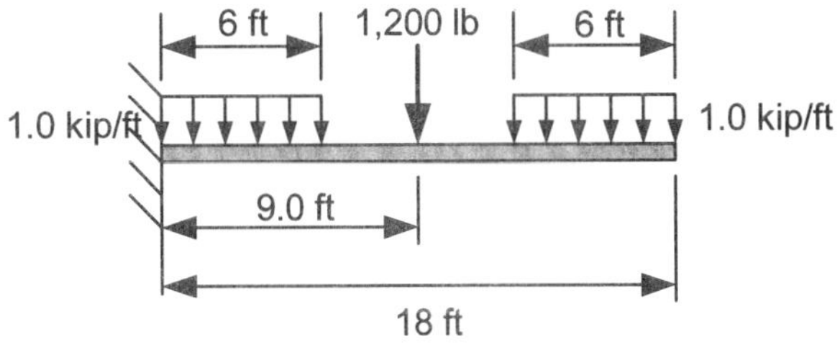

Fig. P5.44

5.45 For the cantilever beam, shown in Fig. P5.45, write the equation for the elastic curve. Also determine the deflection and slope at the free end.

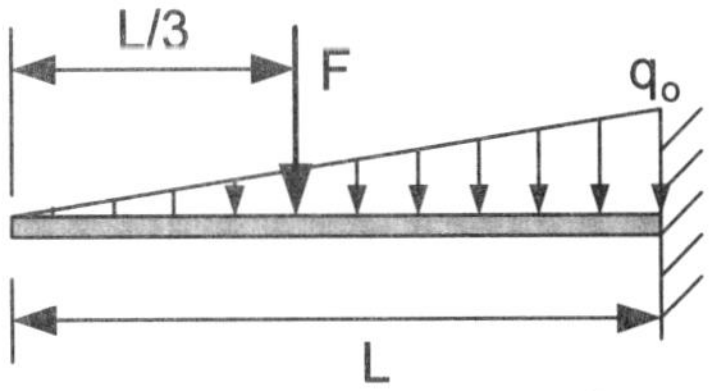

Fig. P5.45

5.46 For the steel cantilever beam, shown in Fig. P5.46, determine the minimum weight wide flange section if the deflection at the free end is limited to 15 mm.

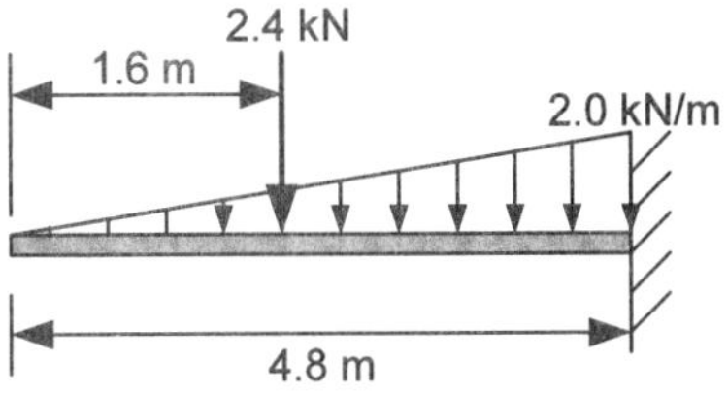

Fig. P5.46

5.47 Using the method of superposition, for the simply supported beam shown in Fig. P5.47, determine the deflection at mid-span and the slope at the left end of the beam. The beam is steel with a W12 × 65 wide flange section.

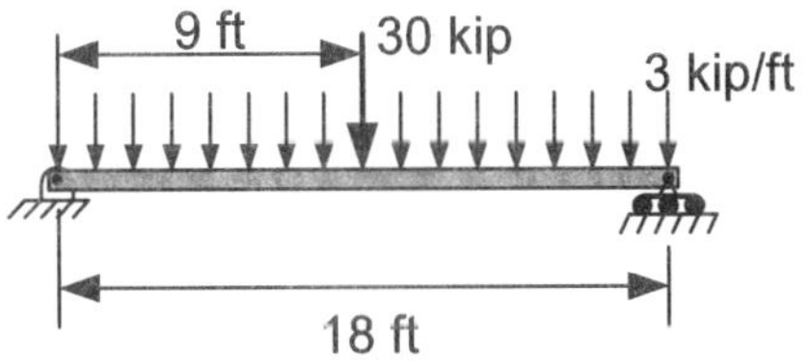

Fig. P5.47

5.48 Using the method of superposition, for the simply supported beam shown in Fig. P5.48, determine the deflection at mid-span and the slope at the left end of the beam.

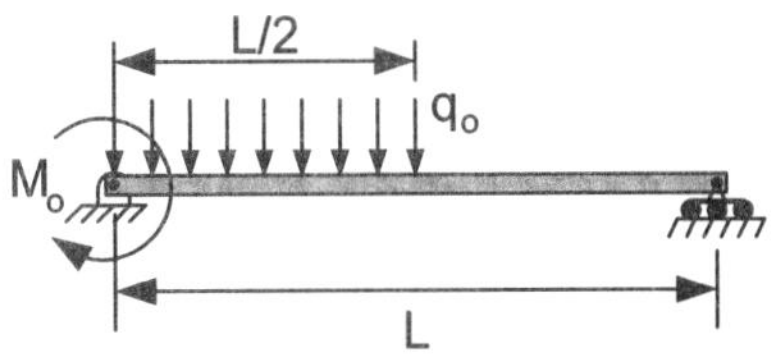

Fig. P5.48

5.49 Using the method of superposition, for the simply supported beam shown in Fig. P5.49, determine the deflection at mid-span and the slope at the right end of the beam. The beam is steel with a W305 × 97 wide flange section.

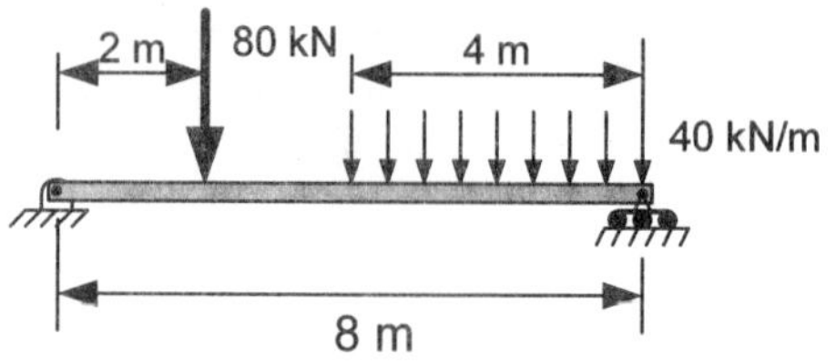

Fig. P5.49

5.50 Using the method of superposition, for the simply supported beam shown in Fig. P5.50, determine the deflection at mid-span and the slope at the right end of the beam.

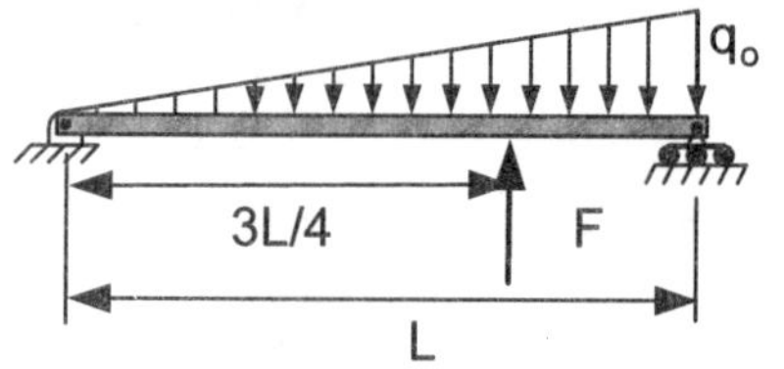

Fig. P5.50

5.51 Using the method of superposition, for the cantilever beam shown in Fig. P5.51, determine the deflection and the slope at the free end of the beam.

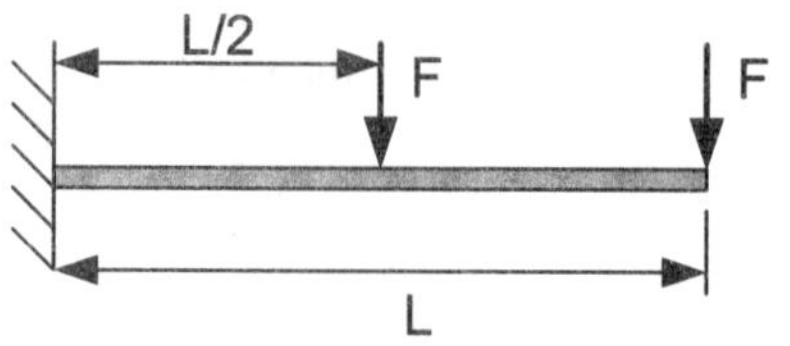

Fig. P5. 51

5.52 Using the method of superposition, for the cantilever beam shown in Fig. P5.52, determine the deflection and the slope at the free end of the beam. The beam is steel with a S457 × 81 American Standard section.

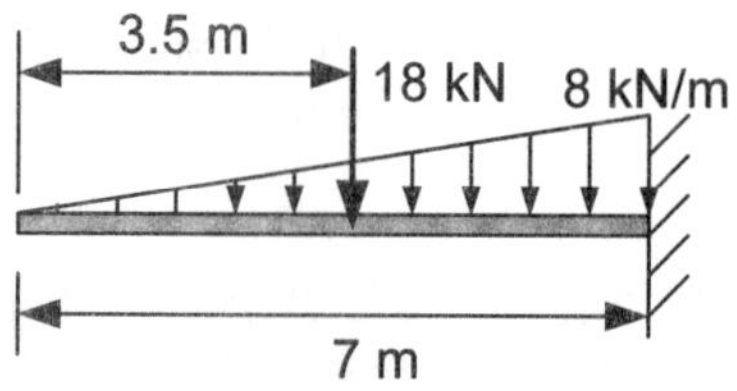

Fig. P5.52

5.53 Using the method of superposition, for the cantilever beam shown in Fig. P5.53, determine the deflection and the slope at the free end of the beam. The beam is steel with a S20 × 66 American Standard section..

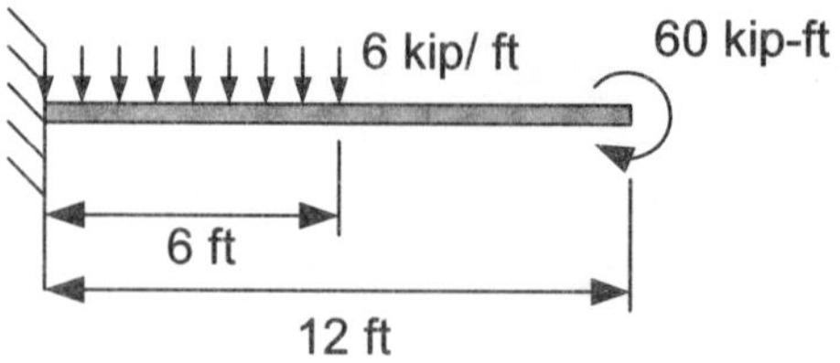

Fig. P5.53

5.54 Using the method of superposition, for the cantilever beam shown in Fig. P5.54, determine the deflection and the slope at the free end of the beam.

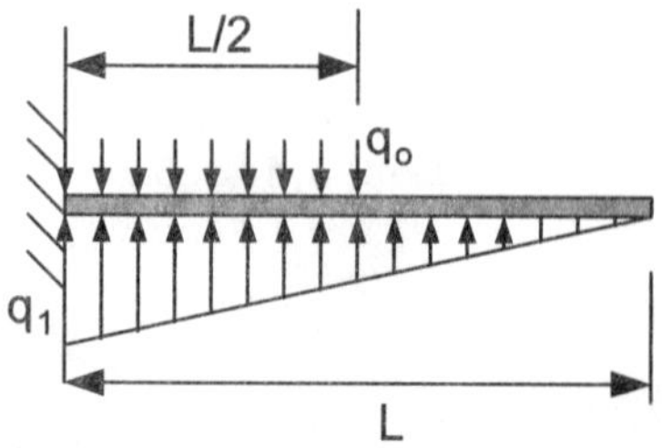

Fig. P5.54

CHAPTER 6

STATICALLY INDETERMINATE MEMBERS

6.1 INTRODUCTION

Structures are considered to be statically determinate when the unknown forces, either internal forces or external reactions, can be determined using only the equilibrium relations. However, in some structures the number of unknown forces exceed the number of applicable equilibrium equations, and a solution is not possible without the introduction of additional equations. When the number of unknown forces exceeds the number of applicable equilibrium equations, the structure is **statically indeterminate.**

The approach for solving for the unknown forces in statically indeterminate structures is to use the equilibrium relations and then to introduce additional equations based on the deformation of the structure. The solution involves two separate but compatible parts:

1. Prepare the traditional FBD together with all of the applicable equations of equilibrium.
2. Prepare displacement diagrams together with deformation equations that are consistent with the forces shown on the FBD.

Statically indeterminate problems arise in structural elements subjected to axial, torsion and transverse (bending) loads. Because the deformation equations depend on the type of loading, we will introduce examples dealing with these three types of loading in separate sections of this chapter. First, let's consider an example to demonstrate this approach in solving for the unknown forces in a statically indeterminate axial member.

6.2 STATICALLY INDETERMINATE AXIAL MEMBERS

EXAMPLE 6.1

A 20 ft. long column supporting the corner of a large building is fabricated from a steel pipe with an outside diameter of 10 in. and an inside diameter of 9 in. The pipe is filled with medium strength concrete to form a composite column that supports a 140-ton axial load as illustrated in Fig. E6.1. The load is transferred to the pipe and concrete through a rigid cap. Determine the forces and stresses in the steel pipe and concrete plug.

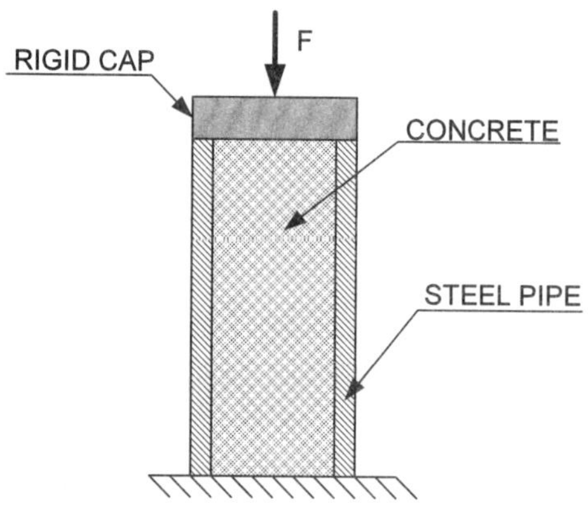

Fig. E6.1

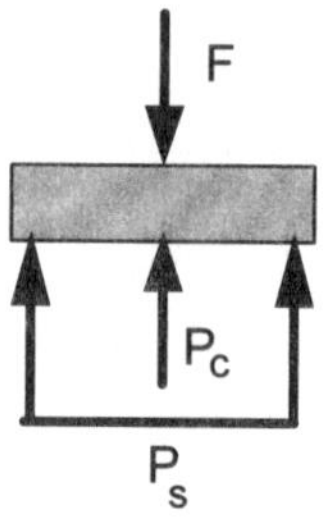

Fig. E6.1a

Solution:

Step 1: Prepare FBDs of the rigid cap, steel pipe and concrete plug as shown in Fig. E6.1a, and write the only applicable equilibrium equation, which is $\Sigma F_y = 0$.

$$\Sigma F_y = P_c + P_s - F = 0$$

$$P_c + P_s = 140 \text{ ton} \qquad \text{(a)}$$

where P_c and P_s are the internal forces in the concrete plug and steel pipe, respectively.

Because we have two unknown forces P_c and P_s and only a single applicable equation of equilibrium, the unknown forces are statically indeterminate.

Step 2: Prepare a drawing shown in Fig. E6.1b depicting an exaggerated view of the deformations occurring in the concrete plug δ_c and the steel pipe δ_s when subjected to the internal forces P_c and P_s. Because the two structural elements deform together under the action of the axial loads, we write the controlling deformation equation as:

$$\delta_c = \delta_s \qquad \text{(b)}$$

Fig. E6.1b

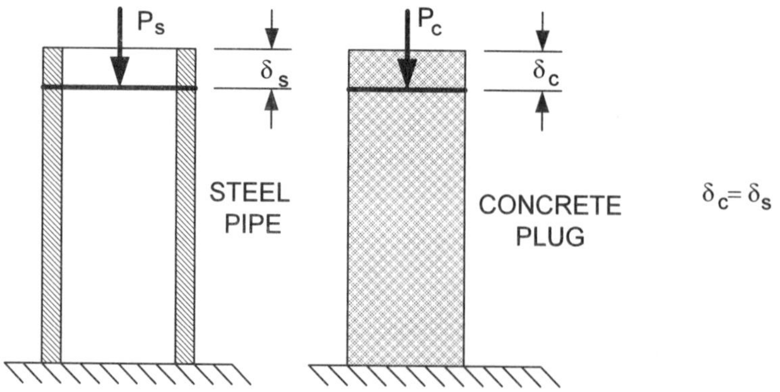

Recall Eq. (2.2) and write:

$$\delta_c = P_c L_c / A_c E_c = \delta_s = P_s L_s / A_s E_s \quad \text{(c)}$$

Solve Eq. (c) for P_c noting that $L_c = L_s$, to obtain:

$$P_c = (A_c/A_s)(E_c/E_s)P_s \quad \text{(d)}$$

Equation (d) provides the second relation needed to solve for the unknown internal forces.

Step 3: Solve for the internal force P_s by substituting Eq. (d) into Eq. (a) to obtain:

$$P_s = (140)/[1 + (A_c/A_s)(E_c/E_s)] \quad \text{(e)}$$

The area ratio is given by:

$$A_c/A_s = [d_i^2/(d_o^2 - d_i^2)] = (9.0)^2/[(10.0)^2 - (9.0)^2] = 4.263 \quad \text{(f)}$$

Using values from Appendix B-1, the modulus ratio is given by:

$$E_c/E_s = (3.6)/(30) = 0.12 \quad \text{(g)}$$

Substituting the results from Eq. (f) and Eq. (g) into Eq. (e) gives:

$$P_s = 140/[1 + (A_c/A_s)(E_c/E_s)] = (140)/[1 + (4.263)(0.12)] = 92.62 \text{ ton} \quad \text{(h)}$$

Then from Eq. (a) and Eq. (h), it is clear that:

$$P_c = 140 - 92.62 = 47.38 \text{ ton} \quad \text{(i)}$$

Step 4: Solve for the stresses in the concrete plug and steel pipe as:

$$\sigma_c = P_c/A_c = [(4)(47.38)(2{,}000)]/[\pi(9.0)^2] = 1{,}490 \text{ psi} \quad \text{(j)}$$

$$\sigma_s = P_s/A_s = [(4)(92.62)(2{,}000)]/\{\pi[(10.0)^2 - (9.0)^2]\} = 12{,}410 \text{ psi} \quad \text{(k)}$$

Note that both of these stresses are compressive and relatively low in value compared to typical strengths of concrete and steel.

EXAMPLE 6.2

A grade 8 steel bolt 1.0 in. in diameter (8 threads/in.) is employed to clamp an aluminum bushing between two rigid platens as illustrated in Fig. E6.2. The aluminum bushing has a 2.5 in. outside diameter and 1.25 in. inside diameter and is 14.00 in. long. After the unit is assembled with a snug fit, the nut is tightened by ½ of a turn. Determine the axial stresses in the bolt and the bushing after the nut is tightened. Also determine the deflection of the aluminum bushing.

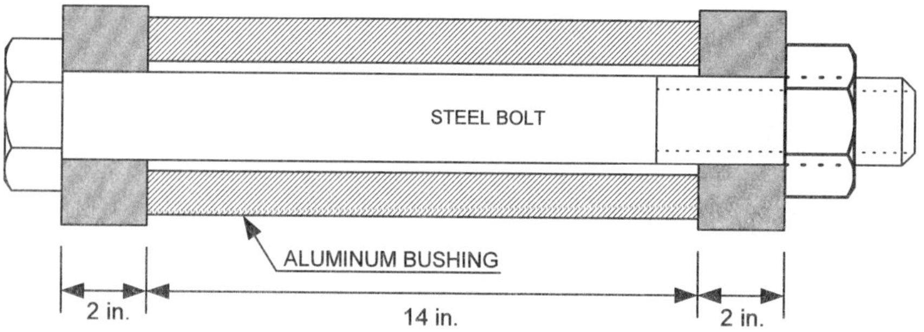

Fig. E6.2

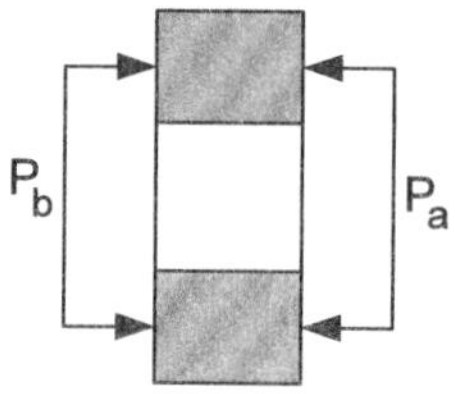

Fig. E6.2a

Solution:

Step 1: Prepare FBDs of one of the rigid platens as shown in Fig. E6.2a, and write the only applicable equilibrium equation, which is $\Sigma F_x = 0$.

$$\Sigma F_x = -P_a + P_b = 0$$

$$P_a = P_b \qquad \text{(a)}$$

where P_a and P_b are the internal forces in the aluminum bushing and the steel bolt, respectively. They are equal in magnitude and opposite in sign. Because we have two unknown forces P_a and P_b and only a single applicable equation of equilibrium, the unknown forces are statically indeterminate.

Step 2: Prepare a drawing shown in Fig. E6.2b that depicts an exaggerated view of the deformations occurring in the bolt and the aluminum bushing when subjected to the internal forces P_a and P_b. When the nut is tightened the steel bolt tends to stretch and the aluminum bushing is compressed (shortened). The total of the two deformations must equal the amount of displacement induced by rotating the nut by ½ of a turn, which is (1/2)(1/8) = 0.0625 in.

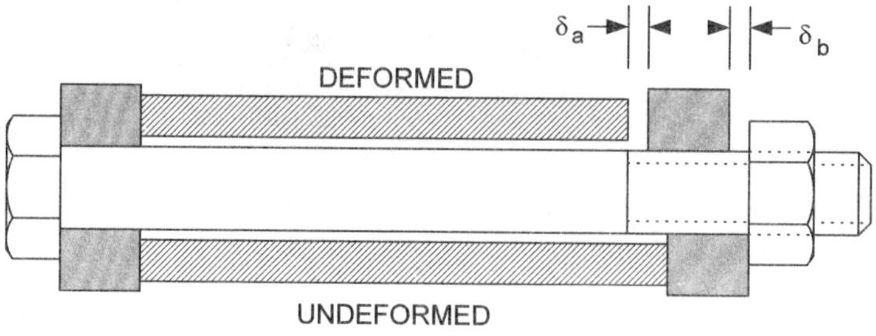

Fig. E6.2b

$$\delta_a + \delta_b = .0625 \text{ in.} \qquad \text{(b)}$$

Step 3: Recall Eq. (2.2) and Eq. (a) and write:

$$\delta_a = P_a L_a / A_a E_a = [(4)(14)/\{\pi[(2.5)^2 - (1.25)^2](10.4 \times 10^6)\}]\, P_a = 0.3656 \times 10^{-6}\, P_a$$

$$\text{(c)}$$

$$\delta_b = P_b L_b / A_b E_b = \{(4)(18)/[\pi(1.0)^2\,(30 \times 10^6)]\}\, P_b = 0.7639 \times 10^{-6}\, P_b$$

Use $P_a = P_b$ and substitute Eq. (c) into Eq. (b) and solve for P_b.

$$P_b\,[0.3656 + 0.7639] = 0.0625 \times 10^6$$

$$P_a = P_b = 55{,}330 \text{ lb} \qquad \text{(d)}$$

Step 4: The stresses are given by Eq. (2.4) as:

$$\sigma_b = P_b/A_b = (4)(55{,}330)/[\pi(1.0)^2] = 70.45 \text{ ksi (tension)}$$

$$\sigma_a = P_a/A_a = (4)(55{,}330)/\{\pi[(2.5)^2-(1.25)^2]\} = 15.03 \text{ ksi (compression)} \qquad \text{(e)}$$

Step 5: The amount of the compression of the aluminum bushing is given by Eq. (2.2) as:

$$\delta_a = P_aL_a/A_aE_a = [(55{,}330)(14)(4)]/\{\pi[(2.5)^2-(1.25)^2](10.4\times 10^6)]\} = 0.02023 \text{ in. (shorter)}$$

These two examples demonstrate the method employed to solve statically indeterminate problems. This approach involves two important steps — writing the applicable equations of equilibrium based on an accurate FBD and writing a deformation equation based on a drawing showing the deformation of the structural elements involved.

6.2.1 Thermal Stresses

Thermal stresses are produced in structural elements by the constraint of the free expansion of a material subjected to a temperature change. To illustrate this fact, consider a long thin rod of length L_o at a temperature T_o. When the temperature of the rod increases to say T_1, the rod undergoes a free expansion with an attendant increase in length δ_T given by:

$$\delta_T = L_o\,\alpha(T_1 - T_o) = L_o\,\alpha\Delta T \qquad (6.1)$$

where α is the temperature coefficient of expansion.

It is clear from the definition of strain and Eq. (2.3) that a thermal strain ε_T accompanies a free expansion.

$$\varepsilon_T = \delta_T/L_o = \alpha\Delta T \qquad (6.2)$$

Thermal stresses in a free expansion process are zero because the temperature change does not produce the internal forces P required to generate stresses. Thermal strains induce thermal stresses if, and only if, the structural element is constrained in some manner. When the structural element is totally constrained and free expansion is not permitted, the thermal stresses in the uniaxial rod are given by:

$$\sigma_T = E\alpha\Delta T \qquad (6.3)$$

To derive Eq. (6.3), consider the free expansion of a long thin rod due to a temperature change ΔT as shown in Fig. 6.1a.

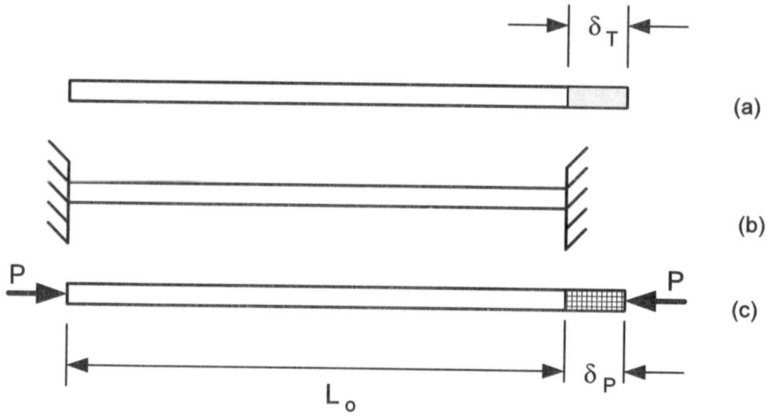

Fig. 6.1 Rod with free expansion, constraint and internal forces P.

If the rod is constrained within rigid walls as illustrated in Fig. 6.1b, the length remains at L_o after the temperature change ΔT. As the rod attempts to expand against the constraint offered by the rigid walls, an internal force P is produced as shown in Fig. 6.1c. The internal force P is sufficiently large to produce an axial displacement (contraction) equal to the thermal expansion. Hence, we can write:

$$\delta_T = \delta_P \tag{6.4}$$

Substituting Eq. (2.2) and Eq. (6.1) into Eq. (6.4) and simplifying yields:

$$\sigma_T = P/A = E\alpha\Delta T \tag{6.3}$$

The results obtained by applying Eq. (6.3) should be considered as an upper bound on the thermal stresses generated by a temperature change ΔT. The derivation of this relation assumed total constraint of the free expansion of the bar. In practice, total constraint is difficult to achieve and because the displacements are small, even slight relief in the constraint markedly reduces the magnitude of the thermal stresses.

We have included a table showing the coefficient of thermal expansion, modulus of elasticity and thermal stresses for a ΔT = 100° F or 100° C in Table 6.1.

Table 6.1
Coefficient of thermal expansion, modulus of elasticity and thermal stress induced by ΔT = 100 °F or 100 °C in various engineering materials.

Material	$E \times 10^6$ psi	$\alpha \times 10^{-6}$/°F	σ_T (ksi)	$E \times 10^9$ (Pa)	$\alpha \times 10^{-6}$/°C	σ_T (MPa)
Steel	30	6.3	18.90	207	11.3	233.9
Aluminum	10.4	12.9	13.42	72	23.2	167.0
Brass	16	11.1	17.76	110	20.0	220.0
Stainless Steel	27.5	9.6	26.40	190	17.3	328.7
Titanium	16.5	4.9	8.09	114	8.8	100.3

EXAMPLE 6.3

Two heavy blocks of steel are permanently fastened together by a steel shrink link that is fitted into pockets machined into the two blocks as illustrated in Fig. E6.3. If a shrink link has a body length of 120.0 mm at a temperature of 200° C, determine the clamping force provided by the shrink link at an ambient temperature of 25° C. Also determine the stress in the link after it has cooled to ambient temperature. The body of the link has a square cross section with a side dimension of 60 mm.

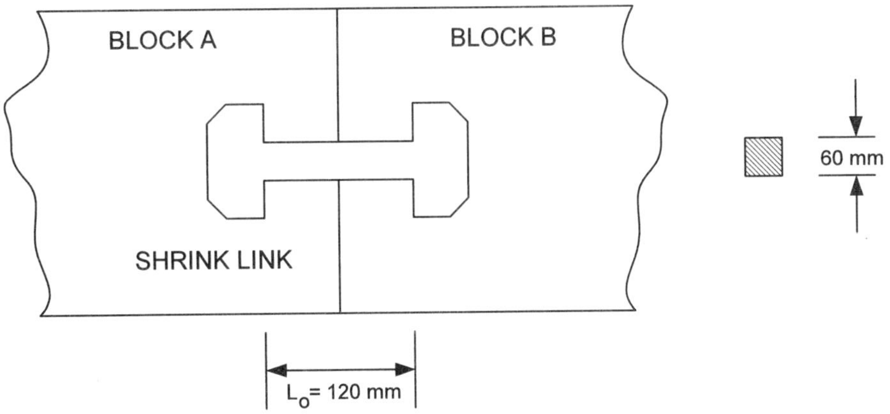

Fig. E6.3

Solution:

Step 1: Upon cooling to ambient temperature the link attempts to shrink an amount δ_T given by Eq. (6.1) as:

$$\delta_T = L_o\, \alpha\Delta T = (120)(11.3 \times 10^{-6})(200 - 25) = 0.2373 \text{ mm} \qquad \text{(a)}$$

Step 2: We assume that the free contraction of the link is totally constrained by the two steel blocks. This constraint condition yields:

$$\delta_T = \delta_P \qquad \text{(b)}$$

Substituting Eq. (2.2) into Eq. (b) gives the internal force P developed in the shrink link as:

$$P = (\delta_P AE)/L = [(0.2373)(3{,}600)(207 \times 10^3)]/120 = 1{,}474 \text{ kN} \qquad \text{(c)}$$

Step 3: The thermal stress induced in the link by the $\Delta T = 175°$ C is given by Eq. (2.4) as:

$$\sigma_T = P/A = E\alpha\Delta T = (1{,}474 \times 10^3)/(0.060)^2 = 409.4 \text{ MPa} \qquad \text{(d)}$$

EXAMPLE 6.4

A thin retaining ring, fabricated from stainless steel is fitted over the polished steel journal of a solid shaft 8.000 inches in diameter. The outside diameter of the retaining ring is 8.25 in. and its length is 0.50 in. To fit the ring over the journal it is heated to 350 °F and slid on the shaft to its designated position. The ring becomes snug at a temperature of 245 °F. The ambient temperature is 75 °F. Determine the stress in the retaining ring and the clamping pressure between the ring and the journal.

Solution:

Step 1: Upon cooling from the snug temperature of 245° F to the ambient temperature of 75° F, the ring attempts to shrink diametrically by an amount δ_T given by Eq. (6.1) as:

$$\delta_T = d_o\,\alpha\Delta T = (8.000)(9.6 \times 10^{-6})(245 - 75) = 13.056 \times 10^{-3} \text{ in.} \qquad \text{(a)}$$

Step 2: We assume that the free contraction of the retaining ring is totally constrained by the polished journal of the solid steel shaft. This constraint condition yields:

$$\delta_T = \delta_P \qquad \text{(b)}$$

Consider the circumference $C = \pi d_o$ of the retaining ring. Then the free contraction ΔC of the circumference of the ring is given by:

$$\Delta C = \pi\Delta d_o = \pi\delta_T = \pi\delta_P \qquad \text{(c)}$$

The increase in the circumference of the ring due to the generation of an internal force P is obtained by substituting into Eq. (2.2) as:

$$\Delta C = (P\pi d_o)/(AE) = \pi\delta_T \qquad \text{(d)}$$

Solving Eq. (d) for the internal force P in the ring gives:

$$P = (\delta_T AE)/d_o = (13.056 \times 10^{-3})(0.250/2)(0.5)(27.5 \times 10^{6})/8.00 = 2.805 \text{ kip} \qquad \text{(e)}$$

Step 3: The thermal stress induced in the retaining ring due to $\Delta T = 170°$ F is given by Eq. (6.3) as:

$$\sigma_T = E\alpha\Delta T = (27.5 \times 10^{6})(9.6 \times 10^{-6})(170) = 44.88 \text{ ksi} \qquad \text{(f)}$$

Step 4: To determine the interfacial pressure between the ring and the journal, consider the FBD of the ring shown in Fig. E6.4. Writing $\Sigma F_y = 0$ gives an expression containing the interfacial pressure p as:

$$\Sigma F = p(d_o b) - 2P = 0 \qquad p = 2P/(d_o b) \qquad \text{(g)}$$

where b = 0.5 in. is the width of the ring.

Fig. E6.4

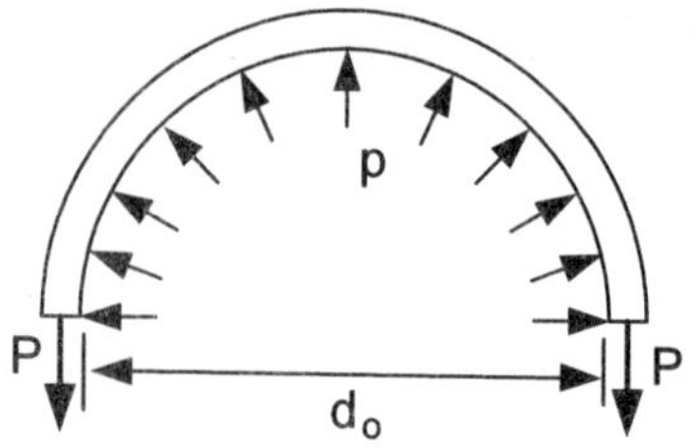

Using Eq. (g), the interfacial pressure is given by:

$$p = (2)(2.805 \times 10^{3})/(8.0)(0.5) = 1{,}402 \text{ psi} \qquad \text{(h)}$$

6.3 STATICALLY INDETERMINATE TORSION MEMBERS

Statically indeterminate shafts are treated in the same manner as statically indeterminate tensile or compression members. A free body diagram is prepared and the applicable equations of equilibrium are written. Displacement diagrams are then drawn that are consistent with the torques shown on the FBD. Deformation equations are used to provide the additional relations necessary to solve for the unknown forces.

Examples will be presented to illustrate the methods employed to solve for stresses and deflections in statically indeterminate shafts subjected to torsion.

EXAMPLE 6.5

A circular shaft fabricated from steel is supported at each end by rigid constraints, as shown in Fig. E6.5. The left side of the shaft is 1.0 in. in diameter and its right side is 0.75 in. in diameter. A torque of 150 ft-lb is applied at the center of the shaft where the diameter discontinuity is located. Determine the reactions at each of the supports.

Fig. E6.5

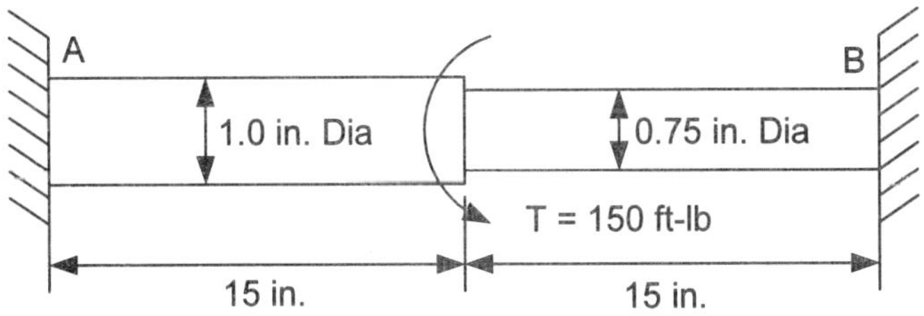

Solution:

Step 1: Prepare a FBD of the shaft showing the reactions at the supports and write the applicable equations of equilibrium.

Fig. E6.5a

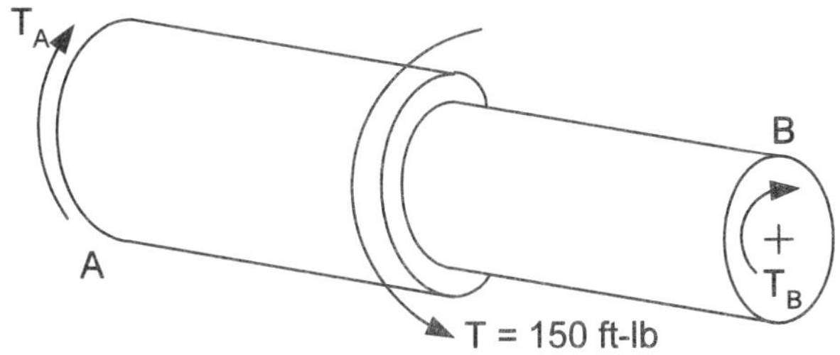

From $\Sigma M = 0$, we may write that:

$$T_A + T_B = 150 \text{ ft-lb} \qquad \text{(a)}$$

Because the beam is not uniform in cross section along its entire length the reactions at the two supports will not be equal. We have two unknowns in Eq. (a); hence, the shaft is statically indeterminate.

Step 2: Examining Fig. E6.5, indicates that the shaft is rigidly constrained implying that:

$$\phi = \phi_A + \phi_B = 0 \qquad \text{(b)}$$

where ϕ_A and ϕ_B are the angles of twist of the left and right side of the shaft, respectively.

Step 3: To determine the angle of twist, let's first draw a FBD of the two different sides of the shaft, as shown in Fig. E6.5b.

Fig. E6.5b

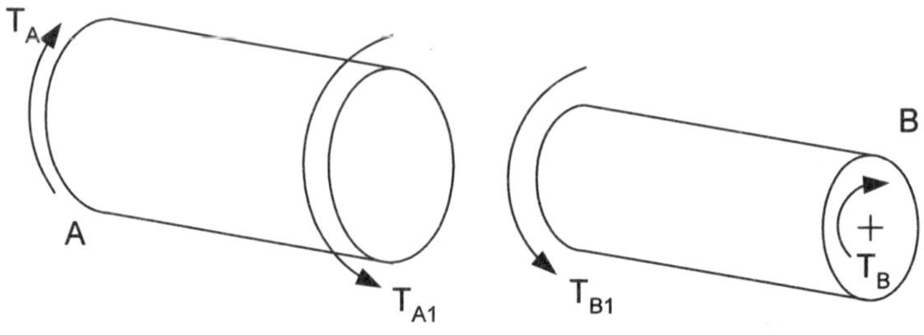

To maintain the ends of the shaft in equilibrium, it is evident that:

$$T_{A1} = T_A \qquad \text{and} \qquad T_{B1} = T_B \tag{c}$$

Recall Eq. (3.35a) and write:

$$\phi = \phi_A + \phi_B = \frac{T_A L_A}{GJ_A} - \frac{T_B L_B}{GJ_B} = 0 \tag{d}$$

Note that the right end of the shaft is twisted in the opposite direction than the left end.

Step 4: Solve Eq. (d) for T_A yields:

$$T_A = \frac{L_B J_A}{L_A J_B} T_B \tag{e}$$

Substituting numerical values into Eq. (e) gives:

$$T_A = \frac{d_A^4}{d_B^4} T_B = \frac{(1.0)^4}{(0.75)^4} T_B = 3.160 T_B \tag{f}$$

Step 5: Substitute Eq. (f) into Eq. (a) and solve for T_B.

$$3.160\ T_B + T_B = 4.160\ T_B = 150 \text{ ft-lb} \tag{g}$$

$$T_B = 36.06 \text{ ft-lb}$$

and (h)

$$T_A = 150 - T_B = 113.94 \text{ ft-lb}$$

EXAMPLE 6.6

The structural member, presented in Fig. E6.6, is fabricated from a steel shaft (core) and a brass tube (cover). The two materials are bonded together to form a composite member. The steel core has a diameter of 25 mm and the brass tube has an inside diameter of 25 mm and an outside diameter of 35 mm. The length of the composite shaft is 1.4 m. A torque T = 150 N-m is applied at its free end. Determine the angle of twist of the composite shaft, the maximum shear stress in the steel core and the brass cover and prepare a graph of the shear stress distribution.

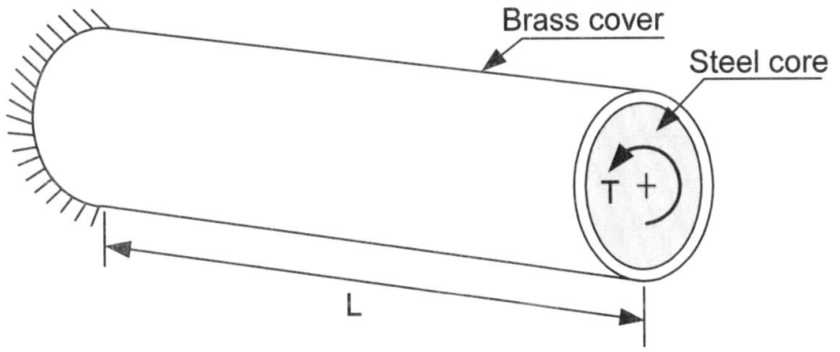

Fig. E6.6

Solution:

Step 1: Prepare the FBD, shown in Fig. E6.6a and write the applicable equilibrium equation.

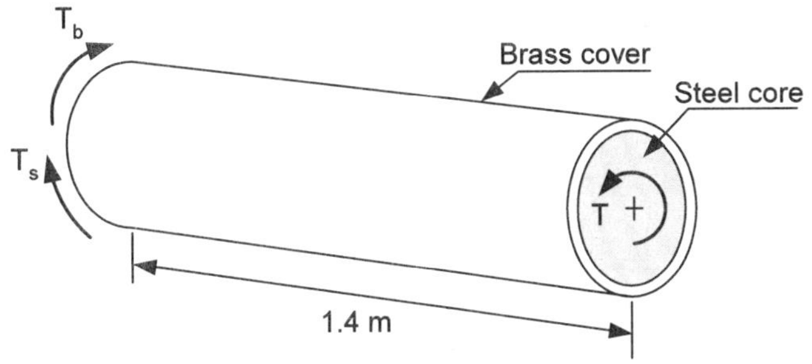

Fig. E6.6a

Using $\Sigma M = 0$ yields:

$$T_s + T_b = T = 150 \text{ N-m} \tag{a}$$

Step 2: Because the brass and the steel are bonded together they must undergo the same angle of twist; hence:

$$\phi = \phi_s = \phi_b \tag{b}$$

Step 3: Use Eq. (3.35) to relate the angle of twist to the torsion loading to obtain:

$$\phi = \phi_s = \phi_b = \frac{T_s L}{G_s J_s} = \frac{T_b L}{G_b J_b} \tag{c}$$

From Appendix B-1 note that G_s = 79 GPa and G_b = 41 GPa. Substitute these values into Eq. (c) and solve for T_s yields:

$$T_s = \frac{G_s J_s}{G_b J_b} T_b = \frac{G_s d_s^4}{G_b\left(d_{0b}^4 - d_{ib}^4\right)} T_b = \frac{79}{41} \frac{(25)^4}{\left[(35)^4 - (25)^4\right]} T_b$$

$$T_s = 0.6781\ T_b \qquad \text{(d)}$$

Step 4: Substituting Eq. (d) into Eq. (a) yields:

$$(0.6781 + 1)T_b = 150 \text{ N-m}$$

$$T_b = 89.39 \text{ N-m} \qquad \text{and} \qquad T_s = 60.61 \text{ N-m} \qquad \text{(e)}$$

Step 5: The angle of twist is given by Eq. (3.35a) as:

$$\phi = \frac{T_s L}{G_s J_s} = \frac{(60.61)(1.4)(32)}{(79 \times 10^9)\pi(0.025)^4} = 0.02801 \text{ Radian} = 1.605 \text{ Degrees} \qquad \text{(f)}$$

Step 6: The torque is constant along the length of the shaft. We determine the maximum shear stress from Eq. (3.16) as:

$$\left(\tau_{Max}\right)_s = \frac{16T_s}{\pi d^3} = \frac{(16)(60.61)}{\pi(0.025)^3} = 19.76 \text{ MPa}$$

$$\text{(g)}$$

$$\left(\tau_{Max}\right)_b = \frac{16T_s}{\pi\left(d_0^3 - d_i^3\right)} = \frac{(16)(89.39)}{\pi\left((0.035)^3 - (0.025)^3\right)} = 16.71 \text{ MPa}$$

Step 7: Prepare a graph showing the distribution of the shear stresses across the cross section of the composite shaft. Note the strains are linearly distributed beginning at zero at the center of the shaft and going to their maximum value at the outside diameter of each material. The stresses are also linearly distributed.

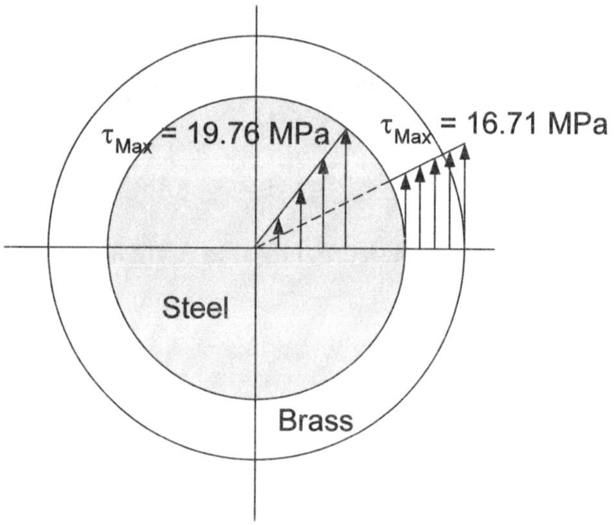

Fig. E6.6b

EXAMPLE 6.7

For the drive shaft arrangement shown in Fig. E6.7, determine the shear stress in the shaft and the angle of twist. The shaft is fabricated from steel with a diameter of 50 mm. The brakes prevent shaft rotation with an applied torque of 750 N-m. The gears are considered as rigid and tooth deflections are neglected in the analysis.

Fig. E6.7

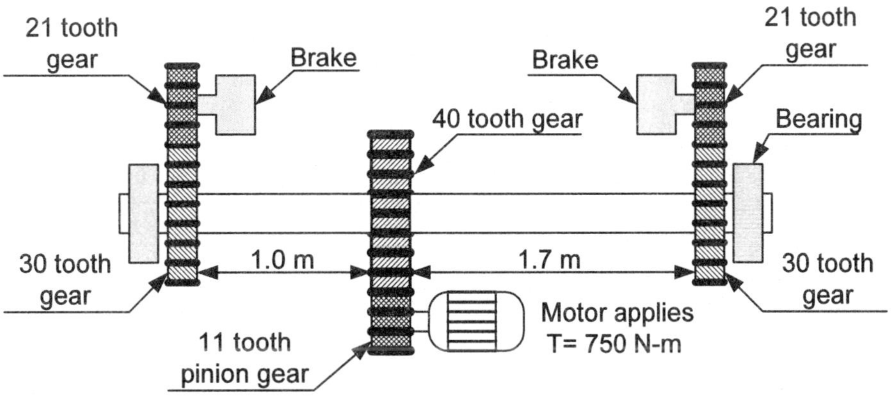

Solution:

Step 1: Prepare the FBD, shown in Fig. E6.7a and write the applicable equilibrium equation.

Fig. E6.7a

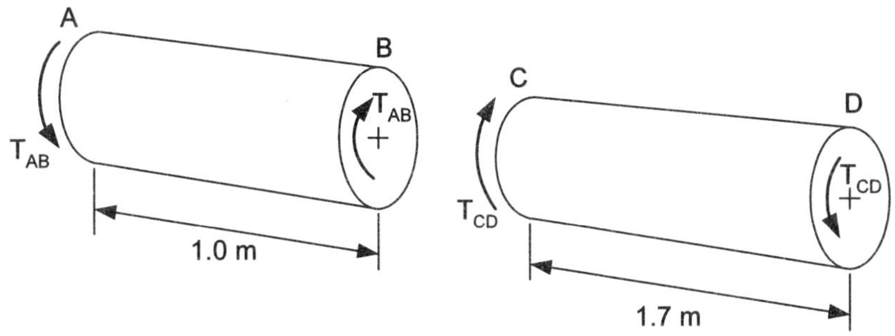

The applied torque is divided between the two sides of the shaft; hence:

$$T_{AB} + T_{CD} = T = 750 \text{ N-m} \quad \text{(a)}$$

Step 2: Because the shaft is continuous from one end to the other, the angle of twist measured at the central gear where the torque is applied must be equal; hence:

$$\phi = \phi_{AB} = \phi_{CD} \quad \text{(b)}$$

Step 3: Use Eq. (3.35a) to relate the angle of twist to the torsion loading to obtain:

$$\phi = \phi_{AB} = \phi_{CD} = \frac{T_{AB}L_{AB}}{GJ} = \frac{T_{CD}L_{CD}}{GJ} \quad \text{(c)}$$

or

$$T_{AB} = (L_{CD}/L_{AB})T_{CD} = (1.7/1.0)T_{CD} = 1.7\ T_{CD} \quad \text{(d)}$$

Step 4: Substitute Eq. (d) into Eq. (a) and solve for the torques to obtain:

$$T_{AB} + T_{CD} = (1.7 + 1.0)T_{CD} = 750 \text{ N-m}$$

$$T_{CD} = 750/2.7 = 277.8 \text{ N-m} \quad \text{and} \quad T_{AB} = 472.2 \text{ N-m} \qquad \text{(e)}$$

Step 5: The angle of twist is given by Eq. (3.35) as:

$$\phi = \frac{T_{AB}L_{AB}}{GJ} = \frac{(472.2)(1.0)(32)}{(79\times 10^9)\pi(0.050)^4} = 0.009741 \text{ Radian} = 0.5581 \text{ Degrees} \qquad \text{(f)}$$

Step 5: The torque is constant along segments AB and CD of the shaft. We determine the maximum shear stress from Eq. (3.16) as:

$$(\tau_{Max})_{AB} = \frac{16T_{AB}}{\pi d^3} = \frac{(16)(472.2)}{\pi(0.05)^3} = 19.24 \text{ MPa}$$

$$(\tau_{Max})_{CD} = \frac{16T_{CD}}{\pi d^3} = \frac{(16)(277.8)}{\pi(0.05)^3} = 11.32 \text{ MPa} \qquad \text{(g)}$$

The examples presented on previous pages illustrate the approach to solve statically indeterminate problems for discontinuous shafts, composite shafts and shafts with gearing. The method is the same for all of the statically indeterminate members. You prepare a FBD and write the applicable equilibrium equation. Then you consider the angle of twist and write the controlling deformation equation. This approach enables you to partition the applied torques and to calculate the shear stresses in the shaft.

6.4 STATICALLY INDETERMINATE BEAMS

In most instances beams are statically determinate. The reactions at the supports may be determined from the three applicable equations of equilibrium — $\Sigma F_x = 0$, $\Sigma F_y = 0$ and $\Sigma M_o = 0$. However, in some cases beams are designed with extra supports that produce additional reaction forces making the beam statically indeterminate. Two common examples of statically indeterminate beams are illustrated in Fig. 6.2 — the propped cantilever beam and the continuously supported beam.

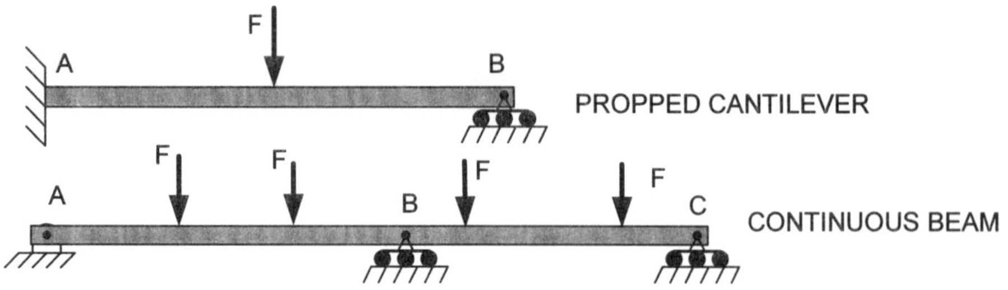

Fig. 6.2 Statically indeterminate beams.

The propped cantilever has one reaction force R_{By} at the prop and three possible reaction forces R_{Ax}, R_{Ay} and M_A at the built-in end. Three possible equilibrium equations and four unknowns yield a statically indeterminate beam. For the continuous beam, two reaction forces are possible at the clevis and one at each of the roller supports at locations B and C. Clearly, the continuous beam is also statically indeterminate.

There are several methods to solve for the additional reaction force; however, in this treatment, we supplement the equilibrium relations with a deformation equation to enable a solution. We will demonstrate two different methods to determine the reaction forces for statically indeterminate beams including the method of superposition and the method of integration with singularity functions.

6.4.1 Superposition Methods

In applying the method of superposition to the solution of statically indeterminate beams, we supplement the equilibrium equations by writing additional equations based on the deformation of the beam. This is accomplished by representing the statically indeterminate beam with two beams, each of which is statically determinate. The deflections of these two beams are added to yield the boundary conditions imposed on the statically indeterminate beam. This process yields the reaction force at one of the supports. Let's consider the propped cantilever beam as an example to demonstrate this approach.

EXAMPLE 6.8

Determine the reaction force at the prop of the cantilever beam shown in Fig. E6.8. The force F = 5,000 lb. The steel beam, 15 ft long, is fabricated from a wide flange section specified as W6 × 25. After solving for the reaction force, solve for the deflection at mid span.

Fig. E6.8

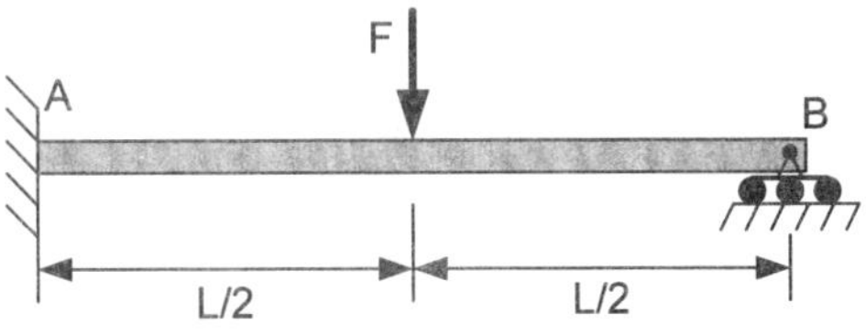

Solution:

The prop at B causes the cantilever beam to be statically indeterminate. It may have been added to reduce the deflection or the stress of the beam; however, the prop complicates the analysis. We begin by replacing the prop with a reaction force R and noting the boundary condition at x = L as:

$$y(L) = 0 \tag{a}$$

We then apply the principle of superposition and represent the beam in Fig. E6.8 with the two statically determinate beams that are shown in Fig. E6.8a.

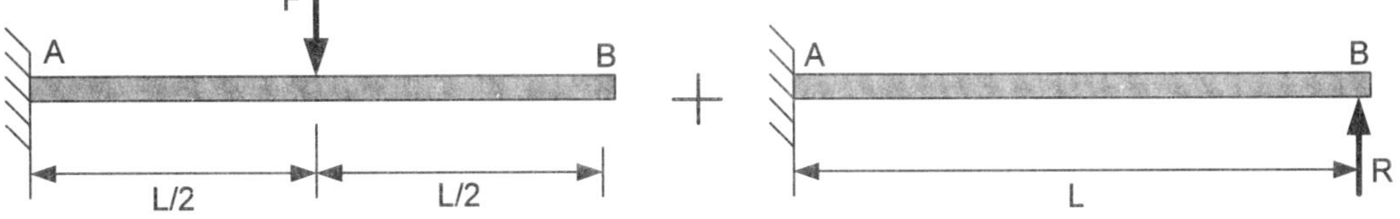

Fig. E6.8a

Let's determine the deflection at the free end for each of the two beams using the solutions tabulated in Appendix E. For the cantilever beam with the force F applied at mid-span, we write:

$$y_{x=L} = -\frac{5FL^3}{48EI_z} \quad \text{(b)}$$

And for the cantilever beam with the upward directed reaction force, we write:

$$y_{x=L} = \frac{RL^3}{3EI_z} \quad \text{(c)}$$

However, the end of the cantilever beam is propped and y(L) = 0. Hence, it is clear from Eq. (b) and Eq. (c) that:

$$y_{x=L} = \frac{RL^3}{3EI_z} - \frac{5FL^3}{48EI_z} = 0 \quad \text{(d)}$$

Solving Eq. (d) and inserting numerical parameters gives:

$$R = 5F/16 = 5(5{,}000)/16 = 1562.5 \text{ lb} \quad \text{(e)}$$

It is interesting that the partitioning of the applied force F between the built-in support and the prop is independent of the length of the beam and its stiffness (EI_z).

Let's continue the analysis using the result for the reaction force R and the method of superposition to determine the deflection at mid-span. From Appendix E, we write the expressions for the deflection at x = L/2 for the two beams illustrated in Fig. E6.8a as:

$$y_{x=L/2} = -\frac{FL^3}{24EI_z} \quad \text{(f)}$$

$$y_{x=L/2} = \frac{5RL^3}{48EI_z} \quad \text{(g)}$$

Substituting R = 5F/16 from Eq. (e) into Eq. (g) yields:

$$y_{x=L/2} = \frac{25FL^3}{768EI_z} \quad \text{(h)}$$

Superimposing the results from Eq. (f) and Eq. (h) and substituting numerical parameter yields:

$$y_{x=L/2} = \frac{FL^3}{EI_z}\left(\frac{25}{768} - \frac{1}{24}\right) = -\frac{7FL^3}{768EI_z} = -\frac{7(5{,}000)(15)^3(12)^3}{768(30\times 10^6)(53.4)} = -0.1659 \text{ in.} \quad \text{(i)}$$

In this example, we employed the principle of superposition twice — first to find the reaction force and then to determine the mid-span deflection. In both applications, the solutions tabulated in Appendix E greatly reduced the computational effort required.

EXAMPLE 6.9

Determine the reaction force at the prop of the cantilever beam shown in Fig. E6.9. The uniform load $q_0 = 1.8$ kN/m. The steel beam, 5 m long, is fabricated from a wide flange section specified as W203 × 46. After solving for the reaction force, solve for the deflection at mid-span.

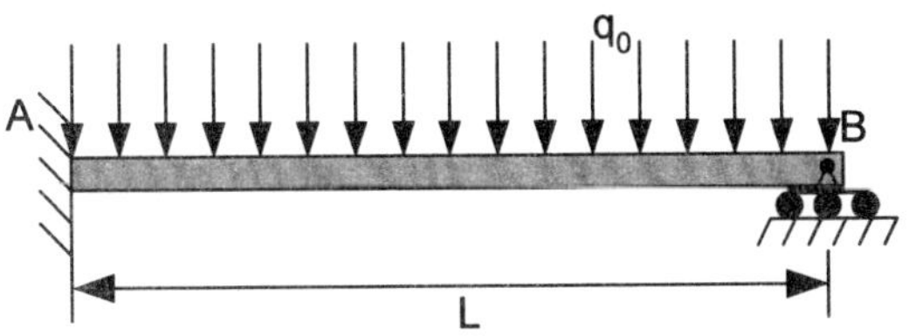

Fig. E6.9

Solution:

The prop at B causes the cantilever beam to be statically indeterminate. It may have been added to reduce the deflection or the stress of the beam; however, the prop complicates the analysis. We begin by replacing the prop with a reaction force R and noting the boundary condition at x = L as:

$$y(L) = 0 \qquad \text{(a)}$$

We then apply the principle of superposition and represent the beam in Fig. E6.9 with two statically determinate beams, as shown in Fig. E6.9a.

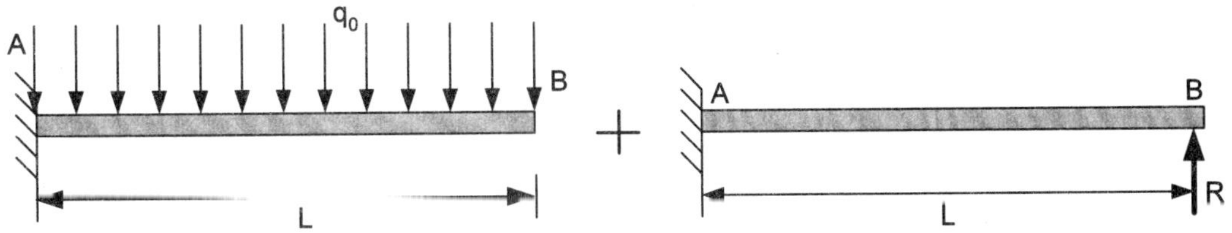

Fig. E6.9a

Let's determine the deflection at the free end for each of the two beams using the solutions tabulated in Appendix E. For the cantilever beam with the uniformly distributed load q_o over the entire length of the beam, we write:

$$y_{x=L} = -\frac{q_0 L^4}{8EI_z} \qquad \text{(b)}$$

And for the cantilever beam with the upward directed reaction force, we write:

$$y_{x=L} = \frac{RL^3}{3EI_z} \qquad \text{(c)}$$

However, the end of the cantilever beam is propped and y(L) = 0. Hence, it is clear from Eq. (b) and Eq. (c) that:

$$y_{x=L} = \frac{RL^3}{3EI_z} - \frac{q_0L^4}{8EI_z} = 0 \qquad \text{(d)}$$

Solving Eq. (d) and inserting numerical parameters gives:

$$R = 3q_0\,L/8 = 3(1.8)(5)/8 = 3.375\text{ kN} \qquad \text{(e)}$$

It is interesting that the partitioning of the force F between the built-in support and the prop is independent of its stiffness (EI_z). Let's continue the analysis using the result for the reaction force R and the method of superposition to determine the deflection at mid span. From Appendix E, we write the expressions for the deflection at x = L/2 for the two beams illustrated in Fig. E6.9a as:

$$y_{x=L/2} = -\frac{17q_0L^4}{384EI_z} \qquad \text{(f)}$$

$$y_{x=L/2} = \frac{5RL^3}{48EI_z} \qquad \text{(g)}$$

Substituting $R = 3q_0L/8$ from Eq. (e) into Eq. (g) yields:

$$y_{x=L/2} = \frac{15q_0L^4}{384EI_z} \qquad \text{(h)}$$

Superimposing the results from Eq. (f) and Eq. (h) and substituting numerical parameters from the problem statement and Appendices B-1 and C yields:

$$y_{x=L/2} = \frac{q_0L^4}{384EI_z}(15-17) = -\frac{2q_0L^4}{384EI_z} = -\frac{2(1{,}800)(5)^4(10)^{15}}{384(207\times10^9)(45.8\times10^6)} = -0.6180\text{ mm} \qquad \text{(i)}$$

In this example, we employed the principle of superposition twice — first to find the reaction force and then to determine the mid-span deflection. In both applications, the solutions tabulated in Appendix E greatly reduced the computational effort required.

6.4.2 Integration Method with Singularity Functions

Singularity functions may also be applied to establish the deformation equation needed to solve for the additional reaction force in statically indeterminate beams. With this approach, we remove one of the supports (usually a roller) and replace the support with an unknown reaction force R. This substitution enables us to write expressions for q(x), V(x) and M(x) over the entire length of the beam. We then integrate twice the M(x) relation to obtain y(x). Of course, the equation for y(x) contains the unknown force R and two integration constants. These three unknowns are then determined from three boundary conditions.

Let's consider an example of a continuous beam to demonstrate the process followed with this approach.

EXAMPLE 6.10

Determine the reaction force at the center support of the continuous beam shown in Fig. E6.10. The forces are both equal to 10 kN. The steel beam is 2L long where L = 8 m and a = b = 4 m. The beam is fabricated from a wide flange section specified as W203 × 36. After solving for the reaction force solve for the deflection at mid span (x = L/2).

Fig. E6.10

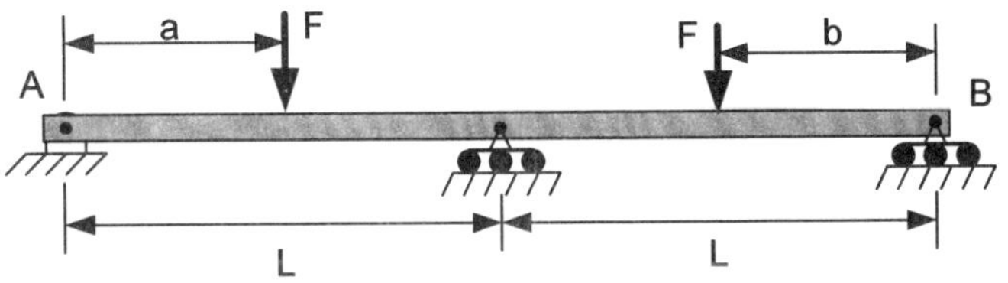

Solution:

Let's remove the support and replace it with a reaction force R directed upwards as illustrated in Fig. E6.10a.

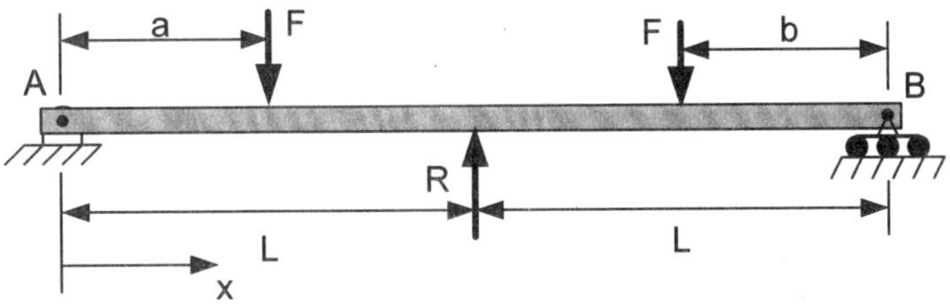

Fig. E6.10a

Next write the expression for q(x) with the singularity functions described in Fig. 5.8.

$$q(x) = -R_A <x - 0>^{-1} + F<x - a>^{-1} - R<x - L>^{-1} + F<x - 3a>^{-1} \quad \text{(a)}$$

where R_A is the reaction force at the left side support.

Integrate Eq. (a) to obtain the equation for the shear force V(x) as:

$$V(x) = R_A <x - 0>^{0} - F<x - a>^{0} + R<x - L>^{0} - F<x - 3a>^{0} + C_1 \quad \text{(b)}$$

Integrate Eq. (b) to obtain the equation for the bending moment M(x) as:

$$M(x) - R_A <x - 0>^{1} - F<x - a>^{1} + R<x - L>^{1} - F<x - 3a>^{1} + C_1x + C_2 \quad \text{(c)}$$

The constants of integration C_1 and C_2 both are zero because M(0) = 0 and V(0) = R_A. Hence, we write:

$$M(x) = R_Ax - F<x - a>^{1} + R<x - L>^{1} - F<x - 3a>^{1} \quad \text{(d)}$$

Substitute Eq. (d) into Eq. (5.4) and integrate to obtain:

$$EI_z \frac{d^2y}{dx^2} = R_A x - F < x - a >^1 + R < x - L >^1 - F < x - 3a >^1 \qquad \text{(e)}$$

$$EI_z \frac{dy}{dx} = \frac{R_A}{2} x^2 - \frac{F}{2} < x - a >^2 + \frac{R}{2} < x - L >^2 - \frac{F}{2} < x - 3a >^2 + C_3 \qquad \text{(f)}$$

$$EI_z y = \frac{R_A}{6} x^3 - \frac{F}{6} < x - a >^3 + \frac{R}{6} < x - L >^3 - \frac{F}{6} < x - 3a >^3 + C_3 x + C_4 \qquad \text{(g)}$$

Examination of Eq. (g) indicates that we have four unknowns — R_A, R, C_3 and C_4. Boundary conditions for the deflection y listed below enable us to write three independent equations.

$$y(0) = 0 \qquad y(L) = 0 \qquad y(2L) = 0 \qquad \text{(h)}$$

An equilibrium relation $\Sigma M_B = 0$ gives the fourth equation as:

$$2R_A + R = 2F \qquad \text{(i)}$$

From the boundary condition y(0) = 0, it is evident that C_4 = 0. From the boundary condition y(L) = 0, we determine C_3 as:

$$EI_z y_{x=L} = \frac{R_A}{6}(L)^3 - \frac{F}{6}\left(L - \frac{L}{2}\right)^3 + 0 - 0 + C_3 L = 0$$

$$C_3 = (L^2/48)[F - 8\ R_A] \qquad \text{(j)}$$

From the boundary condition y(2L) = 0, we can determine another independent equation in terms of the remaining unknowns R_A and R as:

$$EI_z y_{x=2L} = \frac{R_A}{6}(2L)^3 - \frac{F}{6}\left(\frac{3L}{2}\right)^3 + \frac{R}{6}(L)^3 - \frac{F}{6}\left(\frac{L}{2}\right)^3 + \frac{2L^3}{48}(F - 8R_A) = 0$$

$$6R_A + R = (13/4)F \qquad \text{(k)}$$

From Eq. (i) and Eq. (k), it is clear that:

$$R_A = (5/16)F \quad \Rightarrow \quad R = (11/8)F = (11/8)(10) = 13.75\ \text{kN} \qquad \text{(l)}$$

It is interesting that the load partitioning between the supports is independent of the stiffness of the beam and the length of the beam. The partitioning of the loads among the three supports depends only on the placement of the two concentrated forces F as indicated by a = b = L/2.

Let's continue the analysis and determine the deflection at mid-span between the first and second supports located by x = a = L/2 = 4 m. Begin by substituting the values for R and R_A from Eq. (l) into Eq. (g) to give the expression for y(x) as:

$$EI_z y = \frac{5F}{96}x^3 - \frac{F}{6} < x-a >^3 + \frac{11F}{48} < x-L >^3 - \frac{F}{6} < x-3a >^3 - \frac{FL^2}{32}x \quad \text{(m)}$$

Evaluating Eq. (m) at mid span where x = a = L/2 gives:

$$EI_z y_{x=L/2} = -\frac{7FL^3}{768} \quad \text{(n)}$$

Reference to Appendix D gives $I_z = 34.5 \times 10^6$ mm^4 for the W203 × 36 wide flange section. Then substituting numerical parameters into Eq. (n) gives:

$$y_{x=L/2} = -\frac{7FL^3}{768EI_z} = -\frac{7(10{,}000)(8{,}000)^3}{768(207\times10^3)(34.5\times10^6)} = -6.535 \text{ mm} \quad \text{(o)}$$

EXAMPLE 6.11

Determine the reactions at the supports of the continuous beam shown Fig. E6.11, and the relation for its maximum deflection.

Fig. 6E.11

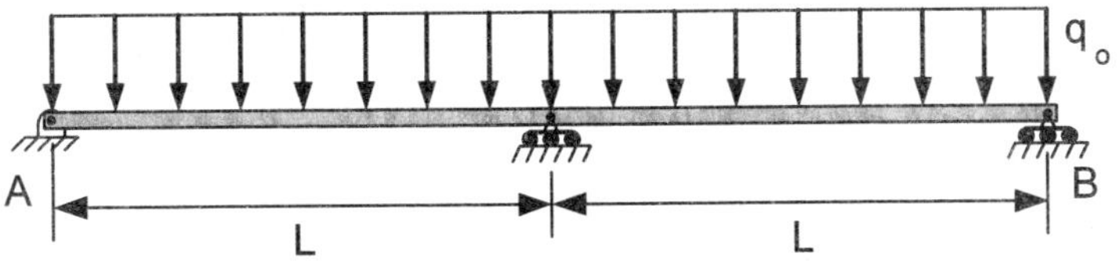

Solution:

Let's remove the supports and replace them with the reaction forces directed upwards as illustrated in Fig. E6.11a.

Fig. E6.11a

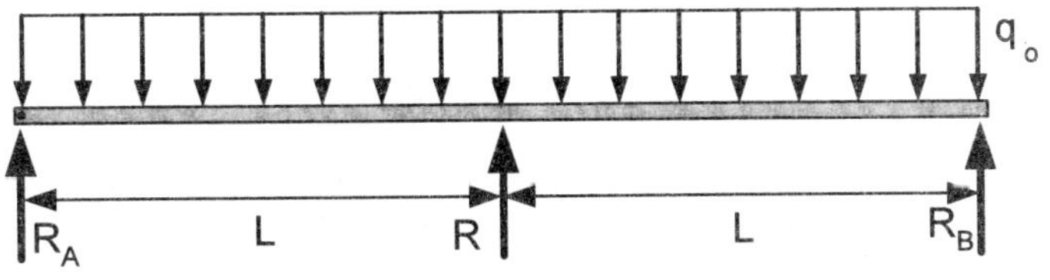

Next write the expression for q(x) with the singularity functions described in Fig. 5.8.

$$q(x) = -R_A <x-0>^{-1} + q_0 <x-0>^0 - R<x-L>^{-1} \quad \text{(a)}$$

where R_A is the reaction force at the left side support.

Integrate Eq. (a) to obtain the equation for the shear force V(x) as:

$$V(x) = R_A <x - 0>^0 - q_0 <x - 0>^1 + R<x - L>^0 + C_1 \quad \text{(b)}$$

Integrate Eq. (b) to obtain the equation for the bending moment M(x) as:

$$M(x) = R_A <x - 0>^1 - (q_0/2)<x - 0>^2 + R<x - L>^1 + C_1 x + C_2 \quad \text{(c)}$$

The constants of integration C_1 and C_2 both are zero because M(0) = 0 and V(0) = R_A. Hence, we write:

$$M(x) = R_A x - (q_0/2)x^2 + R<x - L>^1 \quad \text{(d)}$$

Substitute Eq. (d) into Eq. (5.4) and integrate to obtain:

$$EI_z \frac{d^2y}{dx^2} = R_A x - \frac{q_0}{2} x^2 + R < x - L >^1 \quad \text{(e)}$$

$$EI_z \frac{dy}{dx} = \frac{R_A}{2} x^2 - \frac{q_0 x^3}{6} + \frac{R}{2} < x - L >^2 + C_3 \quad \text{(f)}$$

$$EI_z y = \frac{R_A}{6} x^3 - \frac{q_0 x^4}{24} + \frac{R}{6} < x - L >^3 + C_3 x + C_4 \quad \text{(g)}$$

Examination of Eq. (g) indicates that we have four unknowns — R_A, R, C_3 and C_4. Boundary conditions for the deflection y listed below enable us to write three independent equations.

$$y(0) = 0 \qquad y(L) = 0 \qquad y(2L) = 0 \quad \text{(h)}$$

Symmetry of the continuous beam indicates $R_A = R_B$, and the equilibrium relation $\Sigma F_y = 0$ gives the fourth equation as:

$$2R_A + R = 2q_0 L \quad \text{(i)}$$

From the boundary condition y(0) = 0, it is evident that $C_4 = 0$. From the boundary condition y(L) = 0, we determine C_3 as:

$$EI_z y_{x=L} = \frac{R_A}{6}(L)^3 - \frac{q_0 L^4}{24} + 0 + C_3 L = 0$$

$$C_3 = (1/24L)[q_0 L^4 - 4R_A L^3] = (L^2/24)[q_0 L - 4 R_A] \quad \text{(j)}$$

From the boundary condition y(2L) = 0, we can determine another independent equation in terms of the remaining unknowns R_A and R as:

$$EI_z y_{x=2L} = \frac{R_A}{6}(2L)^3 - \frac{q_0}{24}(2L)^4 + \frac{R}{6}(L)^3 + \frac{2L}{24L}(q_0 L^4 - 4R_A L^3) = 0$$

This expression reduces to:

$$6R_A + R = (7/2)q_0 L \tag{k}$$

From Eq. (i) and Eq. (k), it is clear that:

$$R_A = (3/8)q_0 L \quad \Rightarrow \quad R = (5/4)q_0 L \tag{l}$$

It is interesting that the load partitioning between the supports is independent of the stiffness of the beam and the length of the beam.

Let's continue the analysis and determine the maximum deflection, which occurs at mid span between the first and second supports located by x = L/2. Let's substitute the values for R, R_A and C_3 from Eq. (j) and Eq. (l) into Eq. (g) to give the expression for y(x) at x = a as:

$$EI_z y_{x=L/2} = \frac{R_A}{6}\left(\frac{L}{2}\right)^3 - \frac{q_0 (L/2)^4}{24} + \frac{L^3}{48}(q_0 L - 4R_A) \tag{m}$$

$$EI_z y_{x=L/2} = -\frac{q_0 L^4}{192} \tag{n}$$

6.5 SUMMARY

The approach for solving for the unknown forces in statically indeterminate structures is to use the equilibrium relations and then to introduce additional equations based on the deformation of the structure. The solution involves two separate but compatible parts:

1. Prepare the traditional FBD together with all of the applicable equations of equilibrium.
2. Prepare displacement diagrams together with deformation equations that are consistent with the forces shown on the FBD.

Statically indeterminate problems arise in structural elements subjected to axial loading, torsion and transverse loading. Because the deformation equations depend on the type of loading, we have introduced examples dealing with three types of loading to demonstrate various methods for solving for the indeterminate forces that arise.

Thermal stresses are produced in structural elements by the constraint of the free expansion of a material subjected to a temperature change. When the structural element is totally constrained and free expansion is not permitted, the thermal stresses in the uniaxial rod are given by:

$$\sigma_T = E\alpha\Delta T \tag{6.3}$$

PROBLEMS

6.1 A steel tie rod with a diameter of 1.0 in. and length of 30.0 in. is employed to compress a brass bushing with an outside diameter of 3.0 in. and a length of 20.0 in. as shown in Fig. P6.1. Determine the minimum wall thickness of the bushing if the deflection of the tie rod is limited to $\delta = 0.018$ in. Note that F = 12 kip.

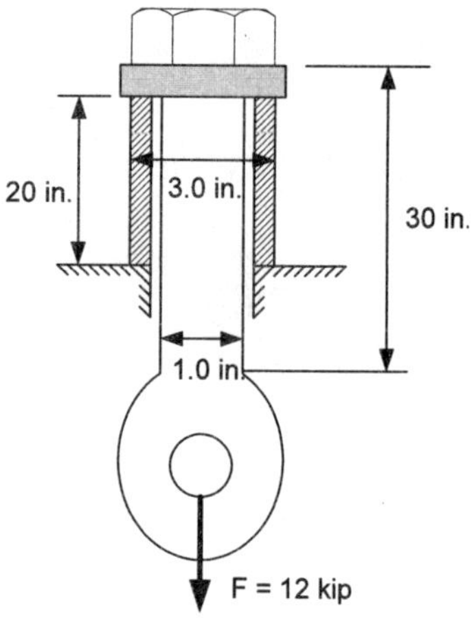

Fig. P6.1

6.2 Repeat Problem 6.1 using aluminum for the bushing instead of brass. All the other parameters remain the same.

6.3 A short column with a height of 1.5 m is fabricated by adhesively bonding aluminum faceplates to a core of plastic foam as shown in Fig. P6.3. The foam plastic core has a square cross section with an elastic modulus of 1,000 psi. Determine the stresses in the aluminum plates and the plastic foam. Also, determine the displacement of the column under the action of the applied force F = 35 kN.

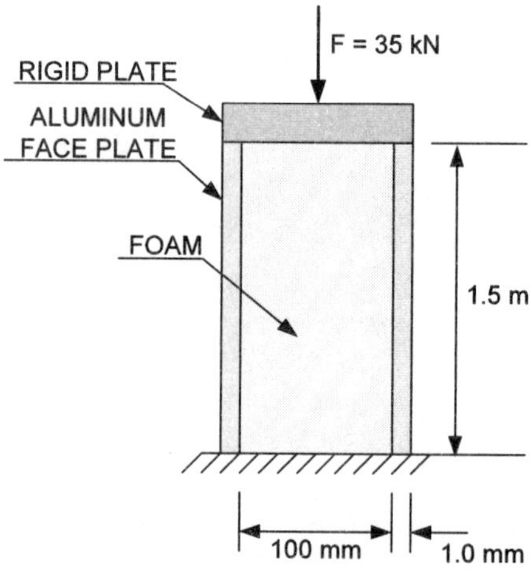

Fig. P6.3

6.4 Repeat Problem 6.3 replacing the foam with Western white pine. All the other parameters remain the same.

6.5 A grade 8 steel bolt, 1.0 in. in diameter (14 threads/in.) is employed to clamp a brass bushing between two rigid platens as illustrated in Fig. P6.5. The brass bushing has a 2.5 in. outside diameter and 1.5 in. inside diameter and is 15.00 in. long. After the unit is assembled with a snug fit, the nut is tightened by 1/2 of a turn. Determine the axial stresses in the bolt and the bushing. Also determine the deflection of the brass bushing.

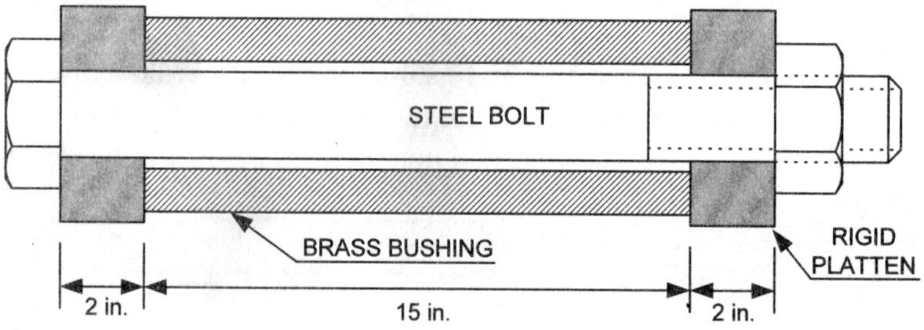

Fig. P6.5

6.6 Repeat Problem 6.5 using aluminum for the bushing instead of brass. All the dimensions remain the same, but the nut is turned 200 degrees after a snug fit has been achieved.

6.7 Twenty-five steel reinforcing rods with a ¼ in. diameter are placed within a high strength concrete column with a square cross section that supports an applied force of 40 kip. Determine the stresses in the steel reinforcing bars and the concrete. Also determine the amount of deflection of the column. Reference Fig. P6.7.

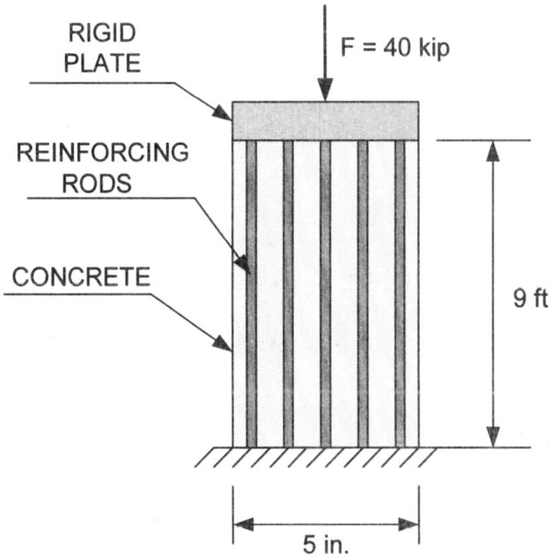

Fig. P6.7

6.8 Repeat Problem 6.7 replacing the 25 rebars bars — ¼ in. in diameter with 20 rebars each 3/8 in. in diameter. All the dimensions remain the same, and the concrete used is high strength.

6.9 A long aluminum rod is connected to a shorter brass cylinder with a bolted flange as shown in Fig. P6.9. Prior to assembly a gap of δ = 0.18 mm occurred between the flange plates. Bolts were inserted and tightened bringing the flange plates together. Determine the stresses induced in both the rod and the cylinder by the assembly operation. Also determine the displacement of the face of each flange.

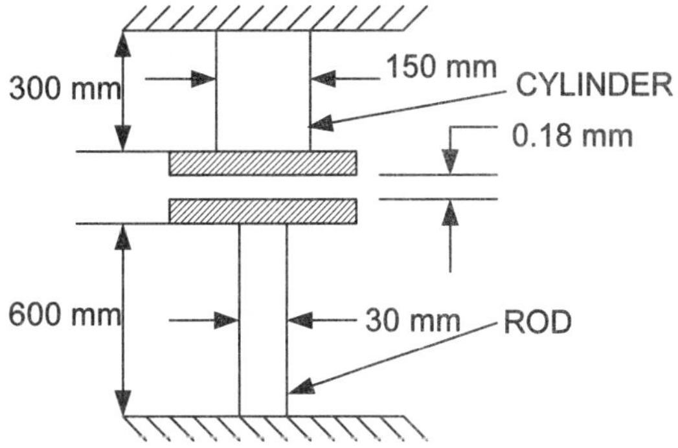

Fig. P6.9

6.10 A copper and stainless steel rod are assembled between two rigid walls at an ambient temperature of 20° C as shown in Fig. P6.10. If the temperature is increased by an amount ΔT = 80 °C, determine the thermal stresses induced in each rod. Also determine the change in length of each member.

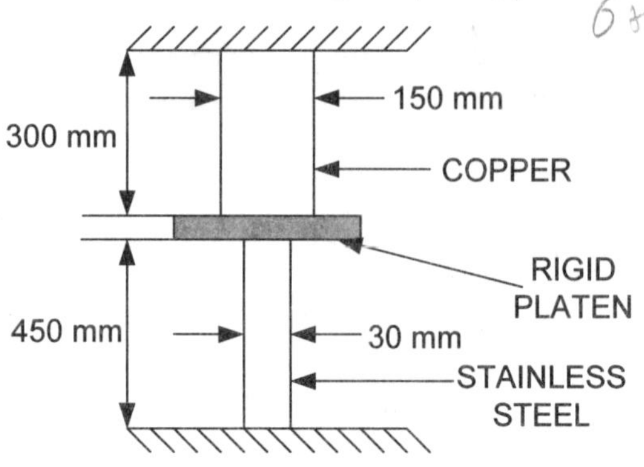

Fig. P6.10

6.11 Repeat Problem 6.10 if the diameter of the copper rod is decreased to 100 mm and the diameter of the stainless steel rod is increased to 60 mm. The length of the rods remains the same but ΔT increases to 110 °C.

6.12 A high strength steel bolt with a diameter of 1.0 in. passes through an aluminum bushing with a cross sectional area of 3.0 in.^{2} as shown in Fig. P6.12. The unit is assembled with a snug fit at an ambient temperature 72 °F. If the temperature of the assembly increases by ΔT = 68 °F, determine the thermal stresses induced in the bolt and the bushing.

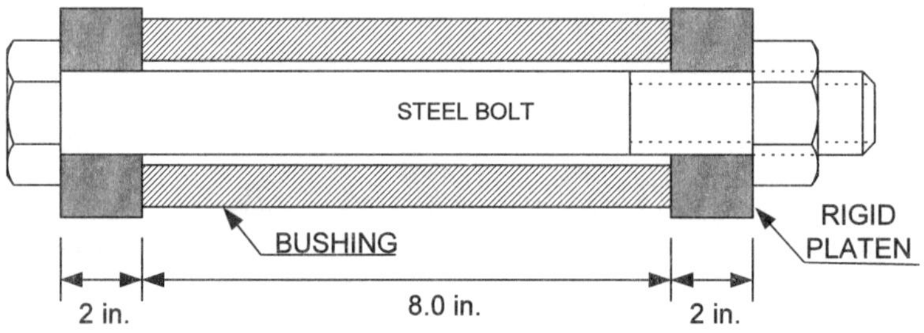

Fig. P6.12

6.13 Repeat Problem 6.12 but replace the aluminum bushing with one made from brass. All other parameters remain the same.

6.14 A three bar suspension system, shown in Fig. P6.14, is assembled at an ambient temperature of 20° C. Determine the axial stresses in each bar after a force F of 120 kN is applied to the rigid platen and the temperature is increased by ΔT = 50 °C. The bars labeled A are fabricated from aluminum with a cross sectional area of 750 mm^2 and the bar labeled B is fabricated from stainless steel with a cross sectional area of 1,250 mm^2.

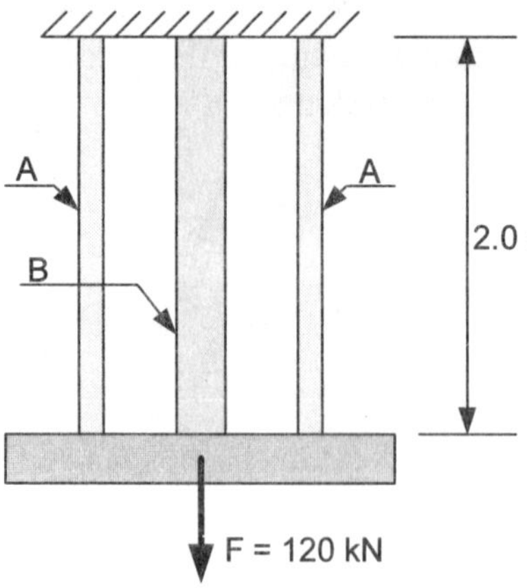

Fig. P6.14

6.15 Repeat Problem 6.14 but increase the force F to 150 kN and increase ΔT to 75 °C. All other parameters remain the same.

6.16 A circular steel shaft is supported at each end by rigid constraints as shown in Fig. P6.16. The left side of the shaft is 1.50 in. in diameter and its right side is 1.00 in. in diameter. A torque of 250 ft-lb is applied at the center of the shaft where the diameter discontinuity is located. Determine the reactions at each of the supports.

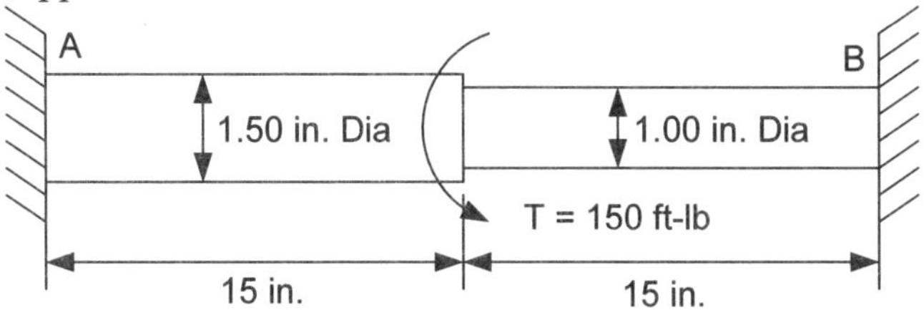

Fig. P6.16

6.17 Repeat Problem 6.16 but decrease the applied torque to 120 ft-lb. All the other parameters remain the same.

6.18 The structural member, presented in Fig. P6.18, is fabricated with a steel shaft (core) and a brass tube (cover). The two materials are bonded together to form a composite member. The steel core has a diameter of 25 mm and the brass tube has an inside diameter of 25 mm and an outside diameter of 35 mm. The length L of the composite shaft is 1.15 m. A torque T = 225 N-m is applied at its free end. Determine the angle of twist of the composite shaft, the maximum shear stress in the steel core and the brass cover and prepare a graph of the shear stress distribution.

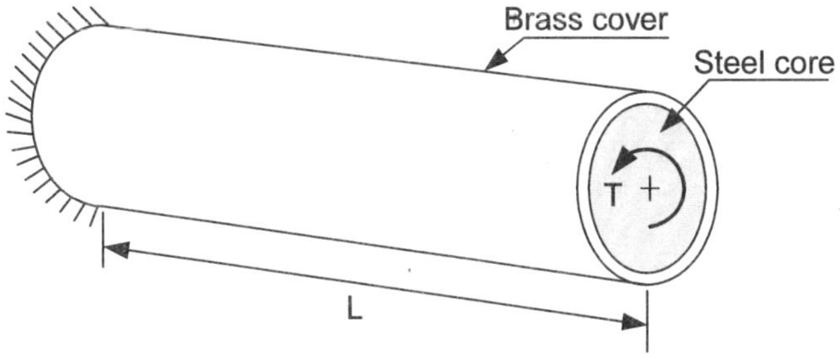

Fig. P6.18

6.19 Repeat Problem 6.18 but replace the brass cover tube with one made of stainless steel. All the other parameters remain the same.

6.20 For the drive shaft arrangement shown in Fig. P6.20, determine the shear stress in the shaft and the angle of twist. The shaft is fabricated from steel with a diameter of 40 mm. The brakes prevent shaft rotation with an applied torque of 600 N-m. The gears are considered as rigid and tooth deflections are neglected in the analysis.

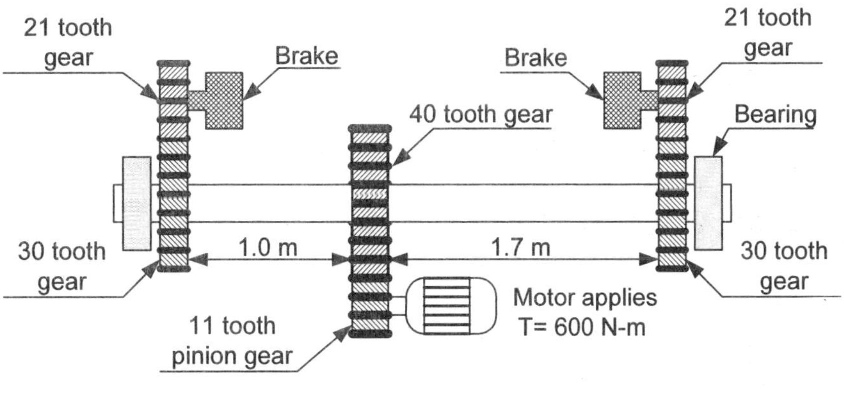

Fig. P6.20

6.21 Repeat Problem 6.20 but decrease the applied torque to 500 N-m and change the shaft material from steel to stainless steel. All the other parameters remain the same.

6.22 A circular steel shaft is supported at each end by rigid constraints as shown in Fig. P6.22. The left side of the shaft is 30 mm in diameter and its right side is 22 mm in diameter. A torque of 250 N-m is applied at the center of the shaft where the diameter discontinuity is located. Determine the reactions at each of the supports.

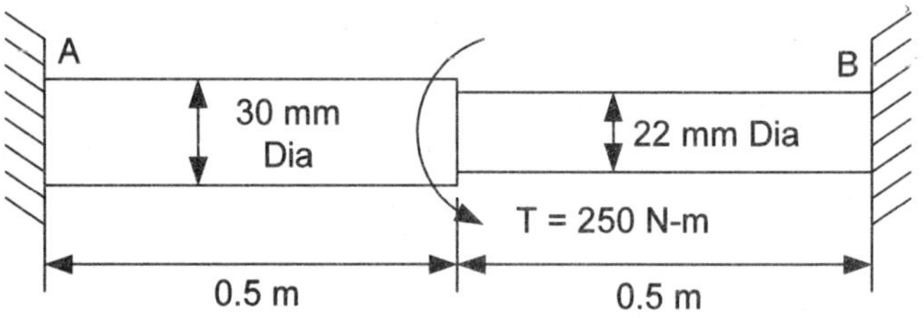

Fig. P6.22

6.23 Repeat Problem 6.22 but decrease the applied torque to 220 ft-lb. Decrease the length of the two shafts from 0.5 m to 0.40 m. All the other parameters remain the same.

6.24 Two circular shafts are joined together at the center of the assembly and supported at each end by rigid constraints as shown in Fig. P6.24. The left side shaft is 30 mm in diameter and fabricated from brass. The right side shaft is 22 mm in diameter and fabricated from steel. A torque of 175 N-m is applied at the center of the shaft where the shafts are joined together. Determine the reactions at each of the supports.

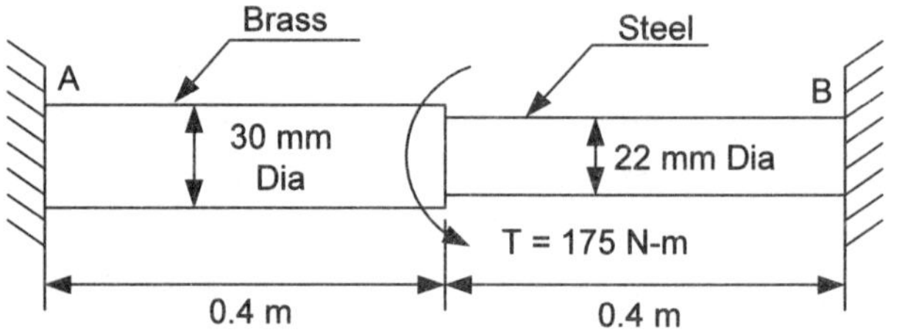

Fig. P6.24

6.25 Repeat Problem 6.24 but switch the materials using steel for the shaft on the left and brass for the shaft on the right. All the other parameters remain the same.

6.26 Two circular shafts are joined together at the center of the assembly and supported at each end by rigid constraints as shown in Fig. P6.26. The left side shaft is 45 mm in diameter and fabricated from brass. The right side shaft is 30 mm in diameter and fabricated from steel. A torque of 225 N-m is applied at the center of the shaft where the shafts are joined together. Determine the reactions at each of the supports.

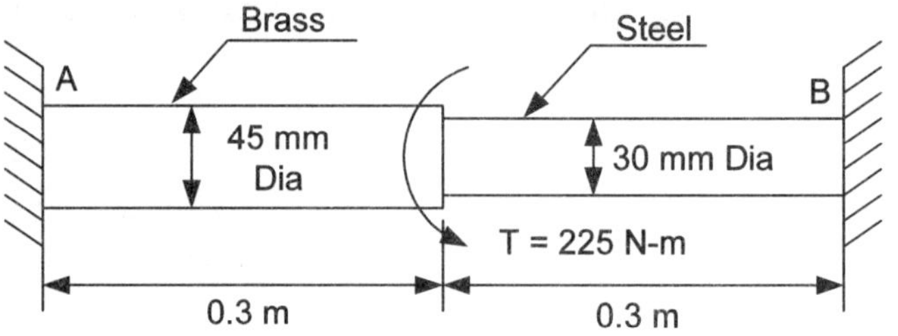

Fig. P6.26

6.27 Repeat Problem 6.26 but switch the materials using steel for the shaft on the left and brass for the shaft on the right. All the other parameters remain the same.

6.28 The structural member, presented in Fig. P6.28, is fabricated with a steel shaft (core) and a brass tube (cover). The two materials are bonded together to form a composite member. The solid steel core has a diameter of 20 mm and the brass tube has an inside diameter of 20 mm and an outside diameter of 30 mm. The length L of the composite shaft is 0.75 m. A torque T = 180 N-m is applied at its free end. Determine the angle of twist of the composite shaft, the maximum shear stress in the steel core and the brass cover and prepare a graph of the shear stress distribution.

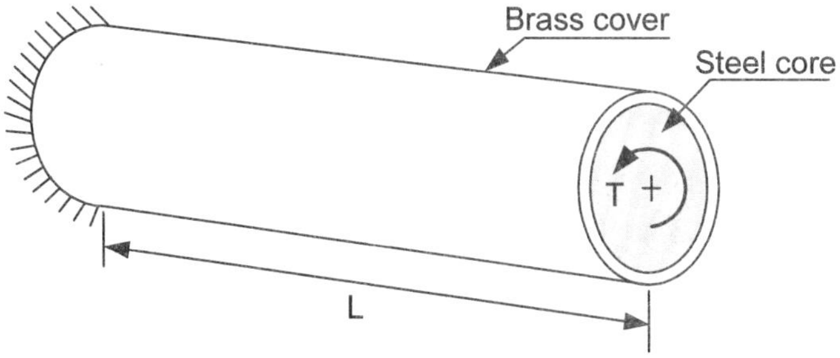

Fig. P6.28

6.29 The structural member, presented in Fig. P6.29, is fabricated with a copper core and a stainless steel cover. The two materials are bonded together to form a composite member. The copper core has a diameter of 1.00 in. and the stainless steel cover has an inside diameter of 1.00 in. outside diameter of 1.20 in. The length L of the composite shaft is 30 in. A torque T = 100 ft-lb is applied at its free end. Determine the angle of twist of the composite shaft, the maximum shear stress in the steel core and the brass cover and prepare a graph of the shear stress distribution.

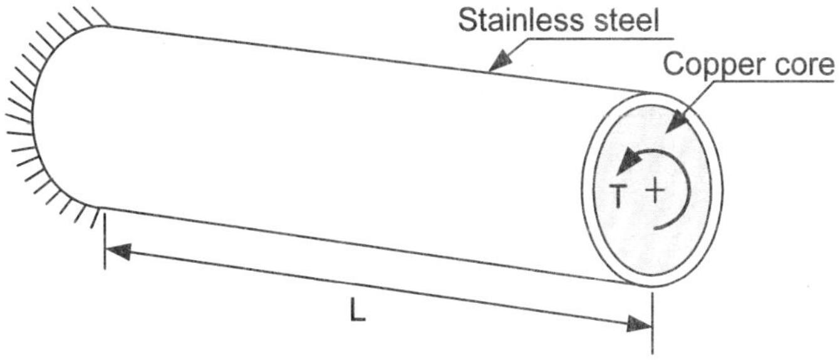

Fig. P6.29

6.30 Repeat Problem 6.29 but switch the materials using stainless steel for the core and copper for the cover. All the other parameters remain the same.

6.31 For the drive shaft arrangement shown in Fig. P6.31, determine the shear stress in the shaft and the angle of twist. The shaft is fabricated from stainless steel with a diameter of 2.00 in. mm. The brakes prevent shaft rotation with an applied torque of 350 ft-lb. The gears are considered as rigid and tooth deflections are neglected in the analysis.

Fig. P6.31

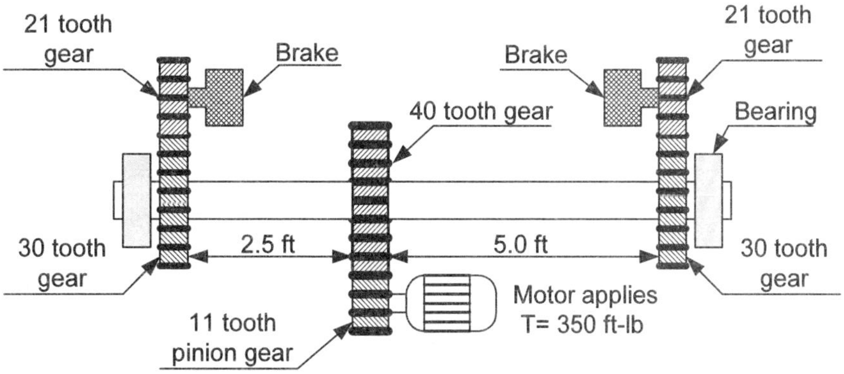

6.32 For the two-shaft gear assembly, shown in Fig. P6.32, determine the angle of twist of disk C when a torque T = 100 ft-lb is applied to gear A. The dimensions are L = 12 in. D_A = 12 in., D_B = 6 in, $d_A = d_B$ = 2.0 in. Shaft A is fixed at its upper end. The bearings are frictionless. The shafts are fabricated from steel.

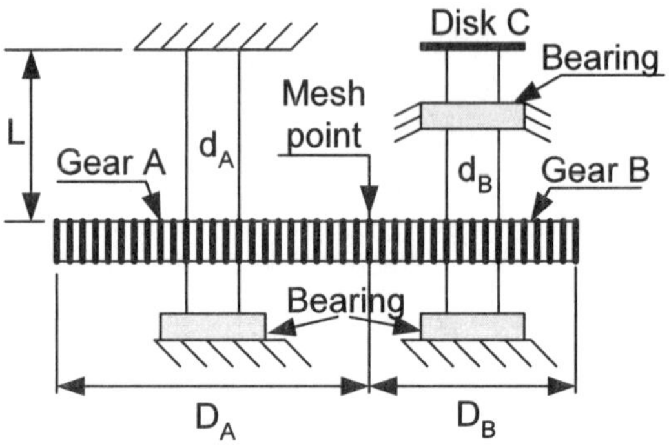

Fig. P6.32

6.33 For the two-shaft gear assembly, shown in Fig. P6.32, determine the angle of twist of disk C when a torque T = 160 N-M is applied to gear A. The dimensions are L = 450 mm, D_A = 400 mm, D_B = 200 mm, $d_A = d_B$ = 40 mm. Shaft A is fixed at its upper end. The bearings are frictionless. The shafts are fabricated from steel

6.34 The tapered circular shaft, shown in Fig. P6.34, is supported by fixed ends. A torque T is applied at L/3 from the smaller end. The diameter of the larger end is twice that of the smaller end. Determine the reactions at the two supports.

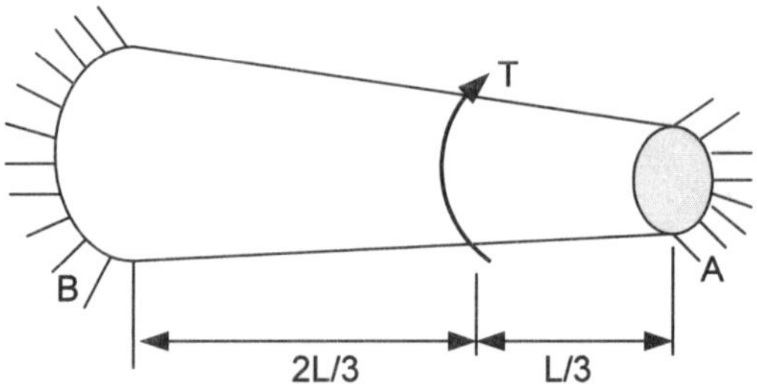

Fig. P6.34

6.35 Repeat Problem 6.34 but change the geometry of the tapered shaft so that the diameter of its larger end is 1.5 times the diameter of its smaller end. All other parameters remain the same.

6.36 Determine the reactions at the prop and the wall on the cantilever beam shown in Fig. P6.36.

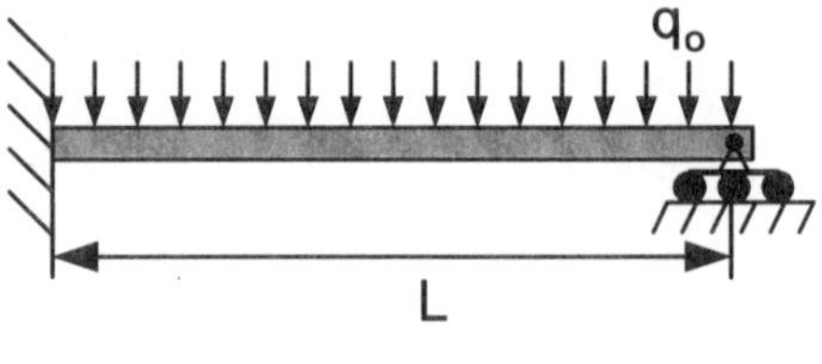

Fig. P6.36

6.37 Determine the reactions at the prop and the wall on the cantilever beam shown Fig. P6.37.

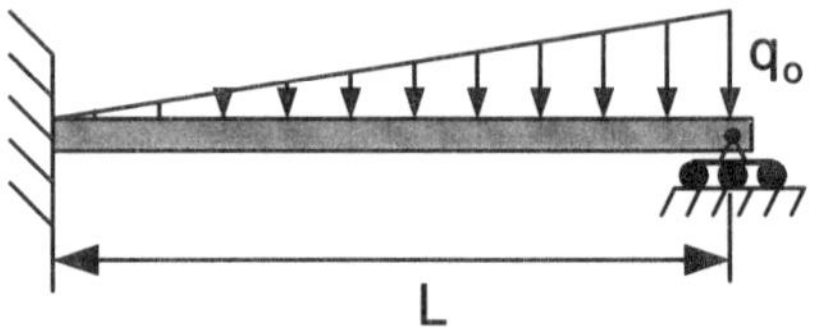

Fig. P6.37

6.38 Determine the reactions at the prop and the wall on the cantilever beam shown Fig. P6.38.

Fig. P6.38

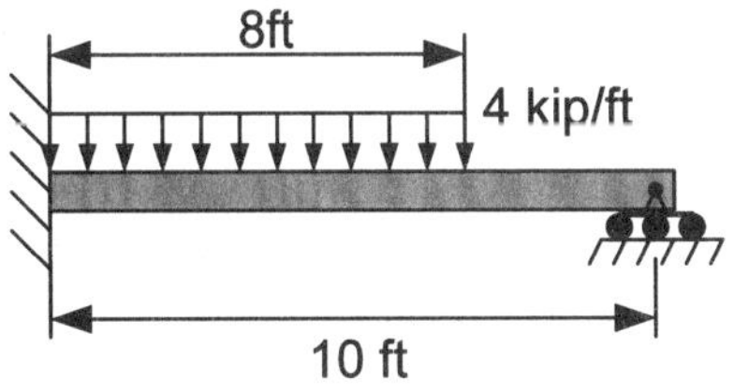

6.39 Determine the reactions at the prop and the wall on the cantilever beam shown Fig. P6.39.

Fig. P6.39

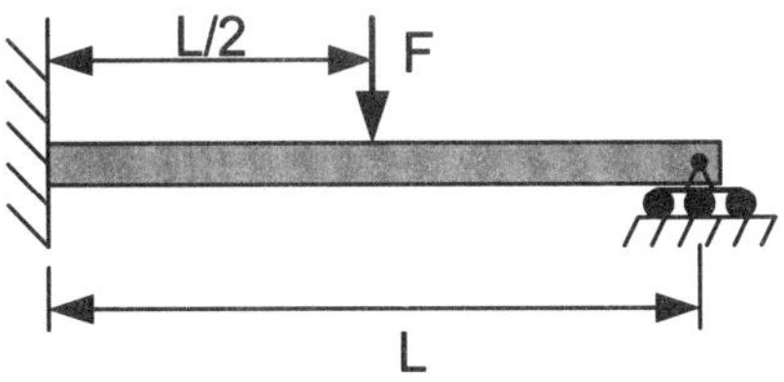

6.40 Determine the reactions at the prop and the wall on the cantilever beam shown Fig. P6.40.

Fig. P6.40

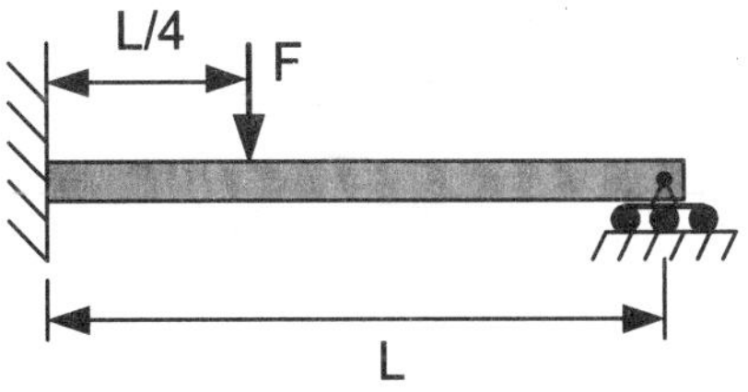

6.41 Determine the reactions at the prop and the wall on the cantilever beam shown in Fig. P6.41

Fig. P6.41

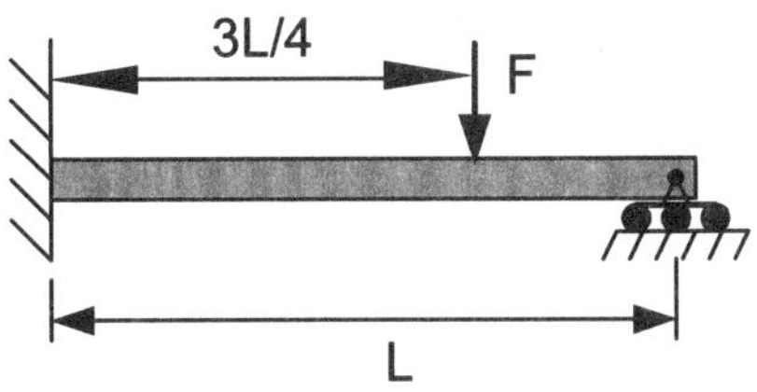

6.42 Determine the reactions at the prop and the wall on the cantilever beam shown in Fig. P6.42.

Fig. P6.42

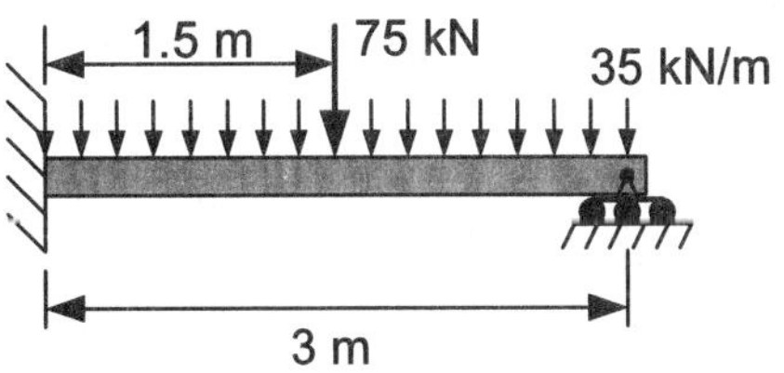

6.43 Determine the reactions at the prop and the wall on the cantilever beam shown in Fig. P6.43.

Fig. P6.43

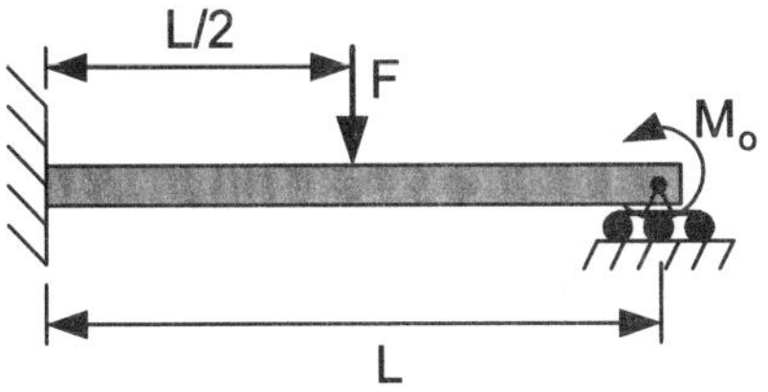

6.44 Determine the reactions at the supports of the continuous beam shown in Fig. P6.44.

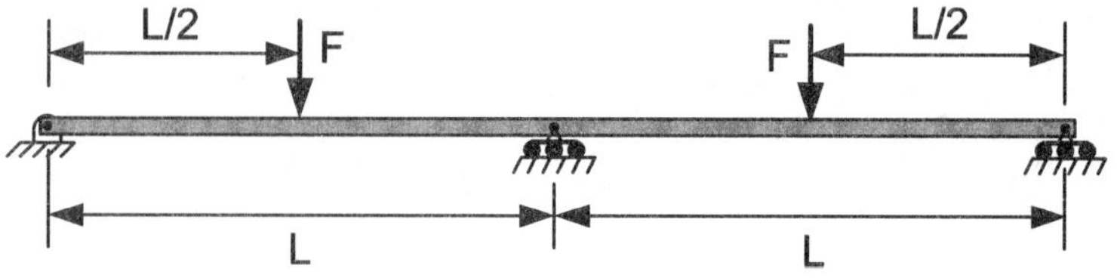

Fig. P6.44

6.45 Determine the reactions at the supports of the continuous beam shown in Fig. P6.45.

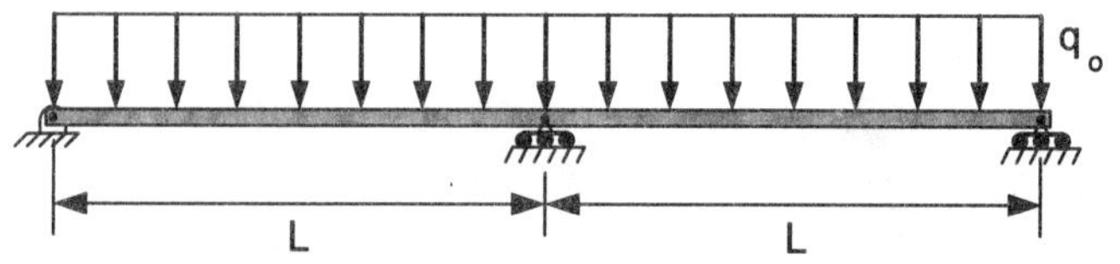

Fig. P6.45

6.46 Determine the reactions at the supports of the continuous beam shown in Fig. P6.46.

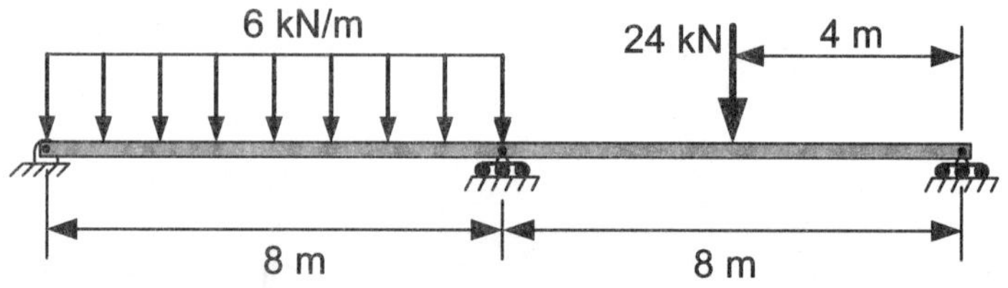

Fig. P6.46

6.47 Determine the reactions at the supports of the continuous beam shown in Fig. P6.47.

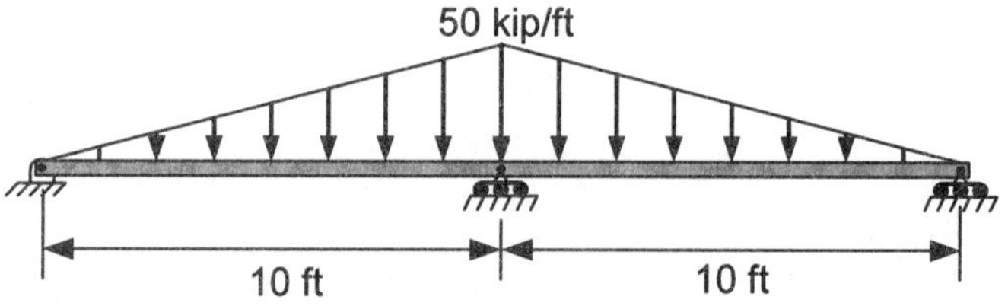

Fig. P6.47

6.48 Determine the reactions at the supports of the continuous beam shown in Fig. P6.48.

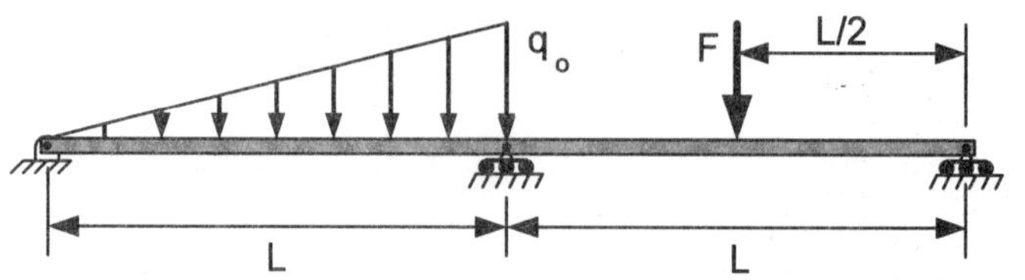

Fig. P6.48

6.49 Determine the reactions at the supports of the continuous beam shown in Fig. P6.49.

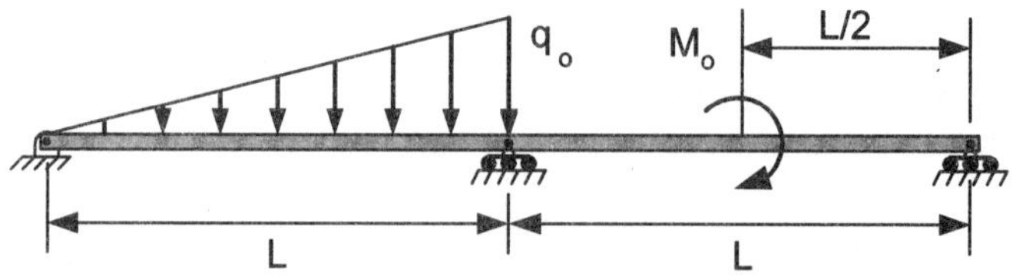

6.50 Determine the reactions at the supports of the built-in beam shown in Fig. P6.50.

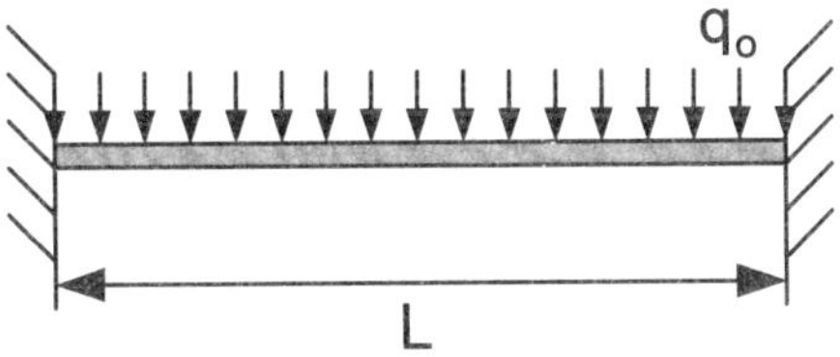

Fig. P6.50

6.51 Determine the reactions at the supports of the built-in beam shown in Fig. P6.51.

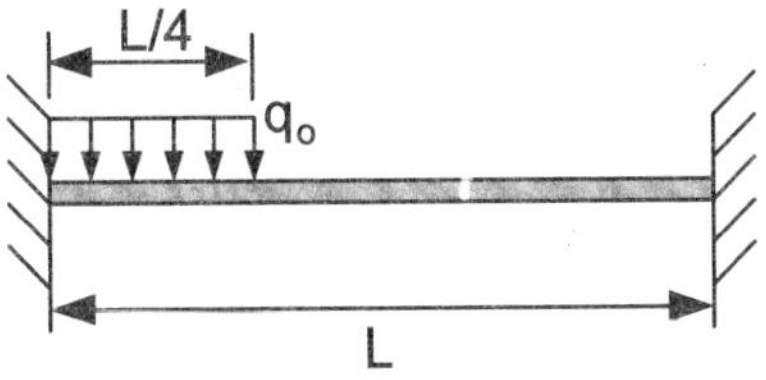

Fig. P6.51

6.52 Determine the reactions at the supports of the built-in beam shown in Fig. P6.52.

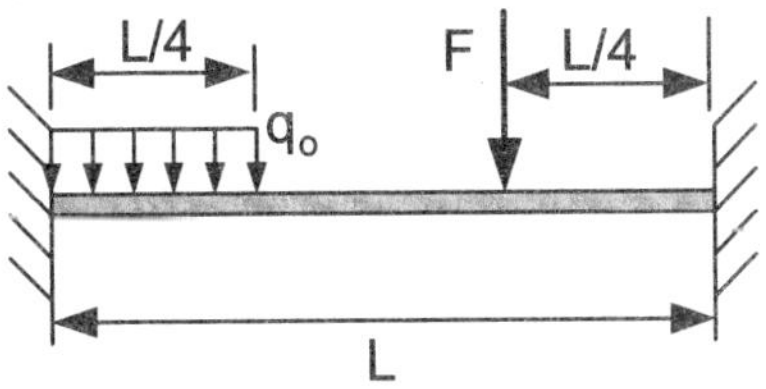

Fig. P6.52

6.53 Determine the reactions at the supports of the built-in beam shown in Fig. P6.53.

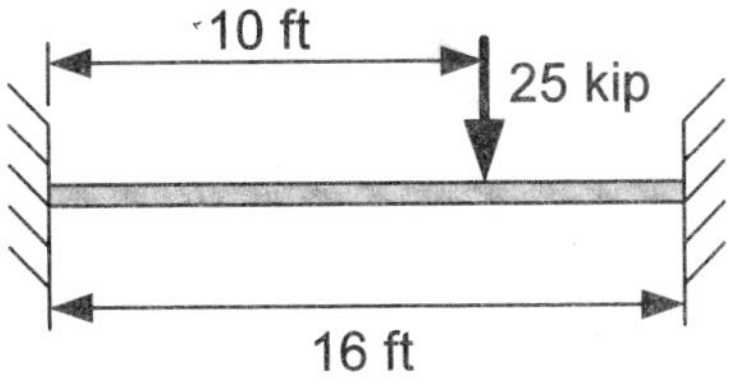

Fig. P6.53

6.54 Determine the reactions at the supports of the built-in beam shown Fig. P6.54.

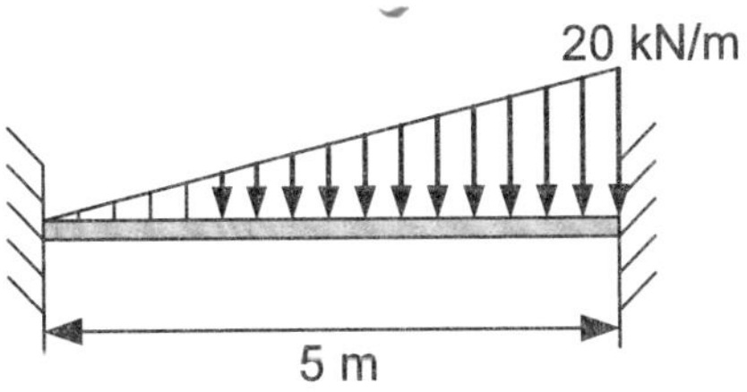

Fig. P6.54

CHAPTER 7

STRESS STATES AND TRANSFORMATIONS

7.1 INTRODUCTION

In our discussions we have, with few exceptions, concentrated on two-dimensional force systems and uniaxial stress systems. Long thin rods used for tension members, beams and torsion bars lend themselves to a simple analysis, which generate uniaxial stresses. In a few instances, we have examined oblique planes and discovered that shear and normal stresses can occur together. However, we have not explored the implication of shear and normal stresses occurring on oblique planes, and we have not discussed multi-dimensional states of stress.

If we consider a general three-dimensional body subjected to forces acting in all three dimensions, the stress system developed contains nine Cartesian components, which include the normal stresses σ_{xx}, σ_{yy} and σ_{zz} and the shear stresses τ_{xy}, τ_{xz}, τ_{yz}, τ_{yx}, τ_{zx}, and τ_{zy}, as illustrated in Fig. 7.1.

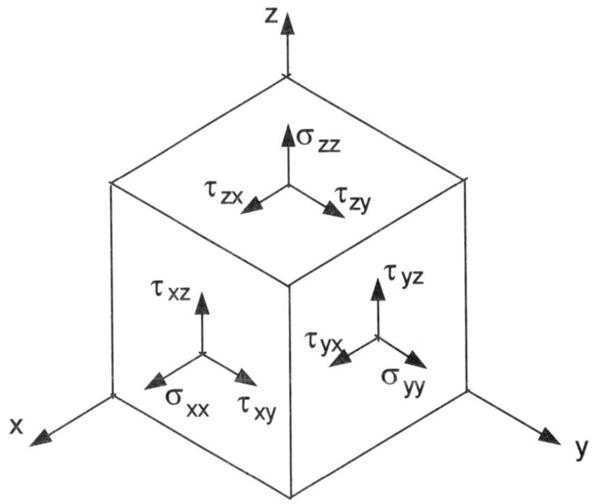

Fig. 7.1 Cartesian components of stress representing a three-dimensional state of stress.

The six Cartesian components of shear stress may be reduced to three by recognizing that:

$$\tau_{xy} = \tau_{yx} \qquad \tau_{yz} = \tau_{zy} \qquad \tau_{xz} = \tau_{zx} \tag{7.1}$$

We have used a double subscript in Fig. 7.1 in designating the normal stresses. The first subscript is to denote the direction of the normal vector of the plane upon which the stress acts and the second is to show the direction of the stress. The subscript convention also applies for the shear stress components.

In a general three-dimensional state of stress, it is necessary to specify six Cartesian components of stress (σ_{xx}, σ_{yy}, σ_{zz}, τ_{xy}, τ_{yz}, and τ_{zx}) to completely define the stress state. These general three-dimensional solutions are beyond the scope of this book. However, we will develop the special case of plane stress, which is an important state of stress with many applications.

For the general three-dimensional state, the strains are related to the stress by:

$$\begin{aligned}
\varepsilon_{xx} &= (1/E)[\sigma_{xx} - \nu(\sigma_{yy} + \sigma_{zz})] \\
\varepsilon_{yy} &= (1/E)[\sigma_{yy} - \nu(\sigma_{xx} + \sigma_{zz})] \\
\varepsilon_{zz} &= (1/E)[\sigma_{zz} - \nu(\sigma_{xx} + \sigma_{yy})] \\
\gamma_{xy} &= \tau_{xy}/G \\
\gamma_{yz} &= \tau_{yz}/G \\
\gamma_{xz} &= \tau_{xz}/G
\end{aligned} \tag{7.2}$$

Solving Eq. (7.2) for the stresses in terms of the strains gives:

$$\begin{aligned}
\sigma_{xx} &= \frac{E}{(1+\nu)(1-2\nu)}\left[(1-\nu)\varepsilon_{xx} + \nu(\varepsilon_{yy} + \varepsilon_{zz})\right] \\
\sigma_{yy} &= \frac{E}{(1+\nu)(1-2\nu)}\left[(1-\nu)\varepsilon_{yy} + \nu(\varepsilon_{zz} + \varepsilon_{xx})\right] \\
\sigma_{zz} &= \frac{E}{(1+\nu)(1-2\nu)}\left[(1-\nu)\varepsilon_{zz} + \nu(\varepsilon_{xx} + \varepsilon_{yy})\right]
\end{aligned} \tag{7.3}$$

$$\tau_{xy} = G\gamma_{xy} \qquad \tau_{yz} = G\gamma_{yz} \qquad \tau_{zx} = G\gamma_{zx}$$

An inspection of Eq. (7.3) shows that Hooke's law ($\sigma_{xx} = E\varepsilon_{xx}$) is not generally valid for three-dimensional states of stress. The simplified form of Hooke's law is valid only for the case of uniaxial tension where $\sigma_{yy} = \sigma_{zz} = 0$ and $\varepsilon_{yy} = \varepsilon_{zz} = -\nu\varepsilon_{xx}$.

EXAMPLE 7.1

A three-dimensional stress state is defined by the six Cartesian components of stress listed below.

$$\sigma_{xx} = 12 \text{ ksi},\ \sigma_{yy} = 15 \text{ ksi},\ \sigma_{zz} = -10 \text{ ksi},\ \tau_{xy} = 13 \text{ ksi},\ \tau_{yz} = 9.0 \text{ ksi and } \tau_{zx} = -8.0 \text{ ksi}$$

Determine the state of strain, if the body is made from an aluminum alloy.

Solution:

From Appendix B-1, we obtain $E = 10.4 \times 10^6$ psi, $G = 3.9 \times 10^6$ psi and $\nu = 0.32$. Substituting the stress components and these values into Eq. (7.2) yields:

$$\varepsilon_{xx} = (1/E)[\sigma_{xx} - \nu(\sigma_{yy} + \sigma_{zz})] = [1/(10.4 \times 10^6)][12 - (0.32)(15 - 10)] \times 10^3 = 1.000 \times 10^{-3}$$

$$\varepsilon_{yy} = (1/E)[\sigma_{yy} - \nu(\sigma_{xx} + \sigma_{zz})] = [1/(10.4\times 10^6)][15 - (0.32)(12 - 10)]\times 10^3 = 1.381 \times 10^{-3}$$

$$\varepsilon_{zz} = (1/E)[\sigma_{zz} - \nu(\sigma_{xx} + \sigma_{yy})] = [1/(10.4\times 10^6)][- 10 - (0.32)(12 + 15)]\times 10^3 = - 1.792 \times 10^{-3}$$

$$\gamma_{xy} = \tau_{xy}/G = (13 \times 10^3)/(3.9 \times 10^6) = 3.333 \times 10^{-3}$$

$$\gamma_{yz} = \tau_{yz}/G = (9.0 \times 10^3)/(3.9 \times 10^6) = 2.308 \times 10^{-3}$$

$$\gamma_{xz} = \tau_{xz}/G = (- 8.0 \times 10^3)/(3.9 \times 10^6) = - 2.051 \times 10^{-3}$$

Examination of the results indicates that the strains are small quantities (of the order of 10^{-3}) even when the stress state is of the order of 10^3.

EXAMPLE 7.2

A three-dimensional strain state is defined by six Cartesian components of strain listed below.

$\varepsilon_{xx} = 1.2 \times 10^{-3}$, $\varepsilon_{yy} = 1.3 \times 10^{-3}$, $\varepsilon_{zz} = - 0.80 \times 10^{-3}$, $\gamma_{xy} = 1.0 \times 10^{-3}$, $\gamma_{yz} = 0.90 \times 10^{-3}$, and $\gamma_{zx} = - 0.70 \times 10^{-3}$

Determine the state of stress, if the body is made from steel.

Solution:

From Appendix B-1, we obtain E = 207 GPa, G = 79 GPa and ν = 0.30. Substituting the strain components and these values into Eq. (7.3) yields:

$$\sigma_{xx} = \frac{E}{(1 + \nu)(1 - 2\nu)}\left[(1 - \nu)\varepsilon_{xx} + \nu(\varepsilon_{yy} + \varepsilon_{zz})\right]$$

$$\sigma_{xx} = \frac{207\times 10^9}{(1.3)(0.4)}\left[(0.7)(1.2) + (0.3)(1.3 - 0.80)\right]\times 10^{-3} = 394.1 \text{ MPa}$$

$$\sigma_{yy} = \frac{E}{(1 + \nu)(1 - 2\nu)}\left[(1 - \nu)\varepsilon_{yy} + \nu(\varepsilon_{zz} + \varepsilon_{xx})\right]$$

$$\sigma_{yy} = \frac{207\times 10^9}{(1.3)(0.4)}\left[(0.7)(1.3) + (0.3)(-0.80 + 1.2)\right]\times 10^{-3} = 410.0 \text{ MPa}$$

$$\sigma_{zz} = \frac{E}{(1 + \nu)(1 - 2\nu)}\left[(1 - \nu)\varepsilon_{zz} + \nu(\varepsilon_{xx} + \varepsilon_{yy})\right]$$

$$\sigma_{zz} = \frac{207\times 10^9}{(1.3)(0.4)}\left[(0.7)(-0.80) + (0.3)(1.2 + 1.3)\right]\times 10^{-3} = 75.63 \text{ MPa}$$

$$\tau_{xy} = G\gamma_{xy} = (79 \times 10^9)(1.0 \times 10^{-3}) = 79.00 \text{ MPa}$$

$$\tau_{yz} = G\gamma_{yz} = (79 \times 10^9)(0.90 \times 10^{-3}) = 71.10 \text{ MPa}$$

$$\tau_{zx} = G\gamma_{zx} = (79 \times 10^9)(- 0.70 \times 10^{-3}) = - 55.30 \text{ MPa}$$

7.1.1 Plane Stress

When a body is thin relative to its lateral dimensions such as that shown in Fig. 7.2, the stresses acting on all of the planes perpendicular to the normal vector z of the thin body are sufficiently small to be disregarded. Also on a free surface of any body, the normal and shear stresses acting on that surface vanish. In these situations, the stress state is called plane stress. For a plane state of stress, the stresses acting in the z direction are set equal to zero to give.

$$\sigma_{zz} = \tau_{xz} = \tau_{yz} = 0 \tag{7.4}$$

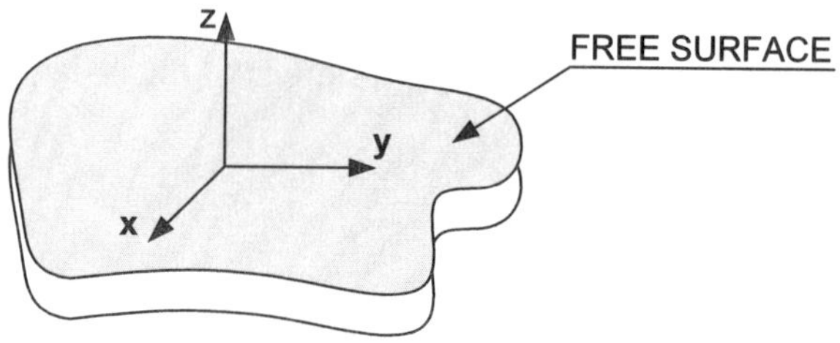

Fig. 7.2 Thin bodies exhibit plane stress conditions.

The remaining stresses σ_{xx}, σ_{yy} and τ_{xy} are specified when defining the stresses associated with a state of plane stress. For a state of plane stress, with $\sigma_{zz} = \tau_{xz} = \tau_{yz} = 0$, Eq. (7.2) reduces to:

$$\varepsilon_{xx} = (1/E)[\sigma_{xx} - \nu(\sigma_{yy})]$$

$$\varepsilon_{yy} = (1/E)[\sigma_{yy} - \nu(\sigma_{xx})] \tag{7.5}$$

$$\varepsilon_{zz} = (1/E)[-\nu(\sigma_{xx} + \sigma_{yy})]$$

$$\gamma_{xy} = \tau_{xy}/G$$

Similarly, the stress-strain relations given in Eq. (7.3) reduce to:

$$\sigma_{xx} = \frac{E}{(1-\nu^2)}\left(\varepsilon_{xx} + \nu\varepsilon_{yy}\right)$$

$$\sigma_{yy} = \frac{E}{(1-\nu^2)}\left(\varepsilon_{yy} + \nu\varepsilon_{xx}\right) \tag{7.6}$$

$$\tau_{xy} = G\gamma_{xy}$$

While the equations for the shear stresses do not change with the dimension of the state of stress, the expressions for the normal stresses differ markedly. Hooke's law ($\sigma_{xx} = E\varepsilon_{xx}$) is valid only for a uniaxial state of stress where $\sigma_{yy} = \sigma_{zz} = 0$.

EXAMPLE 7.3

The stresses on the external surface of a cylindrical pressure vessel in the hoop and axial direction are predicted from a simple stress analysis to be σ_h = 30 ksi and σ_a = 15 ksi, when the vessel is pressurized to 120 psi. If a pair of strain gages is placed on the pressure vessel to measure the strains in the hoop and axial directions, predict the strains that will occur when the pressure of 120 psi is applied. The pressure vessel is fabricated from steel.

Solution:

From Appendix B-1, we note E = 30 × 10^6 psi, G = 11.5 × 10^6 psi and Poisson's ratio ν = 0.30. Substituting the hoop and axial stresses in Eq. (7.5) gives:

$$\varepsilon_{xx} = (1/E)[\sigma_{xx} - \nu(\sigma_{yy})] = [1/(30 \times 10^6)][30 - (0.3)(15)] \times 10^3 = 0.8500 \times 10^{-3}$$

$$\varepsilon_{yy} = (1/E)[\sigma_{yy} - \nu(\sigma_{xx})] = [1/(30 \times 10^6)][15 - (0.3)(30)] \times 10^3 = 0.2000 \times 10^{-3}$$

7.2 STRESS EQUATIONS OF TRANSFORMATION

In developing the stress equations of transformation, we will consider the case of plane stress where $\sigma_{zz} = \tau_{xz} = \tau_{yz} = 0$. Suppose we know the state of stress (σ_{xx}, σ_{yy} and τ_{xy}) in a body relative to a set of coordinates say Oxy. Does this state of stress represent the most important combination of stresses, which will determine the failure loads? Or is some other state of stress, relative to a different coordinate system, the critical state? To answer these questions it is necessary to explore all of the admissible states of stress. We accomplish this task by using the stress equations of transformation.

Consider an elemental area with stresses σ_{xx}, σ_{yy} and τ_{xy} as shown in Fig. 7.3a.

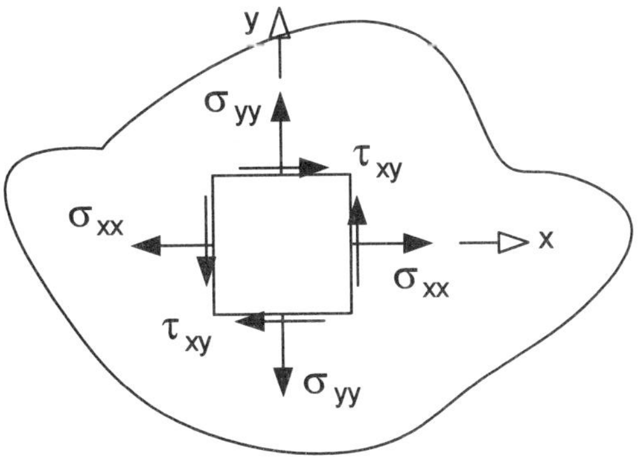

Fig. 7.3a An element with x-y orientation.

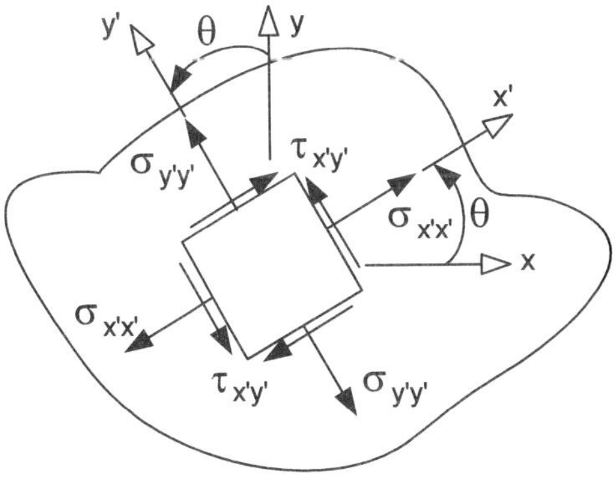

Fig. 7.3b An element with x'-y' orientation.

As we rotate the element about its center through some angle θ, the stresses on the element faces change from σ_{xx}, σ_{yy} and τ_{xy} to $\sigma_{x'x'}$, $\sigma_{y'y'}$ and $\tau_{x'y'}$. To explore stress space, it is necessary to establish relations for $\sigma_{x'x'}$, $\sigma_{y'y'}$ and $\tau_{x'y'}$ in terms of σ_{xx}, σ_{yy} and τ_{xy} and the angle θ.

Let's follow the same procedure as we used in Chapter 3 when considering stresses on oblique planes. Cut the left corner from the element shown in Fig. 7.3a at an angle θ so as to produce a wedge like element with an inclined surface that is parallel to the y' axis and perpendicular to the x' axis. Consider the element thickness in the z direction to be unity, and define the area of the inclined surface as ΔA as indicated in Fig. 7.4. The area of the short side of the wedge is given by ΔA sin θ and the area of the longer side of the wedge is ΔA cos θ. These areas are important because they factor into the equilibrium equations that are employed later in this derivation.

The stresses $\tau_{x'y'}$ and $\sigma_{x'x'}$ act on the inclined surface of the wedge and τ_{xy}, σ_{xx} and σ_{yy} act on the other sides of the wedge. We multiply these stresses with the areas of the three sides of the wedge to obtain the forces shown in Fig. 7.4b. No forces are shown on the face of the wedge, because the element was removed from a body in a plane state of stress where $\sigma_{zz} = \tau_{xz} = \tau_{yz} = 0$.

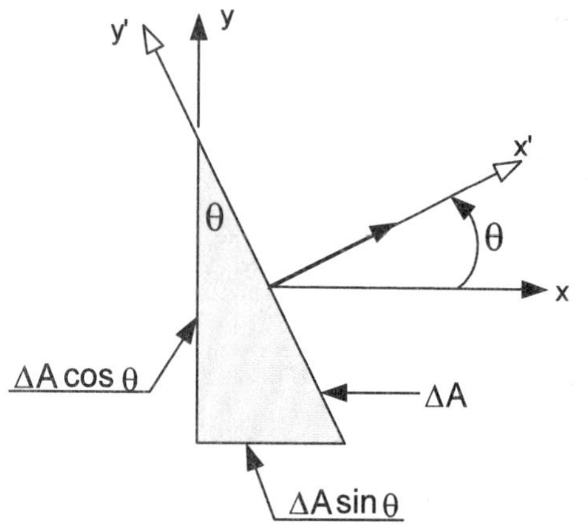

Fig. 7.4a A wedge like element cut from the x-y element at an angle θ.

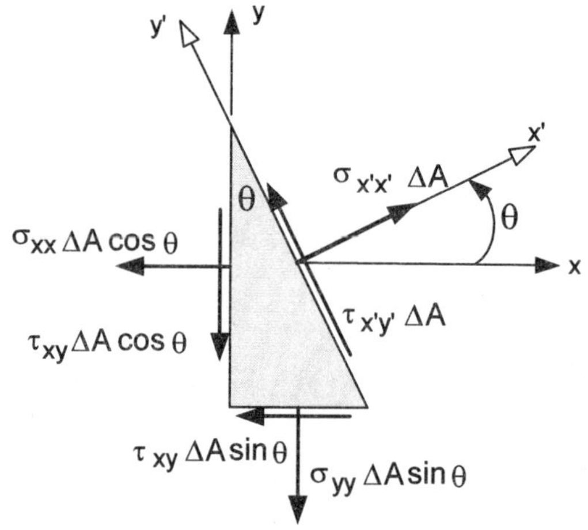

Fig. 7.4b Forces acting on the three sides of the wedge like element.

Next we write two equilibrium relations summing forces in the x' and y' directions:

$$\Sigma F_{x'} = 0 \qquad \begin{aligned} &\sigma_{x'x'}\Delta A - \sigma_{xx}(\Delta A\cos\theta)\cos\theta - \tau_{xy}(\Delta A\cos\theta)\sin\theta \\ &- \sigma_{yy}(\Delta A\sin\theta)\sin\theta - \tau_{xy}(\Delta A\sin\theta)\cos\theta = 0 \end{aligned}$$

$$\Sigma F_{y'} = 0 \qquad \begin{aligned} &\tau_{x'y'}\Delta A + \sigma_{xx}(\Delta A\cos\theta)\sin\theta - \tau_{xy}(\Delta A\cos\theta)\cos\theta \\ &- \sigma_{yy}(\Delta A\sin\theta)\cos\theta + \tau_{xy}(\Delta A\sin\theta)\sin\theta = 0 \end{aligned} \tag{7.7}$$

Simplifying these two equations and solving for $\sigma_{x'x'}$ and $\tau_{x'y'}$ gives:

$$\sigma_{x'x'} = \sigma_{xx}\cos^2\theta + \sigma_{yy}\sin^2\theta + 2\tau_{xy}\sin\theta\cos\theta \tag{7.8}$$

$$\tau_{x'y'} = -(\sigma_{xx} - \sigma_{yy})\sin\theta\cos\theta + \tau_{xy}(\cos^2\theta - \sin^2\theta) \tag{7.9}$$

These relations enable you to search solution space to determine the angle θ, which produces maximum and minimum values of both the normal and shear stresses.

By introducing four trigonometric identities, it is possible to convert Eqs. (7.8) and (7.9) into a double angle (2θ) format as shown below.

$$\sigma_{x'x'} = \frac{\sigma_{xx} + \sigma_{yy}}{2} + \frac{\sigma_{xx} - \sigma_{yy}}{2}\cos 2\theta + \tau_{xy}\sin 2\theta$$

$$\tau_{x'y'} = -\frac{\sigma_{xx} - \sigma_{yy}}{2}\sin 2\theta + \tau_{xy}\cos 2\theta \tag{7.10}$$

A similar relation for $\sigma_{y'y'}$ may be derived by increasing the angle of the cut for the wedge from θ to 90° + θ. Alternatively, you may convert Eq. (7.8) or the first of Eq. (7.10) to an expression for $\sigma_{y'y'}$ by letting $\theta \Rightarrow \theta + 90°$ to obtain:

$$\sigma_{y'y'} = \frac{\sigma_{xx} + \sigma_{yy}}{2} - \frac{\sigma_{xx} - \sigma_{yy}}{2} \cos 2\theta - \tau_{xy} \sin 2\theta \qquad (7.11)$$

The form of the relations for $\sigma_{x'x'}$ and $\sigma_{y'y'}$ is almost identical except for the signs of the last two terms. It is evident from inspection that we can add Eq. (7.10) and Eq. (7.11) to obtain:

$$\sigma_{x'x'} + \sigma_{y'y'} = \sigma_{xx} + \sigma_{yy} \qquad (7.12)$$

Equation (7.12) indicates that the sum of the normal stress components is independent of the angle of θ. The sum of the normal stresses is an invariant that does not depend on the orientation of the planes upon which the stresses act. This is the first of the three invariants of stress states.

EXAMPLE 7.4

Consider a plane state of stress represented at a point by a small elemental area ΔA shown in Fig. E7.4. If the stresses are σ_{xx} = 50 MPa, σ_{yy} = – 32 MPa and τ_{xy} = 24 MPa, determine the stresses on an element that is rotated 35° counterclockwise relative to the element shown in Fig. E7.4.

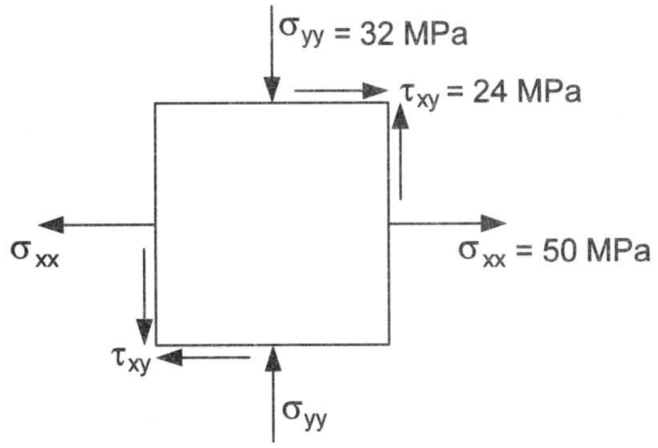

Fig. E7.4

Solution:

Using Eqs. (7.10) and (7.11) and setting θ = 35°, we write:

$$\sigma_{x'x'} = \frac{\sigma_{xx} + \sigma_{yy}}{2} + \frac{\sigma_{xx} - \sigma_{yy}}{2} \cos 2\theta + \tau_{xy} \sin 2\theta$$

$$\sigma_{x'x'} = \frac{50 - 32}{2} + \frac{50 + 32}{2} \cos 70 + 24 \sin 70 = 45.58 \text{ MPa}$$

$$\tau_{x'y'} = -\frac{\sigma_{xx} - \sigma_{yy}}{2} \sin 2\theta + \tau_{xy} \cos 2\theta$$

$$\tau_{x'y'} = -\frac{50 + 32}{2} \sin 70 + 24 \cos 70 = -30.32 \text{ MPa}$$

$$\sigma_{y'y'} = \frac{\sigma_{xx} + \sigma_{yy}}{2} - \frac{\sigma_{xx} - \sigma_{yy}}{2}\cos 2\theta - \tau_{xy} \sin 2\theta$$

$$\sigma_{y'y'} = \frac{50 - 32}{2} - \frac{50 + 32}{2}\cos 70 - 24 \sin 70 = -27.58 \text{ MPa}$$

EXAMPLE 7.5

Consider a plane state of stress represented at a point by a small elemental area shown in Fig. E7.5. If the stresses are σ_{xx} = 12 ksi, σ_{yy} = 15 ksi and τ_{xy} = – 14 ksi, determine the stresses on an element that is rotated 45° clockwise relative to the element shown in Fig. E7.5.

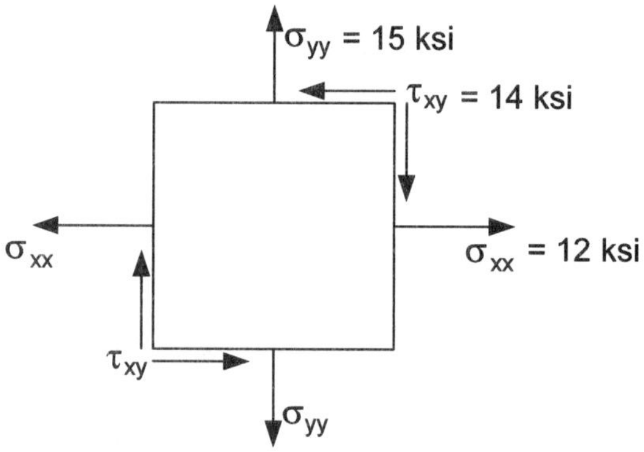

Fig. E7.5

Solution:

Using Eqs. (7.10) and (7.11) and setting θ = – 45°, we write:

$$\sigma_{x'x'} = \frac{\sigma_{xx} + \sigma_{yy}}{2} + \frac{\sigma_{xx} - \sigma_{yy}}{2}\cos 2\theta + \tau_{xy} \sin 2\theta$$

$$\sigma_{x'x'} = \frac{12 + 15}{2} + \frac{12 - 15}{2}\cos(-90) - 14 \sin(-90) = 27.50 \text{ ksi}$$

$$\tau_{x'y'} = -\frac{\sigma_{xx} - \sigma_{yy}}{2}\sin 2\theta + \tau_{xy} \cos 2\theta$$

$$\tau_{x'y'} = -\frac{12 - 15}{2}\sin(-90) - 14 \cos(-90) = -1.500 \text{ ksi}$$

$$\sigma_{y'y'} = \frac{\sigma_{xx} + \sigma_{yy}}{2} - \frac{\sigma_{xx} - \sigma_{yy}}{2}\cos 2\theta - \tau_{xy} \sin 2\theta$$

$$\sigma_{y'y'} = \frac{12 + 15}{2} - \frac{12 - 15}{2}\cos(-90) + 14 \sin(-90) = -0.5000 \text{ ksi}$$

These two examples show the application of the stress equations of transformation for determining the Cartesian components of stress on an arbitrary element rotated an angle θ with respect to the x-y coordinate system. Next the stress equations of transformation are used to locate the planes where the normal and shear stresses are a maximum or minimum.

7.3 PRINCIPAL STRESSES

When considering all of the possible planes upon which normal stresses act, we seek those planes where the normal stresses are either a maximum or a minimum. We will define these planes by determining the angle θ_p, which designates the principal plane. To determine this angle, let's employ the standard calculus approach by differentiating the normal stress $\sigma_{x'x'}$ with respect to θ and set the result equal to zero.

$$\frac{d}{d\theta}\sigma_{x'x'} = -(\sigma_{xx} - \sigma_{yy})\sin 2\theta_p + 2\tau_{xy}\cos 2\theta_p = 0$$

$$\tan 2\theta_p = \frac{2\tau_{xy}}{\sigma_{xx} - \sigma_{yy}} \qquad (7.13)$$

From Eq. (7.13), it is easy to show that:

$$\cos 2\theta_p = \frac{(\sigma_{xx} - \sigma_{yy})/2}{\sqrt{\left(\left(\frac{\sigma_{xx} - \sigma_{yy}}{2}\right)^2 + \tau_{xy}^2\right)}}$$

$$\sin 2\theta_p = \frac{\tau_{xy}}{\sqrt{\left(\left(\frac{\sigma_{xx} - \sigma_{yy}}{2}\right)^2 + \tau_{xy}^2\right)}} \qquad (7.14)$$

Substitute Eq. (7.14) into Eq. (7.10) and simplifying yields:

$$\sigma_{\text{Max, Min}} = \frac{\sigma_{xx} + \sigma_{yy}}{2} + \frac{\sigma_{xx} - \sigma_{yy}}{2}\cos 2\theta_p + \tau_{xy}\sin 2\theta_p$$

$$\sigma_{\text{Max, Min}} = \frac{\sigma_{xx} + \sigma_{yy}}{2} \pm \sqrt{\left(\left(\frac{\sigma_{xx} - \sigma_{yy}}{2}\right)^2 + \tau_{xy}^2\right)} \qquad (7.15)$$

$$\tau_{pp} = -\frac{\sigma_{xx} - \sigma_{yy}}{2}\sin 2\theta_p + \tau_{xy}\cos 2\theta_p = 0$$

The maximum normal stress $\sigma_{Max} = \sigma_1$ is the largest algebraic value of the two numbers obtained in the solution of Eq. (7.15). The minimum normal stress $\sigma_{Min} = \sigma_2$ is the smaller of the two values. Both σ_1 and σ_2 are principal stresses, which act on orthogonal planes defined by Eq. (7.13). The shear stress on the principal planes $\tau_{pp} = 0$. We illustrate a typical principal state of stress in Fig. 7.5. In this illustration, the principal element is inscribed in a traditional Cartesian element although the Cartesian components of stress are not shown to avoid clutter. On the principal element, we have shown σ_1 and σ_2 as well as the shear stress τ_{pp} vanishing on its edges.

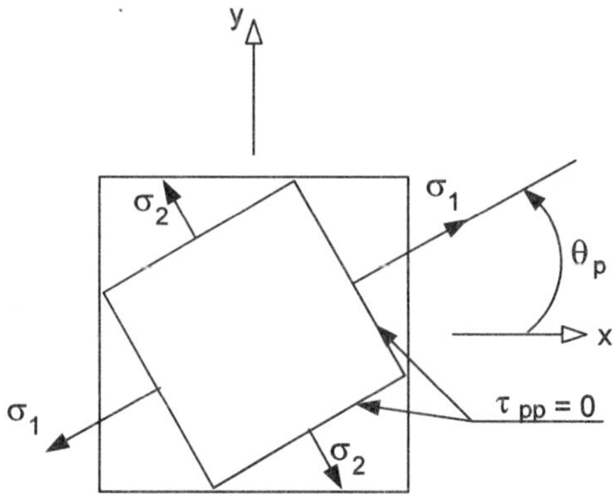

Fig. 7.5 A principal element inscribed in a traditional Cartesian element.

EXAMPLE 7.6

Consider a point, shown here as an elemental area, with Cartesian components of stress defined in Fig. E7.6. Determine the orientation of the principal planes and the stresses that act on the principal planes.

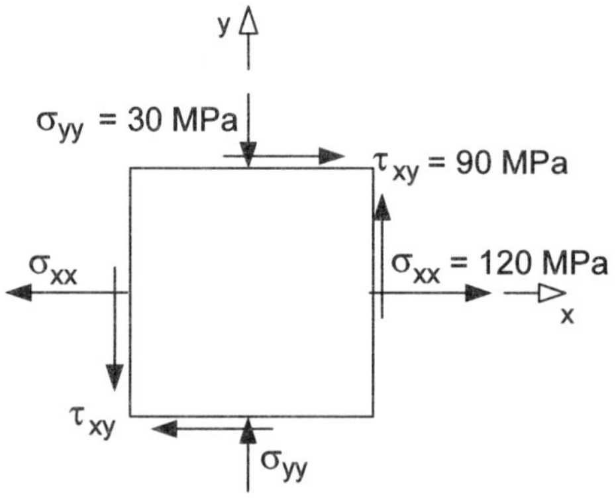

Fig. E7.6

Solution:

The principal angle θ_p is determined from Eq. (7.13) as:

$$\tan 2\theta_p = \frac{2\tau_{xy}}{\sigma_{xx} - \sigma_{yy}} = \frac{2(90)}{120+30} = 1.20$$

$$2\theta_p = \tan^{-1}(1.20) = 50.19^\circ \qquad \text{(a)}$$

$$2\theta_p = 180^\circ + 50.19^\circ = 230.2^\circ$$

$$\theta_p = 25.10^\circ \text{ and } 115.1^\circ \qquad \text{(b)}$$

The first principal angle (25.10°) defines the plane upon which the maximum principal stress σ_1 acts and the second principal angle (115.1°) defines the plane upon which the minimum principal stress σ_2 acts.

Let's determine the magnitude of the principal stresses by using Eq. (7.15) as:

$$\sigma_{\text{Max, Min}} = \frac{\sigma_{xx} + \sigma_{yy}}{2} \pm \sqrt{\left(\left(\frac{\sigma_{xx} - \sigma_{yy}}{2}\right)^2 + \tau_{xy}^2\right)}$$

$$\sigma_{\text{Max, Min}} = \frac{120 - 30}{2} \pm \sqrt{\left(\left(\frac{120 + 30}{2}\right)^2 + (90)^2\right)} \qquad \text{(c)}$$

$$\sigma_{\text{Max, Min}} = 45 \pm 117.15 \text{ MPa}$$

$$\sigma_1 = 162.2 \text{ MPa and } \sigma_2 = -72.15 \text{ MPa} \qquad \text{(d)}$$

We show these stresses acting on the principal element in Fig. E7.6a.

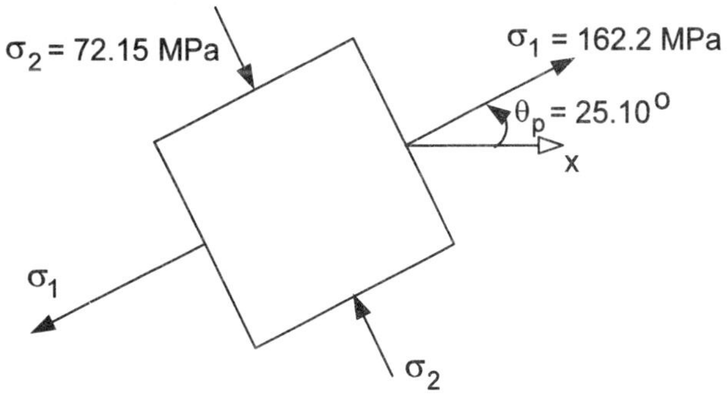

Fig. E7.6a

Of course the shear stresses on the principal element vanish in accordance with Eq. (7.15).

EXAMPLE 7.7

Consider a point, shown here as an elemental area, with Cartesian components of stress defined in Fig. E7.7. Determine the orientation of the principal planes and the stresses that act on the principal planes.

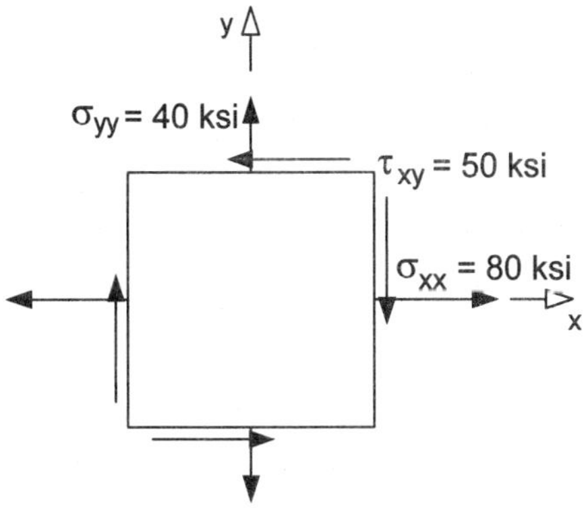

Fig. E7.7

Solution:

The principal angles θ_p are determined from Eq. (7.13) as:

$$\tan 2\theta_p = \frac{2\tau_{xy}}{\sigma_{xx} - \sigma_{yy}} = \frac{2(-50)}{80-40} = -2.50$$

$$2\theta_p = \tan^{-1}(-2.50) = -68.20° \quad \text{(a)}$$

$$2\theta_p = 180° - 68.20° = 111.8°$$

$$\theta_p = -34.10° \text{ and } 55.90° \quad \text{(b)}$$

The first principal angle (– 34.10°) defines the plane upon which the maximum principal stress σ_1 acts and the second principal angle (111.8°) defines the plane upon which the minimum principal stress σ_2 acts.

Let's determine the magnitude of the principal stresses by using Eq. (7.15) as:

$$\sigma_{Max,\,Min} = \frac{\sigma_{xx} + \sigma_{yy}}{2} \pm \sqrt{\left(\left(\frac{\sigma_{xx} - \sigma_{yy}}{2}\right)^2 + \tau_{xy}^2\right)}$$

$$\sigma_{Max,\,Min} = \frac{80+40}{2} \pm \sqrt{\left(\left(\frac{80-40}{2}\right)^2 + (-50)^2\right)} \quad \text{(c)}$$

$$\sigma_{Max,\,Min} = 60 \pm 53.85 \text{ ksi}$$

$$\sigma_1 = 113.85 \text{ ksi and } \sigma_2 = 6.15 \text{ ksi} \quad \text{(d)}$$

We show these stresses acting on the principal element in Fig. E7.7a.

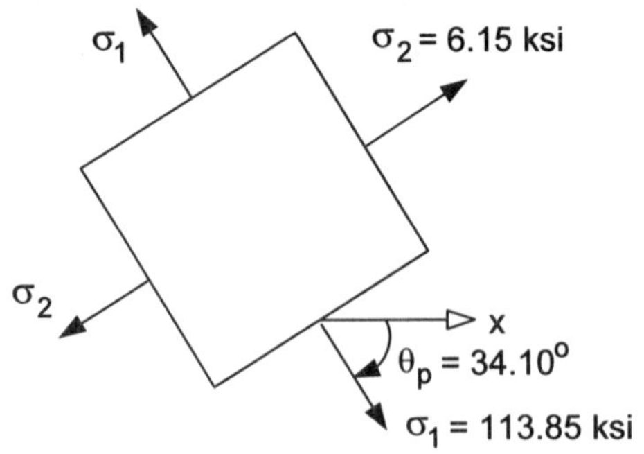

Fig. E7.7a

7.3.1 Maximum Shear Stresses

We used differential calculus to ascertain the principal planes defined by θ_p, which enabled us to determine the maximum and minimum normal stresses. Let's follow the same approach to determine the planes upon which the maximum shear stress occurs. Differentiate the second of Eq. (7.10) with respect to θ, and set the result equal to zero to obtain:

$$\frac{d}{d\theta}\tau_{x'y'} = -\frac{\sigma_{xx}-\sigma_{yy}}{2}(2\cos 2\theta) - 2\,\tau_{xy}\sin 2\theta = 0 \tag{a}$$

Solving Eq. (a) for θ_s gives:

$$\tan 2\theta_s = -\frac{\sigma_{xx}-\sigma_{yy}}{2\tau_{xy}} \tag{7.16}$$

where the angle θ_s defines the planes upon which the maximum shear stresses occur.

Comparing Eq. (7.16) for $2\theta_s$ with Eq. (7.13) for $2\theta_p$, shows that they are negative reciprocals. This fact implies that the angles $2\theta_s$ and $2\theta_p$ are orthogonal. Hence, the angles θ_s and θ_p are separated by 45°. Clearly, the planes of maximum shear and the principal planes are oriented at 45° relative to one another.

Note from Eq. (7.16) that cos $2\theta_s$ and sin $2\theta_s$ are given by:

$$\sin 2\theta_s = \frac{-(\sigma_{xx}-\sigma_{yy})/2}{\sqrt{\left(\left(\frac{\sigma_{xx}-\sigma_{yy}}{2}\right)^2+\tau_{xy}^2\right)}}$$

$$\cos 2\theta_s = \frac{\tau_{xy}}{\sqrt{\left(\left(\frac{\sigma_{xx}-\sigma_{yy}}{2}\right)^2+\tau_{xy}^2\right)}} \tag{7.17}$$

Substituting Eq. (7.17) into Eq. (7.10) and simplifying yields:

$$\tau_{Max} = \sqrt{\left(\left(\frac{\sigma_{xx}-\sigma_{yy}}{2}\right)^2+\tau_{xy}^2\right)} \tag{7.18}$$

EXAMPLE 7.8

Consider a point, shown here as an elemental area, with Cartesian components of stress defined in Fig. E7.8. Determine the orientation of the planes upon which the maximum shear stresses act and also determine the normal stresses that act on these planes.

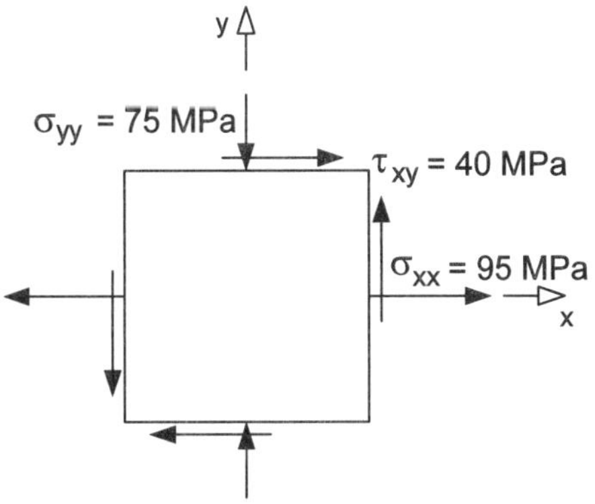

Fig. E7.8

Solution:

The plane upon which the maximum shear stress acts is given by Eq. (7.16) as:

$$\tan 2\theta_s = -\frac{\sigma_{xx} - \sigma_{yy}}{2\tau_{xy}} = -\frac{(95+75)}{2(40)} = -2.125 \qquad \text{(a)}$$

$$2\theta_s = \tan^{-1}(-2.125) = -64.80°$$

$$\theta_s = -\ 32.40° \qquad \text{(b)}$$

The maximum shear stress is calculated from Eq. (7.18) as:

$$\tau_{Max} = \sqrt{\left(\left(\frac{\sigma_{xx} - \sigma_{yy}}{2}\right)^2 + \tau_{xy}^2\right)} = \sqrt{\left(\left(\frac{95+75}{2}\right)^2 + (40)^2\right)} = 93.94 \text{ MPa} \qquad \text{(c)}$$

To determine the normal stress acting on this plane, substitute the value of $2\theta_s = -\ 64.80°$ into Eq. (7.10) to obtain:

$$\sigma_{x'x'} = \frac{\sigma_{xx} + \sigma_{yy}}{2} + \frac{\sigma_{xx} - \sigma_{yy}}{2}\cos 2\theta + \tau_{xy}\sin 2\theta \qquad \text{(d)}$$

$$\sigma_n = \frac{95-75}{2} + \frac{95+75}{2}\cos(-64.7989) + (40)\sin(-64.7989) = 10 \text{ MPa}$$

Using Eq. (7.10) and the angle θ_s is a cumbersome method to determine σ_n. We will show in the next section that on planes of maximum shear stress, σ_n is given by:

$$\sigma_n = (\sigma_{xx} + \sigma_{yy})/2 \qquad (7.19)$$

7.4 MOHR'S CIRCLE

A graphical technique, known as Mohr's circle, often was employed for solving for $\sigma_{x'x'}$, $\sigma_{y'y'}$ and $\tau_{x'y'}$ prior to the development of efficient electronic computers. Today the equations of stress transformation are easy to solve; however, Mohr's circle remains useful because it enables one to visualize how the Cartesian components of stress vary with the angle θ that defines the plane upon which the stresses act. Also the magnitude and orientation of σ_1, σ_2 and τ_{Max} are apparent from a cursory inspection of Mohr's circle.

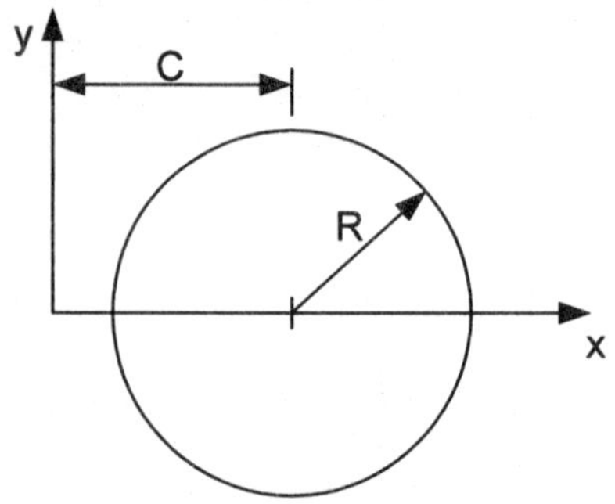

Fig. 7.6 A circle with radius R centered at x = C.

To establish the relation between a circle and the stress state, consider the equation of a circle with a radius R centered at x = C as shown in Fig. 7.6. The equation for this circle is:

$$(x - C)^2 + y^2 - R^2 \qquad (7.20)$$

To show that the stress equations of transformation map into a similar circle, rewrite Eq. (7.10) to obtain:

$$\sigma_{x'x'} - \frac{\sigma_{xx} + \sigma_{yy}}{2} = \frac{\sigma_{xx} - \sigma_{yy}}{2}\cos 2\theta + \tau_{xy}\sin 2\theta$$

$$(7.21)$$

$$\tau_{x'y'} = -\frac{\sigma_{xx} - \sigma_{yy}}{2}\sin 2\theta + \tau_{xy}\cos 2\theta$$

Square both sides of these two equations and add them obtain:

$$\left(\sigma_{x'x'} - \frac{\sigma_{xx} + \sigma_{yy}}{2}\right)^2 + \tau_{x'y'}^{\ 2} = \left(\frac{\sigma_{xx} - \sigma_{yy}}{2}\right)^2 + \tau_{xy}^{\ 2} \qquad (7.22)$$

Comparing the form of Eq. (7.20) with that of Eq. (7.22), permits us to establish several facts about Mohr's circle.

1. The correspondence between x and $\sigma_{x'x'}$ indicates σ will be found along the abscissa.
2. Mohr's circle will be centered at C where:

$$C = (\sigma_{xx} + \sigma_{yy})/2 \qquad (7.23)$$

3. The correspondence between y and $\tau_{x'y'}$ indicates τ will be found along the ordinate.
4. The radius of Mohr's circle R is given by:

$$R = \sqrt{\left(\frac{\sigma_{xx} - \sigma_{yy}}{2}\right)^2 + \tau_{xy}^{\ 2}} \qquad (7.24)$$

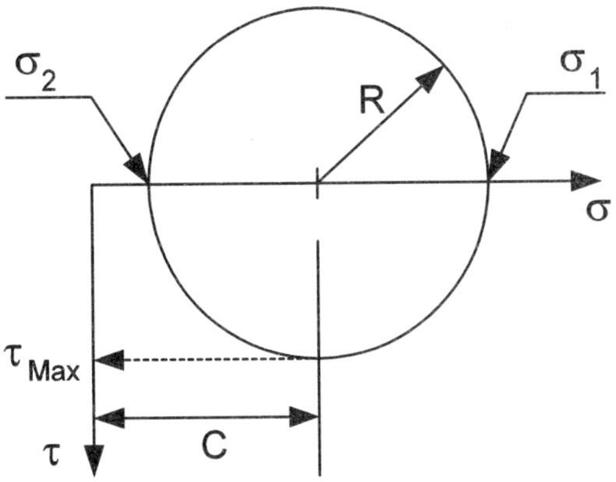

Fig. 7.7 Mohr's circle showing the principal stresses, σ_1 and σ_2 and maximum shear stress τ_{Max}.

An example of Mohr's circle, presented in Fig 7.7, shows the σ and τ axes, the center point located by C, the radius R, the principal stresses σ_1 and σ_2 and the maximum shear stress τ_{Max}. We have shown the τ axis as positive downward in this representation. This choice is consistent with the definition of θ as a positive quantity for counterclockwise rotation and for the sign convention for τ_{xy}. Let's consider two examples to demonstrate the usefulness of Mohr's circle in visualizing a complete state of stress at a point.

EXAMPLE 7.9

Consider a point, shown here as an elemental area, with Cartesian components of stress defined in Fig. E7.9. Determine the principal stresses and the orientation of the principal planes. Also determine the maximum shear stresses and their orientation.

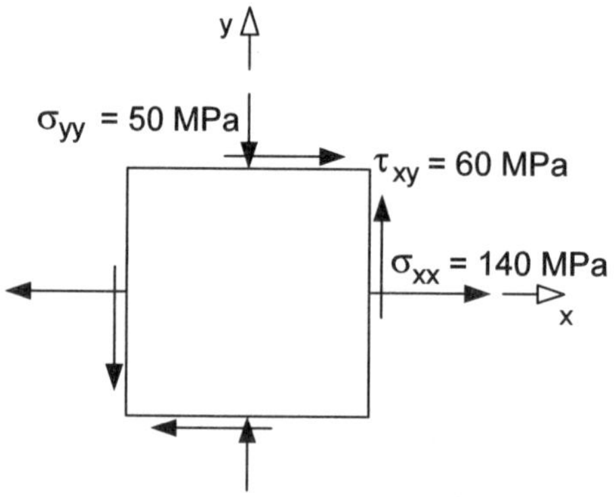

Fig. E7.9

Solution:

Step 1: Use Eq. (7.23) and Eq. (7.24) to determine the position of the center of the circle and its radius R as:

$$C = (\sigma_{xx} + \sigma_{yy})/2 \qquad C = (140 - 50)/2 = 45 \text{ MPa} \qquad \text{(a)}$$

$$R = \sqrt{\left(\frac{\sigma_{xx} - \sigma_{yy}}{2}\right)^2 + \tau_{xy}^{\ 2}} = \sqrt{\left(\frac{140 + 50}{2}\right)^2 + (60)^2} = 112.4 \text{ MPa} \qquad \text{(b)}$$

Step 2: Draw the σ and τ axes, locate the center of the circle on the σ axis at C = 45 MPa and construct a circle with the radius R = 112.4 MPa as shown in Fig. E7.9a. The principal stresses σ_1 and σ_2 are located where the circle intersects the σ axis and given by:

$$\sigma_1 = C + R \qquad \sigma_2 = C - R \qquad (7.25)$$

The maximum shear stress is given by:

$$\tau_{Max} = R \qquad (7.26a)$$

The normal stress acting on the plane associated with τ_{Max} is given by:

$$\sigma_n = C \qquad (7.26b)$$

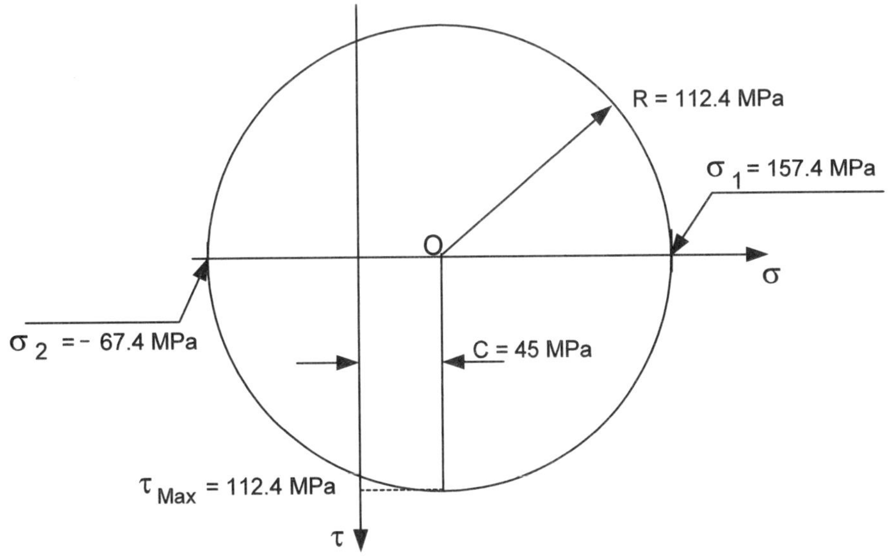

Fig. E7.9a

Step 3: To determine the orientation of the planes upon which the principal stresses and the maximum shear stress act, let's establish the location of the x-axis and y-axes on Mohr's circle. Locate σ_{xx} = 140 MPa on the σ axis and draw a perpendicular line through this point. Measure down the perpendicular a distance equal to the value of τ_{xy} = 60 MPa. We measure downward because τ_{xy} is a positive quantity (counterclockwise) and the positive τ axis is downward. Point A, shown in Fig. E7.9b, represents the location with coordinates σ = 140 MPa and τ = 60 MPa. This point also falls on the circle that was drawn in Step 2. Clearly the line O – A represents the radius of Mohr's circle.

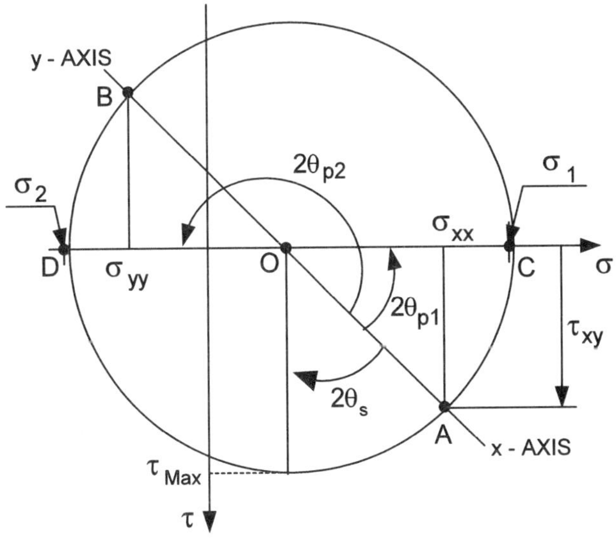

Fig. E7.9b

We have extended line O – A beyond the circle and labeled it as the x –axis. We have also extended this line upward and to the left until it intersect the circle at point B. If we drop a perpendicular line from point B to its intersection with the σ axis, the intersection occurs at σ_{yy} = – 50 MPa verifying the accuracy of the construction of the circle. The line O – B represents the y-axis. Note on this axis that τ_{xy} is negative (it tends to rotate the element clockwise) and the negative τ axis is upward. Having established the positions of the x and y axes relative to the circle, the next step is to measure the angles defining the principal planes and the planes upon which the maximum shear stress acts.

Step 4: From line O-A, we measure the angle AOC as illustrated in Fig. E7.9b, to obtain $2\theta_{p1} = 32°$. This observation indicates that the plane upon which σ_1 acts is located at $\theta_{p1} = 16°$. We also note that the angle $2\theta_{p2} = 2\theta_{p1} + 180°$. Thus, σ_2 acts on the plane located by $\theta_{p2} = 16° + 90° = 106°$. The angle $2\theta_{p1}$ can be verified by substituting the values for σ_{xx}, σ_{yy} and τ_{xy} into Eq. (7.13) to obtain:

$$\tan 2\theta_{p1} = \frac{2\tau_{xy}}{\sigma_{xx} - \sigma_{yy}} = \frac{2(60)}{140+50} = 0.6316 \qquad \text{(d)}$$

$$2\theta_{p1} = \tan^{-1}(0.6316) = 32.28°$$

The angle $2\theta_s$ is measured in the clockwise (negative) direction. The measurement gives $2\theta_s = -32°$ as expected because the expression for $2\theta_s$ is the negative reciprocal of Eq. (7.13).

Step 5: Finally, let's locate the principal planes relative to the x and y axes as shown in Fig. E7.9c.

Fig E7.9c

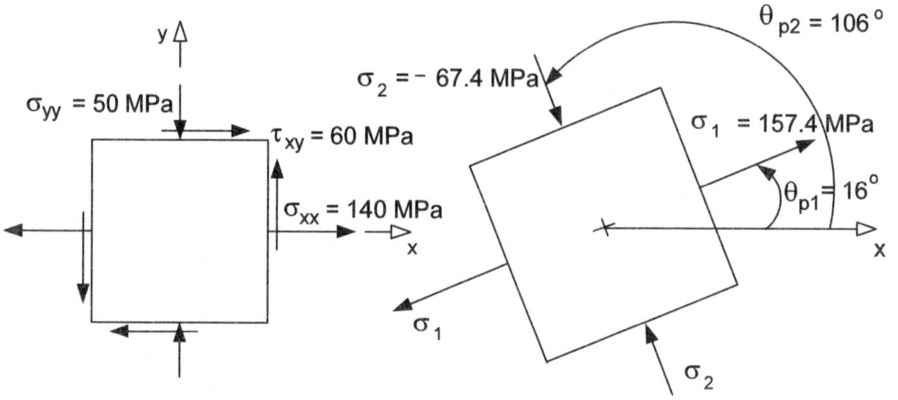

EXAMPLE 7.10

Consider a point, shown here as an elemental area, with Cartesian components of stress defined in Fig. E7.10. Using Mohr's circle, determine the principal stresses and the orientation of the principal planes. Also determine the maximum shear stresses and their orientation.

Fig. E7.10

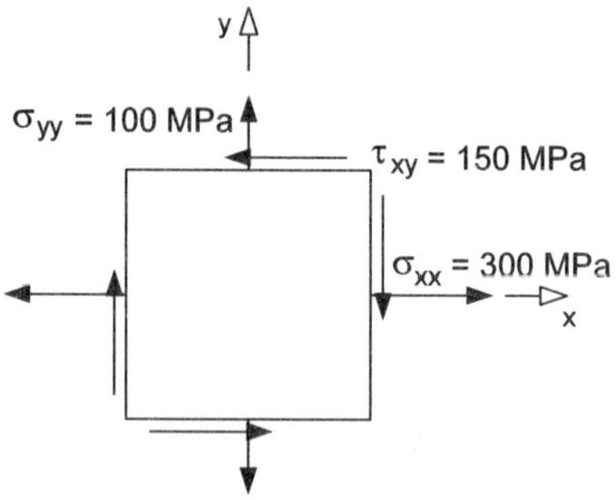

Solution:

Step 1: Use Eq. (7.23) to determine the position of the center of the circle as:

$$C = (\sigma_{xx} + \sigma_{yy})/2 \qquad = (300 + 100)/2 = 200 \text{ MPa} \qquad \text{(a)}$$

Step 2: Layout the axes for Mohr's circle and locate the center point O at $\sigma = C$. Then locate $\sigma_{xx} = 300$ MPa along the σ axis and construct a perpendicular line upward from this intersection. Scale the length of the perpendicular line to be proportional to $\tau_{xy} = 150$ MPa, as shown in Fig E7.10a. Because τ_{xy} is a negative quantity it is plotted in the negative τ direction. Draw the line O – A, which is the radius of Mohr's circle. This line also locates the x – axis relative to Mohr's circle. The radius can be determined from Eq. (7.24) as:

$$R = \sqrt{\left(\frac{\sigma_{xx} - \sigma_{yy}}{2}\right)^2 + \tau_{xy}^{\ 2}} = \sqrt{\left(\frac{300 - 100}{2}\right)^2 + (-150)^2} = 180.3 \text{ MPa} \qquad \text{(b)}$$

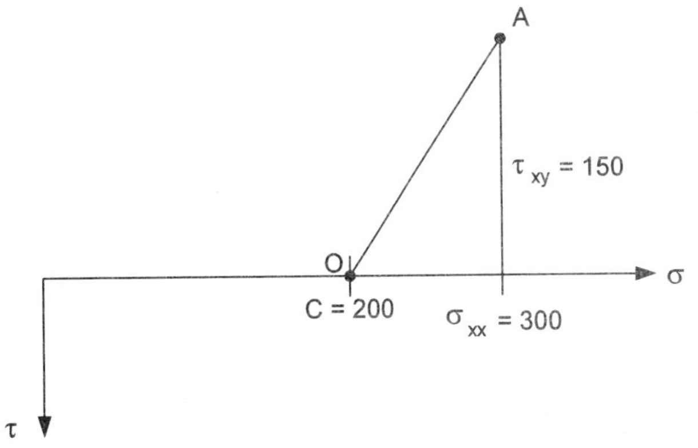

Fig. E7.10a

Step 3: Using the length of the line O – A as the radius R and with the center of the circle at $\sigma = C$, we construct Mohr's circle as shown in Fig. E7.10b. The axes are scaled and the locations of σ_1, σ_2 and τ_{Max} are marked.

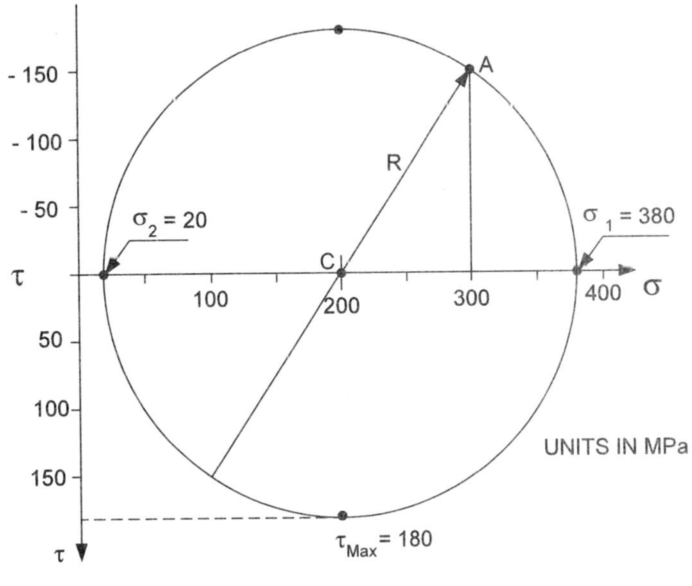

Fig. E7.10b

From the scale imposed on the σ and τ axes we determine the approximate values of the principal and maximum shear stresses as:

$\sigma_1 = 380$ MPa $\quad \sigma_2 = 20$ MPa $\quad \tau_{Max} = 180$ MPa $\quad \sigma_n = 200$ MPa

The accuracy of these results can be verified by employing Eq. (7.15) and Eq. (7.18).

Step 4: The location of the principal planes and the planes of maximum shear stress is determined by measuring the angles $2\theta_p$ and $2\theta_s$ as illustrated in Fig. E7.10c. Measurements of the angles AOC and AOD, both in the clockwise (negative) direction, shows that $2\theta_p = -56°$ and that $\theta_s = -146°$.

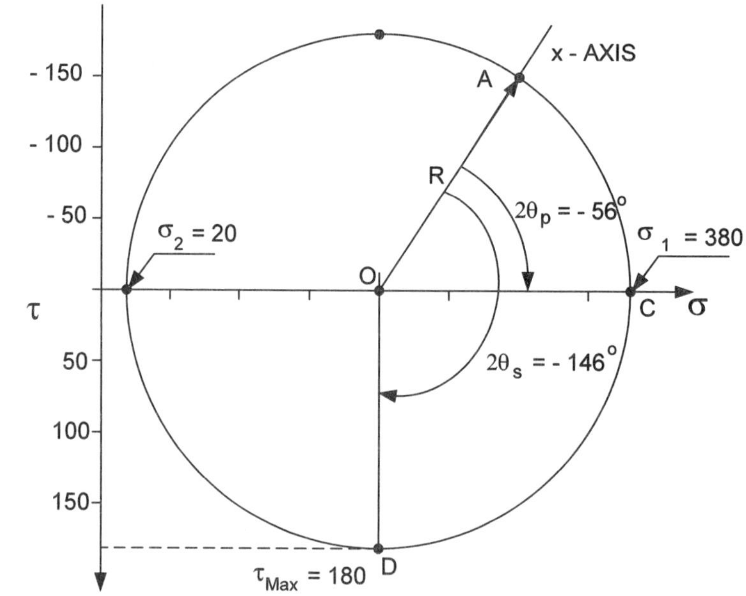

Fig. E7.10c

Step 5: Construct elements showing the planes upon which σ_1 and σ_2 act. We rotate a line through an angle θ_p measured in the clockwise direction from the x-axis to obtain the element shown in Fig. E 7.10d. Construct a similar element showing the plane upon which τ_{MAX} acts. Again we rotate a line an angle θ_s measured in the clockwise direction from the x-axis to obtain the element shown in Fig. E 7.10e.

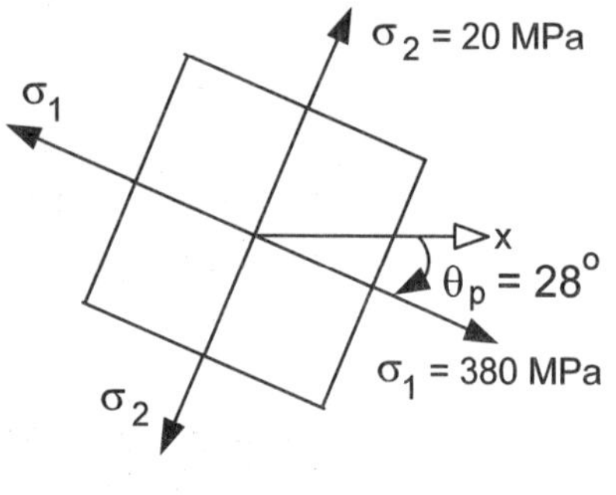

Fig. E7.10d

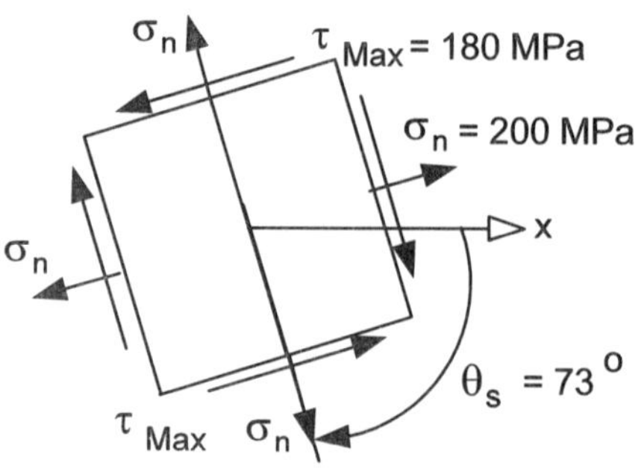

Fig. E7.10e

7.5 FAILURE THEORIES

In previous discussions pertaining to the safety of uniaxial members — beams, truss members, tie rods, etc., we indicated that failure would occur when the stress σ imposed on the member in question exceeded the strength of the material from which the member was fabricated. The equation for failure for these uniaxial members is given by:

$$\sigma_{xx} = \sigma_1 \geq S_y \qquad \sigma_{xx} = \sigma_1 \geq S_u \qquad (7.27)$$

where the choice of yield or ultimate tensile strength, S_y or S_u, depends on the admissible mode of failure.

For uniaxial members the stress state is also uniaxial with $\sigma_{yy} = \sigma_{zz} = 0$ and $\sigma_2 = \sigma_3 = 0$; hence, the conditions for structural failure given in Eq. (7.27) are valid. However, for more complex structural components such as plates and shells or machine components, the state of stress is multi-dimensional and more involved theories of failure are required. We will consider a two-dimensional state of stress — plane stress — where the principal stresses are ordered so that:

$$\sigma_1 \geq \sigma_2 \qquad \sigma_3 = 0 \qquad (7.28)$$

Several different theories of failure are used today, but in the interest of brevity, we will describe only the three most popular ones.

1. The maximum principal stress theory.
2. The maximum shear stress theory.
3. The maximum distortional energy theory.

We will also assume that the failure occurs upon yielding and that the yield strength in tension is the same as the yield strength in compression.

7.5.1 The Maximum Principal Stress Theory

The maximum principal stress theory states that a structural component fails by yielding when the maximum principal stress σ exceeds the yield strength of the material from which it is fabricated.

$$|\sigma_1| \geq S_y \qquad |\sigma_2| \geq S_y \qquad (7.29)$$

If we consider all possible combinations of σ_1 and σ_2, it is possible to construct the yielding diagram presented in Fig. 7.8.

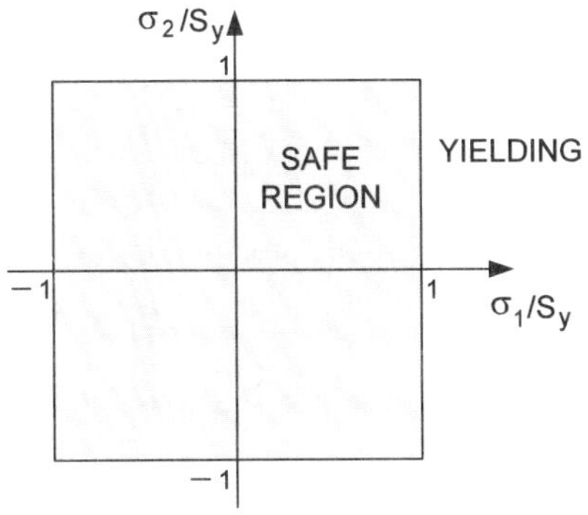

Fig. 7.8 Failure diagram for the maximum principal stress theory for yielding.

If we plot a point with coordinates σ_1/S_y and σ_2/S_y and it falls within the square in Fig. 7.8, the structural component will not yield. However, if the point falls on the boundary or outside the boundary of this box, yielding will occur. This theory is employed in the analysis of uniaxial structural members where the influence of the second principal stress σ_2 is small. Unfortunately, failure of ductile materials subjected to biaxial states of stress occurs due to shear on planes of maximum shear stress. In these cases, the maximum principal stress theory is not conservative. Yielding by shear occurs at stress states lower than predicted by the maximum principal stress theory.

7.5.2 The Maximum Shear Stress Theory

The maximum shear stress theory for yielding, sometimes called the Tresca theory, is often employed to predict the onset of yielding in machine components fabricated from ductile materials. These ductile materials fail on maximum shear planes that are oriented at 45° to the principal planes. This theory indicates that yielding will occur when τ_{Max} in a machine component equals the maximum shear stress achieved at yield in a simple tensile test of the material.

Consider first the simple tension test where:

$$\sigma_1 = S_y \qquad \sigma_2 = \sigma_3 = 0 \qquad \tau_{Max} = (\sigma_1 - \sigma_2)/2 = S_y/2 \tag{7.30}$$

Next, consider the maximum shear stress in the structural component. Two possibilities must be considered:

1. When σ_1 and σ_2 are of opposite signs τ_{Max} is given by:

$$\tau_{Max} = (\sigma_1 - \sigma_2)/2 \tag{7.31}$$

Substituting Eq. (7.30) into Eq. (7.31) gives the equation governing yielding as:

$$|\sigma_1 - \sigma_2| \geq S_y \tag{7.32}$$

2. When σ_1 and σ_2 are the same sign τ_{Max} is given by:

$$\tau_{Max} = (\sigma_1 - \sigma_3)/2 = \sigma_1/2 \tag{7.33}$$

Substituting Eq. (7.30) into Eq. (7.33) gives the equation governing yielding as:

$$|\sigma_1| \geq S_y \tag{7.34}$$

If we consider all possible combinations of σ_1 and σ_2, it is possible to construct the yielding diagram presented in Fig. 7.9. When the principal stresses σ_1 and σ_2 are of like sign, the stress state corresponds to quadrant I or III in Fig. 7.9, and the maximum shear theory corresponds to the maximum principal stress theory. When the signs of σ_1 and σ_2 are opposite, the stress state corresponds to quadrant II and IV. In this instance, there is a marked difference between the two theories, and the maximum shear stress theory is much more conservative.

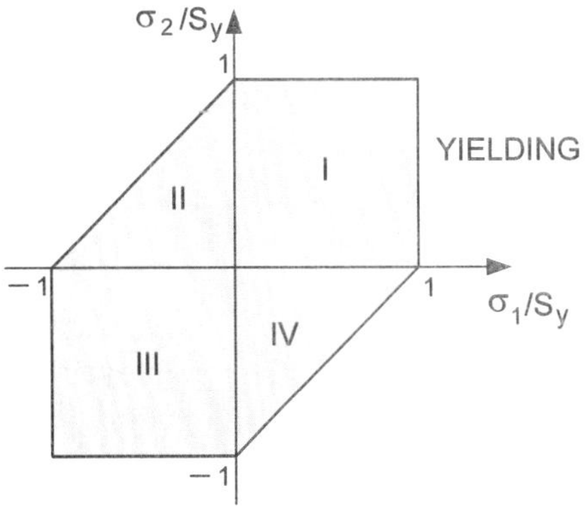

Fig. 7.9 Failure diagram for the Maximum shear stress theory of yielding.

7.5.3 Maximum Distortion Energy Theory

The maximum distortion energy theory, sometimes called the von Mises theory, predicts yielding in a machine component when the distortion energy per unit volume equal the distortion energy per unit volume achieved when the material yields in a simple tensile test.

For a two-dimensional stress state with $\sigma_3 = 0$, the distortion energy per unit volume U_d is given by:

$$U_d = (1/6G)[\sigma_1^2 - \sigma_1\sigma_2 + \sigma_2^2] \tag{7.35}$$

In a tensile test with $\sigma_1 = S_y$ and $\sigma_2 = \sigma_3 = 0$, the distortion energy per unit volume is:

$$U_d = (1/6G)S_y^2 \tag{7.36}$$

By substituting Eq. (7.36) into Eq. (7.35), we obtain the von Mises equation for yielding.

$$(\sigma_1/S_y)^2 - (\sigma_1/S_y)(\sigma_2/S_y) + (\sigma_2/S_y)^2 = 1 \tag{7.37}$$

If we consider all possible combinations of σ_1 and σ_2, it is possible to construct the yielding diagram presented in Fig. 7.10. The boundary of the failure diagram is an ellipse that is slightly less conservative than the maximum principal stress theory for yielding in quadrants I and III. In quadrants II and IV, where the principal stresses are of opposite sign, the von Mises theory is less conservative than the maximum shear theory but more conservative that the maximum principal stress theory. The distortional energy theory is widely accepted as the most accurate theory for predicting yielding in ductile materials commonly used to fabricate structural elements and machine components.

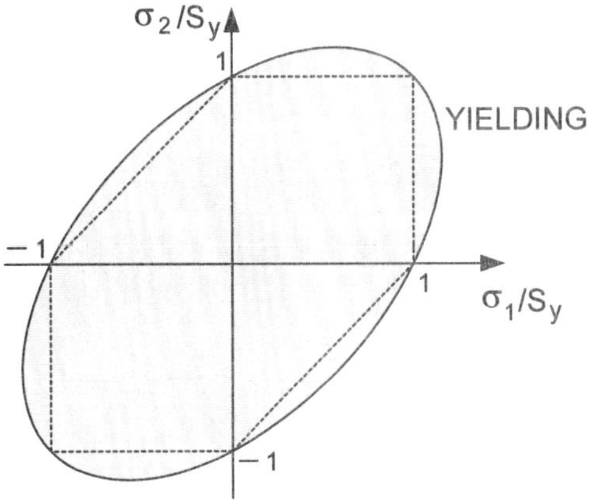

Fig 7.10 Failure diagram for the maximum distortion energy theory for yielding.

EXAMPLE 7.11

Your analysis of the principal stresses in a machine component indicates that $\sigma_1 = 262$ MPa and $\sigma_2 = -138$ MPa. If the component is fabricated from 1020 HR steel, will it yield in service?

Solution:

Because $S_y = 290$ MPa for 1020 HR steel, the prediction of yielding will depend on the theory of yielding employed in the analysis. Let's use the three different theories described in the previous subsections. From the maximum principal stress theory for yielding and Eq. (7.29), it is clear that yielding **will not** occur because:

$$\sigma_1 = 262 \text{ MPa} < S_y = 290 \text{ MPa} \qquad |\sigma_2| = |138| \text{ ksi} < S_y = 290 \text{ MPa} \tag{a}$$

Because σ_1 and σ_2 are of opposite signs, the maximum shear stress theory for yielding and Eq. (7.32) gives:

$$(\sigma_1 - \sigma_2) = (262 + 138) = 400 \text{ MPa} > S_y = 290 \text{ MPa} \tag{b}$$

From the results of Eq. (b), we predict that yielding **will** occur.

Using the maximum distortion energy theory and applying Eq. (7.37), we write:

$$(\sigma_1/S_y)^2 - (\sigma_1/S_y)(\sigma_2/S_y) + (\sigma_2/S_y)^2 \geq 1$$

$$(262/290)^2 - (262/290)(-138/290) + (-138/290)^2 = 1.473 > 1 \tag{c}$$

The maximum distortional energy theory also predicts yielding. Because the two conservative theories of failure that are widely accepted to predict yielding in ductile materials provide the same result, we conclude that the machine component **will fail** by yielding. We indicate the same result on the graphic shown in Fig. E7.11, where the operating point $\sigma_1/S_y = 0.903$ and $\sigma_2/S_y = -0.476$ is plotted.

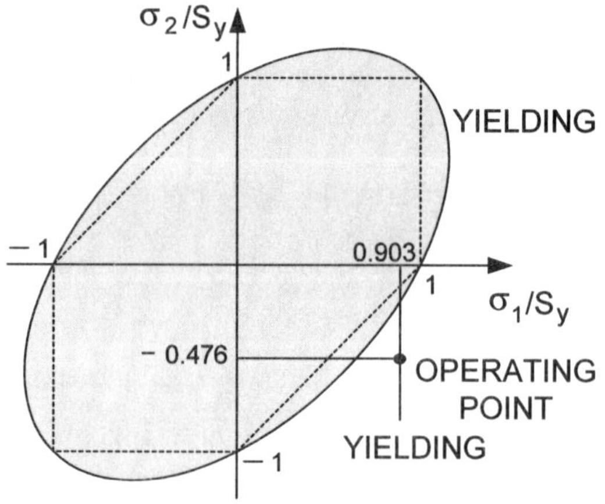

Fig. E7.11

7.6 STRESSES IN THIN WALLED PRESSURE VESSELS

Thin walled[1] pressure vessels (shells) are widely employed as containers for liquids and gasses. They are usually subjected to internal pressure, which generates membrane stresses in their walls. Bending stresses do not occur unless the shell is designed with discontinuities such as nozzles or skirts. Because the state of stress is primarily membrane, the pressure vessels are very efficient structures with stresses that are nearly uniformly distributed through the thickness of the wall.

Applications involving pressure vessels vary widely. Pressure vessels are fabricated in various sizes and shapes. They can be small such as a can for soda, or large such as a storage tank for natural gas. While the most common shape is cylindrical, they may be designed with spherical, conical or toroidal shapes.

7.6.1 Spherical Pressure Vessels

Let's consider a portion of a thin spherical shell, to illustrate the concept of membrane stresses. The portion of a spherical shell with a radius r and wall thickness t subjected to an internal pressure p is illustrated in Fig. 7.11. Writing the equilibrium equation $\Sigma F_y = 0$ yields:

$$p\pi r_x^2 - (N \sin \phi)(2\pi r_x) = 0 \qquad (7.38)$$

where N is the membrane force per unit length, and r_x is the radius defined in Fig. 7.11

Solving Eq. (7.38) for N and noting that $r_x/\sin \phi = r$ gives:

$$N = pr_x/(2 \sin \phi) = pr/2 \qquad (7.39)$$

Fig. 7.11 A portion of a spherical shell subjected to an internal pressure p.

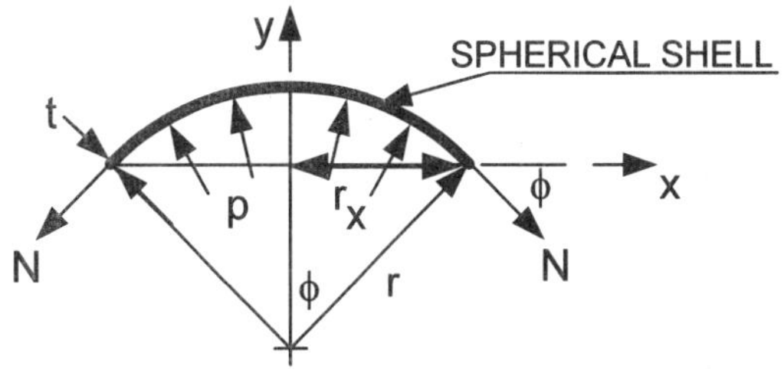

It is evident from Eq. (7.39) that the value of N is independent of the angle ϕ; hence, the membrane force per unit length is independent of position. The membrane stresses σ_m for a spherical pressure vessel are obtained from Eq. (7.39) as:

$$\sigma_m = N/t = pr/2t \qquad (7.40)$$

Because the spherical pressure vessel is symmetric, it is evident that the membrane stresses in the meridian σ_{my} and tangential σ_{mx} directions are the same, and the stress state is biaxial with:

$$\sigma_1 = \sigma_2 = \sigma_{my} = \sigma_{mx} = pr/2t \qquad (7.41)$$

[1] A pressure vessel is considered to be thin walled if the ratio of $r/t > 10$. The membrane stresses in thin walled pressure vessels are considered to be uniformly distributed through the thickness of the wall.

These stresses are also principal stresses because axes of symmetry always coincide with principal planes.

EXAMPLE 7.12

A spherical pressure vessel with a radius r = 6 m and a wall thickness of 10 mm is subjected to a pressure of 500 kPa. Determine the membrane stresses in thc longitudinal and meridian directions. Also determine the maximum shear stress.

Solution:

From Eq. (7.41), we write:

$$\sigma_{my} = \sigma_{mx} = pr/2t = (500 \times 10^3)(6)/[(2)(0.010)] = 150 \text{ MPa} \qquad \text{(a)}$$

Also $\tau_{xy} = 0$ because the meridian and longitudinal membrane stresses are principal stresses.

From Eq. (7.18), the maximum shear stress is given by:

$$\tau_{Max} = \sqrt{\left(\left(\frac{\sigma_{xx} - \sigma_{yy}}{2}\right)^2 + \tau_{xy}^2\right)} = \sqrt{\left(\frac{150 - 150}{2}\right)^2 + 0} = 0 \qquad \text{(b)}$$

The maximum shear stress is zero for in-plane stresses. For out-of-plane shear stresses τ_{Max} is given by:

$$\tau_{Max} = (\sigma_1 - \sigma_3)/2 = \sigma_1/2 = pr/(4t) \qquad \text{(7.41a)}$$

$$\tau_{Max} = 150/2 = 75 \text{ MPa} \qquad \text{(c)}$$

7.6.2 Cylindrical Pressure Vessels

Cylindrical pressure vessels are the most common type employed because the cylindrical shape is easy to fabricate. Thin metal plates are formed into rounds and the longitudinal (axial) seam is welded to produce a thin walled tube. End caps are welded on this tube to produce a thin walled vessel capable of maintaining internal pressures.

To determine the membrane stresses σ_h (hoop or circumferential direction) and σ_a (axial or longitudinal direction) in a thin walled cylindrical pressure vessel, consider a cylinder with a radius r and a wall thickness t as illustrated in Fig. 7.12. Next remove a semi-circular segment of the cylinder as a FBD. The forces due to pressure p and the membrane forces acting on this FBD are shown in Fig. 7.13.

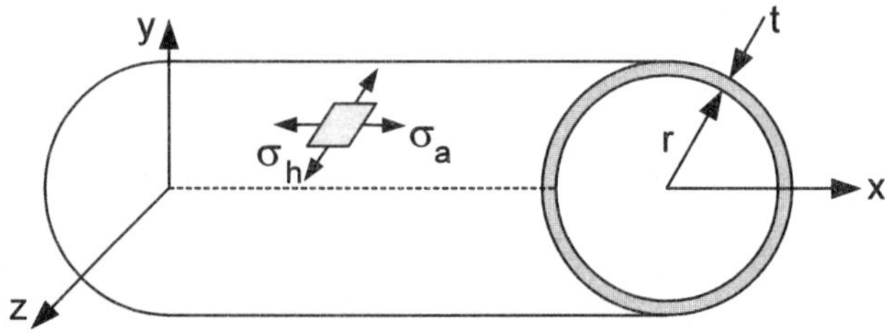

Fig. 7.12 A cylindrical pressure vessel with a radius r and a wall thickness of t.

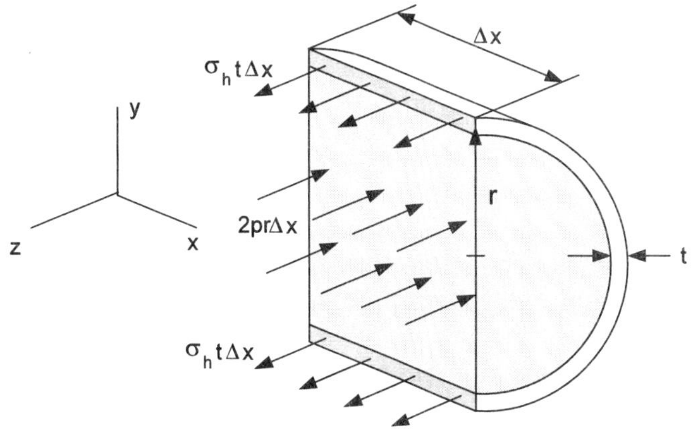

Fig. 7.13 A FBD of a semi-circular segment from the thin walled cylindrical pressure vessel.

To solve for the hoop stress σ_h, write $\Sigma F_z = 0$:

$$2(\sigma_h t\Delta x) - 2pr\Delta x = 0 \quad \text{(a)}$$

$$\sigma_h = pr/t \quad (7.42)$$

The axial stresses are determined by considering a segment of the cylinder formed by a section cut perpendicular to the axis of the cylinder as shown in Fig. 7.14. This FBD shows the forces due to pressure and the stresses in the axial direction. Writing $\Sigma F_x = 0$ yields:

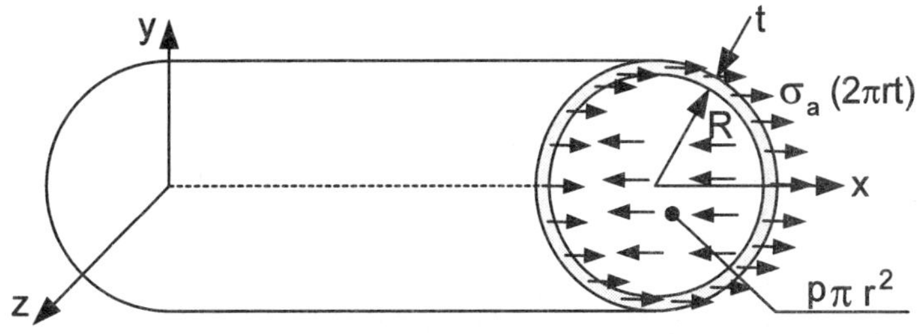

Fig. 7.14 FBD of a cylindrical pressure vessel showing the forces in the axial direction.

$$\sigma_a\,(2\pi rt) - p(\pi r^2) = 0 \quad \text{(b)}$$

Solving Eq. (b) for σ_a gives:

$$\sigma_a = pr/2t \quad (7.43)$$

Comparing Eq. (7.42) and Eq. (7.43) indicates that the hoop stress is twice as large as the axial stress in a thin walled circular pressure vessel. Also, from symmetry it is evident that σ_h and σ_a are principal stresses with:

$$\sigma_1 = \sigma_h \qquad \sigma_2 = \sigma_a \qquad \tau_{ha} = 0 \quad (7.44)$$

The maximum shear stress τ_{Max} is determined from Eq. (7.18) as:

$$\tau_{Max} = \sqrt{\left(\left(\frac{\sigma_{xx} - \sigma_{yy}}{2}\right)^2 + \tau_{xy}^2\right)} = \sqrt{\left(\frac{\sigma_1 - \sigma_2}{2}\right)^2} = \frac{pr}{4t} \tag{7.45}$$

EXAMPLE 7.13

A cylindrical pressure vessel, shown in Fig. E7.13, is employed as a water storage tank for a small municipality. Determine the height of the water h that can be maintained in the tank if the city's engineering director specifies a safety factor of 3.0. The tank is fabricated from 1020 HR steel with a diameter of D = 36 ft., a height H = 60 ft. and a thickness t = 0.375 in. The engineering director also indicates that the safety factor should be based on the maximum shear stress theory of yielding.

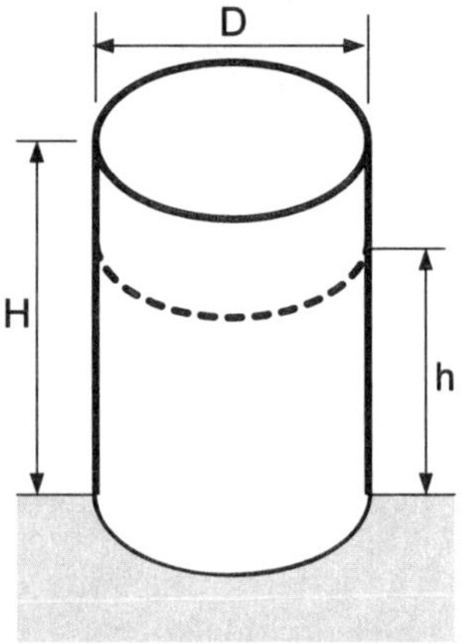

Fig. E7.13

Solution:

The pressure in the water tank varies from zero at the water level to a maximum at the base of the tank. The maximum pressure is given by:

$$p_{Max} = \gamma h \tag{7.46}$$

where $\gamma = 62.4\ \text{lb/ft}^3$ is the density of fresh water.

At the base of the tank, the pressure is:

$$p_{Max} = (62.4)h \quad (\text{lb/ft}^2) \tag{a}$$

The hoop stress is given by Eq. (7.42) as:

$$\sigma_h = \sigma_1 = pr/t = [(62.4)(18)(12)/(0.375)]h = 35{,}940\ h \quad (\text{lb/ft}^2) \tag{b}$$

where h is measured in ft.

From the failure diagram for yielding under maximum shear stress, shown in Fig. E7.13a, we can write:

$$(\sigma_1)_{Design} = S_y/SF \tag{c}$$

Reference to Appendix B-2 for the yield strength of 1020 HR steel gives:

$$(\sigma_1)_{Design} = S_y/SF = 42.0/3.0 = 14.0\ \text{ksi} \tag{d}$$

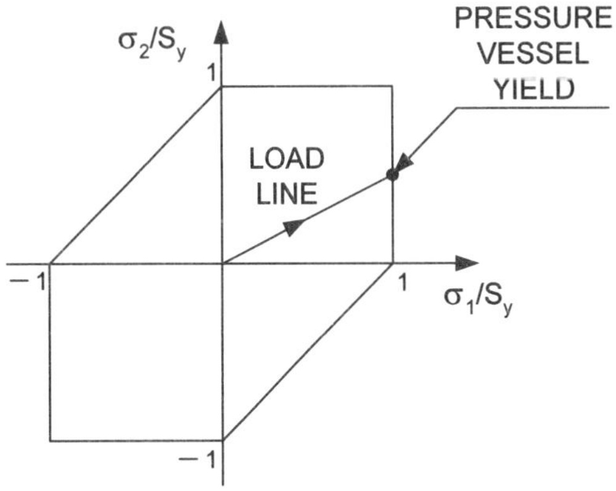

Fig. E7.13a

Converting the units of Eq. (d) from ksi to lb/ft² gives:

$$(\sigma_1)_{Design} = (14 \times 10^3 \text{ lb/in.}^2)(144 \text{ in.}^2/\text{ft}^2) = 2{,}016 \times 10^3 \text{ lb/ft}^2 \qquad \text{(e)}$$

From Eq. (b) and Eq. (e), we solve for h as:

$$h = (2{,}016 \times 10^3)/35{,}940 = 56.09 \text{ ft} \qquad \text{(f)}$$

Reference to Fig. E7.13 shows that the tank is 60 ft high and if filled to the brim, the stresses would exceed the allowable design limit of 14.0 ksi by about one percent. You may avoid even this slight excess by placing an overflow line at a location 56 ft above the tank's base.

7.7 STRAIN EQUATIONS OF TRANSFORMATION

In Section 7.2, we derived the stress equations of transformation and showed that the stresses $\sigma_{x'x'}$, $\sigma_{y'y'}$ and $\tau_{x'y'}$ varied with the angle of rotation θ of the Ox'y' coordinate system relative to the Oxy coordinate system. A remarkably similar set of transformation equations exist for strain. When deriving the stress equations of transformation, we considered a state of plane stress where $\sigma_{zz} = \tau_{xz} = \tau_{yz} = 0$. This derivation of the stress equations of transformation was based solely on the equilibrium equations.

To derive the strain equations of transformation, we will consider a state of plane strain where $\varepsilon_{zz} = \gamma_{xz} = \gamma_{yz} = 0$. This derivation is based only on the geometry of the deformation field. Let's consider the plane body illustrated in Fig 7.15 where the line segment AB is scribed on the body prior to imposing plane strain deformations. After the deformations are imposed, the line segment moves and is designated as A*B*. Point A moves to a new location designated by A*. The displacement in the x direction associated with this movement is u and the movement in the y direction is v. Point B moves to a new location designated by B* with displacements u + Δu in the x direction and v + Δv in the y direction.

By definition the strain along the line segment AB is given by:

$$\varepsilon_{AB} = (A^*B^* - AB)/AB \qquad \text{(a)}$$

From the geometry of Fig. 7.15, it clear that the length of the line segments are given by:

$$(AB)^2 = (\Delta x)^2 + (\Delta y)^2 \tag{b}$$

$$(A^*B^*)^2 = (\Delta x^*)^2 + (\Delta y^*)^2 \tag{c}$$

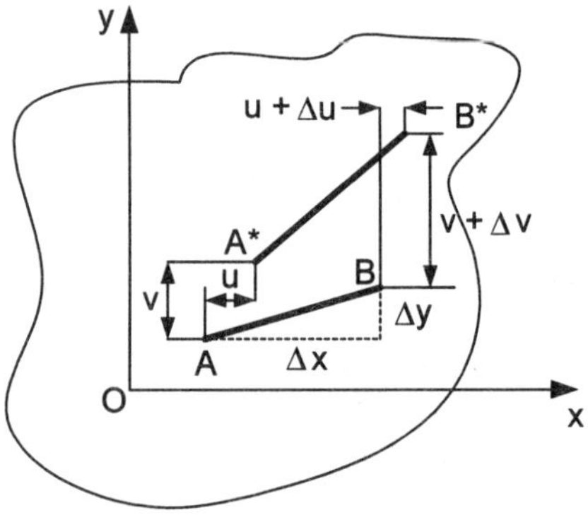

Fig. 7.15 A line segment AB before deformation and A*B* after deformation.

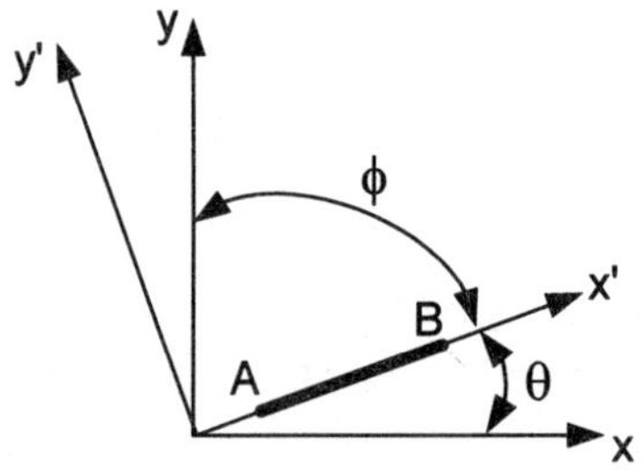

Fig. 7.16 Definition of angles θ and ϕ.

In general, the component Δx^* will have a different length than Δx because of the deformation of the body in the x direction. We express this difference in both Δx^* and Δy^* by writing:

$$\begin{aligned} \Delta x^* &= \left(1+\frac{\partial u}{\partial x}\right)\Delta x + \frac{\partial u}{\partial y}\Delta y \\ \Delta y^* &= \frac{\partial v}{\partial x}\Delta x + \left(1+\frac{\partial v}{\partial y}\right)\Delta y \end{aligned} \tag{d}$$

The length of the line segment A*B* can be determined by substituting Eq. (d) into Eq. (c). Because the deformations are extremely small, the products and squares of the derivatives can be neglected. From the substitution and simplification, we obtain:

$$(A^*B^*) = \left(1+2\frac{\partial u}{\partial x}\right)(\Delta x)^2 + \left(1+2\frac{\partial v}{\partial y}\right)(\Delta y)^2 + 2\left(\frac{\partial u}{\partial y}+\frac{\partial v}{\partial x}\right)(\Delta x)(\Delta y) \tag{e}$$

Let's rewrite Eq. (a) as:

$$(\varepsilon_{AB}+1)^2 = \left(\frac{A^*B^*}{AB}\right)^2 \tag{f}$$

Substituting Eq. (b) and Eq. (e) into Eq. (f) and simplifying gives:

$$(\varepsilon_{AB}+1)^2 = \cos^2\theta + \cos^2\phi + 2\frac{\partial u}{\partial x}\cos^2\theta + 2\frac{\partial v}{\partial y}\cos^2\phi + 2\left(\frac{\partial u}{\partial y}+\frac{\partial v}{\partial x}\right)\cos\theta\cos\phi \tag{g}$$

where θ and ϕ are defined in Fig. 7.16.

Expand the left side of Eq. (g) and neglect ε_{AB}^2 because it is a second order term and note that:

$$\cos^2\theta + \cos^2\phi = 1 \tag{h}$$

We can then express the strain along the line segment AB as:

$$\varepsilon_{AB} = \frac{\partial u}{\partial x}\cos^2\theta + \frac{\partial v}{\partial y}\cos^2\phi + \left(\frac{\partial u}{\partial y} + \frac{\partial v}{\partial x}\right)\cos\theta\cos\phi \tag{7.47}$$

The relationship between strains and displacements can be expressed as:

$$\partial u/\partial x = \varepsilon_{xx} \qquad \partial v/\partial y = \varepsilon_{yy} \qquad (\partial u/\partial y + \partial v/\partial x) = \gamma_{xy} \tag{7.48}$$

If we substitute the strain displacement relations of Eq. (7.48) into Eq. (7.47), we obtain the relation for ε_{AB} as:

$$\varepsilon_{AB} = \varepsilon_{xx}\cos^2\theta + \varepsilon_{yy}\sin^2\theta + \gamma_{xy}\cos\theta\sin\theta \tag{7.49}$$

If we select the line segment AB so that it is parallel to the x' axis, then it is evident that Eq. (7.49) may be written as:

$$\varepsilon_{x'x'} = \varepsilon_{xx}\cos^2\theta + \varepsilon_{yy}\sin^2\theta + \gamma_{xy}\cos\theta\sin\theta \tag{7.50}$$

Selecting the line segment AB parallel to the y' axis gives:

$$\varepsilon_{y'y'} = \varepsilon_{yy}\cos^2\theta + \varepsilon_{xx}\sin^2\theta - \gamma_{xy}\cos\theta\sin\theta \tag{7.51}$$

A similar but somewhat more involved derivation can be used to establish the strain equations of transformation for $\gamma_{x'y'}$. If we consider the angular change in an arbitrary right angle formed by two line segments AB_1 and AB_2 and follow the same procedure, the shear strain $\gamma_{x'y'}$ can be written as:

$$\frac{\gamma_{x'y'}}{2} = -\varepsilon_{xx}\cos\theta\sin\theta + \varepsilon_{yy}\cos\theta\sin\theta + \frac{\gamma_{xy}}{2}\left(\cos^2\theta - \sin^2\theta\right) \tag{7.52}$$

The strain equations of transformation presented in Eqs. (7.50), (7.51) and (7.52) are the same form as the stress equations of transformation given by Eqs. (7.8) and (7.9). A comparison shows that σ_{xx}, σ_{yy}, $\sigma_{x'x'}$ and $\sigma_{y'y'}$ correspond to ε_{xx}, ε_{yy}, $\varepsilon_{x'x'}$ and $\varepsilon_{y'y'}$. The comparison also shows that τ_{xy} and $\tau_{x'y'}$ correspond to $\gamma_{xy}/2$ and $\gamma_{x'y'}/2$.

It is possible to change Eqs. (7.50), (7.51) and (7.52), which show the angle θ into a double angle representation with suitable trigonometric substitutions. The results of these substitutions are:

$$\varepsilon_{x'x'} = \frac{\varepsilon_{xx} + \varepsilon_{yy}}{2} + \frac{\varepsilon_{xx} - \varepsilon_{yy}}{2}\cos 2\theta + \frac{\gamma_{xy}}{2}\sin 2\theta$$

$$\frac{\gamma_{x'y'}}{2} = -\frac{\varepsilon_{xx} - \varepsilon_{yy}}{2}\sin 2\theta + \frac{\gamma_{xy}}{2}\cos 2\theta$$

$$\varepsilon_{y'y'} = \frac{\varepsilon_{xx} + \varepsilon_{yy}}{2} - \frac{\varepsilon_{xx} - \varepsilon_{yy}}{2} \cos 2\theta - \frac{\gamma_{xy}}{2} \sin 2\theta \tag{7.53}$$

Because of the correspondence of the stress and strain transformation equations, it is apparent that a Mohr's strain circle can be constructed to graphically represent the state of strain at a point. The procedure for constructing Mohr's circle for strain is exactly the same as that followed previously for the stress circle. The only difference is to change the abscissa from σ to ε and the ordinate from τ to γ/2. We show a typical Mohr's circle for strain in Fig. 7.17.

The center of the strain circle is located at position C where:

$$C = (\varepsilon_{xx} + \varepsilon_{yy})/2 \tag{7.54}$$

The radius R of the circle is given by:

$$R = \sqrt{\left(\frac{\varepsilon_{xx} - \varepsilon_{yy}}{2}\right)^2 + \left(\frac{\gamma_{xy}}{2}\right)^2} \tag{7.55}$$

It is also evident from Fig. 7.17 that the principal strains are given by:

$$\varepsilon_{1,2} = C \pm R = \frac{\varepsilon_{xx} + \varepsilon_{yy}}{2} \pm \sqrt{\left(\frac{\varepsilon_{xx} - \varepsilon_{yy}}{2}\right)^2 + \left(\frac{\gamma_{xy}}{2}\right)^2} \tag{7.56}$$

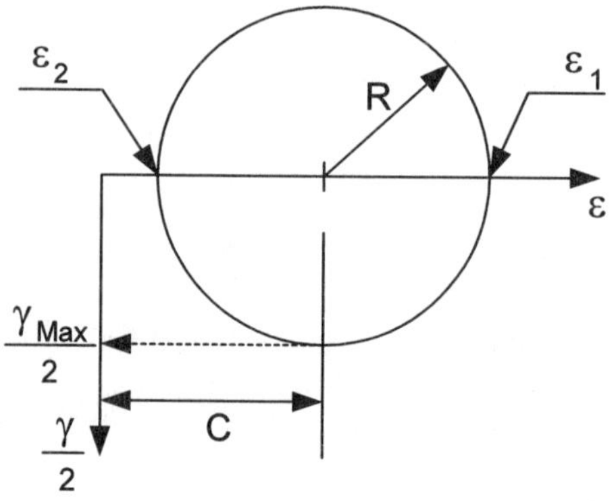

Fig. 7.17 Mohr's circle for strain.

The maximum shear strain γ_{Max} is given by:

$$\frac{\gamma_{Max}}{2} = R = \sqrt{\left(\frac{\varepsilon_{xx} - \varepsilon_{yy}}{2}\right)^2 + \left(\frac{\gamma_{xy}}{2}\right)^2} \tag{7.57}$$

Because of the correspondence in the stress and strain equations of transformation the principal planes are given by:

$$\tan 2\theta_p = \frac{\gamma_{xy}}{\varepsilon_{xx} - \varepsilon_{yy}} \tag{7.58}$$

The planes upon which the maximum shear strain act are rotated 45° relative to the principal planes.

Let's consider an example, which demonstrates the application of these results for determining the state of strain on arbitrary planes.

EXAMPLE 7.14

A state of plane strain exists at point A in a plane body where the Cartesian components of strain are given by:

$\varepsilon_{xx} = 450 \times 10^{-6}$ $\varepsilon_{yy} = -200 \times 10^{-6}$ $\gamma_{xy} = 150 \times 10^{-6}$

Determine the state of strain on an element rotated counterclockwise 40° relative to the Oxy axes.

Solution:

The strains $\varepsilon_{x'x'}$, $\varepsilon_{y'y'}$ and $\gamma_{x'y'}$ are determined from the strain equations of transformation as:

$$\varepsilon_{x'x'} = \frac{\varepsilon_{xx} + \varepsilon_{yy}}{2} + \frac{\varepsilon_{xx} - \varepsilon_{yy}}{2} \cos 2\theta + \frac{\gamma_{xy}}{2} \sin 2\theta$$

$$\varepsilon_{x'x'} = \left[\frac{450-200}{2} + \frac{450+200}{2} \cos 80^{\circ} + \frac{150}{2} \sin 80^{\circ}\right] \times 10^{-6} = 255.3 \times 10^{-6}$$

$$\frac{\gamma_{x'y'}}{2} = -\frac{\varepsilon_{xx} - \varepsilon_{yy}}{2} \sin 2\theta + \frac{\gamma_{xy}}{2} \cos 2\theta$$

$$\gamma_{x'y'} = [-(450+200)\sin 80^{\circ} + (150)\cos 80^{\circ}] \times 10^{-6} = -614.1 \times 10^{-6}$$

$$\varepsilon_{y'y'} = \frac{\varepsilon_{xx} + \varepsilon_{yy}}{2} - \frac{\varepsilon_{xx} - \varepsilon_{yy}}{2} \cos 2\theta - \frac{\gamma_{xy}}{2} \sin 2\theta$$

$$\varepsilon_{y'y'} = (\frac{450-200}{2} - \frac{450+200}{2} \cos 80^{\circ} - \frac{150}{2} \sin 80^{\circ}) \times 10^{-6} = -5.296 \times 10^{-6}$$

EXAMPLE 7.15

For the state of plane strain described in Example 7.14, determine the principal strains, the maximum shear strain and the planes upon which they act.

Solution:

The magnitudes of the principal strains are given by Eq. (7.56) as:

$$\varepsilon_{1,2} = C \pm R = \frac{\varepsilon_{xx} + \varepsilon_{yy}}{2} \pm \sqrt{\left(\frac{\varepsilon_{xx} - \varepsilon_{yy}}{2}\right)^2 + \left(\frac{\gamma_{xy}}{2}\right)^2}$$

$$\varepsilon_{1,2} = \left(\frac{450-200}{2} \pm \sqrt{\left(\frac{450+200}{2}\right)^2 + \left(\frac{150}{2}\right)^2}\right) \times 10^{-6} = \varepsilon_{1,2} = [125 \pm 333.54] \times 10^{-6}$$

$$\varepsilon_1 = 458.5 \times 10^{-6} \quad \text{and} \quad \varepsilon_2 = -208.5 \times 10^{-6}$$

The principal planes are given by Eq. (7.58) as:

$$\tan 2\theta_p = \frac{\gamma_{xy}}{\varepsilon_{xx} - \varepsilon_{yy}} = \frac{150}{450+200} = 0.2308$$

$$2\theta_p = 12.99^\circ \qquad \theta_p = 6.497^\circ$$

The maximum shear strain is given by Eq. (7.57) as:

$$\frac{\gamma_{Max}}{2} = R = \sqrt{\left(\frac{\varepsilon_{xx} - \varepsilon_{yy}}{2}\right)^2 + \left(\frac{\gamma_{xy}}{2}\right)^2} = \sqrt{\left(\frac{450+200}{2}\right)^2 + \left(\frac{150}{2}\right)^2} \times 10^{-6}$$

$$\frac{\gamma_{Max}}{2} = 333.5 \times 10^{-6} \qquad \gamma_{Max} = 667.1 \times 10^{-6}$$

The plane upon which the maximum shear strain acts is given by:

$$\theta_s = \theta_p \pm 45^\circ = 6.497^\circ \pm 45^\circ = 51.497^\circ \text{ or } -38.503^\circ$$

It is usually worth the time and effort to quickly check the results of a calculation by constructing Mohr's circle. The Mohr's circle for this state of strain is presented in Fig. E7.15.

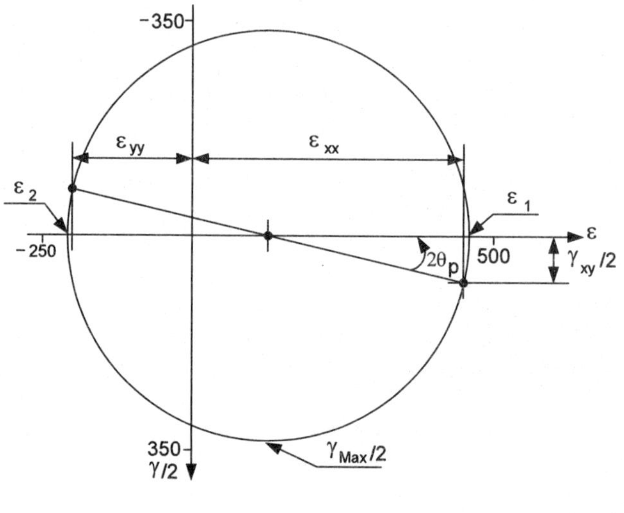

Fig. E7.15 Mohr's strain circle drawn to scale. Multiply strains shown by 10^{-6}.

7.8 DETERMINING PRINCIPAL STRESS WITH STRAIN GAGES

In the laboratory or the field, we usually measure strain with a metal foil resistor called a strain gage. The pattern of the resistor for a typical strain gage is shown in Fig. 7.18. A grid configuration is photoetched from the metallic foil to increase the resistance of the gage and to give the gage high directional sensitivity. Large tabs at each end of the metal foil conductors are provided to accommodate the lead wire connections. The foil is very thin (about 200 μ in.) and fragile; hence, it requires support to avoid damage in normal handling. This support is provided by a thin plastic carrier (illustrated in Fig. 7.18), which facilitates handling the gage.

To employ a strain gage, it is bonded to a mechanical member with an adhesive. The adhesive serves a vital function in the strain measuring system because it transmits the strain from the mechanical component to the gage-sensing element (the foil) without loss. The singularly unimpressive feat of adhesively bonding a strain gage to a mechanical component is one of the most critical steps in the entire process of measuring strain with a bonded resistance strain gage.

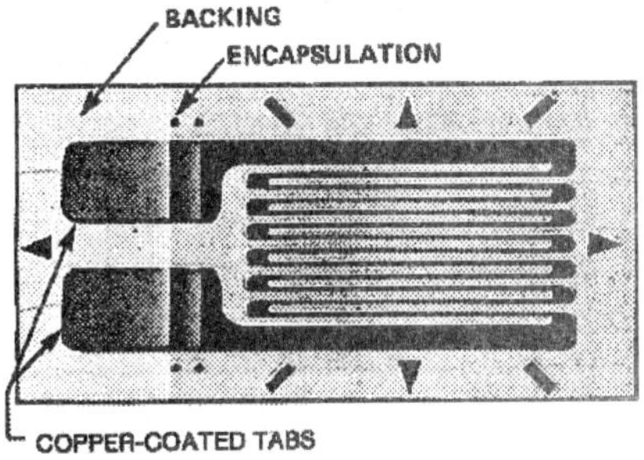

Fig. 7.18 A typical strain gage with a grid pattern and thin film plastic carrier.

A strain gage acts as a variable resistor when subjected to a surface strain in the direction of its grid elements. The relation between the change in resistance ΔR with the strain ε is given by:

$$\Delta R/R_0 = (R_f - R_0)/R_0 = (GF)\,\varepsilon_g \qquad (7.59)$$

where R_0 is the initial resistance of the gage, usually 120, 350 or 500 Ω (ohms).
R_f is the final resistance of the gage after the application of a strain ε.
GF is the gage factor or calibration constant for the gage, usually about 2.0.
ε_g is the strain in the direction of the gage axis.

A strain gage converts strain into a change in the electrical resistance ΔR. Because strains, in structural elements fabricated from common engineering materials, are small quantities (of the order of 10^{-3}), a Wheatstone bridge circuit is employed to transform the small change in resistance of the gage to a voltage that is proportional to the strain.

7.8.1 Determining Principal Stresses from Strain Measurements

In the analysis of certain structural elements, the directions of the principal stresses are known quantities. Consider axially loaded tension members or beams in bending where a uniaxial state of stress exists and $\sigma_{yy} = \tau_{xy} = 0$. In this case, the strain gage is oriented with its axis coincident with the x-axis of the structural element. Then the principal stress σ_1 is given by:

$$\sigma_1 = \sigma_{xx} = E\varepsilon_g \qquad \sigma_2 = \sigma_{yy} = 0 \qquad (7.60)$$

where ε_g is the strain measured in the x direction along the axis of the structural member.

Next, consider a spherical pressure vessel in which an isotropic state of stress exists, where $\sigma_{xx} = \sigma_{yy} = \sigma_1 = \sigma_2$ and $\tau_{xy} = 0$. In this case the strain gage can be mounted with its axis in any direction because all directions are principal. From Eq. (7.6) it is evident that the magnitude of the principal stresses is given by:

$$\sigma_{xx} = \sigma_{yy} = \sigma_1 = \sigma_2 = E\varepsilon_g/(1 - \nu) \qquad (7.61)$$

where ε_g is the strain measured in any direction in the isotropic stress field.

When less is known beforehand regarding the state of stress in the structural element, it is necessary to employ either two or three strain gages to establish the magnitude and directions of the principal stresses. If the structure has an axis of symmetry, the principal directions are known and the magnitude of the stresses can be determined from the output of two orthogonal strain gages that are mounted with their axes coincident with the axes of symmetry. In this case, the principal stresses are given by:

$$\sigma_1 = \frac{E}{1-\nu^2}(\varepsilon_1 + \nu\varepsilon_2)$$
$$\sigma_2 = \frac{E}{1-\nu^2}(\varepsilon_2 + \nu\varepsilon_1) \qquad (7.62)$$

Special strain gage configurations are available for measurements when either two or three strain determinations are required to establish the strain field. When the principal stress directions are known the two-element rectangular rosette shown in Fig. 7.19a is usually employed in measuring the two principal strains ε_1 and ε_2. When the principal stress directions are not known, there are three unknown quantities σ_1, σ_2 and θ_p. In this instance, a three-element strain gage rosette, illustrated in Fig. 7.19b, is employed to completely determine the stress or strain field.

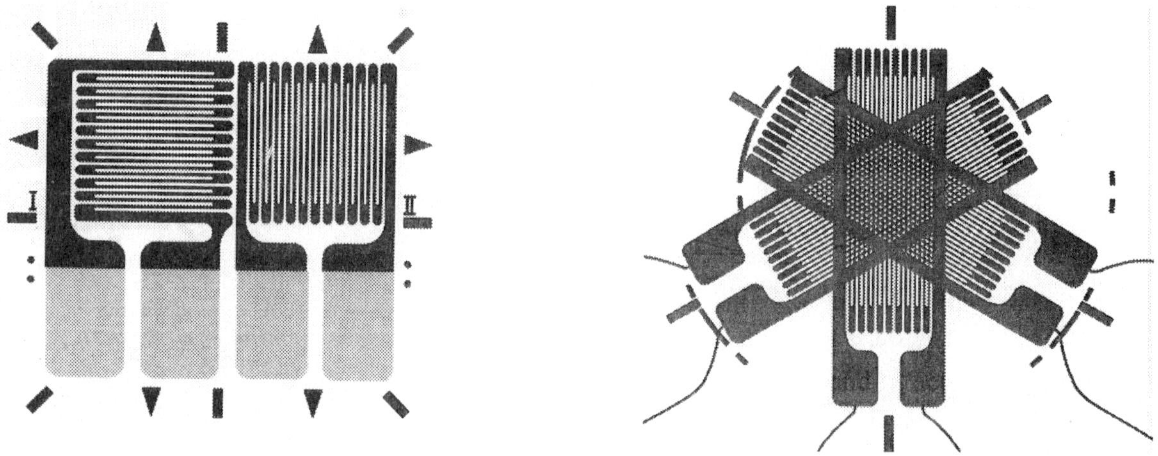

(a) (b)

Fig. 7.19 Two and three-element strain gage rosettes. Courtesy of Vishay Intertechnolgy, Inc., Malvern, PA.

7.8.2 Strain Gage Rosettes

In the most general situation, the directions of the principal stresses are not known prior to conducting an experimental analysis. Three element rosettes that provide three independent strain measurements are necessary in determining the three unknown quantities σ_1, σ_2 and θ_p. To show that three strain measurements are sufficient, consider three strain gages aligned along axes A, B and C as shown in Fig. 7.20.

If we recall the strain equation of transformation given by Eq. (7.50), we can write:

$$\varepsilon_A = \varepsilon_{xx}\cos^2\theta_A + \varepsilon_{yy}\sin^2\theta_A + \gamma_{xy}\cos\theta_A\sin\theta_A$$
$$\varepsilon_B = \varepsilon_{xx}\cos^2\theta_B + \varepsilon_{yy}\sin^2\theta_B + \gamma_{xy}\cos\theta_B\sin\theta_B \qquad (7.63)$$
$$\varepsilon_C = \varepsilon_{xx}\cos^2\theta_C + \varepsilon_{yy}\sin^2\theta_C + \gamma_{xy}\cos\theta_C\sin\theta_C$$

In practice, three-element rosettes with θ_A, θ_B and θ_C fixed at specified values are employed to provide sufficient data to establish the stress field. One of the most popular rosettes is the three-element rectangular rosette that is described in the following subsection.

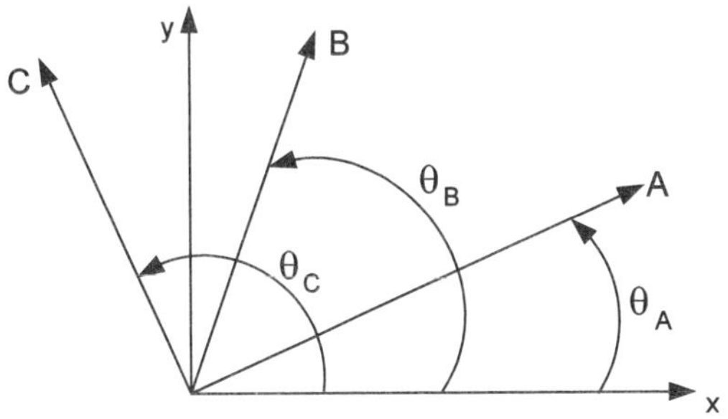

Fig. 7.20 Three strain gages placed at arbitrary angles relative to the x and y-axes.

The Three-Element Rectangular Rosette

The three-element rectangular rosette utilizes gages placed at 0°, 45° and 90° positions as indicated in Fig. 7.21. With this selection of θ_A, θ_B and θ_C, Eqs. (7.63) reduce to:

$$\varepsilon_A = \varepsilon_{xx} \qquad \varepsilon_B = \tfrac{1}{2}(\varepsilon_{xx} + \varepsilon_{yy} + \gamma_{xy}) \qquad \varepsilon_C = \varepsilon_{yy} \qquad (7.64)$$

From Eq. (7.64), it is clear that:

$$\gamma_{xy} = 2\varepsilon_B - \varepsilon_A - \varepsilon_C \qquad (7.65)$$

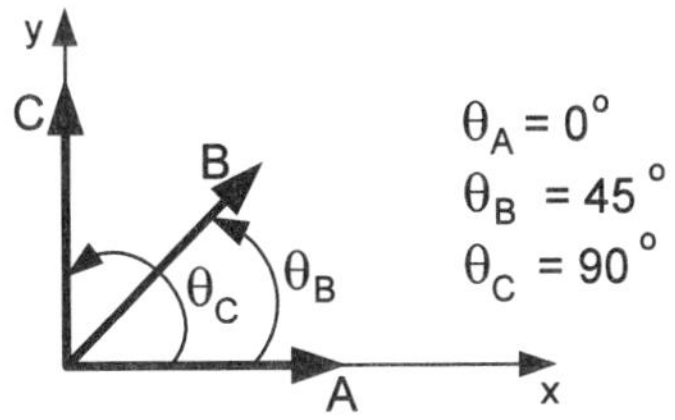

Fig. 7.21 Gage positions in a three-element rectangular rosette.

From Eqs. (7.64) and (7.65), we can determine the Cartesian components of strain from the measurements ε_A, ε_B and ε_C. Next, by employing Eq. (7.56), we write the expression for the principal strains as:

$$\varepsilon_{1,2} = \frac{\varepsilon_A + \varepsilon_C}{2} \pm \sqrt{\left(\frac{\varepsilon_A - \varepsilon_C}{2}\right)^2 + \left(\frac{2\varepsilon_B - \varepsilon_A - \varepsilon_C}{2}\right)^2} \qquad (7.66)$$

The principal angle is established from Eq. (7.58) as:

$$\tan 2\theta_p = \frac{(2\varepsilon_B - \varepsilon_A - \varepsilon_C)}{\varepsilon_A - \varepsilon_C} \qquad (7.67)$$

Finally, the expression for the principal stresses is derived by substituting Eq. (7.66) into Eq. (7.6) and simplifying to obtain:

$$\sigma_{1,2} = E\left[\frac{\varepsilon_A + \varepsilon_C}{2(1-\nu)} \pm \frac{1}{2(1+\nu)}\sqrt{(\varepsilon_A - \varepsilon_C)^2 + (2\varepsilon_B - \varepsilon_A - \varepsilon_C)^2}\right] \qquad (7.68)$$

By employing Eqs. (7.66) to (7.68) together with the results from the three-element rosette, we can determine the principal strains and stresses and the principal angles.

EXAMPLE 7.16

A two-element rectangular rosette is aligned with the principal stress directions. If the strain measurements are $\varepsilon_1 = 1{,}730 \times 10^{-6}$ and $\varepsilon_2 = -620 \times 10^{-6}$, determine the principal stresses. The structural element upon which the strain gages are mounted is fabricated from 1045 HR steel.

Solution:

The principal stresses can be determined from the principal strains by using Eq. (7.62) as:

$$\sigma_1 = \frac{E}{1-\nu^2}(\varepsilon_1 + \nu\varepsilon_2) = \frac{207\times 10^9}{1-(0.3)^2}[1{,}730 + (0.3)(-620)]\times 10^{-6} = 351.2 \text{ MPa}$$

$$\sigma_2 = \frac{E}{1-\nu^2}(\varepsilon_2 + \nu\varepsilon_1) = \frac{207\times 10^9}{1-(0.3)^2}[-620 + (0.3)(1{,}730)]\times 10^{-6} = -22.97 \text{ MPa}$$

EXAMPLE 7.17

A three-element rectangular rosette is mounted on a steel structure. The strain readings from each gage element are: $\varepsilon_A = 1{,}600 \times 10^{-6}$, $\varepsilon_B = 450 \times 10^{-6}$ and $\varepsilon_C = -525 \times 10^{-6}$. Determine the principal strains, the principal stresses and the principal angle.

Solution:

The principal stresses can be determined by substituting the strain gage readings into Eq. (7.66) to obtain:

$$\varepsilon_{1,2} = \frac{\varepsilon_A + \varepsilon_C}{2} \pm \sqrt{\left(\frac{\varepsilon_A - \varepsilon_C}{2}\right)^2 + \left(\frac{2\varepsilon_B - \varepsilon_A - \varepsilon_C}{2}\right)^2}$$

$$\varepsilon_{1,2} = \left(\frac{1{,}600 - 525}{2} \pm \sqrt{\left(\frac{1{,}600 + 525}{2}\right)^2 + \left(\frac{2(450) - 1{,}600 + 525}{2}\right)^2}\right)\times 10^{-6}$$

$$\varepsilon_{1,2} = [537.5 \pm 1{,}066.1]\times 10^{-6} \qquad \varepsilon_1 = 1{,}604\times 10^{-6} \qquad \varepsilon_2 = -528.6\times 10^{-6}$$

To determine the principal stresses, we will substitute the strain gage readings into Eq. (7.68) to obtain:

$$\sigma_{1,2} = E\left[\frac{\varepsilon_A + \varepsilon_C}{2(1-\nu)} \pm \frac{1}{2(1+\nu)}\sqrt{(\varepsilon_A - \varepsilon_C)^2 + (2\varepsilon_B - \varepsilon_A - \varepsilon_C)^2}\right]$$

$$\sigma_{1,2} = 30 \times 10^6\left[\frac{1{,}600 - 525}{2(1-0.3)} \pm \frac{1}{2(1+0.3)}\sqrt{(1{,}600+525)^2 + (2(450) - 1{,}600 + 525)^2}\right] \times 10^{-6}$$

$$\sigma_{1,2} = 23.04 \pm 24.60 \text{ ksi} \qquad \sigma_1 = 47.64 \text{ ksi} \qquad \sigma_2 = -1.56 \text{ ksi}$$

Finally, the principal angle is determined from Eq. (7.67) as:

$$\tan 2\theta_p = \frac{(2\varepsilon_B - \varepsilon_A - \varepsilon_C)}{\varepsilon_A - \varepsilon_C} = \frac{(2(450) - 1{,}600 + 525)}{1{,}600 + 525} = -0.08235$$

$$2\theta_p = -4.708^\circ \qquad \theta_p = -2.354^\circ$$

The minus sign associated with θ_p indicates that the principal element is rotated clockwise relative to the Oxy coordinate system.

7.9 COMBINED LOADING

In most structures fabricated from beams, struts and columns, a single type of load such as an axial or transverse force or a bending moment produces the stresses. However, in the design of vehicles or machines, it is common to encounter two or more different types of loads acting on a machine component. For example, shafts that transmit power are subjected to torsion and transverse forces that produce internal bending moments and shear forces. When dealing with components subjected to two or three different types of loading, locating the point of maximum normal or shear stresses is often difficult. In addition when stresses are due to two or more different types of load, determining the combined stress at a given point must be accomplished with care. A guide to assist you in dealing with both of these difficulties is given below:

1. The bending stress is a maximum at a point located the maximum distance from the neutral axis of the beam.
2. The bending stress is a maximum at a point where the bending moment M is a maximum, which coincides with the location where the shear force V is zero.
3. The transverse and longitudinal shear stresses are equal and a maximum at a point located at the neutral axis of the beam where the first moment of the area Q is also a maximum.
4. The transverse and longitudinal shear stresses are a maximum at a point where the shear force V is a maximum, which occurs at a point of application of a transverse load.
5. The shear stress due to torsion is a maximum at the point on the shaft where the torsion loading T is a maximum.
6. The maximum shear stress on a shaft occurs on its outside surface.

Even with these guides, the location of the maximum stress is not apparent. In many analyses, it is necessary to evaluate the stresses at several points to discover the most critical location. When two or more normal stresses or shear stresses act on the same plane, they can be added together using the method of superposition providing the combined value does not exceed the yield strength of the material. However, when the stresses act on mutually orthogonal planes, appropriate stress equations of transformation must be used to determine the maximum principal and shear stresses.

Let's consider three examples to demonstrate the procedure for performing this type of analysis.

EXAMPLE 7.18

A U shaped machine component, illustrated in Fig. E7.18, is subjected to opposing forces of F = 15 kN. If the component is fabricated from 1045 HR steel, determine the safety factor based on yield strength using the maximum normal stress theory. Comment on the appropriateness of this theory to predict the onset of yielding for this example.

Fig. E7.18

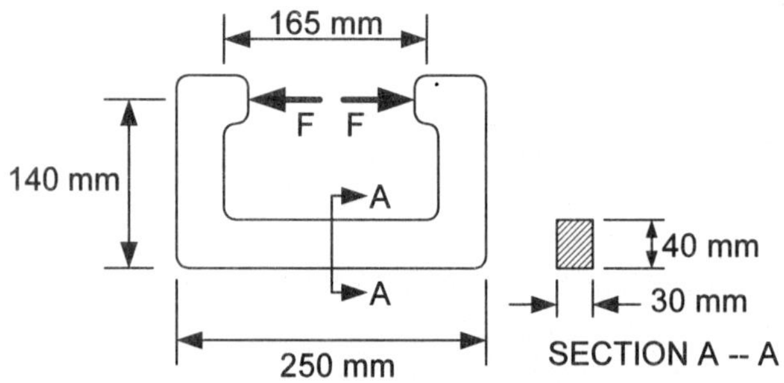

Solution:

Let's begin the analysis by constructing the FBD of the left side of the U shaped member, as shown in Fig. E 7.18a.

Fig. E7.18a

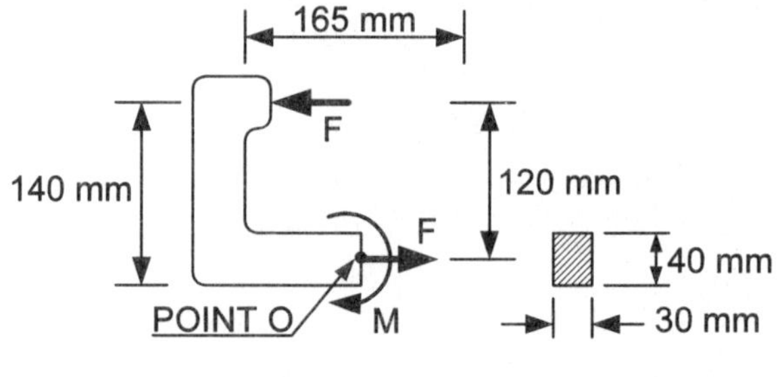

It is evident from the equilibrium relation $\Sigma F_x = 0$, that P = F = 15 kN. This internal force produces a uniformly distributed axial stress σ_{xx} that is given by:

$$\sigma_{xx} = P/A = (15 \times 10^3)/1{,}200 = 12.50 \text{ MPa} \qquad \text{(a)}$$

The equilibrium relation for the moments about the point O gives:

$$\Sigma M_o = 0 \qquad 120F - M = 0 \qquad M = (120)(15 \times 10^3) = 180 \times 10^4 \text{ N-mm} \qquad \text{(b)}$$

The moment M produces a bending stress σ_{xx} that is linearly distributed over the cross section of the component at section A-A. The maximum and minimum bending stresses are given by:

$$\sigma_{xx} = \pm\, Mc/I = \pm\, 6M/bh^2 \qquad \text{(c)}$$

Substituting the results from Eq. (b) into Eq. (c) yields:

$$\sigma_{xx} = \pm\frac{(6)(180\times 10^4)}{(30)(40)^2} = \pm\ 225\ \text{MPa} \qquad \text{(d)}$$

The stresses due to P and M both act on the same plane and are in the x direction; hence, the results can be superimposed to give:

$$\sigma_{Max} = 12.5 + 225 = 237.5\ \text{MPa} \qquad \sigma_{Min} = 12.5 - 225 = -\,212.5\ \text{MPa} \qquad \text{(e)}$$

The superposition process and the resulting distribution of stresses across the section A-A is presented in Fig. 7.18b.

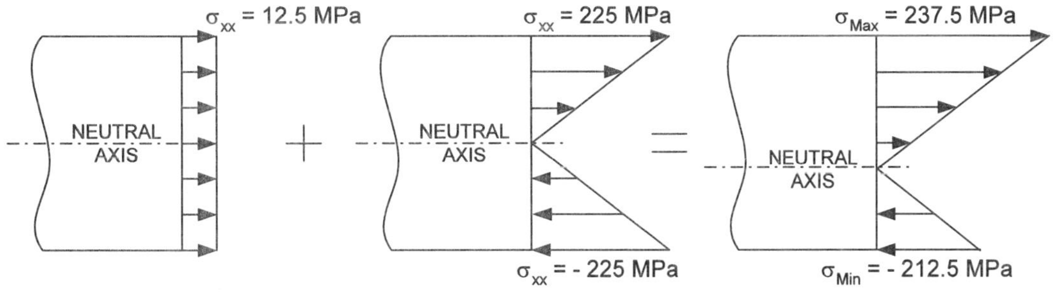

Fig. E7.18b

From Appendix B-2, we determine that S_y = 414 MPa for 1045 HR steel. The maximum normal stress theory for yielding indicates that the onset for yielding occurs when $\sigma_{Max} \geq S_y$. Accordingly the safety factor is determined from:

$$SF = S_y/\sigma_{Max} = 414/237.5 = 1.743$$

The maximum normal stress theory is appropriate in this case because $\sigma_2 = \sigma_3 = 0$. For a uniaxial state of stress, all three of the failure theories described in this chapter predict yielding to occur when $\sigma_{Max} \geq S_y$.

We note that the safety factor is less than 2.0 and warn the design engineer of this fact.

EXAMPLE 7.19

The design engineer responsible for the U shaped machine component, described in Example 7.18, must drill a hole 6 mm in diameter through the member at Section A-A to permit passage of a signal wire. She knows that the hole should pass through the neutral axis to minimize its effects on the maximum stresses and the safety factor. She also is aware that the neutral axis has shifted and requests that you locate it.

Solution:

We locate the position of the neutral axis by using the similar triangles depicted in Fig. E7.18b. Let's redraw the two triangles and define the location of the neutral axis relative to the bottom edge of the U shaped member as illustrated in Fig. E7.19.

Fig. E7.19

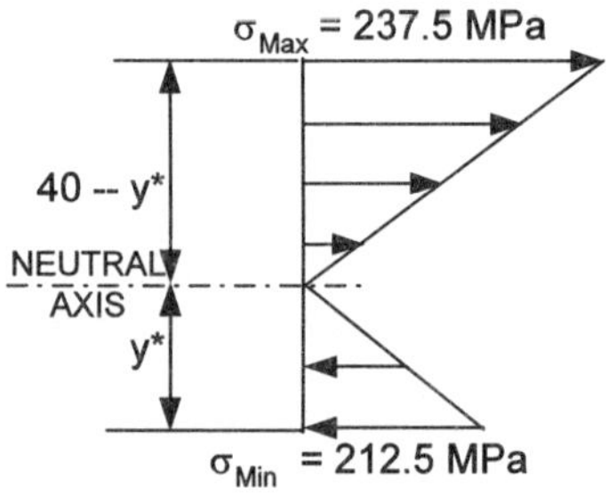

From the proportionality of similar triangles, we write:

$$\frac{y^*}{212.5} = \frac{40 - y^*}{237.5} \qquad \text{(a)}$$

$$y^* = 18.89 \text{ mm} \qquad \text{(b)}$$

You also indicate that drilling a 6 mm hole at the neutral axis will elevate the stresses slightly and reduce the safety factor.

EXAMPLE 7.20

A traffic sign along a city street is cantilevered from a pole as illustrated in Fig. E7.20. The pressure due to the wind impinging on the sign is uniformly distributed over its area and equal to 15 lb/ft^2 in the x direction. The pole is fabricated from a tube with a 12 in. outside diameter and a 0.25 in. wall thickness. Determine the stresses at points A and B located at the base of the pole.

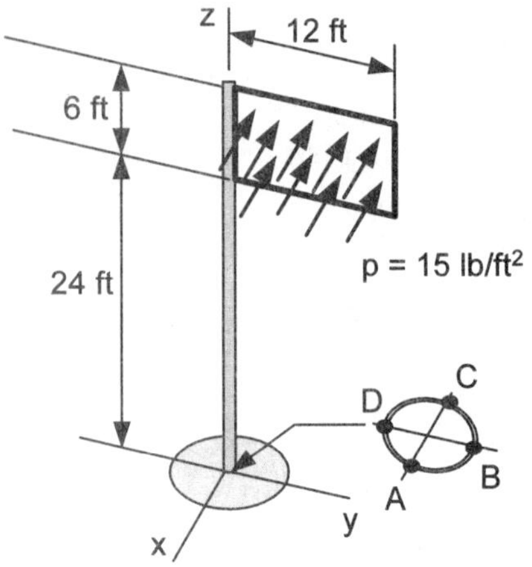

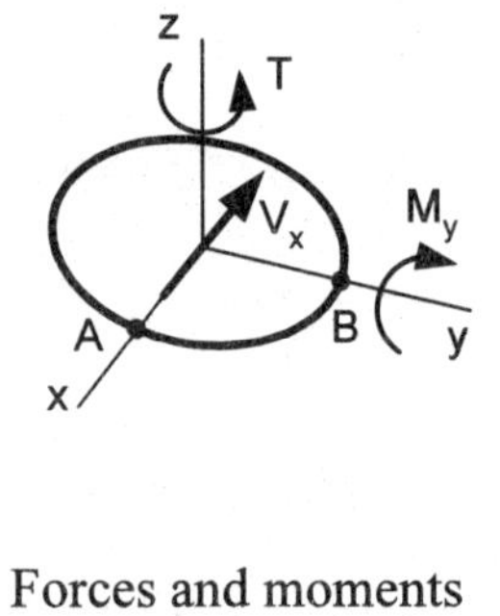

Forces and moments at the base

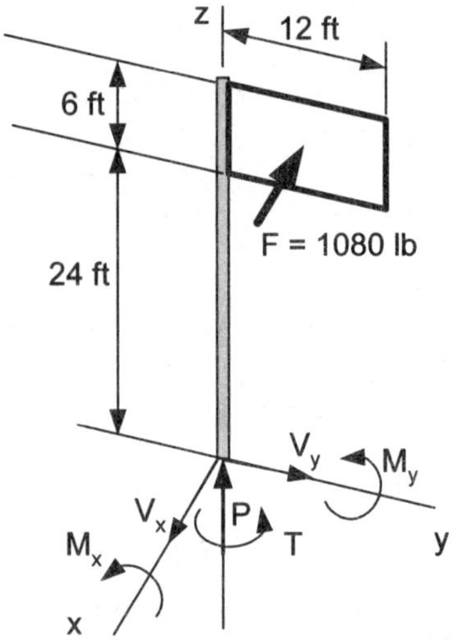

Wind pressure acting on the sign.

Fig. E7.20

Solution:

The effective force due to the wind pressure acts at the center of the sign and is given by:

$$F_x = pA = (15)(6)(12) = 1{,}080 \text{ lb} \qquad (a)$$

Next let's prepare a FBD showing the forces at the base of the pole as indicated in Fig. E7.20. Then we write the six equations of equilibrium to obtain:

$$\Sigma F_x = 0 \qquad V_x = 1{,}080 \text{ lb} \qquad (b)$$

$$\Sigma F_y = 0 \qquad V_y = 0 \qquad (c)$$

$$\Sigma F_z = 0 \qquad P = 0 \qquad (d)$$

$$\Sigma M_x = 0 \qquad M_x = 0 \qquad (e)$$

$$\Sigma M_y = 0 \qquad M_y = (1{,}080)(27) = 29{,}160 \text{ ft-lb} \qquad (f)$$

$$\Sigma M_z = 0 \qquad T = -(1{,}080)(6) = -6{,}480 \text{ ft-lb} \qquad (g)$$

Gravitational forces have been neglected in this analysis. The geometric parameters that are needed to determine the stresses at the base of the pole are:

$$A = (\pi/4)(d_o^2 - d_i^2) = (\pi/4)[(12)^2 - (11.5)^2] = 9.228 \text{ in}^2. \qquad (h)$$

$$I = I_{xx} = I_{yy} = (\pi/64)(d_o^4 - d_i^4) = (\pi/64)[(12)^4 - (11.5)^4] = 159.3 \text{ in.}^4 \qquad (i)$$

$$J = 2I = 318.7 \text{ in.}^4 \qquad (j)$$

$$r = c = 6.0 \text{ in.} \qquad (k)$$

For circular shafts or tubes it can be shown that Q is given by:

$$Q = (2/3)/(r_o^3 - r_i^3) \qquad (l)$$

$$Q = (2/3)/[(6.0)^3 - (5.75)^3] = 17.26 \text{ in.}^3 \qquad (m)$$

Let's determine the stresses due to the three internal forces M_y, V_x and T and, in the process, use the geometric parameters listed above.

$$\sigma_{zz} = M_y c/I = (29{,}160)(12)(6)/159.3 = 13{,}180 \text{ psi} \qquad (n)$$

$$\tau_T = Tr/J = (6{,}480)(12)(6)/318.7 = 1{,}464 \text{ psi} \qquad (o)$$

$$\tau_{Vx} = (V_x Q)/(It) = [(1{,}080)(17.26)]/[(159.3)(2)(0.25)] = 234.0 \text{ psi} \qquad (p)$$

Consider point A, which is on the tension side of the pole, and show the stresses on an elemental volume removed from the annular ring at the base of the pole.

$$(\sigma_{zz})_A = \sigma_{zz} = 13{,}180 \text{ psi} \qquad \text{(q)}$$

$$(\tau_T)_A = \tau_T = 1{,}464 \text{ psi} \qquad \text{(r)}$$

$$(\tau_{Vx})_A = 0 \qquad \text{(s)}$$

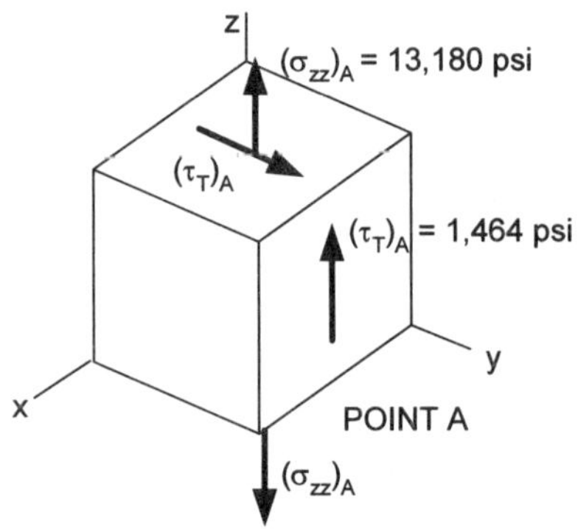

Fig. E7.20b

For point A, only the shear stress (τ_T) due to the torque appears and it acts in the + y direction. The shear stress (τ_{Vx}) due to the shear force V_x does not appear because of the location of point A. Recall from the analysis of beams that the shear stress due to transverse loadings was a maximum at the neutral axis and zero at the top and bottom edges of the beam. For the shear force V_X, point A is at the top edge of the cross section; hence, $\tau_{Vx})_A$ = 0.

Finally consider point B, which is on the neutral axis of the pole and show the stresses on an elemental volume removed from the annular ring at the base of the pole.

$$(\sigma_{zz})_B = 0 \qquad \text{(t)}$$

$$(\tau)_B = -\tau_T - \tau_{Vx} = (-1{,}464 - 234)$$

$$(\tau)_B = -1{,}698 \text{ psi} \qquad \text{(u)}$$

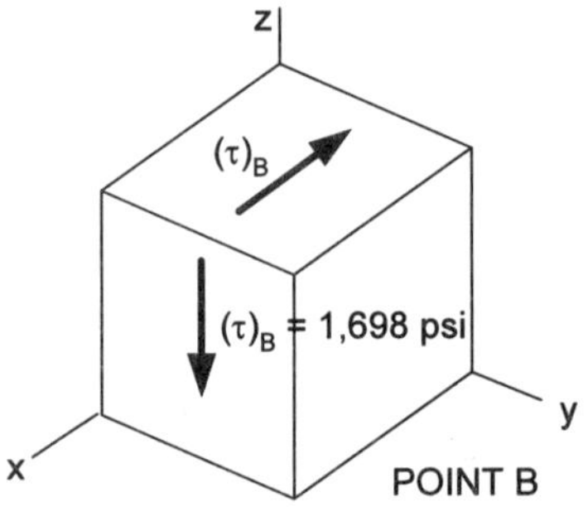

Fig. E7.20c

For point B, the normal stress component $(\sigma_{zz})_A$ vanishes because point B is located on the y-axis, which acts as the neutral axis for M_y. Also both shear stress components are present and algebraically sum because they both act in the same direction (– x axis).

EXAMPLE 7.21

A machine component is fabricated from a tube that has been formed into a 90° bend as illustrated in Fig. E7.21. The outside diameter of the tube is 50 mm and its inside diameter is 40 mm. A design engineer wants to place an access hole in the tube at a location 150 mm from its base and is concerned with the possibility of failure by doing so. He requests you to determine the maximum principal stress and the maximum shear stress at point A at this elevation on the tube. A problem is included at the end of this chapter to determine the same quantities at point B.

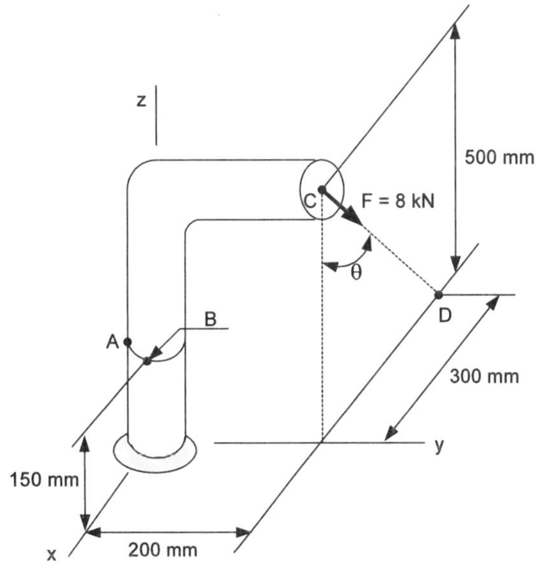

Fig. E7.21

Solution:

Let's first determine the angle θ and resolve the force **F** into its components F_x and F_z.

$$\theta = \tan^{-1}(300/500) = 30.96° \qquad \text{(a)}$$

$$F_x = F \sin\theta = 8 \sin(30.96°) = 4.116 \text{ kN} \qquad \text{(b)}$$

$$F_z = F \cos\theta = 8 \cos(30.96°) = 6.860 \text{kN} \qquad \text{(c)}$$

Next prepare a FBD of the segment of the tube with a section cut at the 150 mm elevation as shown in Fig. E7.21a.

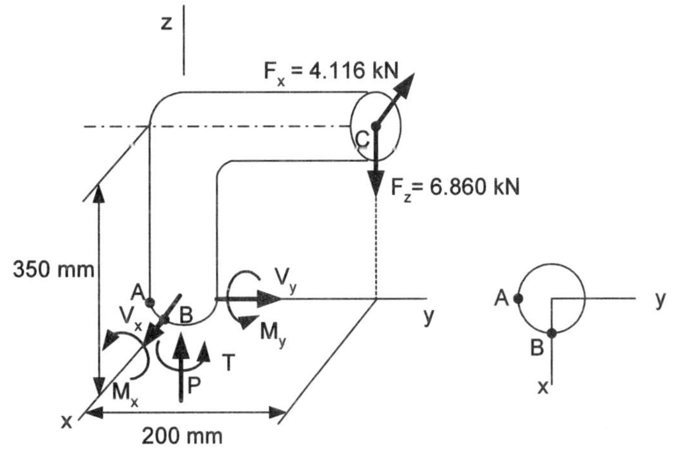

Fig. E7.21a

Let's use this FBD together with the equilibrium relations to determine the internal forces at the section cut.

$\Sigma F_x = 0$ $\quad V_x = 4.116$ kN (d)

$\Sigma F_y = 0$ $\quad V_y = 0$ (e)

$\Sigma F_z = 0$ $\quad P = 6.860$ kN (f)

$\Sigma M_x = 0$ $\quad M_x = (6.860 \times 10^3)(0.200) = 1{,}372$ N-m (g)

$\Sigma M_y = 0$ $\quad M_y = (4.116 \times 10^3)(0.350) = 1{,}441$ N-m (h)

$\Sigma M_z = 0$ $\quad T = -(4.116 \times 10^3)(0.200) = -823.2$ N-m (i)

The geometric parameters that are needed to determine the stresses at points A and B are:

$A = (\pi/4)(d_o^2 - d_i^2) = (\pi/4)[(50)^2 - (40)^2] = 706.9 \text{ mm}^2.$ (j)

$I = I_{xx} = I_{yy} = (\pi/64)(d_o^4 - d_i^4) = (\pi/64)[(50)^4 - (40)^4] = 181.1 \times 10^3 \text{ mm}^4$ (k)

$J = 2I = 362.2 \times 10^3 \text{ mm}^4$ (l)

$r = c = 25$ mm (m)

$Q = (2/3)(r_o^3 - r^{i3}) = (2/3)[(25)^3 - (20)^3] = 5{,}083 \text{ mm}^3$ (n)

Let's determine the stresses at point A due to the five internal forces P, M_x, M_y, V_x and T. In the process, we will use the geometric parameters listed above.

$\sigma_{zz} = P/A = (6{,}860)/706.9 = 9.704$ MPa (compressive) (o)

$\sigma_{zz} = M_x c/I = (1{,}372 \times 10^3)(25)/(181.1 \times 10^3) = 189.4$ MPa (p)

$\sigma_{zz} = M_y y/I = 0$ because $y = 0$ (q)

$\sigma_{xx} = \sigma_{yy} = 0$ (r)

$(\sigma_{zz})_{Total} = 189.4 - 9.704 = 179.7$ MPa (s)

$\tau_T = Tr/J = (823.2 \times 10^3)(25)/(362.2 \times 10^3) = 56.82$ MPa (t)

$\tau_{Vx} = (V_x Q)/(It) = [(4.116 \times 10^3)(5{,}083)]/[(181.1 \times 10^3)(10)] = 11.55$ MPa (u)

$(\tau)_{Total} = \tau_T - \tau_{Vx} = 56.82 - 11.55 = 45.27$ MPa (v)

Before proceeding to determine the principal stresses and the maximum shear stress, let's draw an element removed from the tube at point A as shown in Fig. E7.21b. Let's also examine a two-dimensional element representing the x-z plane at point A.

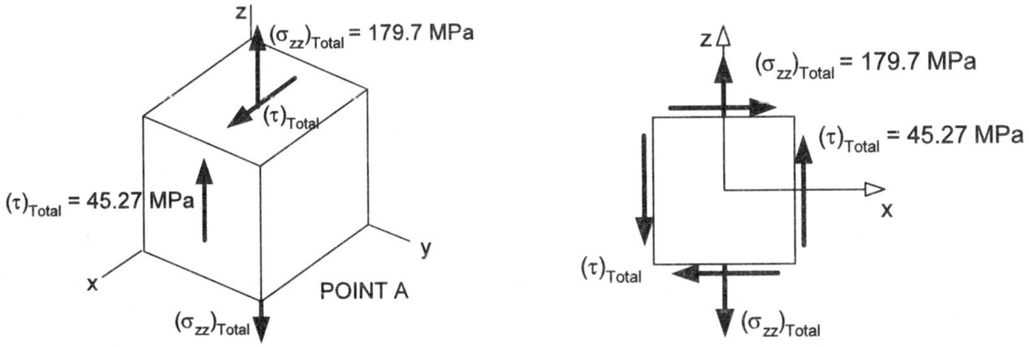

Fig. E 7.21b

The principal stresses are given by:

$$\sigma_{\text{Max, Min}} = \frac{\sigma_{xx} + \sigma_{zz}}{2} \pm \sqrt{\left(\left(\frac{\sigma_{xx} - \sigma_{zz}}{2}\right)^2 + \tau_{xz}^2\right)} \qquad \text{(w)}$$

$$\sigma_{\text{Max, Min}} = \frac{0 + 179.7}{2} \pm \sqrt{\left(\left(\frac{0 - 179.7}{2}\right)^2 + (45.27)^2\right)} = 89.85 \pm 100.6 \text{ MPa} \qquad \text{(x)}$$

$$\sigma_{Max} = 190.5 \text{ MPa} \qquad \sigma_{Min} = -\ 10.75 \text{ MPa} \qquad \text{(y)}$$

The maximum shear stress is given by:

$$\tau_{\text{Max}} = \sqrt{\left(\left(\frac{\sigma_{xx} - \sigma_{zz}}{2}\right)^2 + \tau_{xz}^2\right)} = \sqrt{\left(\left(\frac{0 - 179.7}{2}\right)^2 + (45.25)^2\right)} = 100.6 \text{ MPa} \qquad \text{(z)}$$

7.10 SUMMARY

In earlier chapters, we considered only uniaxial states of stress that occurred in tension members and beams. In this chapter multi-dimensional states of stress were introduced, which gave rise to nine Cartesian components of stress. However, we used equilibrium conditions to show a relation among the six shear stresses that is given below. This relation reduced the number of unique Cartesian components of stress to six.

$$\tau_{xy} = \tau_{yx} \qquad \tau_{yz} = \tau_{zy} \qquad \tau_{xz} = \tau_{zx} \qquad (7.1)$$

For the three-dimensional state of stress, Hooke's law must be generalized to give the stress-strain relations presented in Eq. (7.3).

$$\sigma_{xx} = \frac{E}{(1+\nu)(1-2\nu)}\left[(1-\nu)\varepsilon_{xx} + \nu(\varepsilon_{yy}+\varepsilon_{zz})\right]$$
$$\sigma_{yy} = \frac{E}{(1+\nu)(1-2\nu)}\left[(1-\nu)\varepsilon_{yy} + \nu(\varepsilon_{zz}+\varepsilon_{xx})\right] \qquad (7.3)$$
$$\sigma_{zz} = \frac{E}{(1+\nu)(1-2\nu)}\left[(1-\nu)\varepsilon_{zz} + \nu(\varepsilon_{xx}+\varepsilon_{yy})\right]$$
$$\tau_{xy} = G\gamma_{xy} \qquad \tau_{yz} = G\gamma_{yz} \qquad \tau_{xz} = G\gamma_{xz}$$

The geometric and loading conditions for plane stress were introduced and the stress strain relations for plane stress were written as:

$$\sigma_{xx} = \frac{E}{(1-\nu^2)}\left(\varepsilon_{xx} + \nu\varepsilon_{yy}\right)$$
$$\sigma_{yy} = \frac{E}{(1-\nu^2)}\left(\varepsilon_{yy} + \nu\varepsilon_{xx}\right) \qquad (7.6)$$
$$\tau_{xy} = G\gamma_{xy}$$

The equations of stress transformation were derived to provide expressions for $\sigma_{x'x'}$, $\sigma_{y'y'}$ and $\tau_{x'y'}$ in terms of σ_{xx}, σ_{yy} and τ_{xy}.

$$\sigma_{x'x'} = \frac{\sigma_{xx}+\sigma_{yy}}{2} + \frac{\sigma_{xx}-\sigma_{yy}}{2}\cos 2\theta + \tau_{xy}\sin 2\theta$$
$$\sigma_{y'y'} = \frac{\sigma_{xx}+\sigma_{yy}}{2} - \frac{\sigma_{xx}-\sigma_{yy}}{2}\cos 2\theta - \tau_{xy}\sin 2\theta \qquad (7.11)$$
$$\tau_{x'y'} = -\frac{\sigma_{xx}-\sigma_{yy}}{2}\sin 2\theta + \tau_{xy}\cos 2\theta$$

After establishing the stress equations of transformation, we showed that the principal stresses were given by:

$$\sigma_{Max,\,Min} = \frac{\sigma_{xx}+\sigma_{yy}}{2} + \frac{\sigma_{xx}-\sigma_{yy}}{2}\cos 2\theta_p + \tau_{xy}\sin 2\theta_p$$
$$\sigma_{Max,\,Min} = \frac{\sigma_{xx}+\sigma_{yy}}{2} \pm \sqrt{\left(\left(\frac{\sigma_{xx}-\sigma_{yy}}{2}\right)^2 + \tau_{xy}^2\right)} \qquad (7.15)$$

Also, we showed that the principal planes were located at θ_p:

$$\tan 2\theta_p = \frac{2\tau_{xy}}{\sigma_{xx}-\sigma_{yy}} \qquad (7.13)$$

In a similar manner, we derived the relation for the maximum shear stress and the location of the plane θ_s upon which this stress acts as:

$$\tau_{Max} = \sqrt{\left(\left(\frac{\sigma_{xx} - \sigma_{yy}}{2}\right)^2 + \tau_{xy}^2\right)} \qquad (7.18)$$

$$\tan 2\theta_s = -\frac{\sigma_{xx} - \sigma_{yy}}{2\tau_{xy}} \qquad (7.16)$$

A graphical technique, Mohr's circle, was described for visualizing the variation in the Cartesian components of stress with the angle of the plane upon which these stresses act. Examples were presented demonstrating the use of Mohr's circle for determining principal stresses, principal planes and maximum shear stresses.

Three different failure theories were introduced including:

1. The maximum principal stress theory.
2. The maximum shear stress theory.
3. The maximum distortional energy theory.

The maximum principal stress theory indicates that yielding occurs when:

$$|\sigma_1| \geq S_y \qquad |\sigma_2| \geq S_y \qquad (7.29)$$

The maximum shear stress theory indicates yielding occurs when:

$$|\sigma_1 - \sigma_2| \geq S_y \qquad \text{Opposite sign stresses} \qquad (7.32)$$

$$|\sigma_1| \geq S_y \qquad \text{Same sign stresses} \qquad (7.34)$$

The maximum distortional energy theory indicates yielding occurs when:

$$(\sigma_1/S_y)^2 - (\sigma_1/S_y)(\sigma_2/S_y) + (\sigma_2/S_y)^2 \geq 1 \qquad (7.37)$$

The maximum distortional energy theory is widely accepted as the most accurate method for determining the onset of yielding in ductile materials commonly used to fabricate structural element and machine components.

Equations for the stresses in thin-walled pressure vessels were derived. For spherical pressure vessels the stress state is isotropic with $\sigma_1 = \sigma_2$.

$$\sigma_1 = \sigma_2 = \sigma_{my} = \sigma_{mx} = pr/2t \qquad (7.41)$$

For cylindrical pressure vessels, it was shown that the hoop stress σ_h and axial stress σ_a are given by:

$$\sigma_h = pr/t \qquad (7.42)$$

$$\sigma_a = pr/2t \qquad (7.43)$$

The strain equations of transformation were also derived. While the derivation was based only on geometric considerations, the results obtained were very similar to the equations of transformation for stresses. You will note the similarity between Eqs. (7.53) and Eqs. (7.10).

$$\begin{aligned}
\varepsilon_{x'x'} &= \frac{\varepsilon_{xx}+\varepsilon_{yy}}{2} + \frac{\varepsilon_{xx}-\varepsilon_{yy}}{2}\cos 2\theta + \frac{\gamma_{xy}}{2}\sin 2\theta \\
\varepsilon_{y'y'} &= \frac{\varepsilon_{xx}+\varepsilon_{yy}}{2} - \frac{\varepsilon_{xx}-\varepsilon_{yy}}{2}\cos 2\theta - \frac{\gamma_{xy}}{2}\sin 2\theta \\
\frac{\gamma_{x'y'}}{2} &= -\frac{\varepsilon_{xx}-\varepsilon_{yy}}{2}\sin 2\theta + \frac{\gamma_{xy}}{2}\cos 2\theta
\end{aligned} \qquad (7.53)$$

Principal strains and the planes upon which principal strains act were also described and equations provided for their determination.

Strain gages were introduced as a method for experimentally determining stresses from gage measurements. A strain gage acts as a variable resistor and undergoes a change in resistance when subjected to strain. This change in resistance is related to strain by:

$$\Delta R/R_0 = (R_f - R_0)/R_0 = (GF)\,\varepsilon_g \qquad (7.59)$$

The number of strain gages required for determining the stress at a point depends on the number of unknown quantities. For uniaxial states of stress, a single gage is sufficient. For biaxial states of stress, two gages are sufficient if the principal directions are known. However, for a biaxial state of stress, three gages are required when the directions of the principal stresses are not known. The three strain measurements are made with a three-element strain gage rosette with three strain gages oriented at angles θ_A, θ_B and θ_C. The readings from the gages are related to the Cartesian components of strain by:

$$\begin{aligned}
\varepsilon_A &= \varepsilon_{xx}\cos^2\theta_A + \varepsilon_{yy}\sin^2\theta_A + \gamma_{xy}\cos\theta_A\sin\theta_A \\
\varepsilon_B &= \varepsilon_{xx}\cos^2\theta_B + \varepsilon_{yy}\sin^2\theta_B + \gamma_{xy}\cos\theta_B\sin\theta_B \\
\varepsilon_C &= \varepsilon_{xx}\cos^2\theta_C + \varepsilon_{yy}\sin^2\theta_C + \gamma_{xy}\cos\theta_C\sin\theta_C
\end{aligned} \qquad (7.63)$$

A three-element strain gage rosette is made with gages oriented with $\theta = 0°$, $\theta = 45°$ and $\theta = 90°$. Strain measurements from these three gages give the principal stresses and the principal planes as:

$$\sigma_{1,2} = E\left[\frac{\varepsilon_A+\varepsilon_C}{2(1-\nu)} \pm \frac{1}{2(1+\nu)}\sqrt{(\varepsilon_A-\varepsilon_C)^2+(2\varepsilon_B-\varepsilon_A-\varepsilon_C)^2}\right] \qquad (7.68)$$

$$\tan 2\theta_p = \frac{(2\varepsilon_B - \varepsilon_A - \varepsilon_C)}{\varepsilon_A - \varepsilon_C} \qquad (7.67)$$

Finally, a section on stresses due to combined loading of machine components was presented. While no new equations were derived in this section, several examples were included to demonstrate the method of superposition of stresses and combining shear and normal stresses.

PROBLEMS

7.1 A three-dimensional stress state is defined by six Cartesian components of stress listed in the table below. Determine the state of strain, if the body is made from the material specified.

Prob. No.	σ_{xx}	σ_{yy}	σ_{zz}	τ_{xy}	τ_{yz}	τ_{zx}	Material
7.1a	13 ksi	18 ksi	−11.50 ksi	19 ksi	10.4 ksi	−12.85 ksi	Steel
7.1b	90 MPa	– 51MPa	77MPa	45 MPa	– 58 MPa	46 MPa	Aluminum
7.1c	11 ksi	– 11 ksi	6.4 ksi	9.5 ksi	– 8.9 ksi	7.6 ksi	Titanium
7.1d	64 MPa	78MPa	– 52MPa	– 47MPa	33MPa	– 29MPa	Brass
7.1e	18 ksi	24 ksi	– 15 ksi	22 ksi	– 13 ksi	– 19 ksi	Nickel Alloy
7.1f	−95 MPa	84 MPa	– 68 MPa	52 MPa	– 27 MPa	54 MPa	Stainless St.

7.2 A three-dimensional strain state is defined by six Cartesian components of strain listed in the table below. Determine the state of stress, if the body is made from the material specified.

Prob. No.	$\varepsilon_{xx} \times 10^{-6}$	$\varepsilon_{yy} \times 10^{-6}$	$\varepsilon_{zz} \times 10^{-6}$	$\gamma_{xy} \times 10^{-6}$	$\gamma_{yz} \times 10^{-6}$	$\gamma_{zx} \times 10^{-6}$	Material
7.2a	600	– 600	– 450	650	– 800	– 650	Steel
7.2b	1150	– 1025	725	865	– 875	1225	Aluminum
7.2c	– 450	– 625	345	– 421	322	– 374	Titanium
7.2d	354	425	298	223	305	– 112	Brass
7.2e	– 453	524	– 426	– 385	– 296	333	Nickel Alloy
7.2f	– 294	– 439	388	251	274	– 115	Stainless St.

7.3 The stresses on the external surface of a cylindrical pressure vessel, in the hoop and axial directions, are predicted to be σ_h and σ_a when the vessel is subjected to a pressure p. If two strain gages are placed on the pressure vessel to measure the strains in the hoop and axial directions, predict the strains that are expected to occur at this pressure. The pressure vessel is fabricated from material specified in the table below.

Prob. No.	σ_h	σ_a	p	Material
7.3a	30 ksi	15 ksi	105 psi	Steel
7.3b	140 MPa	70 MPa	700 kPa	Stainless steel
7.3c	22 ksi	11 ksi	195 psi	Aluminum
7.3d	200 MPa	100 MPa	900 kPa	Titanium
7.3e	34 ksi	17 ksi	95 psi	Steel

7.4 A plane state of stress at a point is represented by a small elemental area ΔA as shown in Fig. P7.4. The stresses are σ_{xx} = 18 ksi, σ_{yy} = 24 ksi and τ_{xy} = – 15 ksi. Determine the stresses $\sigma_{x'x'}$, $\sigma_{y'y'}$ and $\tau_{x'y'}$ on an element that is rotated (a) + 25° and (b) – 35° degrees (counterclockwise is positive) relative to the element shown in this figure.

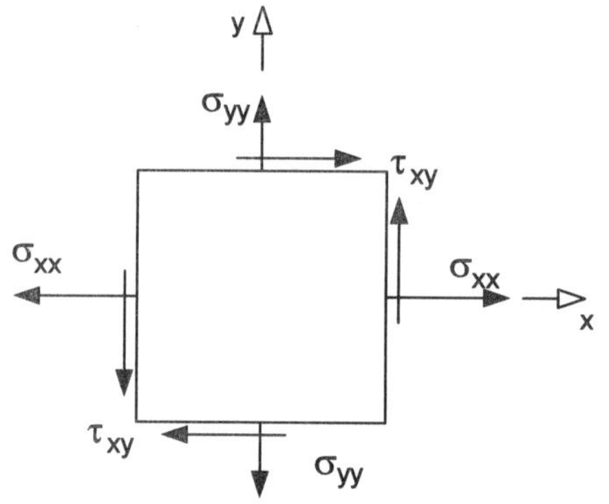

Fig. P7.4

7.5 Consider a point, shown in Fig. P7.4, as an elemental area ΔA with Cartesian components of stress σ_{xx} = 21 ksi, σ_{yy} = – 28 ksi and τ_{xy} = – 19 ksi. Determine the orientation of the principal planes and the stresses that act on these planes. Also determine the maximum shear stress, the corresponding normal stress, and the planes upon which they act.

7.6 Repeat Problem 7.5 for the following stress state: σ_{xx} = 110 MPa, σ_{yy} = – 75 MPa and τ_{xy} = 25 MPa. Determine the orientation of the principal planes and the stresses that act on these planes. Also determine the maximum shear stress, the corresponding normal stress, and the planes upon which they act.

7.7 Repeat Problem 7.4 using Mohr's circle for the solution.

7.8 Repeat Problem 7.5 using Mohr's circle for the solution.

7.9 Repeat Problem 7.6 using Mohr's circle for the solution.

7.10 Determine the pressure p required to cause yielding in a spherical pressure vessel if its radius is 1.00 m and its wall thickness is 8.0 mm. The pressure vessel is fabricated from 80-20 brass. Use the maximum shear stress failure theory.

7.11 Repeat Problem 7.10 but change the thickness of the wall to 12 mm and increase the radius to 1.8 m. All the other parameters remain the same.

7.12 Determine the pressure p required to cause yielding in a cylindrical pressure vessel if its radius is 1.2 m and its wall thickness is 7.5 mm. The pressure vessel is fabricated from 304 stainless steel. Use the von Mises failure theory.

7.13 Repeat problem 7.12, but change the thickness of the wall to 12 mm and increase its radius to 1.6 mm. All the other parameters remain the same.

7.14 A pressure vessel, shown in Fig. P7.14, is employed as a water storage tank for a small municipality. Determine the height of the water, h, which can be maintained in the tank if the city's engineering director specifies a safety factor of 2.75. The tank is fabricated from 1020 HR steel with a 32.0 ft diameter, a height of 60.0 ft and a thickness of 3/16 in. The city's engineering director also indicates that the safety factor should be based on maximum normal stress theory for failure. Recall the density for water is 62.4 lb/ft^3.

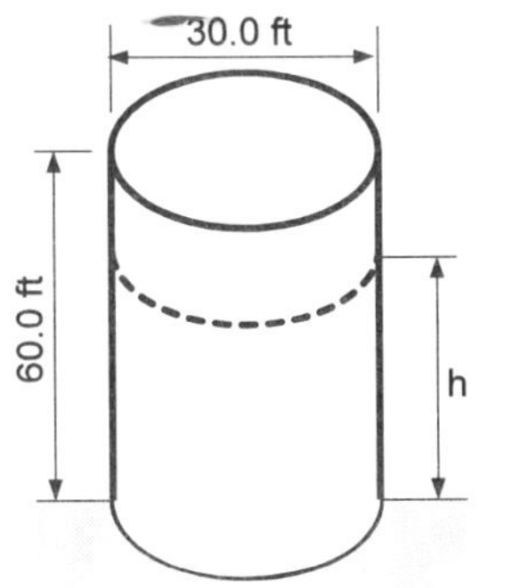

Fig. P7.14

7.15 A cylindrical pressure vessel is fabricated by wrapping thin steel plate in a spiral about a mandrel with a diameter of 3.0 m and butt-welding the seam as illustrated in Fig. P7.15. The weld seam forms an angle of 45° with the axis of the cylinder. Determine the normal stress σ and the shear stress τ acting on the weld when the vessel is subjected to a pressure p = 900 kPa and is fabricated with 7.0 mm thick plate.

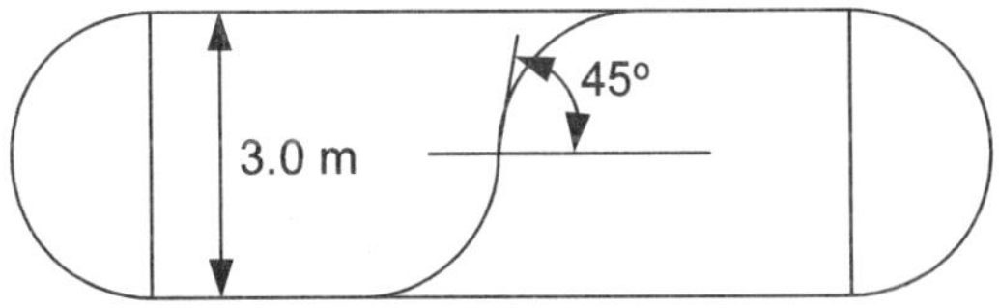

Fig. P7.15

7.16 Repeat Problem 7.15 but change the plate thickness to 12 mm and increase the pressure to 1.5 MPa. All the other parameters remain the same.

7.17 A 36 in. diameter pipeline is to be designed to transmit a variety of fluids. It is to operate at a maximum pressure of 350 psi. Determine the thickness of the steel plate used in its fabrication if the pipeline is designed with a safety factor of 3.5. The pipeline is fabricated from 1018 A steel. The design is based on von Mises theory for yielding.

7.18 Repeat Problem 7.17 but change the maximum pressure to 225 psi and reduce the diameter of the pipeline to 30 in. All other parameters remain the same.

7.19 A pair of orthogonal strain gages is mounted on a cylindrical pressure vessel with the orientation indicated in Fig. P7.19. The strains measured were $\varepsilon_A = 646 \times 10^{-6}$ and $\varepsilon_B = 330 \times 10^{-6}$. The pressure vessel is fabricated from 1018 A steel plate that is 7.5 mm thick. Determine the hoop and axial stresses in the cylinder, the internal pressure applied when the strains were measured and the factor of safety based on the von Mises theory for yielding.

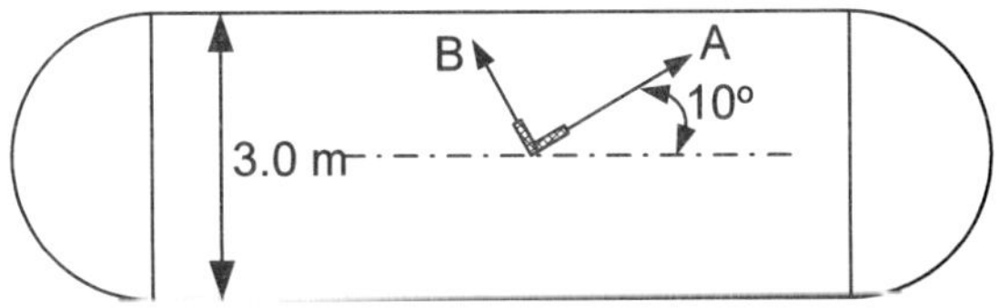

Fig. P7.19

7.20 You have been informed that the data provided for your analysis of Problem 7.19 was in error. The pressure vessel was fabricated from stainless steel not steel and the plate thickness was 9.0 mm, not 7.5 mm. All the other parameters specified were correct. Determine the hoop and axial stresses in the cylinder, the internal pressure applied when the strains were measured and the factor of safety based on the von Mises theory for yielding.

7.21 A thin walled spherical water tank, presented in Fig. P7.21, is filled with water and vented to the atmosphere. Determine the meridional σ_m and tangential σ_t stresses anywhere along the equator of the sphere. Your result should be written as an equation in terms of the water density γ, the tank diameter D and its wall thickness t.

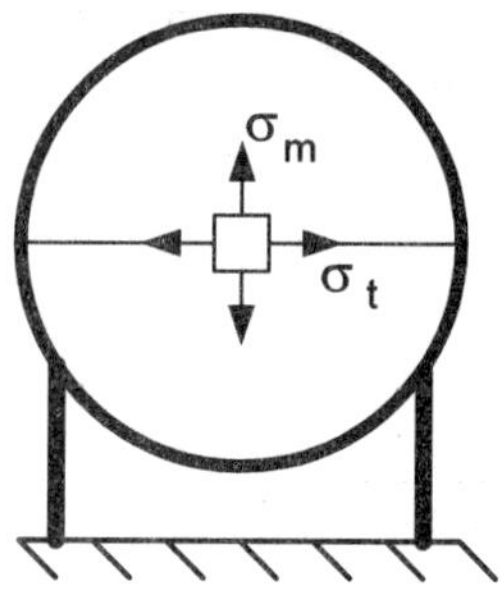

Fig. P7.21

7.22 A state of plane strain exists at a specified point in a plane body where the Cartesian components of strain are $\varepsilon_{xx} = 880 \times 10^{-6}$, $\varepsilon_{yy} = 275 \times 10^{-6}$ and $\gamma_{xy} = -700 \times 10^{-6}$. Determine the state of strain on an element rotated through an angle $\theta = +30°$ (counterclockwise is positive) relative to the Oxy axes.

7.23 Repeat Problem 7.22 but change the angle of rotation to − 50 degrees. All the other parameters remain the same.

7.24 For the Cartesian components of strain $\varepsilon_{xx} = 1050 \times 10^{-6}$, $\varepsilon_{yy} = -395 \times 10^{-6}$ and $\gamma_{xy} = 315 \times 10^{-6}$, determine the principal strains, the maximum shear strains and the angles θ_p and θ_s. Also determine the normal strains on the planes of maximum shear strain.

7.25 Repeat Problem 7.22 using Mohr's strain circle for the solution.

7.26 Repeat Problem 7.24 using Mohr's strain circle for the solution.

7.27 A thin rubber membrane (dental dam) is stretched in such a manner that a uniform strain field is produced over the area of the membrane. The Cartesian components of strain are $\varepsilon_{xx} = 6{,}520 \times 10^{-6}$, $\varepsilon_{yy} = 2{,}130 \times 10^{-6}$ and $\gamma_{xy} = -4{,}420 \times 10^{-6}$. A rectangle is scribed on the membrane before it is deformed. Determine the orientation of the membrane relative to the Cartesian axes if its angles are to remain at 90° after stretching.

7.28 Repeat Problem 7.27 if the Cartesian components of strain are changed to $\varepsilon_{xx} = 4{,}520 \times 10^{-6}$, $\varepsilon_{yy} = 1{,}250 \times 10^{-6}$ and $\gamma_{xy} = 3{,}420 \times 10^{-6}$.

7.29 A thin aluminum plate 100 mm wide and 500 mm long is subjected to a state of stress that produces a uniform strain field with Cartesian components of $\varepsilon_{xx} = 1{,}220 \times 10^{-6}$, $\varepsilon_{yy} = -472 \times 10^{-6}$ and $\gamma_{xy} = 315 \times 10^{-6}$. Determine the change in length of the diagonals of the plate and determine the maximum shear strain in the plate.

7.30 Repeat Problem 7.29 if the Cartesian components of strain are change to $\varepsilon_{xx} = 1{,}110 \times 10^{-6}$, $\varepsilon_{yy} = -624 \times 10^{-6}$ and $\gamma_{xy} = 254 \times 10^{-6}$.

7.31 A two-element rectangular rosette is aligned with the principal stress directions. If the principal strain measurements are $\varepsilon_1 = 825 \times 10^{-6}$ and $\varepsilon_2 = -423 \times 10^{-6}$, determine the principal stresses. The structural element upon which the strain gages are mounted is fabricated from steel.

7.32 Repeat Problem 7.31 if the principal strain measurements are changed to $\varepsilon_1 = 1125 \times 10^{-6}$ and $\varepsilon_2 = -552 \times 10^{-6}$.

7.33 Repeat Problem 7.31 if the principal strain measurements are changed to $\varepsilon_1 = 918 \times 10^{-6}$ and $\varepsilon_2 = 154 \times 10^{-6}$.

7.34 For the three-element rectangular rosette, derive Eq. (7.64), Eq. (7.67) and Eq. (7.68).

7.35 A three-element rectangular rosette is mounted on an aluminum structure. The strain readings from each gage element are $\varepsilon_A = 1{,}500 \times 10^{-6}$, $\varepsilon_B = 480 \times 10^{-6}$ and $\varepsilon_C = -275 \times 10^{-6}$. Determine the principal strains, the principal stresses and the principal angle.

7.36 Repeat Problem 7.35 if the strain readings from each gage element are $\varepsilon_A = 1{,}200 \times 10^{-6}$, $\varepsilon_B = 528 \times 10^{-6}$ and $\varepsilon_C = -212 \times 10^{-6}$.

7.37 Repeat Problem 7.36 if the strain readings from each gage element are $\varepsilon_A = 985 \times 10^{-6}$, $\varepsilon_B = 639 \times 10^{-6}$ and $\varepsilon_C = -355 \times 10^{-6}$.

7.38 Prepare a spreadsheet that will automatically compute σ_1, σ_2, ε_1, ε_2 and θ_p from the strains ε_A, ε_B and ε_C obtained from measurements with a three-element rectangular rosette for three different materials (steel, aluminum and stainless steel).

7.39 Another three-element rosette in common usage, illustrated in Fig. P7.39, is the delta-rosette with angles $\theta_A = 0°$, $\theta_B = 120°$, and $\theta_C = 240°$. Determine the equation for the principal strains ε_1 and ε_2 in terms of ε_A, ε_B and ε_C for this rosette.

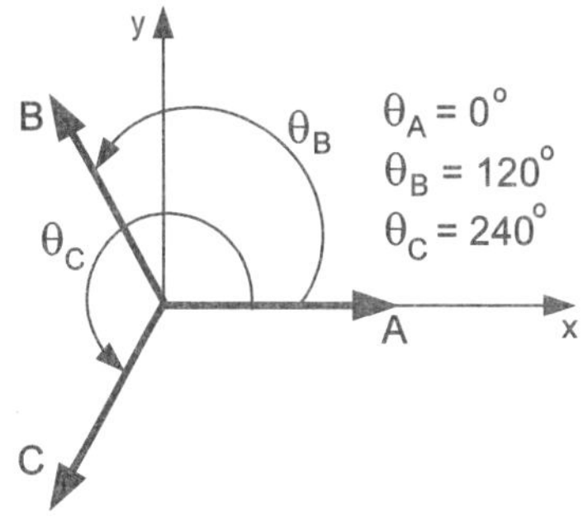

Fig. P7.39

7.40 An axle of an all-terrain vehicle is subjected to the forces and torque shown in Fig. P7.40. If the axle diameter is 18 mm, determine the principal stresses and the maximum shear stresses at point A and B on the surface of the axle. Note that point A lies along the z-axis and point B lies along the y-axis.

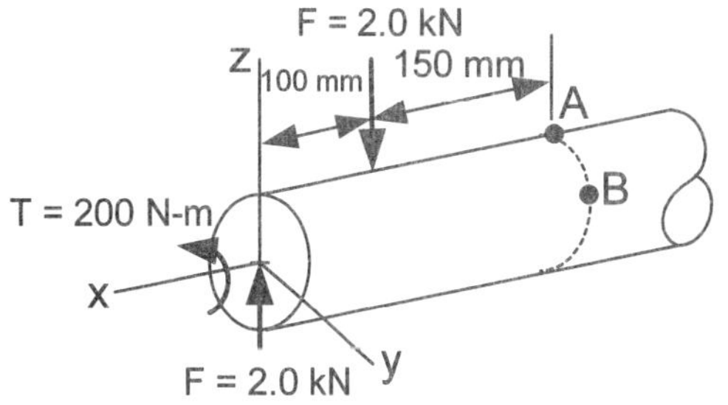

Fig. P7.40

7.41 Repeat Problem 7.40 but change the axle diameter from 18 mm to 21 mm. All other parameters remain the same.

7.42 An advertising sign located along a city street is cantilevered from a pole as illustrated in Fig. P7.42. The pressure due to the wind impinging on the sign is uniformly distributed over its area and equal to 12 lb/ft^2 in the x direction. The pole is fabricated from a tube with an outside diameter of 9 in. and a wall thickness of 0.25 in. Determine the stresses at points A and B located at the base of the pole.

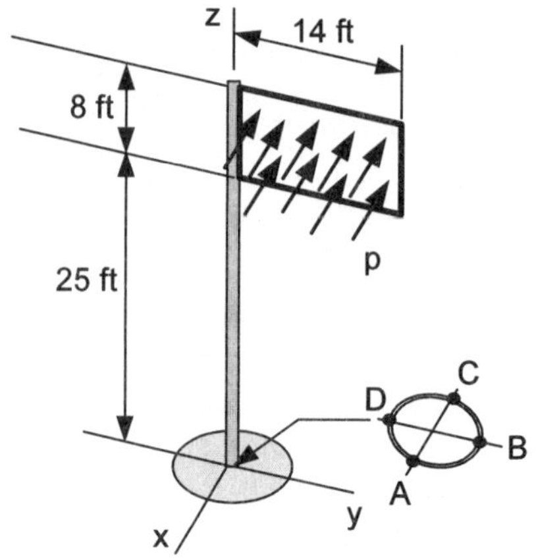

Fig. P7.42

7.43 Repeat Problem 7.42; however, solve for the stresses at points C and D located at the base of the pole.

7.44 A machine component is fabricated from a tube that has been formed into a 90° bend as illustrated in the Fig. P7.44. The outside diameter of the tube is 120 mm and its inside diameter is 104 mm. Determine the principal stresses and the maximum shear stresses at points A and B. Note that point A lies along the y-axis and point B lies along the x-axis.

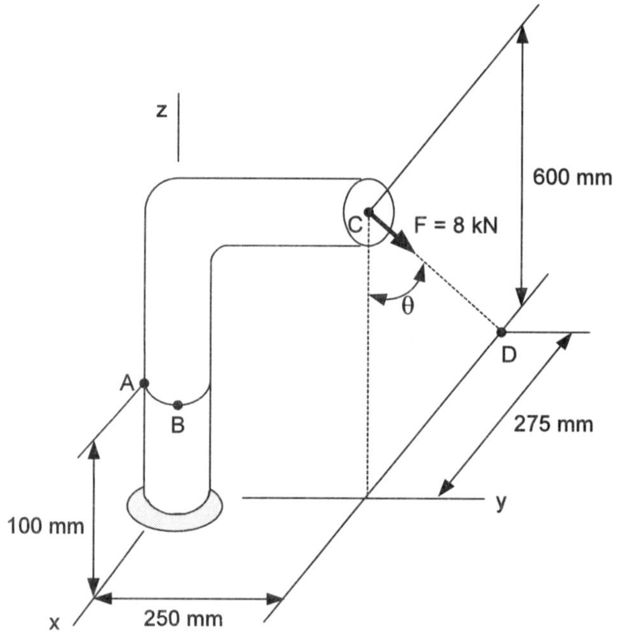

Fig. P7.44

7.45 A U shaped machine component, illustrated in Fig. P7.45, is subjected to opposing forces of 12 kN. If the component is fabricated from 1020 HR A steel, determine the safety factor based on yield strength using the maximum normal stress theory.

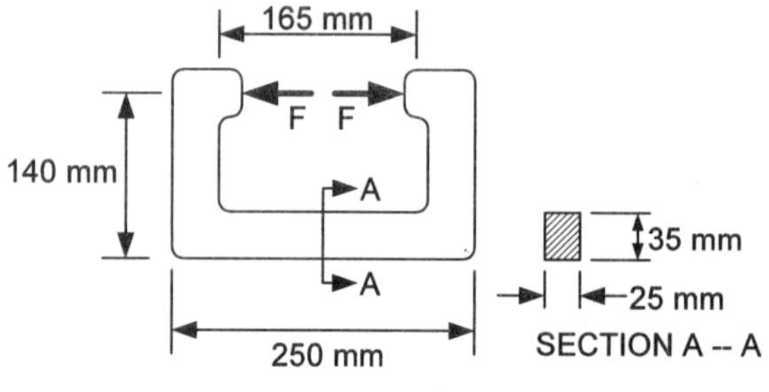

Fig. P7.45

7.46 Determine the maximum normal stress on the vertical section A -- A of the cantilever beam shown in Fig. P7.46.

Fig. P7.46

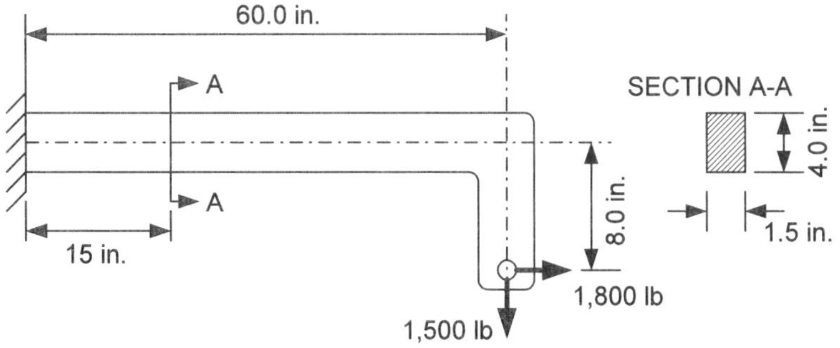

7.47 Repeat Problem 7.46 by changing the 1,800 lb force to 2,400 lb and the 1,500 lb force to 1,000 lb. All the other parameters remain the same.

7.48 The large bracket, shown in Fig. P7.48, is loaded in its plane of symmetry with a force F = 5 kN inclined by an angle $\theta = 10°$. Determine the principal stresses and the maximum shear stresses at points A, B and C. Points A and C are in the web adjacent to the flange of the bracket.

Fig. P7.48

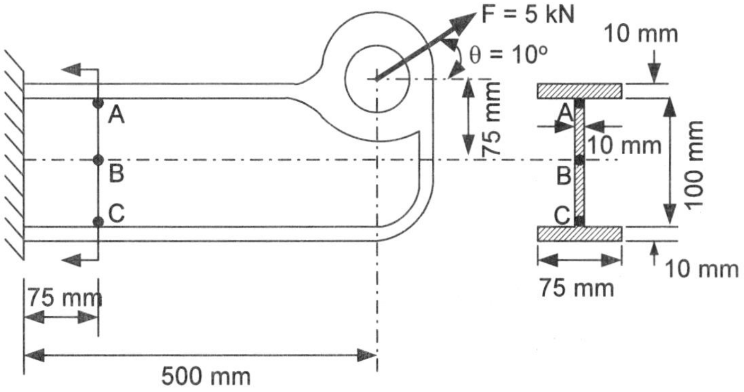

7.49 Repeat Problem 7.48 by changing the 5 kN force to 6.4 kN and increasing the angle θ from 10 degrees to 15 degrees. All the other parameters remain the same.

7.50 A thin walled cylindrical pressure vessel with an inner diameter 600 mm and a wall thickness of 10 mm, shown in Fig. P7.50, is subjected to an internal pressure of 0.80 MPa. It is also subjected to a torque of 56 kN-m and an axial force of 250 kN, which act through heavy plates attached to the ends of the cylinder. Determine the principal stresses and the maximum shear stresses at point A located on the outer surface of the cylinder.

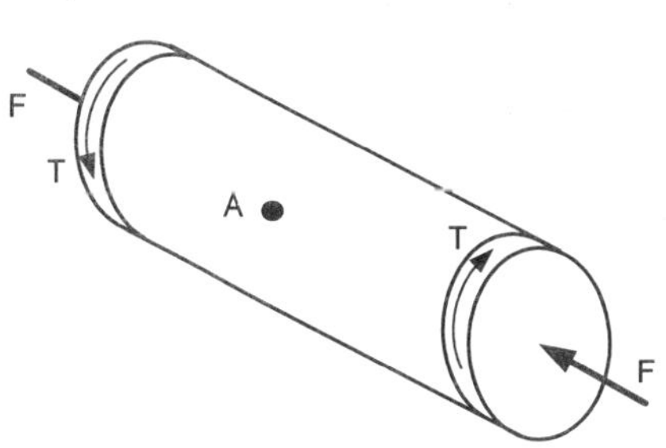

Fig. P7.50

7.51 Repeat Problem 7.50 if the wall thickness of the cylinder is increased to 12 mm. All other parameters remain the same.

7.52 An angled strut 6 in. thick is subjected to a force F = 50 kip and a uniformly distributed load q = 20 kip/ft, as illustrated in Fig. P7.52. Determine the principal stresses at points A, B and C.

Fig. P7.52

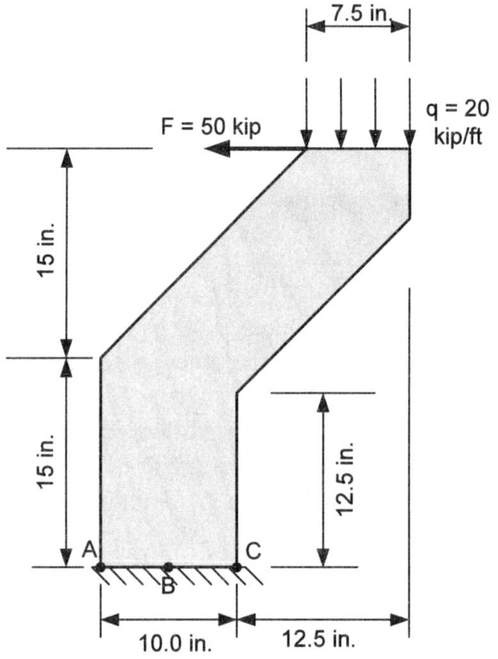

7.53 Repeat problem 7.52 if the loading is changed from 50 kip to 62 kips and from 20 kip/ft to 15 kip/ft. All other parameters remain the same.

CHAPTER 8

BUCKLING OF COLUMNS

8.1 INTRODUCTION

In this chapter, the concept of instability of columns under the action of a compressive force is introduced. This is a new concept that leads to a markedly different mode of failure of many structural elements such as columns, plates and shells. Even the analysis employed differs from our normal approach. In the previous chapters, we were concerned with stresses and deflections. If the stresses were less than the material's strength, the structural element was safe. If the deflections did not exceed some specified limit, the structural element was satisfactory. The concept of stability requires a designer to determine a critical load to insure that the structural element will not become unstable and collapse prior to either yield or fracture.

When the compressive force on a column exceeds some critical value P_{CR}, the column becomes unstable and collapses. This mode of failure is extremely dangerous because the collapse is catastrophic. When a column buckles, without shedding load, it initially deforms in the shape of a half sine wave and then simply folds when a plastic hinge forms at its center as illustrated in Fig. 8.1.

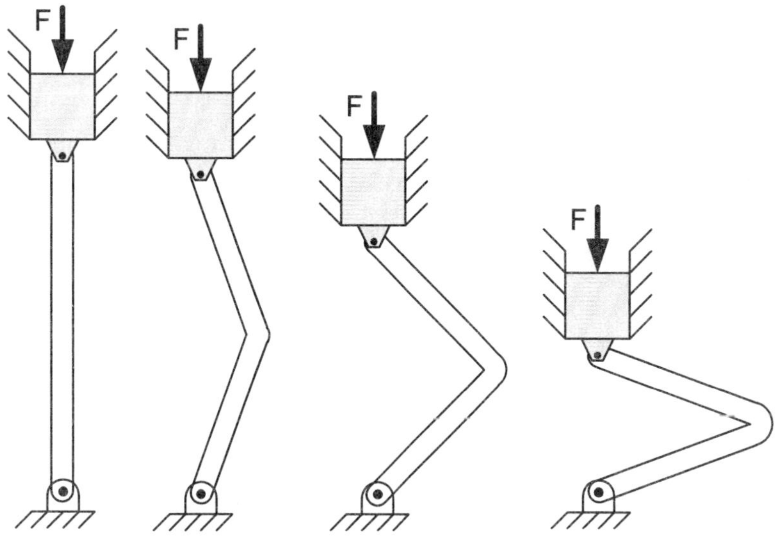

Fig. 8.1 Catastrophic collapse of a column with pinned ends during a buckling event.

In developing the equations for predicting the buckling of a column, we deviate from our previous practice of neglecting the small deformations of a structural element under the action of a load. When computing stress from $\sigma = P/A$, we do not take into account the change in A due to the strains induced by the force P. However, the entire concept of elastic instability is based on load-induced deformations. In analyzing columns, we consider the moment produced by the axial force P times the column's transverse deflection y. To show this new analytical approach, consider a column with both ends pinned subjected to a centric force P.

8.2 BUCKLING OF COLUMNS WITH BOTH ENDS PINNED

Consider a column of length L with both ends pinned subjected to a centric force P as illustrated in Fig. 8.2a. As the magnitude of the centric force increases, the column will bow slightly as indicated in Fig 8.2b. The column is, at this stage of loading, elastic and stable. To perform the analysis, we model the pinned end supports and the column as shown in Fig. 8.2c. We have selected the x-axis in the vertical direction and the y-axis in the horizontal direction to adapt the column coordinate system to that previously used in developing beam theory. The origin is placed at point A at the top of the column.

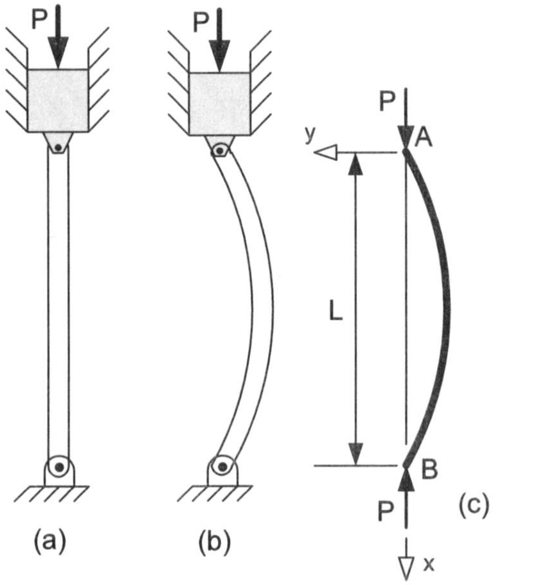

Fig. 8.2 Modeling a column with pinned ends.

Next, let's make a section cut and remove a portion of the top of the column as a FBD as shown in Fig. 8.3b.

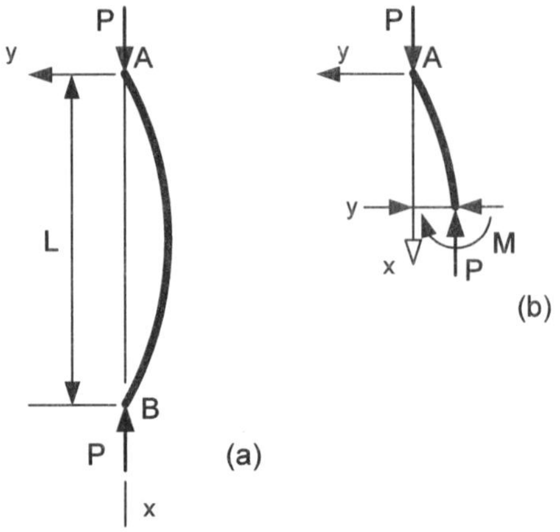

Fig. 8.3 FBD of the top portion of the column.

An examination of the axial forces in the FBD shows a couple, which produces a moment M = – Py. This is a bending moment and Eq. (5.4) is valid. Hence, we write:

$$\frac{d^2y}{dx^2} = \frac{M(x)}{EI} = -\frac{Py}{EI} \tag{8.1}$$

Rearranging Eq. (8.1) to write the differential equation in standard format yields:

$$\frac{d^2y}{dx^2} + p^2y = 0 \tag{8.2}$$

where $p = \sqrt{\frac{P}{EI}}$ (8.3)

Equation (8.2) is a linear, second-order differential equation with constant coefficients, which can be solved for y to obtain:

$$y = C_1 \sin(px) + C_2 \cos(px) \qquad (8.4)^1$$

where C_1 and C_2 are constants of integration.

We follow the procedure established in Chapter 5 and solve for the constants of integration using boundary conditions. Because both ends of the column are pinned, we write:

$$y(0) = 0 \qquad\qquad y(L) = 0 \tag{8.5}$$

It is clear from the first of the boundary conditions listed in Eq. (8.5) that $C_2 = 0$. Substituting the second boundary condition (y = 0 at x = L) into Eq. (8.4) yields:

$$C_1 \sin pL = 0 \tag{8.6}$$

There are two interpretations for Eq. (8.6). First, the equation is satisfied if $C_1 = 0$, which gives y = 0 for all of x. This is not realistic, because it implies that the column remains straight and will never buckle. Because buckling has been demonstrated in the laboratory and observed in field applications, this solution is discarded. The remaining solution to Eq. (8.6) is obtained by seeking values of pL which permit sin pL = 0.

$$\text{If} \quad pL = n\pi \qquad \text{then} \qquad \sin pL = 0 \tag{a}$$

Then from Eq. (8.3), we write:

$$p = \sqrt{\frac{P}{EI}} = \frac{n\pi}{L} \tag{8.7a}$$

and

$$P = \frac{n^2 EI\pi^2}{L^2} \tag{8.7b}$$

---

[1] This solution can be verified by differentiating Eq. (8.4) twice with respect to x to obtain d^2y/dx^2. Then substitute d^2y/dx^2 and y into Eq. (8.2).

It is necessary to interpret Eq. (8.7b) because it contains a counter n, which can be 0, 1, 2, etc. We seek the lowest meaningful value of n. Clearly n = 0 does not produce a realistic result because this value gives P = 0 indicating the column is unstable prior to loading. We seek a value for P > 0, and if n = 1 is selected, we obtain:

$$P_{CR} = \frac{\pi^2 EI}{L^2} \tag{8.8}$$

where P_{CR} is the critical centric compression load that initiates buckling and catastrophic collapse of the column. The moment of inertia I is the minimum value for the cross sectional area of the column.

Equation (8.8) is known as the Euler relation for elastic buckling. It is valid for long slender columns[2] with both ends pinned.

Returning to Eq. (8.4), we may use Eq. (8.7a) and express the deflection of the column as:

$$y = C_1 \sin\frac{\pi x}{L} \tag{8.9}$$

This result indicates that the column deflects as a sinusoid when the load $P = P_{CR}$. The fact that we cannot determine the amplitude C_1 of the sin wave is not important, because the column has become unstable and will quickly collapse.

Let's apply the Euler buckling theory to determine the critical load for two different columns both with pinned ends.

EXAMPLE 8.1

A column 20 feet long is fabricated from an aluminum tube with a 6 in. outside diameter and a 5.5 in. inside diameter. Determine the critical buckling force if the tube is pinned at both ends.

Solution:

We employ Eq. (8.8) to write the expression for the critical buckling force as:

$$P_{CR} = \frac{\pi^2 EI}{L^2} \tag{a}$$

The modulus of elasticity $E = 10.4 \times 10^6$ psi for an aluminum alloy is from Appendix B-1.

The minimum value of the moment of inertia for a tube is:

$$I = (\pi/64)[d_o^4 - d_i^4] = (\pi/64)[(6)^4 - (5.5)^4] = 18.70 \text{ in.}^4 \tag{b}$$

Substituting Eq. (b) into Eq. (a) yields:

---

[2] We will discuss the distinction among long slender columns, intermediate columns and short columns later in this chapter.

$$P_{CR} = \frac{\pi^2 EI}{L^2} = \frac{\pi^2 (10.4 \times 10^6)18.70}{(20)^2 (12)^2} = 33.32 \text{ kip} \qquad \text{(c)}$$

EXAMPLE 8.2

A column 8 m long is fabricated from a square tube (1020 HR steel) shown in Fig. E8.2. Determine the critical buckling force if the tube is pinned at both ends. Also determine the compressive stress in the tube and comment on its magnitude.

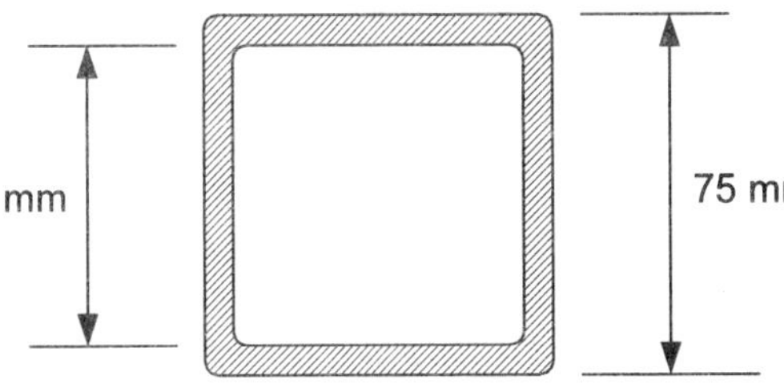

Fig. E8.2

Solution:

We employ Eq. (8.8) to write the expression for the critical buckling force as:

$$P_{CR} = \frac{\pi^2 EI}{L^2} \qquad \text{(a)}$$

The modulus of elasticity E = 207 GPa for the steel tube is from Appendix B-1.

The minimum value of the moment of inertia for the square tube is:

$$I = (1/12)[h_o^4 - h_i^4] = (1/12)[(75)^4 - (50)^4] = 2.116 \times 10^6 \text{ mm}^4 \qquad \text{(b)}$$

Substituting Eq. (b) into Eq. (a) yields:

$$P_{CR} = \frac{\pi^2 EI}{L^2} = \frac{\pi^2 (207 \times 10^3)(2.116 \times 10^6)}{(8 \times 10^3)^2} = 67.55 \text{ kN} \qquad \text{(c)}$$

The axial stress produced by the critical force P_{CR} is:

$$\sigma_{CR} = P_{CR}/A = 67.55 \times 10^3/[(75)^2 - (50)^2] = 21.62 \text{ MPa} \qquad \text{(d)}$$

The yield strength of 1020 HR steel is listed in Appendix B-2 as 290 MPa; hence, the stress at the critical load that produces buckling is only 7.5% of the yield strength. This example illustrates the danger of collapse due to buckling when columns are long and slender.

8.3 INFLUENCE OF END CONDITIONS

The critical buckling load is profoundly affected by the end conditions of the column. Increasing the constraint at either end markedly increases the critical load required for the onset of elastic instability. Three additional sets of boundary conditions are considered to show the influence of constraint on buckling load.

1. Top — pinned Bottom — built-in.
2. Top — free Bottom — built-in.
3. Top — built-in Bottom — built-in.

8.3.1 Column Buckling with One Pinned and One Built-in End.

Consider the column with its bottom built-in and its top pinned as shown in Fig. 8.4. It is subjected to an axial load P as shown in Fig. 8.5. To begin the analysis, draw the deformed shape of the column in its initial stages of instability. In preparing this drawing, recognize that the slope of the elastic curve at the built-in end and the deflection at its ends must be zero.

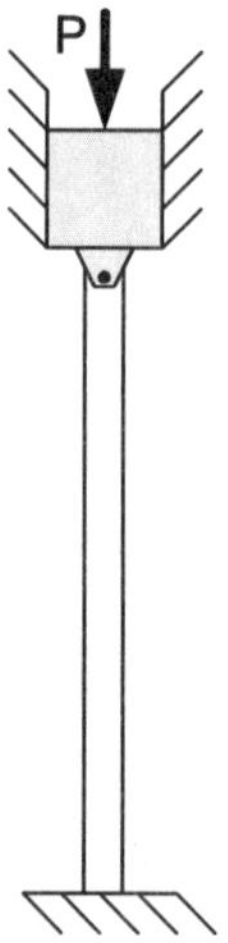

Fig. 8.4 A column with one end pinned and one end built-in.

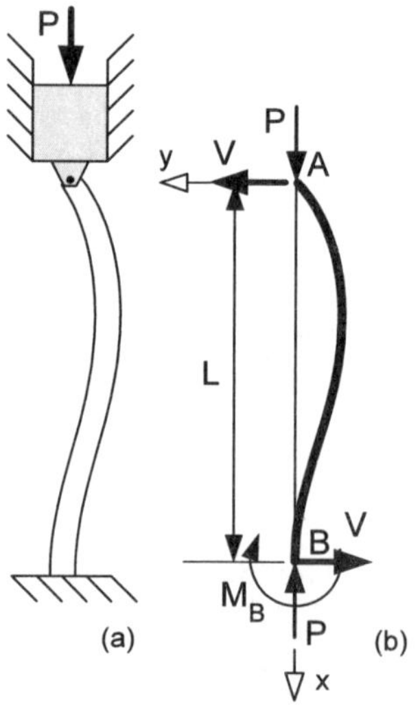

Fig. 8.5 Deformation of the column at initiation of elastic instability.

Next, make a section cut and remove a portion of the top of the column to represent the FBD as shown in Fig. 8.6b.

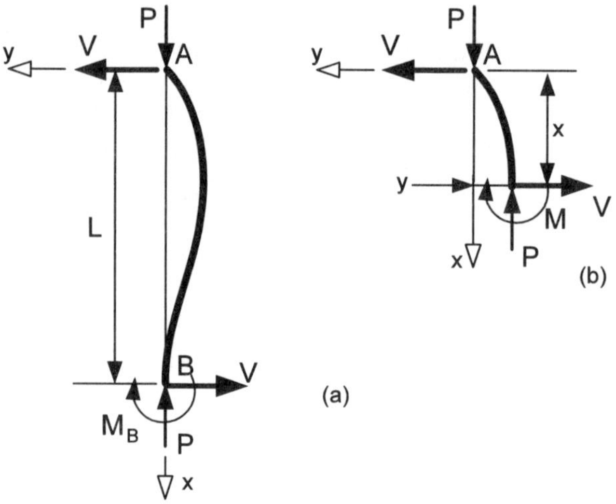

Fig. 8.6 FBD of the top portion of the column.

An examination of the FBD shows two couples produced by the equal and opposite forces V and P. These couples result in a bending moment M given by:

$$M = -Py - Vx \tag{8.10}$$

Substituting Eq. (8.10) into Eq. (5.4) yields:

$$\frac{d^2y}{dx^2} = \frac{M(x)}{EI} = -\frac{1}{EI}(Py + Vx) \tag{8.11}$$

Rearranging Eq. (8.11) to write the differential equation in standard format gives:

$$\frac{d^2y}{dx^2} + p^2y = -\frac{Vx}{EI} \tag{8.12}$$

recall $p = \sqrt{\frac{P}{EI}}$

Equation (8.12) is a linear, second-order differential equation with constant coefficients; however, it is not homogeneous. We obtain the homogeneous solution by setting the right hand side of Eq. (8.12) equal to zero and solving for y_h to obtain:

$$y_h = C_1 \sin(px) + C_2 \cos(px) \tag{8.13}$$

where C_1 and C_2 are constants of integration.

The particular solution is an expression for y_p that satisfies Eq. (8.12). Consider the expression for y_p shown below:

$$y_p = -Vx/P \tag{8.14}$$

The expression in Eq. (8.14) satisfies Eq. (8.12); hence, it represents the particular solution. The general solution is given by adding the homogeneous and particular solutions to obtain:

$$y = y_h + y_p = C_1 \sin(px) + C_2 \cos(px) - Vx/P \tag{8.15}$$

We follow the usual procedure to solve for the constants of integration using boundary conditions. Because the top of the column is pinned, we write:

$$y(0) = 0 \tag{8.16}$$

The boundary conditions for the built-in end where x = L are given by:

$$y(L) = 0 \qquad \frac{dy}{dx}(L) = 0 \tag{8.17}$$

It is clear from the boundary condition listed in Eq. (8.16) that $C_2 = 0$. Substituting the first boundary condition (y = 0 at x = L) from Eq. (8.17) into Eq. (8.15) yields:

$$C_1 \sin pL = VL/P \tag{8.18}$$

Next differentiate Eq. (8.15) with respect to x to obtain:

$$dy/dx = pC_1 \cos(px) - V/P \tag{8.19}$$

Substituting the boundary condition (dy/dx = 0 at x = L) from Eq. (8.17) into Eq. (8.19) gives:

$$pC_1 \cos pL = V/P \tag{8.20}$$

Dividing Eq. (8.18) by Eq. (8.20) leads to the transcendental equation:

$$\tan pL = pL \tag{8.21}$$

Solving this transcendental equation by trial and error gives the first meaningful solution for pL as:

$$pL = 4.4934 \tag{8.22}$$

Then substituting Eq. (8.3) into Eq. (8.22) and solving, we obtain:

$$P_{CR} = \frac{20.19EI}{L^2} \approx \frac{\pi^2 EI}{(0.7L)^2} \tag{8.23}$$

Comparing the result in Eq. (8.23) with that in Eq. (8.8) shows that the two equations differ only by the coefficient multiplying the term (EI/L^2). Recognizing this similarity, let's write a general equation for the buckling of columns as:

$$P_{CR} = \frac{\pi^2 EI}{(kL)^2} \tag{8.24}$$

For the column with two pinned ends k = 1, and for the column with one end pinned and the other built–in k = 0.7. Clearly, building-in one end of the column increased the critical load required for buckling by a factor of slightly more than two.

8.3.2 Column Buckling with One Free and One Built-in End.

This case deals with a column with a free end, where the load is applied, and a built-in end as depicted in Fig. 8.7. A FBD of the free end of the cantilever column is shown in Fig. 8.7d. From this FBD we write the moment equation as:

$$M = P(\delta - y) \tag{8.25}$$

Substituting Eq. (8.25) into Eq. (5.4) and rearranging to write the differential equation in standard format gives:

$$\frac{d^2y}{dx^2} + p^2y = p^2\delta \tag{8.26}$$

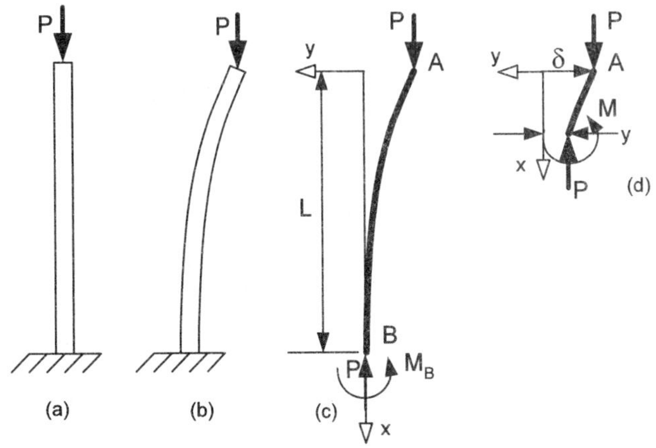

Fig. 8.7 A cantilever type column with one end free and one end built-in.

Using similar procedures to solve Eq. (8.26), we obtain:

$$y = y_h + y_p = C_1 \sin (px) + C_2 \cos (px) + \delta \qquad (8.27)$$

Solve for the constants of integration using boundary conditions. Because the top of the column undergoes a deflection δ, we write:

$$y(0) = \delta \qquad (8.28)$$

The boundary conditions for the built-in end are:

$$y(L) = 0 \qquad \frac{dy}{dx}(L) = 0 \qquad (8.29)$$

It is clear from the boundary condition listed in Eq. (8.28) that $C_2 = 0$. Next differentiate Eq. (8.27) with respect to x to obtain:

$$dy/dx = pC_1 \cos (px) \qquad (8.30)$$

Substituting the boundary condition (dy/dx = 0 at x = L) into Eq. (8.30) gives:

$$pC_1 \cos pL = 0 \qquad (8.31)$$

It is evident that Eq. (8.31) is satisfied when $pL = n\pi/2$. The first bucking mode occurs when n = 1; hence, $pL = \pi/2$. Substituting this value into Eq. (8.3) gives the critical buckling load as:

$$P_{CR} = \frac{\pi^2 EI}{4L^2} \qquad (8.32)$$

Comparison of Eq. (8.32) with Eq. (8.23) shows a remarkable reduction in the critical buckling load when the pin at the top of the column is removed and the axial compression load is applied to the column's free end. The reduction is a factor of about eight.

8.3.3 Column Buckling with Two Built-in Ends.

The final case considered is the column with both ends built-in as shown in Fig. 8.8. The procedure for deriving the Euler equation for the critical load for buckling is similar to that described previously. Begin with the FBD, shown in Fig. 8.8d and write the moment equation as:

$$M = -Py + M_A \tag{8.33}$$

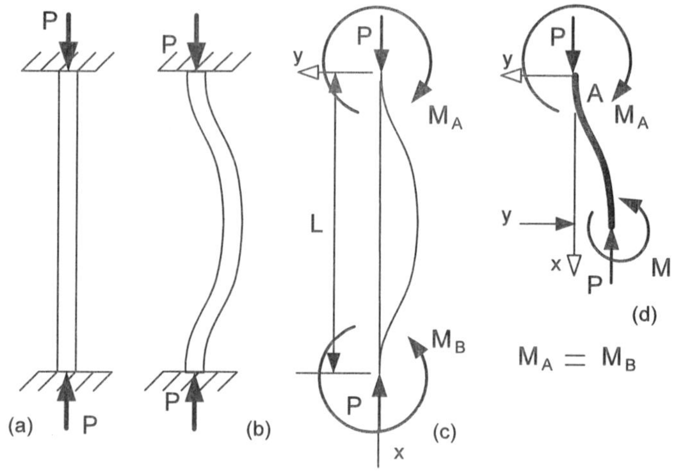

Fig. 8.8 A column with both ends built-in subjected to axial compression loading.

Substituting Eq. (8.33) into Eq. (5.4) and rearranging gives the differential equation in standard format as:

$$\frac{d^2y}{dx^2} + p^2 y = \frac{M_A}{EI} \tag{8.34}$$

Solving Eq. (8.34) for the homogeneous and particular solutions gives the general solution as:

$$y = y_h + y_p = C_1 \sin(px) + C_2 \cos(px) + M_A/P \tag{8.35}$$

We follow the usual procedure to solve for the constants of integration using boundary conditions. At the top of the column (x = 0), y = 0 and dy/dx = 0. At the middle of the column symmetry exists so that dy/dx = 0 at x = L/2. At the bottom of the column (x = L), y = 0 and dy/dx = 0. It is clear from the boundary condition (y = 0 at x = 0) and Eq. (8.35) that:

$$C_2 = -M_A/P \tag{8.36}$$

Differentiating Eq. (8.35) with respect to x and substituting Eq. (8.36) into the resulting relation yields:

$$dy/dx = C_1 p \cos(px) + (M_A/P) p \sin(px) \tag{8.37}$$

Substituting the boundary condition (dy/dx = 0 at x = 0) into Eq. (8.37) gives $C_1 = 0$. We can now write Eq. (8.35) as:

$$y = C_2[\cos(px) - 1] \tag{8.38}$$

From the boundary condition (y = 0 at x = L) and Eq. (8.38), we can write:

$$\cos(pL) - 1 = 0 \tag{8.39}$$

Equation (8.39) is satisfied when $pL = 2n\pi$. The first mode of buckling occurs with n = 1, which lcads to:

$$pL = 2\pi \tag{8.40}$$

Then substituting Eq. (8.3) into Eq. (8.40), we obtain:

$$P_{CR} = \frac{4\pi^2 EI}{L^2} \tag{8.41}$$

Let's apply these new relations to determine the critical load for two different columns with various end conditions.

EXAMPLE 8.3

A column 18 feet long is fabricated from a steel tube with the rectangular cross section presented in Fig. E8.3. The column is pinned at one end and built-in at the other. Determine the critical buckling force.

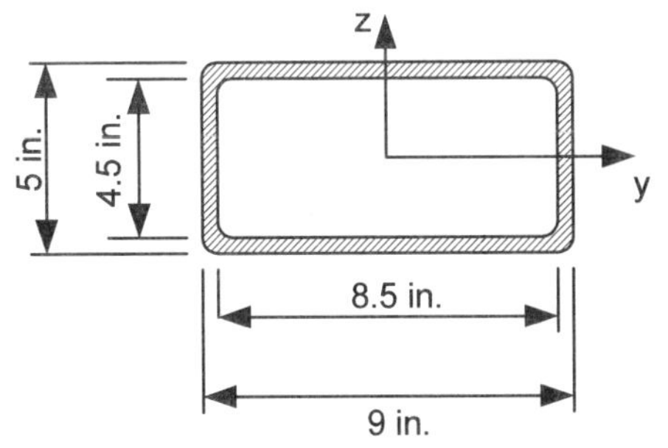

Fig. E8.3

Solution:

We employ Eq. (8.23) to write the expression for the critical buckling force for this column as:

$$P_{CR} = \frac{20.19EI}{L^2} \tag{a}$$

The modulus of elasticity $E = 30 \times 10^6$ psi for the steel tube is from Appendix B-1.

The cross section is rectangular; hence the moment of inertia is a function of the choice of axis. For this reason, we will determine both I_y and I_z below:

$$I_y = (1/12)[b_o h_o^3 - b_i h_i^3] = (1/12)[(9)(5)^3 - (8.5)(4.5)^3] = 29.20 \text{ in.}^4 \tag{b}$$

$$I_z = (1/12)[b_o h_o^3 - b_i h_i^3] = (1/12)[(5)(9)^3 - (4.5)(8.5)^3] = 73.45 \text{ in.}^4 \tag{c}$$

Substituting the lower value of the moment of inertia from Eq. (b) into Eq. (a) yields:

$$(P_{CR})_y = \frac{20.19EI_y}{L^2} = \frac{(20.19)(30\times 10^6)(29.20)}{(18)^2(12)^2} = 379.1 \text{ kip} \tag{d}$$

Examination of the results indicates the importance of the choice of axis when determining the moment of inertia when the cross section is not circular or square. In this case, the difference in the inertia is about a factor of about 2.5.

EXAMPLE 8.4

A column 5.8 m long is fabricated from a steel wide flange section with a designation of W152 × 24. Determine the critical buckling force for the following two cases: (a) the column is free at one end and built-in at the other, and (b) the column is built-in at both ends.

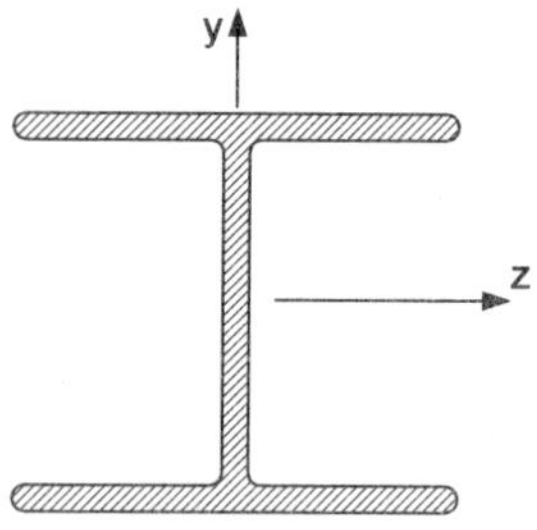

Fig. E8.4

Solution:

Employ Eq. (8.32) to write the expression for the critical buckling force for the column with the top end free as:

$$P_{CR} = \frac{\pi^2 EI}{4L^2} \quad \text{(a)}$$

The modulus of elasticity (207 GPa) for the steel column is from Appendix B-1. The moment of inertia is a function of the choice of axis. Both I_y and I_z are given in Appendix D as:

$$I_y = 1.84 \times 10^6 \text{ mm}^4 \qquad I_z = 13.4 \times 10^6 \text{ mm}^4 \quad \text{(b)}$$

We select the minimum value of the moment of inertia I_y given in Eq. (b) and substitute this value into Eq. (a) to obtain:

$$(P_{CR})_y = \frac{\pi^2 EI_y}{4L^2} = \frac{\pi^2(207\times 10^3)(1.84\times 10^6)}{(4)(5{,}800)^2} = 27.94 \text{ kN} \quad \text{(c)}$$

Examination of the results indicates the importance of the choice of the end conditions for column buckling. In this case, the difference in the critical buckling load is in excess of a factor of sixteen.

Next, employ Eq. (8.41) to obtain the expression for the critical buckling force for the column with both ends built-in:

$$(P_{CR})_y = \frac{4\pi^2 EI_y}{L^2} = \frac{4\pi^2(207\times 10^3)(1.84\times 10^6)}{(5{,}800)^2} = 447.0 \text{ kN} \quad \text{(d)}$$

Again, we have selected the minimum value of the moment of inertia I_y for evaluating the critical buckling force.

8.3.4 Summary of Equations For Critical Column Buckling Loads

We have derived four equations for the buckling of columns under the action of centric compressive loads. These equations all are of the form $P_{CR} = \pi^2 EI/(kL)^2$. We summarize the results for the parameter k as a function of the various end constraints imposed on the column in Table 8.1

Table 8.1 Constant k as a function of column end constraints

Case No.	End Constraints	k
1	Pinned—Pinned	1
2	Pinned—Built-in	0.7
3	Free—Built-in	2
4	Built-in—Built-in	0.5

The determination of the critical buckling load for columns subjected to centric compressive forces involves identifying the end constraints and substituting the correct value of k into Eq. (8.24). Care must also be exercised in selecting the correct axis about which to determine the moment of inertia I as two choices exist in most cases. The minimum inertia usually is employed in the determination. Four examples have been described to demonstrate the method for computing the Euler buckling loads.

The critical buckling stress σ_{CR} has not been emphasized in this section, as we were more concerned with determining the critical buckling force. The topic of stresses produced in columns is discussed in much more detail in the next section.

8.4 COLUMN STRESSES AND LIMITATIONS OF EULER'S THEORY

When a centric load is applied to a column, an axial compressive stress develops that increases until the column becomes unstable. At the inception of buckling, the applied stress is called the critical stress and is given by:

$$\sigma_{CR} = P_{CR}/A \qquad (8.42)$$

If we consider the column pinned at both ends, then $P_{CR} = \pi^2 EI/L^2$. Substituting this value into Eq. (8.42) and rearranging symbols yields:

$$\sigma_{CR} = \frac{\pi^2 EI}{L^2 A} = \frac{\pi^2 EAr^2}{L^2 A} = \frac{\pi^2 E}{(L/r)^2} \qquad (8.43)$$

Note $I = Ar^2$ in the expansion of Eq. (8.43), where A is the cross sectional area of the column and r is the radius of gyration of the area.

The term (L/r) is known as the slenderness ratio of the column. As (L/r) increases the column becomes more flexible and will buckle at lower and lower stress levels. Let's consider an example to illustrate the reduction in the critical stress σ with increasing (L/r).

EXAMPLE 8.5

Consider a steel column with E = 207 GPa and S_y = 300 MPa. Prepare a graph showing σ_{CR} as a function of the slenderness ratio (L/r).

Solution:

The solution involves evaluating Eq. (8.43) as (L/r) is varied from 10 to 200 in steps of 10.

$$\sigma_{CR} = \frac{\pi^2 E}{(L/r)^2} = S_y \qquad \text{(a)}$$

The results obtained from a spreadsheet calculation using Eq. (a) are presented in Fig. E8.5. Examination of this figure indicates that the critical stress σ_{CR} exceeds the yield strength S_y of the steel specified in the example statement for (L/r) < 82.5. This fact means that the Euler theory for buckling is valid only when (L/r) ≥ 82.5. For slenderness ratios less than this value, failure of the column will occur by compressive yielding.

The limiting value of (L/r) depends on the column constraint and both the modulus of elasticity and the yield strength of the material from which the column is fabricated. We will explore this dependency in the next example.

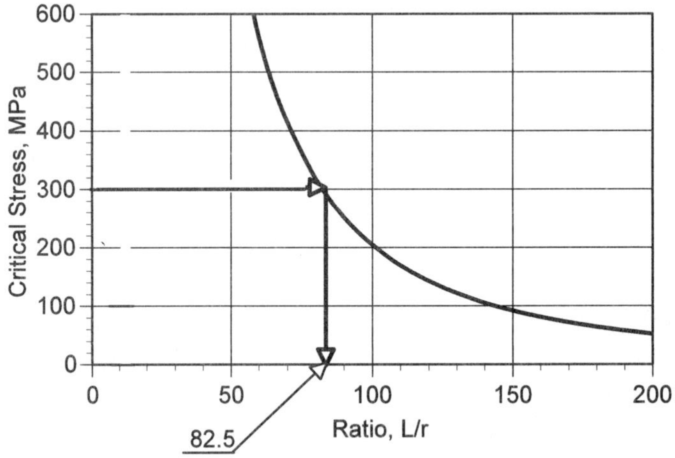

Fig. E8.5 Critical stress σ_{CR} as a function of slenderness ratio (L/r).

EXAMPLE 8.6

Consider a column with both ends pinned. Determine the limiting value of (L/r) as a function of yield strength for columns fabricated from both steel and aluminum. Consider the yield strength varying from 20 to 200 ksi.

Solution:

Set $\sigma_{CR} = S_y$ in Eq. (8.43) and solve for (L/r) to obtain:

$$\frac{L}{r} = \sqrt{\frac{\pi^2 E}{S_y}} \qquad \text{(a)}$$

Let E = 30 × 10^6 pi and 10.4 × 10^6 psi for steel and aluminum, respectively. Using a spreadsheet to evaluate Eq. (a) and varying S_y from 20 to 200 ksi in steps of 10, we obtain the results presented in Fig. E8.6.

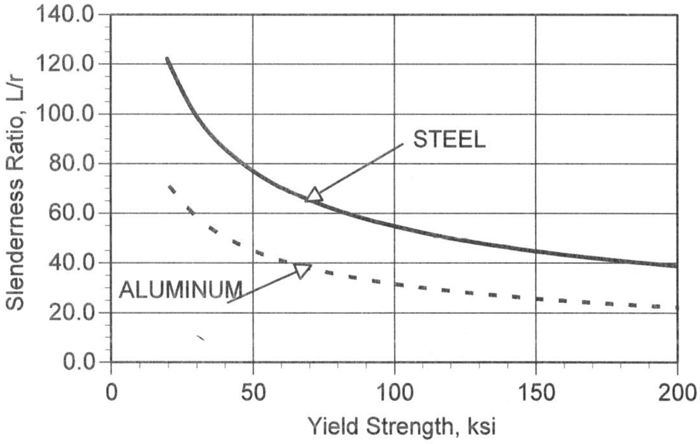

Fig. E8.6 The limiting value of the slenderness ratio as a function of yield strength for a column with both ends pinned.

The marked difference in the limiting value of the slenderness ratio for steel and aluminum alloy is due to the fact that aluminum is less resistant to buckling because of its much lower modulus of elasticity.

These two examples have illustrated that the Euler theory of buckling has limits of applicability. Long slender columns with high values of (L/r) will buckle under the action of centric compressive loads and Euler's equations are valid. However, if (L/r) for the column is less than the limit value, as is the case for shorter columns with larger radii of gyration, then the Euler theory is not valid. In these cases, the column does not buckle. The failure mode is one of yielding due to excessive compressive stress. The two different modes of failure are illustrated in Fig. 8.9.

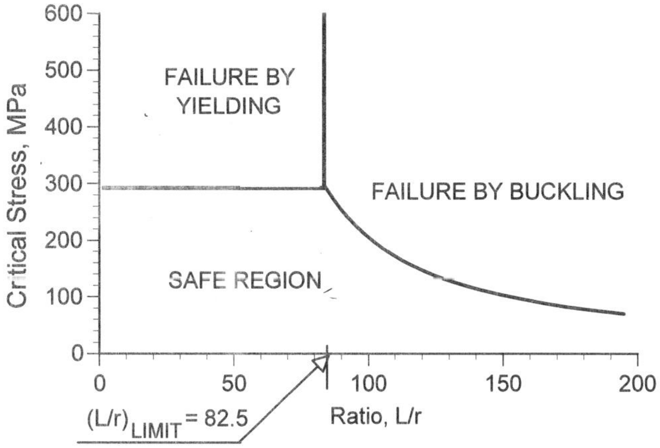

Fig. 8.9 Safety and failure regions for a centric loaded, pin-pin ended column. Yield strength 300 MPa.

8.5 ECCENTRICALLY LOADED COLUMNS

The developments in the previous sections of this chapter assumed that the axial compressive load was applied to the column through the centroid of its cross section. In practice this centric loading is nearly impossible to achieve. Even if the load is placed at the centroid of the cross section, columns are never perfectly straight. As a consequence the loading always exhibits some small eccentricity e. Let's explore the effect of the eccentricity of the load on the buckling relations by considering the pin-pin ended column shown in Fig. 8.10.

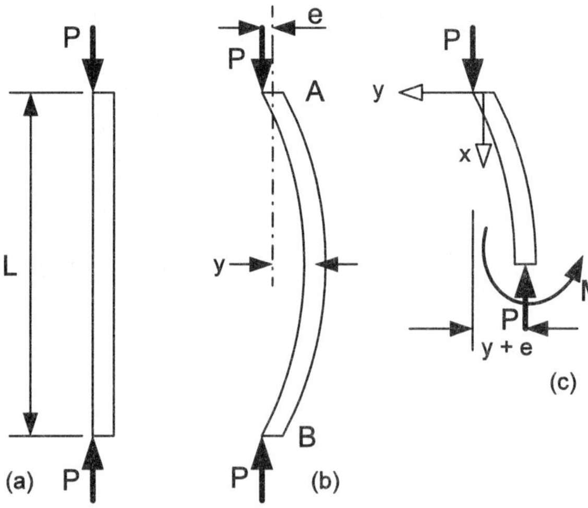

Fig. 8.10 A column with an eccentric axial load P.

The analysis follows the same procedure as described previously. The deformed shape of the column is represented as a sine wave because the ends are pinned. The column is cut at a location x measured from the top end and a FBD of this end is made as shown in Fig. 8.10c. Writing the equation for the moment M gives:

$$M = -P(y + e) \tag{8.44}$$

Substituting Eq. (8.44) into Eq. (5.4) yields:

$$\frac{d^2y}{dx^2} = \frac{M(x)}{EI} = -\frac{1}{EI}(Py + Pe) \tag{8.45}$$

Rearranging Eq. (8.45) to write the differential equation in standard format gives:

$$\frac{d^2y}{dx^2} + p^2 y = -p^2 e \tag{8.46}$$

where p is given in Eq. (8.3)

Solving Eq. (8.46) yields:

$$y = y_h + y_p = C_1 \sin(px) + C_2 \cos(px) - e \tag{8.47}$$

We follow the usual procedure to solve for the constants of integration using boundary conditions. Because both ends of the column are pinned, we write:

$$y(0) = 0 \qquad\qquad y(L) = 0 \tag{8.48}$$

From the first boundary condition ($y = 0$ at $x = 0$), it is clear that $C_2 = e$.

From the second boundary condition (y = 0 at x = L), we can show that:

$$C_1 = e[1 - \cos (pL)]/\sin (pL) \tag{8.49}$$

Using the following trigometric identities:

$$1 - \cos (pL) = 2 \sin^2 (pL/2) \qquad \sin (pL) = 2 \sin (pL/2) \cos (pL/2)$$

the expression for C_1 can be rewritten as:

$$C_1 = e \tan (pL/2) \tag{8.50}$$

Substituting the values for C_1 and C_2 into Eq. (8.47) yields:

$$y = = e[\tan (pL/2) \sin (px) + \cos (px) - 1] \tag{8.51}$$

This relation shows that the amplitude of the deflection of the column prior to the initiation of buckling depends upon the eccentricity e. We will show a graph illustrating this fact later in this section. The maximum value of y occurs at the mid point of the column where x = L/2. At that location, we can write the expression for y_{Max} as:

$$y_{Max} = e[\sec (pL/2) - 1] \tag{8.52}$$

The column will buckle when y_{Max} becomes large. For small eccentricity, y_{Max} becomes large when:

$$\sec (pL/2) \rightarrow \infty \qquad \Rightarrow \qquad pL/2 = \pi/2$$

From this result and Eq. (8.3), it is clear that:

$$P_{CR} = \frac{\pi^2 EI}{L^2} \tag{8.53}$$

The buckling load is identical with that derived for centrically loaded columns when e = 0. While the end result is the same, the bucking process differs. With centric loading the column remained straight as the load P was increased until P_{CR} was achieved. At the critical load P_{CR}, the column became unstable and suddenly buckled (collapsed). With eccentricity the column deflects laterally with increasing magnitude until the critical load is achieved. We will illustrate this behavior in the next example.

EXAMPLE 8.7

Consider a column with both ends pin loaded with an axial force P. The force P is applied with an eccentricity e. Determine y_{Max} as a function of the axial force P as the quantity pL/2 varies from 0 to π/2. Let e = 1 and 2 in. The column is 30 ft long and fabricated from a square steel tube depicted in Fig. E8.7.

Fig. E8.7

Solution:

Before determining y_{Max}, establish the critical buckling load from Eq. (8.53) as:

$$P_{CR} = \frac{\pi^2 EI}{L^2} = \frac{\pi^2(30\times 10^6)[(6)^4 - (5)^4]}{(12)(30)^2(12)^2} = 127.8 \text{ kip} \quad \text{(a)}$$

This result enables us to bound the calculations needed in preparing a graph of y_{Max} as a function of P. Recall Eq. (8.52) and rewrite it as:

$$y_{Max} = e\left(\sec\left(\frac{pL}{2}\right) - 1\right) = e\left(\sec\sqrt{\frac{PL^2}{4EI}} - 1\right) \quad \text{(b)}$$

Substituting numerical parameters into Eq. (b) gives:

$$y_{Max} = e\left(\sec\sqrt{\frac{PL^2}{4EI}} - 1\right) = e\left(\sec\sqrt{\frac{P(360)^2}{4(30\times 10^6)(55.92)}} - 1\right) = e\left(\sec\sqrt{19.31\times 10^{-6} P} - 1\right) \quad \text{(c)}$$

Next, employ a spreadsheet to evaluate Eq. (c) for P varying from 0 to 130 kip to obtain the graph shown in Fig. E8.7a.

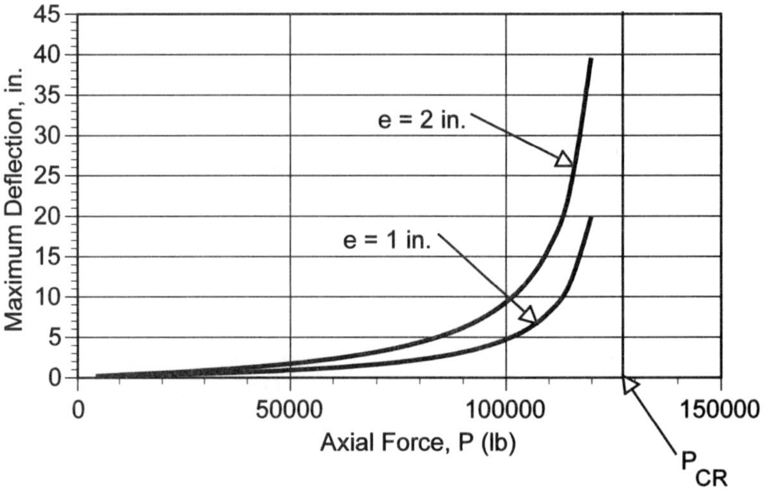

Fig. E8.7a

Examination of the results in Fig. E8.7a shows that the deflection is not a linear function of the axial load P. Instead the deflection increases exponentially as the critical buckling load is approached. This response is due to the non-linear behavior of moment M = P(e + y), because the deflection y increases together with the axial load P.

8.6 STRESSES IN COLUMNS WITH ECCENTRIC LOADING

In some structural applications, it is necessary to apply loads to columns with significant eccentricity. While this practice does not affect the critical buckling load as determined by the Euler theory, it may result in failure of the column due to excessive compressive stress at loads less than P_{CR}. Let's consider the free-ended column, shown in Fig. 8.11, with an axial force P that is applied with an eccentricity e.

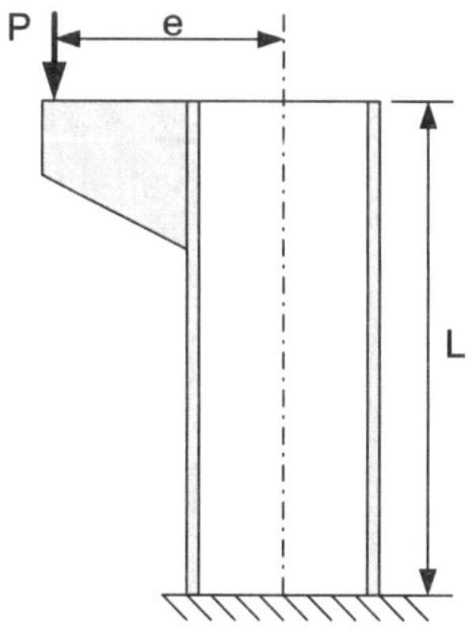

Fig. 8.11 A free-ended column with an eccentric load P.

The load P generates an internal force and a bending moment both of which are constant over the length of the column. A FBD of the top portion of the column, presented in Fig. 8.12, shows this force and moment.

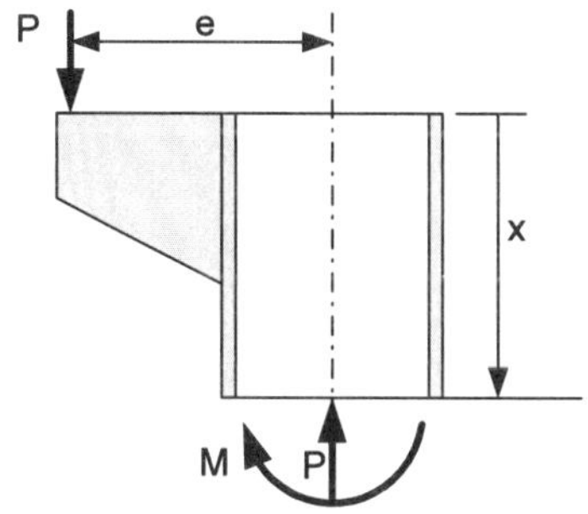

Fig. 8.12 A FBD showing an internal force P and a bending moment M.

Considering equilibrium permits us to write:

$$M = P\,e \tag{8.54}$$

The axial stresses produced in the column due to P and M are:

$$\sigma_c = \sigma_a + \sigma_b = -\,P/A \pm Mc/I \tag{8.55}$$

It is evident from Eq. (8.55) that the axial stresses due to the axial force and the bending moment combine. The combined distribution of axial stresses across the column is illustrated in Fig. 8.13.

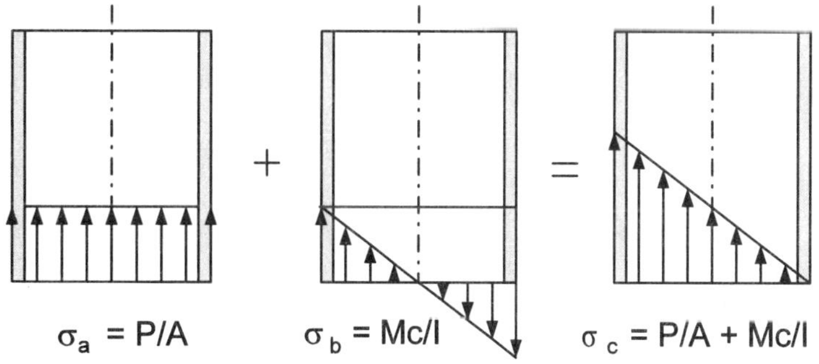

Fig. 8.13 Combined stresses due to eccentric loading of a column.

For an axial compressive force applied to a column, the maximum combined stress produced is a compressive stress given by:

$$\sigma_c = \sigma_a + \sigma_b = -\,(P/A + Mc/I) \tag{8.56}$$

In the design of an eccentrically loaded column, the procedure is to determine the combined stress using Eq. (8.56) and the critical stress using the appropriate relation that depends on the end conditions of the column. We then compare these two values to determine the mode of failure for the column. We will illustrate this procedure in the next example.

EXAMPLE 8.8

Consider a column with both ends pin loaded with an axial force P as shown in Fig. E8.8. The force P is applied with an eccentricity e = 350 mm. Determine the maximum load P that can be applied if a safety factor SF = 2.5 is to be maintained against failure by excessive compressive stress or by buckling. The steel column is 8.0 m long and is fabricated from an American Standard section with a designation of S127 × 22. The steel is 1020 HR with $S_y = 290$ MPa.

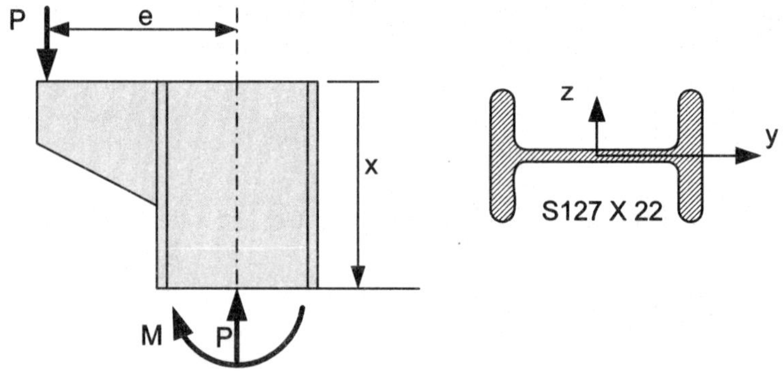

Fig. E8.8

Solution:

We employ Eq. (8.8) to write the expression for the critical buckling force for this pinned ended column as:

$$P_{CR} = \frac{\pi^2 EI}{L^2} \qquad \text{(a)}$$

The modulus of elasticity E = 207 GPa for the steel column is from Appendix B-1.

The moment of inertia is a function of the orientation of the pin. If the pin is inserted along the y axis (see Fig. E8.8), then the end of the column will rotate about this axis. However, if the pin is inserted in the z direction, the column will rotate about this axis. Both I_y and I_z are given in Appendix D as:

$$I_y = 0.695 \times 10^6 \text{ mm}^4 \qquad \text{(b)}$$

$$I_z = 6.33 \times 10^6 \text{ mm}^4 \qquad \text{(c)}$$

Substituting the minimum value I_y into Eq. (a) yields:

$$(P_{CR})_y = \frac{\pi^2 EI_y}{L^2} = \frac{\pi^2(207\times 10^3)(0.695\times 10^6)}{(8{,}000)^2} = 22.19 \text{ kN} \qquad \text{(d)}$$

Examination of the results indicates the importance of the direction of the pin when the cross section is not circular or square. In this case, the difference in the moment of inertia I is in excess of a factor of nine. Clearly, for the section shown in Fig. E8.8, the pin should be inserted in the z direction. Many conservative designers will base their recommendations on the minimum critical load, even with the column end free to rotate about the z-axis. Let's follow this conservative approach. Then the allowable load P is given by:

$$P_{Allowable} = P_{CR}/SF = 22.19/2.5 = 8.876 \text{ kN} \tag{e}$$

The compressive stress is given by Eq. (8.56) as:

$$\sigma_c = \sigma_a + \sigma_b = -(P/A + Mc/I_y) = = -(P/A + M/Z_y) = S_y/SF \tag{f}$$

Substituting the numerical parameters for the S127 × 22 section, and the yield strength of the 1020 HR steel into Eq. (f) gives:

$$P/2{,}800 + 350P/(16.6 \times 10^3) = 290/2.5 \tag{g}$$

$$P_{Allowable} = 5.410 \text{ kN} \tag{h}$$

8.7 DESIGN CODES

Design codes have been developed by several industrial associations to facilitate the design of columns fabricated from steel, aluminum and wood. These codes accommodate both long slender columns and intermediate length columns. Local governments controlling building permits have adopted these codes and structural engineers employ the formulas contained in the codes when sizing columns.

8.7.1 Steel Columns

The American Institute for Steel Construction (AISI) has adopted two different equations for the design of steel columns. These equations permit a designer to determine the maximum allowable stress for centric loaded columns for specified slenderness ratios. The first of these two equations for long slender columns is based on Euler's theory, but with a safety factor SF = 1.92.

$$\sigma_{Allowable} = \frac{\pi^2 E}{1.92(kL/r)^2} \tag{8.57}$$

where k depends on the column's end conditions and is given in Table 8.1.

Equation (8.57) is applied for specified values of (kL/r) as indicated below:

$$SR_C \leq \left(\frac{kL}{r}\right) \leq 200 \tag{8.58}$$

where $SR_C = \sqrt{\dfrac{2\pi^2 E}{S_y}}$ is the critical slenderness ratio.

The limitations Eq. (8.57) imposed by Eq. (8.58) insure that the column will remain elastic and that $\sigma_{Allowable} \leq S_y$ even when the residual stresses in the rolled steel section approach one half of the yield strength of the steel.

For columns with slenderness ratios less than $SR_C = [(2\pi^2 E)/S_y]^{1/2}$, a more conservative equation is employed to determine the allowable stress. Because of plastic behavior of the steel with these lower slenderness ratios, a larger safety factor is incorporated in the design equation. The safety factor specified in the design code is a variable depending on (kL/r).

$$SF = 1.667 + 0.375\,[(kL/r)/SR_c] - 0.125\,[(kL/r)^3/SR_C^{\,3})] \qquad (8.59)$$

The allowable stress in this range of (kL/r) is given by:

$$\sigma_{Allowable} = \left(1 - \frac{(kL/r)^2}{2(SR_C)^2}\right)\left(\frac{S_y}{SF}\right) \qquad (8.60)$$

Equation (8.60) is employed for columns with $(kL/r) < SR_c$. A graph showing the allowable stress as a function of the slenderness ratio (kL/r) is presented in Fig. 8.14.

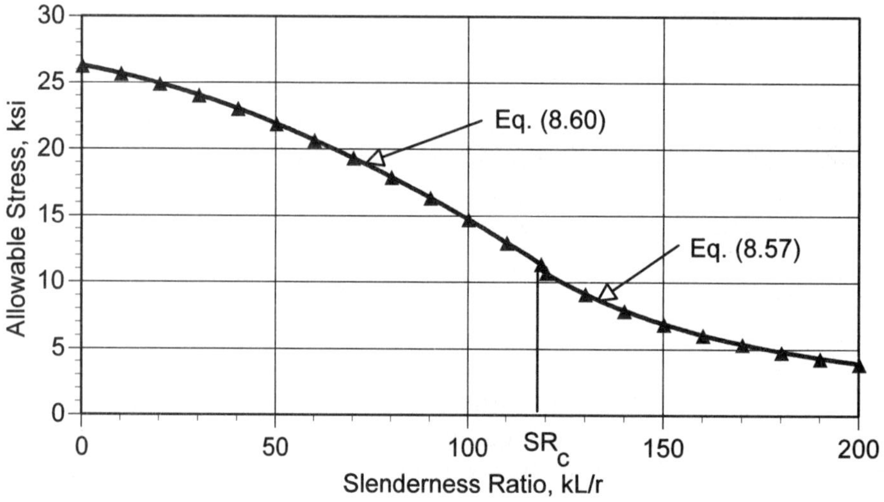

Fig. 8.14 Design curve for pin ended column fabricated from 1020 HR steel with $S_y = 42$ ksi.

A smooth transition from one equation to the other occurs at the critical slenderness ratio when $SR_c = 118.7$ for a steel with $S_y = 30 \times 10^3$ ksi.

EXAMPLE 8.9

A column fabricated from a steel wide flange section W 12 × 50 is pinned at both ends. Use the curve resulting from the code equations that is shown in Fig. 8.14 to determine the allowable centric load applied to the column. The column is 24 ft long.

Solution:

First reference Appendix D and note for the W 12 × 50 section that the minimum value of r = 1.96 in. and A = 14.7 in^2. Also note k = 1 for a column with pinned ends. Determine the slenderness ratio (kL/r):

$$(kL/r) = (1.0)(24)(12)/1.96 = 146.9 \qquad \text{(a)}$$

Employing the graph in Fig. 8.14, we locate the point (kL/r) = 146.9 and draw a line upward to intersect the curve as shown in Fig. E8.9. We then construct a horizontal line from the intersection point to the ordinate to obtain the value of $\sigma_{Allowable}$ = 7.15 ksi.

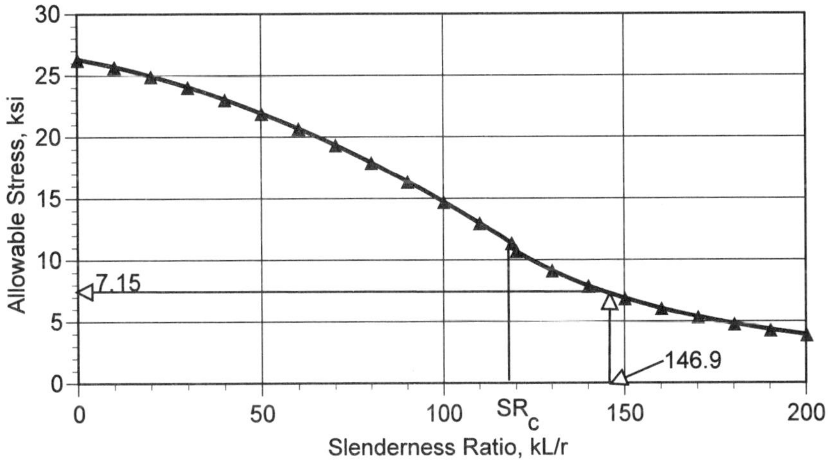

Fig. E8.9

The maximum allowable load on the column is then given by:

$$P_{Allowable} = \sigma_{Allowable}\, A = (7.15)(14.7) = 105.1 \text{ kip} \qquad \text{(b)}$$

Clearly, the use of the design curve and the geometric properties of the wide flange section from Appendix D enable a rapid determination of the maximum allowable centric force applied to the column.

8.7.2 Aluminum Columns

The Aluminum Association has also developed a design code for aluminum columns. It accounts for the elastic and plastic behavior of aluminum by using three different equations to determine the allowable stress. Because the physical properties of aluminum alloys vary considerably from one alloy to another, three equations are provided by the Aluminum Association for each alloy commonly employed in construction. The relations presented below are valid for the alloy 2014 T-6.

$$\sigma_{Allowable} = 28 \text{ ksi} \qquad 0 \leq (kL/r) \leq 12 \qquad (8.61)$$

$$\sigma_{Allowable} = [30.7 - 0.23(kL/r)] \text{ ksi} \qquad 12 \leq (kL/r) \leq 55 \qquad (8.62)$$

$$\sigma_{Allowable} = [54{,}000/(kL/r)^2] \text{ ksi} \qquad 55 \leq (kL/r) \qquad (8.63)$$

The allowable stress $\sigma_{Allowable}$ as a function of (kL/r) was determined from these three equations to develop the design curve presented in Fig. 8.15. Recall that this curve is limited in its use to the aluminum alloy 2014 T-6.

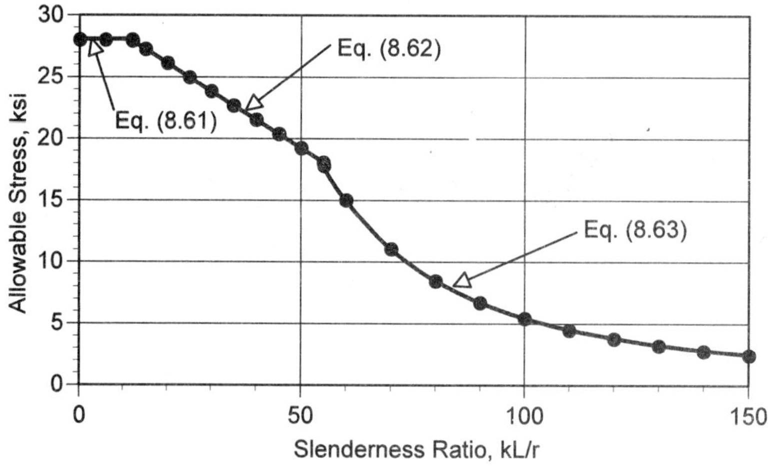

Fig. 8.15 Design curve for a column fabricated from aluminum alloy 2014 T-6 (S_y = 41 ksi).

EXAMPLE 8.10

A column fabricated from an aluminum (2014 T-6) structural T section WT 6 × 48 is pinned at one end and built-in at the other. Use the curve resulting from the code equations that is shown in Fig. 8.15, to determine the allowable centric load applied to the column. The column is 18 ft long.

Solution:

First reference Appendix D and note for the WT 6 × 48 section that the minimum value of r is 1.51 in. Also the area A is 14.1 in^2. Note k = 0.7 for a column pinned at one end and built-in at the other. Determine the slenderness ratio (kL/r):

$$(kL/r) = (0.7)(18)(12)/(1.51) = 100.1 \quad \text{(a)}$$

Employing the graph in Fig. 8.15, we locate the point (kL/r) = 101.1 and draw a line upward to intersect the curve as shown in Fig. E8.10. We then construct a horizontal line from the intersection point to the ordinate to obtain the value of $\sigma_{Allowable}$ = 5.40 ksi.

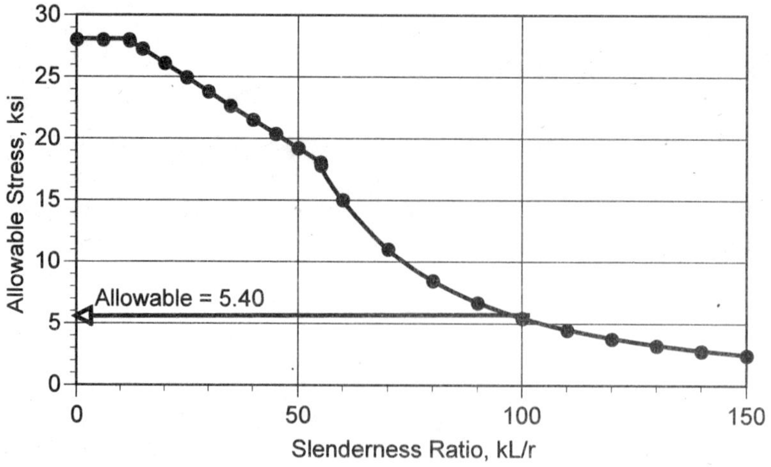

Fig. E8.10

The maximum allowable load on the column is then given by:

$$P_{Allowable} = \sigma_{Allowable} A = (5.40)(14.1) = 76.14 \text{ kip} \quad \text{(b)}$$

Clearly, the use of the design curve and the geometric properties of the structural tee section from Appendix D enable a rapid determination of the maximum allowable centric force applied to the column.

8.7.3 Wood Columns

Design of both columns and beams fabricated from wood is difficult because the physical properties of wood depend on the type of tree used to produce the structural members and the region in the country where the tree was grown. Also the moisture content of the wood affects its properties. To deal with these many variables, the American Forest and Paper Association has published the National Design Specification for Wood Construction. The Western Woods Products Association has incorporated these design specifications in an excellent reference for designing structural members fabricated from many types of woods in their Western Woods Use Book[3].

A computer program is provided with the Western Woods Use Book that has merged the physical properties of several types of woods with the design relations adopted by the wood products and construction industries. This program enables the user to determine allowable column loading and beam loading while taking into account several factors affecting the physical properties of the wood such as section size, duration of the load, temperature and moisture content.

8.8 SUMMARY

The concept of elastic instability was introduced. Columns can fail by buckling at stress levels lower than the yield strength of the materials from which they are fabricated. Failure by buckling is catastrophic as the column collapses suddenly. The critical load P_{CR} depends on the end conditions of the column, with its critical load increasing as the constraint at its ends increase.

Equations for P_{CR} were derived for four different end conditions. The results are given by:

$$P_{CR} = \frac{\pi^2 EI}{(kL)^2} \quad (8.24)$$

where k, given in the table below, accounts for the constraint provided by the column supports.

Case No.	End Constraints	k
1	Pinned—Pinned	1
2	Pinned—Built-in	0.7
3	Free—Built-in	2
4	Built-in—Built-in	0.5

[3] Available from Western Woods Products Association, 522 SW 5th Avenue, Suite 400, Portland, OR 97204.

The moment of inertia I of the cross section of the column in Eq. (8.24) is almost always taken as the minimum value.

The critical stress σ_{CR} in centric loaded columns was defined as:

$$\sigma_{CR} = P_{CR}/A \qquad (8.42)$$

The critical stress may be written as:

$$\sigma_{CR} = \frac{\pi^2 EI}{L^2 A} = \frac{\pi^2 EAr^2}{L^2 A} = \frac{\pi^2 E}{(L/r)^2} \qquad (8.43)$$

where A is the cross sectional area of the column and r is the radius of gyration of the area.

The term (L/r) is known as the slenderness ratio of the column. As (L/r) increases, the column becomes more flexible and will buckle at lower stress levels. When the slenderness ratio is large, columns buckle in accordance with Eq. (8.24); however, for shorter and stiffer columns $\sigma_{CR} > S_y$. In these cases the column fails by yielding. The transition from the Euler theory of buckling to yielding occurs at a limit value of (L/r), which depends on the modulus of elasticity and yield strength of the column material as indicated in Fig. E8.6. Safety and failure regions for a typical column are illustrated in Fig. 8.9.

When the load applied to a column, which exhibits some eccentricity, a bending moment is produced that affects the stresses in the column. However, the eccentricity does not affect the critical bucking load. While the result for P_{CR} is the same, the bucking process differs. With centric loading the column remains straight as the load P is increased until P_{CR} was achieved. At that load, the column becomes unstable and suddenly buckles (collapses). With eccentricity, the column deflects laterally with increasing magnitude until the critical load is achieved and then it collapses.

The stress in an eccentrically loaded column is due to a combination of a compressive stress σ_a due to P and a bending stress σ_b due to the moment M = Pe. The two stresses superimpose as indicated by:

$$\sigma_c = \sigma_a + \sigma_b = -(P/A + Mc/I) \qquad (8.56)$$

Finally, a sampling of the design codes for columns fabricated from steel and aluminum were described. These codes are extensive and in practice control the design of columns placed in most major structures. Reference was also given for design codes for columns and beams fabricated from timber.

PROBLEMS

8.1 Write an engineering brief explaining why understanding buckling is important in ensuring public safety.

8.2 An 20 ft long column is fabricated from an aluminum tube with an outside diameter of 8.5 in. and an inside diameter of 7.5 in. as shown in Fig. P8.2 Determine the critical buckling force P_{CR} if the tube is pinned at both ends.

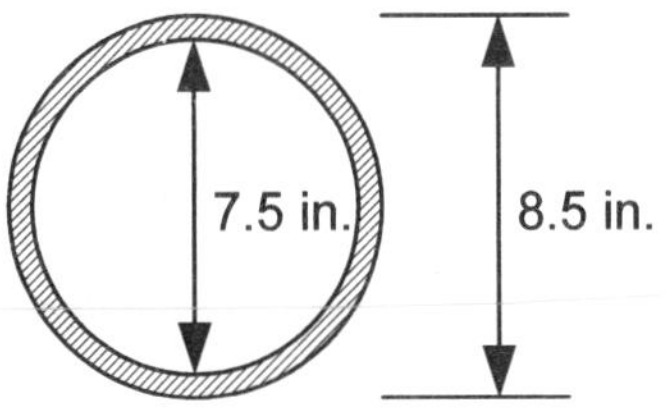

Fig. P8.2

8.3 Repeat Problem 8.2 if the column is fabricated from steel and its length is changed to 24 ft. All the other parameters remain the same.

8.4 A 6.5 m long column is fabricated from a square steel tube as illustrated in Fig. P8.4. Determine the critical buckling force P_{CR} if the tube is pinned at both ends. Also determine the compressive stress in the tube at the critical load and comment on its magnitude.

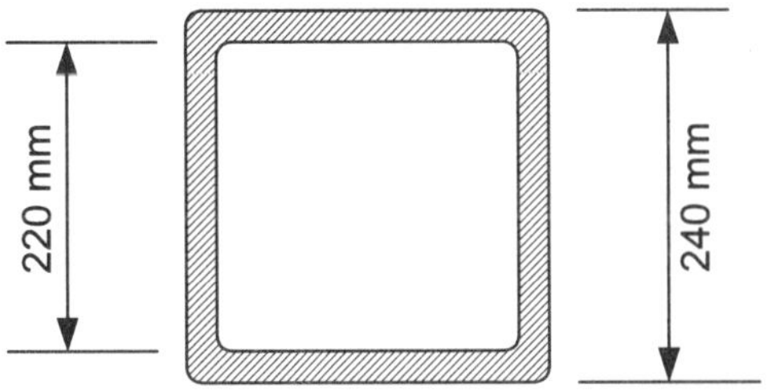

Fig. P8.4

8.5 Repeat Problem 8.4 if the column is fabricated from aluminum and its length is changed to 5.3 m. All the other parameters remain the same.

8.6 A 5.8 m long column is fabricated from an aluminum tube with the rectangular cross section defined in Fig. P8.6. The column is pinned at one end and built-in at the other. Determine the critical buckling force P_{CR}.

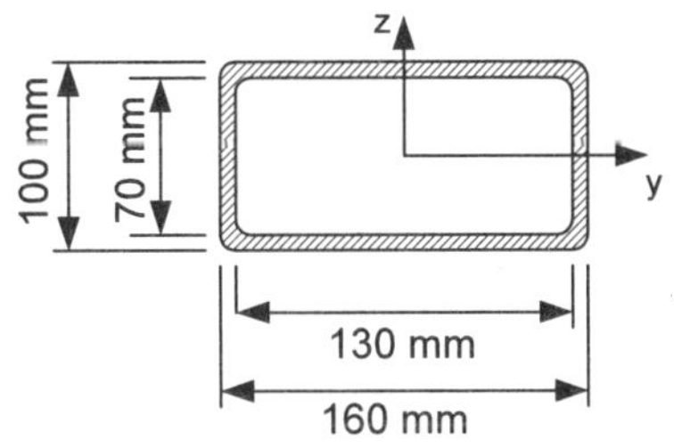

Fig. P8.6

8.7 Repeat Problem 8.6 if the column is fabricated from steel and its length is changed to 4.9 m. All the other parameters remain the same.

8.8 Design a round tubular column for a construction firm that is to be fabricated from aluminum. The column is 7.0 m long and is expected to support a critical load of 340 kN. The ratio of its inside to outside diameter is 0.85. Pins support both of its ends.

8.9 Design a column fabricated from an aluminum, square-tubular section for a construction firm. The column is 20 ft long and is expected to support a critical load of 120 kip. The ratio of its inside to outside dimensions is 0.90. Pins support both of its ends.

8.10 Design a column that is fabricated from a steel rectangular section. The column is 24 ft long and is expected to support a critical load of 150 kip. The ratio of its inside to outside dimensions is 0.85 ($w_i/w_o = d_i/d_o = 0.85$). Both of its ends are built-in.

8.11 Select the most suitable wide flange section for the design of a steel column 7.6 m long. The column is expected to support a load of 450 kN and is built-in on both ends.

8.12 Select the most suitable American Standard section for the column described in Problem 8.11 if the loading is increased to 500 kN. All the other parameters remain the same.

8.13 Select the most suitable American Standard section for the design of an aluminum column 19 ft long. The column is expected to support a load of 140 kip and is built-in on one end and pinned on the other.

8.14 Select the most suitable American Standard section for the column described in Problem 8.14 if the length of the column is decreased to 15 ft. All the other parameters remain the same.

8.15 Select the most suitable structural tee section for the design of a steel column 5.8 m long. The column is expected to support a load of 210 kN and is built-in on both ends.

8.16 Repeat Problem 8.15 if the load on the column is increased to 305 kN. All the other parameters remain the same.

8.17 A control rod in a vehicle is subjected to axial forces of ± 3,200 lb. If it is fabricated from stainless steel determine its diameter if the design incorporates a safety factor of 2.8. Consider its ends pinned.

8.18 Repeat Problem 8.17 if the material of the control rod is changed to aluminum and the safety factor is increased to 3.0. All the other parameters remain the same.

8.19 A lever is used to provide an axial force to a 30 in. long vertical member as shown in Fig. P8.19. Determine the maximum force F that may be exerted if the vertical link is fabricated from an aluminum bar with a rectangular cross section. The dimensions of the rectangular bar are 0.75 in. by 1.5 in. Note all of the joints are pinned.

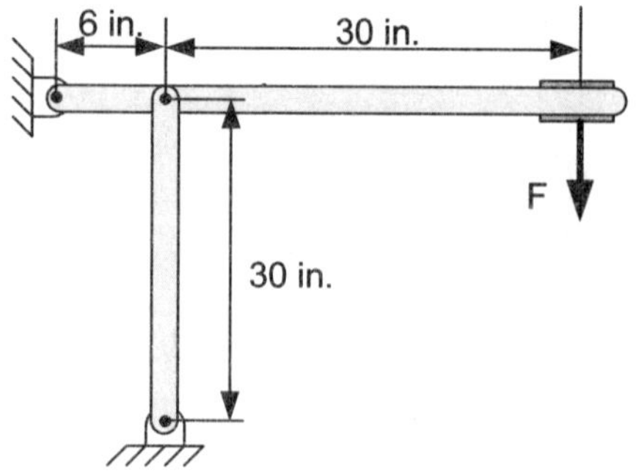

Fig. P8.19

8.20 The truss, shown in Fig. P8.20, is fabricated from round, steel tubes. If the tubes all have the same outside diameter of 80 mm, determine the inside diameter of the compression members required to prevent buckling. Employ a safety factor of 4.0.

Fig. P8.20

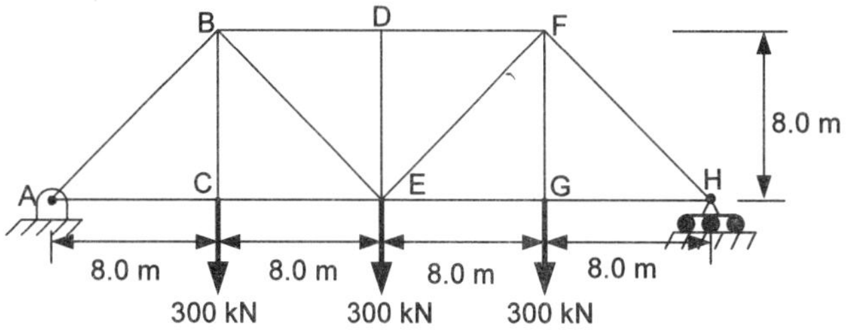

8.21 Repeat Problem 8.20 if the three loads are changed from 300 kN to 400 kN. All the other parameters remain the same.

8.22 The truss, shown in Fig. P8.22, is fabricated from square, steel tubes. If the tubes all have the same outside dimension of $s_o = 4.0$ in., determine the inside dimension s_i of the compression members required to prevent buckling. Employ a safety factor of 2.5.

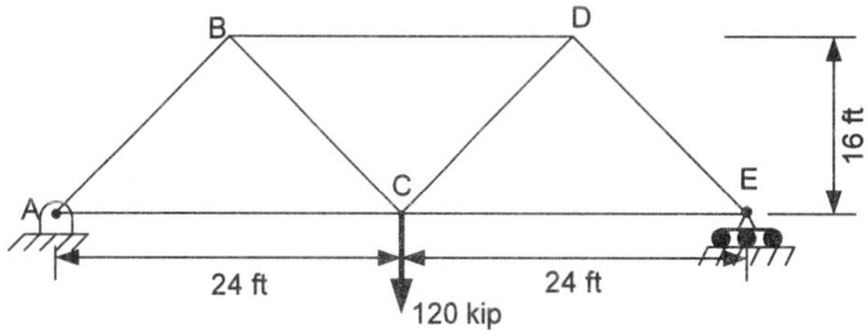

Fig. P8.22

8.23 Repeat Problem 8.22 if the load is increased to 180 kip. All the other parameters remain the same.

8.24 A force F acts on a simple truss containing a horizontal tie rod and an inclined strut, as shown in Fig. P8.24. The strut, fabricated from an aluminum alloy, is rectangular with dimensions w and d. Determine those dimensions if w = 2d and a safety factor of 2.75 is required.

Fig. P8.24

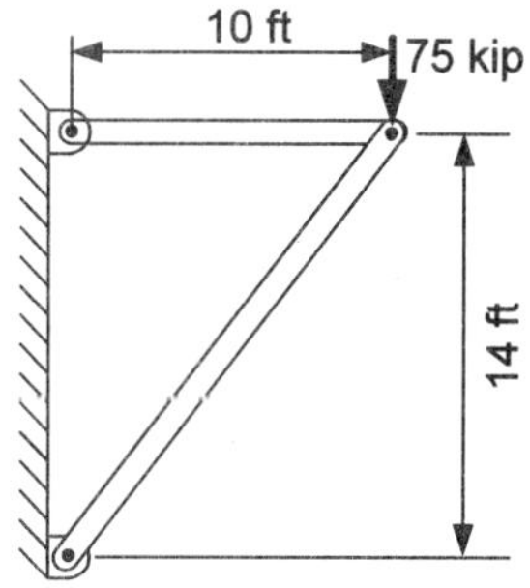

8.25 Repeat Problem 8.24 if the load is increased to 120 kip. All the other parameters remain the same.

8.26 For the frame, shown in Fig. P8.26, determine the maximum force that can be supported before the inclined member buckles. The inclined member is fabricated from a rectangular steel bar with dimensions w = 2.5 in. and d = 1.5 in.

Fig. P8.26

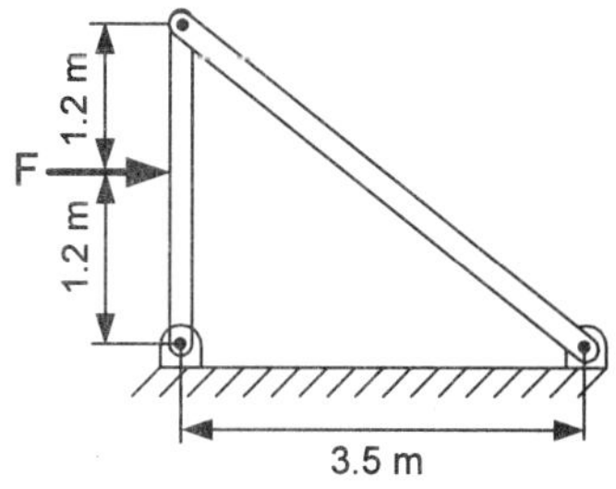

8.27 The truss, shown in Fig. P8.27, is fabricated from rectangular, steel tubes. If the tubes all have the same outside dimension of w_o = 150 mm in. and d_o = 75 mm determine the wall thickness of the compression members required to prevent buckling. Employ a safety factor of 3.3.

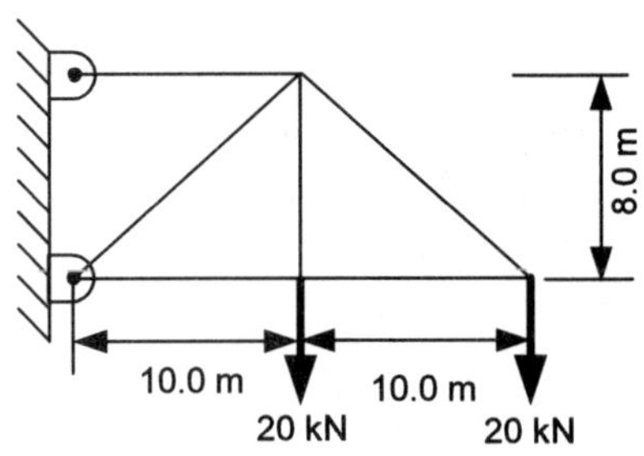

Fig. P8.27

8.28 Repeat Problem 8.27 if the two loads are increased to 30 kN. All the other parameters remain the same.

8.29 A wooden column, with a square cross section, is subjected to an eccentric load as shown in Fig. P8.29. The column is embedded in a concrete footer at one end and free at the other. Determine the load that can be applied to the column without causing it to fail by either buckling or breaking. The column is fabricated from Western white pine.

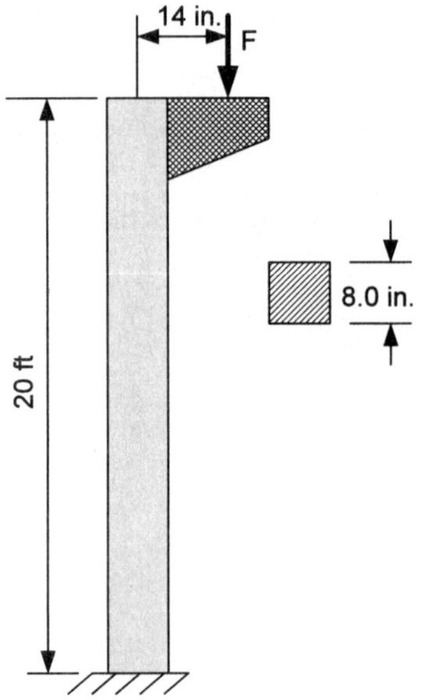

Fig. P8.29

8.30 A column fabricated from a W305 × 74 wide flange section is loaded eccentrically as indicated in Fig. P8.30. Determine the force F required for the column to fail by either buckling or yielding. The wide flange section is fabricated from 1020 HR steel. The column is braced so that it does not buckle about its minimum inertia axis. Assume the top of the column is free.

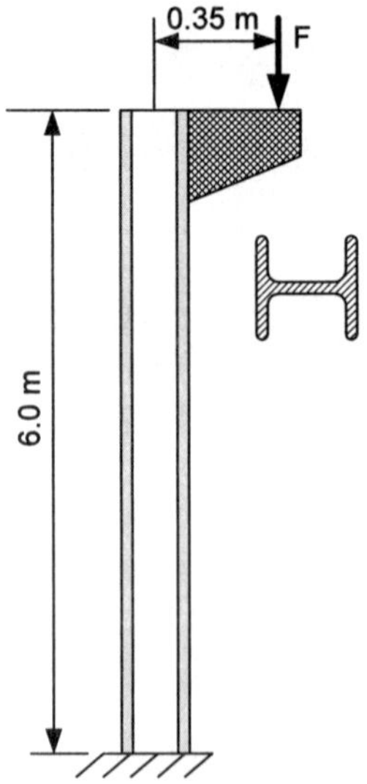

Fig. P8.30

8.31 Repeat Problem 8.30 if the column is replaced with an American Standard section S381 × 64. All the other parameters remain the same.

8.32 Determine the deflection y_{Max} at the top of the column, shown in Fig. P8.30, when the applied load F is equal to 75% of the failure load.

8.33 A column, fabricated from a S 203 × 34 American Standard section, is loaded eccentrically as indicated in Fig. P8.33. Determine the force F required for the column to fail by either buckling or yielding. The American Standard section is fabricated from 1020 HR steel. Assume both ends of the column are built-in, and that bracing prevents buckling about the minimum inertia axis.

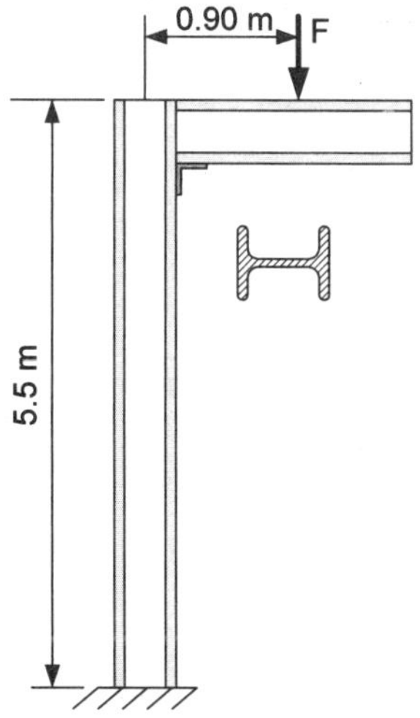

Fig. P8.33

8.34 Repeat Problem 8.33 if the column is replaced with an wide flange W305 × 74. All the other parameters remain the same.

8.35 A column is fabricated from a solid aluminum rod with a diameter of 80 mm as shown in Fig. P8.35. It is loaded with a force F with an eccentricity e = 40 mm. Determine the maximum force F that can be applied to the column before it fails by either buckling or yielding. The aluminum alloy employed is 2024-T-4.

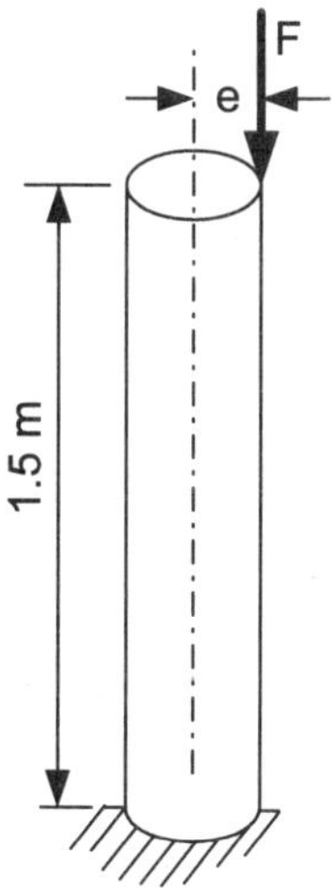

Fig. P8.35

8.36 Develop a design curve similar to the one shown in Fig. 8.14 for steel columns with pinned/pinned ends and with a yield strength of 75 ksi. Also determine the limiting value of the slenderness ratio SR_c for this case.

8.37 Develop a design curve similar to the one shown in Fig. 8.14 for steel columns with pinned/pinned ends and with a yield strength of 100 ksi. Also determine the limiting value of the slenderness ratio SR_c for this case.

8.38 Determine the safety factor as a function of (kL/r) that is employed using the design code for steel columns. Consider yield strengths of 30, 40, 50 and 60 ksi.

8.39 A 7.2 m long column is fabricated from a W 254 × 45 steel wide flange section with pinned/pinned ends. Use the curve resulting from the code equations that is shown in Fig. 8.14, to determine the allowable centric load applied to the column.

8.40 A 6.8 m long column is fabricated from a S 178 × 23 steel American Standard section with pinned/pinned ends. Use the curve resulting from the code equations that is shown in Fig. 8.14, to determine the allowable centric load applied to the column.

8.41 A 5.0 m long column is fabricated from aluminum (2014 T-6) in the form of a WT 178 × 36 structural tee section. Use the curve resulting from the code equations that is shown in Fig. 8.15, to determine the allowable centric load applied to the column. The ends are both built-in.

8.42 An aluminum (2014-T6) tube with a square cross section, shown in Fig. P8.42, is to be employed in a building lobby. The column length is 6.2 m and its ends are both built in. Use the curve resulting from the code equations that is shown in Fig. 8.15, to determine the allowable centric load applied to the column.

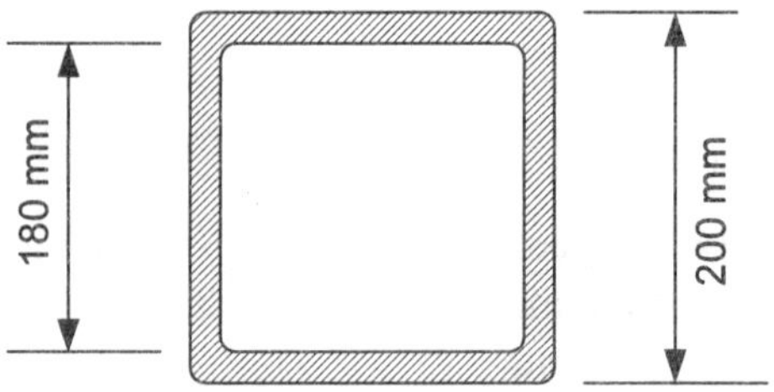

Fig. P8.42

8.43 Repeat Problem 8.42, but change its length to 5.6 m. All other parameters remain the same.

CHAPTER 9

STRESS CONCENTRATIONS

9.1 INTRODUCTION

In our discussion of stresses in uniform, tapered or stepped bars in Chapter 2, we assumed that the stresses were uniformly distributed over the cross sectional area of the bar. For the uniform and the tapered bars, this is a valid assumption except near the ends of the bar where the external forces are applied. However, for the stepped bar, the stresses are not uniformly distributed across the section in the vicinity of the step. Indeed, whenever we encounter a discontinuity such as a step or a hole in a bar, the stresses tend to concentrate at that discontinuity. As a consequence, the use of Eq. (2.4) to compute the stresses seriously underestimates their actual value. We must account for the effect of the structural discontinuities by determining a suitable stress concentration factor.

Stress concentrations also occur at discontinuities in shafts subjected to torsion loads and beams in bending. The stress concentrations result in a significant elevation of the stresses in a local region adjacent to the discontinuity. Methods for determining stresses at discontinuities in bars subjected to axial loading using stress concentration factors are introduced in Section 9.2. Similarly methods for determining stresses at discontinuities in shafts and beams using stress concentration factors are introduced in Section 9.4 and Section 9.5, respectively. Because the topic of stress concentration factors is extremely important, the reader is referred to an excellent book by R. E. Peterson for an extended coverage that includes many more structural members [1].

The influence of the stress concentration factors on the failure of structural members is dependent on the ductility of the material from which the member is fabricated as well as the nature of the loading. If the material used to fabricate the structural member is brittle, the elevated stresses in the local region adjacent to the discontinuity are effective in initiating failure with little evidence of ductility. However, if the material from which the structural member is fabricated is ductile, then local yielding of the region of elevated stresses occurs that relieves the concentrated stresses and the effect of the stress concentration is largely mitigated.

Relief of the concentrated stresses for ductile materials avoids failure only if the applied load is static. With static loading, the load is applied once and is maintained on the structure during its entire life. Static loading is common in buildings that are loaded slowly during construction. However, loading of structural members found in vehicles and many bridges is not static, because the structures are loaded, unloaded and reloaded many thousands of times. When cyclic loading is applied to structures, the elevated stresses due to stress concentrations must be taken into account, because fatigue cracks are initiated in the region of elevated stress adjacent to the discontinuity. Methods to estimate fatigue life in structures with stress concentrations are presented in Section 9.3.

9.2 STRESS CONCENTRATION FACTORS IN TENSION MEMBERS

9.2.1 Stress Concentration Factors Due to Circular Holes in Bars

Let's consider the bar with a centrally located circular hole subjected to an axial tension force as shown in Fig. 9.1.

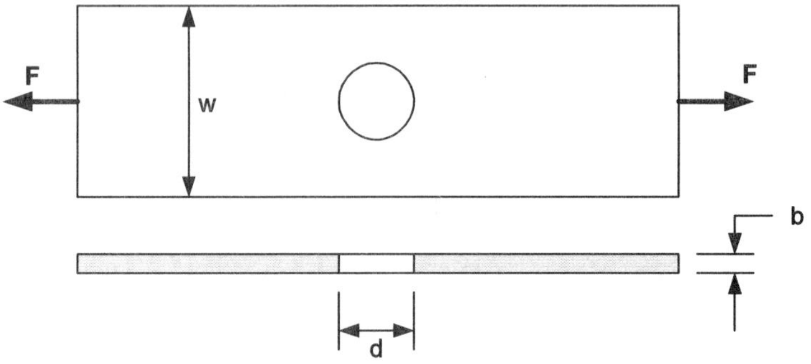

Fig. 9.1 A centrally located circular hole in an axially loaded bar.

The stress distribution in a section removed three or more diameters from the hole is uniform with a magnitude given by Eq. (2.4) as $\sigma_o = F/(bw)$. However, on the section through the center of the hole the stress distribution shows significant variation. The stresses increase sharply adjacent to the discontinuity (the hole) and concentrate at this location. The maximum value of the normal stress occurs adjacent to the hole as indicated in Fig 9.2.

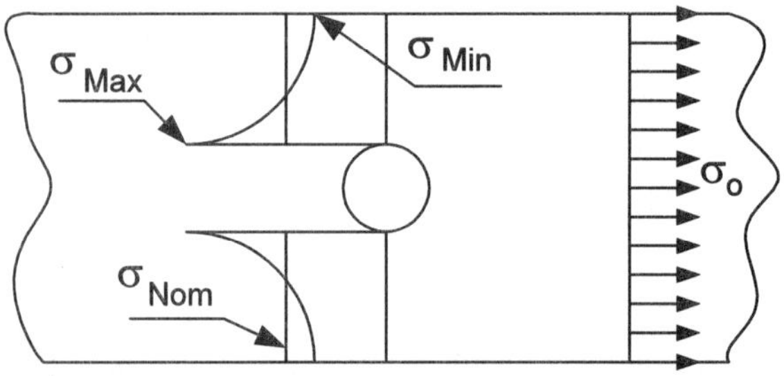

Fig. 9.2 Distribution of stress across a section through the center of the hole shows the concentration of stresses adjacent to the boundary of the hole.

We are interested in determining the maximum stress, σ_{Max} adjacent to the hole. It is convenient to express the maximum stresses in terms of a stress concentration factor by employing:

$$\sigma_{Max} = K\,\sigma_{Nom} \tag{9.1}$$

where K is the stress concentration factor and σ_{Nom} is the nominal stress.

The **nominal stress** is the average stress across the net section containing the hole, and is given by:

$$\sigma_{Nom} = F/A_{Nom} = F/[(w-d)b] \tag{9.2}$$

where b is the thickness of the bar, w is the bar width and d is the hole diameter.

The uniform stress σ_o and the nominal stress σ_{Nom} are related by:

$$F = \sigma_{Nom} A_{Nom} = \sigma_o A_{Uniform} \quad (a)$$

Substituting for the areas in Eq. (a) and simplifying yields:

$$\sigma_{Nom} = [w/(w - d)]\sigma_o \quad (9.3)$$

The nominal stress σ_{Nom} is always greater than the uniform stress σ_0, because the factor w/(w – d) is always greater than one.

The **stress concentration factor** K for a uniform thickness bar with a central circular hole subjected to axial loading is a function of the ratio of d/w as shown in Fig. 9.3.

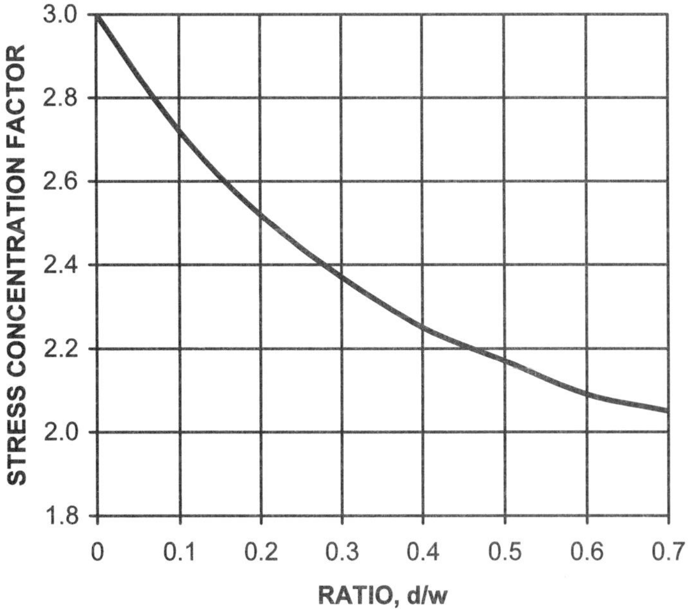

Fig. 9.3 Stress concentration factor for a central circular hole in an axially loaded bar.

EXAMPLE 9.1

A centrally located hole of diameter d = 0.5 in. is drilled in a long thin bar that is subjected to an axial load of 8,000 lb. If the bar is defined by w = 1.5 in., and b = 0.50 in., determine the nominal stress, the stress concentration and the maximum stress.

Solution:

The nominal stress is given by Eq. (9.2) as:

$$\sigma_{Nom} = F/[b(w - d)] = (8{,}000)/[(1.5 - 0.5)(0.5)] = 16{,}000 \text{ psi} \quad (a)$$

The stress concentration K is determined from Fig. 9.3, by locating the intercept of a vertical line originating at d/w = 0.5/1.5 = 0.3333 with the curve. This intercept gives K = 2.33.

Finally, the maximum stress is given by Eq. (9.1) as:

$$\sigma_{Max} = K\, \sigma_{Nom} = (2.33)(16{,}000) = 37.28 \text{ ksi} \quad (b)$$

By drilling a hole in the bar, we have increased the maximum stress significantly. The procedure using the stress concentration factor provides a simple yet effective approach for solving a very difficult stress analysis problem. Also, you should be aware that the uniform stress in the bar prior to drilling the hole was σ_o = 10.67 ksi; therefore, the presence of the hole increased the stresses by a factor of 3.49.

9.2.2 Stress Concentrations in Shouldered Bars

The stepped bar is another configuration with an abrupt change in the section of the bar. This geometric discontinuity produces a non-uniform distribution of stresses and a concentration of stress at the fillet used in transitioning from one section of the bar to the other. The geometric parameters involved in characterizing the stress concentration factor are w_2/w_1 and r/w_1 as defined in Fig. 9.4.

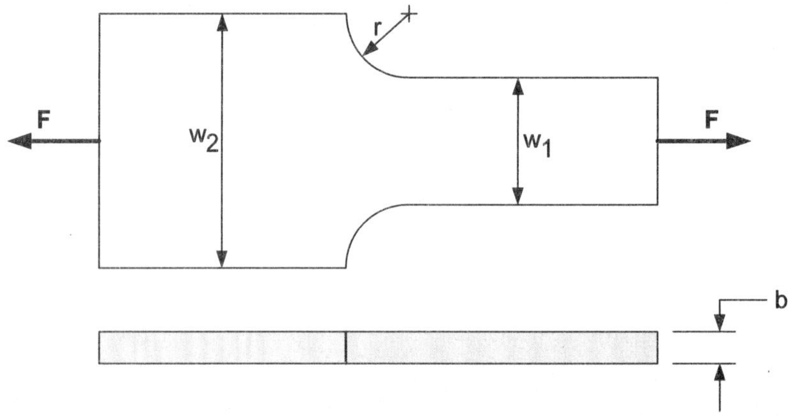

Fig. 9.4 Geometric parameters controlling the stress concentration in a stepped bar.

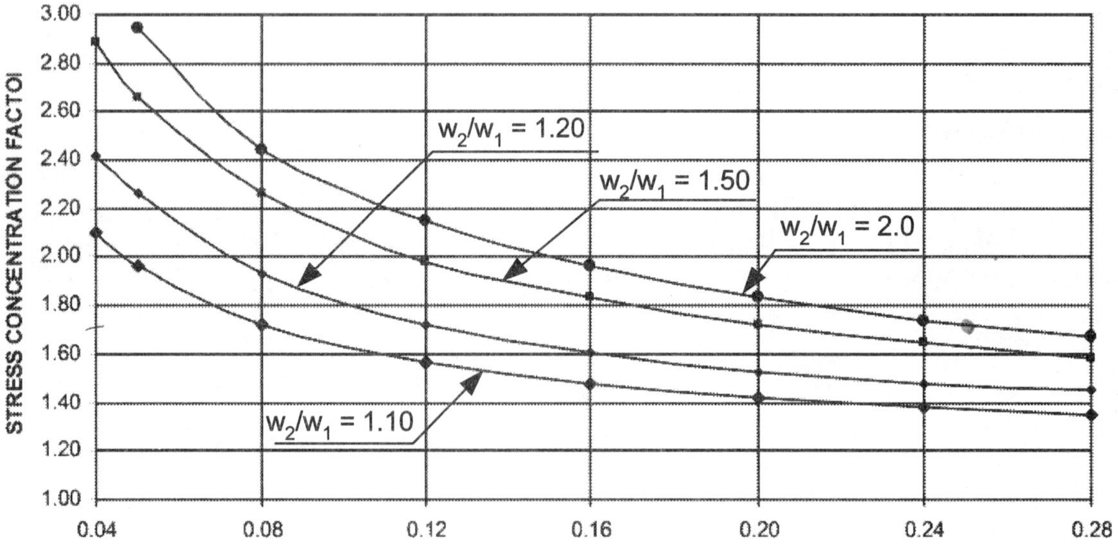

Fig. 9.5 Stress concentration factor for a stepped bar subjected to axial forces.

The maximum stress occurs at the fillet in the transition from the narrow section of the bar (w_1) to the wider section (w_2). The maximum stress is determined from Eq. (9.1). However, for the case of the stepped bar the nominal stress is defined as:

$$\sigma_{Nom} = P/(w_1 b) \qquad (9.4)$$

The stress concentration factor K for the stepped bar depends on two different ratios r/w_1 and w_2/w_1. as shown in Fig 9.5.

EXAMPLE 9.2

Consider the axially loaded stepped bar shown in Fig. E9.2, and determine the maximum stress at the fillet in the transition region of the bar.

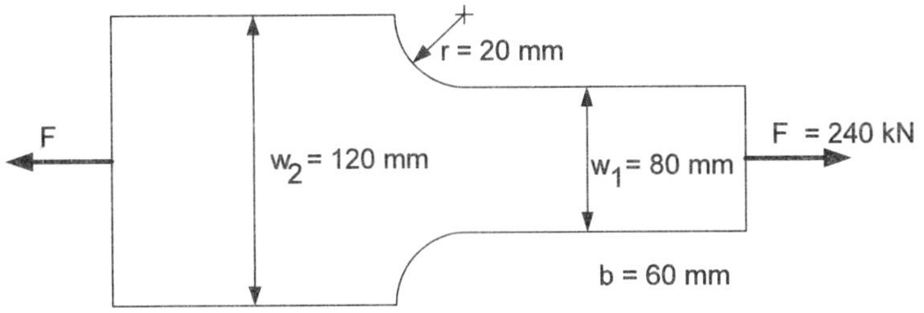

Fig. E9.2

Solution:

From Eq. (9.1), we write $\sigma_{Max} = K\,\sigma_{Nom}$.

From Eq. (9.4), write:

$$\sigma_{Nom} = P/(w_1 b) = (240 \times 10^3)/[(80)(60)] = 50 \text{ MPa} \qquad (a)$$

To determine the stress concentration factor K, we note that $r/w_1 = 20/80 = 0.25$, and $w_2/w_1 = 120/80 = 1.5$. Reading the chart for the stress concentration factor in Fig. 9.5, we establish that K is:

$$K = 1.63 \qquad (b)$$

Finally, Eq. (9.1) yields:

$$\sigma_{Max} = K\,\sigma_{Nom} = (1.63)(50) = 81.5 \text{ MPa} \qquad (c)$$

9.3 FATIGUE STRENGTH

Many structures are loaded only once. For example, the structural members in the Sears tower in Chicago were loaded by the dead weight of all of the structural components as the tower was constructed. The people, furnishings and equipment going into the tower added some weight, but this additional load was small when compared to the weight of the basic structure. For structures and machine components loaded only once, either the yield strength or the ultimate tensile strength is adequate to predict the safety of the structure.

However, many structures and machine components are subjected to repeated loading. Very heavy tractor-trailer trucks, for example, traverse a bridge. With the passage of each truck every bridge member is subjected to another cycle of loading. Consider the engine of your automobile. If you are driving along a highway with the tachometer registering 3,600 RPM, you are subjecting the crankshaft in your engine to 3,600 cycles of load for each minute of its operation.

There are two detrimental effects due to the cyclic loading of structures and machine components. First, the design strength of the material from which the structure is fabricated is lowered. We design to a fatigue strength S_f that is a function of the cyclic stresses and the number of cycles of load imposed onto the structure.

Second, fatigue failures in **ductile** materials are of a **brittle** nature (i.e., structural failure and collapse occur catastrophically). The failure mechanism in fatigue is markedly different from that observed in yielding or rupture. In fatigue, microscopic cracks are initiated due to accumulated irreversible slip in a very thin layer of material adjacent to the surface. These cracks grow larger and extend into the material until reaching a critical size. At this time, the cracks become unstable and extend at high speed across the structural member producing sudden and catastrophic collapse. Examination of a surface of a fatigue failure shows the brittle nature of the phenomena. Although the material may be classified as ductile based on the results of a tensile test, there is no visible sign of coarse slip or necking associated with failure in fatigue.

9.3.1 The S_f - N Diagram

To accommodate for the degrading effects of cyclic loading, we compare the applied stresses with the **fatigue strength, S_f** of the material from which the structure is fabricated. A typical example of the fatigue strength for low carbon steel is presented in the S_f-N diagram of Fig. 9.6.

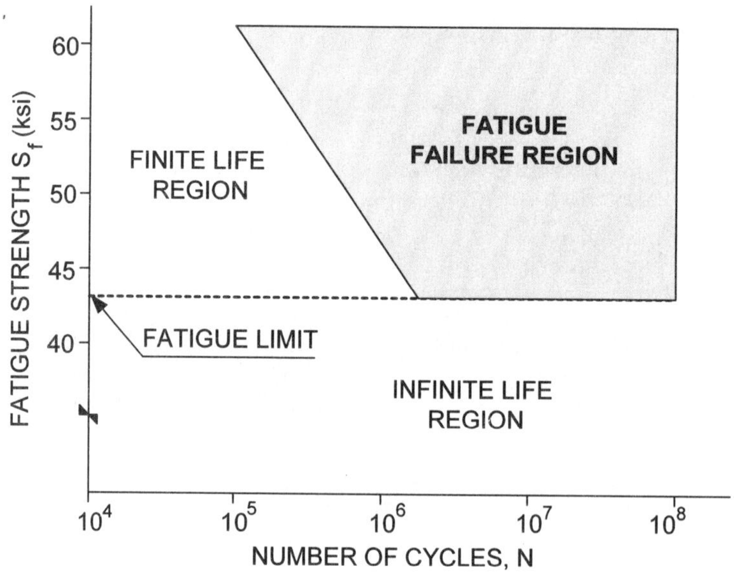

Fig. 9.6 S_f – N curve for high strength low alloy steel.

The S_f - N diagram is a graphical representation showing both safe and critical states of cyclic stresses. This diagram is divided into three different regions:

1. The failure region (shaded) where many cycles of high stresses produce a fatigue crack leading to fracture.

2. Safe regions where component stresses lower than the fatigue (endurance) limit ensure infinite cyclic life.
3. A finite-life region where a finite number of cycles can be endured at a specified stress level that is greater than the fatigue limit.

For infinite life, the fatigue strength is often called the endurance limit S_e where:

$$S_e = S_f \qquad \text{for } N > 10^6 \text{ cycles} \tag{9.5}$$

For finite life, with the number of cycles less than about 10^6, the fatigue strength S_f is larger than S_e. The value of S_f used in a design analysis is determined from the S_f-N diagram for the material used to fabricate the structural elements. Example 9.4 demonstrates the technique used to determine the strength S_f associated with finite life.

In comparing the cyclic stresses with the strength as defined in Fig. 9.6, we use the alternating portion of the applied stresses. The alternating stress, σ_a, and the mean stress, σ_m, for different types of cyclic loading are defined in the stress-time diagrams presented in Fig. 9.7. We compute the mean stress for cyclic loading by identifying the maximum and minimum stress in a given cycle of applied loading. The mean cyclic stress is the average of the maximum and minimum stress, which is given by:

$$\sigma_m = (\sigma_{Max} + \sigma_{Min})/(2) \tag{9.6}$$

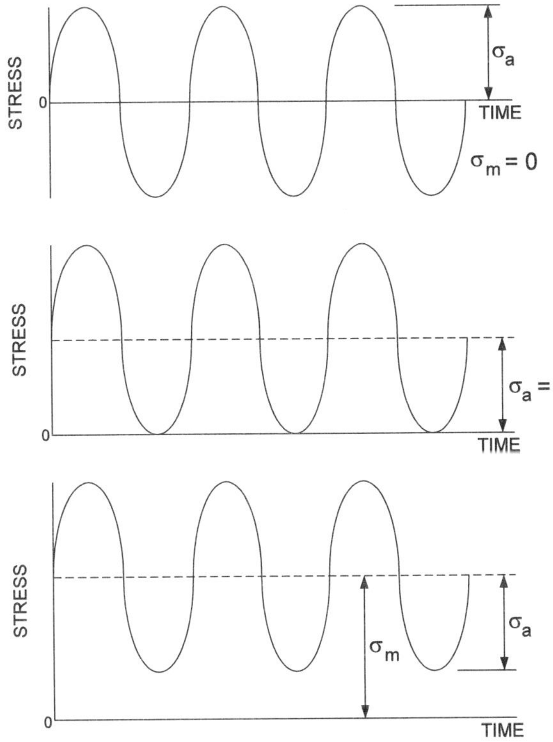

Fig. 9.7 Different types of cyclic stresses imposed on a structure.

The alternating stress is determined from the difference in the maximum and minimum stress during a typical load cycle. The relation used to determine the alternating cyclic stress is given by:

$$\sigma_a = (\sigma_{Max} - \sigma_{Min})/(2) \tag{9.7}$$

The method used to determine the safety of a structural member when subjected to cyclic loading is described in Examples 9.3 and 9.4.

EXAMPLE 9.3

Consider a cross beam used in constructing a bridge. The dead weight of the bridge structure produces a stress of 22,000 psi in this beam. However, when a fully loaded tractor-trailer crosses over the beam the stress increases to 65,000 psi. The beam is fabricated from a material with the fatigue properties described in Fig. 9.6. The strengths, yield and ultimate tensile, of this material are 66 ksi and 96 ksi, respectively. Will the beam fail in fatigue? If failure occurs, predict the cyclic life of the structure. Neglect the effect of the mean stress on fatigue strength in this example.

Solution:

Determine the alternating stresses imposed on the bridge beam from Eq. (9.7).

$$\sigma_a = (\sigma_{Max} - \sigma_{Min})/(2) = (65{,}000 - 22{,}000)/(2) = 21.5 \text{ ksi} \qquad \text{(a)}$$

Next, compare this value to the fatigue limit of 43 ksi that is obtained by reading the S_f - N curve in Fig. 9.6. Clearly $S_f = 43$ ksi $> \sigma_a = 21.5$ ksi. The alternating stresses are less than the endurance limit and the bridge beam is safe. Indeed, the safety factor is determined from a modified form of Eq. (2.31) as:

$$\mathbf{SF_f} = S_f/\sigma_a \qquad (9.8)$$

$$\mathbf{SF_f} = (43)/(21.5) = 2.00$$

The mean stress imposed on the bridge beam during the cyclic loading is determined from Eq. (9.6) as:

$$\sigma_m = (\sigma_{Max} + \sigma_{Min})/(2) = (65{,}000 + 22{,}000)/(2) = 43.5 \text{ ksi} \qquad \text{(b)}$$

This is a relatively large mean stress to impose on a beam. As a consequence, the fatigue strength will be lower than that obtained from the S_f–N curve to account for the effects of the large tensile mean stress. This solution is modified in Example 9.5 to account for the effects of mean stresses in reducing the allowable alternating stresses.

EXAMPLE 9.4

Consider the crankshaft of a high performance racecar which is subjected to maximum and minimum stresses of + 345 MPa and – 345 MPa. If the crankshaft is fabricated from the high strength low alloy steel described in Fig. 9.6, determine its fatigue life.

Solution:

Let's first determine the alternating stress σ_a for the crankshaft from Eq. (9.7).

$$\sigma_a = (\sigma_{Max} - \sigma_{Min})/(2) = [345 - (-345)]/(2) = 345 \text{ MPa} \qquad \text{(a)}$$

Next convert this result from MPa units to ksi units so that we may employ a graphical approach using the fatigue properties of the high-strength, low-alloy steel shown in Fig. 9.6.

$$\sigma_a = (345 \text{ MPa})(1 \text{ ksi}) /(6.895 \text{ MPa}) = 50.0 \text{ ksi} \qquad \text{(b)}$$

Plot σ_a = 50.0 ksi at point A on the ordinate of the S_f-N diagram shown in Fig. E9.4. Extend a line parallel to the abscissa until it intersects the shaded (fatigue failure) region and plot point B. Drop a vertical line from point B until it intersects the axis defining the cyclic life to establish point C. Point C gives the anticipated cyclic life, which in this example is less than 10^6 cycles. For a crankshaft operating at 5,000 RPM in a high-performance racing car, the anticipated life is less than three hours. Clearly, this life is too short by several orders of magnitude and the design of the crankshaft is inadequate. Either the crankshaft size must be increased to lower the stress level or a different material with a higher endurance limit S_e must be selected.

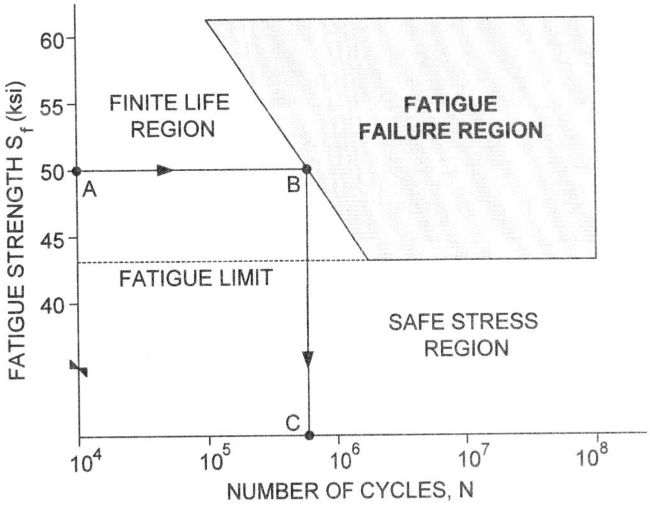

Fig. E9.4

9.3.2 The Goodman Diagram

In some instances, the cyclic loading on a structural member produces a combination of alternating and mean stresses. When mean stresses are superimposed on the alternating stresses, the effect is to decrease the fatigue strength of the material. Goodman [2] developed an empirical method to determine a modified fatigue strength that accounts for the detrimental effects of combined alternating and mean stresses. The modified fatigue strength S_a is presented as a function of the cyclic mean stress in Fig. 9.8. Examination of Fig. 9.8 reveals that the modified fatigue strength S_a is equal to the endurance limit when $\sigma_m = 0$. The decrease in the modified fatigue strength is linear with the increase in σ_m, and S_a becomes zero when $\sigma_m = S_u$.

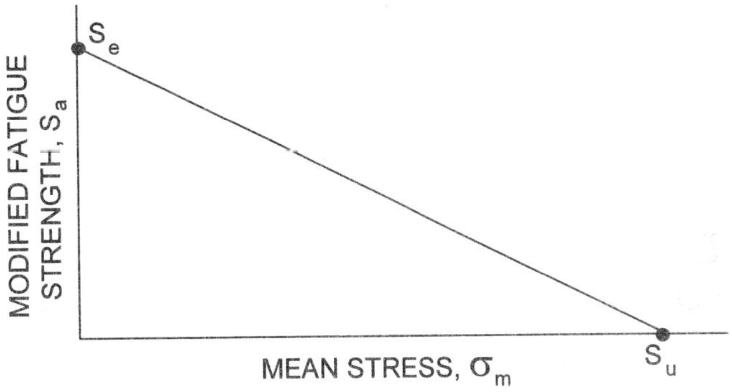

Fig. 9.8 Modified fatigue strength S_a decreases as the cyclic mean stresses increase.

We may also characterize the modified fatigue strength S_a in equation format as:

$$S_a = S_e\,[1 - (\sigma_m/S_u)] \qquad (9.9)$$

where S_e is the endurance limit when $\sigma_m = 0$; S_u is the ultimate tensile strength and σ_m is the cyclic mean stress.

EXAMPLE 9.5

Let's reconsider the bridge described in Example 9.3. In the previous solution, we neglected the influence of the mean stress on the fatigue strength. In this solution, let's account for the degrading effect of the cyclic mean stress on the fatigue strength.

Solution:

Recall the results for the alternating and mean stresses from Example 9.3.

$$\sigma_a = (\sigma_{Max} - \sigma_{Min})/(2) = (65{,}000 - 22{,}000)/(2) = 21.5 \text{ ksi} \qquad (a)$$

$$\sigma_m = (\sigma_{Max} + \sigma_{Min})/(2) = (65{,}000 + 22{,}000)/(2) = 43.5 \text{ ksi} \qquad (b)$$

Next, compare the value of the alternating stress with the modified fatigue strength that is obtained from Eq. (9.9) as:

$$S_a = S_e\,[1 - (\sigma_m/S_u)] = (43)[1 - (43.5/96)] = 23.52 \text{ ksi} \qquad (c)$$

Clearly $S_a = 23.52$ ksi $> \sigma_a = 21.5$ ksi; the alternating stresses are slightly less than the modified fatigue strength. The bridge beam is safe, but the margin of safety is very small. The safety factor is determined from Eq. (9.8) as:

$$\mathbf{SF_f} = S_a/\sigma_a \qquad (d)$$

$$\mathbf{SF_f} = (23.52)/(21.5) = 1.094 \qquad (e)$$

In this more accurate solution, which accounts for the effect of the mean cyclic stresses on fatigue strength, the safety factor was reduced. In the previous solution $\mathbf{SF_f} = 2.00$; whereas, in this solution the safety factor is reduced to 1.01. Clearly, the effect of the mean stress is to reduce the modified fatigue strength S_a of the steel beam. With safety factors this small, the beam size should be increased or a substitute material employed with higher fatigue strength.

EXAMPLE 9.6

A centrally located hole of diameter d = 0.5 in. is drilled in a long thin bar that is subjected to a cyclic load that varies from + 4,000 to – 4,000 lb. The bar is fabricated from a 1045 HR steel with an estimated fatigue strength of $S_f = 45$ ksi. If the bar is defined by w = 1.5 in., and b = 0.50 in., determine the safety factor for an infinite fatigue life.

Solution:

The nominal stress is given by Eq. (9.2) as:

$$\sigma_{Nom} = P/[b(w - d)] = (4{,}000)/[(1.5 - 0.5)(0.5)] = 8{,}000 \text{ psi} \qquad \text{(a)}$$

The stress concentration K is determined from Fig. 9.3, by locating the intercept of a vertical line originating at d/w = 0.5/1.5 = 0.3333 with the curve. This intercept gives K = 2.33.

The maximum stress is given by Eq. (9.1) as:

$$\sigma_{Max} = K\,\sigma_{Nom} = \sigma_a = (2.33)(8{,}000) = 18.64 \text{ ksi} \qquad \text{(b)}$$

Finally, the safety factor for an infinite fatigue life is determined from Eq. (9.8) as:

$$\mathbf{SF_f} = S_f/\sigma_a = (45.0)/(18.64) = 2.41 \qquad \text{(c)}$$

EXAMPLE 9.7

Consider the axially loaded stepped bar shown in Fig. E9.7, and determine the expected fatigue life. The bar is fabricated from HR 1020 HR with an ultimate tensile strength of 455 MPa and an endurance limit of S_e = 227 MPa. The cyclic load varies zero to a maximum value of 960 kN.

Fig. E9.7

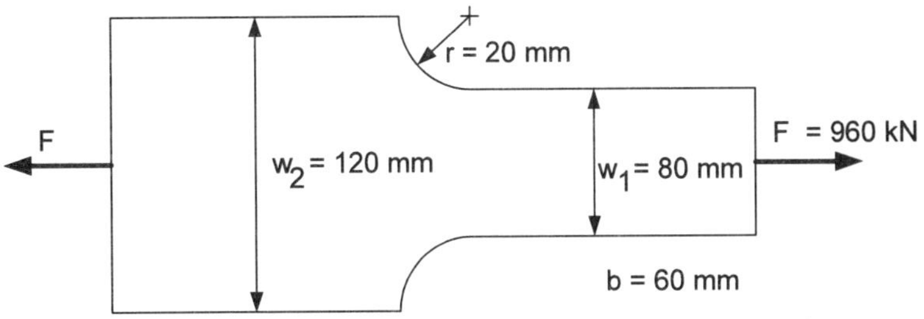

Solution:

From Eq. (9.1), we write $\sigma_{Max} = K\,\sigma_{Nom}$.

From Eq. (9.4), write:

$$\sigma_{Nom} = P/w_1 b = (960 \times 10^3)/[(80)(60)] = 200 \text{ MPa} \qquad \text{(a)}$$

To determine the stress concentration factor K, we note that r/w_1 = 20/80 = 0.25, and w_2/w_1 = 120/80 = 1.5. Reading the chart for the stress concentration factor in Fig. 9.5, we establish that K is:

$$K = 1.63 \qquad \text{(b)}$$

Finally, Eq. (9.1) yields:

$$\sigma_{Max} = K\,\sigma_{Nom} = (1.63)(200) = 326.0 \text{ MPa} \qquad \text{(c)}$$

Note that the minimum stress is:

$$\sigma_{Min} = 0 \quad \text{(d)}$$

From Eq. (9.7) the alternating stress is given by:

$$\sigma_a = (\sigma_{Max} - \sigma_{Min})/(2) = (326.0 - 0)/(2) = 163.0 \text{ MPa} \quad \text{(e)}$$

From Eq. (9.6) the mean stress is given by:

$$\sigma_m = (\sigma_{Max} + \sigma_{Min})/(2) = (326.0 + 0)/(2) = 163.0 \text{ MPa} \quad \text{(f)}$$

From Eq. (9.9) the modified fatigue strength of the 1020 HR steel is given by:

$$S_a = S_e\,[1 - (\sigma_m/S_u)] = 227[1 - (163.0/455)] = 145.7 \text{ MPa} \quad \text{(g)}$$

Comparison of S_a with σ_a shows that $\sigma_a = 163.0$ MPa > $S_a = 145.7$ MPa, which indicates that the stepped bar will fail in fatigue with a life of 10^5 to 10^6 cycles.

9.4 STRESS CONCENTRATIONS IN CIRCULAR SHAFTS SUBJECT TO TORSION

In many applications, shafts are stepped with different diameters to accommodate gears and bearings. Stress concentrations occur at the fillets adjacent to a shaft's shoulder where one diameter transitions into another. The geometry leading to a stress concentration of this type is illustrated in Fig. 9.9. In applications where the loads are cyclic, the shafting is subjected to fatigue failure and the stress concentrations must be this mode of failure must be accounted for in the design analysis.

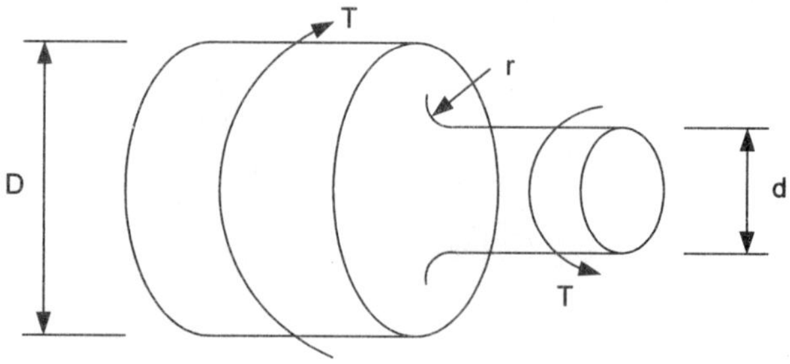

Fig. 9.9 Stress concentrations occur at the fillet located at the transition of the shaft diameters.

The effect of the stress concentration on elevating the shear stresses due to the applied torque is accommodated by introducing a torsion stress concentration factor K_{TS}. In this case, the maximum shear stress at the fillet is given by:

$$\tau_{Max} = K_{TS}\,\tau_{Nom} = 16K_{TS}\,T/(\pi d^3) \quad (9.10)$$

where the nominal shear stress $\tau_{Nom} = 16T/(\pi d^3)$ occurs in the smaller diameter shaft.

The stress concentration factor depends on the radius of the fillet and the mismatch in the diameters as shown in Fig. 9.10.

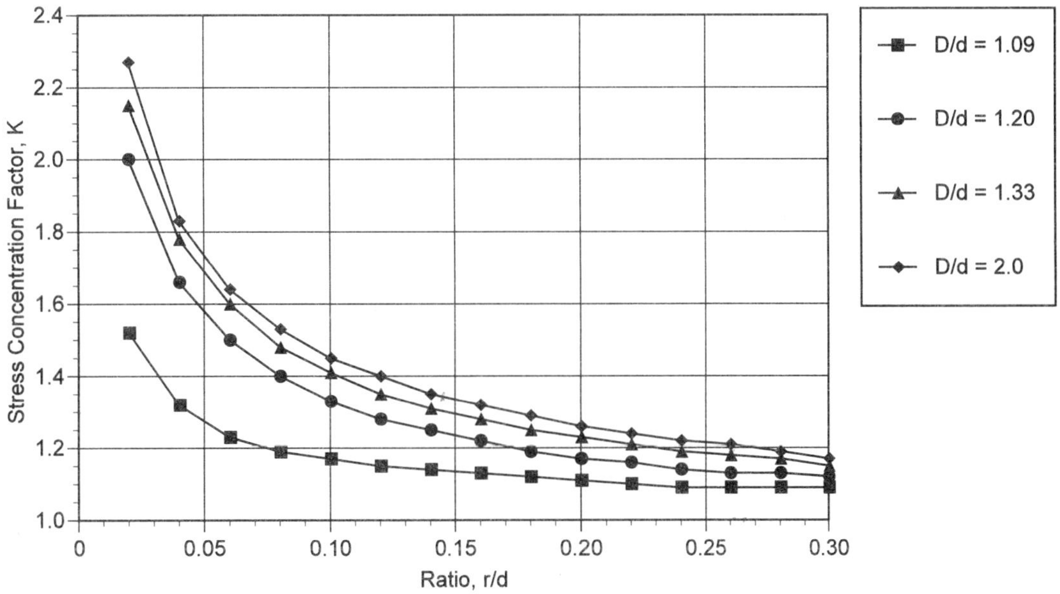

Fig. 9.10 Stress concentration factor for a shouldered shaft subject to torsion.

EXAMPLE 9.8

A shouldered shaft is subjected to a torque T = 1,500 N-m. The diameters are D = 120 mm and d = 60 mm. The radius of the transition fillet is 6.0 mm. Determine the maximum shear stress at the fillet.

Solution:

The nominal shear stress is given by:

$$\tau_{Nom} = 16T/(\pi d^3) = (16)(1{,}500)/[\pi\ (0.060)^3] = 35.37 \text{ MPa} \qquad \text{(a)}$$

To determine the stress concentration factor compute the ratios D/d and r/d as:

$$D/d = (120)/(60) = 2.00 \qquad \text{and} \qquad r/d = (6.0)/(60) = 0.10$$

Reference to the graph for the stress concentration factor K_{TS} shown in Fig. 9.10 gives:

$$K_{TS} = 1.45 \qquad \text{(b)}$$

Then from Eq. (9.10), we write:

$$\tau_{Max} = K_{TS}\ \tau_{Nom} = (1.45)(35.37) = 51.29 \text{ MPa} \qquad \text{(c)}$$

Examination of these results indicates that the presence of the shoulder on the shaft increased the shear stresses in the fillet from 35.37 MPa to 51.28 MPa. This increase is significant and it is clear that stress concentrations must be taken into account whenever we are dealing with cyclic loading or brittle materials.

EXAMPLE 9.9

A shouldered shaft is subjected to a cyclic torque that varies from zero to 2,500 N-m. The diameters are D = 150 mm and d = 75 mm. The radius of the transition fillet is 7.5 mm. Determine the maximum shear stress at the fillet. Also determine the allowable alternating shear stress T_a in fatigue, if the shaft's material exhibits an ultimate tensile strength of 350 MPa.

Solution:

The nominal shear stress is given by:

$$\tau_{Nom} = 16T/(\pi d^3) = (16)(2,500)/[\pi\ (0.075)^3] = 30.18 \text{ MPa} \qquad \text{(a)}$$

To determine the stress concentration factor compute the ratios D/d and r/d as:

$$D/d = (150)/(75) = 2.00 \qquad \text{and} \qquad r/d = (7.5)/(75) = 0.10$$

Reference to the graph for the stress concentration factor K_{TS} shown in Fig. 9.10 gives:

$$K_{TS} = 1.45 \qquad \text{(b)}$$

Then from Eq. (9.10), we write:

$$\tau_{Max} = K_{TS}\ \tau_{Nom} = (1.45)(30.18) = 43.76 \text{ MPa} \qquad \text{(c)}$$

The minimum shear stress is zero. The mean and alternating shear stresses are both equal to:

$$\tau_a = \tau_m = \tau_{Max}/2 = (43.76)/(2) = 21.88 \text{ MPa}$$

Applying the Goodman relation to cyclic shear stresses gives the allowable alternating shear stress T_a as:

$$T_a = T_e\ (1 - \tau_m/T_u\ ) = [0.5774\ (S_u\ /2)]\{1 - [\tau_m/(0.5774S_u)]\} \qquad (9.11)$$

where the ultimate strength T_u in shear is given by:

$$T_u = 0.5774\ S_u \qquad (9.12)$$

and the endurance strength in shear T_e is approximated by:

$$T_e = 0.5774\ (S_u\ /2) \qquad (9.13)$$

From Eqs. (9.11), (9.12) and (9.13), we determine T_a as:

$$T_a = [0.5774\ (S_u\ /2)]\{1 - [\tau_m/(0.5774S_u)]\} = (0.5774/2)(350)\{1 - 21.88/[(0.5774)(350)]\}$$

$$T_a = 90.10 \text{ MPa} \qquad \text{(d)}$$

9.5 STRESS CONCENTRATIONS IN BEAMS

In our study of methods to analyze stresses in beams, we have assumed that the beams were continuous along their entire length. However, in design of structures it is common to cut notches in beams for one reason or another. In some instances, shouldered shafts or beams are employed and occasionally transverse holes are drilled in shafts to enable lubricant transfer. These geometric discontinuities produce stress concentrations in regions adjacent to the hole or notch. To determine the maximum stress, we account for these discontinuities by establishing the appropriate stress concentration factor. The stress concentration factor multiplies a nominal stress to give the maximum stress at the discontinuity. This procedure is identical to that described previously in Section 9.2 and Section 9.4.

9.5.1 Stress Concentration Factors

Due to Notches in Beams

Let's consider a beam with a rectangular cross section that is notched on its top and bottom surfaces as shown in Fig. 9.11. The stresses in the region adjacent to the notch are elevated due to the presence of the discontinuity. The maximum stress σ_{Max} occurs at the base of the notch, and is given by:

$$\sigma_{Max} = K\,\sigma_{Nom} \qquad (9.1)$$

where σ_{Nom} is the nominal stress and K is the stress concentration factor.

Fig. 9.11 A notched beam subjected to bending moments.

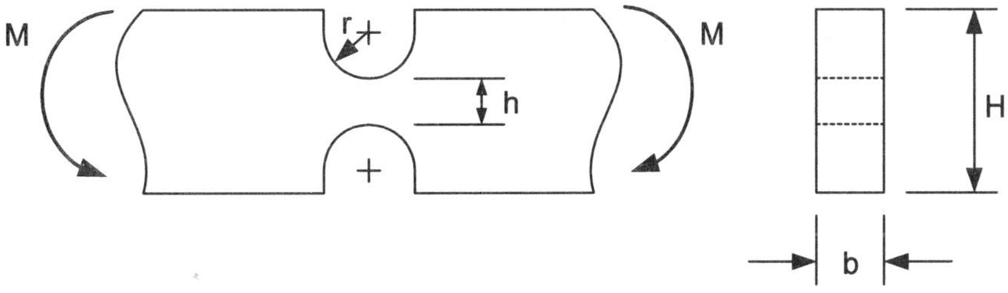

The nominal stress is the bending stress at the notched section that is given by:

$$\sigma_{Nom} = Mc/I_z = 6M/(bh^2) \qquad (9.14)$$

where b, r, h and H are defined in Fig. 9.11.

The stress concentration factor is a function of the geometry of the discontinuity and depends on the ratios H/h and r/h as shown in Fig. 9.12

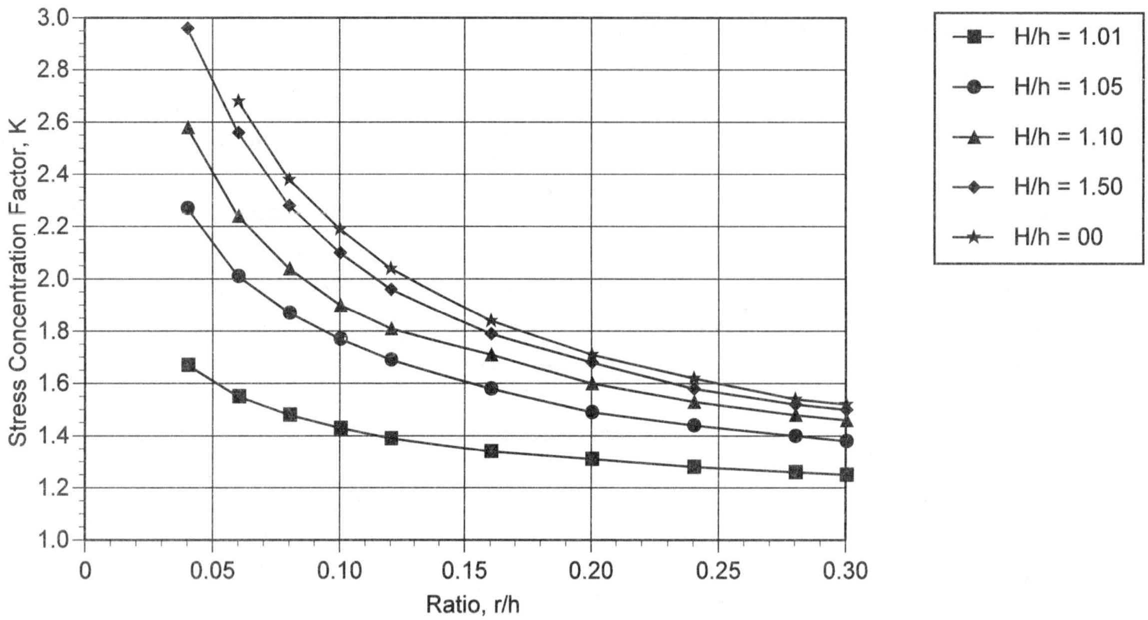

Fig. 9.12 Stress concentration factor for a notched beam in bending.

EXAMPLE 9.10

A simply supported beam with a uniform load is shown in Fig. E9.10. If notches are cut on the top and bottom surfaces at the center span of the beam, determine the nominal stresses, the stress concentration factor and the maximum stresses at the notches. The beams dimensions are L= 20 ft, b = 2.5 in., H = 8 in. and h = 5 in. The notch radius r = 0.5 in. is centered on the top and bottom edges of the beam. The distributed load q = 0.8 kip/ft.

Fig. E9.10

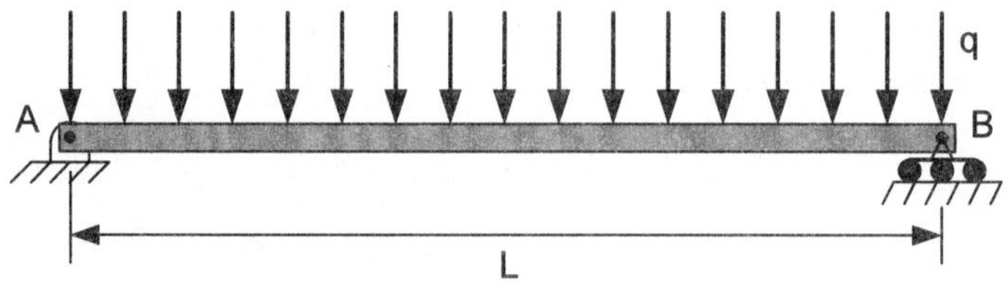

Solution:

Let's begin by determining the moment at the midspan of the beam. In Example 4.2, we showed that the moment for a beam with a uniformly distributed load was a maximum at midspan given by:

$$M_{Max} = qL^2/8 = (800)(20)^2/(8) = 40 \text{ kip-ft} = 480 \text{ kip-in.} \qquad \text{(a)}$$

Next calculate the nominal stress σ_{Nom} from Eq. (9.14) as:

$$\sigma_{Nom} = Mc/I_z = 6M/(bh^2) = 6(480 \times 10^3)/[(2.5)(5)^2] = 46.08 \text{ ksi} \qquad \text{(b)}$$

Reference Fig. 9.12 to determine the stress concentration factor. The ratios giving the coordinates for K are r/h = (0.50)/(5.0) = 0.10 and H/h = (8.0)/(5) = 1.60. Then from Fig. 9.12, we establish that:

$$K = 2.12 \qquad \text{(c)}$$

Substituting Eqs. (b) and (c) into Eq. (9.1) yields:

$$\sigma_{Max} = K\,\sigma_{Nom} = (2.12)(46.08) = 97.69 \text{ ksi} \qquad \text{(d)}$$

EXAMPLE 9.11

A simply supported beam with a uniform load is shown in Fig. E9.11. If notches are cut on the top and bottom surfaces at the center span of the beam, determine the nominal stresses, the stress concentration factor and the maximum stresses at the notches. Also determine the fatigue safety factor, if the beam is fabricated from steel with an endurance limit of 60 ksi. The beam's dimensions are L= 20 ft, b = 4.0 in., H = 10 in. and h = 8 in. The notch radius r =1.0 in. is centered on the top and bottom edges of the beam. The distributed load of q = 1.2 kip/ft is cyclic.

Fig. E9.11

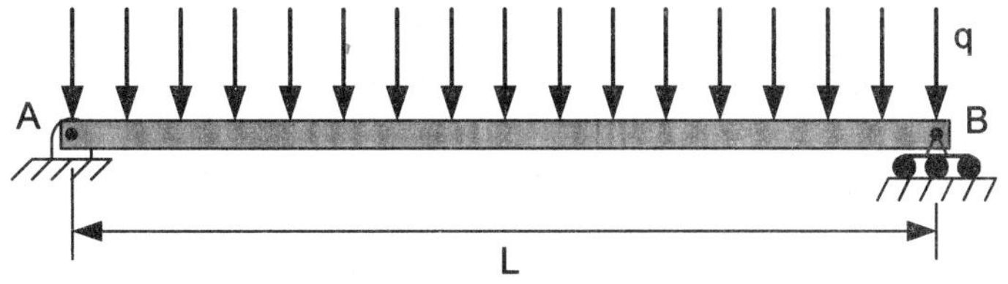

Solution:

Let's begin by determining the moment at the midspan of the beam. In Example 4.2, we showed that the moment for a beam with a uniformly distributed load was a maximum at midspan given by:

$$M_{Max} = qL^2/8 = (1{,}200)(20)^2/(8) = 60 \text{ kip-ft} = 720 \text{ kip-in.} \qquad \text{(a)}$$

Next calculate the nominal stress σ_{Nom} from Eq. (9.14) as:

$$\sigma_{Nom} = Mc/I_z = 6M/(bh^2) = (6)(720 \times 10^3)/[(4.0)(8)^2\,] = 16.875 \text{ ksi} \qquad \text{(b)}$$

Reference Fig. 9.12 to determine the stress concentration factor. The ratios giving the coordinates for K are r/h = (1.0)/(8.0) = 0.125 and H/h = (10.0)/(8) = 1.25. Then from Fig. 9.12, we establish that:

$$K = 1.88 \qquad \text{(c)}$$

Substituting Eqs. (b) and (c) into Eq. (9.1) yields:

$$\sigma_{Max} = K\,\sigma_{Nom} = (1.88)(16.875) = 31.725 \text{ ksi} \qquad \text{(d)}$$

The safety factor for failure in fatigue is given by Eq. (9.8) as:

$$\mathbf{SF_f} = S_f/\sigma_a = (60.00)/(31.72) = 1.891 \qquad \text{(e)}$$

Due to Grooves in Circular Shafts

Let's consider a shaft with a circular cross section that has a groove machined about its circumference as shown in Fig. 9.13. When the shaft is subjected to a bending moment M, the stresses in the region at the root of the groove are elevated due to the presence of the discontinuity. The procedure is the same as we described previously — we multiply a nominal value for the bending stresses by a suitable stress concentration factor to determine the maximum stresses in accordance with Eq. (9.1).

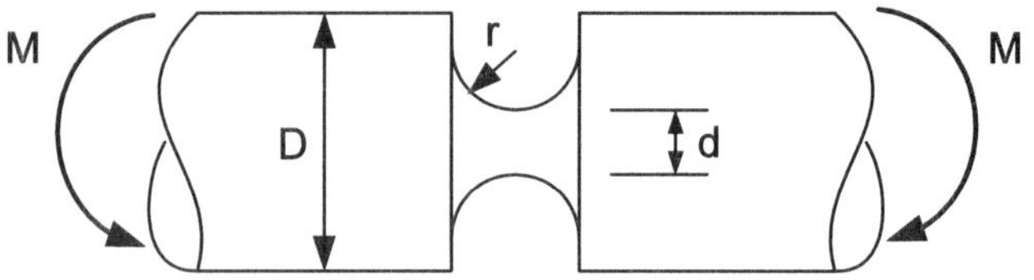

Fig. 9.13 A grooved shaft subjected to bending moments.

The nominal stress at the neck section where the groove is located is given by:

$$\sigma_{Nom} = 32M/\pi d^3 \qquad (9.15)$$

The curves defining the stress concentration factors are presented in Fig. 9.14.

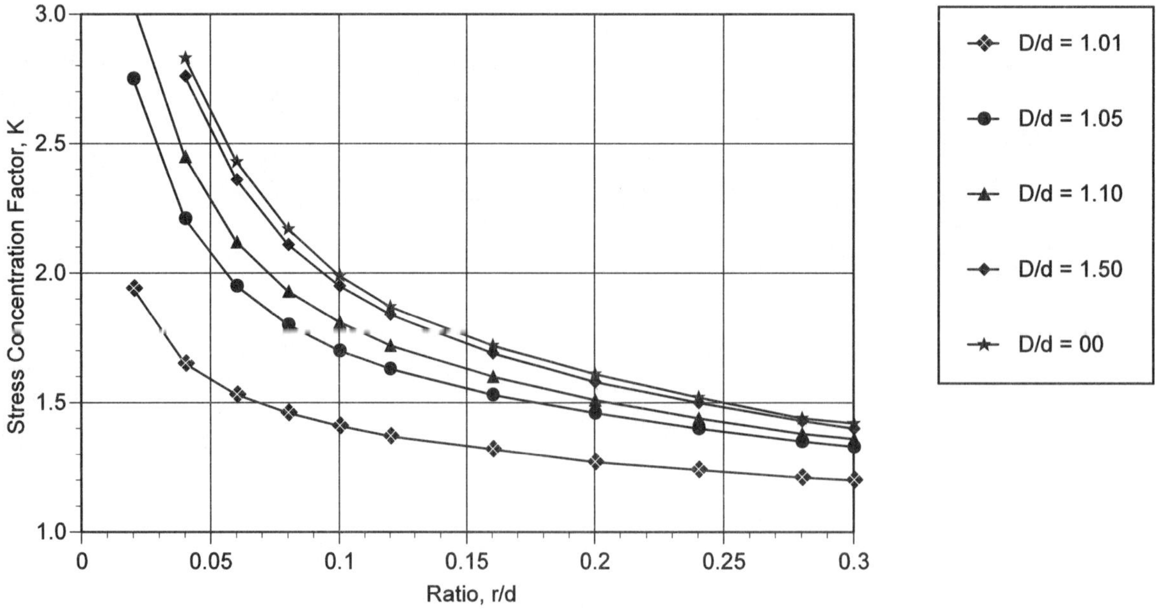

Fig. 9.14 Stress concentration factor for a grooved shaft.

EXAMPLE 9.12

The circular shaft, illustrated in Fig. 9.13, is loaded in four-point bending producing a bending moment M = 5.0 kN-m over the central region of a circular shaft. If a groove is cut about the perimeter of the shaft at its midspan point, determine the nominal stresses, the stress concentration factor and the maximum stress at the base of the groove. The shaft's dimensions are D = 100 mm, d = 75 mm. The notch radius r = 15 mm is centered near the bottom of the grove.

Solution:

Let's begin by determining the calculating the nominal stress at the location of the groove from Eq. (9.15) as:

$$\sigma_{Nom} = 32M/\pi d^3 = (32)(5.0 \times 10^3)/[\pi(0.075)^3] = 120.7 \text{ MPa} \qquad \text{(a)}$$

Reference Fig. 9.14 to determine the stress concentration factor. The ratios giving the coordinates for K are r/d = (15)/(75) = 0.20 and D/d = (100)/(75) = 1.3333. Then from Fig. 9.14, we establish that K = 1.53.

Substituting the results for σ_{Nom} and K into Eq. (9.1) yields:

$$\sigma_{Max} = K\, \sigma_{Nom} = (1.53)(120.7) = 184.7 \text{ MPa} \qquad \text{(b)}$$

EXAMPLE 9.13

The circular shaft, illustrated in Fig. 9.13, is loaded in four-point bending producing a bending moment M = 10.0 kN-m over the central region of a circular shaft. The shaft is rotating so that the stresses alternate from a tension peak to a compression peak. If a groove is cut about the perimeter of the shaft at its midspan point, determine the nominal stresses, the stress concentration factor and the maximum stress at the base of the groove. Also determine the shaft's safety factor against failure by fatigue. The shaft's dimensions are D = 150 mm, d = 100 mm. The notch radius r = 25 mm is centered near the bottom of the grove. The material from which the shaft is fabricated exhibits an endurance strength of 250 MPa.

Solution:

Let's begin by determining the calculating the nominal stress at the location of the groove from Eq. (9.15) as:

$$\sigma_{Nom} = 32M/\pi d^3 = (32)(10.0 \times 10^3)/[\pi(0.100)^3] = 101.9 \text{ MPa} \qquad \text{(a)}$$

Reference Fig. 9.14 to determine the stress concentration factor. The ratios giving the coordinates for K are r/d = (250/(100) = 0.25 and D/d = (150)/(100) = 1.50. Then from Fig. 9.14, we establish that K = 1.48.

Substituting the results for σ_{Nom} and K into Eq. (9.1) yields:

$$\sigma_{Max} = K\,\sigma_{Nom} = (1.48)(101.9) = 150.8 \text{ MPa} \qquad \text{(b)}$$

The safety factor for failure in fatigue is given by Eq. (9.8) as:

$$\mathbf{SF_f} = S_f/\sigma_a = (250)/(150.8) = 1.658 \qquad \text{(c)}$$

Due to Shoulder Fillets in a Stepped Beam

Some beams do not exhibit a uniform cross section along their length and are of two different heights — H and h. We show such a stepped beam in Fig. 9.15, which is acted upon by a bending moment M. A circular fillet is placed at the transition to mitigate the concentration of stresses at the reentrant corner. When the beam is subjected to bending, the stresses in the region adjacent to the fillet are elevated due to the presence of the step. The procedure to determine the stresses at the fillet is the same as described previously.

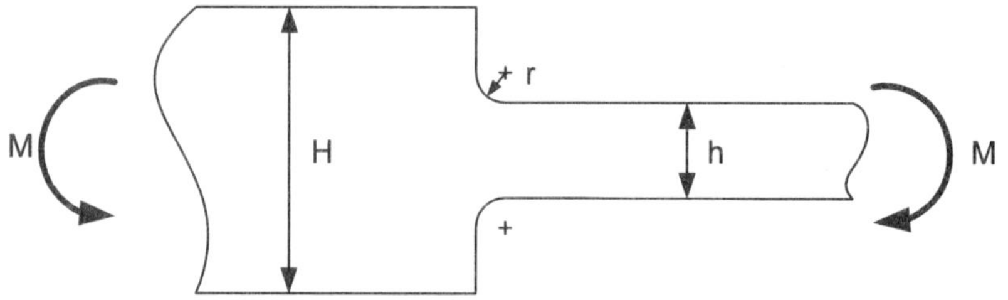

Fig. 9.15 A stepped beam subjected to bending.

The nominal stress σ_{Nom} for this case is determined from by Eq. (9.14), and the stress concentration factor is given in Fig. 9.16.

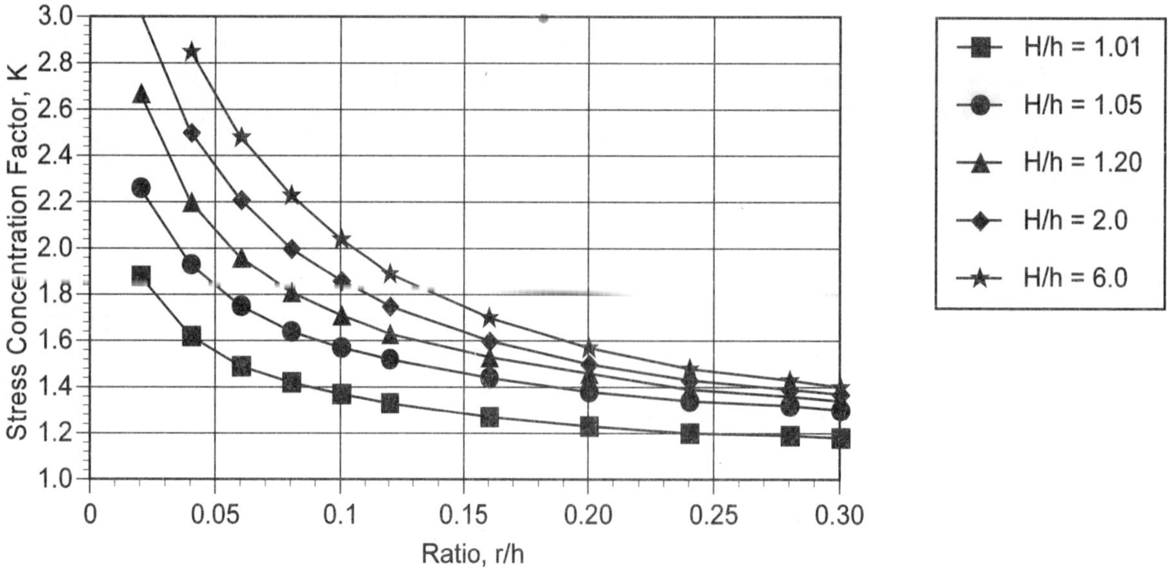

Fig. 9.16 Stress concentration factors for a stepped beam with shoulders.

EXAMPLE 9.14

A stepped beam subjected to moment loading M = 20 kN-m is shown in Fig. E9.14. If the step is located at the center span of the beam, determine the nominal stresses, the stress concentration factor and the maximum stresses at the fillets. The beams dimensions are L= 5 m, b = 50 mm, H = 250 mm and h = 125 mm. The fillet radius is r = 25 mm.

Fig. E9.14

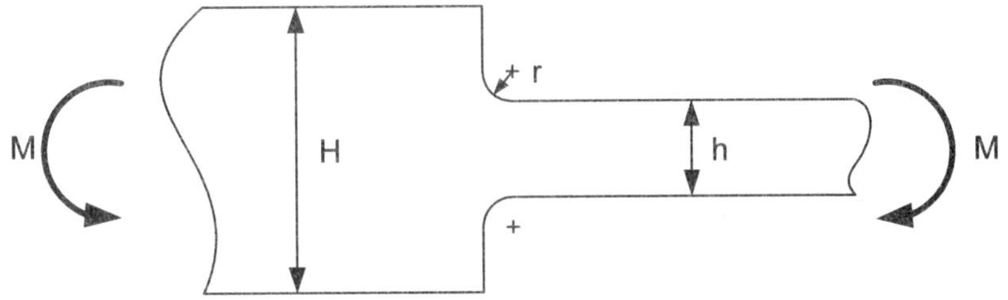

Solution:

Let's begin by calculating the nominal stress σ_{Nom} from Eq. (9.14) as:

$$\sigma_{Nom} = Mc/I_z = 6M/(bh^2) = 6(20 \times 10^6)/[(50)(125)^2] = 153.6 \text{ MPa} \qquad \text{(a)}$$

Reference Fig. 9.16 to determine the stress concentration factor. The ratios giving the coordinates for K are r/h = (25)/(125) = 0.20 and H/h = (250)/(125) = 2.0. Then from Fig. 9.16, we establish that:

$$K = 1.52 \qquad \text{(b)}$$

Substituting Eqs. (a) and (b) into Eq. (9.1) yields:

$$\sigma_{Max} = K\,\sigma_{Nom} = (1.52)(153.6) = 233.5 \text{ MPa} \qquad \text{(c)}$$

Due to Shoulder Fillets in a Stepped Shaft

Many shafts are stepped with two or more different diameters to accommodate the installation of gears, bearings, etc. We show such a stepped shaft in Fig. 9.17, which is acted upon by a bending moment M. A circular fillet is placed at the transition to mitigate the concentration of stresses at the reentrant corner. When the shaft is subjected to bending, the stresses in the region adjacent to the fillet are elevated due to the presence of the step. The procedure to determine the stresses at the fillet is the same as we described previously.

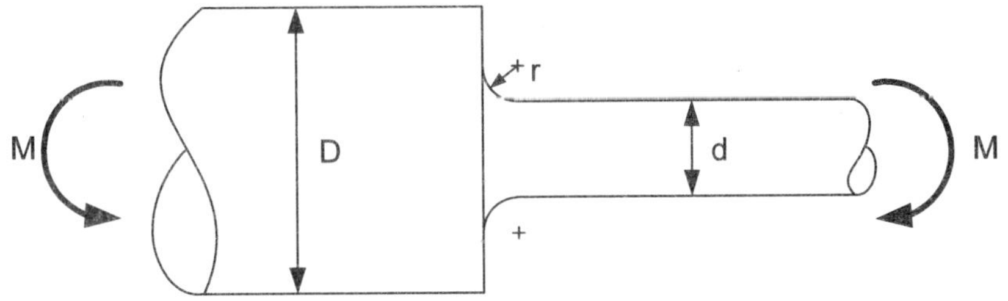

Fig. 9.17 Stepped shaft subjected to a bending moment M.

The nominal stress σ_{Nom} for this case is determined from Eq. (9.15), and the stress concentration factor is given in Fig. 9.18.

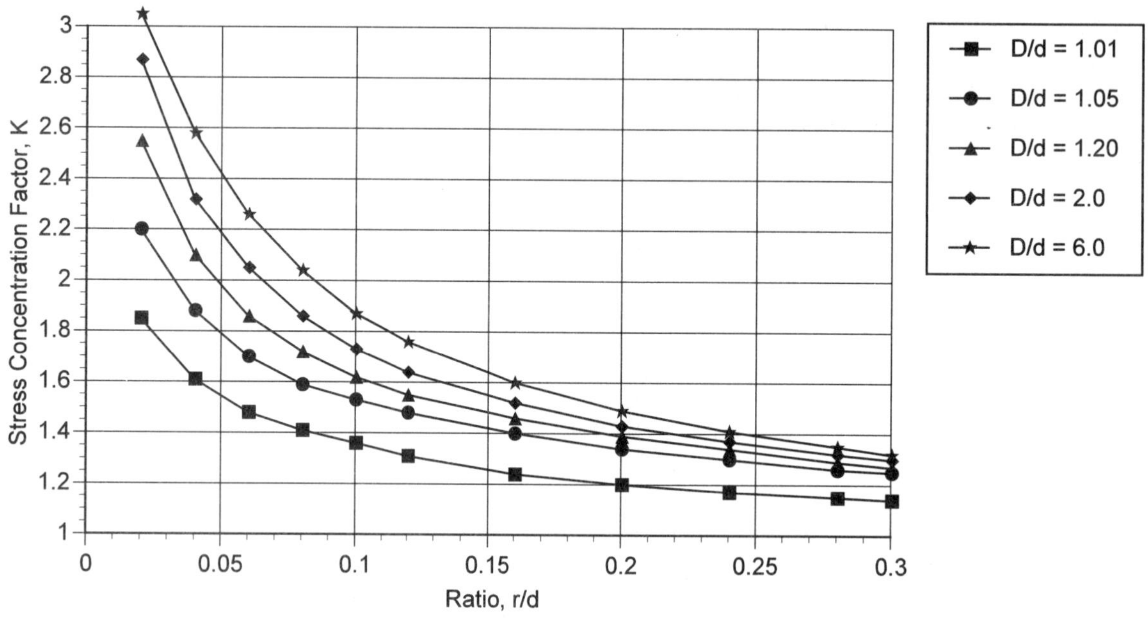

Fig. 9.18 Stress concentration factors for a stepped shaft.

EXAMPLE 9.15

A shaft with a circular cross section is designed with a step transition between two diameters — D = 2.0 in. and d = 1.0 in. The shaft is subjected to a bending moment of M = 150 ft-lb at the transition point. Determine the minimum radius of the fillet at the transition region, if the maximum stress is not to exceed 40.0 ksi.

Solution:

Let's solve for the nominal stress at the transition region by using Eq. (9.15).

$$\sigma_{Nom} = My/I_z = 32M/(\pi d^3) = (32)(150)(12)/[\pi(1.0)^3] = 18.33 \text{ ksi} \qquad \text{(a)}$$

Next, determine the maximum allowable stress concentration factor from Eq. (9.1) as:

$$K_{Max} = \sigma_{Max}/\sigma_{Nom} = (40)/(18.33) = 2.182 \qquad \text{(b)}$$

Note that D/d = (2.0)/(1.0) = 2.0. Then select the diamond curve for D/d = 2.0 from Fig. 9.18. Project a line horizontally from K = 2.182 and locate the intercept with the diamond curve. Project a second line downward and read the intercept for r/d as 0.05. The radius of the fillet at the transition section must exceed r = (0.05)(1.0) = 0.05 in. so that $\sigma_{Max} \leq 40$ ksi.

EXAMPLE 9.16

A rotating shaft with a circular cross section is designed with a step transition between two diameters — D = 3.0 in. and d = 1.5 in. The shaft is subjected to a bending moment of M = 400 ft-lb at the transition point. The radius of the fillet at the transition region is r = 0.15 in. Determine the safety factor against fatigue failure, if the endurance limit from which the shaft is fabricated is 45 ksi.

Solution:

Let's solve for the nominal stress at the transition region by using Eq. (9.15).

$$\sigma_{Nom} = My/I_z = 32M/(\pi d_3) = (32)(400)(12)/[\pi(1.5)^3] = 14.49 \text{ ksi} \qquad (a)$$

Reference Fig. 9.18 to determine the stress concentration factor. The ratios giving the coordinates for K are r/d = (0.15)/(150) = 0.10 and D/d = (3.0)/(1.5) = 2.00. Then from Fig. 9.18, we establish that K = 1.73

Substituting the results for σ_{Nom} and K into Eq. (9.1) yields:

$$\sigma_{Max} = K\,\sigma_{Nom} = (1.73)(14.49) = 25.07 \text{ ksi} \qquad (b)$$

The safety factor for failure in fatigue is given by Eq. (9.8) as:

$$\mathbf{SF_f} = S_f/\sigma_a = (45)/(25.07) = 1.795 \qquad (c)$$

Due to a Transverse Hole in a Circular Shaft

Many shafts are designed with transverse holes to enable the flow of lubricants or coolants to some other component in the system. We show a shaft with a small diameter transverse hole in Fig. 9.19. When the shaft is subjected to bending, the stresses in the region adjacent to the hole are elevated due to the presence of the discontinuity. The procedure to determine the maximum stresses at the hole is the same as we described previously.

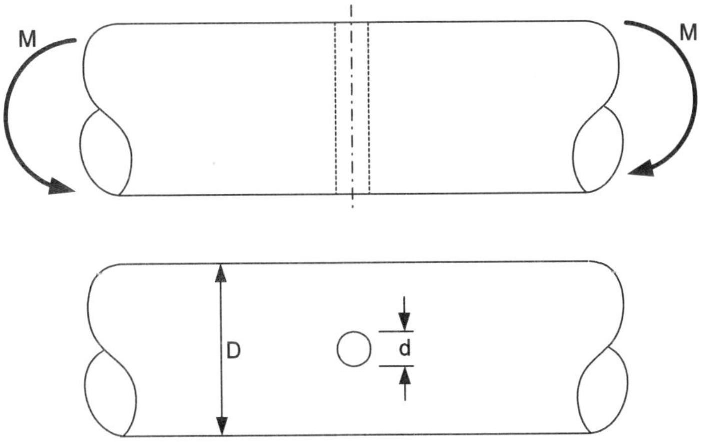

Fig. 9.19 A transverse hole in shaft with circular cross-section that is subjected to a moment M.

The nominal stress σ_{Nom} at the location of the transverse hole is approximated by:

$$\sigma_{Nom} = \frac{M}{\dfrac{\pi D^3}{32} - \dfrac{D^2 d}{6}} \quad (9.16)$$

The stress concentration factor, which is a function of the ratio of d/D, is presented in Fig. 9.20.

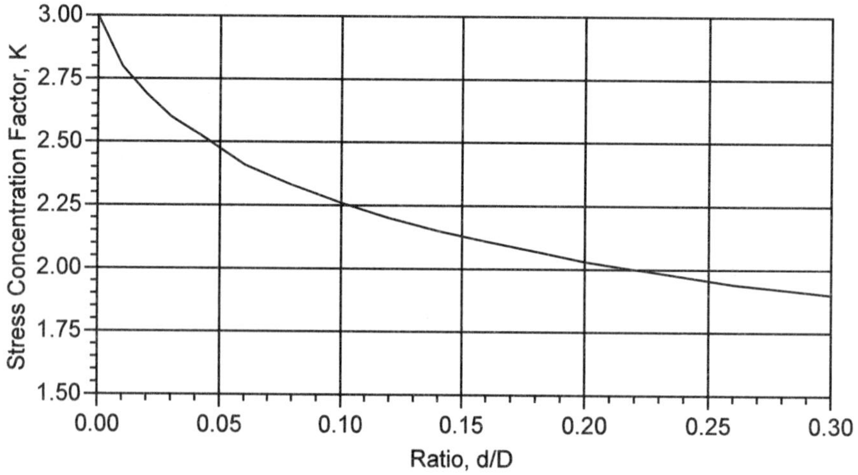

Fig. 9.20 Stress concentration factor for a shaft with a transverse hole.

EXAMPLE 9.17

A circular shaft with a diameter D = 125 mm is drilled with a transverse hole having a diameter d = 6 mm. If the shaft is subjected to a bending moment of 25 kN-m, determine the maximum stress adjacent the hole.

Solution:

The nominal stress is determined from Eq. (9.16) as:

$$\sigma_{Nom} = \frac{M}{\dfrac{\pi D^3}{32} - \dfrac{D^2 d}{6}} = \frac{25 \times 10^6}{\dfrac{\pi(125)^3}{32} - \dfrac{(6)(125)^2}{6}} = 141.9 \text{ MPa} \quad (a)$$

Using the ratio d/D = (6.0)/(125) = 0.048 and the curve in Fig. 9.20, we establish that K = 2.49. Then from Eq. (9.1) we write:

$$\sigma_{Max} = K\,\sigma_{Nom} = (2.49)(141.9) = 353.3 \text{ MPa} \quad (b)$$

EXAMPLE 9.18

A circular shaft with a diameter D = 4.0 in. is drilled with a transverse hole having a diameter d = 0.25 in. If the shaft is subjected to a bending moment of 125 × 10^3 in.-lb, determine the maximum stress adjacent the hole. If the material from which the shaft is fabricated exhibits an endurance limit of 70 ksi, determine the safety factor again failure by fatigue at the transverse hole.

Solution:

The nominal stress is determined from Eq. (9.16) as:

$$\sigma_{Nom} = \frac{M}{\dfrac{\pi D^3}{32} - \dfrac{D^2 d}{6}} = \frac{125 \times 10^3}{\dfrac{\pi (4)^3}{32} - \dfrac{(4.0)^2 (0.25)}{6}} = 22.26 \text{ ksi} \qquad \text{(a)}$$

Using the ratio d/D = (0.25)/(4.0) = 0.0625 and the curve in Fig. 9.20, we establish that K = 2.40. Then from Eq. (9.1) we write:

$$\sigma_{Max} = K\,\sigma_{Nom} = (2.40)(22.26) = 53.42 \text{ ksi} \qquad \text{(b)}$$

The safety factor for failure in fatigue is given by Eq. (9.8) as:

$$\mathbf{SF_f} = S_f/\sigma_a = (70)/(53.42) = 1.310 \qquad \text{(c)}$$

The safety factor in this example is marginal and the analyst should inform the design engineer that his or her design might fail in fatigue due to the variation often encountered in fatigue strength.

9.6 SUMMARY

Discontinuities such as a step or a hole in a bar, cause an increases in the stresses that concentrate at that discontinuity. As a consequence, the use of Eq. (2.4) to compute the stresses seriously underestimates their actual value. We account for the effect of the structural discontinuities by determining a suitable stress concentration factor, which multiplies a minimal stress according to:

$$\sigma_{Max} = K\,\sigma_{Nom} \qquad (9.1)$$

where the nominal stress for an axial bar with a central hole of diameter d is given by:

$$\sigma_{Nom} = F/A_{Nom} = F/[(w - d)b] \qquad (9.2)$$

The influence of the stress concentration factors on the failure of structural members is dependent on the ductility of the material from which the member is fabricated as well as the nature of the loading.

If the material used to fabricate the structural member is brittle, the elevated stresses in the local region adjacent to the discontinuity are effective in initiating failure with little evidence of ductility. However, if the material from which the structural member is fabricated is ductile, then local yielding of the region of elevated stresses occurs that relieves the concentrated stresses and the effect of the stress concentration is largely mitigated.

Many structures and machine components are subjected to repeated loading. There are two detrimental effects due to this cyclic loading. First, the design strength of the material from which the structure is fabricated is lowered. We design to a fatigue strength S_f that is a function of the cyclic stresses and the number of cycles of load imposed onto the structure.

Second, fatigue failures in **ductile** materials are of a **brittle** nature (i.e., structural failure and collapse occur catastrophically). The failure mechanism in fatigue is markedly different from that observed in yielding or rupture. In fatigue, microscopic cracks are initiated due to accumulated irreversible slip in a very thin layer of material adjacent to the surface. These cracks grow larger and extend into the material until reaching critical size. At this point, the cracks become unstable and extend at high speed across the structural member producing sudden and catastrophic collapse.

To accommodate for the degrading effects of cyclic loading, we compare the applied stresses with the **fatigue strength, S_f** of the material from which the structure is fabricated. A typical example of the fatigue strength for low carbon steel is presented in the S_f-N diagram of Fig. 9.6. This diagram is a graphical representation showing both safe and critical states of cyclic stresses. For infinite life, the fatigue strength is often called the endurance limit S_e where:

$$S_e = S_f \qquad \text{for } N > 10^6 \text{ cycles} \tag{9.5}$$

In comparing the cyclic stresses with the strength as defined in Fig. 9.6, we use the alternating portion of the applied stresses. The alternating stress σ_a, and the mean stress σ_m are is given by:

$$\sigma_m = (\sigma_{Max} + \sigma_{Min})/2 \tag{9.6}$$

$$\sigma_a = (\sigma_{Max} - \sigma_{Min})/2 \tag{9.7}$$

The safety factor in a cyclic loading application where fatigue is a consideration is given by:

$$\mathbf{SF_f} = S_f/\sigma_a \tag{9.8}$$

Tensile mean stresses lower the allowable fatigue strength according to the Goodman law that is given by:

$$S_a = S_e\,[1 - (\sigma_m/S_u)] \tag{9.9}$$

Fatigue strength in torsion is treated with modified relations as indicated below:

$$\tau_{Max} = K_{TS}\,\tau_{Nom} = 16K_{TS}\,T/(\pi d^3) \tag{9.10}$$

$$T_a = T_e\,(1 - \tau_m/T_u) = [0.5774\,(S_u/2)]\{1 - [\tau_m/(0.5774 S_u)]\} \tag{9.11}$$

$$T_u = 0.5774\,S_u \tag{9.12}$$

$$T_e = 0.5774 (S_u / 2) \qquad (9.13)$$

REFERENCES

1. Petersen, R. E., Stress Concentration Design Factors, 2nd Ed., Wiley & Sons, New York, 1990.
2. Hertzberg, R. W., Deformation and Fracture Mechanics of Engineering Materials, 4th Edition, John Wiley, New York, NY 1996.
3. Madayag, A. F. Metal Fatigue, John Wiley, New York, NY, 1969.
4. Forrest, P. G., Fatigue of Metals, Pergamon Press, Oxford, UK, 1962.

PROBLEMS

9.1 A centrally located hole of diameter d = 20 mm is drilled in a long thin bar that is subjected to an axial load of 25 kN as shown in Fig. P9.1. If the bar is defined by w = 80 mm, and b = 12 mm, determine the nominal stress, the stress concentration and the maximum stress.

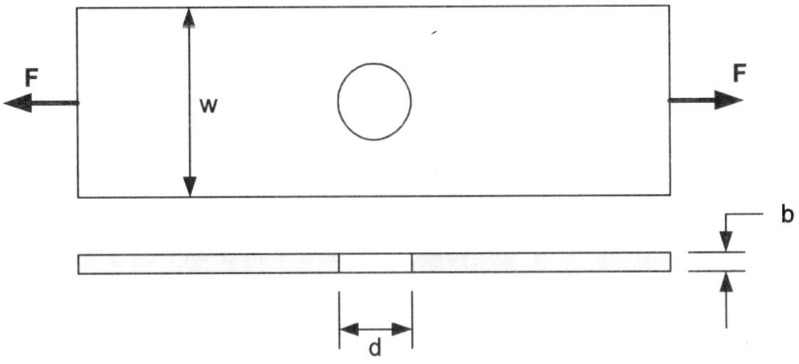

Fig. P9.1

9.2 Repeat Problem 9.1 if the bar is defined by w = 120 mm and b = 8 mm. All the other parameters remain the same.

9.3 A tensile bar 40 in. long, shown in Fig. P9.3, is subjected to an axial force of 12 kip. Determine: (a) the nominal stress, (b) the stress concentration factor K, and (c) the maximum stress.

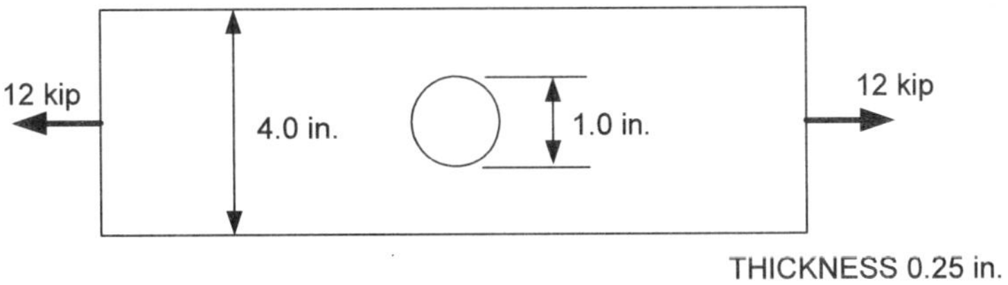

Fig. P9.3

9.4 Repeat Problem 9.4 if the hole diameter is decreased from 1.0 in. to 0.75 in. All the other parameters remain the same.

9.5 A stepped tensile bar, illustrated in Fig. P9.5, with fillets at the transition between the small and the large sections, is subjected to an axial tensile force of 85 kN. Determine the maximum stress at the fillets.

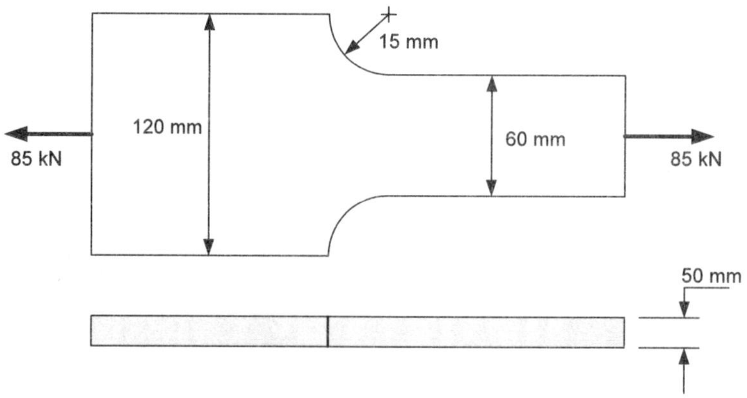

Fig. P9.5

9.6 Repeat Problem 9.5 if the fillet radius is decreased from 15 mm to 8 mm. All the other parameters remain the same.

9.7 For the stepped tensile bar, illustrated in Fig. P9.5, determine the maximum stress at the fillets if the bar is subjected to an axial tensile force of 120 kN and the fillet radii are increased from 15 mm to 25 mm.

9.8 Consider a cross beam used in constructing a bridge. The dead weight of the bridge structure produces a stress of 14,000 psi in this beam. However, when a fully loaded tractor-trailer crosses over the beam the stress increases to 45,000 psi. The beam is fabricated from a material with the fatigue properties described in Fig. 9.6. The strengths, yield and ultimate tensile, are 50 ksi and 75ksi respectively. Will the beam fail in fatigue? If failure is expected to occur, predict the cyclic life of the structure. Neglect the effect of the mean stress on fatigue strength in this example.

9.9 Consider a cross beam used in constructing a bridge. The dead weight of the bridge structure produces a stress of 120 MPa in this beam. However, when a fully loaded tractor-trailer crosses over the beam the stress increases to 330 MPa. The beam is fabricated from a material with the fatigue properties described in Fig. 9.6. The strengths, yield and ultimate tensile, are 380 MPa and 600 MPa respectively. Will the beam fail in fatigue? If failure occurs, predict the cyclic life of the structure. Neglect the effect of the mean stress on fatigue strength in this example.

9.10 Consider the crankshaft of a high performance racecar, which is subjected to maximum and minimum stresses of + 250 MPa and – 250 MPa. If the crankshaft is fabricated from the high-strength, low-alloy steel described in Fig. 9.6, determine its fatigue life.

9.11 Consider the crankshaft of a high performance racecar which is subjected to maximum and minimum stresses of + 35 ksi and – 35 ksi. If the crankshaft is fabricated from the high-strength, low-alloy steel described in Fig. 9.6, determine its fatigue life.

9.12 Reconsider the bridge beam described in Problem 9.8. In the previous solution, the influence of the mean stress on the fatigue strength was neglected. In this solution, account for the degrading effect of the cyclic mean stress on the fatigue strength.

9.13 Reconsider the bridge beam described in Problem 9.9. In the previous solution, the influence of the mean stress on the fatigue strength was neglected. In this solution, account for the degrading effect of the cyclic mean stress on the fatigue strength.

9.14 A centrally located hole of diameter d = 0.75 in. is drilled in a long thin bar that is subjected to a cyclic axial load that varies from + 3,500 to – 3,500 lb. The bar is fabricated from 1045 HR steel with an estimated fatigue strength of S_f = 45 ksi. If the bar width is 2.5 in. and its thickness is 0.375 in., determine the safety factor for an infinite fatigue life.

9.15 Repeat Problem 9.14 if the cyclic axial load varies from + 2,500 to – 2,500 lb. All the other parameters remain the same.

9.16 A centrally located hole of diameter d = 20 mm is drilled in a long thin bar that is subjected to a cyclic axial load that varies from + 12 kN to – 12 kN. The bar is fabricated from a 1045 HR steel with an estimated fatigue strength of S_f = 320 MPa. If the bar width is 70 mm and its thickness is 10 mm, determine the safety factor for an infinite fatigue life.

9.17 Repeat Problem 9.16 if the bar is fabricated from 52100 A alloy steel with an estimated fatigue strength of 550 MPa. The bar thickness is decreased to 6 mm. All the other parameters remain the same.

9.18 Consider the axially loaded stepped bar shown in Fig. P9.18, and determine the expected fatigue life. The bar is fabricated from HR 1018A with an ultimate tensile strength of 341 MPa and an endurance limit of S_e = 170 MPa. The cyclic load varies zero to a maximum value of 500 kN.

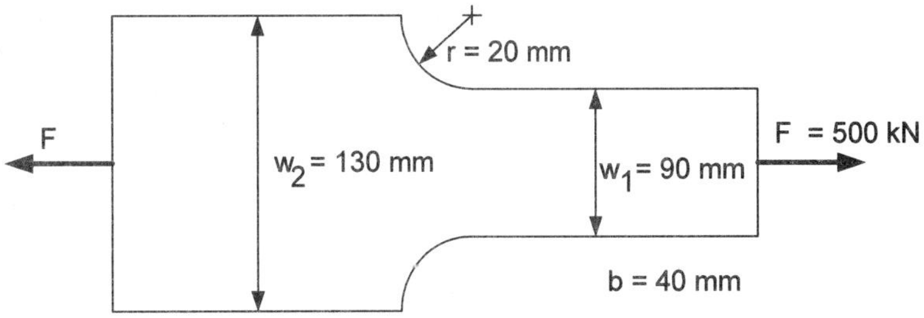

Fig. P9.18

9.19 Repeat Problem 9.18 if the cyclic load varies zero to a maximum value of 400 kN and the radius of the fillet is decreased to 15mm. All the other parameters remain the same.

9.20 Consider the axially loaded stepped bar shown in Fig. P9.18, and determine the expected fatigue life. The bar is fabricated from HR 1020A with an ultimate tensile strength of 455 MPa and an endurance limit of S_e = 227 MPa. The cyclic load varies zero to a maximum value of 500 kN.

9.21 Determine the nominal and maximum shear stresses for a shouldered shaft shown in Fig. P9.21. The shaft is defined with a diameter D = 1.75 in. and a diameter d = 1.0 in. subjected to a torque of 600 ft-lb. The fillet radius at the shoulder of the shaft is 0.375 in.

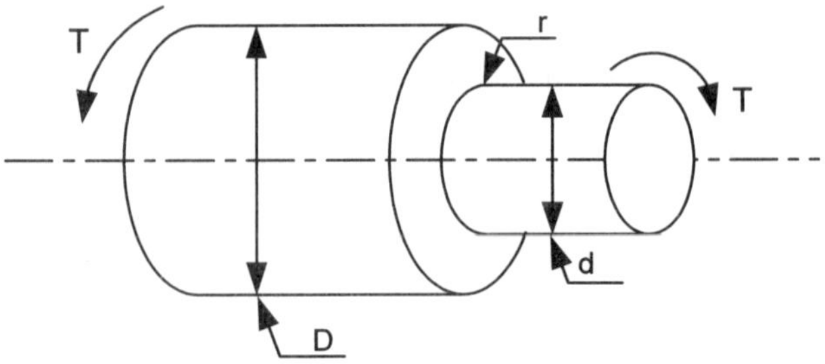

Fig. P9.21

9.22 A shouldered shaft is designed such that the maximum shear stress τ_{Max} cannot exceed a critical value of 50 MPa. The shouldered shaft shown in Fig. P9.21, has a diameter D = 46 mm and a diameter d = 30 mm. The fillet radius at the shoulder of the shaft is 8 mm. Determine the largest torque that the shaft can support.

9.23 A shouldered shaft is subjected to a cyclic torque that varies from zero to 2,000 N-m. The diameters are D = 140 mm and d = 70 mm. The radius of the transition fillet is 10 mm. Determine the maximum shear stress at the fillet. Also determine the allowable alternating shear stress in fatigue, if the shaft's material exhibits an ultimate tensile strength of 350 MPa.

9.24 The electric motor shown in Fig. P9.24 has a power rating of 5.0 kW and operates at 1,180 RPM. It powers a gear drive with a variable load, which sometimes requires the motor to operate at its maximum rating. The shaft is supported by two bearings — one on each side of the gear drive. The shaft from the motor has a diameter d and the shaft at the gear has a diameter D. The radius at the transition is specified as r/d = 0.15 and the diameter mismatch ratio is specified as D/d = 1.33. Select a material for the shaft and determine the diameters d and D if the maximum shear stress in the material is not to exceed 1/4 of the yield strength of the material in shear. Another constraint on the design is the angle of twist ϕ, which is not to exceed 2.0° measured from the motor to the gear drive.

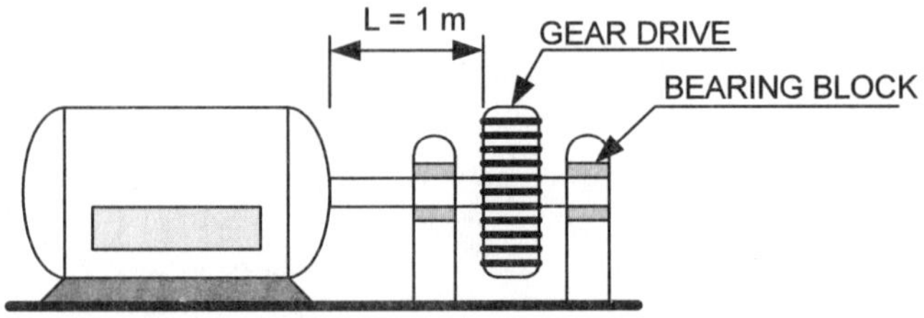

Fig. P9.24

9.25 Repeat Problem 9.24 if the constraint on the design is the angle of twist ϕ is changed so that it is not to exceed 5.0° measured from the motor to the gear drive. All the other parameters remain the same.

9.26 The electric motor, shown in Fig. P9.26, has a power rating of 20.0 HP and operates at 1780 RPM. It powers a drive shaft with three gears. When the motor is operating at rated capacity, gear A removes 1/2 of the power developed by the motor, while gear B and gear C remove 1/3 and 1/6 of the power, respectively. The shaft is supported by four bearings as shown in Fig. P9.26. The shaft from the motor has a diameter d but it is shouldered with a diameter D at each of the three gear locations. The radius at the transition is specified as r/d = 0.20 and the diameter mismatch ratio is specified as D/d = 1.50. If an alloy steel with a yield strength in shear of 150 ksi is used to fabricate the shaft, determine the diameters d and D if the maximum shear stress in the material is not to exceed 1/3 of the yield strength of the material in shear.

Another constraint on the design is the angle of twist ϕ, which is not to exceed 4.4° measured from the motor to the gear C.

Fig. P9.26

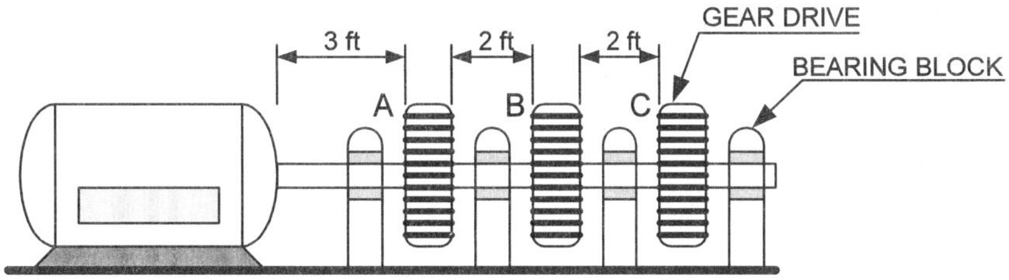

9.27 A notched cantilever beam, illustrated Fig. P9.27, is notched at position x = 3.8 ft. Determine the maximum tensile stress on the beam.

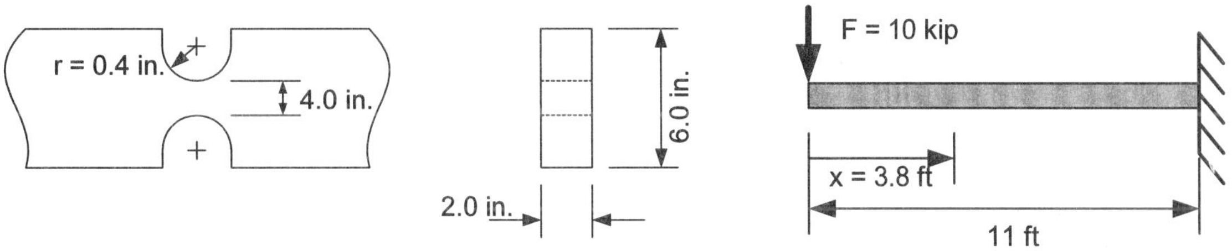

Fig. P9.27

9.28 Repeat Problem 9.27 if the position of the notch is changed to x = 4.6 ft. All the other parameters remain the same.

9.29 If the force in Problem 9.27 is cyclic varying from + 10 kip to – 10 kip, determine if the beam will fail in fatigue. The beam is fabricated from 1020 HR with an endurance limit of 33 ksi.

9.30 A simply supported beam with a uniform load is shown in Fig. P9.30. If notches are cut on the top and bottom surfaces at the center span of the beam, determine the nominal stresses, the stress concentration factor and the maximum stresses at the notches. The beams dimensions are L= 20 ft, b = 2.5 in., H = 8 in. and h = 5 in. The notch radius r = 0.5 in. is centered on the top and bottom edges of the beam. The distributed load q = 0.8 kip/ft.

Fig. P9.30

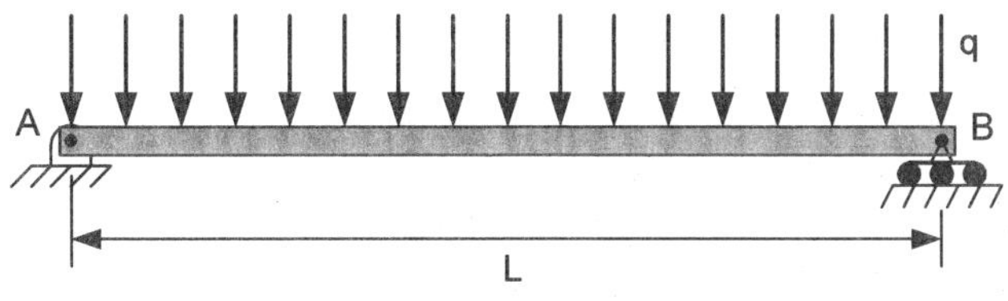

9.31 Repeat Problem 9.30 if the notch radius is changed to r = 0.25 in. All the other parameters remain the same.

9.32 If the distributed load in Problem 9.30 is cyclic, varying from + 8 kip/ft to + 8 kip/ft, determine if the beam will fail in fatigue. The beam is fabricated from 1045 HR with and endurance limit of 46 ksi.

9.33 The circular shaft, illustrated in Fig. P9.33, is loaded in four-point bending producing a bending moment $M = 40 \times 10^3$ in-lb over the central region of a circular shaft. If a groove is cut about the perimeter of the shaft at its midspan point, determine the nominal stresses, the stress concentration factor and the maximum stress at the base of the groove. The shaft's dimensions are D = 4.0 in. and d = 2.5 in. The notch radius r = 0.75 in. is centered near the bottom of the grove.

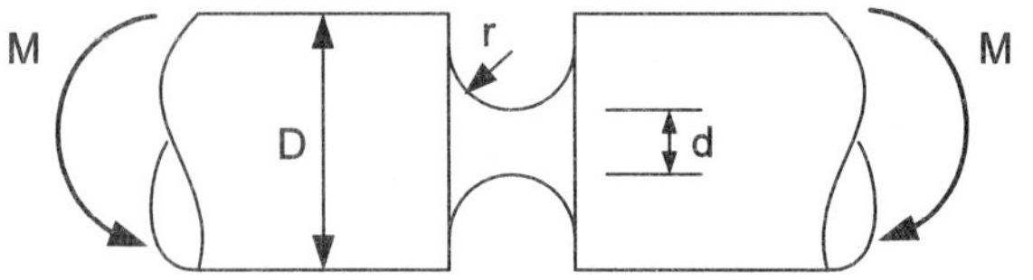

Fig. P9.33

9.34 Repeat Problem 9.33 if the notch radius is changed to r = 0.375 in. All the other parameters remain the same.

9.35 The circular shaft, illustrated in Fig. P9.33, is loaded in four-point bending producing a bending moment M = 7.0 kN-m over the central region of a circular shaft. If a groove is cut about the perimeter of the shaft at its midspan point, determine the nominal stresses, the stress concentration factor and the maximum stress at the base of the groove. The shaft's dimensions are D = 125 mm, d = 100 mm. The notch radius r = 12.5 mm is centered near the bottom of the grove.

9.36 Repeat Problem 9.35 if the shaft's dimensions are D = 110 mm, d = 80 mm. The notch radius r = 10.0 mm is centered near the bottom of the grove. All the other parameters remain the same.

9.37 The circular shaft, illustrated in Fig. P9.33, is loaded in four-point bending producing a bending moment M = 8.0 kN-m over the central region of a circular shaft. The shaft is rotating so that the stresses produced alternate from a tension peak to a compression peak. If a groove is cut about the perimeter of the shaft at its midspan point, determine the nominal stresses, the stress concentration factor and the maximum stress at the base of the groove. Also determine the shaft's safety factor against failure by fatigue. The shaft's dimensions are D = 140 mm, d = 100 mm. The notch radius r = 20 mm is centered near the bottom of the grove. The material from which the shaft is fabricated exhibits an endurance strength of 225 MPa.

9.38 An architect has proposed a series of stepped roof beams to provide a visual impact for a public building with high pedestrian traffic. A representative beam with its loading is presented in Fig. P9.38. The beam's depth is 60 mm, and its yield strength is 240 MPa. As the city's structural engineer, you have the responsibility to approve or disapprove the design. Justify your decision.

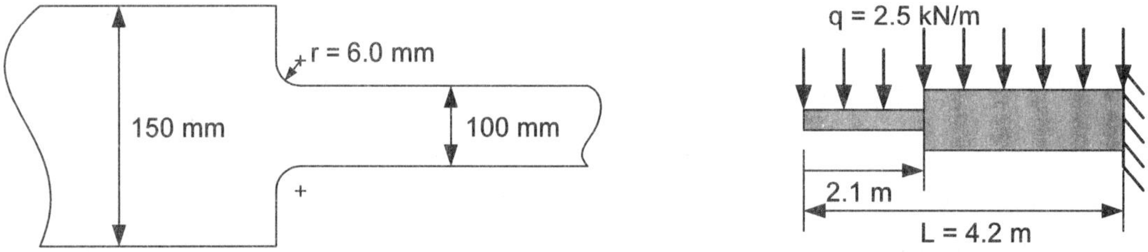

Fig. P9.38

9.39 A stepped beam subjected to moment loading M = 17 kN-m is shown in Fig. P9.39. If the step is located at the center span of the beam, determine the nominal stresses, the stress concentration factor and the maximum stresses at the fillets. The beams dimensions are L= 4.5 m, b = 40 mm, H = 200 mm and h = 112 mm. The fillet radius is r = 20 mm.

Fig. P9.39

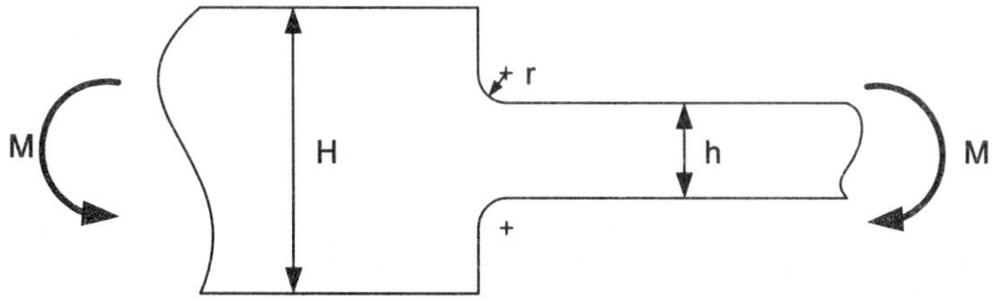

9.40 Repeat Problem 9.39 if the beams dimensions are L= 3.4 m, b = 30 mm, H = 150 mm, h = 100 mm and r = 15 mm. All the other parameters remain the same.

9.41 A shaft in a drive train, illustrated in Fig. P9.41, is subjected to bending moments due to a transverse force of 3.5 kN imposed by a gear set. Determine the maximum stresses at the fillet due to the gear load.

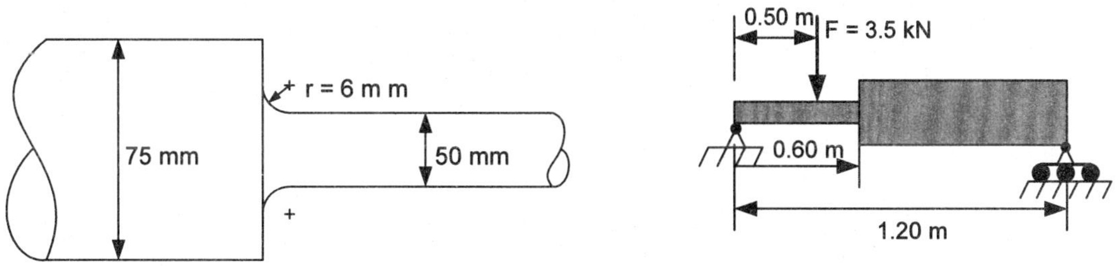

Fig. P9.41

9.42 If the shaft in Problem 9.41 is fabricated from steel with an endurance limit of 280 MPa, determine its safety factor against failure by fatigue.

9.43 A shaft with a circular cross section is designed with a step transition between two diameters, D = 2.5 in. and d = 1.25 in. The shaft is subjected to a bending moment of M = 175 ft-lb at the transition point. Determine the minimum radius of the fillet at the transition region, if the maximum stress is not to exceed 35.0 ksi.

9.44 Repeat Problem 9.43 if the maximum stress is not to exceed 30 ksi. All the other parameters remain the same.

9.45 A rotating shaft with a circular cross section is designed with a step transition between two diameters, D = 4.0 in. and d = 2.0 in. The shaft is subjected to a bending moment of M = 500 ft-lb at the transition point. The radius of the fillet at the transition region is r = 0.25 in. Determine the safety factor against fatigue failure, if the endurance limit from which the shaft is fabricated is 40 ksi.

9.46 A shaft in a turbine engine is used as a conduit to transport coolant to the root of the turbine blades. The coolant enters and exits the shaft through small holes as shown in Fig. P9.46. Determine the maximum stress adjacent to the hole, if the shaft supports a bending moment M = 400 N-m at the location of the hole.

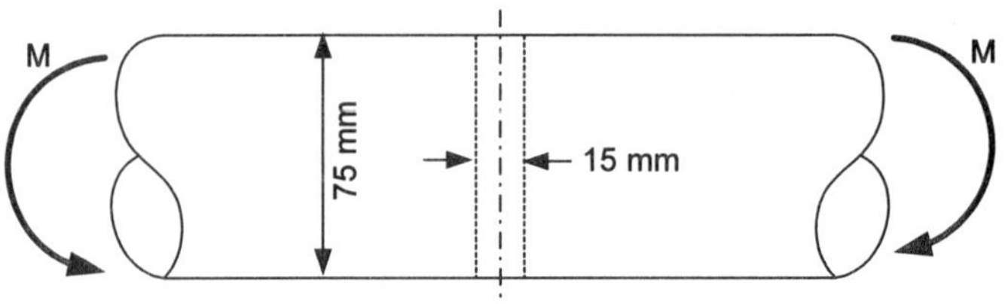

Fig. P9.46

9.47 A circular shaft with a diameter D = 100 mm is drilled with a transverse hole having a diameter d = 5 mm. If the shaft is subjected to a bending moment of 90 kN-m, determine the maximum stress adjacent the hole.

9.48 A circular shaft with a diameter D = 60 mm is drilled with a transverse hole having a diameter d = 6 mm. If the shaft is subjected to a bending moment of 20 kN-m, determine the maximum stress adjacent the hole.

9.49 A circular shaft with a diameter D = 3.0 in. is drilled with a transverse hole having a diameter d = 0.25 in. If the shaft is subjected to a bending moment of 75×10^3 in.-lb, determine the maximum stress adjacent the hole. If the material from which the shaft is fabricated exhibits an endurance limit of 54 ksi, determine the safety factor again failure by fatigue at the transverse hole.

9.50 A circular shaft with a diameter D = 2.0 in. is drilled with a transverse hole having a diameter d = 0.125 in. If the shaft is subjected to a bending moment of 25×10^3 in.-lb, determine the maximum stress adjacent the hole. If the material from which the shaft is fabricate exhibits an endurance limit of 54 ksi, determine the safety factor again failure by fatigue at the transverse hole.

CHAPTER 10

ENERGY METHODS

10.1 INTRODUCTION

To introduce the concept of energy in the analysis of structural elements, let's consider the tie bar subjected to an axial tension force F. The tie bar extends an amount δ as the force is applied. Because we have moved a force F through a distance δ, work $\boldsymbol{W}$ has been performed. The amount of work is established from the force-displacement graph presented in Fig. 10.1.

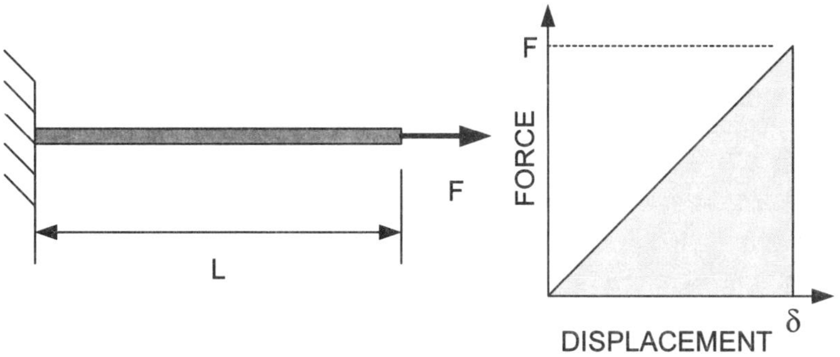

Fig. 10.1 Force-displacement graph for a tie rod with an applied force F.

The work performed on the tie rod is the shaded area under the F-δ curve in Fig. 10.1. Hence:

$$\boldsymbol{W} = F\delta/2 \qquad (10.1)$$

The tie bar may be considered as a system in which energy is conserved. This fact implies that work performed on the bar is conserved as strain energy $\boldsymbol{E}_\varepsilon$. Accordingly, we equate the work and strain energy and express the strain energy stored in the tie rod as:

$$\boldsymbol{E}_\varepsilon = F\delta/2 \qquad (10.2)$$

In later sections of this chapter, we will derive the equations for the strain energy stored in beams and torsion bars. The ability to compute the strain energy stored in structural members is important because three different energy theorems can be employed to extend our methods of analysis including:

1. Theorem of virtual work.
2. Theorem of Castigliano.
3. Theorem of least work (minimum potential energy).

10.2 THE ENERGY THEOREMS

10.2.1 The Theorem of Virtual Work

Consider a structural member subjected to a number of forces that maintain the member in equilibrium, as illustrated in Fig. 10.2.

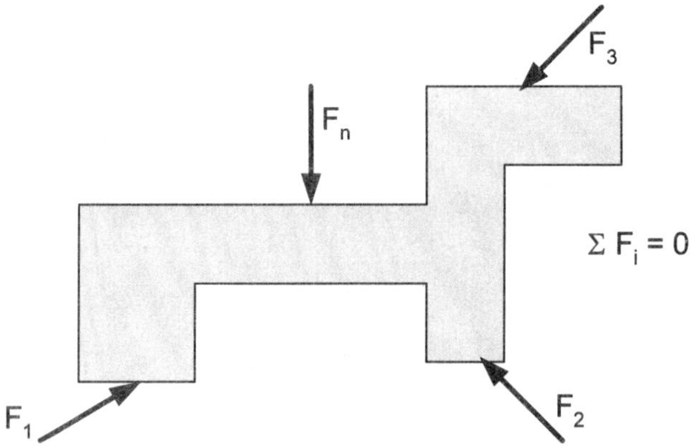

Fig. 10.2 A structural member in equilibrium subjected to forces F_1, F_2, F_3 and F_n.

Suppose we apply a virtual[1] displacement $\Delta\delta_n$ at the location and in the direction of F_n. Then the strain energy is increased by a small amount given by:

$$\Delta \boldsymbol{E}_{\varepsilon} = F_n \Delta\delta_n \tag{10.3}$$

In writing Eq. (10.3), we have assumed that the other external forces F_1, F_2 and F_3 do not move when the virtual displacement is applied. With this assumption, we can rewrite Eq. (10.3) as:

$$\frac{\partial \boldsymbol{E}_{\varepsilon}}{\partial \delta_n} = F_n \tag{10.4}$$

In applying Eq. (10.4), the strain energy E_ε is expressed in terms of displacements so that the applied loads F_1, F_2 and F_3 do not appear and are not an issue. Equation (10.4) is used in determining the force F_n, when the loading of a structural element is accomplished by applying displacements at specified locations.

10.2.2 The Theorem of Castigliano

Consider again the structural member in Fig. 10.2, which is in equilibrium when subjected to forces F_1, F_2, F_3 and F_n. Let's increase the force F_n by a virtual amount ΔF_n. Accordingly, the increase in the strain energy is given by:

$$\Delta \boldsymbol{E}_{\varepsilon} = \delta_n \Delta F_n \tag{10.5}$$

Again we have assumed that ΔF_n is sufficiently small that the external forces F_1, F_2 and F_3 do not move as ΔF_n is applied. We can then rewrite Eq. (10.5) as:

---

[1] The word virtual implies that the displacement $\Delta\delta_n$ is small when compared to δ_n.

$$\frac{\partial \boldsymbol{E}_{\varepsilon}}{\partial F_n} = \delta_n \tag{10.6}$$

In applying Eq. (10.6), we write the expression for $\boldsymbol{E}_{\varepsilon}$ so that the displacements δ_1, δ_2, δ_3 and δ_n do not appear. Equation (10.6) is used to determine displacements at selected locations on structural members or in solving for reactions in statically indeterminate structures.

10.2.3 The Theorem of Least Work[2]

Consider a number of different stress distributions that are possible for some structural member subjected to external loading. Moreover, assume that all of these different stress distributions yield internal forces that satisfy the equations of equilibrium. Only one of these distributions is correct, because the others violate the compatibility conditions[3].

The correct (compatible) stress distribution minimizes the strain energy stored in the structural member. We can express this fact by writing:

$$\partial \boldsymbol{E}_{\varepsilon} = 0 \tag{10.7}$$

All three of these theorems are useful in the analysis of structures. Castigliano's theorem is often employed to determine the reaction at the redundant support in a statically indeterminate structure. The theorem of virtual work is helpful in solving for the critical load in the buckling of structural members. The theorem of least work is used with finite elements to determine displacement fields that satisfy the compatibility conditions. Energy methods can also be used to solve for forces generated during impact events. We will demonstrate many of the applications of Castigliano's theorem later in this chapter. Applications of the theorems of virtual work and least work are deferred to a more advanced course in Mechanics.

10.3 STRAIN ENERGY DENSITY

Consider an arbitrary element removed from the tie rod shown previously in Fig. 10.1. When the tie rod is subjected to an axial force F, a normal stress σ_{xx} results on opposites sides of the element as shown in Fig. 10.3a.

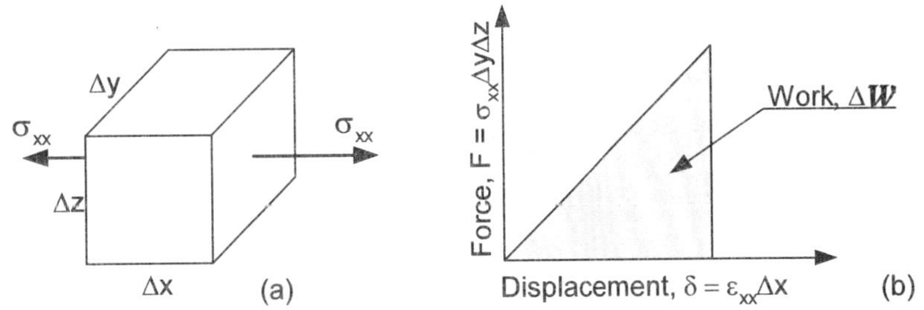

Fig. 10.3 An element from the tie rod is subjected to a uniaxial stress σ_{xx}.

---

[2] The theorem of least work is also referred to as the theorem for minimum potential energy.

[3] Many different stress distributions can be devised to satisfy equilibrium; however, only the true (correct) distribution will yield the correct displacement field for the structural member. This requirement, given in Eq. (10.7), couples the stress and displacement fields and is referred to as the compatibility condition.

The work performed on the element, illustrated in Fig. 10.3b, is the shaded area under the force-displacement line. We equate this work to strain energy and write:

$$\Delta \boldsymbol{W} = \Delta \boldsymbol{E}_\varepsilon = (1/2)(\sigma_{xx}\, \varepsilon_{xx})\Delta x\Delta y\Delta z \tag{10.8}$$

Let's rewrite Eq. (10.8) as:

$$\boldsymbol{e}_\varepsilon = \Delta \boldsymbol{E}_\varepsilon / \boldsymbol{V} = (1/2)\sigma_{xx}\, \varepsilon_{xx} \tag{10.9}$$

where $\boldsymbol{e}_\varepsilon$ is the strain energy density, which is the amount of strain energy stored per unit volume of the member. $\boldsymbol{V} = \Delta x\Delta y\Delta z$ is the volume of the element.

Equation (10.9) is valid for a uniaxial state of stress where $\sigma_{yy} = \sigma_{zz} = \tau_{xy} = \tau_{yz} = \tau_{zx} = 0$. However, if the member is subjected to a general three-dimensional state of stress, we write the expression for $\boldsymbol{e}_\varepsilon$ as:

$$\boldsymbol{e}_\varepsilon = (1/2)(\sigma_{xx}\, \varepsilon_{xx} + \sigma_{yy}\, \varepsilon_{yy} + \sigma_{zz}\, \varepsilon_{zz} + \tau_{xy}\gamma_{xy} + \tau_{yz}\gamma_{yz} + \tau_{zx}\gamma_{zx}) \tag{10.10}$$

If the state of stress in the structural member is a principal state, then x, y and z are principal axes and $\gamma_{xy} = \gamma_{yz} = \gamma_{zx} = 0$. Then Eq. (10.10) reduces to:

$$\boldsymbol{e}_\varepsilon = (1/2)(\sigma_1\, \varepsilon_1 + \sigma_2\, \varepsilon_2 + \sigma_3\, \varepsilon_3) \tag{10.11}$$

where $\sigma_{xx} = \sigma_1$, $\varepsilon_{xx} = \varepsilon_1$, etc.

Let's consider two examples to illustrate the methods for computing strain energy density.

EXAMPLE 10.1

A point in a machine component is subjected to a three-dimensional state of stress that is described in terms of three principal stresses given by σ_1 = 15,000 psi, σ_2 = 10,000 psi and σ_3 = – 5,000 psi. Determine the strain energy density for this point, if the machine component is fabricated from steel.

Solution:

Let's begin by writing the expression of the strain energy density in terms of the principal stresses and strains, which is given by Eq. (10.11) as:

$$\boldsymbol{e}_\varepsilon = (1/2)(\sigma_1\, \varepsilon_1 + \sigma_2\, \varepsilon_2 + \sigma_3\, \varepsilon_3) \tag{a}$$

Recall the stress-strain relations as:

$$\varepsilon_1 = (1/E)[\sigma_1 - \nu(\sigma_2 + \sigma_3)]$$

$$\varepsilon_2 = (1/E)[\sigma_2 - \nu(\sigma_1 + \sigma_3)] \tag{b}$$

$$\varepsilon_3 = (1/E)[\sigma_3 - \nu(\sigma_1 + \sigma_2)]$$

Substituting Eq. (b) into Eq. (a) gives:

$$\mathscr{e}_\varepsilon = (1/2E)[\sigma_1^2 + \sigma_2^2 + \sigma_3^2 - 2\nu(\sigma_1 \sigma_2 + \sigma_2 \sigma_3 + \sigma_3 \sigma_1)] \qquad (10.12)$$

Substituting numerical parameters from the problem statement into Eq. (10.12) gives:

$$e_\varepsilon = \frac{1}{2(30\times 10^6)}\{(15.0)^2 + (10.0)^2 + (-5.0)^2 - (2)(0.30)[(15.0)(10.0) + (10.0)(-5.0) + (-5.0)(15.0)]\}(10^6)$$

$$e_\varepsilon = 5.583 \text{ in.-lb/in}^3$$

We have used the unit in.-lb/in.^{3} instead of lb/in^2 for the strain energy density, because the former conveys the concept of energy per unit volume. Actually both representations of the units are correct.

EXAMPLE 10.2

A point in a structural member is subjected to a three dimensional state of stress described by the six Cartesian stress components σ_{xx} = 200 MPa, σ_{yy} = – 120 MPa, σ_{zz} = 80.0 MPa, τ_{xy} = 90 MPa, τ_{yz} = 85 MPa, τ_{zx} = 70 MPa. Determine the strain energy density if the member is fabricated from aluminum alloy 2024 T-4.

Solution:

Let's begin by writing the expression for the strain energy density in terms of the Cartesian components of stress, which is given by Eq. (10.10) as:

$$\mathscr{e}_\varepsilon = (1/2)(\sigma_{xx}\,\varepsilon_{xx} + \sigma_{yy}\,\varepsilon_{yy} + \sigma_{zz}\,\varepsilon_{zz} + \tau_{xy}\gamma_{xy} + \tau_{yz}\gamma_{yz} + \tau_{zx}\gamma_{zx}) \qquad (a)$$

Recall the stress strain relations as:

$$\varepsilon_{xx} = (1/E)[\sigma_{xx} - \nu(\sigma_{yy} + \sigma_{zz})] \qquad \gamma_{xy} = \tau_{xy}/G$$

$$\varepsilon_{yy} = (1/E)[\sigma_{yy} - \nu(\sigma_{xx} + \sigma_{zz})] \qquad \gamma_{yz} = \tau_{yz}/G \qquad (b)$$

$$\varepsilon_{zz} = (1/E)[\sigma_{zz} - \nu(\sigma_{xx} + \sigma_{yy})] \qquad \gamma_{zx} = \tau_{zx}/G$$

Substituting Eq. (b) into Eq. (a) gives:

$$\mathscr{e}_\varepsilon = (1/2E)[\sigma_{xx}^2 + \sigma_{yy}^2 + \sigma_{zz}^2 - 2\nu(\sigma_{xx}\sigma_{yy} + \sigma_{yy}\sigma_{zz} + \sigma_{zz}\sigma_{xx})] + (1/2G)[\tau_{xy}^2 + \tau_{yz}^2 + \tau_{zx}^2] \qquad (10.13)$$

Substituting numerical parameters from the problem statement into Eq. (10.13) gives:

$$\mathscr{e}_\varepsilon = \frac{10^{12}}{2(72\times 10^9)}\left[(200)^2 + (-120)^2 + (80)^2 - (2)(0.32)[(200)(-120) + (-120)(80) + (80)(200)]\right]$$

$$+ \frac{10^{12}}{2(27\times 10^9)}\left[(90)^2 + (85)^2 + (70)^2\right] = 875.0\times 10^3 \text{ N-m/m}^3$$

10.4 STRAIN ENERGY IN STRUCTURAL ELEMENTS

This section describes methods employed to determine the strain energy stored in common structural elements such as tie rods, beams in bending and torsion bars. First, consider the tie rod from Fig. 10.1.

10.4.1 Strain Energy in Tie Rods

Previously we described a technique for determining the strain energy stored in an axially loaded rod in Section 10.1. Let's consider a second approach based on strain energy density. Recall Eq. (10.9) and substitute Hooke's law into this relation to obtain:

$$\mathscr{e}_\varepsilon = (1/2)(\sigma_{xx}\,\varepsilon_{xx}) = (1/2)\,E\varepsilon_{xx}^2 = [1/(2E)]\sigma_{xx}^2 \qquad (10.14)$$

Integrate Eq. (10.14) over the volume $\boldsymbol{V}$ of the tie rod to obtain:

$$\boldsymbol{E}_\varepsilon = \frac{1}{2E}\int \sigma_{xx}^2\, d\boldsymbol{V} \qquad (10.15)$$

Because $\sigma_{xx} = F/A$ for each volume element in the tie rod, we can rewrite Eq. (10.15) as:

$$\boldsymbol{E}_\varepsilon = \frac{1}{2E}\frac{F^2}{A^2}AL = \frac{F^2L}{2AE} \qquad (10.16)$$

Let's consider two examples to demonstrate this approach for determining the strain energy in a tie bar.

EXAMPLE 10.3

A tie rod, 15 ft long fabricated from steel with a yield strength $S_y = 42$ ksi is subjected to an axial force of 12,000 lb. If the bar diameter is 0.80 in., determine the strain energy stored in the tie rod and the strain energy density.

Solution:

We employ Eq. (10.16) to determine the strain energy $\boldsymbol{E}_\varepsilon$ as:

$$\boldsymbol{E}_\varepsilon = \frac{F^2L}{2AE} = \frac{(12{,}000)^2(15)(12)}{2(\pi)(0.40)^2(30\times 10^6)} = 859.4 \text{ in.-lb} \qquad \text{(a)}$$

The strain energy density is given by Eq. (10.14) as:

$$\mathscr{e}_\varepsilon = \frac{\sigma_{xx}^2}{2E} = \left(\frac{12{,}000}{\pi(0.40)^2}\right)^2\left(\frac{1}{(2)(30\times 10^6)}\right) = 9.499 \text{ in.-lb/in.}^3 \qquad \text{(b)}$$

It is difficult to physically interpret the significance of these results, because we do not have a basis for comparison. What is a large strain energy or strain energy density? The total strain energy increases with the volume of the member. Consequently, the strain energy stored in a member depends upon both the square of the stress and the rod volume. To assess the results of this analysis, it is advantageous to examine the strain energy density, which is independent of the volume. Hence we seek a maximum value of the strain energy density to be used for comparison purposes. From Eq. (10.14) it is evident that:

$$(e_\varepsilon)_{Max} = [1/(2E)]S_y^2 \tag{10.17}$$

$$(e_\varepsilon)_{Max} = (42{,}000)^2/[(2)(30\times 10^6)] = 29.40 \text{ in.-lb/in.}^3 \tag{c}$$

Comparing the results of Eq. (b) with Eq. (c) indicates that the tie rod in this example was loaded to a strain energy density of (9.499)/(29.40) = 0.3231, or 32.31% of the maximum possible value.

EXAMPLE 10.4

A tie rod, fabricated from stainless steel is shown in Fig. E10.4. If the axial loading is F = 500 kN, determine the strain energy stored in the tie rod and the strain energy density.

Fig. E10.4

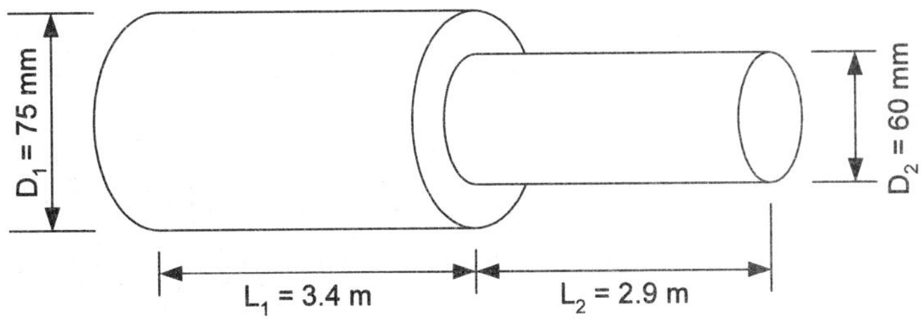

Solution:

Let's begin by computing the stress in each segment of the tie rod as:

$$\sigma_1 = \frac{4F}{\pi D_1^2} = \frac{(4)(500\times 10^3)}{\pi(75)^2} = 113.2 \text{ MPa}$$

$$\sigma_2 = \frac{4F}{\pi D_2^2} = \frac{(4)(500\times 10^3)}{\pi(60)^2} = 176.8 \text{ MPa} \tag{a}$$

Using Eq. (10.14) and Eq. (a), we determine the strain energy density for each segment of the bar as:

$$(e_\varepsilon)_1 = \frac{\sigma_1^2}{2E} = \frac{(113.2)^2\times 10^{12}}{2(190\times 10^9)} = 33.72\times 10^3 \text{ N-m/m}^3 \tag{b}$$

$$(e_\varepsilon)_2 = \frac{\sigma_2^2}{2E} = \frac{(176.8)^2 \times 10^{12}}{2(190 \times 10^9)} = 82.26 \times 10^3 \text{ N-m/m}^3 \qquad \text{(c)}$$

The total strain energy stored in the tie rod is determined from Eq. (10.9) as:

$$E_\varepsilon = (e_\varepsilon)_1 V_1 + (e_\varepsilon)_2 V_2 = (33.72 \times 10^3)(.0375)^2\pi(3.4)$$

$$+ (82.26 \times 10^3)(.03)^2\pi(2.9) = 1{,}181 \text{ N-m} \qquad \text{(d)}$$

Because the bar was not of constant diameter, it was necessary to divide it into two segments and determine the strain energy density in each segment. The total strain energy is then computed by multiplying each value of e_ε by the appropriate volume and summing the two quantities.

10.4.2 Strain Energy for a Beam in Bending

For a beam subjected to transverse loading, as shown in Fig. 10.4, the flexural stress σ_{xx} can be determined from:

$$\sigma_{xx} = My/I_z \qquad (10.18)$$

where M is the bending moment at any location defined by x.

Fig. 10.4 A beam subjected to transverse forces.

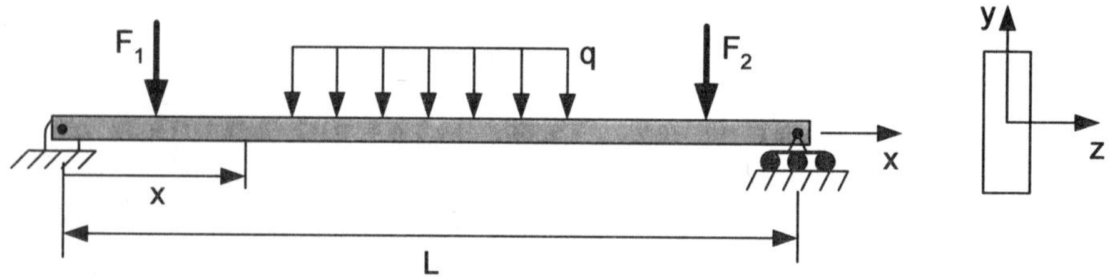

To determine the strain energy density, we use Eq. (10.14), which is valid for uniaxial states of stress. Combing Eq. (10.14) and Eq. (10.18), we obtain:

$$e_\varepsilon = \left(\frac{1}{2E}\right)\left(\frac{My}{I_z}\right)^2 \qquad (10.19)$$

An examination of Eq. (10.19) shows that the strain energy density varies with the location x over the length of the beam, because M is a function of x. The strain energy density also depends on the position y measured from the neutral axis of the beam.

We integrate Eq. (10.19) over the volume to obtain the strain energy stored in the beam as:

$$E_\varepsilon = \int \frac{1}{2E}\left(\frac{My}{I_z}\right)^2 dA dx = \int \frac{1}{2E}\left(\frac{M}{I_z}\right)^2 \left[\int y^2 dA\right] dx \qquad (10.20)$$

In Eq. (10.20), we recognize $\int y^2\, dA = I_z$. Hence, we rewrite Eq. (10.20) as:

$$\boldsymbol{E}_{\varepsilon} = \left(\frac{1}{2EI_z}\right)\int_0^L M^2 dx \tag{10.21}$$

We have assumed that both E and I_z are constant over the volume of the beam in the derivation of Eq. (10.21). Let's consider two examples to demonstrate the use of Eq. (10.21) in determining the strain energy stored in a beam subjected to transverse loading.

EXAMPLE 10.5

For the beam shown in Fig. E10.5, determine the expression for the strain energy due to the normal stress σ_{xx}.

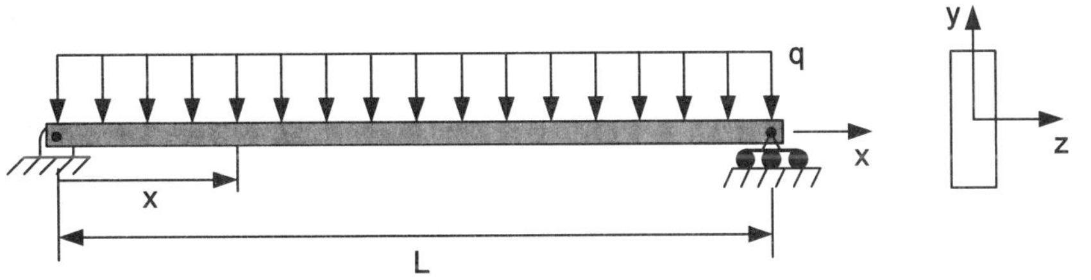

Fig. E10.5

Solution:

The reactions at the simple supports are determined from an appropriate FBD and the application of the equilibrium equations as:

$\Sigma F_x = 0 \quad \Rightarrow \quad R_{Lx} = 0$

$\Sigma M_L = 0 \quad \Rightarrow \quad R_R = qL/2 \qquad$ (a)

$\Sigma F_y = 0 \quad \Rightarrow \quad R_{Ly} = qL/2$

Next prepare a FBD of the left-hand portion of the beam as shown in Fig. E10.5a.

Fig. E10.5a

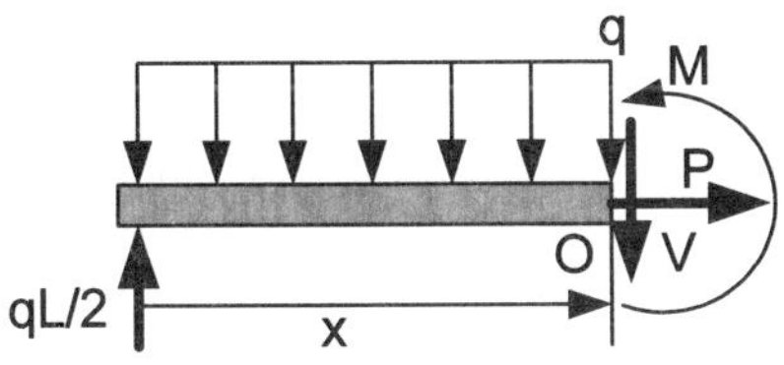

Applying the equilibrium equation yields:

$\Sigma F_x = 0 \quad \Rightarrow \quad P = 0$

$\Sigma F_y = 0 \quad \Rightarrow \quad qL/2 - qx - V = 0 \qquad$ (b)

$\Sigma M_O = 0 \quad \Rightarrow \quad (qL/2)x - (qx)(x/2) + M = 0$

Solving Eqs. (b) for V and M yields:

$$V = (q/2)(L - 2x) \qquad \text{(c)}$$

$$M = (qx/2)(x - L) \qquad \text{(d)}$$

Substituting Eq. (d) into Eq. (10.21) gives:

$$\boldsymbol{E}_\varepsilon = \frac{1}{2EI_z}\int_0^L \left[\left(\frac{qx}{2}\right)(x - L)\right]^2 dx \qquad \text{(e)}$$

Integrating Eq. (e) and simplifying gives:

$$\boldsymbol{E}_\varepsilon = \frac{q^2L^5}{240EI_z} \qquad (10.22)$$

It is important to recognize that the strain energy represented in Eq. (10.22) is due to the normal stress σ_{xx}, which in turn is produced by the bending moment M. However, a shear stress τ_{xy} due to the shear force V exists. This shear stress τ_{xy} produces additional strain energy so that the total strain energy includes contributions from both σ_{xx} and τ_{xy}. We will describe methods to determine the strain energy due to shear stresses later in this chapter.

EXAMPLE 10.6

For the beam shown in Fig. E10.6, determine the expression for the strain energy due to the normal stress σ_{xx}.

Fig. E10.6

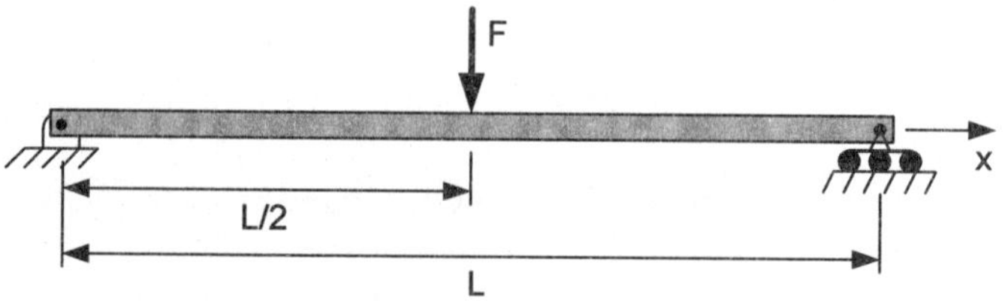

Solution:

The reactions at the simple supports are determined from an appropriate FBD and the application of the equilibrium equations to obtain:

$$R_L - F/2 \qquad\qquad R_R - F/2 \qquad \text{(a)}$$

Next prepare a FBD of the left-hand portion of the beam as shown in Fig. E10.6a.

Fig. E10.6a

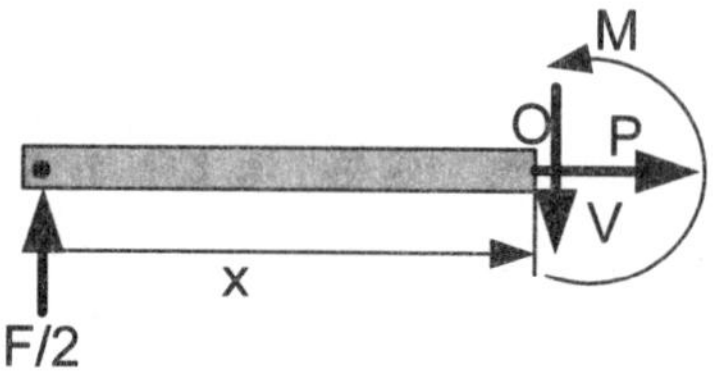

Applying the equilibrium equations yields:

$$\Sigma F_x = 0 \quad \Rightarrow \quad P = 0 \quad 0 \le x \le (L/2)$$

$$\Sigma F_y = 0 \quad \Rightarrow \quad V = F/2 \quad 0 \le x \le (L/2) \qquad \text{(b)}$$

$$\Sigma M_O = 0 \quad \Rightarrow \quad M = (F/2)x \quad 0 \le x \le (L/2)$$

Substituting the expression for the moment M in Eq. (b) into Eq. (10.21) gives a relation that is valid for the left half of the beam.

$$\boldsymbol{E}_\varepsilon = \frac{1}{2EI_z}\int_0^{L/2}\left(\frac{Fx}{2}\right)^2 dx \qquad \text{(c)}$$

Integrating Eq. (c) gives:

$$\boldsymbol{E}_\varepsilon = \frac{F^2L^3}{192EI_z} \qquad \text{(d)}$$

The result in Eq. (d) represents the strain energy due to σ_{xx} in the left half of the beam. Because the loading on the beam is symmetric, we multiply this result by two to obtain the strain energy over the entire volume of the beam as:

$$\boldsymbol{E}_\varepsilon = \frac{F^2L^3}{96EI_z} \qquad (10.23)$$

Again, it is important to recognize that the strain energy represented in Eq. (10.23) is due to the normal stress σ_{xx}; however, a shear stress τ_{xy} due to the shear force V exists. This shear stress τ_{xy} produces additional strain energy so that the total strain energy includes contributions from both σ_{xx} and τ_{xy}.

10.4.3 Strain Energy Due to Shear Stresses

The most general expression for strain energy density is given in Eq. (10.10), where the contributions due to all six Cartesian components of stress are included. To develop a simpler form of this expression, consider the state of stress where $\sigma_{xx} = \sigma_{yy} = \sigma_{zz} = \tau_{yz} = \tau_{zx} = 0$. Then we can rewrite Eq. (10.10) as:

$$\boldsymbol{e}_\varepsilon = \tau_{xy}\gamma_{xy}/2 = \tau_{xy}^2/(2G) \qquad (10.24)$$

Integrate Eq. (10.24) over the volume $\boldsymbol{V}$ of a structural member to obtain the relation for the strain energy due to τ_{xy} as:

$$\boldsymbol{E}_\varepsilon = \frac{1}{2G}\int \tau_{xy}^2 d\boldsymbol{V} \qquad (10.25)$$

Let's consider a circular shaft subjected to a torsional load to demonstrate the application of Eq. (10.25) in the determination of strain energy due to shear stress.

EXAMPLE 10.7

A 60 in. long steel shaft is subjected to a torque T = 40,000 in.-lb. If the shaft is 2.0 in. in diameter, compute the strain energy stored in the shaft.

Solution:

Let's begin by writing the relation for the shear stress τ_{xy} as a function of its radial position ρ.

$$\tau_{xy} = T\rho/J \tag{a}$$

Substituting Eq. (a) into Eq. (10.25) gives:

$$\boldsymbol{E}_\varepsilon = \frac{1}{2G}\int\left(\frac{T\rho}{J}\right)^2 dAdx = \frac{1}{2G}\int\left(\frac{T}{J}\right)^2\left[\int\rho^2 dA\right]dx \tag{b}$$

Recognizing that $\int\rho^2 dA = J$, we rewrite Eq. (b) as:

$$\boldsymbol{E}_\varepsilon = \frac{1}{2GJ}\int_0^L T^2 dx = \frac{T^2L}{2GJ} \tag{10.26}$$

Note that T and J are considered constant over the length of the shaft in Eq. (10.26). Substituting numerical parameters into this relation yields:

$$\boldsymbol{E}_\varepsilon = \frac{T^2L}{2GJ} = \frac{(40\times 10^3)^2(60)(32)}{(2)(11.5\times 10^6)\pi(2.0)^4} = 2{,}657 \text{ in.-lb} \tag{c}$$

EXAMPLE 10.8

Let's again consider the beam with the uniformly distributed load q that we studied in Example 10.5. In this re-examination, determine the relation for the strain energy stored in the beam due to the shear stress τ_{xy}. The beam has a rectangular cross section as shown in Fig. E10.8.

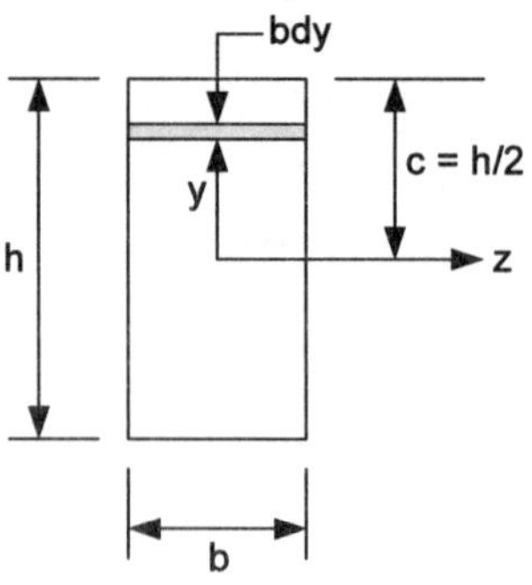

Fig. E10.8

Solution:

For a beam with a rectangular cross section, it can be shown that:

$$\tau_{xy} = \frac{3V}{2A}\left(1 - \frac{y^2}{c^2}\right) \tag{a}$$

Recall from Example 10.5 that the shear force V was given by:

$$V = (q/2)(L - 2x) \tag{b}$$

Substitute Eq. (b) into Eq. (a) to obtain:

$$\tau_{xy} = \frac{3q}{2A}\left(1 - \frac{y^2}{c^2}\right)\left(\frac{L}{2} - x\right) \tag{c}$$

Substitute Eq. (c) into Eq. (10.25) and note that $d\boldsymbol{V}$ = bdydx to obtain:

$$(\boldsymbol{E}_\varepsilon)_\tau = \frac{1}{2G}\left(\frac{3q}{2A}\right)^2 \int \left(1 - \frac{y^2}{c^2}\right)^2 \left(\frac{L}{2} - x\right)^2 \text{bdydx} \tag{d}$$

Expanding Eq. (d) gives:

$$(\boldsymbol{E}_\varepsilon)_\tau = \frac{1}{8G}\left(\frac{9q^2}{bh^2}\right)\int_{-c}^{+c}\left(1 - \frac{2y^2}{c^2} + \frac{y^4}{c^4}\right)dy \int_0^L \left(\frac{L^2}{4} - Lx + x^2\right)dx \tag{e}$$

Integrating and substituting the upper and lower limits into the results yields:

$$(\boldsymbol{E}_\varepsilon)_\tau = \frac{q^2 L^3}{20Gbh} \tag{10.27}$$

A comparison of the strain energies stored in the beam due to shear and normal stress is obtained from the ratio of the strain energies given by Eqs. (10.22) and (10.27) as:

$$\frac{(\boldsymbol{E}_\varepsilon)_\tau}{(\boldsymbol{E}_\varepsilon)_\sigma} = \frac{12q^2 L^3 EI_z}{bhGq^2 L^5} \tag{a}$$

Noting that $I_z = bh^3/12$ and $G = E/[2(1 + \nu)]$, we can reduce Eq. (a) to:

$$\frac{(\boldsymbol{E}_\varepsilon)_\tau}{(\boldsymbol{E}_\varepsilon)_\sigma} = 2(1 + \nu)\left(\frac{h}{L}\right)^2 \tag{10.28}$$

Evaluating Eq. (10.28) for a series of beams with different ratios of h/L gives the strain energy ratio for uniformly distributed loaded beams, shown in Table 10.1.

Examination of the results of Table 10.1 shows that the fraction of strain energy due to shear stresses is very small if the beam is long and slender. The shear stress becomes an important contributor to strain energy only for short deep beams. For this reason, we neglect the contribution of the shear stresses in beams to the total strain energy stored when h/L < 1/10.

Table 10.1
Strain energy ratio $(E_\varepsilon)_\tau/(E_\varepsilon)_\sigma$ for steel beams with different ratios of h/L

h/L	$(E_\varepsilon)_\tau/(E_\varepsilon)_\sigma$	$(E_\varepsilon)_\tau/(E_\varepsilon)_\sigma$	Type of Beam
0.2	0.104	10.4%	Deep
0.1	0.026	2.6%	Long and Slender
0.05	0.0065	0.65%	Long and Slender
0.02	0.0010	0.10%	Long and Slender

10.5 DYNAMIC (IMPACT) LOADING

All of the methods introduced thus far in this textbook, apply to structures with loadings, which are gradually applied. Typical force-time and force-displacement curves for gradual application of loads to structures are presented in Fig. 10.5.

Fig. 10.5 Force-time and force-displacement functions associated with gradual (static) loading.

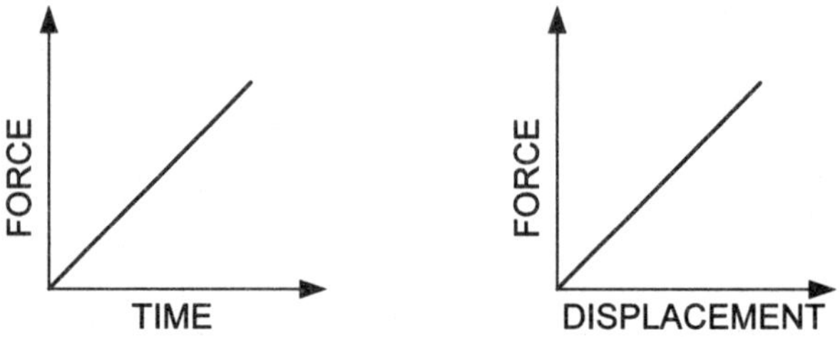

For dynamically applied forces, sometimes called impact forces, we treat the force as if it were applied instantaneously with the force-time trace as illustrated in Fig. 10.6. The instantaneous application of load on a structural element has a dramatic effect on the magnitude of the stresses generated.

Fig. 10.6 Force-time trace for impact loading.

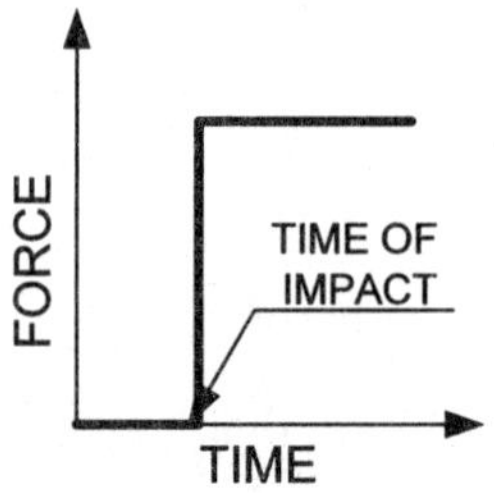

We are able to use energy methods to solve for the stresses in rods and beams when they are subjected to impact loading. With this approach, two assumptions are made:

1. Energy is conserved, which implies that the impact is elastic and that no work is converted to heat or used to produce plastic deformation at the point of contact.
2. The impacting body remains in contact with the structure during the impact period and transfers all of its kinetic energy to the structure.

Next, we will describe the application of energy methods for determining the maximum stresses developed due to impact of both rods and beams.

10.5.1 Impact Loading of Rods

Consider the axial rod shown in Fig. 10.7 that is impacted by a ball traveling with a velocity v at the instant it strikes the rod. If the ball remains in contact with the rod during the entire impact period, the kinetic energy in the ball is converted into strain energy stored in the rod. To determine the stresses produced by the impact of the ball, recall that the expression for the kinetic energy $\boldsymbol{E}_k$ of the ball is given by:

$$\boldsymbol{E}_k = mv^2/2 \tag{10.29}$$

where: m is the mass of the ball and v is the velocity of the ball at the instant of impact.

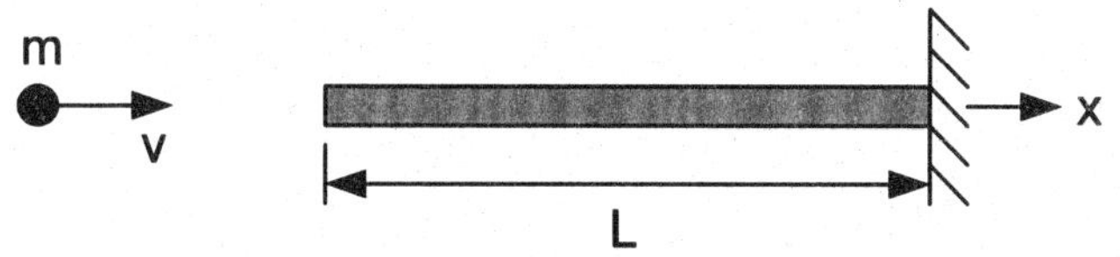

Fig. 10.7 Ball impacting rod with kinetic energy (½)mv^2.

If energy is conserved, the kinetic energy is converted to strain energy and we can write:

$$\boldsymbol{E}_k = \boldsymbol{E}_\varepsilon \tag{10.30}$$

Substituting Eqs. (10.16) and (10.29) into Eq. (10.30) yields:

$$(F^2L)/(2AE) = mv^2/2 \tag{10.31}$$

Solving Eq. (10.31) for the maximum impact force gives:

$$F_{Max} = \sqrt{\frac{mv^2AE}{L}} \tag{10.32}$$

The axial stress developed during impact is then given by:

$$\sigma_{Max} = \frac{F_{Max}}{A} = \sqrt{\frac{mv^2E}{AL}} = \sqrt{\frac{mv^2E}{\boldsymbol{V}}} \tag{10.33}$$

Let's consider an example to demonstrate the application of this approach to the solution of impact problems involving rods.

EXAMPLE 10.9

A hammer strikes a steel rod with an axial impact. Determine the maximum force and the maximum stress produced if the hammer weighs 1.5 lb. The rod is 32 in. long with a square cross section having dimensions of 1.25 by 1.25 in. The velocity of the head of the hammer at impact was 10 ft/s.

Solution:

Substitute the numerical parameters from the problem statement into Eq. (10.32) to obtain the impact force as:

$$F_{Max} = \sqrt{\frac{mv^2AE}{L}} = \sqrt{\frac{1.5(10\times 12)^2(1.25)^2(30\times 10^6)}{(386)(32)}} = 9{,}054 \text{ lb} \qquad \text{(a)}$$

Note that g = 386 in./s^2 must be used in Eq. (a) to convert the 1.5 lb weight into mass.

The axial stress developed during impact is determined from:

$$\sigma_{Max} = \frac{F_{Max}}{A} = \frac{9{,}054}{(1.25)^2} = 5{,}795 \text{ psi} \qquad \text{(b)}$$

The result of this simple example clearly demonstrates that very large impact forces can be generated with small masses during an impact event. In this example, a dynamic force approaching three tons was produced with a 1.5 lb hammer traveling with a velocity of 6.82 MPH.

10.5.2 Impact Loading of Beams

Consider a simply supported beam that is subjected to impact by a falling weight W as illustrated in Fig. 10.8.

Fig. 10.8 A simply supported beam subjected to impact by a falling weight W.

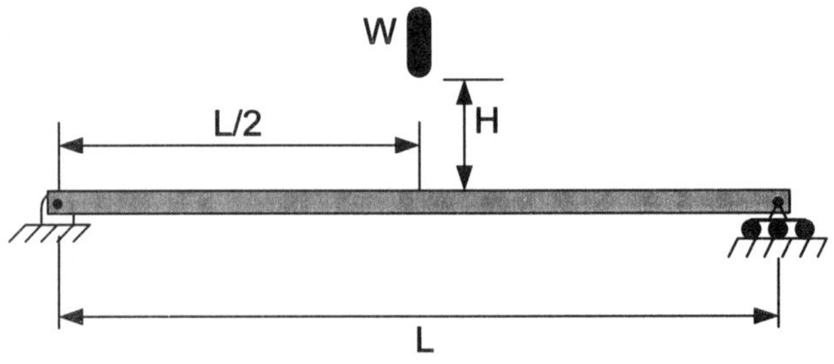

We approach this problem by recognizing that the potential energy of the weight $\boldsymbol{E}_p$ is converted to kinetic energy prior to impact. Upon impact the kinetic energy $\boldsymbol{E}_k$ is converted to strain energy $\boldsymbol{E}_\varepsilon$ stored in the beam. Accordingly, we can write:

$$\boldsymbol{E}_p = \boldsymbol{E}_k = \boldsymbol{E}_\varepsilon = W(H + \delta) \qquad (10.34)$$

where δ is the deflection of the beam at the point of impact.

The strain energy stored in the beam at impact is determined from Eq. (10.21) as:

$$\boldsymbol{E}_\varepsilon = \left(\frac{1}{2EI_z}\right)\int_0^L M^2 dx \qquad \text{(a)}$$

For the simply supported beam with a force F applied at the beam's midpoint, we can write the moment equation as:

$$M = Fx/2 \qquad 0 \le x \le (L/2) \qquad \text{(b)}$$

This equation is identical to the moment relation written for the beam in Example 10.6. Using the results from Example 10.6, we recall Eq. (10.23) as:

$$\boldsymbol{E}_\varepsilon = \frac{F^2L^3}{96EI_z} \qquad \text{(c)}$$

Let's first assume that the deflection of the beam is small with respect to the drop height H. Then the potential energy is reduced to $\boldsymbol{E}_p = WH$. Equating Eq. (c) and Eq. (10.34) gives:

$$WH = \frac{F^2L^3}{96EI_z} \qquad \text{(d)}$$

Solving Eq. (d) for the maximum force gives:

$$F_{Max} = \sqrt{\frac{96EI_zWH}{L^3}} \qquad (10.35)$$

The maximum bending stress occurs at the midpoint of the beam under the impact point. The bending moment at this location is given by:

$$M_{Max} = \frac{F_{Max}L}{4} = \sqrt{\frac{6EI_zWH}{L}} \qquad (10.36)$$

The stress at the midpoint of the beam's span is given by:

$$(\sigma_{xx})_{Max} = M_{Max}c/I_z = M_{Max}/Z \qquad \text{(e)}$$

where $Z = I_z/c$ is the section modulus.

If the beam's cross section is rectangular with $c = h/2$ and $I_z = bh^3/12$, then Eq. (10.36) can be rewritten as:

$$(\sigma_{xx})_{Max} = \sqrt{\frac{18EWH}{Lbh}} = \sqrt{\frac{18EWH}{\boldsymbol{V}}} \qquad (10.37)$$

where $\boldsymbol{V}$ is the volume of the beam.

EXAMPLE 10.10

An experimental impact machine is to be employed in testing the integrity of welds made in steel beams. A schematic diagram of the impact machine is shown in Fig. E10.10. A cross section of a typical test beam is b = 50 mm, h = 75 mm and its length L = 400 mm. For a hammer height H set at 1.5 m, determine the effective weight of the hammer necessary to break the weld, if its estimated strength is 500 MPa.

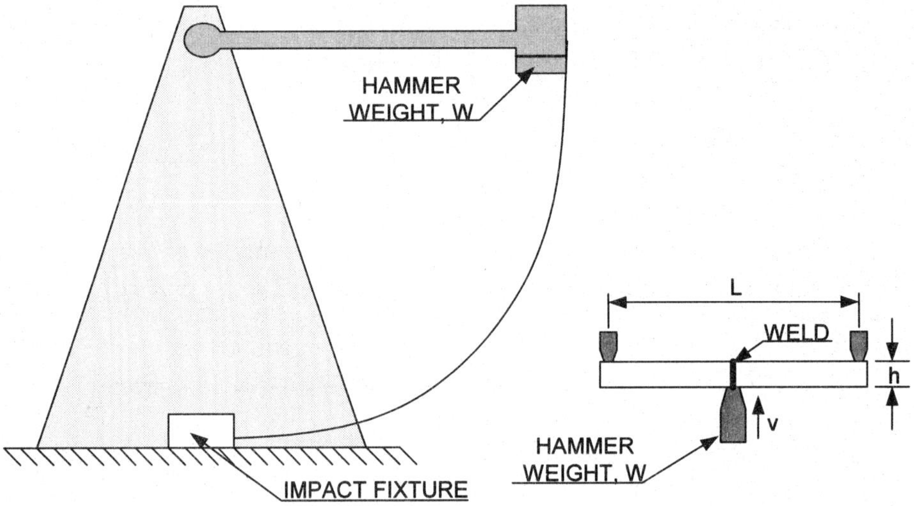

Fig. E10.10

Solution:

While the hammer swings through an arc, the equivalent drop of 1.5 meters must be sufficient to generate a maximum stress that is equal to or greater than the strength of the weld material. Accordingly, we can write:

$$(\sigma_{xx})_{Max} = (S_u)_{Weld} \tag{a}$$

Substituting Eq. (a) into Eq. (10.37) and squaring both sides yields:

$$\frac{18EWH}{Lbh} = S_u^2 \tag{b}$$

Solving Eq. (b) for the hammer weight W using the numerical parameters in the problem statement gives:

$$W = \frac{S_u^2 bhL}{18EH} = \frac{(500\times 10^6)^2(0.05)(0.075)(0.4)}{(18)(207\times 10^9)(1.5)} = 67.10 \text{ N} \tag{c}$$

This solution shows that an impact machine incorporating a relatively small weight (about 15 lb) dropped through a short distance (1.5 m) can develop sufficiently high stress to produce failure of a relatively large steel test specimen. Of course, we are assuming an elastic impact. If plastic bending occurs prior to the failure of the weld, the amount of energy necessary to deform the beam increases dramatically.

The maximum force developed during impact is given by Eq. (10.35) as:

$$F_{Max} = \sqrt{\frac{96EI_zWH}{L^3}} = \sqrt{\frac{8EWHbh^3}{L^3}} = \sqrt{\frac{8(207\times 10^9)(67.10)(1.5)(0.05)(0.075)^3}{(0.4)^3}} = 234.4 \text{ kN}$$

In this example, we observe that the impact force of 234.4 kN is almost 3,500 times larger than the weight (67.10 N) attached to the impact machine. Clearly, dynamic loading is a very important consideration in the design of structures and machine components.

EXAMPLE 10.11

A weight W is positioned at the midpoint on a simply supported beam as shown in Fig. E10.11. While the weight is in contact with the beam (H = 0), its gravitational force has not been applied to the beam. The weight is suddenly released to produce an impact event, although the height of the drop is zero. Determine the equations for the maximum stress, the displacement of the load point and the maximum force developed during the impact.

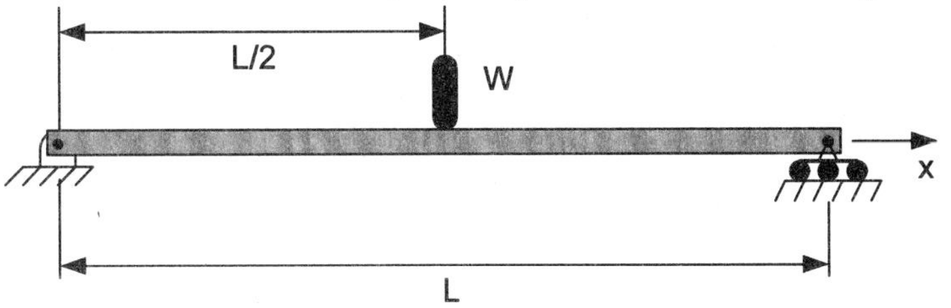

Fig. E10.11

Solution:

The potential energy of the weight in contact with the beam before it is released is given by:

$$\boldsymbol{E}_p = W\delta \tag{a}$$

where δ is the beam's deflection at midpoint due to the sudden application of the weight W.

Let's assume that the elastic curve for the beam during impact is identical to that produced by static loading. Then reference to Appendix E indicates that the force F required to produce the deflection during impact is given by:

$$F = \left(\frac{48EI_z}{L^3}\right)\delta \tag{b}$$

The strain energy stored in the beam is equal to the work performed on the beam by this force and is given by:

$$\boldsymbol{E}_\varepsilon = \boldsymbol{W} = F\delta/2 \tag{c}$$

Substituting Eq. (b) into Eq. (c) yields:

$$\boldsymbol{E}_\varepsilon = \left(\frac{24EI_z}{L^3}\right)\delta^2 \tag{d}$$

Noting that $\boldsymbol{E}_p = \boldsymbol{E}_\varepsilon$, we can write:

$$W\delta = \left(\frac{24EI_z}{L^3}\right)\delta^2 \tag{e}$$

Solving Eq. (e) for δ gives:

$$\delta = \frac{WL^3}{24EI_z} = 2\delta_{st} \tag{f}$$

where δ_{st} is the static deflection of the beam as given in Appendix E.

The maximum force F_{Max} during this impact event is given by substituting Eq. (f) into Eq. (b) to obtain:

$$F_{Max} = \left(\frac{48EI_z}{L^3}\right)\left(\frac{WL^3}{24EI_z}\right) = 2W \tag{g}$$

The results from Eqs. (f) and (g) show the effect of suddenly applying a weight W to a simply supported beam doubles the maximum force and the beam deflection when compared to the case where the weight W is slowly applied.

Now that we have established the importance of the potential energy due to the deflection of the beam during an impact event let's reconsider the assumption made in the derivation of Eq. (10.36). In this derivation, we assumed $\delta << H$ and dropped δ in writing the energy balance. Let's repeat this derivation retaining δ in the energy balance. Begin by recalling Eq. (10.34) as:

$$\boldsymbol{E}_p = \boldsymbol{E}_k = \boldsymbol{E}_\varepsilon = W(H + \delta) \tag{a}$$

For the simply supported beam impacted by a weight W at its midpoint, we recall Eq. (10.23) and write:

$$\boldsymbol{E}_\varepsilon = \frac{F^2L^3}{96EI_z} \tag{b}$$

Again, let's assume that the elastic curve for the beam during impact is identical to that produced by static loading. Then the force F required to produce the deflection during impact is given by:

$$F = \left(\frac{48EI_z}{L^3}\right)\delta \tag{c}$$

Substituting Eq. (c) into (b) and equating the strain energy with the potential energy gives:

$$\left(\frac{48EI_z}{2L^3}\right)\delta^2 - W\delta - WH = 0 \tag{d}$$

Recall from Appendix E that the static deflection δ_{st} is given by:

$$\delta_{st} = \frac{WL^3}{48EI_z} \tag{e}$$

Combining Eqs. (d) and (e) and rearranging yields a quadratic equation in terms of δ:

$$\delta^2 - 2\delta_{St}\delta - 2\delta_{St}H = 0 \qquad \text{(f)}$$

Solving Eq. (f) gives:

$$\delta = \delta_{St}\left(1+\sqrt{1+2\left(\frac{H}{\delta_{St}}\right)}\right) \qquad (10.38)$$

$$\delta = \boldsymbol{M}\delta_{St} \qquad (10.38a)$$

where the term $\boldsymbol{M} = \left(1+\sqrt{1+2\left(\frac{H}{\delta_{St}}\right)}\right)$ is a multiplier on the static deflection.

The magnitude of this multiplier as a function of the ratio H/δ_{st} is presented in Table 10.2.

Table 10.2
Multiplier for beam deflection for different ratios of H/δ_{St}.

H/δ_{st}	$\boldsymbol{M}$	H/δ_{st}	$\boldsymbol{M}$
0	2.00	50	11.05
1	2.73	100	15.17
2	3.24	200	21.02
5	4.32	500	32.64
10	5.58	1000	45.73
20	7.40	2000	64.25

This multiplier is the same for the maximum force developed during impact. Because δ_{st} is usually a small quantity, the ratio of H/δ_{st} becomes large even for relatively small values of the drop height H.

10.6 CASTIGLIANO'S THEOREM

In a previous section, we have developed relations for the strain energy for rods in tension or compression, beams in bending, and shafts in torsion. These expressions are useful because they may be employed in the application of Castigliano's theorem. Castigliano's theorem enables the determination of the relations for the displacement of a structural member at any point where a force is applied. To illustrate this concept consider the strain energy stored in a tie rod, which is given by Eq. (10.16) as:

$$\boldsymbol{E}_\varepsilon = \frac{F^2L}{2AE} \qquad \text{(a)}$$

If we differentiate this relation with respect to the force F, in accordance with Castigliano's theorem and Eq. (10.6), we obtain:

$$\frac{\partial \boldsymbol{E}_\varepsilon}{\partial F} = \frac{FL}{AE} = \delta \tag{b}$$

Differentiating the expression for the strain energy with respect to a force gives the displacement at the point of application of the force. Moreover, the displacement is in the direction of the applied force.

The general procedure for applying Castigliano's theorem is to write an expression for the strain energy of a structural member in terms of the applied loads F_1, F_2, F_3 and F_n. The expression for the strain energy is then differentiated with respect to one of the forces to obtain the displacement at the point of application of that force. The differentiation is repeated for other forces to obtain additional solutions for displacements. Several examples will be described below to demonstrate the application of Castigliano's theorem.

EXAMPLE 10.12

For the simply supported beam shown in Fig. E10.12, determine the deflection at midspan using Castigliano's theorem.

Fig. E10.12

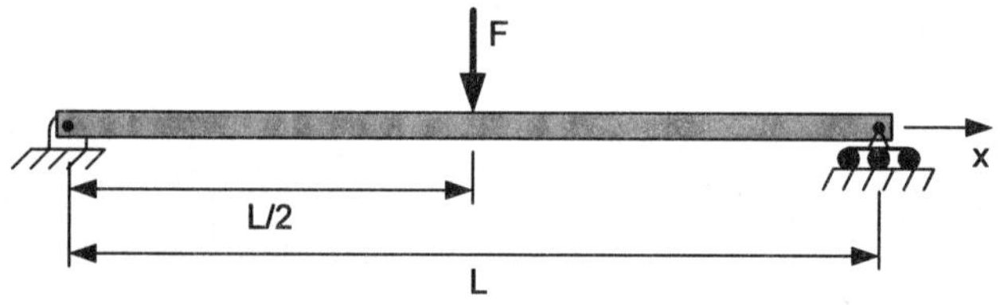

Solution:

We make use of Eq. (10.23) for the strain energy stored in this beam, which was derived in Example 10.6 as:

$$\boldsymbol{E}_\varepsilon = \frac{F^2L^3}{96EI_z} \tag{a}$$

Employ Eq. (10.6) with Eq. (a) to obtain the deflection at the midspan of the beam as:

$$\delta = \frac{\partial \boldsymbol{E}_\varepsilon}{\partial F} = \frac{FL^3}{48EI_z} \tag{b}$$

This result matches the result given in Appendix E for the identical case.

It is clear that Castigliano's method provides a useful approach to determine the deflection at a point on a structure where a concentrated load is applied. But what if we find it necessary to determine the displacement at some other point on the structure? The next example describes a clever approach to provide a solution for this type of problem.

EXAMPLE 10.13

For the cantilever beam, shown in Fig. E10.13, determine the deflection at its free end.

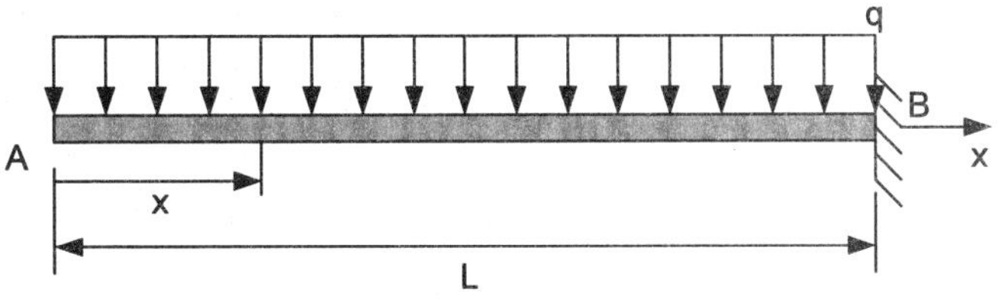

Fig. E10.13

Solution:

The application of Castigliano's theorem to the solution of this problem requires a concentrated force to be located at the point where the deflection is to be determined. However, in this case the cantilever beam is subjected to a uniformly distributed load and a concentrated force is not available. To circumvent this difficulty, we apply a fictitious concentrated force f at the free end of the beam as shown in Fig. E10.13a.

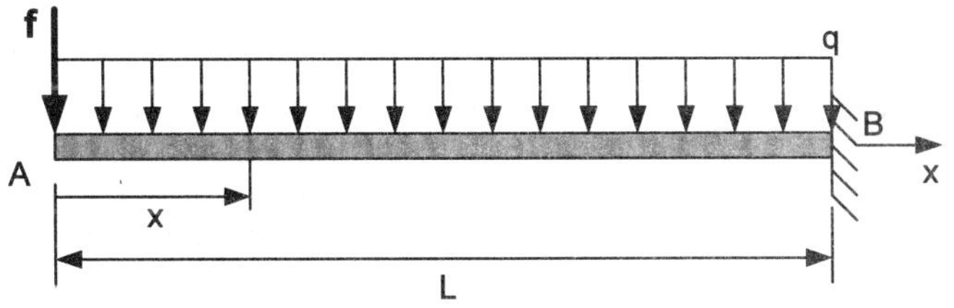

Fig. E10.13a

To apply Castigliano's theorem it is necessary to determine the strain energy stored in the beam shown in Fig. E10.13a. We begin this determination by preparing a FBD of a segment of the beam as shown in Fig. E10.13b.

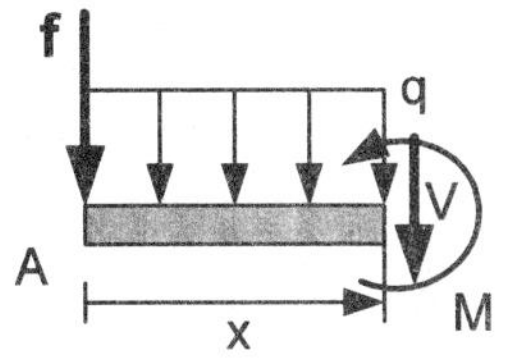

Fig. E10.13b

Writing the moment equation for this segment, we obtain:

$$M = -fx - qx^2/2 \qquad \text{(a)}$$

Next, use Eq. (10.21) to express the relation for the strain energy stored in the beam as:

$$\boldsymbol{E}_\varepsilon = \left(\frac{1}{2EI_z}\right)\int_0^L M^2 dx \qquad \text{(b)}$$

If we differentiate Eq. (b) with respect to f and employ Eq. (10.6), it is possible to write the expression for the deflection at the free end of the beam as:

$$\delta = \frac{\partial \boldsymbol{E}_\varepsilon}{\partial f} = \left(\frac{1}{EI_z}\right)\int_0^L M\frac{\partial M}{\partial f}dx \qquad (10.39)$$

From Eq. (a), it is evident that:

$$\frac{\partial M}{\partial f} = -x \qquad \text{(c)}$$

Substituting Eqs. (a) and (c) into Eq. (10.39) gives:

$$\delta = \left(\frac{1}{EI_z}\right)\int_0^L \left(fx^2 + \frac{qx^3}{2}\right)dx \qquad \text{(d)}$$

Integrating Eq. (d) yields:

$$\delta = \left(\frac{1}{EI_z}\right)\left[\frac{fx^3}{3} + \frac{qx^4}{8}\right]_0^L = \left(\frac{1}{EI_z}\right)\left[\frac{fL^3}{3} + \frac{qL^4}{8}\right] \qquad \text{(e)}$$

Let the fictitious force $f \Rightarrow 0$ and Eq. (e) becomes:

$$\delta = \left(\frac{qL^4}{8EI_z}\right) \qquad (10.40)$$

Again, this result agrees with the answer given in Appendix E for the identical case.

EXAMPLE 10.14

For the simply supported beam shown in Fig. E10.14, use Castigliano's theorem to determine the deflection at the midpoint of the span. Note that $b = L - 2a$.

Fig. E10.14

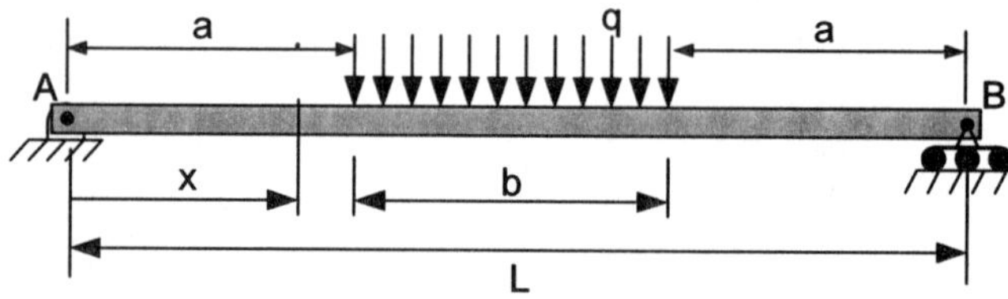

Solution:

We first add the fictitious force f at the midpoint of the span and prepare a FBD of the entire beam as shown in Fig. E10.14a.

Fig. E10.14a

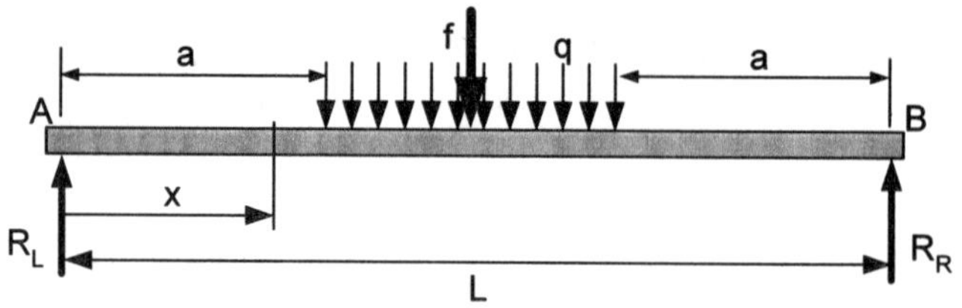

From the equilibrium relations and the statement that $b = L - 2a$, it is clear that:

$$R = R_L = R_R = (1/2)(qb + f) \qquad \text{(a)}$$

An FBD of the beam segment for $x \leq a$ is presented in Fig. E10.14b.

Fig. E10.14b

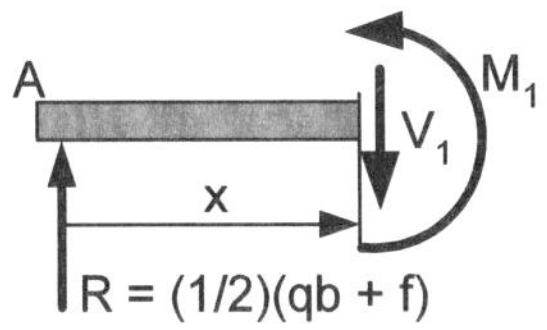

Writing the equation for the moment M from this FBD yields:

$$M_1 = \frac{x}{2}(qb + f) \qquad \text{for } x \leq a \qquad \text{(b)}$$
$$\frac{\partial M_1}{\partial f} = \frac{x}{2}$$

The FBD presented in Fig. E10.14c is helpful in writing the equation for the moment M_2 which is valid from $a \leq x \leq L/2$.

Fig. E10.14c

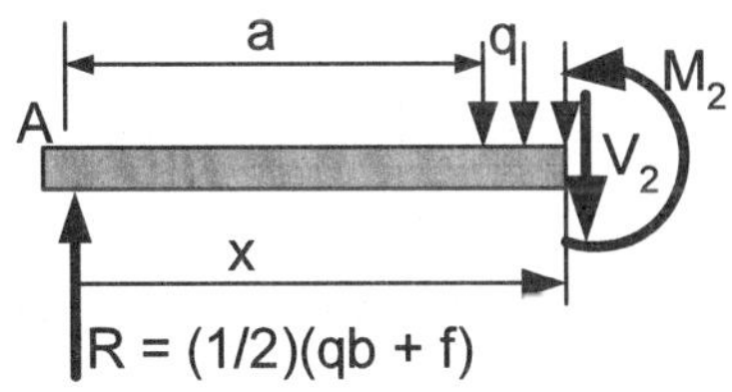

Writing the equation for the moment M_2 from this FBD yields:

$$M_2 = \frac{x}{2}(qb + f) - \frac{q}{2}(x - a)^2 \qquad \text{for } a \leq x \leq L/2 \qquad \text{(c)}$$
$$\frac{\partial M_2}{\partial f} = \frac{x}{2}$$

Note that the loading of the beam is symmetric with respect to x even after the addition of the fictitious force f. We will use this symmetry in simplifying the calculations needed to determine the midspan deflection. Let's write Eq. (10.39) and adapt it to account for the symmetry of loading by setting the limits of integration from zero to L/2 and multiplying the resulting relation by two.

$$\delta = \left(\frac{1}{EI_z}\right)\left\{\int_0^a M_1 \frac{\partial M_1}{\partial f} dx + \int_a^{L/2} M_2 \frac{\partial M_2}{\partial f} dx\right\} 2 \qquad \text{(d)}$$

Substituting Eqs. (b) and (c) into Eq. (d) yields:

$$\delta = \left(\frac{2}{EI_z}\right)\left\{\int_0^a \left(\frac{x}{2}\right)(qb + f)\left(\frac{x}{2}\right) dx + \int_a^{L/2} \left(\left(\frac{x}{2}\right)(qb + f) - \frac{q}{2}(x - a)^2\right)\left(\frac{x}{2}\right) dx\right\} \qquad \text{(e)}$$

Let's simplify Eq. (e) by letting $f \Rightarrow 0$ to obtain:

$$\delta = \left(\frac{2}{EI_z}\right)\left\{\int_0^a \left(\frac{qbx^2}{4}\right)dx + \int_a^{L/2}\left(\frac{qbx^2}{4} - \frac{qx(x-a)^2}{4}\right)dx\right\}$$
$$= \left(\frac{q}{2EI_z}\right)\left\{\int_0^a bx^2 dx + \int_a^{L/2}\left[bx^2 - x(x-a)^2\right]dx\right\} \tag{f}$$

Integrating Eq. (f) gives:

$$\delta = \left(\frac{q}{2EI_z}\right)\left\{\left[\frac{bx^3}{3}\right]_0^a + \left[\frac{bx^3}{3}\right]_a^{L/2} - \left[\frac{x^4}{4} - \frac{2ax^3}{3} + \frac{a^2x^2}{2}\right]_a^{L/2}\right\} \tag{g}$$

Substitute the upper and lower limits in Eq. (g), replace a with (1/2)(L – b), and simplify to obtain:

$$\delta = \left(\frac{qb}{384EI_z}\right)\left(8L^3 + b^3 - 4Lb^2\right) \tag{h}$$

The result is the same as the deflection determined by the double integration method in Chapter 5 [see Eq. (5.19)]. In this case, the sign of the deflection is positive because the fictitious force was directed downward. The positive sign indicates that the deflection is in the same direction of the fictitious force.

10.6.1 Castigliano's Method Applied to Statically Indeterminate Beams

In Chapter 6, we described techniques for solving for the reaction forces in statically indeterminate beams by employing either the superposition or the integration method. We can also solve for the reaction forces by using Castigliano's theorem. This approach utilizes Eq. (10.6) applied at one of the structure's supports. We rewrite Eq. (10.6) as:

$$\frac{\partial \boldsymbol{E}_\varepsilon}{\partial F_n} = \frac{\partial \boldsymbol{E}_\varepsilon}{\partial R} = \delta_R = 0 \tag{10.41}$$

where $\delta_R = 0$ is the displacement of the reactive force R at the support.

In applying Eq. (10.41), we differentiate the expression for the strain energy in the beam with respect to an appropriate reaction force R. The result of the differentiation gives the displacement at the support; however, because the support is fixed this displacement is zero. Thus Eq. (10.41) provides the additional relation that can be used together with the usual equilibrium equations to solve for unknown reaction forces in statically indeterminate beams.

Let's consider two examples to demonstrate this method of analysis.

EXAMPLE 10.15

For the uniformly loaded cantilever beam, shown in Fig. E10.15, use Castigliano's theorem to determine the reaction force at the prop.

Fig. E10.15

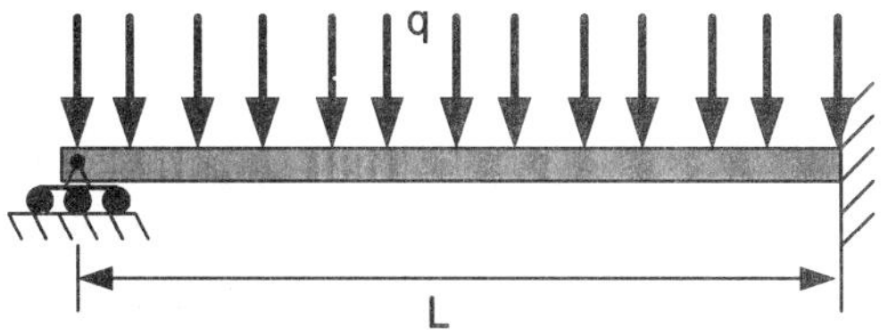

Solution:

The propped cantilever beam is statically indeterminate because we have three unknown reactive forces — the reaction R at the prop, and the moment and the reaction force at the built-in end of the beam. Let's begin the solution by drawing a FBD of a portion of the left end of the beam that includes the reaction force R at the prop as shown in Fig. E10.15a.

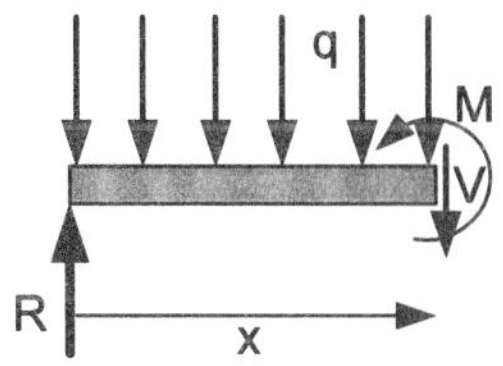

Fig. E10.15a

Writing the equation for the moment M from this FBD yields:

$$M = Rx - \frac{qx^2}{2} \qquad \text{(a)}$$
$$\frac{\partial M}{\partial R} = x$$

Let's write Eq. (10.41) and use Eq. (10.39) to obtain:

$$\delta = \frac{\partial \boldsymbol{E}_e}{\partial R} = \left(\frac{1}{EI_z}\right)\int_0^L M\frac{\partial M}{\partial R}dx = 0 \qquad \text{(b)}$$

Substituting Eq. (a) into Eq. (b) and integrating gives:

$$\int_0^L M\frac{\partial M}{\partial R}dx = \int_0^L\left(Rx - \frac{qx^2}{2}\right)xdx = 0 \qquad \text{(c)}$$
$$\left[\frac{Rx^3}{3} - \frac{qx^4}{8}\right]_0^L = 0$$

Substituting the limits into Eq. (c) and simplifying yields:

$$R = 3qL/8 \qquad \text{(d)}$$

This example illustrates another useful approach for determining unknown reactive forces acting on statically indeterminate structures.

EXAMPLE 10.16

For the uniformly loaded continuous beam, shown in Fig. E10.16, use Castigliano's theorem to determine the reaction force at the center support.

Fig. E10.16

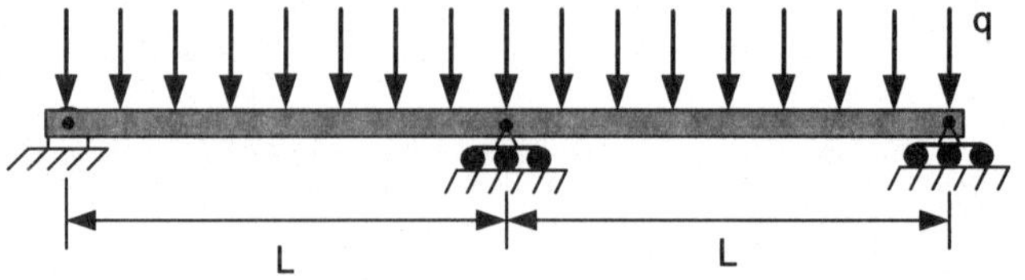

Solution:

The propped continuous beam is statically indeterminate because we have three unknown reactive forces — the three reactions at the simple supports — and only two useful equations of equilibrium. Let's begin the solution by writing the equilibrium relation $\Sigma F_y = 0$ for the entire beam to obtain:

$$R_L + R_C + R_R = 2qL \qquad (a)$$

Because of symmetry $R_L = R_R$, and we can rewrite Eq. (a) as:

$$R_C = 2qL - 2R_L \qquad (b)$$

Now draw a FBD of a portion of the left end of the beam that includes the reaction force R_L at the left hand end as shown in Fig. E10.16a.

Fig. E10.16a

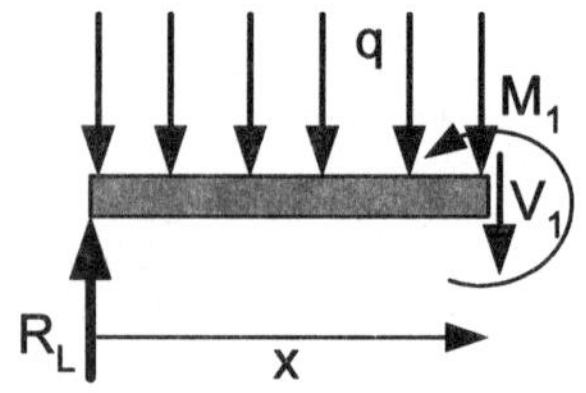

Writing the equation for the moment M_1 from this FBD yields:

$$M_1 = R_L x - \frac{qx^2}{2} \qquad \text{for } 0 \le x \le L \qquad (c)$$

$$\frac{\partial M_1}{\partial R_L} = x$$

Next, we prepare another FBD that includes the reaction R_C at the center support as shown in Fig. E10.16b.

E10.16b

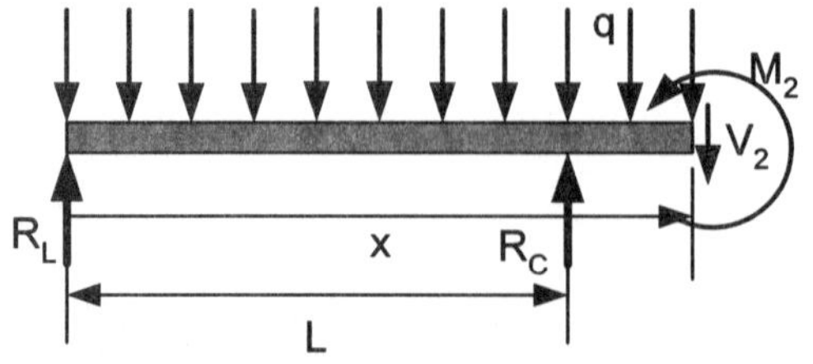

Writing the equation for the moment M_2 from this FBD yields:

$$M_2 = R_L x - \frac{qx^2}{2} + R_C(x - L) \qquad \text{for } L \le x \le 2L \qquad \text{(d)}$$

Substituting Eq. (b) into Eq. (d) and simplifying gives:

$$M_2 = R_L(2L - x) - \frac{qx^2}{2} + 2qL(x - L)$$

$$\frac{\partial M_2}{\partial R_L} = 2L - x \qquad \text{for } L \le x \le 2L \qquad \text{(e)}$$

Let's write Eq. (10.41) and adopt the form of the strain energy shown in Eq. (10.39) to obtain:

$$\delta_L = \frac{\partial E_\varepsilon}{\partial R_L} = \left(\frac{1}{EI_z}\right)\left\{\int_0^L M_1 \frac{\partial M_1}{\partial R_L} dx + \int_L^{2L} M_2 \frac{\partial M_2}{\partial R_L} dx\right\} = 0 \qquad \text{(f)}$$

Substituting Eqs. (c) and (e) into Eq. (f) and integrating gives:

$$\delta_L = \int_0^L \left(R_L x - \frac{qx^2}{2}\right)(x)dx + \int_L^{2L} \left(R_L(2L - x) - \frac{qx^2}{2} + 2qL(x - L)\right)(2L - x)dx = 0$$

$$\left[\frac{R_L x^3}{3} - \frac{qx^4}{8}\right]_0^L + \left[R_L\left(4L^2x - 2Lx^2 + \frac{x^3}{3}\right) + q\left(\frac{x^4}{8} - Lx^3 + 3L^2x^2 - 4L^3x\right)\right]_L^{2L} = 0 \qquad \text{(g)}$$

Substituting the limits into Eq. (g) and simplifying yields:

$$(2L^3/3)R_L - qL^4/4 = 0 \qquad \text{(h)}$$

Solving for R_L yields:

$$R_L = R_R = 3qL/8 \qquad \text{(i)}$$

Finally from Eq. (i) and Eq. (b), it is clear that:

$$R_C = 5qL/4 \qquad \text{(j)}$$

This example illustrates that the center support in a continuous beam carries a large portion of the loading. In this case, the center support carries over three times as much load as each end support. Note that these same results can be obtained by using the methods (i.e. superposition and singularity functions) presented in Chapter 6.

10.6.2 Castigliano's Method Applied to Determining Rotation

In previous sections, we considered a structural element subjected to forces F_1, F_2, F_3 and F_n to derive the relation:

$$\frac{\partial \mathbf{E}_\varepsilon}{\partial F_n} = \delta_n \qquad (10.6)$$

In the derivation of Eq. (10.6), we equated the incremental changes in the work $\Delta \mathbf{W} = \delta_n \Delta F_n$ with the incremental changes in the strain energy $\Delta \mathbf{E}_\varepsilon$. However, Castigliano's method is more general and can also accommodate incremental changes in the work due either to the application of a concentrated moment M or a torque T. When a concentrated moment is applied to a structural member, the work is given by:

$$\mathbf{W} = (1/2)M\theta \qquad (10.42)$$

where θ is the angle through which the moment rotates.

Similarly when applying a torque T to a shaft, the resulting work is:

$$\mathbf{W} = (1/2)T\phi \qquad (10.43)$$

where ϕ is the angle of twist of the shaft.

Recognizing these alternative forms for expressing work, enables us to write the expressions for the angular displacements (rotations) as:

$$\theta_n = \partial \mathbf{E}_\varepsilon / \partial M_n \qquad (10.44)$$

$$\phi_n = \partial \mathbf{E}_\varepsilon / \partial T_n \qquad (10.45)$$

Let's demonstrate the use of these relations in the solution of two example problems.

EXAMPLE 10.17

A cantilever beam is formed in the shape of a quarter circle as illustrated in Fig. E10.17. If the cantilever beam is loaded with a concentrated moment M_o and a concentrated force F at its free end, determine the angular displacement and the beam's deflection in the direction of the force F.

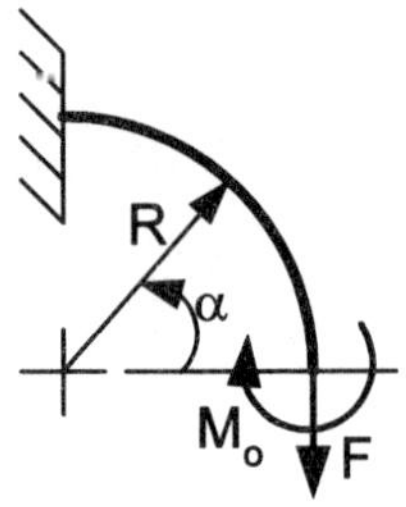

Fig. E10.17

Solution:

Let's begin by preparing a FBD of a segment of the circular arc as shown in Fig. E10.17a. Writing the equation for the moment M at some arbitrary position defined by the angle α, as shown in the FBD gives:

Fig. E10.17a

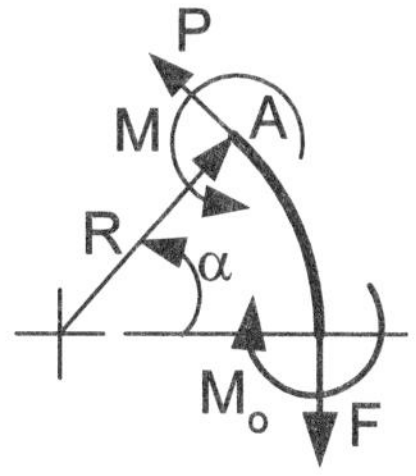

Writing the equation for the moment M at an arbitrary point A defined by the angle α as shown in the FBD gives:

$$M = M_0 + FR(1 - \cos\alpha) \qquad \text{(a)}$$

The cantilever beam in this example is in the form of a circular arc; hence, it is necessary to modify Eq. (10.21) to read as:

$$\boldsymbol{E}_\varepsilon = \left(\frac{1}{2EI_z}\right)\int_0^{\pi/2} M^2 R d\alpha \qquad (10.46)$$

where $Rd\alpha = dx$

In this case, the upper limit on the integral is π/2 because the cantilever is formed as a quarter circle. The upper limit is adjusted to accommodate the shape of the circular arc. Let's determine the deflection downward δ_y in the direction of the force F by using Eq. (10.6) to obtain:

$$\delta_y = \frac{\partial \boldsymbol{E}_\varepsilon}{\partial F} = \left(\frac{1}{EI_z}\right)\int_0^{\pi/2} M\frac{\partial M}{\partial F} R d\alpha \qquad \text{(b)}$$

Substitute Eq. (a) into Eq. (b) and integrate to obtain:

$$\delta_y = \left(\frac{1}{EI_z}\right)\int_0^{\pi/2}[M_0 + FR(1-\cos\alpha)][R(1-\cos\alpha)]Rd\alpha$$

$$\delta_y = \left(\frac{R^2}{EI_z}\right)\int_0^{\pi/2}\left[M_0(1-\cos\alpha) + FR(1-\cos\alpha)^2\right]d\alpha \qquad \text{(c)}$$

$$\delta_y = \left(\frac{R^2}{EI_z}\right)\left[M_0\alpha - M_0\sin\alpha + FR\left(\alpha - 2\sin\alpha + \frac{\alpha}{2} + \frac{\sin 2\alpha}{4}\right)\right]_0^{\pi/2}$$

Substituting the limits into Eq. (c) and simplifying yields:

$$\delta_y = \frac{R^2}{EI_z}\left\{\frac{M_0}{2}(\pi - 2) + \frac{FR}{4}(3\pi - 8)\right\} \qquad \text{(d)}$$

To determine the rotation at the free end of the cantilever beam, substitute Eq. (a) into Eq. (10.44) to obtain:

$$\theta = \frac{\partial \boldsymbol{E}_\varepsilon}{\partial M_0} = \left(\frac{1}{EI_z}\right)\int_0^{\pi/2} M\frac{\partial M}{\partial M_0}R d\alpha \qquad \text{(e)}$$

Integrating Eq. (e) gives:

$$\theta = \frac{\partial \boldsymbol{E}_\varepsilon}{\partial M_0} = \left(\frac{1}{EI_z}\right)\int_0^{\pi/2} [M_0 + FR(1-\cos\alpha)][1]R d\alpha$$

$$\theta = \left(\frac{R}{EI_z}\right)\left[M_0\alpha + FR\alpha - FR\sin\alpha\right)\Big]_0^{\pi/2}$$

$$\theta = \left(\frac{R}{EI_z}\right)\left[M_0\frac{\pi}{2} + FR\left(\frac{\pi}{2} - 1\right)\right] \qquad \text{(f)}$$

Castigliano's theorem has provided an approach for solving for the deflection and rotation at select points on **thin** curved beams. Additional exercises of this type will be given in the Problems section of this chapter.

EXAMPLE 10.18

A shaft is fabricated by brazing together two sections of round tubing as shown in Fig. E10.18. The shaft is fixed at one end and a torque T is applied at its free end. Determine the equation for the angle of twist ϕ. Assume the thickness of the braze metal is negligible.

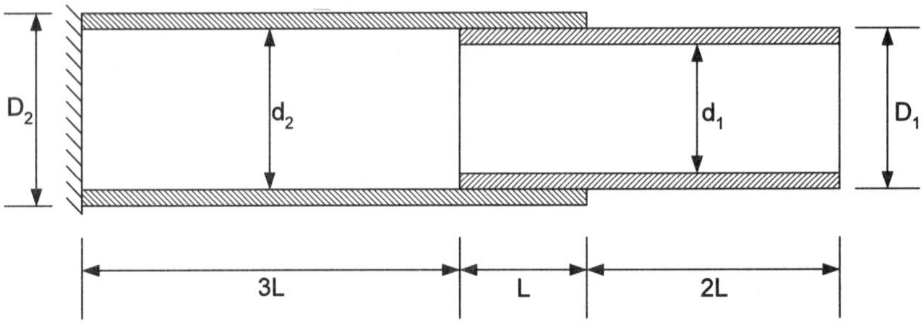

Fig. E10.18

Solution:

The strain energy for a shaft subjected to torsion loading is given by Eq. (10.26) as:

$$\boldsymbol{E}_\varepsilon = \frac{1}{2GJ}\int_0^L T^2 dx = \frac{T^2L}{2GJ} \qquad \text{(a)}$$

We can apply this relation if it is adjusted to account for the variation of the polar moment of inertia J along the length of the shaft. Accordingly we divide the shaft into three parts — the left side, the center portion, and the right side and rewrite Eq. (a) as:

$$\boldsymbol{E}_\varepsilon = \frac{T^2L}{2G}\left[\frac{3}{(\pi/32)(D_2^4 - d_2^4)} + \frac{1}{(\pi/32)(D_2^4 - d_1^4)} + \frac{2}{(\pi/32)(D_1^4 - d_1^4)}\right] \qquad \text{(b)}$$

Recalling Eq. (10.45), substitute Eq. (b) into this relation and simplify to obtain:

$$\phi = \frac{\partial \boldsymbol{E}_\varepsilon}{\partial T} = \frac{32TL}{\pi G}\left[\frac{3}{(D_2^4 - d_2^4)} + \frac{1}{(D_2^4 - d_1^4)} + \frac{2}{(D_1^4 - d_1^4)}\right] \tag{c}$$

Again Castigliano's method provides another independent approach to determining displacements (angular or linear) at one point on the structural member.

10.6.3 Castigliano's Method Applied to Truss Deflections

In our previous discussion of trusses, we were concerned with determining forces, stresses, and safety factors for the individual members. However, in many instances, it is important to determine the displacement of the joints in the truss. There are two approaches for determining these displacements. The first is to calculate the extension or contraction of the individual members, and then to solve a complex geometry problem to establish the movement of each of the joints. The second approach, which is described in this section, is the application of Castigliano's method for this determination.

We have derived the relation for the strain energy stored in a tie rod in Eq. (10.16). This equation is also valid for truss members because the forces are always applied along the axis of the individual members. Let's rewrite this relation as:

$$\boldsymbol{E}_\varepsilon = \frac{P_i^2 L_i}{2A_i E} \tag{10.47}$$

where P_i is the internal force and A_i is the cross sectional area in truss member i and L_i is its length.

The total strain energy in the truss system is then obtained by summing the strain energy stored in the individual members. Hence, we can write:

$$\boldsymbol{E}_\varepsilon = \sum_{i=1}^{n} \frac{P_i^2 L_i}{2A_i E} \tag{10.48}$$

where n is the number of members in the truss.

Substituting Eq. (10.48) into Eq. (10.6) yields:

$$\delta_k = \frac{\partial \boldsymbol{E}_\varepsilon}{\partial F_k} = \frac{\partial}{\partial F_k} \sum_{i=1}^{n} \frac{P_i^2 L_i}{2A_i E} \tag{10.49}$$

Differentiating Eq. (10.49) gives:

$$\delta_k = \frac{1}{E} \sum_{i=1}^{n} \frac{P_i L_i}{A_i}\left(\frac{\partial P_i}{\partial F_k}\right) \tag{10.50}$$

Care must be exercised in the application of Eq. (10.50). To determine the $(\partial P_i/\partial F_k)$, it is necessary to write equations for the internal forces P_i in each member of the truss in terms of the external force

F_k applied at a specified joint in the truss. Numbers must not be substituted into the equations until after Eq. (10.50) has been executed in symbolic format.

Let's consider three examples to demonstrate this approach for determining the displacement of a joint in a truss.

EXAMPLE 10.19

Determine the displacement of joint B in the vertical direction for the two-member truss depicted in Fig. E10.19 using Castigliano's method. Truss members AB and BC are fabricated from the same material, with identical length L and cross sectional area A.

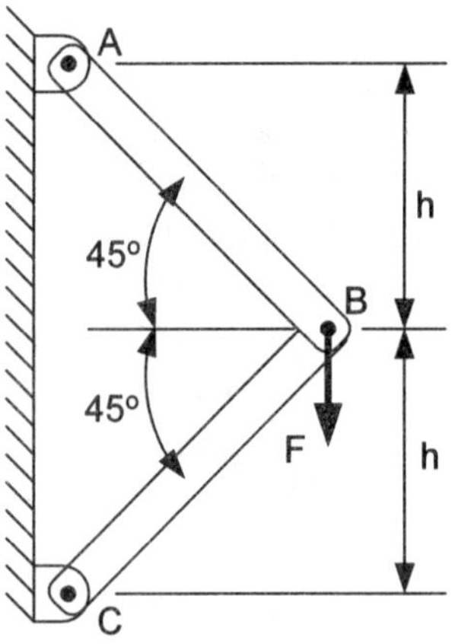

Fig. E10.19

Solution:

We begin by preparing a FBD of the joint at Pin B as shown in Fig. E10.19a.

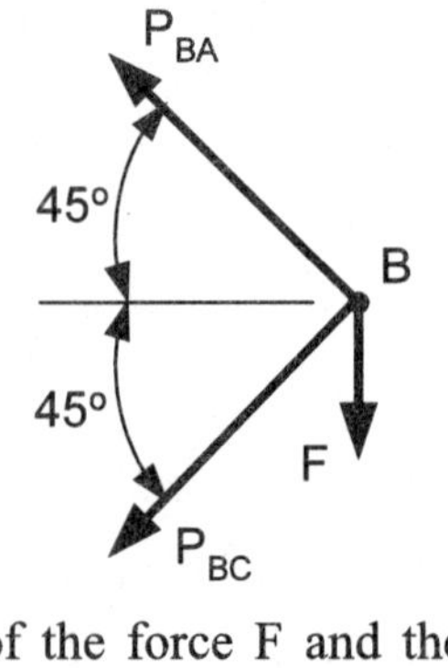

Fig. E10.19a

Writing the equations for the internal forces P_{AB} and P_{BC} in terms of the force F and the geometric parameters describing the truss, we obtain.

$$\Sigma F_x = -P_{BA} \cos 45° - P_{BC} \cos 45° = 0; \qquad P_{BA} = -P_{BC} \qquad \text{(a)}$$

$$\Sigma F_y = P_{BA} \sin 45° - P_{BC} \sin 45° - F = 0; \qquad P_{BA} = F/\sqrt{2}; \qquad P_{BC} = -F/\sqrt{2} \qquad \text{(b)}$$

Taking the partial derivatives of the two internal forces gives:

$$\partial P_{BA}/\partial F = 1/\sqrt{2} \qquad \partial P_{BC}/\partial F = -1/\sqrt{2} \qquad \text{(c)}$$

Substituting the results of Eqs. (b) and (c) into Eq. (10.50) yields:

$$\delta_B = \frac{L}{AE}\sum_{1}^{2}\left(\frac{\partial P_i}{\partial F_B}\right)P_i = \frac{L}{AE}\left[\left(\frac{F}{\sqrt{2}}\right)\left(\frac{1}{\sqrt{2}}\right)+\left(\frac{-F}{\sqrt{2}}\right)\left(\frac{-1}{\sqrt{2}}\right)\right] \quad \text{(d)}$$

Reducing Eq. (d) gives:

$$\delta_B = FL/AE \quad \text{(e)}$$

This result gives the deflection of the pin at joint B in the downward direction. The question of whether the pin at joint B moves in the horizontal direction is given as a problem at the end of the chapter.

EXAMPLE 10.20

Determine the displacement in the vertical direction at joint C for the seven-member truss depicted in Fig. E10.20 using Castigliano's method. All of the truss members are fabricated from the same material. The cross sectional area of members BC, AE, BD and DE is A; the area of AB is 2A, and the area of members BE and CD is $(2/\sqrt{2})A$.

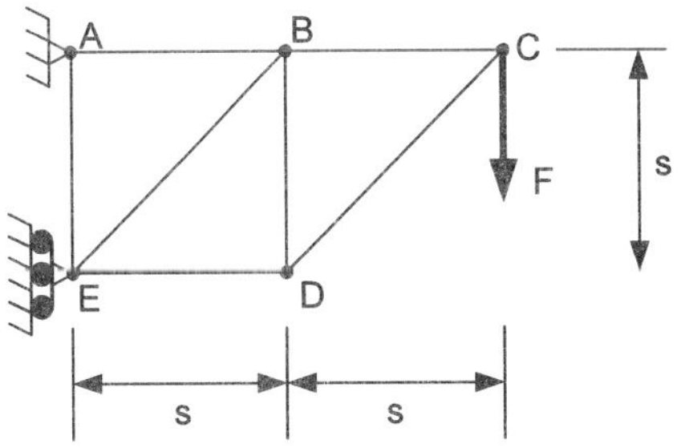

Fig. E10.20

Solution:

Prepare FBDs for the entire truss and for the individual pins A, B, C and E and write the equilibrium relations to determine the reaction forces and the forces in the seven truss members. The FBDs are shown below, and the forces, determined by applying the equilibrium relations for each of the FBDs, are listed in Table E10.20.

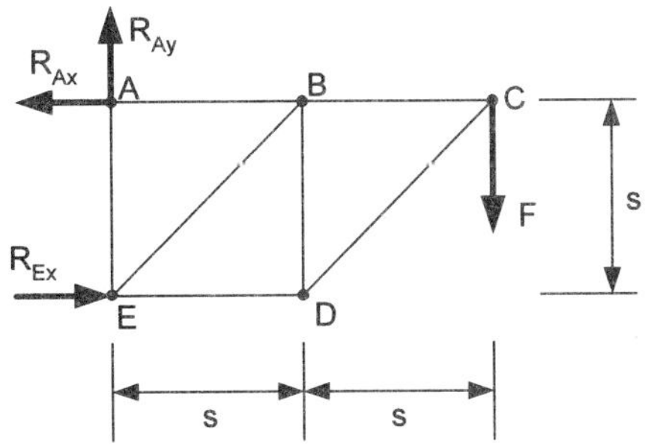

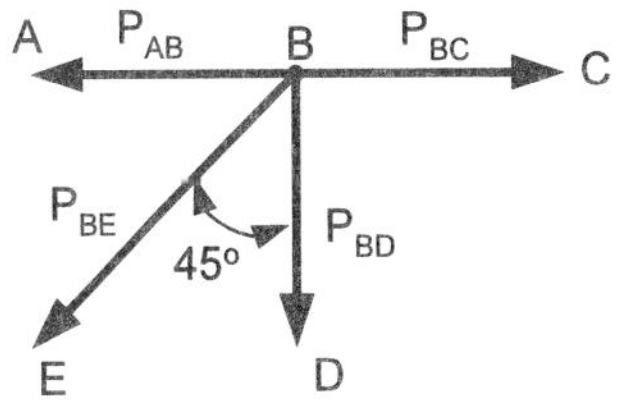

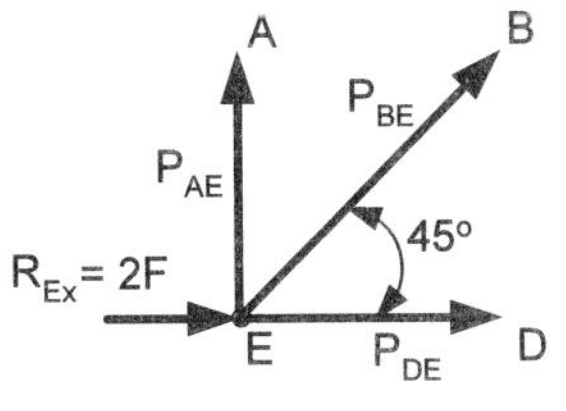

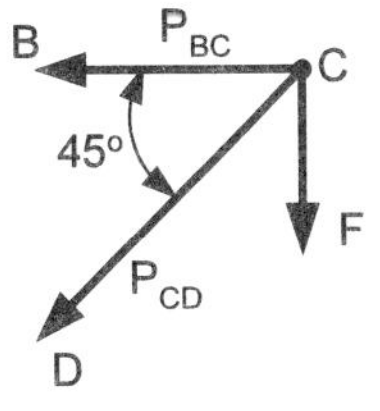

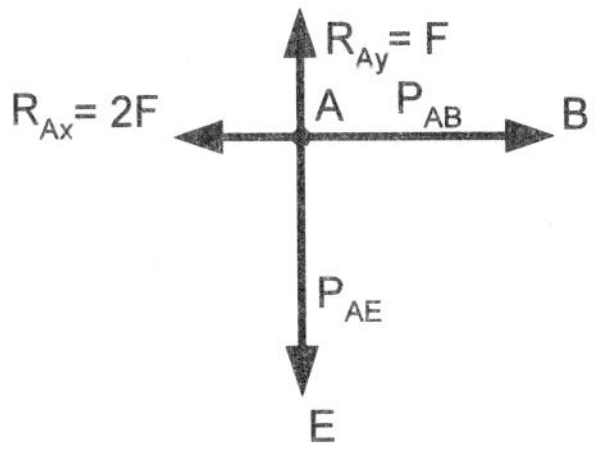

Table E10.20
Arrangement of results for internal forces, length and areas of truss members.

Member	P_i	$\partial P_i/\partial F$	Length. L_i	Area, A_i	$(P_iL_i/A_i)(\partial P_i/\partial F)$
AB	2F	2	s	2A	2Fs/A
BC	F	1	s	A	Fs/A
AE	F	1	s	A	Fs/A
BE	$-2F/\sqrt{2}$	$-2/\sqrt{2}$	$\sqrt{2}$ s	$(2/\sqrt{2})A$	2Fs/A
BD	F	1	s	A	Fs/A
DE	− F	− 1	s	A	Fs/A
CD	$-2F/\sqrt{2}$	$-2/\sqrt{2}$	$\sqrt{2}$ s	$(2/\sqrt{2})A$	2Fs/A
					$\Sigma = 10(Fs/A)$

In the last row in Table E10.20, we have determined the sum of $(P_iL_i/A_i)(\partial P_i/\partial F)$ for the seven different truss members. Then it is evident from Eq. (10.50) that the downward deflection of the joint at C is given by:

$$\delta_y = (10Fs)/(AE)$$

The question remains regarding the horizontal deflection of the joint at C. Let's determine this deflection in the next example.

EXAMPLE 10.21

Determine the displacement in the horizontal direction at joint C for the seven-member truss depicted in Fig. E10.20 using Castigliano's method. All of the truss members are fabricated from the same material. The cross sectional area of members BC, AE, BD and DE is A; the area of AB is 2A, and the area of members BE and CD is $(2/\sqrt{2})A$

Solution:

To determine the horizontal displacement of the pin at joint C, it is necessary to apply a fictitious force f acting in the horizontal direction at that location. The approach is the same as with Example 10.20. We prepare FBDs for the entire truss and for the individual pins A, B, C and E and write the equilibrium relations to determine the reaction forces and the forces in the seven truss members. Because the reactions and the internal forces due to the force F have already been determined, we will consider only the fictitious force f. We will then superimpose the result due to f on the previous results for F in Table E10.21.

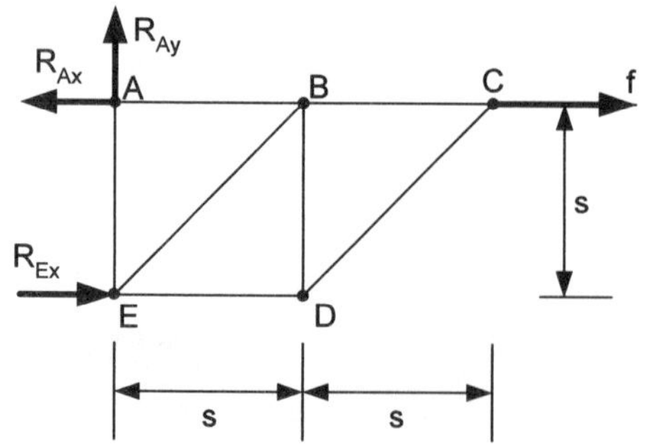

Fig. E10.21

Considering equilibrium of the entire truss enables us to write:

$$R_{Ax} = f \qquad R_{Ay} = 0 \qquad R_{Ex} = 0$$

Considering the pin at joint A, it is clear that $P_{AB} = f$ and $P_{AE} = 0$.

Considering the pin at joint C, it is clear that $P_{BC} = f$ and $P_{CD} = 0$.

Considering the pin at joint B, it is clear that $P_{BE} = 0$ and $P_{BD} = 0$.

Finally, considering the pin at joint E, it is clear that $P_{DE} = 0$.

We superimpose these results for P_i with those obtained in Example 10.20 to give:

Table E10.21
Revision of Table E10.20 showing results for internal forces, length and areas of truss members.

Member	P_i	$\partial P_i/\partial f$	Length. L_i	Area, A_i	$(P_iL_i/A_i)(\partial P_i/\partial f)$
AB	2F + f	1	s	2A	(2F + f)(s/2A)
BC	F + f	1	s	A	(F + f)(s/A)
AE	F	0	s	A	0
BE	– 2F/√2	0	√2 s	(2/√2)A	0
BD	F	0	s	A	0
DE	– F	0	s	A	0
CD	– 2F/√2	0	√2 s	(2/√2)A	0
					Σ = (2Fs/A)+(3fs/2A)

In the last row in Table E10.21, we have determined the sum of $(P_iL_i/A_i)(\partial P_i/\partial f)$ for the seven different truss members. Then it is evident from Eq. (10.50) that the deflection in the positive x direction of the joint at C is given by:

$$\delta_x = (2Fs)/(AE) \qquad \text{(a)}$$

In writing Eq. (a), we permitted the fictitious force f to go to zero. In this solution, we have only considered the displacement of one joint in the truss. We could determine the displacement of any joint by applying fictitious forces at the joint in question and repeating the analysis described in Examples 10.20 and 10.21.

10.7 SUMMARY

When a force F is applied to a structural member, it undergoes a displacement δ and work is performed. This work is conserved and stored as strain energy $\mathbf{E}_\varepsilon$.

$$\mathbf{E}_\varepsilon = F\delta/2 \qquad (10.2)$$

The ability to compute the strain energy stored in structural members is important, because three different energy theorems can be employed to extend our methods of analysis. These include: the theorem of virtual work, the theorem of Castigliano and the theorem of least work (minimum potential energy). We described several applications of Castigliano's theorem in this chapter.

The application of Castigliano's theorem involves the partial differentiation of the strain energy with respect to an applied force F to give the displacement δ as:

$$\frac{\partial \mathbf{E}_\varepsilon}{\partial F_n} = \delta_n \qquad (10.6)$$

The concept of strain energy density was introduced and methods for computing this quantity were demonstrated based on the following equations:

$$\boldsymbol{e}_\varepsilon = \Delta \mathbf{E}_\varepsilon / \boldsymbol{V} = (1/2)\sigma_{xx}\,\varepsilon_{xx} \qquad (10.9)$$

$$\boldsymbol{e}_\varepsilon = (1/2)(\sigma_{xx}\,\varepsilon_{xx} + \sigma_{yy}\,\varepsilon_{yy} + \sigma_{zz}\,\varepsilon_{zz} + \tau_{xy}\gamma_{xy} + \tau_{yz}\gamma_{yz} + \tau_{zx}\gamma_{zx}) \qquad (10.10)$$

$$\boldsymbol{e}_\varepsilon = (1/2)(\sigma_1\,\varepsilon_1 + \sigma_2\,\varepsilon_2 + \sigma_3\,\varepsilon_3) \qquad (10.11)$$

The strain energy density served a useful function because it could be integrated over the volume of the structural member to establish the strain energy stored in the element.

$$\mathbf{E}_\varepsilon = \frac{1}{2E}\int \sigma_1^2\, d\boldsymbol{V} \qquad \text{if } \sigma_2 = \sigma_3 = 0 \qquad (10.15)$$

We showed that the strain energy stored in a tie rod is given by:

$$\mathbf{E}_\varepsilon = \frac{1}{2E}\frac{F^2}{A^2}AL = \frac{F^2L}{2AE} \qquad (10.16)$$

We also showed the strain energy stored in a beam is given by:

$$\mathbf{E}_\varepsilon = \left(\frac{1}{2EI_z}\right)\int_0^L M^2 dx \qquad (10.21)$$

And the strain energy stored in a shaft subjected to a torque T is given by:

$$\boldsymbol{E}_{\varepsilon} = \frac{1}{2GJ}\int_0^L T^2 dx = \frac{T^2 L}{2GJ} \qquad (10.26)$$

After describing and demonstrating techniques for determining the strain energy in structural members, we used energy concepts to write relations for impact stresses developed in rods and beams. For a rod subjected to axial impact by an object with a mass m traveling with a velocity v, we derived the relation for the stress as:

$$\sigma_{Max} = \sqrt{\frac{mv^2 E}{AL}} = \sqrt{\frac{mv^2 E}{\boldsymbol{V}}} \qquad (10.33)$$

We also considered impact of a beam by a weight W falling through a distance H. If the deflection of the beam was small relative to H, then the maximum stress is given by:

$$(\sigma_{xx})_{Max} = \sqrt{\frac{18EWH}{Lbh}} = \sqrt{\frac{18EWH}{\boldsymbol{V}}} \qquad (10.37)$$

When the displacement of the beam is not negligible relative to the height H of the falling weight, both the stress and the displacement is increased. The relation for the displacement is given by:

$$\delta = \delta_{st}\left(1 + \sqrt{1 + 2\left(\frac{H}{\delta_{st}}\right)}\right) = \boldsymbol{M}\delta_{st} \qquad (10.38)$$

where $\delta_{st} = \dfrac{WL^3}{48EI_z}$ and $\left(1 + \sqrt{1 + 2\left(\dfrac{H}{\delta_{st}}\right)}\right)$ is a multiplier $\boldsymbol{M}$ on the static deflection.

Castigliano's theorem and different variations of Eq. (10.6) were applied to four different types of problems, which included determining the displacement of beams under an applied load, solving for unknown reactions in statically indeterminate beams, determining rotations in curved beams and shafts, and determining displacements of select pins in trusses. These applications were demonstrated with several examples.

PROBLEMS

10.1 An aluminum rod with a cross sectional area A = 400 mm^2 and length L = 1.0 m is subjected to an axial force of 32.5 kN as shown in Fig. P10.1. Determine the work $\boldsymbol{W}$ performed on the rod and the strain energy stored in the rod.

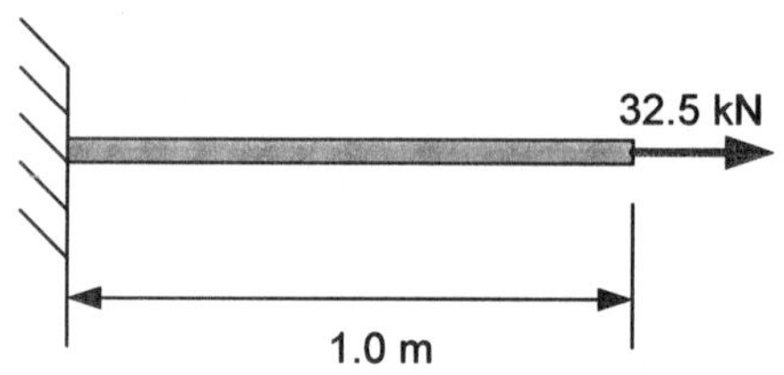

Fig. P10.1

10.2 A point in a machine component is subjected to a three-dimensional state of stress that is described in terms of three principal stresses σ_1 = 120 MPa, σ_2 = 85 MPa and σ_3 = – 99.4 MPa. Determine the strain energy density at this point if the machine component is fabricated from steel.

10.3 A point in a structural member is subjected to a three dimensional state of stress described by the six Cartesian stress components σ_{xx} = 60.2 MPa, σ_{yy} = 51.1 MPa, σ_{zz} = 34.2 MPa, τ_{xy} = – 25.3 MPa, τ_{yz} = 48.7 MPa and τ_{zx} =38.8 MPa. Determine the strain energy density at this point if the structural member is fabricated from brass.

10.4 A tie rod, 25 ft long with a 10 in. diameter is fabricated from steel. If the tie rod is subjected to an axial force of 1570 ton, determine the strain energy stored in the tie rod and the strain energy density.

10.5 For the simply supported beam shown in Fig. P10.5, determine the strain energy stored in it due to the normal stresses σ_{xx} produced by the uniformly distributed load q = 500 N/m. The beam is fabricated from steel.

Fig. P10.5

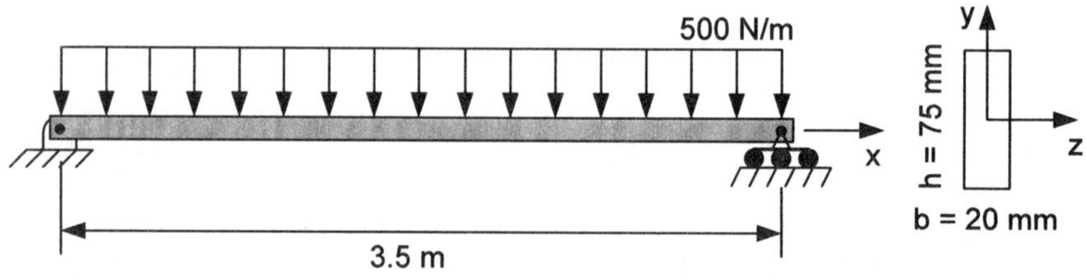

10.6 For the simply supported beam shown in Fig. P10.6, determine the expression for the strain energy due to the normal stress σ_{xx}. Assume that EI_z is a constant.

Fig. P10.6

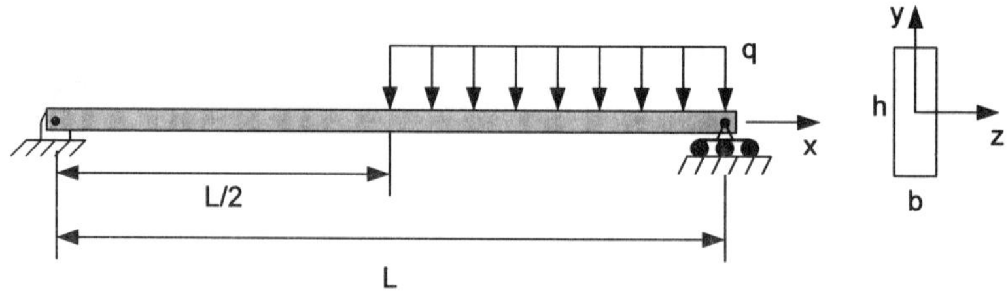

10.7 For the simply supported beam shown in Fig. P10.7, determine the expression for the strain energy due to the normal stress σ_{xx}. Assume that EI_z is a constant.

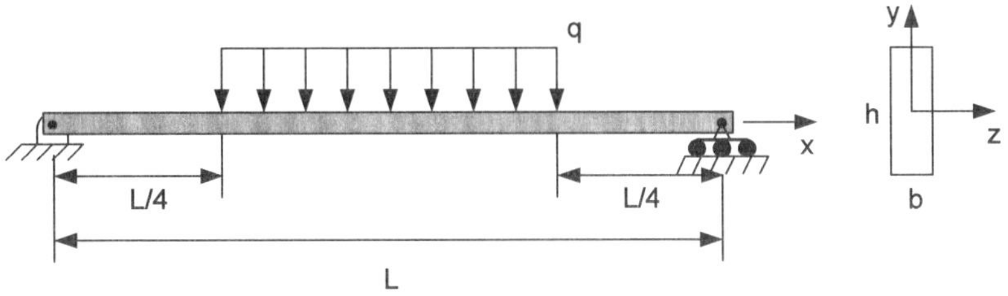

Fig. P10.7

10.8 For the simply supported beam shown in Fig. P10.8, determine the expression for the strain energy due to the normal stress σ_{xx}. Assume that EI_z is a constant.

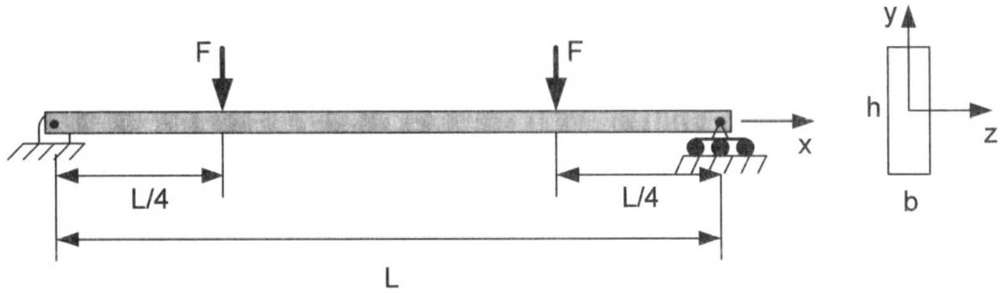

Fig. P10.8

10.9 For the simply supported beam shown in Fig. P10.9, determine the expression for the strain energy due to the normal stress σ_{xx}. Assume that EI_z is a constant.

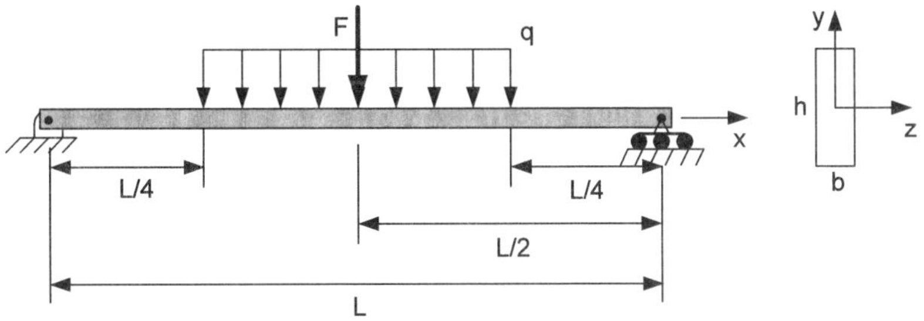

Fig. P10.9

10.10 For the cantilever beam shown in Fig. P10.10, determine the expression for the strain energy due to the normal stress σ_{xx}. Assume that EI_z is a constant.

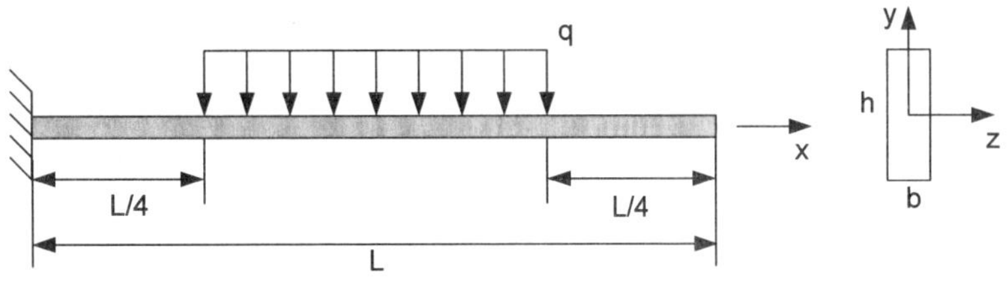

Fig. P10.10

10.11 For the cantilever beam shown in Fig. P10.11, determine the expression for the strain energy due to the normal stress σ_{xx}. Assume that EI_z is a constant.

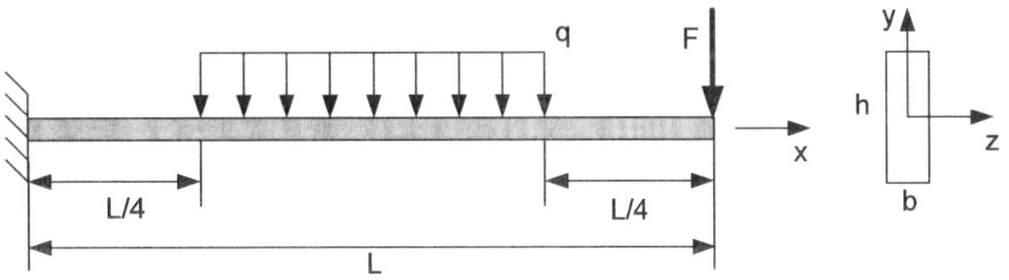

Fig. P10.11

10.12 For the simply supported beam shown in Fig. P10.12, determine the relation for the strain energy stored due to the shear stress τ_{xy}. The beam has a rectangular cross section with dimensions h and b.

Fig. P10.12

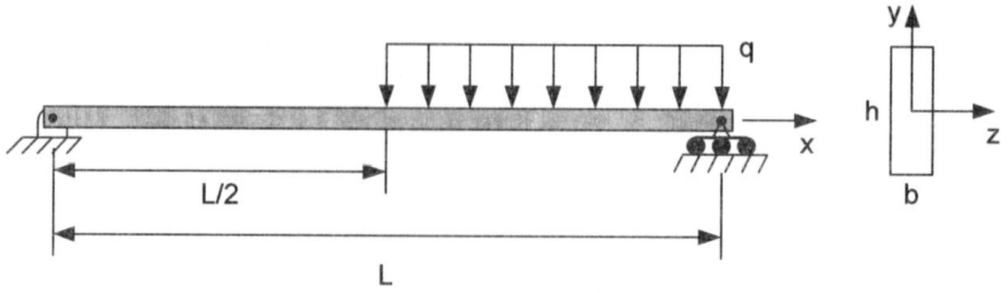

10.13 For the simply supported beam in shown in Fig. P10.13, determine the relation for the strain energy stored due to the shear stress τ_{xy}. The beam has a rectangular cross section with dimensions h and b.

Fig. P10.13

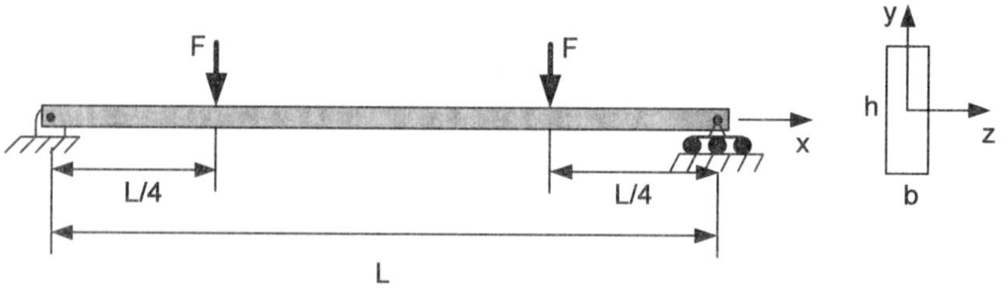

10.14 For the simply supported beam shown in Fig. P10.14, determine the relation for the strain energy stored due to the shear stress τ_{xy}. The beam has a rectangular cross section with dimensions h and b.

Fig. P10.14

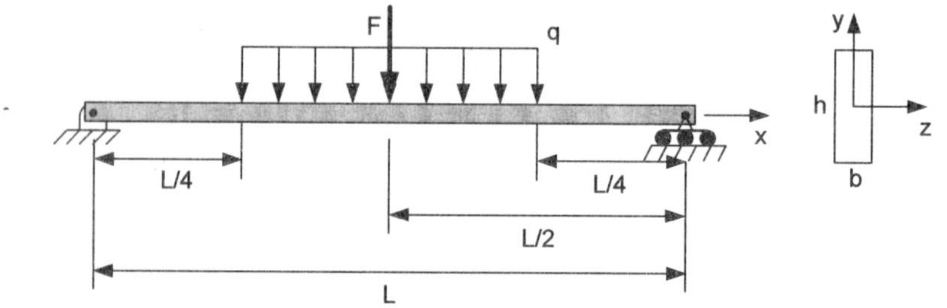

10.15 For the cantilever beam in shown in Fig. P10.15, determine the relation for the strain energy stored due to the shear stress τ_{xy}. The beam has a rectangular cross section with dimensions h and b.

Fig. P10.15

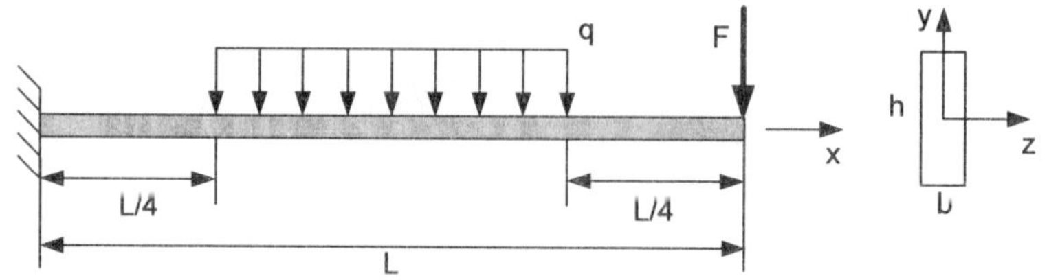

10.16 A 3.0 m long shaft with a 75 mm diameter, shown in Fig. P10.16, is subjected to a torque T = 450 N-m. Compute the strain energy stored in the shaft. The shaft is fabricated from brass.

Fig. P10.16

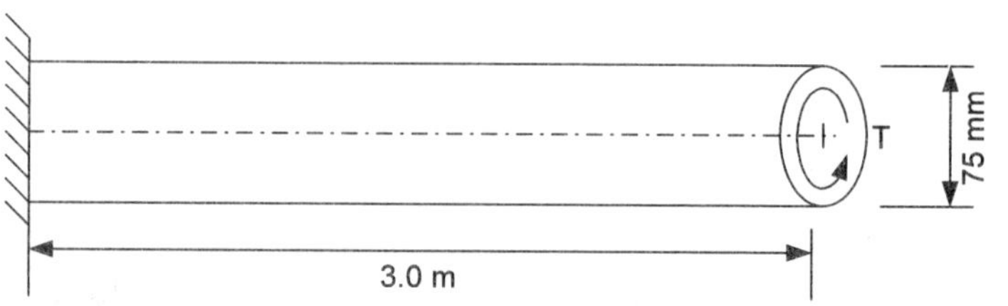

10.17 A stepped shaft, with lengths and diameters defined in Fig. P10.17, is subjected to a torque T = 110 ft-lb N-m. Compute the strain energy stored in the shaft. The shaft is fabricated from stainless steel.

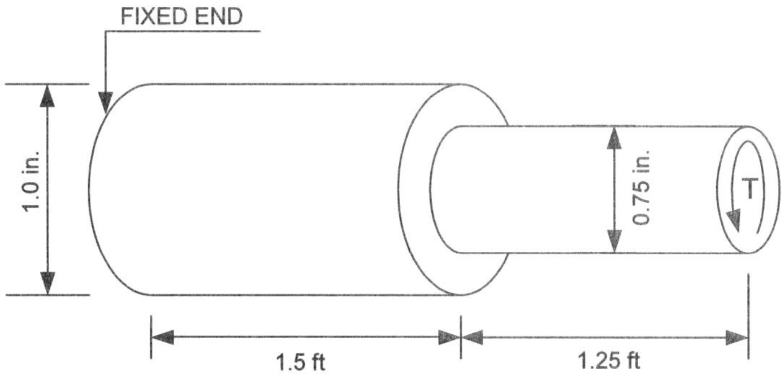

Fig. P10.17

10.18 A sphere fired from an air gun strikes an aluminum rod with an axial impact as illustrated in Fig. P10.18. Determine the maximum force and the maximum stress produced if the sphere weighs 150 gm. The velocity of the sphere at the instant of impact is 200 m/s. The rod has a solid, circular cross section.

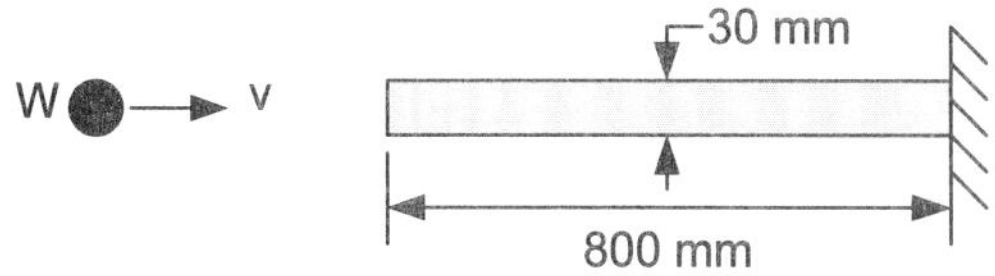

Fig. P10.18

10.19 A short, steel cylinder of diameter d = 0.750 in. and length l = 2.25 in. is fired from an air gun and strikes a long, steel rod with an axial impact as shown in Fig. P10.19. Determine the maximum force and the maximum stress produced if the cylinder has a density of γ = 0.284 lb/in.^{3} The velocity of the cylinder at the instant of impact is 500 ft/s. The rod has a solid, circular cross section.

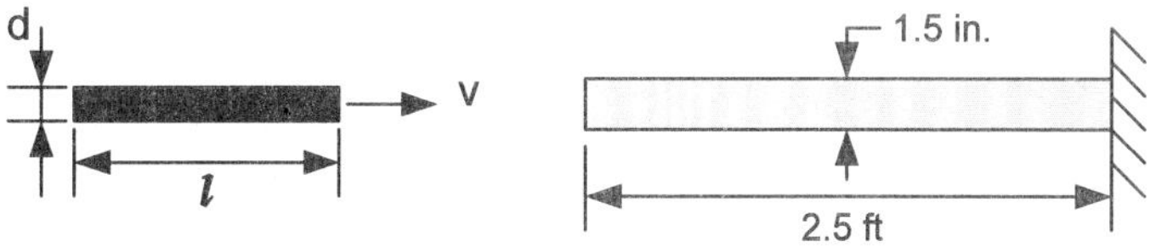

Fig. P10.19

10.20 Consider a simply supported beam that is subjected to impact by a falling weight W as illustrated in Fig. P10.20. Derive the relation for the maximum force and the maximum bending stress in the beam. Assume that the deflection of the beam is small relative to the drop height H.

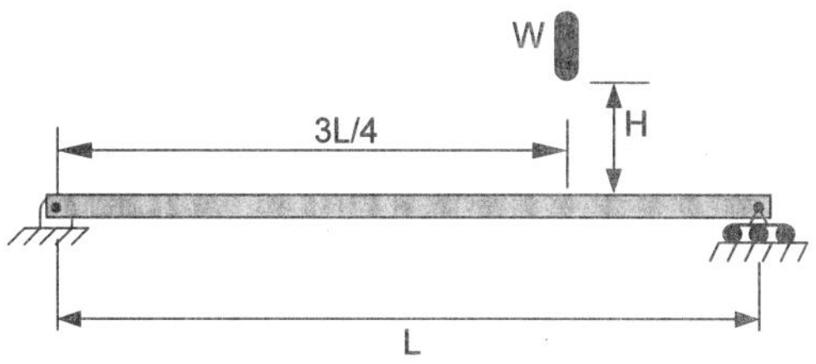

Fig. P10.20

10.21 A weight W is positioned at the free end of a cantilever beam as shown in Fig. P10.21. While the weight is in contact with the beam (H = 0), its gravitational force has not been released. The weight is suddenly released to produce an impact event, although the height of the drop is zero. Determine the equations for the maximum stress, the displacement of the load point and the maximum force developed during the impact.

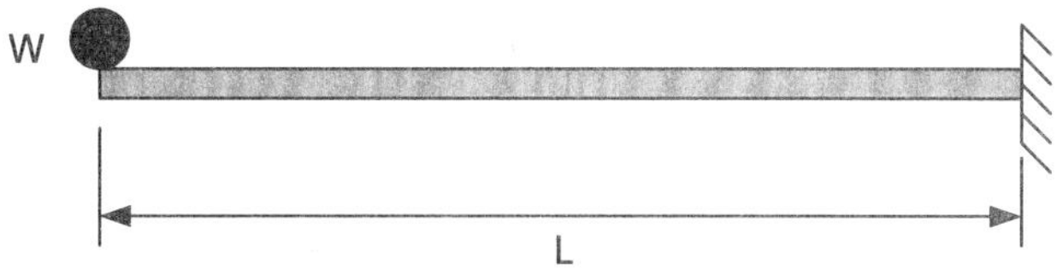

Fig. P10.21

10.22 For the simply supported steel beam shown in Fig. P10.22, determine the maximum force and the maximum stress when the weight impacts the beam. The beam is fabricated from a W 12 × 50 wide flange section.

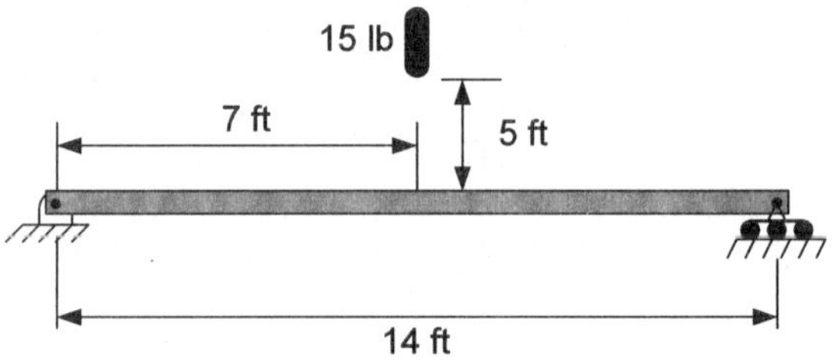

Fig. P10.22

10.23 For the aluminum alloy cantilever beam shown in Fig. P10.23, determine the maximum force and maximum stress when the mass impacts the beam. The beam is fabricated from a S 127 × 22 American Standard section.

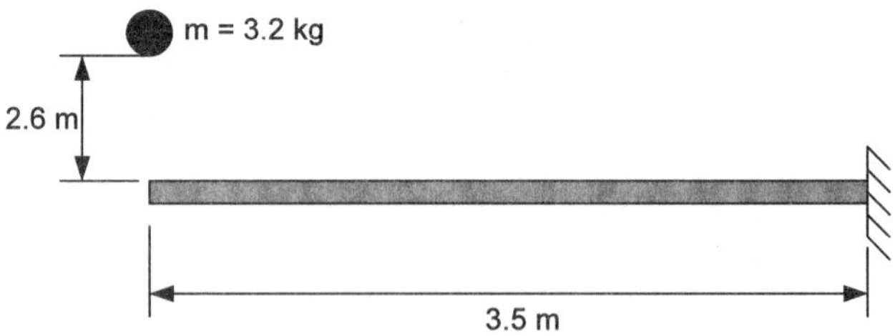

Fig. P10.23

10.24 For the simply supported beam shown in Fig. P10.24, write the equation for the deflection at the quarter span (x = L/4) using Castigliano's theorem.

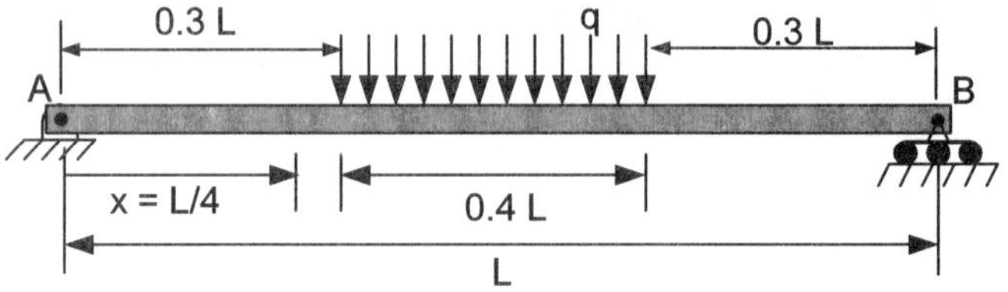

Fig. P10.24

10.25 For the cantilever beam shown in Fig. P10.25, write the equation for the deflection at its free end using Castigliano's theorem.

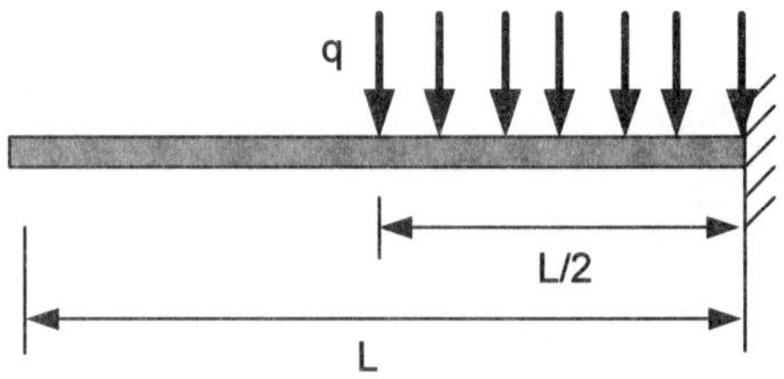

Fig. P10.25

10.26 For the cantilever beam shown in Fig. P10.26, write the equation for the deflection at midspan and its free end using Castigliano's theorem.

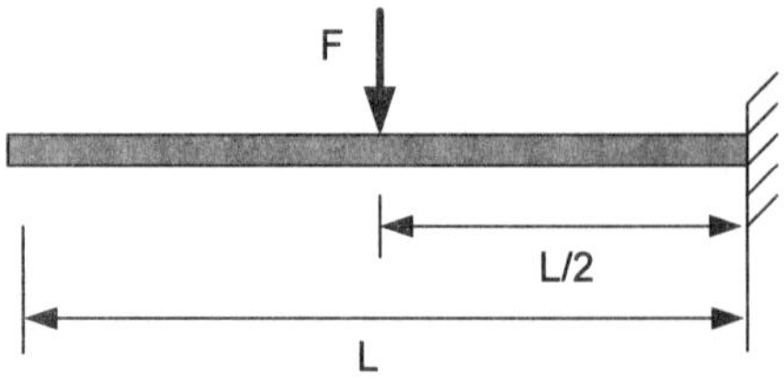

Fig. P10.26

10.27 For the simply supported beam shown in Fig. P10.27, use Castigliano's theorem to write the equation for the deflection at the midpoint of the span.

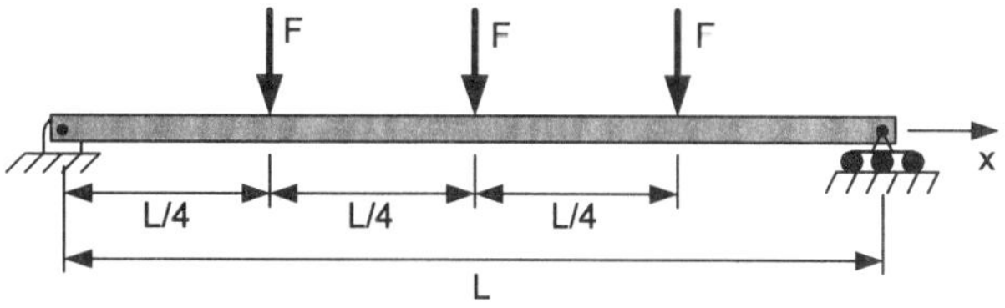

Fig. P10.27

10.28 For the simply supported beam shown in Fig. P10.28, write the equation for the deflection at midspan and both quarter points using Castigliano's theorem.

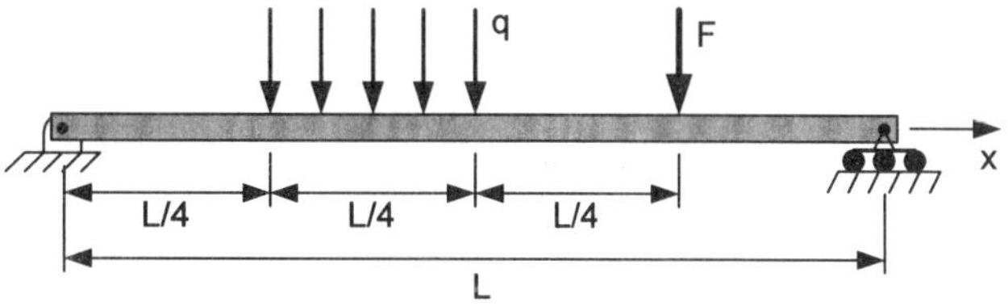

Fig. P10.28

10.29 For the cantilever beam shown in Fig. P10.29, write the equation for the deflection at midspan and its free end using Castigliano's theorem.

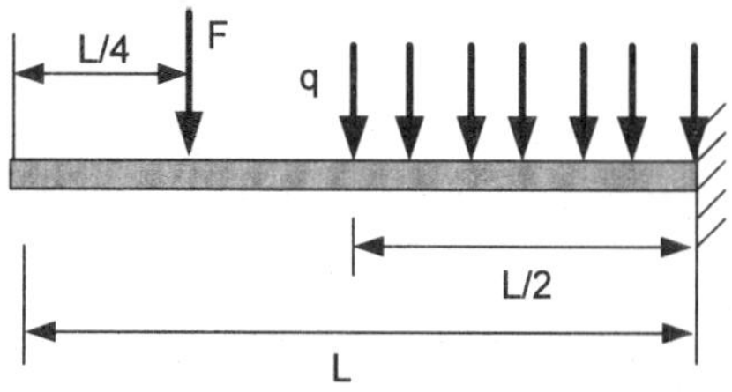

Fig. P10.29

10.30 For the cantilever beam shown in Fig. P10.30, use Castigliano's theorem to write the equation for the reaction force at the prop.

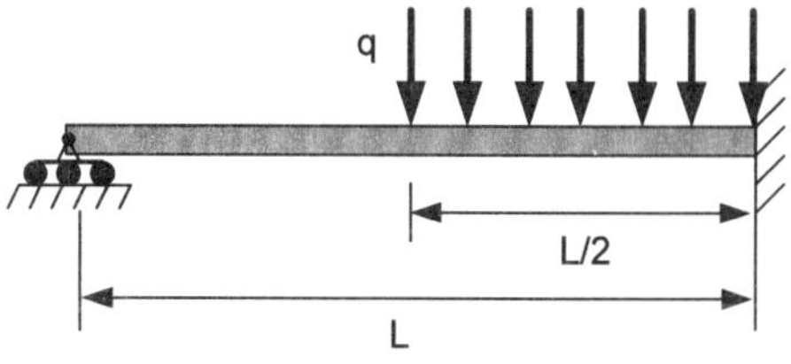

Fig. P10.30

10.31 For the cantilever beam shown in Fig. P10.31, use Castigliano's theorem to write the equation for the reaction force at the prop.

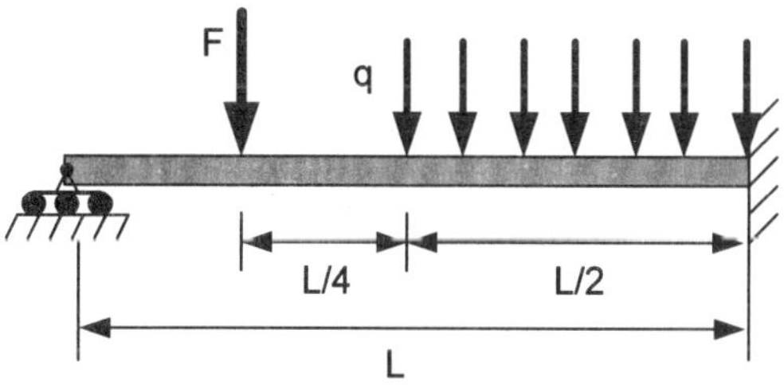

Fig. P10.31

10.32 For the continuous beam shown in Fig. P10.32, use Castigliano's theorem to write the equation for the reaction force at the center support.

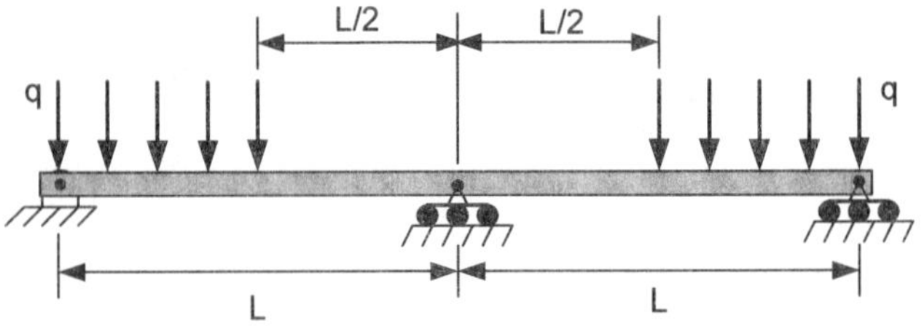

Fig. P10.32

10.33 For the continuous beam, shown in Fig. P10.33, use Castigliano's theorem to write the equation for the reaction force at the center support.

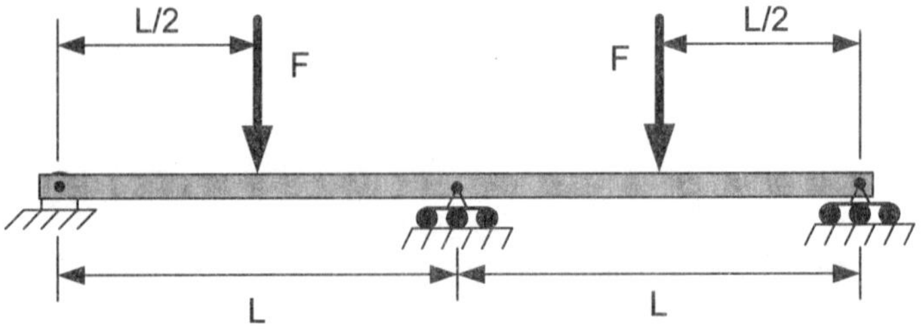

Fig. P10.33

10.34 A cantilever beam is formed in the shape of a quarter circle as illustrated in Fig. P10.34. If the cantilever beam is loaded with a vertical force F at its free end, write the equation for the beam's deflection in the direction of the applied force. Assume that EI_z is a constant.

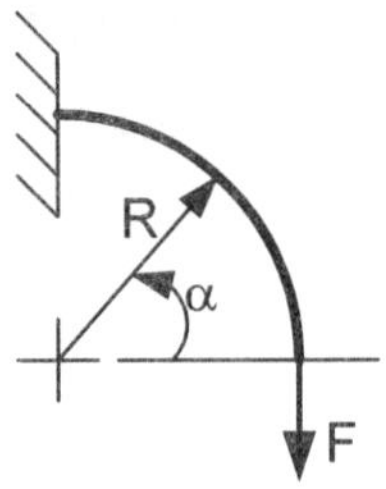

Fig. P10.34

10.35 A cantilever beam is formed in the shape of a quarter circle as illustrated in Fig. P10.35. If the cantilever beam is loaded with a horizontal force F at its free end, write the equation for the beam's deflection in the direction of the applied force. Assume that EI_z is a constant.

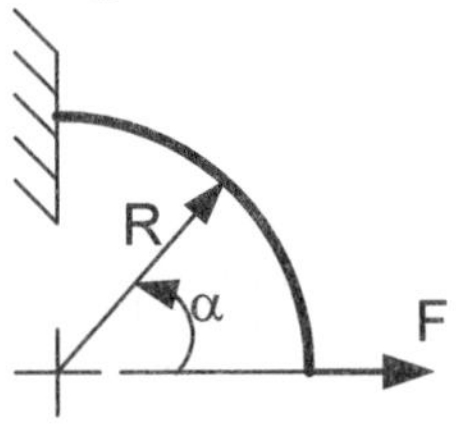

Fig. P10.35

10.36 A cantilever beam is formed in the shape of a semicircle as illustrated in Fig. P10.36. If the cantilever beam is loaded with a horizontal force F at its free end, write the equation for the beam's deflection in the direction of the applied force. Assume that EI_z is a constant.

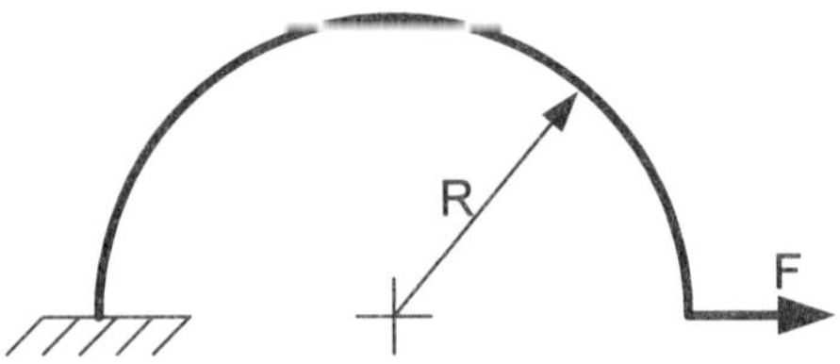

Fig. P10.36

10.37 A cantilever beam is formed in the shape of a semicircle as illustrated in Fig. P10.36. If the cantilever beam is stretched by an amount δ in the horizontal direction, determine the force that must be applied to produce this deflection.

10.38 A shaft is fabricated by brazing together two sections of round tubing as shown in Fig. P10.38 below. The shaft is fixed at one end and a torque T is applied to it at its free end. Use Castigliano's theorem to write the equation for the angle of twist ϕ. Assume the thickness of the braze metal is negligible.

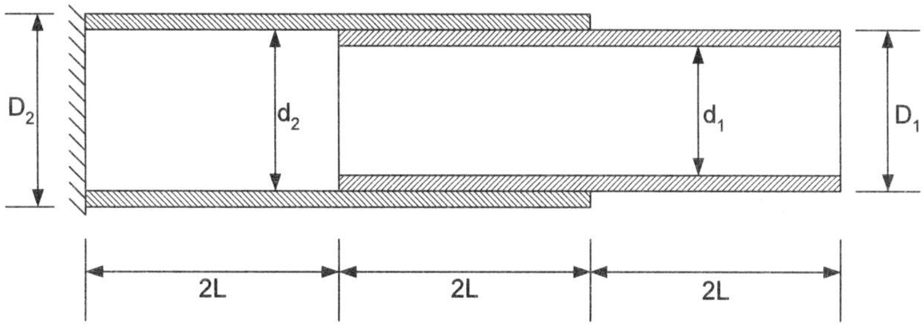

Fig. P10.38

10.39 A shaft is fabricated by brazing together two sections of round tubing as shown in Fig. P10.39. The shaft is fixed at one end and a torque T is applied to it at its free end. Use Castigliano's theorem to write the equation for the angle of twist ϕ. Assume the thickness of the braze metal is negligible.

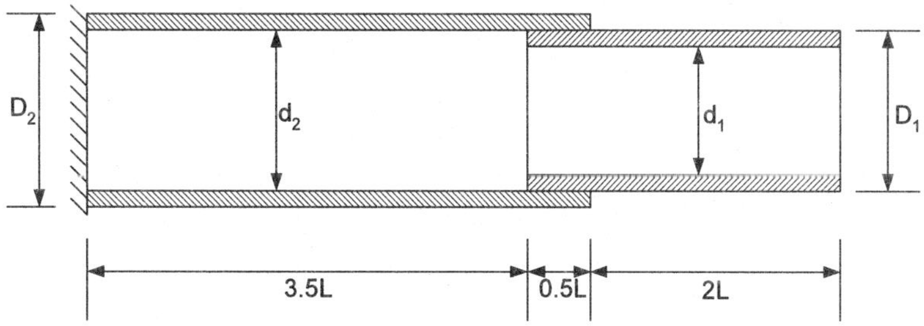

Fig. P10.39

10.40 Write the equation for the displacement in the (a) vertical and (b) horizontal direction at joint B for the two-member truss, shown in Fig. P10.40, using Castigliano's method. Truss members AB and BC are identical of the same material, length L, and area A. The ratio of h/w is 4/3.

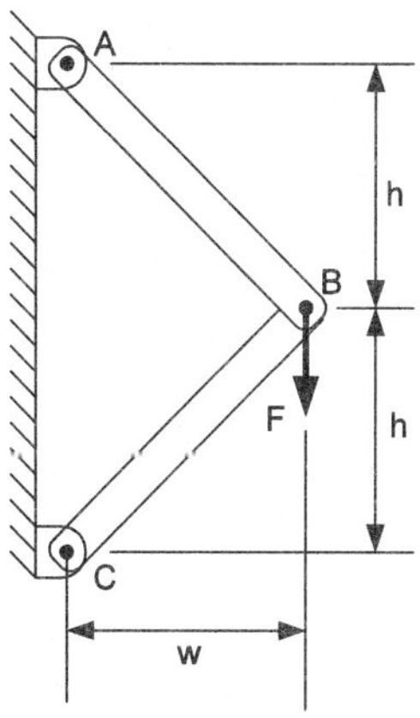

Fig. P10.40

10.41 Determine the displacement in the (a) vertical and (b) horizontal direction at joint B for the two-member truss, shown in Fig. P10.40, using Castigliano's method. Truss members AB and BC are identical of the same material, length L, and area A. The ratio h/w = 1.00.

10.42 Write the equation for the displacement in the vertical direction at joint C for the seven-member truss, shown in Fig. P10.42 figure to the left, using Castigliano's method. All of the truss members are fabricated from the same material. The cross sectional area of members BC, AE, BD and DE is 2A; the area of AB is A; and the area of members BE and CD is 3A.

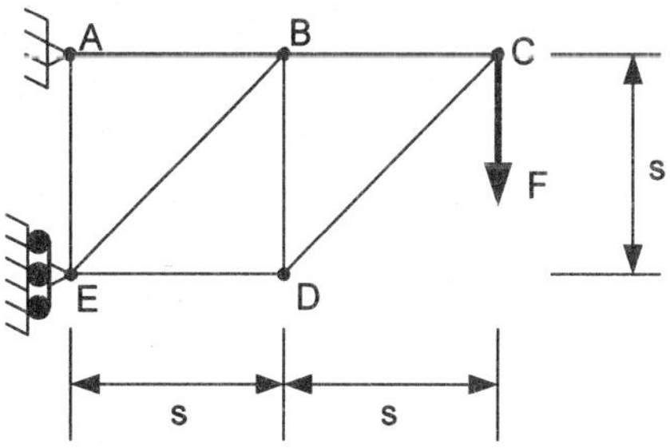

Fig. P10.42

10.43 Write the equation for the displacement in the vertical direction at joint D for the five-member truss, illustrated in Fig. P10.43, using Castigliano's method. All of the truss members are fabricated from the same material with the same cross sectional area of A. The ratio h/s = 1.5.

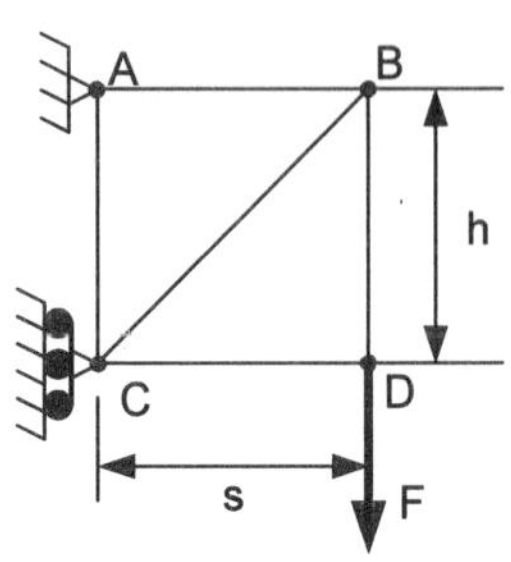

Fig. P10.43

10.44 Write the equation for the displacement in the vertical direction at joint C for the seven-member truss, shown in Fig. P10.44, using Castigliano's method. All of the truss members are fabricated from the same material with the same cross sectional area of A. The ratio of h/s is 0.85.

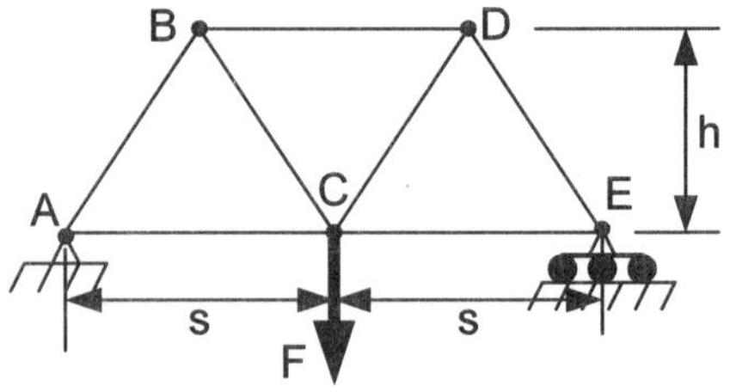

Fig. P10.44

10.45 Write the equation for the displacement in the vertical direction at joint B for the seven-member truss, illustrated in Fig. P10.45, using Castigliano's method. All of the truss members are fabricated from the same material with the same cross sectional area of A. The ratio of h/s is 0.85.

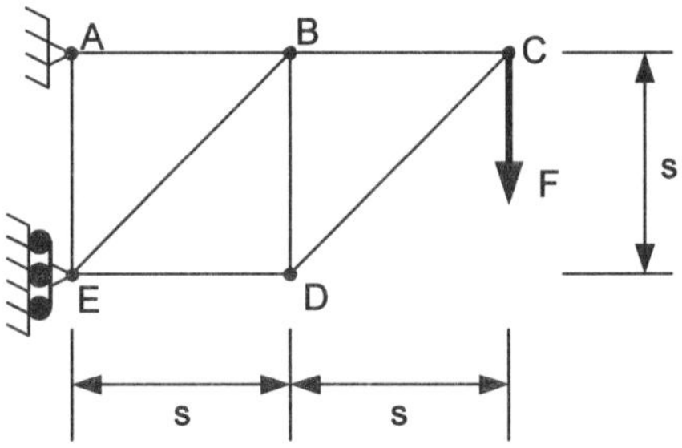

Fig. P10.45

10.46 Write the equation for the displacement in the vertical direction at joint D for the five-member truss, shown in Fig. P10.46, using Castigliano's method. All of the truss members are fabricated from the same material with the same cross sectional area of A. The ratio of h/s is 1.20.

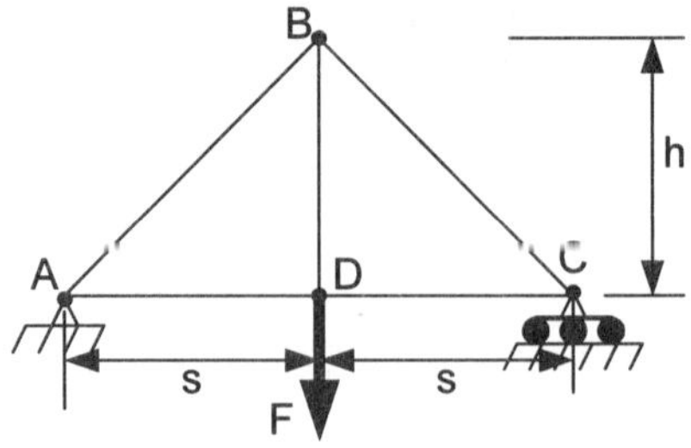

Fig. P10.46

10.47 Write the equation for the displacement in the horizontal direction at joint C for the five-member truss, illustrated in Fig. P10.46, using Castigliano's method. All of the truss members are fabricated from the same material with the same cross sectional area of A. The ratio of h/s is 1.20.

CHAPTER 11

FRACTURE MECHANICS

11.1 INTRODUCTION

In the all of the previous chapters, theories were described showing procedures for determining stresses and strains in structural members that were free of flaws. However, when flaws such as cracks exist in the structure, these theories are not sufficient to predict the onset of failure. The difficulty is due to the geometry of the crack tip. The crack tip is sharp with a radius of curvature approaching zero and this sharpness produces local stresses σ_{xx}, σ_{yy} and τ_{xy}, which tend to infinity as one approaches the crack tip. Because these stresses approach infinity for any loading of the structure, the theories of failure, such as Tresca or Von Mises, cannot be applied and the load required producing either localized yielding or the onset of crack propagation cannot be predicted.

To analyze structural members containing cracks, it is necessary to introduce a method that deals with the singular state of stress at the crack tip, where the stresses approach infinity for even the very small loads. Fracture mechanics, developed by Irwin [1] from the earlier work of Inglis [2], Griffith [3] and Westergaard [4], treats singular stress fields by introducing a quantity known as a **stress intensity factor** K_I defined as:

$$K_I = \lim_{r \Rightarrow 0} (\sigma_{yy} \sqrt{2\pi r}) \tag{11.1}$$

The coordinate system for Eq. (11.1) is defined in Fig. 11.1 and σ_{yy} is evaluated in the limit along the $\theta = 0°$ line.

Fig. 11.1 Coordinate system defining a double-ended crack.

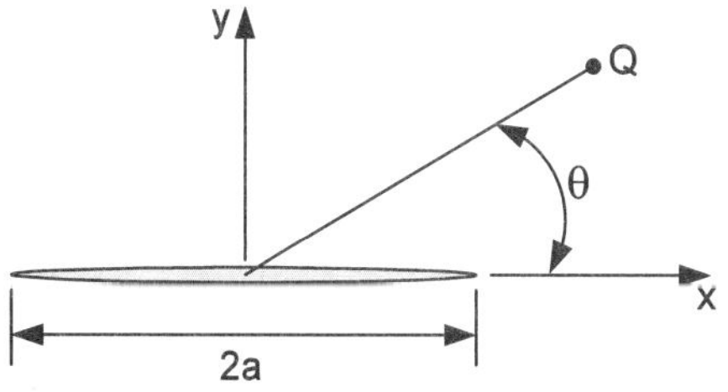

The limit process in Eq. (11.1) gives a stress intensity factor K_I that is a linear function of the loads applied to the structure. The stress intensity factor remains finite and provides a basis for determining the critical load. The critical condition in fracture mechanics is the onset of crack initiation, when the crack extends suddenly at high velocity in cleavage failure, or when the crack extends at a much lower velocity by tearing in a shear failure. With either type of crack extension, the structure has failed. The introduction of the stress intensity factor K_I provides a means, which is dependent upon the applied state of stress (i.e. σ_o) and the crack length, for judging the criticality of a crack.

The second and equally important aspect of fracture mechanics is the characterization of a material property that defines the onset of crack initiation. This property is termed **toughness,** and it is determined using well-defined testing procedures. For example, **the plane strain crack initiation toughness** K_{Ic} defines the resistance of the material to crack initiation.

$$K_I \geq K_{Ic} \qquad \Rightarrow \text{crack initiation} \tag{11.2}$$

When the applied stress intensity factor K_I equals or exceeds the plane strain crack initiation toughness K_{Ic}, the crack initiates and extends into the structure. Because K_I is a linear function of the applied load F, the failure criterion given in Eq. (11.2) provides an approach for predicting the critical load F_{CR} associated with crack initiation. This concept is illustrated in Fig. 11.2.

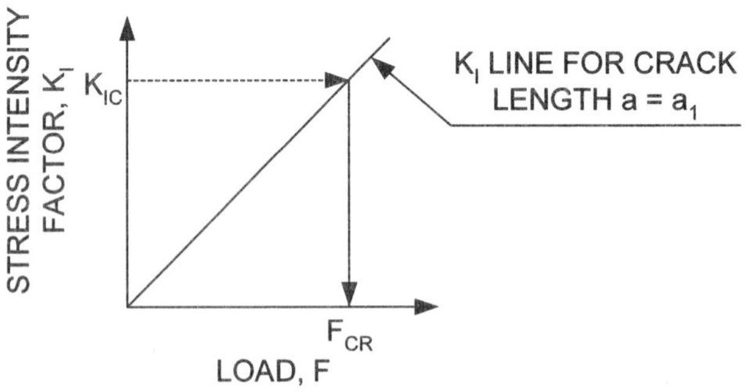

Fig. 11.2 An approach for predicting the critical load F_{CR} associated with crack initiation.

Before beginning a study of fracture mechanics, it is important to understand singular stress fields, where all of the Cartesian components of stress tend to infinity at the crack tip, while the loads applied to the structural element remain finite. To better describe a singular stress state, consider the solution for a very wide plate under uniaxial load with an elliptical hole.

11.2 STRESSES DUE TO AN ELLIPTICAL HOLE IN A UNIFORMLY LOADED PLATE

In Chapter 9, we have introduced the concept of stress concentration factors where discontinuities in a structural element, such as holes and notches, elevate the stresses in the vicinity of the discontinuity. We treated the increase in the stresses by introducing a stress concentration factor K that was a multiplier on the nominal stress as indicated in Eq. (11.3).

$$\sigma_{Max} = K\,\sigma_{Nom} \tag{11.3}$$

where σ_{Max} represents the maximum stress adjacent to the discontinuity.

K is the stress concentration factor that depends on the geometry of the discontinuity, the structural member (tie rod, beam, shaft) and the type of loading.

σ_{Nom} is the nominal stress at a location removed from the discontinuity.

In typical structural applications, where discontinuities are inevitable, stress concentration factors usually range from 2 to 5. The stresses are elevated, but they remain finite. Theories of failure can be applied to predict the onset of local yielding with considerable success.

Now consider a discontinuity that produces much higher stress concentrations than the typical values referenced above. Suppose we have a very wide plate with a centrally located elliptical hole subjected to remote uniaxial loading σ_0, as shown in Fig. 11.3.

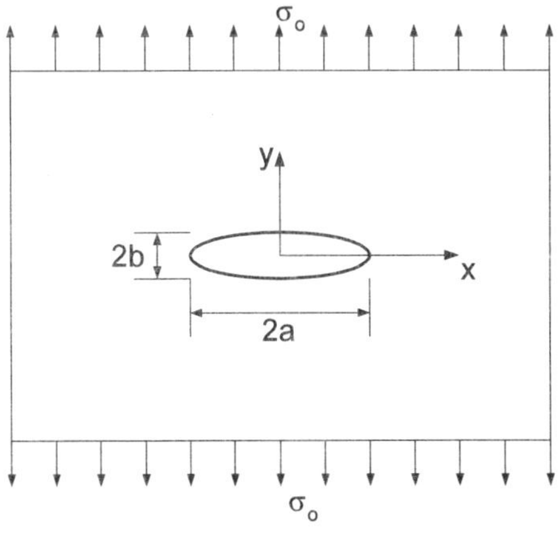

Fig. 11.3 Elliptical hole in an infinite plate with a uniform stress σ_o applied perpendicular to the crack.

Inglis [2] considered an infinite plate with an elliptical hole subjected to a uniform stress σ_o, as shown in Fig. 11.3. He found that σ_{Max} occurs at the ends of the major axis (± a) of the ellipse and is given by:

$$\sigma_{Max} = \sigma_0 \left(1 + \frac{2a}{b}\right) \tag{11.4a}$$

Comparing this result to Eq. (11.3), it is clear that the stress concentration K for the elliptical hole in a very wide (infinite) plate can be written as:

$$K = \left(1 + \frac{2a}{b}\right) \tag{11.4b}$$

It is instructive to examine the results of Eq. (11.4) for two limit cases. First, when a = b, the elliptical hole becomes circular and $\sigma_{Max} = 3\sigma_o$. This result confirms the stress concentration of K = 3 for a circular hole in an infinite plate with a uniaxial load as indicated in Chapter 9. Second, when $b \Rightarrow 0$, the elliptical hole approaches a flat opening that represents a crack. In this case, Eq. (11.4) shows that $\sigma_{Max} \Rightarrow \infty$ as $b \Rightarrow 0$. Note that σ_{Max} goes to infinity regardless of the magnitude of the applied stress σ_o. This fact indicates that localized yielding will occur at the crack tips **for any nonzero load**. The commonly employed failure theories such as Tresca and von Mises predict yielding for a specific load; therefore, they cannot provide useful information regarding the stability of the crack.

When the applied stress σ_o is applied in a direction parallel to the major axis of the elliptical hole, the value of σ_{Max} on the boundary of the hole is at the ends of the minor axes (± b) and is given by:

$$\sigma_{Max} = \sigma_0 \left(1 + \frac{2b}{a}\right) \tag{11.5}$$

In the limit as $b \Rightarrow 0$, the ellipse represents a crack and the stress $\sigma_{Max} = \sigma_o$; thus, concentration of the stress does not occur. At the ends of the major axis of the elliptic hole, Eq. (11.5) does not apply; however, $\sigma = -\sigma_o$ at these two points for all values of b/a.

Equation (11.4) describes the stresses at the tip of a crack in the limit as $b \Rightarrow 0$. It is evident that the stresses at the crack tip are singular when the crack is perpendicular to the applied stress σ_o. This fact indicates local yielding will occur for any nonzero stress σ_o and that methods for predicting structural stability based on classical failure theories for yielding are inadequate. Concepts of crack stability based on fracture mechanics must be introduced to predict if the crack will initiate at a specified value of the applied stress σ_o.

EXAMPLE 11.1

Using Eq. (11.4b), prepare a graph of the stress concentration K for an elliptical hole in a very wide (infinite) plate as b ⇒ 0.05 units.

Solution:

Let's arbitrarily set a = 1 unit and permit b to decrease from 1 to 0.05 in steps of 0.05 units. Evaluating Eq. (11.4b) in a spreadsheet yields the graph shown in Fig. E11.1.

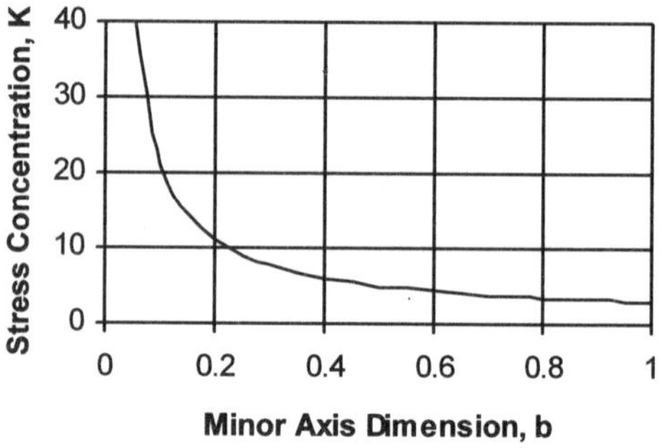

Fig. E11.1

The stress concentration K increases exponentially to a value exceeding 40 as the minor dimension of the ellipse b ⇒ 0.05 units.

EXAMPLE 11.2

Let's repeat the calculation of the stress concentration factor given in Eq. (11.4b), but in this case explore the value of K as the dimension b decreases from 0.05 to 0.001 unit.

Solution:

Let's arbitrarily set a = 1 unit and permit b to decrease from 0.05 to 0.001 unit. Evaluating the stress concentration K in a spreadsheet yields the results presented in Fig. E11.2. Note that the stress concentration K increases exponentially to a value exceeding 2,000 as the minor dimension of the ellipse b ⇒ 0.001 unit.

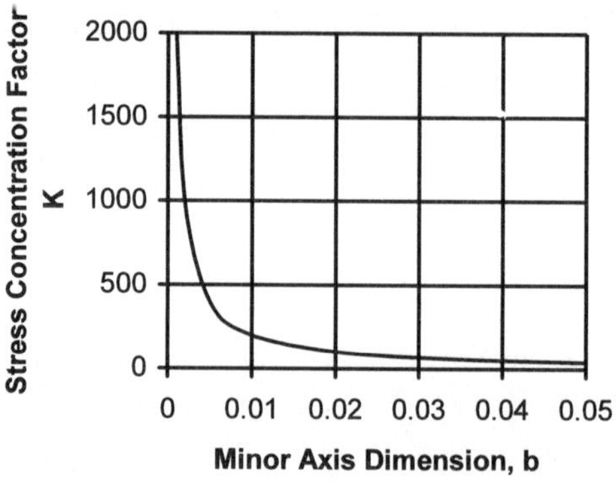

Fig. E11.2

As the elliptical hole is collapsed into a crack by letting the dimension of the minor axis b $\Rightarrow$ 0, it is clear that the stress σ_{Max} becomes infinite. These two examples illustrate this fact with numerical values of the stress concentration, as the elliptical hole is collapsed. Because of the stress singularity, traditional methods of predicting failure are not applicable. This dilemma baffled engineers responsible for designing safe structures for many decades and it was not until the early 1950s that we began to understand a method for dealing with the stress singularities that exist at crack tips.

11.3 STRESSES NEAR THE CRACK TIP

Westergaard [4] employed advanced theories of elasticity and mathematics to develop a solution for the stress near a crack tip. While this development is beyond the scope of this book, we will use his results to develop an expression for the stress intensity factor.

The classic problem in fracture mechanics, shown in Fig 11.4a, is an infinite plate with a central crack of length 2a. The plate is subjected to biaxial tension with σ_o applied in both the x and y directions at its remote boundaries. It is convenient to relocate the origin of the coordinate system and place it at the tip of the crack as shown in Fig. 11.4b.

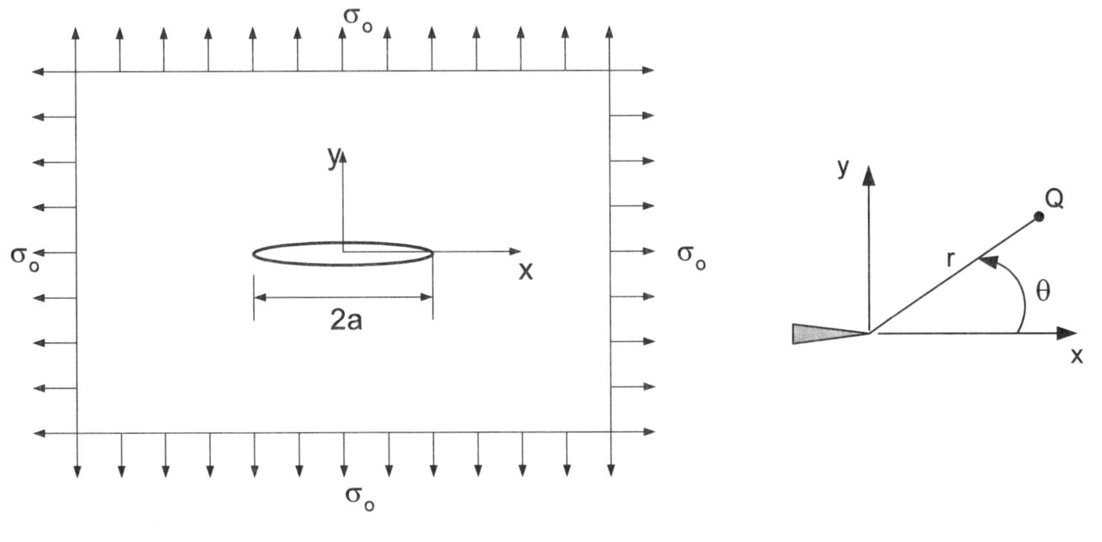

(a) (b)

Fig. 11.4 (a) A crack of length 2a in an infinite plate subjected to biaxial stress σ_o.
(b) Coordinates defined with the origin at the crack tip.

Next, consider a small region near the crack tip where r << a. In this small region, the Westergaard results enable us to write an equation for σ_{yy} that is valid along the crack line where θ and y are both equal to zero.

$$\sigma_{yy} = \sqrt{\frac{a}{2r}}\,\sigma_0 \qquad (11.6)$$

Equation (11.6) shows that the stress $\sigma_{yy} \Rightarrow \infty$, which indicates that it is singular with order $1/\sqrt{r}$ as the crack tip is approached along the x-axis. Finally, substitute Eq. (11.6) into Eq. (11.1) and take the limit of σ_{yy} as $r \Rightarrow 0$ to obtain the stress intensity factor K_I as:

$$K_I = \sigma_0 \sqrt{\pi\, a} \tag{11.7}$$

This result shows that the stress intensity factor K_I varies as a linear function of the applied stress σ_o and increases with crack length as a function of $\sqrt{a}$, as illustrated in Fig. 11.5.

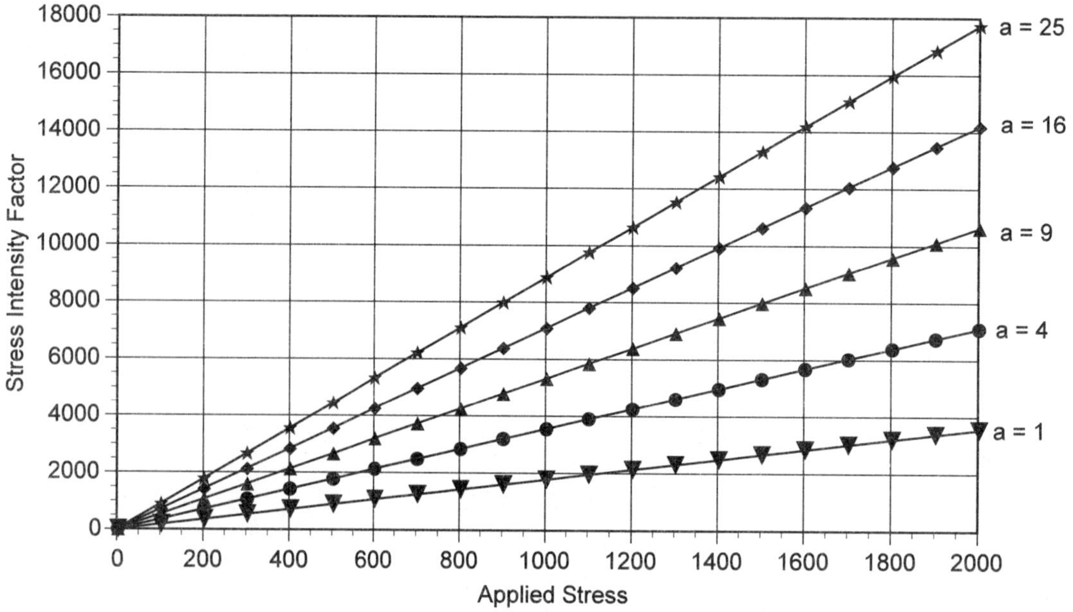

Fig. 11.5 Stress intensity factor K_I (psi -$\sqrt{in.}$) as a function of applied stress σ_o (psi).

The stress intensity factor K_I and the stress concentration factor K are two different quantities and they should not be confused. The stress concentration factor K is used to predict the increase in stresses due to geometric discontinuities that result in elevated but finite stresses. The stress intensity factor K_I is used to accommodate the stresses at crack tips, which are singular in nature. The units of the two quantities differ. The stress concentration factor is dimensionless. The stress intensity factor has units of psi-$\sqrt{in.}$ or MPa-$\sqrt{m}$.

EXAMPLE 11.3

Quality control inspectors discover a crack in the weld of a wide steel plate that is to be subjected to biaxial loading with a stress σ_o = 9,000 psi. They estimate that the crack is 6.0 in. long. You are asked to determine the stress intensity factor.

Solution:

We will employ Eq. (11.7) to estimate the stress intensity associated with this crack as:

$$K_I = \sigma_0 \sqrt{\pi\ a} = (9{,}000)\sqrt{\pi(3.0)} = 27.63\ \text{ksi}\sqrt{\text{in.}} \qquad \text{(a)}$$

At this stage in the development, we cannot interpret the significance of this result. Clearly, a comparison to some material property is necessary before an assessment of the stability of the weld crack can be made. We will discuss material properties and crack initiation toughness in the next section.

EXAMPLE 11.4

A supplier of large, wide plate aluminum castings indicates that cracks up to 50 mm long may be generated as the castings cool to room temperature. The castings are subjected to loads that produce a stress of σ_o = 65 MPa. You are asked to estimate a stress intensity factor for the worst case.

Solution:

In the worst case, the crack will be perpendicular to the applied stress and located away from the boundaries of the casting; hence, difficult for the inspectors to locate. We will assume that the result of Eq. (11.7) represents the worst-case scenario. Then the estimate of the stress intensity factor associated with this crack is given by:

$$K_I = \sigma_0 \sqrt{\pi\ a} = (65)\sqrt{\pi(25)} = 576.0\ \text{MPa}\sqrt{\text{mm}} \qquad \text{(a)}$$

Again, we will postpone interpretation of this result until the information on the aluminum's resistance to crack initiation has been introduced.

11.4 FRACTURE TOUGHNESS

In the previous section, we showed that the stress intensity factor K_I could be determined for a wide plate with a central crack. However, we were not able to predict the safety of the structure (wide plate) because the material property defining resistance to crack initiation was not available. We must have a second quantity — the material's **fracture toughness** — to predict crack behavior.

Fracture toughness K_c is a measure of a material's ability to resist crack initiation. Fracture toughness is a material property, which depends on the type of material (steel, aluminum, titanium, etc.), the alloy, its heat treatment and operating temperature. Fracture toughness also depends on the thickness of the structural element containing the crack, and the thickness of the test specimen used in measuring the toughness.

We noted previously that the stresses were singular at the crack tip. Accordingly any non-zero stress applied to the structure should cause the crack to initiate and propagate. Fortunately, **this statement is not true**. Cracks remain stable until the applied stress σ_o is increased to some critical value. At this critical loading the cracks initiate and extend. We describe the **condition for crack initiation** with:

$$K_I \geq K_c \qquad (11.8)$$

where K_c is the fracture toughness.

After initiation, the crack often propagates at high speed across the width of the structural element causing catastrophic failure. Cracks are **stable** when the applied stress σ_o produces a stress intensity factor K_I that is:

$$K_I < K_c \tag{11.9}$$

The reason cracks are stable, when the stresses at the crack tip are singular, is the presence of local plastic deformation at the crack tip. When the stresses increase at the crack tip, localized yielding occurs in the immediate neighborhood of the crack tip. A plastic zone is formed and the crack tip becomes blunted as illustrated in Fig. 11.6.

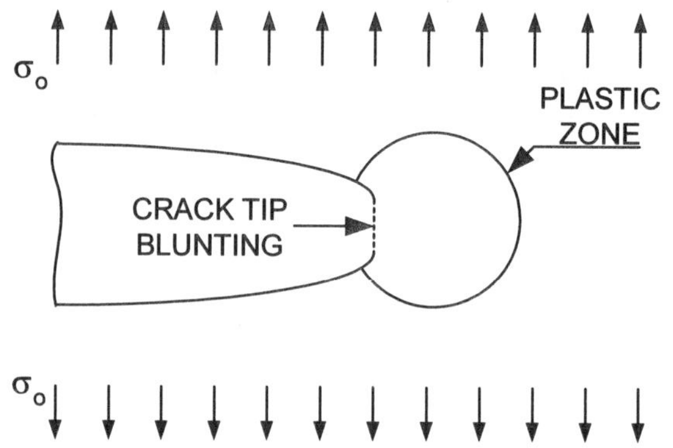

Fig. 11.6 Localized yielding produces a small plastic zone that blunts the crack tip.

The size and shape of the plastic zone depends on the magnitude of the applied stress σ_o and the material thickness. As the material thickness is increased the material in the center of the plate is constrained, the size of the plastic zone diminishes, and the blunting of the crack tip is less pronounced. These changes affect the material toughness K_c as shown in Fig. 11.7. As the specimen thickness increases, the fracture toughness K_c decreases until it reaches a limiting value K_{Ic}. This limiting value K_{Ic} is known as the **plane strain fracture toughness**. This material property is often used to predict the safety of structures because it provides the most conservative estimates of the allowable stress.

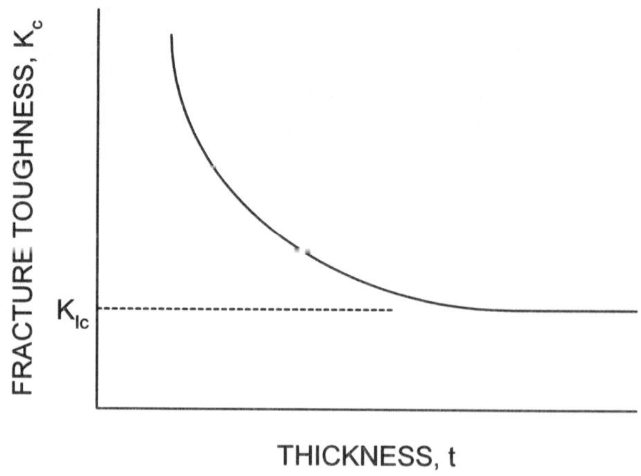

Fig. 11.7 Fracture toughness decreases with increasing specimen thickness.

A table showing the fracture properties of several common engineering materials is presented in Table 11.1. R. J. Sanford [5] presents a more complete listing of these properties in his textbook.

Table 11.1
Strength and fracture toughness of several engineering materials

Material	S_y, ksi	S_u, ksi	K_{Ic}, ksi$\sqrt{in.}$		S_y, MPa	S_u, MPa	K_{Ic}. MPa$\sqrt{mm}$
Steel—1010 HR	25	45	70		172	310	2432
Steel—1020 HR	30	58	70		207	400	2432
Steel—4340	195	210	80		1344	1448	2780
Steel—18 Ni	240	260	75		1655	1793	2606
Stainless Steel 301 ½ Hard	125	165	100		862	1138	3475
Stainless Steel 440C Tempered	270	290	17		1862	1199	591
Aluminum 2024-T852	57	70	28		393	483	973
Aluminum 2124-T851	53	55	31		365	379	1077
Aluminum 6061-T651	44	47	27		303	324	938
Titanium—70	70	80	50		483	552	1737
Titanium 6Al-6V-2Sn	150	160	50		1034	1103	1737
Al-Bronze—630	82	117	53		565	807	1842
Magnesium—AM503	16	29	12		110	200	417

EXAMPLE 11.5

In Example 11.3, the quality control inspectors discovered a 6.0 in. long crack in the weld of a wide steel plate that is subjected to biaxial loading with a stress σ_o = 9,000 psi. We determined the stress intensity factor as $K_I = \sigma_0 \sqrt{\pi\ a} = (9,000)\sqrt{\pi(3.0)} = 27.63\ \text{ksi}\sqrt{\text{in.}}$; however, in executing this solution we could not predict the stability of the crack. If the steel used is 1020 HR, predict if the crack is stable or unstable.

Solution:

Let's use the stability condition presented in Eq. (11.9) and write:

$$K_I < K_c \qquad \text{(a)}$$

Substituting numerical results from Table 11.1 and Example 11.3 into this equation gives:

$$K_I = 27.63\ \text{ksi}\sqrt{\text{in.}} < K_{Ic} = 70\ \text{ksi}\sqrt{\text{in.}} \qquad \text{(b)}$$

The stress intensity factor is less than the plane strain fracture toughness; hence, the crack is stable.

EXAMPLE 11.6

In Example 11.4 your supplier of large aluminum castings indicated that cracks up to 50 mm long may be generated as the castings cool to room temperature. The casting are subjected to loads that produce a stress of $\sigma_o = 65$ MPa. You determined the stress intensity factor for the worst case as:

$$K_I = \sigma_0 \sqrt{\pi\ a} = (65)\sqrt{\pi(25)}\ = 576.0\ \text{MPa}\sqrt{\text{mm}}$$

If the casting is made from an alloy with a fracture toughness of $K_c = 15$ MPa√m, determine if the crack is stable.

Solution:

Let's use the stability condition presented in Eq. (11.9) and write:

$$K_I < K_c \qquad \text{(a)}$$

Substituting numerical results from the problem statement and Example 11.4 into this equation gives:

$$K_I = 576.0\ \text{MPa}\sqrt{\text{mm}} > K_c = 474.3\ \text{MPa}\sqrt{\text{mm}} \qquad \text{(b)}$$

Note in Eq. (b), we converted the units for K_c as follows: (15 MPa√m)(1000 mm/m)$^{1/2}$ = 474.3 MPa√mm. The stress intensity factor is greater than the fracture toughness K_c; hence, the crack is unstable. The structure must be redesigned to lower the applied stress to prevent catastrophic failure.

11.5 STRESS INTENSITY FACTORS FOR SELECT GEOMETRIES

Cracks in plane bodies of finite size are important because cracks pose a threat to the stability and safety of the entire structure even though only one member may be cracked. It is important to determine the stress intensity factor for the specific geometry and loading involved to assess the safety factor for the member with a flaw. Many solutions for boundary value problems with cracks exist and a few of the more commonly encountered geometries and loadings will be presented in this section. A much more complete listing of solutions is given in reference [6].

First, consider the tension strip with a centrally located crack as shown in Fig. 11.8. The loading at the ends of the strip, well removed from the crack, is a uniaxial stress σ_o. An approximate solution for K_I is:

$$K_I = \sqrt{\sec\frac{\pi\ a}{w}}\ \sigma_0\sqrt{\pi\ a} \qquad (11.10)$$

Note that Eq. (11.10) may be written as:

$$K_I = \alpha\ K_{I\infty} = \alpha\ \sigma_0\sqrt{\pi\ a} \qquad (11.11)$$

where: $\alpha = \sqrt{\sec\dfrac{\pi a}{w}}$ is a multiplier; (11.12)

and $K_{I\infty}$ is the stress intensity factor for an infinite plate given by Eq. (11.7).

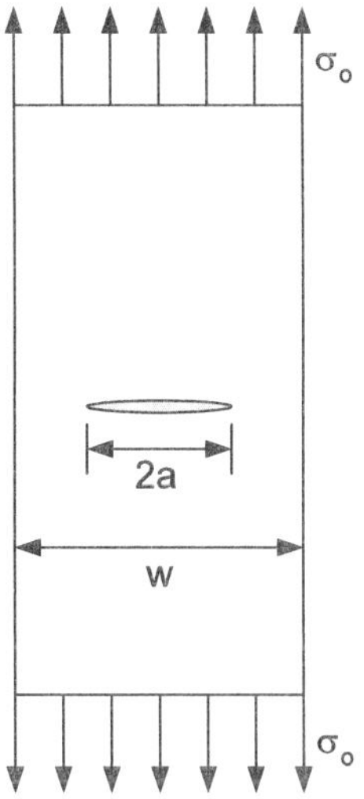

Fig. 11.8 A tension strip with a central crack of length 2a.

With K_I expressed in the form shown in Eq. (11.11), the effect of the finite boundaries of the member is given in terms of a multiplying factor α that acts on $K_{I\infty}$. The magnitude of α depends on (a/w) and ranges from $\alpha = 1.00$ for $(a/w) \Rightarrow 0$ to $\alpha = 4.00$ for $(a/w) = 0.4801$.

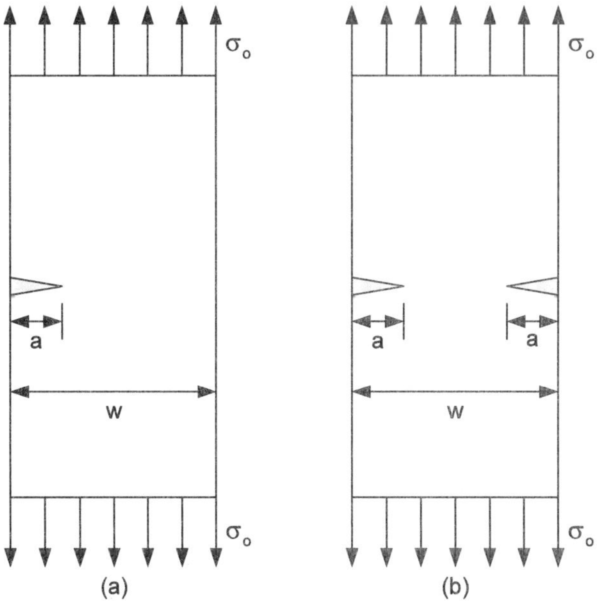

Fig. 11.9 Tension panels with edge cracks: (a) Single-edge crack. (b) Double edge crack.

Next, consider single and double edge cracks in a tension strip as shown in Figs. 11.9a and 11.9b. Series solutions for K_I for these two problems yield the following expressions for the multiplier α in terms of (a/w). For the tension panel with a single edge crack (SEC), the multiplier term α in Eq. (11.11) is given by:

$$\alpha = 1.12 - 0.231\left(\frac{a}{w}\right) + 10.55\left(\frac{a}{w}\right)^2 - 21.71\left(\frac{a}{w}\right)^3 + 30.38\left(\frac{a}{w}\right)^4 \quad (11.13)$$

For the tension panel with a double edge crack (DEC), the multiplier term α in Eq. (11.11) is given by:

$$\alpha = 1.12 + 0.429\left(\frac{a}{w}\right) - 4.78\left(\frac{a}{w}\right)^2 + 15.44\left(\frac{a}{w}\right)^3 \quad (11.14)$$

Results for multipliers of tension panels with cracks are presented in Table 11.2.

Table 11.2
Multiplier α as a function of (a/w) for single (SEC) and double edge cracked (DEC) tension panels

(a/w)	α (SEC)	α (DEC)
0	1.12	1.12
0.10	1.18	1.13
0.20	1.37	1.14
0.30	1.66	1.24
0.40	2.10	1.52
0.45	2.42	1.75

Another common case is a beam with a crack subjected to three-and four-point bending as shown in Figs. 11.10a and 11.10b.

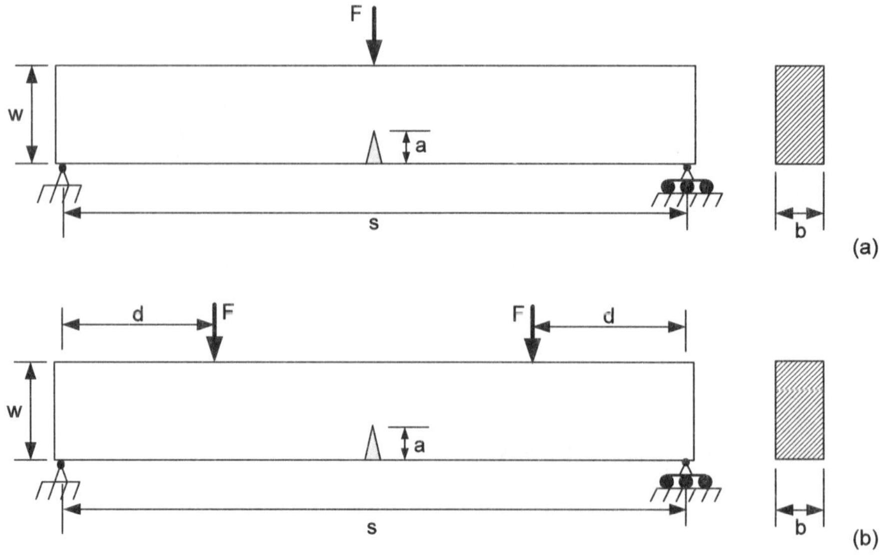

Fig. 11.10 Beams in bending with crack on tension side:
(a) Symmetric three-point bending and (b) Four-point (pure) bending.

With bending applications, the form of the solution changes and the multiplying factor α is not used. Instead, the stress intensity factor K_I is expressed in terms of beam parameters s (span), w (height), b (thickness), as defined in Fig. 11.10, and a power series of the (a/w) ratio. For the beam subjected to three-point bending, K_I is given by:

$$K_I = \frac{Fs}{bw^{3/2}}\left[2.9\left(\frac{a}{w}\right)^{1/2} - 4.6\left(\frac{a}{w}\right)^{3/2} + 21.8\left(\frac{a}{w}\right)^{5/2} - 37.6\left(\frac{a}{w}\right)^{7/2} + 38.7\left(\frac{a}{w}\right)^{9/2}\right] \quad (11.15)$$

For the beam subjected to four-point (pure) bending, K_I is given by:

$$K_I = \frac{6M}{bw^2}\sqrt{\pi a}\left[1.122 - 1.4\left(\frac{a}{w}\right) + 7.33\left(\frac{a}{w}\right)^2 - 13.08\left(\frac{a}{w}\right)^3 + 14.0\left(\frac{a}{w}\right)^4\right] \quad (11.16)$$

EXAMPLE 11.7

Table 11.2 provides the multiplier α for tension panels containing a single and double edge crack as a function of the panel's (a/w) ratio. Prepare a similar table for the tension panel containing a central crack of length 2a.

Solution:

Calculate the value of the multiplier $\alpha = \sqrt{\sec\frac{\pi a}{w}}$ from Eq. (11.12) and evaluate α as $(a/w) \Rightarrow 0$ to 0.45 and tabulate the results as shown below:

(a/w)	Multiplier, α		(a/w)	Multiplier, α
0	1.000		0.30	1.304
0.10	1.025		0.40	1.799
0.20	1.112		0.45	2.528

You may prepare a graph with these results to obtain a curve showing α as a continuous function of (a/w). Alternatively, you can use a spreadsheet to prepare a more complete table with many more values of (a/w).

EXAMPLE 11.8

A tension panel with a central crack is subjected to a uniaxial loading of $\sigma_o = 7.0$ ksi. Determine the value of K_I if the crack length 2a = 1.6 in. and the panel width w = 8.0 in.

Solution:

To calculate K_I, let's use Eq. (11.11):

$$K_I = \alpha\, K_{I\infty} \quad (a)$$

Next, calculate the value of the multiplier α from Eq. (11.12) as:

$$\alpha = \sqrt{\sec\frac{\pi\,a}{w}} = \sqrt{\sec\frac{\pi(0.8)}{8.0}} = 1.025 \qquad \text{(b)}$$

Calculate $K_{I\infty}$ as:

$$K_{I\infty} = \sigma_0\sqrt{\pi\,a} = (7.0)\sqrt{\pi(0.8)} = 11.10 \text{ ksi}\sqrt{\text{in.}} \qquad \text{(c)}$$

Substituting Eqs. (b) and (c) into Eq. (a) yields:

$$K_I = \alpha\,K_{I\infty} = (1.025)(11.10) = 11.38 \text{ ksi}\sqrt{\text{in.}} \qquad \text{(d)}$$

EXAMPLE 11.9

A tension strip, 200 mm wide, contains a single edge crack that is 60 mm deep. If K_I is limited to 450 MPa$\sqrt{\text{mm}}$, determine the maximum axial stress σ_o that can be applied to the tension strip.

Solution:

For a tension panel with a single edge crack (SEC), the multiplier term α in Eq. (11.11) is given by Eq. (11.13) as:

$$\alpha = 1.12 - 0.231\left(\frac{a}{w}\right) + 10.55\left(\frac{a}{w}\right)^2 - 21.71\left(\frac{a}{w}\right)^3 + 30.38\left(\frac{a}{w}\right)^4 \qquad \text{(a)}$$

Substitute (a/w) = (60/200) = 0.30 into Eq. (a) to obtain:

$$\alpha = 1.12 - 0.231(0.30) + 10.55(0.30)^2 - 21.71(0.30)^3 + 30.38(0.30)^4 = 1.660 \qquad \text{(b)}$$

From Eq. (11.11), we can write:

$$K_{I\infty} = K_I/\alpha \qquad \text{(c)}$$

Substituting the results from Eq. (b) and the problem statement into Eq. (c) gives:

$$K_{I\infty} = 450/1.660 = 271.1 \text{ MPa}\sqrt{\text{mm}} \qquad \text{(d)}$$

Recall Eq. (11.7) and write:

$$\sigma_o = K_{I\infty}/(\pi a)^{1/2} = 271.1/\sqrt{[\pi(60)]} = 19.75 \text{ MPa} \qquad \text{(e)}$$

EXAMPLE 11.10

A tension strip, 5.0 in. wide, contains a double edge crack — each 0.50 in. long. If an axial stress σ_o = 10.7 ksi is applied to the tension strip, determine the stress intensity factor. Comment on the stability of these cracks if the tension strip is fabricated from 440C tempered stainless steel.

Solution:

For the tension panel with a double edge crack (DEC), the multiplier term α in Eq. (11.11) is given by Eq. (11.14) as:

$$\alpha = 1.12 + 0.429\left(\frac{a}{w}\right) - 4.78\left(\frac{a}{w}\right)^2 + 15.44\left(\frac{a}{w}\right)^3 \qquad \text{(a)}$$

Substitute (a/w) = (0.50/5.0) = 0.10 into Eq. (a) to obtain:

$$\alpha = 1.12 + (0.429)(0.10) - 4.78(0.10)^2 + 15.44(0.10)^3 = 1.131 \qquad \text{(b)}$$

Calculate $K_{I\infty}$ as:

$$K_{I\infty} = \sigma_0\sqrt{\pi\ a} = (10.7)\sqrt{\pi(0.5)} = 13.41\ \text{ksi}\sqrt{\text{in.}} \qquad \text{(c)}$$

Substituting Eqs. (b) and (c) into Eq. (a) yields:

$$K_I = \alpha\ K_{I\infty} = (1.131)(13.41) = 15.17\ \text{ksi}\sqrt{\text{in.}} \qquad \text{(d)}$$

Reference to Table 11.1 shows that K_{Ic} = 17 ksi$\sqrt{\text{in}}$ for 440C tempered stainless steel. Hence, $K_I < K_{Ic}$ and we conclude that the crack is stable. However, if the applied stress σ_o is increased from 10.7 ksi to 11.99 ksi, the crack will initiate.

EXAMPLE 11.11

A simply supported beam with a span of 5.0 m is loaded with a force F applied at its centerline. Determine the maximum length of a stable crack located below the load point. The beam, fabricated from aluminum 6061-T651, has a rectangular cross section with a height of 110 mm and a thickness of 50 mm. The applied force F = 12 kN.

Solution:

For the beam subjected to three-point bending, K_I is given by Eq. (11.15) as:

$$K_I = \frac{Fs}{bw^{3/2}}\left[2.9\left(\frac{a}{w}\right)^{1/2} - 4.6\left(\frac{a}{w}\right)^{3/2} + 21.8\left(\frac{a}{w}\right)^{5/2} - 37.6\left(\frac{a}{w}\right)^{7/2} + 38.7\left(\frac{a}{w}\right)^{9/2}\right] \qquad \text{(a)}$$

Let's rewrite Eq. (a) as:

$$K_I = \frac{Fs}{bw^{3/2}} \boldsymbol{M}_1 \tag{b}$$

where $\boldsymbol{M}_1$ is given by:

$$\boldsymbol{M}_1 = \left[2.9\left(\frac{a}{w}\right)^{1/2} - 4.6\left(\frac{a}{w}\right)^{3/2} + 21.8\left(\frac{a}{w}\right)^{5/2} - 37.6\left(\frac{a}{w}\right)^{7/2} + 38.7\left(\frac{a}{w}\right)^{9/2}\right] \tag{c}$$

Substituting numerical parameters into the first term in Eq. (b) yields:

$$\frac{Fs}{bw^{3/2}} = \frac{(12\times 10^3)(5\times 10^3)}{(50)(110)^{3/2}} = 1{,}040 \text{ MPa}\sqrt{\text{mm}} \tag{d}$$

We predict crack instability when $K_I \geq K_{Ic}$; hence, we can use Eq. (b) to write:

$$\boldsymbol{M}_1 = \frac{K_{Ic}}{\left(\dfrac{Fs}{bw^{3/2}}\right)} \tag{e}$$

From Table 11.1 we note that K_{Ic} = 938 MPa√mm. Then substituting this value and the result from Eq. (d) into Eq. (e) yields:

$$\boldsymbol{M}_1 = 938/1{,}040 = 0.9019 \tag{f}$$

Finally, we use Eq. (f) in Eq. (c) and a spreadsheet to solve for (a/w) by trial and error and obtain:

$$(a/w) \approx 0.1199 \tag{g}$$

The maximum crack length that can be tolerated prior to crack initiation is then predicted as:

$$a = (0.1199)w = (0.1199)(110) = 13.19 \text{ mm} \tag{h}$$

EXAMPLE 11.12

A simply supported beam with a span of 20 ft is loaded in four-point (pure) bending with the two active loads spaced a distance d = 5 ft from the beam's supports. The beam, fabricated from aluminum 2124-T851, has a rectangular cross section with a height of 6.0 in. and a thickness of 1.00 in. The inspection department assures you that they can find cracks that are at least 1.25 in. long. Determine the maximum force F that can be applied at each of the two load points before the crack initiates.

Solution:

For the beam subjected to four-point (pure) bending, K_I is given by Eq. (11.16) as:

$$K_I = \frac{6M}{bw^2}\sqrt{\pi a}\left[1.122 - 1.4\left(\frac{a}{w}\right) + 7.33\left(\frac{a}{w}\right)^2 - 13.08\left(\frac{a}{w}\right)^3 + 14.0\left(\frac{a}{w}\right)^4\right] \quad \text{(a)}$$

Let's determine the value of the term in the brackets of Eq. (a) for (a/w) = (1.25/6) = 0.2083.

$$\left[1.122 - 1.4(0.2083) + 7.33(0.2083)^2 - 13.08(0.2083)^3 + 14.0(0.2083)^4\right] = 1.057 \quad \text{(b)}$$

We employ the data for the fracture toughness of this alloy listed in Table 11.1 and write:

$$(K_I)_{Max} = K_{Ic} = 31 \text{ ksi}\sqrt{\text{in}}. \quad \text{(c)}$$

Note the bending moment M = Fd = F(5)(12) = F(60 in). Substituting Eqs (b) and (c) and numerical parameters into Eq. (a) yields:

$$31 = \frac{6[F(60)]}{(1)(6)^2}\sqrt{\pi(1.25)}\,[1.057] \quad \text{(d)}$$

Eq. (d) can be rearranged to solve for F_{Max} as:

$$F_{Max} = 1{,}480 \text{ lb} \quad \text{(e)}$$

11.5.1 Cracks at Holes in Tensile Panels

In Chapter 9, we introduced the concept of stress concentration factors that arise when discontinuities such as holes occur in bars subjected to axial loading. When structural members containing holes are subjected to cyclic loading, fatigue cracks often initiate and grow slowly with an increase in the number of cycles of applied load. When a crack becomes sufficiently long, $K_I \geq K_{Ic}$, the crack becomes unstable and propagates at high speed causing catastrophic failure.

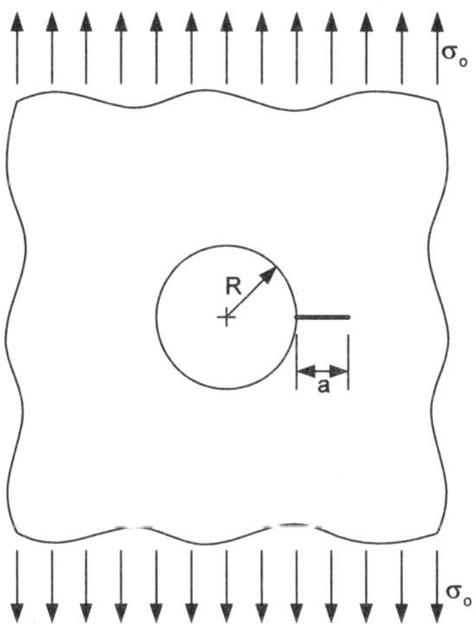

Fig. 11.11 Remotely loaded tension panel with fatigue cracks emanating from a circular hole.

Let's consider a crack emanating from a centrally located circular hole in a tension strip as shown in Fig. 11.11. If the crack is shallow relative to the diameter of the hole, the crack tip is located in a region of high stress concentration where $\sigma = 3\sigma_o$. In this instance, we can write an expression approximating K_I as:

$$K_I \approx (1.12)(3\sigma_o)\sqrt{(\pi a)} \approx (3.36)\sigma_o\sqrt{(\pi a)} \quad (11.17)$$

Equation (11.17) is a good approximation for very short cracks; however, when the cracks become longer this relation is prone to error. A more accurate formula due to Bowie [7] incorporates a factor β that accounts for the length of the crack relative to the radius of the hole as indicated below:

$$K_I = \beta\sigma_o\sqrt{(\pi a)} \quad (11.18)$$

where the factor β is a function of a/R given in Table 11.3.

Table 11.3
β Factors for a single crack extending from a circular hole in a tension panel

a/R	β		a/R	β
0.00	3.39		0.80	1.47
0.10	2.73		1.00	1.37
0.20	2.30		1.50	1.18
0.30	2.04		2.00	1.06
0.40	1.86		3.00	0.94
0.50	1.73		5.00	0.81
0.60	1.64		10.00	0.75

EXAMPLE 11.13

An inspector locates a crack adjacent to a 40 mm diameter circular hole in a tension panel, fabricated from aluminum 2024-T852, that is occasionally loaded with a uniaxial stress σ_o = 100 MPa. After measuring the crack length a = 8 mm, she recommends replacing the panel. You are to review her recommendation.

Solution:

Let's first determine the stress intensity factor due to the crack adjacent to a hole by employing Eq. (11.18).

$$K_I = \beta\sigma_o\sqrt{(\pi a)} \quad (a)$$

Note that a/R = 8/20 = 0.4; hence from Table 11.3 we find that β = 1.86. Substituting numerical parameters into Eq. (a) yields:

$$K_I = (1.86)(100)\sqrt{[\pi(8)]} = 932.5 \text{ MPa}\sqrt{\text{mm}} \quad (b)$$

Reference to Table 11.1 reveals that the fracture toughness K_{Ic} = 973 MPa√mm for aluminum 2024-T852. You conclude that the panel is safe, but by a very narrow margin because K_I is almost as large as K_{Ic}. You agree with the inspector's recommendation.

11.5.2 The Penny-Shaped Crack

In the previous sections, we considered through thickness cracks in two-dimensional bodies and provided solutions for the stress intensity factor K_I. However, cracks occur in three-dimensional bodies and we may be called upon to determine the safety of structures with embedded cracks. In some structural members, the cracks extend only a fraction of the way through the thickness of the structural member creating still another three-dimensional crack stability condition.

The penny shaped crack, illustrated in Fig. 11.12, is a flat crack with a circular shape of diameter 2a that is embedded within an infinite body. The applied stress σ_o is perpendicular to the embedded crack surface.

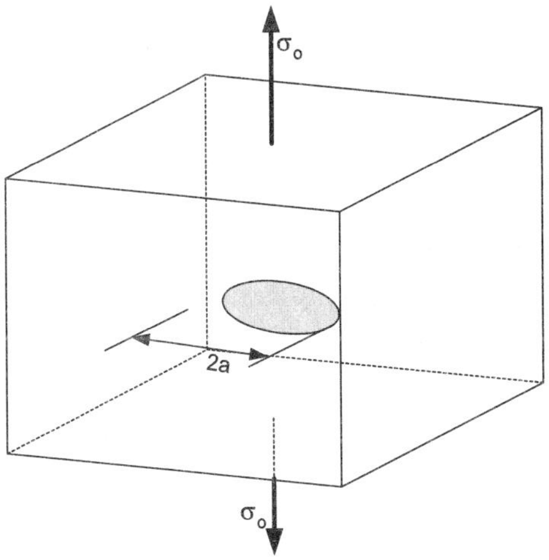

Fig. 11.12 Penny shaped crack embedded in an infinite body.

The stress intensity factor is a constant around the crack edge and is given by:

$$K_I = \frac{2}{\pi}\sigma_0\sqrt{\pi a} \tag{11.19}$$

As the crack grows under the action of cyclic loading, it advances as a series of expanding concentric circles.

EXAMPLE 11.14

Determine the maximum size of embedded shrinkage cracks that can form in a casting of 18 Ni steel if the casting is to be subjected to an applied stress of 150 ksi.

Solution:

Let's begin by using Eq. (11.19) and write the expression for the stress intensity factor for the embedded crack as:

$$K_I = \frac{2}{\pi}\sigma_0\sqrt{\pi a} \tag{a}$$

Next we note the fracture toughness for this steel is $K_{Ic} = 75$ ksi$\sqrt{\text{in}}$. Setting $K_{Ic} = K_I$ in Eq. (a) and solving for the maximum crack length a gives:

$$a_{Max} = \frac{\pi}{4}\left(\frac{K_{Ic}}{\sigma_0}\right)^2 \tag{b}$$

Substituting numerical parameters in Eq. (b) yields:

$$a_{Max} = \frac{\pi}{4}\left(\frac{75}{150}\right)^2 = 0.1963 \text{ in.} \tag{c}$$

If the applied stress is perpendicular to the crack face, then the diameter of the penny shaped crack that can be tolerated at this relatively high stress level is $2a_{Max} = 0.3926$ in.

11.5.3 Semicircular Corner Crack

The stress intensity factor for a semicircular corner crack, illustrated in Fig. 11.13, is approximated by combining the results from the penny shaped crack and the edge cracked panel to give:

Fig. 11.13 Semicircular corner crack with a radius a.

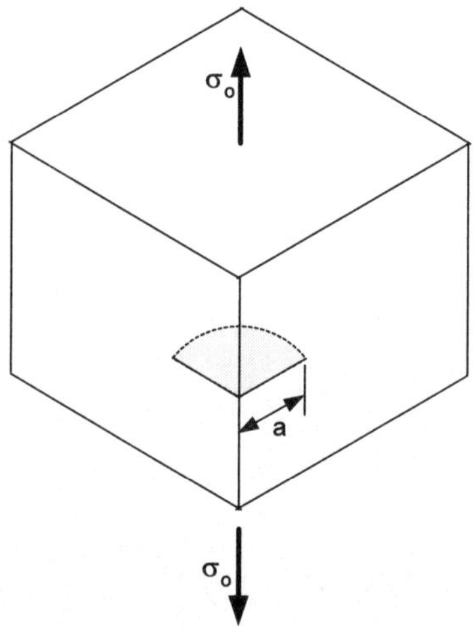

$$K_I = (1.12)^2 \frac{2}{\pi}\sigma_0\sqrt{\pi a} = \frac{2.509}{\pi}\sigma_0\sqrt{\pi a} \tag{11.20}$$

where $(1.12)^2$ is the correction factor to account for the two surface flaws and $(2/\pi)$ is the correction factor to account for the embedded circular crack.

EXAMPLE 11.15

Damage to external corners of very heavy machine components often occurs prior to installation when they are handled in chain slings before and after shipping. If a surface flaw is introduced on one of these corners with a maximum radius of 6 mm, determine the applied stress the component can withstand before the crack (flaw) becomes unstable. The component is fabricated from 4340 steel.

Solution:

The stress intensity factor for a corner crack is given by Eq. (11.20) as:

$$K_I = (1.12)^2 \frac{2}{\pi}\sigma_0\sqrt{\pi a} = \frac{2.509}{\pi}\sigma_0\sqrt{\pi a} \tag{a}$$

Next we note the fracture toughness for this steel is K_{Ic} = 2,780 MPa√mm. Setting $K_{Ic} = K_I$ in Eq. (a) and solving for the maximum stress σ_o that can be applied to the component gives:

$$(\sigma_0)_{Max} = \left(\frac{K_{Ic}}{2.509}\right)\sqrt{\frac{\pi}{a}} \tag{b}$$

Substituting numerical parameters in Eq. (b) yields:

$$(\sigma_0)_{Max} = \left(\frac{K_{Ic}}{2.509}\right)\sqrt{\frac{\pi}{a}} = \frac{2,780}{2.509}\sqrt{\frac{\pi}{6}} = 801.8 \text{ MPa} \tag{c}$$

The stress that may be imposed before the flaw becomes unstable and initiates is 801.8 MPa, which is only about 60% of the yield strength of 1,344 MPa for this type of steel. Clearly, even small flaws are detrimental and significantly compromise the strength of structures.

11.5.4 Elliptical Corner Crack at a Circular Hole

The formation of an elliptical crack emanating from a circular hole is depicted in Fig 11.14. This geometry is complex because of the presence of the hole and the shape of the crack; hence, the solution for the stress intensity factor K_I incorporates many correction factors as indicated in Eq. (11.21).

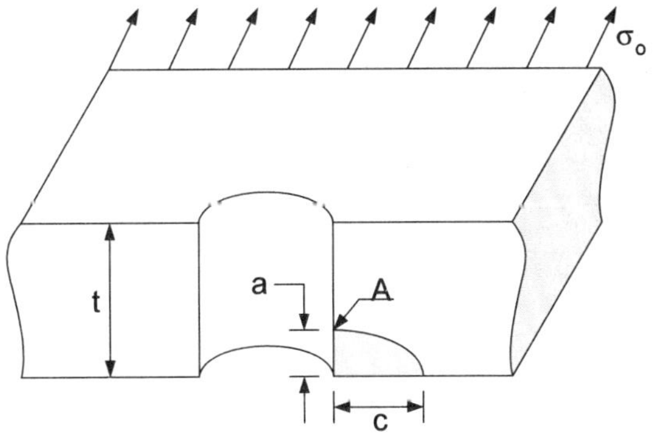

Fig. 11.14 An elliptical crack emanating from a circular hole.

The stress intensity factor K_I varies with position around the elliptical crack front. Its maximum value occurs at point A in Fig. 11.14, and is given by:

$$K_I = (1.12)(3\sigma_0)\sqrt{\frac{\pi a}{Q}}\sqrt{\sec\frac{\pi a}{2t}} \tag{11.21}$$

where a is the depth of the elliptical crack; c is the width of the crack; t is the thickness of the plate; (1.12) is the surface flaw correction factor; ($3\sigma_o$) is the correction factor for the presence of the circular hole; $\sqrt{\sec\frac{\pi a}{2t}}$ is the correction factor for the effect of the finite plate thickness and Q is the elliptical flaw correction factor defined in Table 11.4.

Table 11.4
Flaw shape parameter Q

Flaw Shape, (a/2c)	Correction Factor, Q		Flaw Shape, (a/2c)	Correction Factor, Q
0	0.91		0.30	1.53
0.05	0.95		0.35	1.62
0.10	1.02		0.40	1.82
0.15	1.11		0.45	2.04
0.20	1.23		0.50	2.23
0.25	1.37			

EXAMPLE 11.16

An inspector has located a shallow surface crack at the edge of hole in a tension panel that is fabricated from aluminum 2024-T852. His measurements indicate a crack depth a = 0.25 in. and a crack width c = 0.50 in. The plate is 1.25 in. thick and the hole diameter is 1.00 in. The tension panel is loaded with an applied stress σ_o = 12 ksi. You are to assess the safety of the tension panel.

Solution:

The stress intensity factor K_I for this example is determined from Eq. (11.21) with appropriate substitutions for the various correction factors.

$$K_I = (1.12)(3\sigma_0)\sqrt{\frac{\pi a}{Q}}\sqrt{\sec\frac{\pi a}{2t}} \tag{a}$$

The shape factor Q = 1.37 is found in Table 11.4 corresponding to (a/2c) = 0.25. Substituting numerical parameters into Eq. (a) yields:

$$K_I = (1.12)(3)(12.0)\sqrt{\frac{\pi(0.25)}{1.37}}\sqrt{\sec\frac{\pi(0.25)}{2(1.25)}} = 31.30 \text{ ksi}\sqrt{\text{in.}} \tag{b}$$

Reference to Table 11.1 gives K_{Ic} = 28 ksi$\sqrt{\text{in.}}$ for the aluminum 2024-T852 used in fabricating the plate. Comparing K_I = 31.30 ksi$\sqrt{\text{in.}}$ with K_{Ic} = 28 ksi$\sqrt{\text{in.}}$ indicates that the tension panel is at risk of failing by crack instability. The equation employed is an approximation containing many correction factors. A more accurate analysis using advanced methods of three-dimensional finite element analysis may be justified, if many tension panels are damaged and replacement of all of them is expensive.

11.6 THE THREE MODES OF LOADING

A crack in a structural member can be subjected to three different types of loading. The opening mode, illustrated in Fig. 11.15a, involves loads that produce displacements of the crack surfaces perpendicular to the plane of the crack. In this case, the crack line or the x-axis, as shown in Fig. 11.4b, is a principal axis. The subscript I on K_I indicates that the stress intensity factor is due to opening mode loading.

The shearing mode, illustrated in Fig. 11.15b, is due to in-plane shear loads, which cause the two crack surfaces to slide on one another. The displacement of the crack surfaces is in the plane of the crack and perpendicular to the leading edge of the crack. The subscript II on K_{II} implies that the stress intensity factor is due to shear mode loading. Of course, opening and shear mode loading conditions can occur together. In this case the loading is defined as mixed-mode where both K_I and K_{II} exist in the region near the crack tip.

The tearing mode, shown in Fig. 11.15c, is due to out-of-plane shear loading. The displacements of the crack surfaces are in the plane of the crack and parallel to the leading edge of the crack. The subscript III on K_{III} is used to depict the tearing mode. While the superposition of the three modes of loading gives the most general loading condition, one usually is interested in mode I or mixed-mode loading, since they occur more frequently in engineering applications. In this description, only the opening mode loading will be considered.

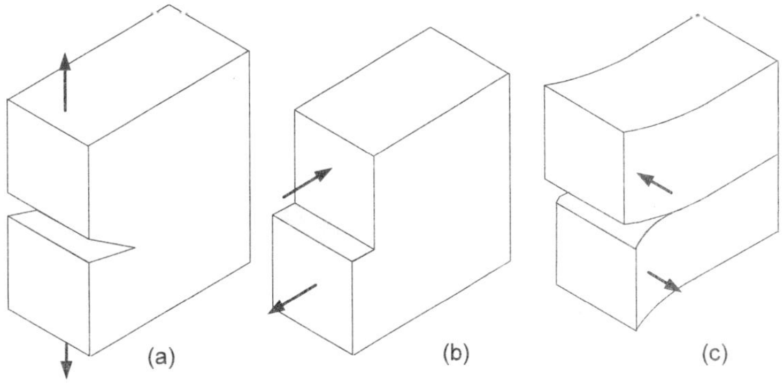

Fig. 11.15 Three modes of crack loading: (a) Opening mode; (b) Shearing mode; (c) Tearing mode.

11.7 CRACK TIP PLASTICITY

The elasticity solutions of structural members with cracks show that a stress singularity exists at the tip of the crack. This fact implies that the material, at the tip of the crack and in a small region near the tip, has exceeded the yield strength of the specimen material. In this region, plastic deformation occurs, and because the stresses are limited by yielding, a stress singularity cannot occur. This region of plastic deformation is called the crack-tip plastic zone.

The size of the plastic zone is important because most of the developments in fracture mechanics are valid only if the size of the plastic zone is small relative to the length of the uncracked ligament from the crack tip to the nearest boundary. To study the size of the plastic zone, consider first the magnitude of σ_{yy} given by Eq. (11.6) along the x-axis where $\theta = 0$. Setting $\sigma_{yy} = S_y$, where S_y is the yield strength of the material, gives:

$$\sigma_{yy} = \sqrt{\frac{a}{2r_p^*}}\sigma_0 = S_y \qquad (11.22)$$

where r_p^* is the apparent distance along the x-axis to the boundary of the plastic zone.

Solving Eq. (11.22) for r_p^* gives:

$$r_p^* = \frac{a}{2}\left(\frac{\sigma_0}{S_y}\right)^2 \qquad (11.23)$$

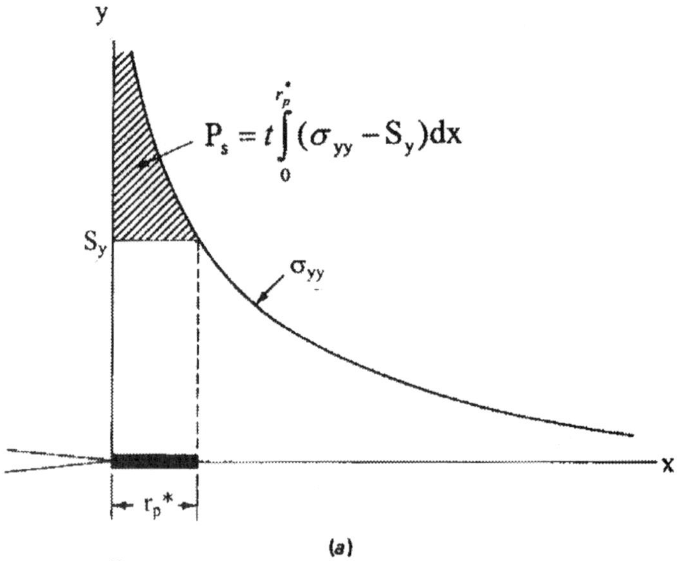

Fig. 11.16 (a) Stress distribution showing yielding in a region at the front of the crack tip.

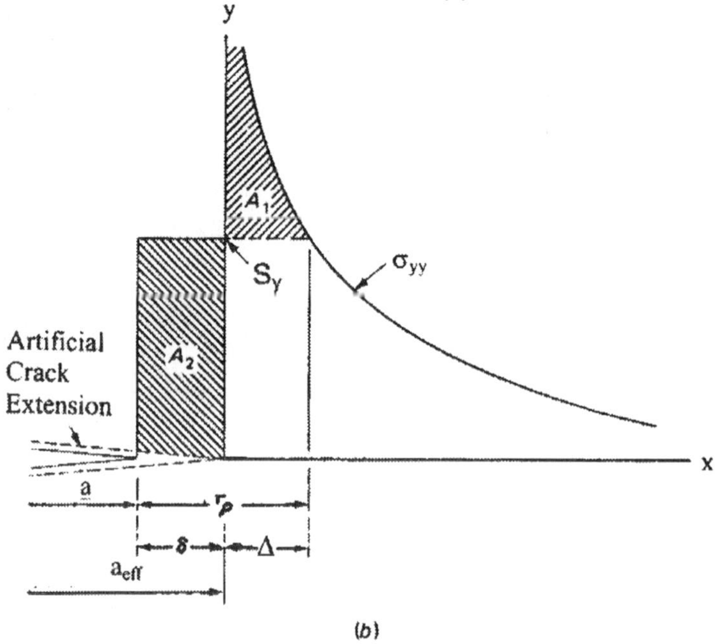

(b) An improved yield model incorporating artificial crack extension.

The apparent distance r_p^* is shown in Fig. 11.16a, where the distribution of σ_{yy} along the x-axis is presented. The shaded area shown in Fig. 11.16a indicates load-shedding P_s due to yielding. Thus,

$$P_s = t\int_0^{r_p^*}(\sigma_{yy} - S_y)dx \qquad (11.24)$$

The result of load loss due to local yielding is to increase the size of the plastic zone because the member must carry P_s. The effect of the plastic zone is to artificially extend the crack by a distance δ as shown in Fig. 11.16b. The coordinate system is translated by δ to the extended crack tip and the elastic stresses σ_{yy} are again limited by the yield strength S_y. Two areas, A_1 and A_2, are shown in Fig. 11.16b. Area A_1 is related to load shedding; however, area A_2 is related to load loss by the crack extension. To maintain equilibrium these two areas must be equal. Modifying Eq. (11.23) to account for changes due to the artificial extension Δ of the crack tip gives:

$$\Delta = \frac{a+\delta}{2}\left(\frac{\sigma_0}{S_y}\right)^2 \qquad (11.25)$$

Because $\delta \ll a$, it is evident by comparing Eqs. (11.23) and (11.25) that $\Delta \approx r_p^*$. The equilibrium requirement that $A_1 = A_2$ together with Eqs. (11.24) and (11.22) can be used to obtain:

$$\sigma_0\int_0^{r_p^*}\sqrt{\frac{a+\delta}{2x}}dx = S_y(r_p^* + \delta) \qquad (a)$$

Integrating and simplifying Eq. (a) yields:

$$(r_p^* + \delta)^2 = 2(a+\delta)(r_p^*)\left(\frac{\sigma_0}{S_y}\right)^2 \qquad (b)$$

Because δ is small when compared to the original crack length a, Eq. (b) and Eq. (11.23) can be combined to obtain:

$$r_p^* + \delta = 2r_p^* \quad \Rightarrow \quad r_p^* = \delta \qquad (c)$$

Then the true length r_p of the plastic zone in front of the crack is given by:

$$r_p = \delta + \Delta = 2r_p^* \qquad (11.26)$$

To account for the effect of the plastic zone, an effective crack length a_{eff} is introduced such that:

$$a_{eff} = a + r_p^* \qquad (11.27)$$

The value of a_{eff} is used to determine K_I and relations like Eq. (11.7) are modified to give:

$$K_I = \sigma_0 \sqrt{\pi \, (a + r_p^*)} \tag{11.28}$$

Note that $r_p^* \approx \Delta$ and Eq. (11.25) gives:

$$r_p^* = \frac{a}{2}\left(\frac{\sigma_0}{S_y}\right)^2 \tag{11.29}$$

Substituting Eq. (11.29) into Eq. (11.28) yields K_I corrected for the plastic deformation at the crack tip as:

$$K_I = \sigma_0 \sqrt{\pi \, a \left[1 + \frac{1}{2}\left(\frac{\sigma_0}{S_y}\right)^2\right]} \tag{11.30}$$

Similar corrections are made to Eqs. (11.10) thru (11.16) to determine K_I for ductile materials, where localized yielding in the region about the crack tip occurs.

The value of r_p is the measure of the size of the plastic zone along the x-axis. Apart from correcting the determination of K_I, r_p is important in establishing if the body is in a state of small scale yielding or large scale yielding. When r_p is small compared to the length of the uncracked ligament, the structural member is subjected to small scale yielding. In this state, it responds in nearly an elastic manner with strains and displacements, outside the small plastic enclave, varying linearly with respect to load. At some critical load, the crack becomes unstable and propagates at a very high velocity (500 to 1,000 m/s in steel). The failure is a cleavage type often with little or no evidence of ductility. This behavior is classified as **linear elastic fracture mechanics** (LEFM) and the stability of the crack may be predicted using the methods introduced in previous sections of this chapter.

In large scale yielding, r_p is large when compared to the length of the unbroken ligament. The structural member does not respond elastically due to the significant redistribution of stress caused by large scale yielding. With large plastic deformation, the crack tip becomes blunted. In some materials, the crack will become unstable and extend at relatively low velocities by tearing. This behavior is classified as elastic plastic fracture mechanics (EPFM). Failure by crack tearing is an advanced topic and is beyond the scope of this book.

In other cases of large scale yielding, the size of the plastic zone increases until it reaches a boundary. The specimen then fails by plastic instability. For failure by plastic instability, limit load analysis is the preferred approach for predicting the critical load. This approach is described in the next section of this chapter.

These three classifications of the effect of localized yielding on crack stability are illustrated in Fig. 11.17, where a graph is presented that shows stress intensity factor as a function of net section stress. When the local yielding is contained in a small region near the crack tip, the net section stress is significantly less than S_y, LEFM methods are applicable and crack instability occurs when $K_I = K_{Ic}$. When yielding becomes global, the entire net section yields, and failure is by plastic collapse when $\sigma_{yy} = S_y$. For yielding, which is significant but not global, failure occurs by plastic tearing with considerable ductility. In this case, the approach employed for analysis is EPFM. The regions inside the exterior bounding curve are considered safe, because the cracks will remain stable for these conditions.

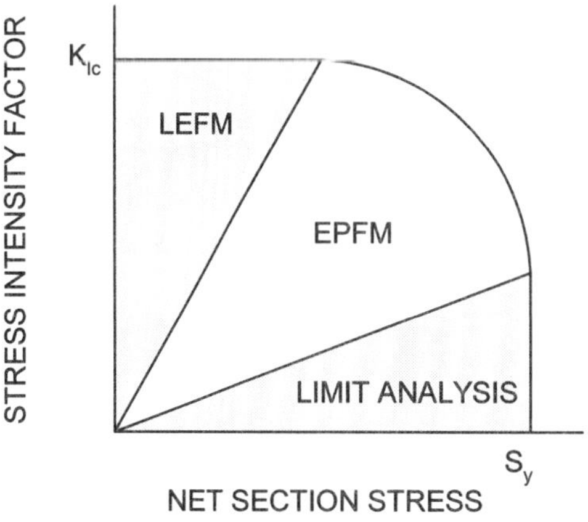

Fig. 11.17 A failure analysis diagram for ductile materials.

EXAMPLE 11.17

Let's reconsider Example 11.4 taking into account the effect of the plastic zone size on the determination of the stress intensity factor K_I. Recall that your supplier of large, wide plate aluminum castings (aluminum 2124-T851) indicates that cracks up to 50 mm long may be generated as the castings cool to room temperature. The castings are subjected to loads that produce a stress of $\sigma_o = 65$ MPa. You are asked to estimate a stress intensity factor for the worst case.

Solution:

In the worst case, the crack will be perpendicular to the applied stress and located some distance from the boundaries of the casting; hence, difficult for the inspectors to locate. We will assume that the result of Eqs. (11.28) and (11.30) will represent the worst-case scenario. Then the estimate of the stress intensity associated with the cooling crack is given by:

$$K_I = \sigma_0 \sqrt{\pi\,(a + r_p^*)} \tag{a}$$

$$K_I = \sigma_0 \sqrt{\pi\, a \left[1 + \frac{1}{2}\left(\frac{\sigma_0}{S_y}\right)^2\right]} \tag{b}$$

Reference to Table 11.1 gives S_y = 365 MPa for the aluminum alloy 2124-T851. Substituting the numerical parameters into Eq. (b) yields:

$$K_I = (65)\sqrt{\pi(25)\left[1 + \frac{1}{2}\left(\frac{65}{365}\right)^2\right]} = (65)\sqrt{\pi(25)\,[1.0159]} = 580.6 \text{ MPa}\sqrt{\text{mm}} \tag{c}$$

The term in the brackets under the square root symbol represents the correction for the effect of the small plastic zone in front of the crack tip. In this example, the correction is small because the bracketed term is only 1.0159 — a correction of the crack length of less than 2%. Reference to Table 11.1 indicates that K_{Ic} = 1077 MPa√mm for this aluminum alloy. Hence, the crack should remain stable, but the margin of safety is only 85%.

EXAMPLE 11.18

Let's reconsider Example 11.3 taking into account the effect of the plastic zone size on the determination of the stress intensity factor K_I. Recall that the quality control inspectors discovered a crack in the weld of a wide steel plate that is to be subjected to biaxial loading with a stress σ_o = 9,000 psi. They estimate that the crack is 6.0 in. long. You are asked to determine the stress intensity factor if the plate is fabricated from 4340 steel.

Solution:

We will employ Eq. (11.30) to estimate the stress intensity associated with the weld crack as:

$$K_I = \sigma_0 \sqrt{\pi \, a \left[1 + \frac{1}{2}\left(\frac{\sigma_0}{S_y}\right)^2\right]} \tag{a}$$

Reference to Table 11.1 gives S_y = 195 ksi for 4340 steel. Substituting the numerical parameters into Eq. (a) yields:

$$K_I = (9.0)\sqrt{\pi(3.0)\left[1 + \frac{1}{2}\left(\frac{9.0}{195}\right)^2\right]} = 27.64 \text{ ksi}\sqrt{\text{in.}} \tag{b}$$

In this case, the correction term in the brackets (1.0011) was negligible. The value of K_I determined in Examples 11.3 and 11.18 are essentially the same.

Reference to Table 11.1 indicates that K_{Ic} = 80 ksi$\sqrt{}$in. for this alloy steel. Hence, the crack should remain stable with a comfortable margin of safety.

11.8 LIMIT ANALYSIS OF PLATES WITH CRACKS

For materials that exhibit sufficient ductility, the plastic zone size that develops in the front of the crack becomes large. Consequently, the crack tip is blunted and the stress singularity is inhibited in its development. In such cases, linear elastic fracture mechanics (LEFM) is not a valid approach. As the load applied to a cracked plate is increased, the plastic zone size increases and if the crack does not initiate by tearing, this plastic zone will extend across the entire net section. We will discuss two approaches to describing the plastic behavior of cracked plates — the Dugdale model [8] and the limit analysis method.

11.8.1 The Dugdale Model

The Dugdale model provides a method for determining the extent of the plastic zone as it grows with increasing load across the uncracked ligament. The method is applied to relatively thin plates, where plane stress conditions exist, and to materials that yield without significant strain hardening. Dugdale considered the plastic zone to take the form of thin triangular strips as shown in Fig. 11.18.

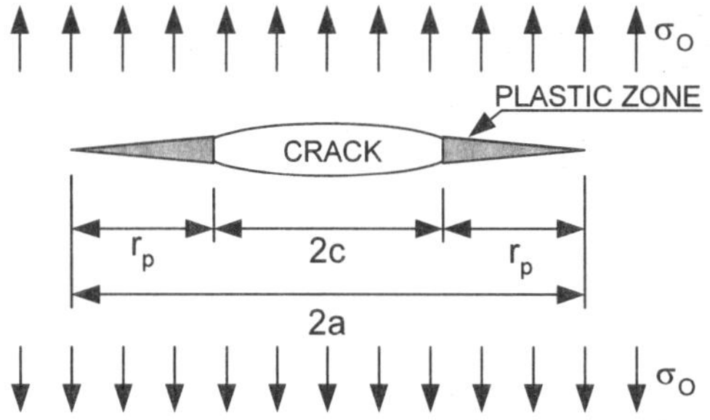

Fig. 11.18 The Dugdale model exhibits plastic zones as thin triangular strips ahead of the crack tips.

Dugdale proved that the length of the plastic strips is given by:

$$\frac{r_p}{c} = \sec\left(\frac{\pi}{2}\frac{\sigma_0}{S_y}\right) - 1 \qquad (11.31)$$

We will evaluate the ratio r_p/c as a function of σ_o/S_y in the next example to illustrate the extension of the plastic zone across a ligament with increasing load σ_o.

EXAMPLE 11.19

Prepare a table showing the extension of the Dugdale plastic strip as a function of the ratio of σ_o/S_y.

Solution:

Use a spreadsheet to evaluate Eq. (11.31) as shown below:

Ratio, σ_0/S_y	r_p/c		Ratio, σ_0/S_y	r_p/c		Ratio, σ_0/S_y	r_p/c
0.00	0.0000		0.35	0.1728		0.70	1.2027
0.05	0.0031		0.40	0.2361		0.75	1.6131
0.10	0.0125		0.45	0.3151		0.80	2.2361
0.15	0.0284		0.50	0.4142		0.85	3.2837
0.20	0.0515		0.55	0.5398		0.90	5.3925
0.25	0.0824		0.60	0.7013		0.95	11.7455
0.30	0.1223		0.65	0.9139		0.99	62.6646

Examination of this table shows that extension of the plastic strip is highly non-linear with increasing load σ_o. For small ratios of σ_o/S_y, the extension of the plastic strip is a small fraction of the crack length. However, when the ratio σ_o/S_y becomes large, the extension of the plastic strip is much more significant with each increment of load.

11.8.2 Limit Load Analysis

Let's consider a center cracked tension panel of width w that is fabricated from a ductile material subjected to an axial stress σ_o. Because of plastic flow, the crack tips have been blunted. Moreover, we will assume that the cracks do not extend by tearing. The maximum applied stress prior to rupture by excessive plastic flow can be determined with limit analysis. In a limit analysis, we assume that the material is perfectly plastic with a yield strength of S_y. The analysis treats the uncracked ligaments of the tension panel as uniformly stressed, as indicated in Fig. 11.19.

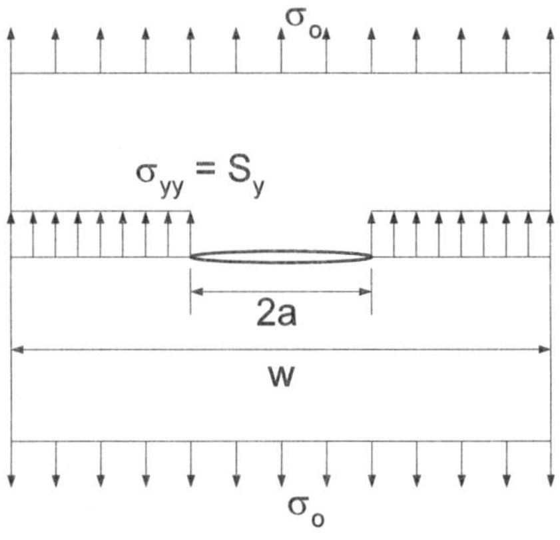

Fig. 11.19 The ligament of the cracked plate is stressed to the yield limit with $\sigma_{yy} = S_y$.

To begin cut the tension panel at the crack line, and write the equilibrium equation for forces in the y direction to obtain:

$$(w - 2a)(t)S_y = (wt)\sigma_o \tag{a}$$

Solving Eq. (a) for the limit stress $(\sigma_o)_{Limit}$ gives:

$$(\sigma_o)_{Limit} = [1 - (2a/w)]S_y \tag{11.32}$$

EXAMPLE 11.20

Determine the limit stress that can be achieved prior to plastic rupture of a cracked tension plate. Use a spreadsheet to calculate $(\sigma_o)_{Limit}/S_y$ as a function of (2a/w) as this ratio varies from 0 to 0.99.

Solution:

Evaluating Eq. (11.32) in a spreadsheet gives the results presented in the table below:

(2a/w)	$(\sigma_o)_{Limit}/S_y$		(2a/w)	$(\sigma_o)_{Limit}/S_y$		(2a/w)	$(\sigma_o)_{Limit}/S_y$
0.00	1.00		0.35	0.65		0.70	0.30
0.05	0.95		0.40	0.60		0.75	0.25
0.10	0.90		0.45	0.55		0.80	0.20
0.15	0.85		0.50	0.50		0.85	0.15
0.20	0.80		0.55	0.45		0.90	0.10
0.25	0.75		0.60	0.40		0.95	0.05
0.30	0.70		0.65	0.35		0.99	0.01

These results show the linear decrease in the limit stress for a cracked tension panel fabricated from a perfectly plastic material.

11.9 FACTORS THAT AFFECT FRACTURE TOUGHNESS

In the preceding sections, we have treated fracture toughness as a material property without addressing many of the factors that affect it. These factors include plate thickness, alloy heat treatment (strength), temperature and rate of loading (strain rate). The influence of the first three of these factors on fracture toughness will be described in subsequent subsections. The effect of strain rate is to decrease the fracture toughness because high stress levels can be achieved at the tip of a crack before yielding by slip mechanisms can occur.

11.9.1 Plate Thickness

We showed in Fig. 11.7 that the fracture toughness K_c decreased with increasing plate thickness. For sufficiently thick plates, the value of K_c reached a minimum called the plane strain fracture toughness K_{Ic}. The reason for the marked difference in fracture toughness with plate thickness is due to the amount of deformation in the local neighborhood about the crack tip. For thin plates fabricated from ductile material, plastic slip occurs at the crack front and the material shears on 45° planes as shown in Fig. 11.20. The formation of these slip planes enables local necking to occur along the crack line with extensive plastic deformation. This plastic deformation increases the energy required to initiate the crack and markedly increases the fracture toughness.

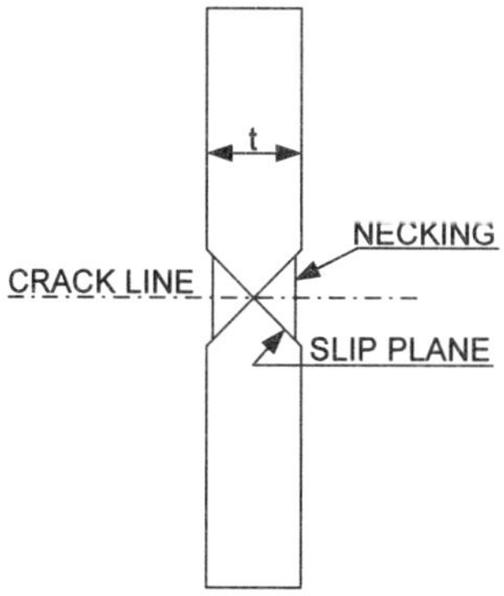

Fig. 11.20 Plastic slip on 45° planes through the plate thickness enables local necking at the crack line.

As the plate thickness increases, plane stress conditions no longer exist and an out-of-plane tensile stress σ_{zz} begins to develop at an interior region of the body near the crack tip. The presence of σ_{zz} constrains yielding at the interior region, and slip cannot occur in the presence of sufficiently large out-of-plane tension stress. As the plate thickness increases, the size of the interior region where yielding is constrained grows and the amount of plastic deformation is suppressed. We show the effect of the constraint, due to the plate thickness, on the appearance of the fracture surface in Fig. 11.21.

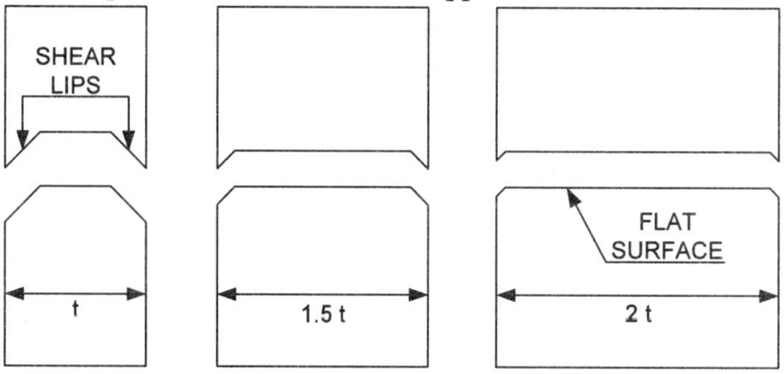

Fig. 11.21 Appearance of the fracture surface of a typical steel with increasing plate thickness.

The effect of the thickness-induced constraint is to suppress the slip planes in the center region of the specimen. As a consequence, the shear lips become smaller and the plastic zone size is suppressed. Flat surface failures exhibit significant amounts of cleavage. The energy consumed in this fracture process is reduced and the fracture toughness diminishes. For sufficiently thick plates, the fracture toughness reaches a minimum that is referred to as the plane strain fracture toughness K_{Ic}.

11.9.2 Strength

Designers dealing with structural failures will sometimes redesign the structure by changing only the material selection. Will increasing the yield strength fix the problem? **Perhaps not.** Selecting a higher strength alloy or a heat treatment that will increase strength will often eliminate structural failures if the problem was due to stresses that exceeded the yield strength of the material specified in the original design. However, if failure was due to the initiation of inherent flaws in the structure, increasing the strength of the material will exacerbate the problem.

A typical curve showing fracture toughness as a function of tensile strength of high quality alloy steel is presented in Fig. 11.22. It is clear that the plane strain fracture toughness decreases markedly as the tensile strength increases.

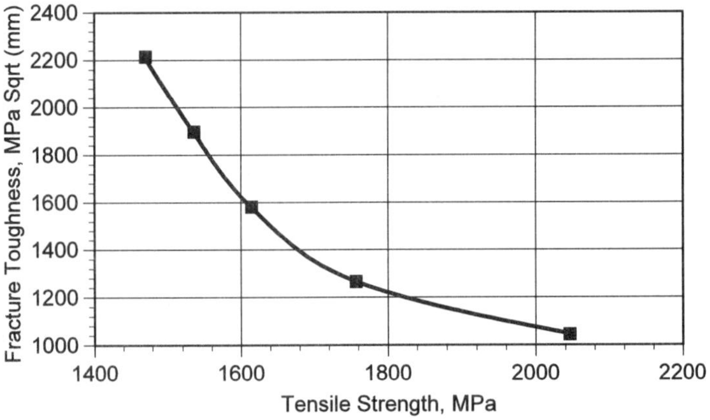

Fig. 11.22 Plane strain fracture toughness with tensile strength for a high quality alloy steel.

11.9.3 Temperature

At low temperatures, ductile steel often behaves in a brittle manner with fractures that exhibit reduced plastic deformation. We conduct Charpy impact tests to determine the temperature for the transition from ductile to brittle behavior. Charpy tests involve striking a small, notched three-point beam specimen with a pendulum-hammer swung from a height sufficient to cause the specimen to fracture. The energy absorbed by the beam in the failure process is measured. At higher temperatures, the failed beams exhibit plastic deformation and the energy required to fracture them is high. However, at lower temperatures the plastic deformation is reduced significantly and the energy required for fracture is greatly diminished. A typical graph presenting Charpy energy with temperature is shown in Fig. 11.23.

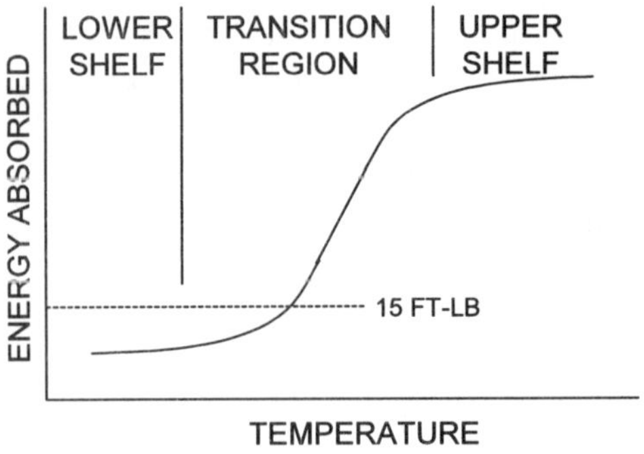

Fig. 11.23 Charpy test results showing energy absorbed at different temperatures for typical steel.

Examination of Fig. 11.23 shows that at higher temperatures the energy absorbed is relatively high, with upper shelf absorbed energy levels in the neighborhood of 100 ft-lb. At lower temperatures, the absorbed energy is much lower and often is as low as 5 to 10 ft-lb. The temperatures between the upper and lower energy shelves are termed transition temperatures, where the fracture process is mixed. At low temperatures, the fracture process is dominated by cleavage with little plastic flow. At high temperatures, the fracture process is dominated by slip with large plastic deformations. In the transition regions, these two failure mechanisms compete, and the fracture surfaces show evidence of both processes. In specifying a steel for structural applications, it is essential that the service temperature, to which the structure is exposed, be above the lower shelf temperature. In fact, 15 ft-lb is often the specified energy level because it is usually located above the lower energy shelf.

A second means for ascertaining the effect of temperature on toughness is to measure K_c or K_{Ic} as a function of temperature. The graph showing fracture toughness as a function of temperature is similar to the results from a Charpy test as indicated in Fig. 11.24.

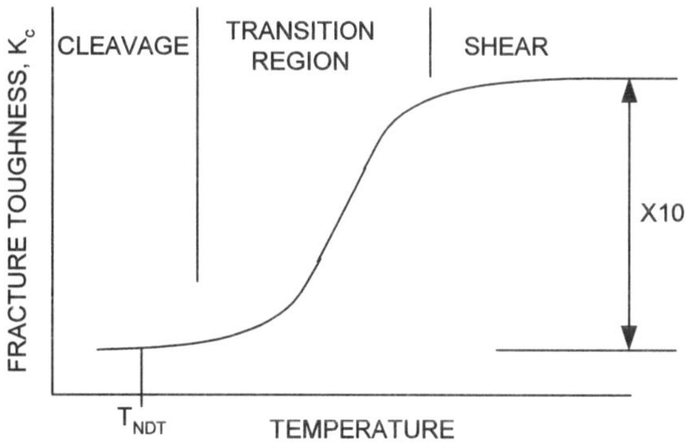

Fig. 11.24 Variations in fracture toughness over a wide range of temperature.

The region with relatively high levels of fracture toughness in Fig. 11.24 is dominated by failure with significant evidence of plastic deformation induced by local shear. The region with relatively low levels of fracture toughness is dominated by cleavage type fracture with little evidence of plastic deformation. In the transition region, these two failure mechanisms compete and the failure region is considered as mixed. The temperature where the fracture toughness reaches a minimum is called the nil-ductility-temperature and is given the symbol T_{NDT}. Allowable service temperatures are often based on the T_{NDT}. For example, a service temperature of T_{NDT} + 30° F is allowable if the design stress is less than (S_y/2), and T_{NDT} + 60° F if the design stress is less than S_y.

Unfortunately tests to measure fracture toughness are expensive to conduct. To avoid these significant costs, we often convert Charpy data to provide an approximation of the plane strain fracture toughness. One of the approximations for the plane strain fracture toughness of bridge steel in the temperature transition region is given by:

$$K_{Ic} = \sqrt{655E\boldsymbol{\mathcal{E}}_{CVN}} \qquad (11.33)$$

where K_{Ic} is the plane strain fracture toughness, with units of Pa√m.

E is the modulus of elasticity, in units of Pa.

$\boldsymbol{\mathcal{E}}_{CVN}$ is the absorbed energy in a Charpy test, in units of joules J.

EXAMPLE 11.21

Determine an approximate value for the fracture toughness of bridge steel if the Charpy V-notch test results for the absorbed energy were 40 J. The test temperature and the service temperature are both in the transition range.

Solution:

Let's substitute the numerical parameters into Eq. (11.33) to obtain:

$$K_{Ic} = \sqrt{(655)E\boldsymbol{\mathcal{E}}_{CVN}} = \sqrt{(655)(207\times 10^9)(40)} = 73.64 \text{ MPa}\sqrt{m} \qquad (a)$$

$$K_{Ic} = \left(73.64 \text{ MPa}\sqrt{m}\right)\sqrt{1{,}000 \text{ mm/m}} = 2{,}329 \text{ MPa}\sqrt{mm} \qquad (b)$$

11.10 CRACK GROWTH UNDER CYCLIC LOADING

Material failure by cyclic loading was introduced in Chapter 9, and the use of the S-N diagram to predict failure or safety of structural components was described. The S-N diagram is employed when the structural component is subjected to large numbers of cycles (many thousand if not millions). It is also employed for components that are initially flaw free. For high cycle fatigue, a significant fraction of the cycles to failure are expended in generating a fatigue crack large enough to find under close inspection. However, in some structural applications, flaws are inherent and fatigue life is measured in hundreds of cycles[1]. In these cases, it is important to locate and track the size of the cracks in structures.

Initially, the cracks inherent in structures are small and stable. However, the cracks grow under cyclic loading and become longer. Eventually one of the cracks will grow to critical size, initiate under load and propagate at high velocity. In most instances, this crack will propagate across the structure and result in catastrophic failure. Clearly, we seek to avoid these failures by exercising fracture control procedures. Part of the process of fracture control is to predict the growth rates for each of the cracks in the structure.

Cracks grow a small amount each time they undergo a stress cycle. A typical graph showing the growth of a crack as a function of the number of stress cycles is presented in Fig. 11.25. Inspection of Fig. 11.25 indicates two important aspects of crack growth. First, that the rate of crack growth (da/dN), given by the slope of each curve, increases as the cracks grow longer. Second, that cracks exposed to higher stress levels grow faster than cracks exposed to lower level stresses. Attempts have been made to develop empirical relations for (da/dN) as a function of the applied stress and crack length; however, too many variables affected the growth rate, and these empirical relations have found limited application.

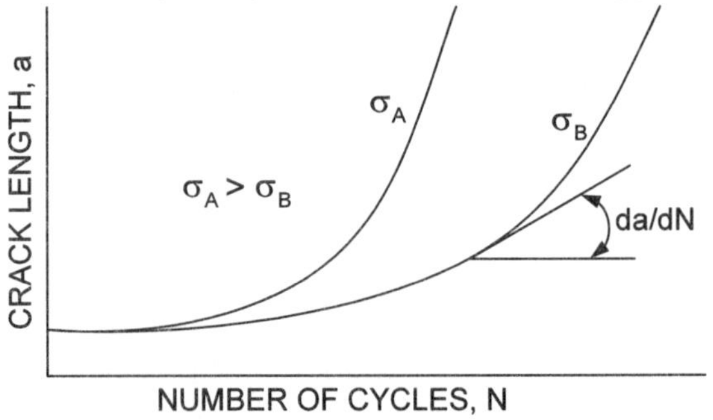

Fig. 11.25 Cyclic crack growth at two different stress levels.

More recently, Paris [9] related crack growth rate to the range in the stress intensity factor that occurs under the action of cyclic loading as:

$$(da/dN) = C(\Delta K)^n \qquad (11.34)$$

where (da/dN) is the crack growth rate, C and n are material properties and ΔK is the range in the stress intensity factor ($K_{Max} - K_{Min}$).

Many experiments have been conducted to prove the validity of Eq. (11.34). Typical results of these crack growth experiments reveal three different phases of the crack growth process as indicated in Fig. 11.26.

---

[1] An example is the pressure vessel that houses a nuclear reactor. One cycle of loading is produced by the thermal stress generated each time a unit is shut down and restarted. Over a thirty-year design life with three or four cycles per year, we are concerned with about 100 to 200 cycles of thermal stress.

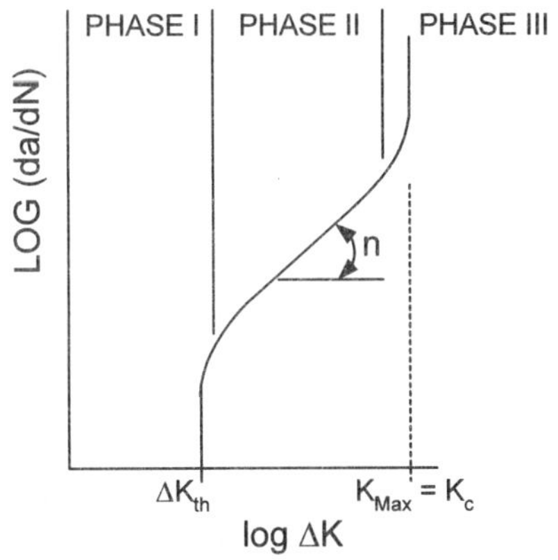

Fig. 11.26 Log-log graph of growth rate with range in stress intensity factor.

The results in Fig. 11.26 indicate that there is a threshold value of ΔK. This fact implies that cracks will remain stable for essentially an infinite number of cycles if $\Delta K < \Delta K_{th}$. During phase II, the cracks grow at a rate predicted by Eq. (11.34). The slope of the log-log curve over this linear region relation gives the exponent n in this relation. Phase III defines rapid crack growth behavior when K_{Max} approaches the fracture toughness K_c.

In a fracture control procedure, it is necessary to predict the number of cycles to failure. It is possible to make this prediction by substituting Eq. (11.11) into Eq. (11.34) to obtain:

$$\frac{da}{dN} = C(\Delta K)^n = C\left(\alpha(\Delta\sigma_0)\sqrt{\pi\, a}\right)^n \tag{11.35}$$

where the stress range $\Delta\sigma_o = (\sigma_{Max} - \sigma_{Min})$. Integrating Eq. (11.35) yields:

$$\int_{a_i}^{a_c} a^{\frac{-n}{2}}\, da = C\left(\alpha(\Delta\sigma_0)\sqrt{\pi}\right)^n \int_0^{N_f} dN \tag{a}$$

Completing the integration and solving for the number of cycles to failure N_f gives:

$$N_f = \left(\frac{2}{2-n}\right)\left(a_c^{\left(1-\frac{n}{2}\right)} - a_i^{\left(1-\frac{n}{2}\right)}\right)\left(\frac{1}{C\left(\alpha(\Delta\sigma_0)\sqrt{\pi}\right)^n}\right) \quad \text{not valid for } n = 2 \tag{11.36}$$

where a_c is the critical crack length, and a_i is the initial crack length.

The constants C and n are determined by conducting crack growth experiments under cyclic loading. Sanford [5] provides an extensive listing of these constants for a number of different materials. For more advanced work, it is recommended that a computer program for predicting life developed by NASA [10] be employed. This program known as NASGRO contains three modules that include:

1. Numerical stress analysis to determine geometric stress intensity factors.
2. A database for material properties.
3. Analysis of critical crack size and determination of safe life.

In the following examples, we will demonstrate the techniques for predicting the remaining life in a structure that is subjected to cyclic loading where crack growth by fatigue processes occurs.

EXAMPLE 11.22

A wide and thick steel plate contains an edge crack 0.25 in. long. The plate is subjected to alternating stresses between 0 and 22 ksi. Experiments conducted with a similar steel provided data for the material constants in Eq. (11.35) as $C = 5 \times 10^{-10}$ and $n = 4$ when ΔK is expressed in units of ksi√in. The plane strain fracture toughness for this steel is $K_{Ic} = 52$ ksi√in. Determine the number of cycles for this crack to grow to a critical size that produces failure.

Solution:

Let's first determine the length of the crack that will initiate under the maximum stress (critical crack length). Using Eqs. (11.11) and (11.13) with (a/w) ⇒ 0 for the edge cracked plate, we write:

$$K_I = K_{Ic} = (1.12)\sigma_{Max}\sqrt{\pi\, a_c} \tag{a}$$

Solve Eq. (a) for the critical crack length a_c as:

$$a_c = \frac{1}{\pi}\left(\frac{K_{Ic}}{(1.12)\sigma_{Max}}\right)^2 = \frac{1}{\pi}\left(\frac{52}{(1.12)(22)}\right)^2 = 1.418 \text{ in.} \tag{b}$$

Substituting numerical values into Eq. (11.36) gives:

$$N_f = \left(\frac{2}{2-4}\right)\left(a_c^{(1-2)} - a_i^{(1-2)}\right)\left(\frac{1}{\left(5\times 10^{-10}\right)\left((1.12)(22-0)\sqrt{\pi}\right)^4}\right) \tag{c}$$

$$N_f = -\left(\frac{1}{1.418} - \frac{1}{0.25}\right)(549.8) = 1{,}811 \text{ cycles} \tag{d}$$

EXAMPLE 11.23

A finite width plate (w = 300 mm) contains a central crack with 2a = 18 mm. The plate is subjected to alternating stresses between 100 and 200 MPa. Experiments conducted with a similar material provided data for the material constants in Eq. (11.35) as $C = 3 \times 10^{-10}$ and $n = 3$ when ΔK is expressed in units of MPa√mm. The plane strain fracture toughness for this steel is $K_{Ic} = 1{,}800$ MPa√mm. Determine the number of cycles for this crack to grow to a critical size, which produces failure.

Solution:

Let's first determine the length of the crack that will initiate under the maximum stress (critical crack length). Using Eq. (11.11) for the center cracked plate, we write:

$$K_I = K_{Ic} = \alpha\,\sigma_{Max}\sqrt{\pi\, a_c} \qquad \text{(a)}$$

Substituting numerical parameters into the multiplier term α given by Eq. (11.12) yields:

$$\alpha = \sqrt{\sec\frac{\pi\, a}{w}} = \sqrt{\sec\frac{\pi(9)}{300}} = 1.0022 \qquad \text{(b)}$$

Solve Eq. (a) for the critical crack length a_c as:

$$a_c = \frac{1}{\pi}\left(\frac{K_{Ic}}{\alpha\sigma_{Max}}\right)^2 = \frac{1}{\pi}\left(\frac{1{,}800}{(1.0022)(200)}\right)^2 = 25.67\text{ mm} \qquad \text{(c)}$$

where σ_{Max} = 200 MPa is used in Eq. (c).

Substituting numerical values into Eq. (11.36) gives:

$$N_f = \left(\frac{2}{2-3}\right)\left(a_c^{(1-1.5)} - a_i^{(1-1.5)}\right)\left(\frac{1}{\left(3\times 10^{-10}\right)\left((1.0022)(200-100)\sqrt{\pi}\right)^3}\right) \qquad \text{(d)}$$

$$N_f = -2\left(\frac{1}{\sqrt{25.67}} - \frac{1}{\sqrt{9.0}}\right)(594.7) = 161.7\text{ cycles} \qquad \text{(e)}$$

11.11 FRACTURE CONTROL

Large complex structures usually have inherent flaws of one type or another. These flaws are often introduced in fabrication during the welding process where incomplete welds, embedded slag, holes, inadequate fusion bonding and shrinkage cracks are common. Flaws are sometimes introduced during service. Mechanisms that produce flaws include fatigue, stress-corrosion cracking and impact damage. Regardless of the source of the flaws, they are common and the history of technology contains many examples of dramatic and catastrophic failures, which caused significant losses in life and property. Indeed as recently as 1972, a 584-ft-long tank barge [11] broke almost completely in half while in port with calm seas. The vessel was only one year old indicating that relatively modern methods of design, material procurement and welding procedures do not always insure safe structures.

Because flaws in structures and components are common, it is essential in the design, fabrication and maintenance of a structure to establish a fracture-control procedure. If properly implemented, the fracture-control plan can insure the safety of the structure during its entire service life. Fracture control involves the recognition that flaws exist and that these flaws must be maintained in a stable state. To describe the technical aspects of fracture control, consider a simple structure, namely a large plate, with the stress-intensity factor given by:

$$K_I = \alpha \sigma_0 \sqrt{\pi \text{ a}} \tag{11.7}$$

The crack in this structure will remain stable if:

$$K_I < K_{Ic} \tag{11.2}$$

Combining these two equations gives the stability relation for this simple structure as:

$$\alpha \sigma_0 \sqrt{\pi \text{ a}} < K_{Ic} \tag{11.37}$$

This stability relation illustrates the three elements in all fracture-control procedures; namely,

1. Flaw size, a
2. Load or stress imposed, σ_o
3. Material fracture toughness, K_{Ic}

Clearly, to insure the integrity of a structure requires that the variables in the stability relation be maintained so that equality in Eq. (11.37) never occurs during the life of a structure.

A typical fracture-control plan usually considers material resistance (i.e. the crack-initiation toughness K_c or K_{Ic}) as the first step in maintaining cracks in a stable state. The material selection sets the upper limit for K_I and it is controlled by the designer in the specification of the material for the structure. Typical values of K_{Ic} for common engineering materials are presented in Table 11.1. To ensure that the material meets the specification, the supplier provides a certification indicating that tests have been conducted using representative samples and that the test results exceed the minimum required strength and toughness.

With welded structures, selection and certification of the base plate is only the first step in insuring the specified toughness. Weld materials and weld processes must be selected and then certified. The weld material is often under matched (lower yield strength) relative to the base plate with a higher toughness. The difficulty is in certifying the weld process, because this certification requires extensive testing of specimens containing the weld and the heat-affected zone. Testing is expensive but necessary, because experience shows that welds often degrade the toughness of the base plate in the heat-affected zone.

In some applications, K_c or K_{Ic} decreases with service life. For instance, in nuclear reactor pressure vessels, radiation damage due to high neutron flux occurs and the toughness degrades with extended service. Also, some alloys that age-harden will exhibit losses in K_c or K_{Ic} during service life, which is often measured in decades.

The second step in a fracture-control plan involves inspection to determine the flaw size a. It is evident from the examples illustrated in the previous section that the critical crack length a_c is given by:

$$a_c = \frac{1}{\pi}\left(\frac{K_{Ic}}{\alpha \sigma_0}\right)^2 \tag{11.38}$$

Inspection with x-rays, eddy current sensors, and ultrasonic waves are employed to locate cracks. Large cracks, which approach or exceed a_c, are repaired. However, small cracks with a length a_d below the minimum detectable length or with a length a_r below the repairable limit remain in the structure. These three crack lengths are depicted in Fig. 11.27 as a function of the time the structural element is in service. These cracks may grow during service due to fatigue loading or stress-corrosion cracking, and they degrade the strength of the structure as shown in Fig. 11.28. The growth period represents the time interval during which one or more cracks extend from a_r to a_c. This period is usually long and provides the opportunity for periodic inspections during the service life. It is important in the fracture-control plan to specify inspection intervals, which are sufficiently short relative to the growth period, to provide two or more opportunities to detect the cracks before they achieve critical length. When longer cracks are detected, they are repaired (in the field) and the growth period is extended.

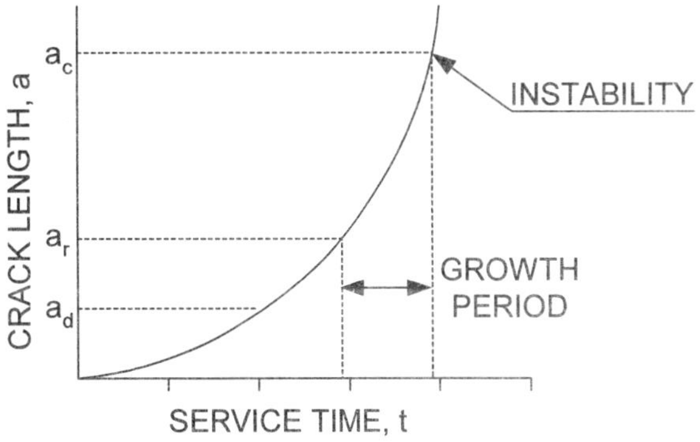

Fig. 11.27 Graph of crack growth with time-in-service showing three stages of crack development.

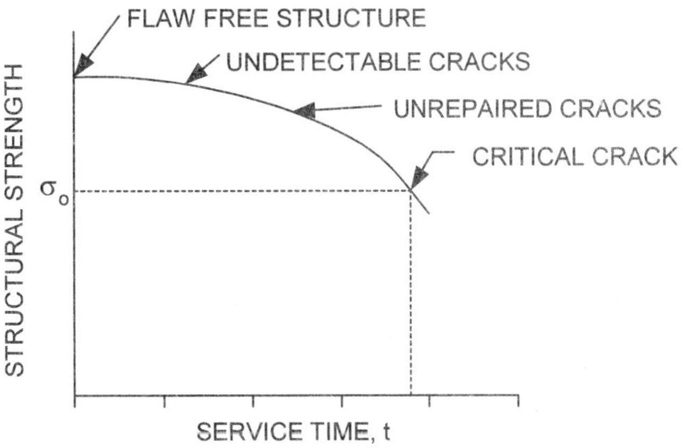

Fig. 11.28 Graph of degradation of structural strength with time-in-service as the crack grows.

The third step in the fracture-control plan involves the applied loads, which establishes the stress σ_o. From Fig. 11.28, it is evident that the structural strength will exceed σ_o provided $a < a_c$. In many types of structures, periodic inspections and field repair insure that crack growth is controlled and that the cracks do not approach critical length. In these structures, structural stability is achieved simply by maintaining the loads so that $\sigma < \sigma_o$. However, in some structures, accessibility is limited and complete inspection is difficult if not impossible. In these instances, a proof-testing procedure can be applied to the structure to insure safety. In proof testing, loads are applied to the structure, which are larger than the normal loading that produces σ_o. These proof loads produce an elevated stress σ_p and if the structure does not fail, the cracks in the structure are less than the critical length as shown in Fig. 11.29. The single cycle of proof load provides confidence that the cracks in the structure are short and stable. Indeed, depending upon the ratio σ_p/σ_o a growth period can be predicted where the safety of the structure can be ensured. It is important to divide the growth period into two or more parts to determine the proof-test interval. One repeats proof testing at these intervals to continue to extend the growth period. In this sense, repeated proof testing is similar to repeated inspections. However, with an inspection procedure, the cracks that grow with time in service can be located and repaired; but with a proof test procedure, the cracks cannot be located or repaired. They continue to grow and when $a_p \geq a_c$, the structure will fail during the proof test.

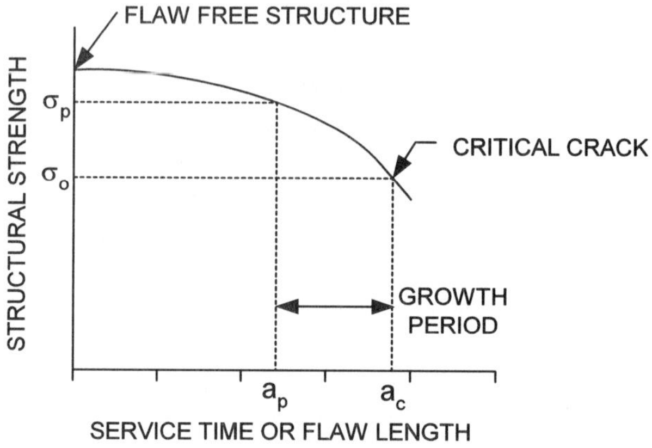

Fig. 11.29 An illustration of proof testing at σ_p to ensure that $a_p < a_c$.

11.12 SUMMARY

The concept of singular stresses and the stress intensity factor K_I was introduced as a means for analyzing structures containing cracks. The stress intensity factor is compared to some fracture toughness K_c or K_{Ic} to determine if the crack is stable or unstable. To introduce the concept of singular stresses at a crack tip, an equation for the stress concentration K at an elliptical hole in a tension panel was given. As the minor axis b approaches zero, the stress concentration K approaches infinity. Clearly, a stress singularity exists at the crack tip.

$$K = \left(1 + \frac{2a}{b}\right) \tag{11.4b}$$

The stress σ_{yy} at the crack tip was determined by Westergaard as:

$$\sigma_{yy} = \sqrt{\frac{a}{2r}}\ \sigma_0 \tag{11.6}$$

Using the definition of the stress intensity factor, we showed that K_I for a central crack of length 2a in a very wide plate is given by:

$$K_I = \sigma_0 \sqrt{\pi\, a} \tag{11.7}$$

The crack initiation criterion was introduced as:

$$K_I \geq K_c \tag{11.8}$$

Fracture toughness K_c is a material property; however, many factors affect its value. Plate thickness is one of these factors. When the plate becomes sufficiently thick, the toughness decreases to a minimum value known as the plane strain fracture toughness K_{Ic}.

We then presented relations giving the stress intensity factor K_I for a number of different two-dimensional geometries. These relations were similar to Eq. (11.7) except for the multiplying term α in the expression to account for the effects of the finite boundaries of these geometries.

$$K_I = \alpha\, K_{I\infty} = \alpha\, \sigma_0 \sqrt{\pi a} \qquad (11.11)$$

A few solutions for the stress intensity factor associated with cracks in three-dimensional structural members containing cracks were given in Eqs. (11.19) to (11.21).

Three modes of loading a structural member containing a crack were introduced. These included the opening, shear and tearing modes. The treatment in this book is limited to the opening mode.

The effect of plastic flow at the crack tip when σ_{yy} exceeds the yield strength S_y was described. The result of load loss due to local yielding is to increase the size of the plastic zone, which in turn artificially extends the crack by a distance δ. To account for the effect of the plastic zone, an effective crack length a_{eff} is introduced such that:

$$a_{eff} = a + r_p^* \qquad (11.27)$$

The value of a_{eff} is used to determine a corrected estimate for K_I as:

$$K_I = \sigma_0 \sqrt{\pi\,(a + r_p^*)} \qquad (11.28)$$

$$r_p^* = \frac{a}{2}\left(\frac{\sigma_0}{S_y}\right)^2 \qquad (11.29)$$

Three different treatments of yielding on crack stability were described. When the local yielding is small, LEFM methods are applicable and crack instability occurs when $K_I \geq K_{Ic}$. When yielding becomes global, the entire net section yields, and failure is by plastic collapse when $\sigma_{yy} \geq S_y$. For yielding that is significant but not global, failure occurs by plastic tearing with considerable ductility. Two approaches describing the plastic behavior of cracked plates, the Dugdale model and the limit analysis method, were described.

Many factors that affect fracture toughness: plate thickness, strength and temperature were discussed. The concept of crack growth under cyclic loading was introduced. The Paris law that estimates the cyclic rate of crack growth was given as:

$$(da/dN) = C(\Delta K)^n \qquad (11.34)$$

An expression predicting the life of a cracked structure was derived from this law as:

$$N_f = \left(\frac{2}{2-n}\right)\left(a_c^{\left(1-\frac{n}{2}\right)} - a_i^{\left(1-\frac{n}{2}\right)}\right)\left(\frac{1}{C\left(\alpha(\Delta\sigma_0)\sqrt{\pi}\right)^n}\right) \quad \text{not valid for } n = 2 \qquad (11.36)$$

Finally, a method for insuring the safety of cracked structures over an extended service life was discussed. A typical fracture-control plan usually considers the crack-initiation toughness K_c or K_{Ic} as the first step in maintaining cracks in a stable state. The material selection sets the upper limit for K_I and it is controlled by the designer in the specification of the material for the structure. The second step in a fracture-control plan involves inspection to determine the flaw size a. Inspection with x-rays, eddy current sensors, and ultrasonic waves are employed to locate cracks. Large cracks, which approach or exceed the critical crack length a_c, are repaired and opportunity for frequent periodic inspections during the service life is provided. When cracks cannot be detected, proof testing is performed to insure that the cracks will remain stable under design loads.

REFERENCES

1. Irwin, G. R.: Fracture I, Handbuch der Physik VI, Flügge Ed., pp. 558-590, Springer, 1958.
2. Inglis, C. E.: “Stresses in a Plate Due to the Presence of Cracks and Sharp Corners,” Trans. Inst. Naval Architects, 55, pp. 219-241, 1913.
3. Griffith, A. A.: "The Phenomena of Rupture and Flow in Solids,” Phil. Trans. Roy. Soc. of London, A 221, pp 163-197, 1921.
4. Westergaard, H. M.: "Bearing Pressures and Cracks", J. Applied Mechanics, 61, pp A49-A53, 1939.
5. Sanford, R. J. Principles of Fracture Mechanics, Prentice Hall, Upper Saddle River, NJ, 2003.
6. Tada, H., Paris, P. and G. R. Irwin: The Stress Analysis of Cracks Handbook, Del Research, Hellertown, PA, 1973.
7. Bowie, O. L., “Analysis of an Infinite Plate Containing Radial Cracks Originating at the Boundary of an Internal Circular Hole,” J. Mathematics and Physics, Vol. 35, pp. 60-71, 1956.
8. Dugdale, D. S., “Yielding of Steel Sheets Containing Slits,” J. Mechanics and Physics of Solids, Vol. 8, pp. 100-104, 1960.
9. Paris, P., and Erdogan, F., “A Critical Analysis of Crack Propagation Laws,” J. Basic Engineering, Vol. 85, pp. 528-534, 1963.
10. NASA/NASGRO Computer Program, http:/mmptdpublic.jsc.nasa.gov/nasgro/NasgroMain.html.
11. Marine Casualty Report, "Structural Failure of the Tank Barge I.O.S. 3301 Involving the Motor Vessel Martha R. Ingram on 10 January 1972 Without Loss of Life", Report No. SDCG/NTSB, March 1974.

PROBLEMS

11.1 Your manager directs you to perform a stress analysis of a machine component containing a well-defined crack, and to employ the von-Mises theory of yielding to predict when the structure will fail. How do you respond to this directive?

11.2 Determine the stress concentration at an elliptical hole of length 2a, when a uniaxial stress σ_o is applied in a direction perpendicular to the length of the hole. Let b = a/40 and b = a/80. Where does σ_{Max} occur?

11.3 Determine the stress concentration at an elliptical hole of length 2a, when a uniaxial stress σ_o is applied in a direction parallel to the length of the hole. Let b = a/40 and b = a/80. Where does σ_{Max} occur?

11.4 A crack 50 mm long develops in a very wide plate, which is to support a uniaxial stress of 70 MPa. Determine the stress intensity factor K_I. What assumption did you make in this determination? If the crack grows at a rate of 12 mm/month, determine the service life remaining before crack initiation if K_{Ic} = 1,265 MPa$\sqrt{}$mm.

11.5 For a very wide plate subjected to a uniaxial stress of 120 MPa, prepare a graph showing the stress intensity factor as a function of crack length 2a.

11.6 Using a spreadsheet program, prepare a graph showing α as a function of (a/w) for a tension strip with a centrally located crack. Let (a/w) vary from 0.02 to 0.40 in steps of 0.02.

11.7 A steel strap 2.0 mm thick and 20 mm wide with a central crack of 4.0 mm long is loaded to failure. Determine the failure stress σ_o and the critical load F_c if the strap material is fabricated from 4340 alloy steel. Compare σ_o to the yield and tensile strengths of 4340 alloy steel. How will the strap fail?

11.8 Use a spreadsheet program to compute the multiplier α for SEC and DEC cracked tension strips. Evaluate α for $0 < (a/w) < 0.49$ in increments of 0.01. Display the results in graphical form.

11.9 A steel tension bar, 80 mm thick and 250 mm wide with a single edge crack 40 mm long, is subjected to a uniaxial stress of 85 MPa. If K_{Ic} = 2,000 MPa$\sqrt{}$mm for the steel used to fabricate the bar, will the crack initiate?

11.10 Determine the critical crack length a_c for the tension bar in Problem 11.9 if K_{Ic} = 2,000 MPa$\sqrt{}$mm.

11.11 Determine the critical load F_c for the tension bar in Problem 11.9 if K_{Ic} = 2,000 MPa$\sqrt{}$mm.

11.12 A steel tension bar, 1.25 in. thick and 15 in. wide with double edge cracks each 2 in. long, is subjected to a uniaxial stress of 20 ksi. If K_{Ic} = 60 ksi$\sqrt{}$in. for the steel used to fabricate the bar, will the crack initiate?

11.13 Determine the critical crack length a_c for the tension bar in Problem 11.12 if K_{Ic} = 60 ksi$\sqrt{}$in.

11.14 Determine the critical load F_c for the tension bar in Problem 11.12 if $K_{Ic} = 60$ ksi$\sqrt{in}$.

11.15 Using a spreadsheet program, determine the normalized stress intensity factor $\frac{K_I b w^{3/2}}{Fs}$ as a function of (a/w) for a beam subjected to three-point bending. Let (a/w) vary from 0.02 to 0.40 in steps of 0.02. Display the results in graphical form.

11.16 Using a spreadsheet program, determine the normalized stress intensity factor $\frac{K_I b w^2}{M\sqrt{a}}$ as a function of (a/w) for a beam subjected to four-point bending. Let (a/w) vary from 0.02 to 0.40 in steps of 0.02. Display the results in graphical form.

11.17 Find the critical load F_c that can be applied to a beam subjected to three-point bending as illustrated in Fig. P11.17. Note that $K_{Ic} = 1{,}800$ MPa$\sqrt{mm}$.

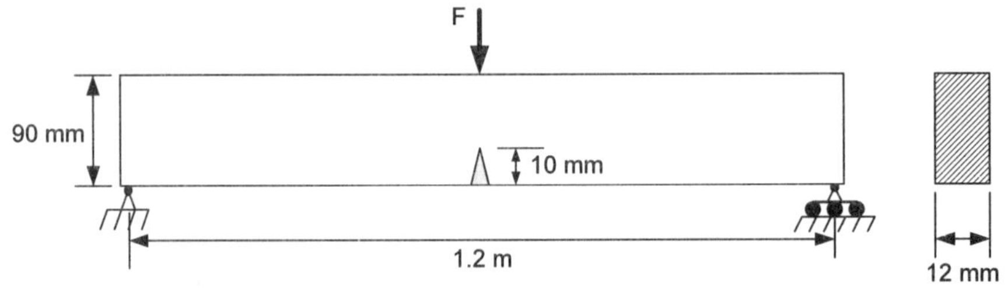

Fig. P11.17

11.18 Find the critical moment M_c that can be applied to a beam in pure bending as illustrated in Fig. P11.18. Note that $K_{Ic} = 55$ ksi $\sqrt{in}$.

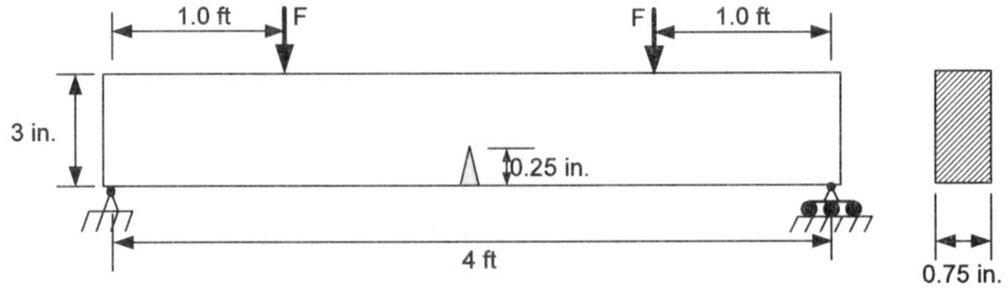

Fig. P11.18

11.19 An inspector locates a 6.0 mm long crack adjacent to a 40 mm diameter circular hole in a tension panel, fabricated from aluminum 2124-T851. The tension panel is occasionally loaded with a uniaxial stress $\sigma_o = 160$ MPa. The inspector recommends replacing the panel. Do you agree with this recommendation? Justify your answer.

11.20 An inspector locates a 0.5 in. long crack adjacent to a 2 in. diameter circular hole in a tension panel, fabricated from 301 stainless steel. The tension panel is occasionally loaded with a uniaxial stress $\sigma_o = 25$ ksi. The inspector recommends replacing the panel. Do you agree with this recommendation? Justify your answer.

11.21 Determine the critical crack length a_c for the geometry shown in Fig. P11.21. Note that K_{Ic} = 100 ksi$\sqrt{in}$.

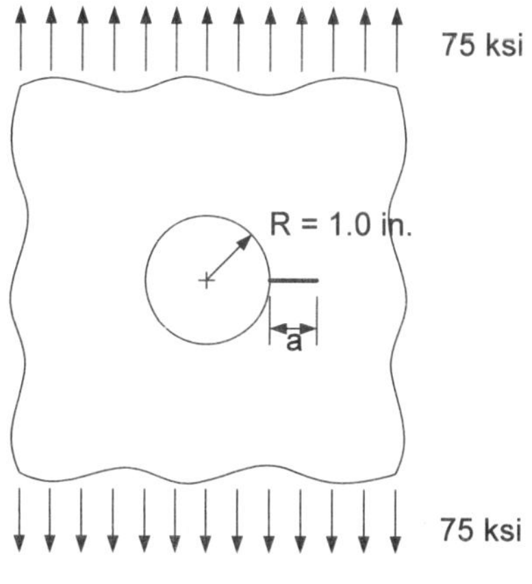

Fig. P11.21

11.22 Determine the maximum size of an embedded shrinkage crack a_{Max} that can form and remain stable in an 18 Ni-steel casting, if the crack is subjected to an applied stress of 950 MPa.

11.23 A surface flaw is introduced on an external corner of a 630-aluminum bronze component, as shown in Fig. P11.23. Determine the applied stress σ_o the component can withstand before the crack (flaw) becomes unstable.

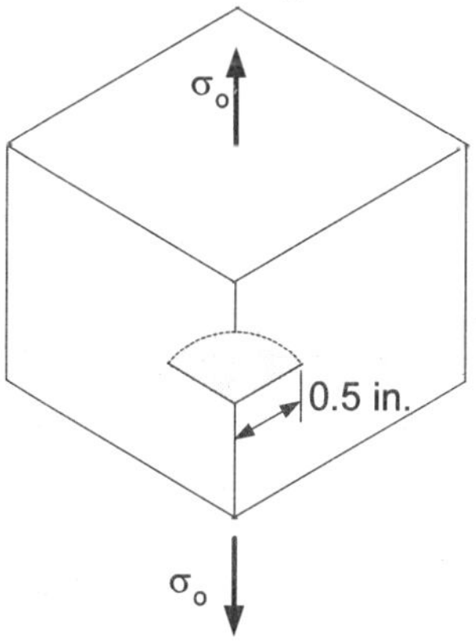

Fig. P11.23

11.24 An inspector has located a shallow surface crack at the edge of hole in a tension panel, as illustrated in Fig. P11.24. The crack dimensions are given in the figure. You are to establish the stress σ_o that will initiate the crack. Note the panel material is 70-titanium.

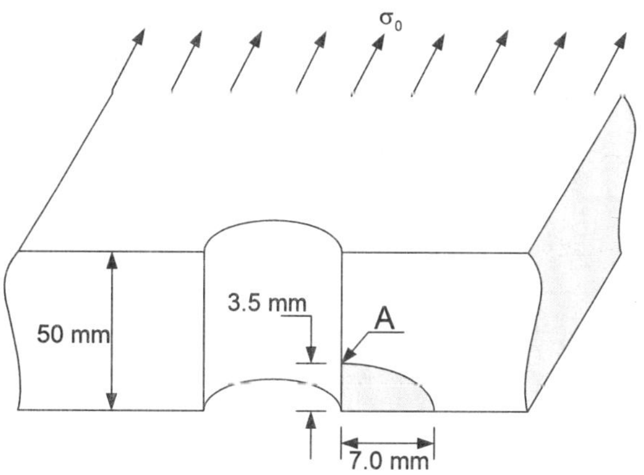

Fig. P11.24

11.25 Give an example of:

a. Opening mode loading.
b. In-plane shear mode loading.
c. Out-of-plane shear mode loading.
d. Mixed mode (I and II) loading.

11.26 Determine r_p at the critical load for the beam shown in Fig. P11.26 if S_y = 800 MPa and K_{Ic} = 1,800 MPa$\sqrt{mm}$. Compare r_p to the crack length and the ligament length and comment.

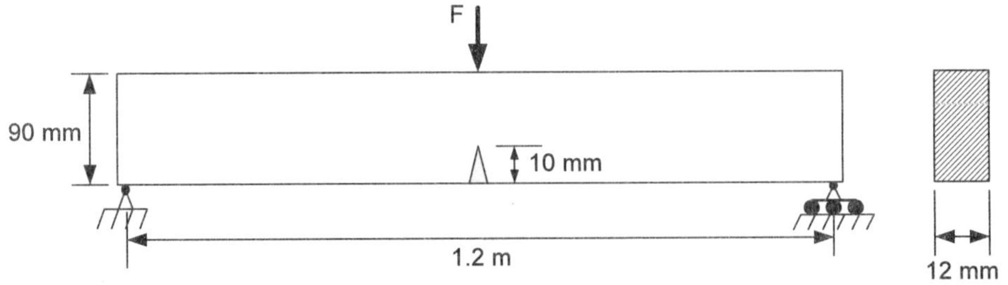

Fig. P11.26

11.27 For the beam shown in Fig. P11.26, which is the same as defined Problem 11.17, adjust the crack length to accommodate the effect of yielding if S_y = 800 MPa and then determine the new critical load F_c. Compare this result to that found in the original solution for Problem 11.17. Note that K_{Ic} = 1,800 MPa$\sqrt{mm}$.

11.28 Consider a thin but wide tension panel, shown in Fig. P11.28. The panel is fabricated from a ductile material that is perfectly plastic when it yields at a stress of 130 ksi. Use the Dugdale model to determine the length of the plastic zone r_p.

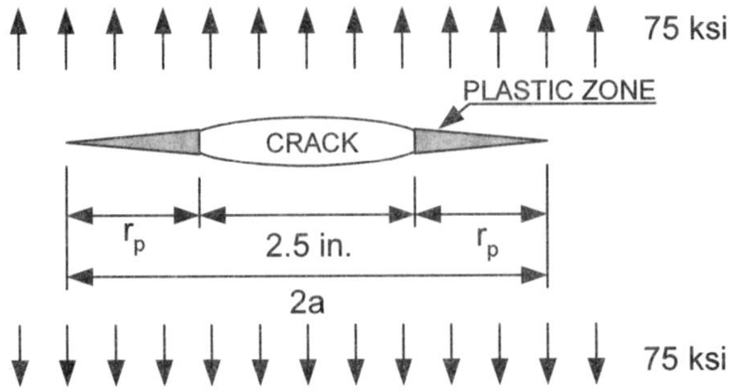

Fig. P11.28

11.29 Determine the limit moment M_{Limit} that can be achieved prior to plastic rupture of a cracked beam subjected to pure bending. Use a spreadsheet to calculate M_{Limit}/S_y as a function of (a/w) as this ratio varies from 0 to 0.75 in steps of 0.05. Display the results in graphical form.

11.30 Describe the effect of plate thickness on the fracture toughness of ductile metals.

11.31 Describe the effect of increasing tensile strength on the fracture toughness of a metallic alloy.

11.32 Describe the effect of decreasing temperature on fracture toughness of typical structural steels.

11.33 Determine an approximate value for the fracture toughness of a structural steel if the Charpy V-notch test result for the absorbed energy is 22 J. The test temperature and the service temperature are both in the transition range.

11.34 A structural design requires steel with a minimum K_{Ic} = 2400 MPa$\sqrt{mm}$. Charpy V-notch test results on a proposed steel gave an absorbed energy of 30 J. The test and service temperatures are both in the transition range. Is this steel appropriate for the design? Justify your answer.

11.35 A wide and thick steel plate contains an edge crack 0.75 in. long. The plate is subjected to alternating stresses between $\sigma_{Min} = 0$ ksi and $\sigma_{Max} = 24$ ksi. Experiments conducted with similar steel provided data for the material constants in Eq. (11.35) as $C = 5.8 \times 10^{-10}$ and $n = 4.0$, when ΔK is expressed in units of ksi$\sqrt{\text{in}}$. The plane strain fracture toughness for this steel is $K_{Ic} = 65$ ksi$\sqrt{\text{in}}$. Determine the number of cycles N_f for this crack to grow to a critical size that produces failure.

11.36 A wide and thick steel plate contains an edge crack 24 mm long. The plate is subjected to alternating stresses between $\sigma_{Min} = 130$ MPa and $\sigma_{Max} = 230$ MPa. Experiments conducted with similar steel provided data for the material constants in Eq. (11.35) as $C = 9.8 \times 10^{-15}$ and $n = 4.0$, when ΔK is expressed in units of MPa$\sqrt{\text{mm}}$. The plane strain fracture toughness for this steel is $K_{Ic} = 2{,}900$ MPa$\sqrt{\text{mm}}$. Determine the number of N_f cycles for this crack to grow to a critical size that produces failure.

11.37 Describe the three steps involved in fracture control plans.

11.38 Using a spreadsheet program, construct a graph showing the critical crack length a_c as a function of K_{Ic}/σ_o over the range from 0.01 to 0.15 $\sqrt{\text{m}}$ in steps of 0.005. Assume $\alpha = 1$ for simplicity.

11.39 Write a fracture control plan for a large natural gas storage tank that is to be located adjacent to a densely populated metropolitan area. Clearly state the assumptions made in preparing your plan.

11.40 Why is proof testing used to insure structural integrity?

APPENDIX A

WIRE AND SHEET METAL GAGES (Dimensions are in inches)

Gage No. of Wire	B & S[1] Non Ferrous Metals	American S. & W Steel Wire	American S. & W Music Wire	Steel Manufactures' Sheet	Gage No. of Wire
7-0s	0.651354	0.4900	......	......	7-0s
6-0s	0.580049	0.4615	0.004	......	6-0s
5-0s	0.516549	0.4305	0.005	......	5-0s
4-0s	0.4600	0.3938	0.006	......	4-0s
000s	0.40964	0.3625	0.007	......	000s
00	0.3648	0.3310	0.008	......	00
0	0.32486	0.3065	0.009	......	0
1	0.2893	0.2830	0.010	......	1
2	0.25763	0.2625	0.011	......	2
3	0.22942	0.2437	0.012	0.2391	3
4	0.20431	0.2253	0.013	0.2242	4
5	0.18194	0.2070	0.014	0.2092	5
6	0.16202	0.1920	0.016	0.1943	6
7	0.14428	0.1770	0.018	0.1793	7
8	0.12849	0.1620	0.020	0.1644	8
9	0.11443	0.1483	0.022	0.1495	9
10	0.10189	0.1350	0.024	0.1345	10
11	0.090742	0.1205	0.026	0.1196	11
12	0.080808	0.1055	0.029	0.1046	12
13	0.071961	0.0915	0.031	0.0897	13
14	0.064084	0.0800	0.033	0.0747	14
15	0.057068	0.0720	0.035	0.0763	15
16	0.05082	0.0625	0.037	0.0598	16
17	0.045257	0.0540	0.039	0.0538	17
18	0.040303	0.0475	0.041	0.0478	18
19	0.03589	0.0410	0.043	0.0418	19
20	0.031961	0.0348	0.045	0.0359	20
21	0.028462	0.0317	0.047	0.0329	21
22	0.025347	0.0286	0.049	0.0299	22
23	0.022571	0.0258	0.051	0.0269	23
24	0.02010	0.0230	0.055	0.0239	24
25	0.01790	0.0204	0.059	0.0209	25
26	0.01594	0.0181	0.063	0.0179	26
27	0.014195	0.0173	0.067	0.0164	27
28	0.012641	0.0162	0.071	0.0149	28
29	0.011257	0.0150	0.075	0.0135	29
30	0.010025	0.0140	0.080	0.0120	30
31	0.008928	0.0132	0.085	0.0105	31
32	0.00795	0.0128	0.090	0.0097	32
33	0.00708	0.0118	0.095	0.0090	33
34	0.006304	0.0104	......	0.0082	34
35	0.005614	0.0095	......	0.0075	35
36	0.00500	0.0090	......	0.0067	36
37	0.004453	0.0085	......	0.0064	37
38	0.003965	0.0080	......	0.0060	38
39	0.003531	0.0075	......	......	39
40	0.003144	0.0070	......	......	40

[1] Courtesy of Brown and Sharpe Manufacturing Company.

APPENDIX B-1

PHYSICAL PROPERTIES OF COMMON STRUCTURAL MATERIALS

Material	Elastic Modulus, E		Shear Modulus, G		Poisson's Ratio, ν	Coefficient Thermal Expansion, α	
	Mpsi	GPa	Mpsi	GPa	—	$\times 10^{-6}/°F$	$\times 10^{-6}/°C$
METAL							
Aluminum Alloy	10.4	72	3.9	27	0.32	12.9	23.2
Brass, Bronze	16	110	6.0	41	0.33	11.1	20.0
Copper	17.5	121	6.6	46	0.33	9.4	16.9
Cast Iron - Gray	15	103	6.0	41	0.26	6.7	12.1
Cast Iron - Malleable	25	170	9.9	68	0.26	6.7	12.1
Magnesium Alloy	6.5	45	2.4	17	0.35	14.4	25.9
Nickel Alloy	30	207	11.5	79	0.30	7.8	14.0
Steel	30	207	11.5	79	0.30	6.3	11.3
Stainless Steel	27.5	190	10.6	73	0.30	9.6	17.3
Titanium Alloy	16.5	114	6.2	43	0.33	4.9	8.8
WOOD[1]							
Douglas Fir	1.9	13	0.1	0.7	—	2.1	3.8
Sitka Spruce	1.5	10	0.07	0.5	—	2.1	3.8
Western White Pine	1.5	10	—	—	—	2.1	3.8
White Oak	1.8	12	—	—	—	2.1	3.8
Red Oak	1.8	12	—	—	—	2.1	3.8
Redwood	1.3	9	—	—	—	2.1	3.8
CONCRETE							
Medium Strength	3.6	25	—	—	—	5.5	9.9
High Strength	4.5	31	—	—	—	5.5	9.9
PLASTIC							
Nylon Type 6/6	0.4	2.8	—	—	—	80	144
Polycarbonate	0.35	2.4	—	—	—	68	122
Polyester, PBT	0.35	2.4	—	—	—	75	135
Polystyrene	0.45	3.1	—	—	—	70	125
Vinyl, Rigid PVC	0.45	3.1	—	—	—	75	135
STONE							
Granite	10	70	4	28	0.25	4	7.2
Marble	8	55	3	21	0.33	6	10.8
Sandstone	6	40	2	14	0.50	5	9.0
GLASS	9.6	65	4.1	28	0.17	44	80
RUBBER	0.22[2]	0.0015	0.073[2]	0.0005	0.50	125	225

The values for the properties given above are representative. Because processing methods and exact composition of the material influence the properties to some degree, the exact values may differ from those presented here.

1. Wood is an orthotropic material with different properties in different directions. The values given here are parallel to the grain.
2. The modulus for rubber is given in ksi.

APPENDIX B-2

TENSILE PROPERTIES OF COMMON STRUCTURAL MATERIALS

Material	Ultimate Tensile Strength, S_u		Yield Strength, S_y		Density, ρ	
	ksi	MPa	ksi	MPa	lb/in.^{3}	Mg/m^3
CARBON & ALLOY STEELS						
1010 A	44	303	29	200	0.284	7.87
1018 A	49.5	341	32	221	0.284	7.87
1020 HR	66	455	42	290	0.284	7.87
1045 HR	92.5	638	60	414	0.284	7.87
1212 HR	61.5	424	28	193	0.284	7.87
4340 HR	151	1041	132	910	0.283	7.84
52100 A	167	1151	131	903	0.284	7.87
STAINLESS STEELS						
302 A	92	634	34	234	0.286	7.92
303 A	87	600	35	241	0.286	7.92
304 A	83	572	40	276	0.286	7.92
440C A	117	807	67	462	0.286	7.92
CAST IRON						
Gray	25	170	—	—	0.260	7.20
Malleable	50	340	32	220	0.266	7.37
ALUMINUM ALLOYS						
1100-0	12	83	4.5	31	0.098	2.71
2024-T4	65	448	43	296	0.100	2.77
6061-T6	38	260	35	240	0.098	2.71
7075-0	34	234	14.3	99	0.100	2.77
7075 T6	86	593	78	538	0.100	2.77
MAGNESIUM ALLOYS						
HK31XA-0	25.5	176	19	131	0.066	1.83
HK31XA-H24	36.2	250	31	214	0.066	1.83
NICKEL ALLOYS						
Monel 400 A	80	550	32	220	0.319	8.83
Cupronickel A	53	365	16	110	0.323	8.94
COPPER ALLOYS						
Oxygen-free (99.9%) A	32	220	10	70	0.322	8.91
90-10 Brass A	36.4	251	8.4	58	0.316	8.75
80-20 Brass A	35.8	247	7.2	50	0.316	8.75
70-30 Brass A	44.0	303	10.5	72	0.316	8.75
Naval Brass	54.5	376	17	117	0.316	8.75
Tin Bronze	45	310	21	145	0.318	8.80
Aluminum Bronze	90	620	40	275	0.301	8.33
TITANIUM ALLOY						
Annealed	155	1070	135	930	0.167	4.63

A = Annealed and HR = Hot Rolled

APPENDIX B-3

TENSILE PROPERTIES OF NON-METALLIC MATERIALS

Materials	Ultimate Tensile Strength, S_u		Yield Strength, S_y		Density, ρ	
	ksi	MPa	ksi	MPa	lb/in.^{3}	Mg/m^3
WOOD						
Douglas Fir	15	100	—	—	0.017	0.470
Sitka Spruce	8.6	60	—	—	0.015	0.415
Western White Pine	5.0	34	—	—	0.014	0.390
White Oak	7.4	51	—	—	0.025	0.690
Red Oak	6.8	47	—	—	0.024	0.660
Redwood	9.4	65	—	—	0.015	0.415
CONCRETE[1]						
Medium Strength	4.0	28	—	—	0.084	2.32
High Strength	6.0	40	—	—	0.084	2.32
PLASTIC						
Nylon Type 6/6	11	75	6.5	45	0.0412	1.14
Polycarbonate	9.5	65	9	62	0.0433	1.20
Polyester, PBT	8	55	8	55	0.0484	1.34
Polystyrene	8	55	8	55	0.0374	1.03
Vinyl, Rigid PVC	6.5	45	6	40	0.0520	1.44
STONE[1]						
Granite	35	240	—	—	0.100	2.77
Marble	18	125	—	—	0.100	2.77
Sandstone	12	85	—	—	0.083	2.30
GLASS[1]						
98% Silica	7	50	—	—	0.079	2.19
RUBBER						
Natural, Vulcanized	4	28	—	—	0.034	0.95

1. The tensile strength of concrete, stone and bulk glass is negligible. Only the compressive strength of these materials is reported in this table.

APPENDIX C

PROPERTIES OF AREAS

C.1 AREA

The cross sectional area, A of structural members plays an extremely important role in the efficiency and the adequacy of any member in the design of the structure. For example, the stress in a uniaxial tension or compression member is given by $\sigma = P/A$.

The force P is in the numerator and the area A of the cross section is in the denominator of the relation for the stresses. To lower the stresses we have only two options—decrease the force P or increase the area A. The area A of the cross section depends on its shape as indicated in Fig. C.1:

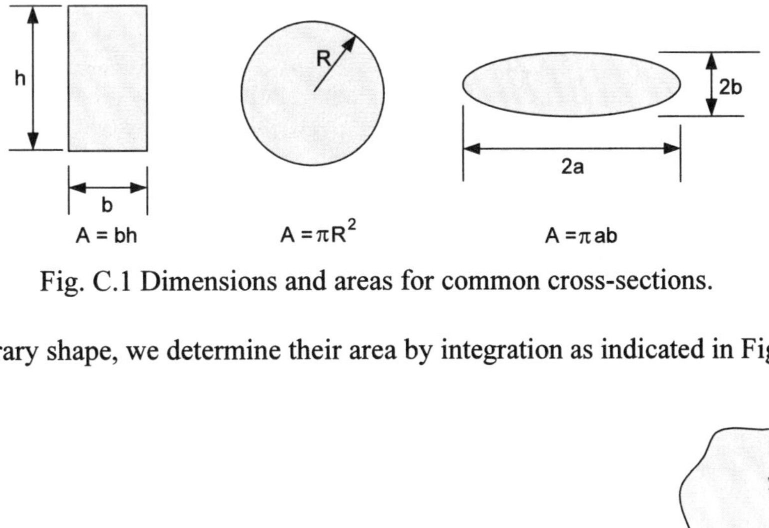

Fig. C.1 Dimensions and areas for common cross-sections.

For areas of arbitrary shape, we determine their area by integration as indicated in Fig. C.2:

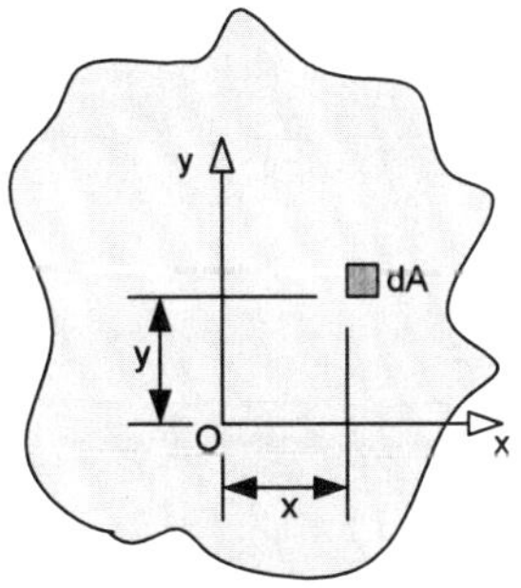

Fig. C.2 An arbitrary area A.

The area, A is determined by summing the incremental area dA in an integration process:

$$A = \int_A dA \qquad \text{(C.1)}$$

If the boundaries of the area are not known in terms of well-defined mathematical expressions, it is not possible to integrate to determine the area A. However, it is always possible to divide the area into many small squares or rectangles each with an area ΔA. These squares or rectangles follow the boundary of the shape in question and completely fill the interior region. The area is then given by:

$$A = \sum_{i=1}^{N} \Delta A_i = N\Delta A \tag{C.2}$$

where N is the number of small squares or rectangles.

C.2 FIRST MOMENT OF AN AREA

The first moment of an area is important because it is useful in locating the position of the centroid of a given cross sectional area. Let's consider an arbitrary area with the coordinate system Oxy as shown in Fig. C.2. The first moment of the area A about the x-axis is defined as:

$$Q_x = \int_A y dA \tag{C.3}$$

Also, the first moment of the area A with respect to the y-axis is defined as:

$$Q_y = \int_A x dA \tag{C.4}$$

Depending on the location of the coordinate system relative to the area, the numerical values obtained for the first moment Q_x and Q_y may be either positive or negative. The units for Q_x and Q_y are mm^3 in the SI system or in^3 in the U. S. Customary system.

C.3 CENTROID OF THE AREA A

The centroid of an area A is defined by point C located relative to an arbitrary coordinate system Oxy in Fig. C.3. Indeed, the definition of a centroid is the point, which is considered the center of gravity of a line, an area or a volume.

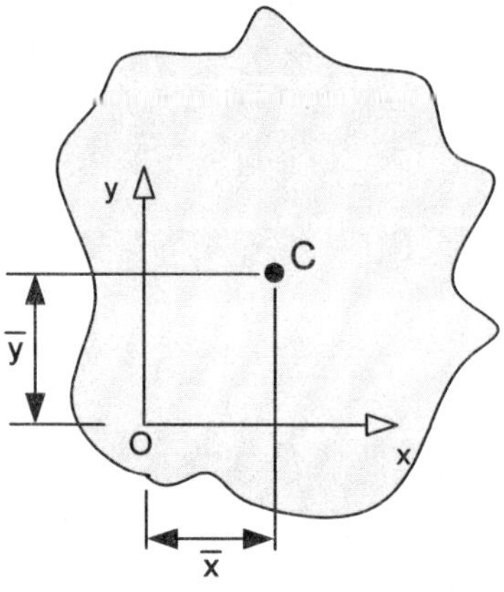

Fig. C.3 The centroid C of an area A is located with coordinates x and y.

The coordinates $\bar{x}$ and $\bar{y}$ for the centroid of an area are determined from the first moments as:

$$Q_y = \int_A x dA = A\bar{x} \qquad Q_x = \int_A y dA = A\bar{y} \tag{C.5}$$

where $\bar{x}$ and $\bar{y}$ are dimensions locating the centroid as shown in Fig. C.3.

Let's illustrate the method for determining the first moment of the area and the location of a centroid by considering a few simple shapes the examples presented below.

EXAMPLE C.1

Consider the rectangular area illustrated in Fig C.4, with the origin of the Oxy coordinate system positioned at its corner. Determine the first moments of the rectangular area and the location of its centroid relative to this coordinate system.

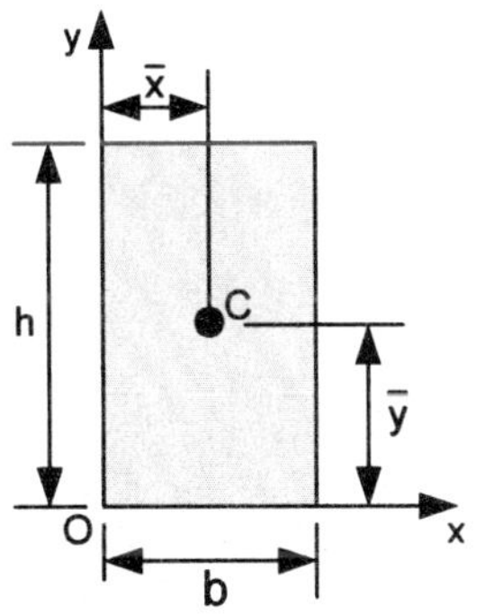

Fig C.4 A rectangle with the coordinate system located along its edges.

Solution:

For the rectangle area presented in Fig. C.4, the first moments of the area about are given by Eq. (C.5) as:

$$Q_x = A\bar{y} = (bh)\frac{h}{2} = \frac{bh^2}{2} \quad \text{and} \quad Q_y = A\bar{x} = (bh)\frac{b}{2} = \frac{b^2h}{2} \tag{a}$$

It was possible to quickly solve for the first moments, Q_x and Q_y, because we recognized the location of the centroid for the rectangular area. When an axis of symmetry exists for a given area, the centroid is located somewhere on this axis of symmetry. With the rectangle, two axes of symmetry exist, and the location of the centroid is obviously at the intersection of the axes.

For the circular cross section shown in Fig. C.5, the center of the circle clearly locates the centroid. The center also serves as the origin for the centroidal axes x_c and y_c.

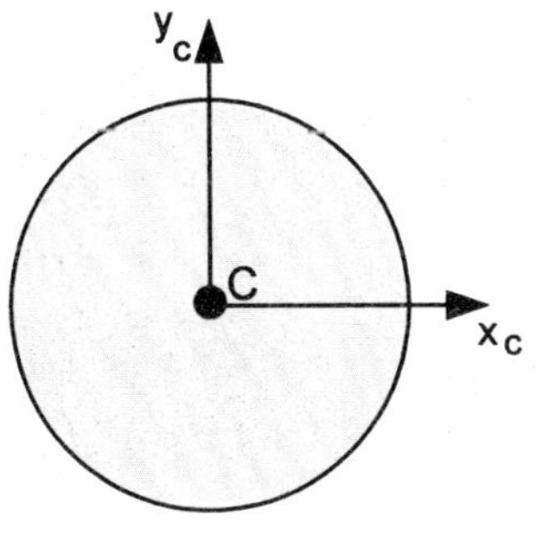

Fig. C.5 The centroid serves as the origin for the centroidal axes Cx_cy_c.

For cross sectional shapes such as ellipses, circles, squares and rectangles, the center may be located by inspection because these geometries have two axes of symmetry. However, for non-symmetric figures, such as triangles, portions of circles, parabolic areas, etc., locating the center of the area is not obvious. We will show methods for determining the location of the centroid of areas that do not exhibit two axes of symmetry.

With respect to a centroidal coordinate system, the first moment of the area must vanish for both axes. Therefore:

$$Q_{\bar{x}} = \int_A y dA = 0 \quad \text{and} \quad Q_{\bar{y}} = \int_A x dA = 0 \tag{C.6}$$

These relations are employed to locate the centroid of an area of any shape providing its boundary is defined with some mathematical function.

EXAMPLE C.2

For a right triangle, determine the first moment of the area about its base and vertical side and the position of its centroid relative to its two sides. The right triangle with a base b and a height h is illustrated in Fig. C.6:

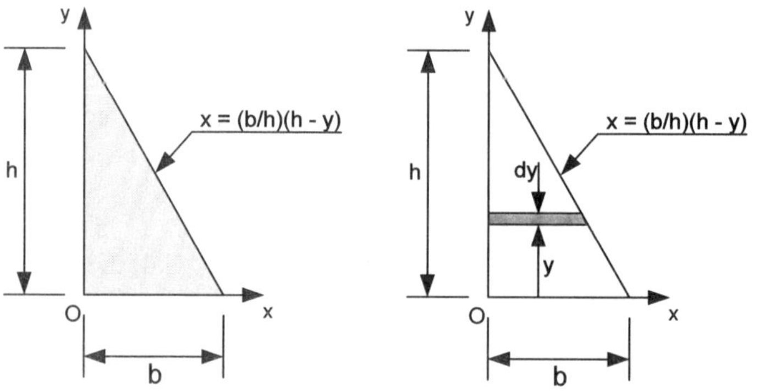

Fig C.6 A right triangle with a coordinate system coincident with its base and vertical side.

Solution:

To begin, let's determine the first moment of the area, A of the right triangle relative to the x-axis (its base side). Writing Eq. C.3 gives:

$$Q_x = \int_A y dA = \int_y xydy \tag{a}$$

Note, the equation for the diagonal boundary of the triangle is given by:

$$x = (b/h)(h - y) \tag{b}$$

The limits on the integral go from 0 to h to encompass the area of the triangle. We substitute Eq. (b) and the limits on the integral into Eq. (a), and write:

$$Q_x = \frac{b}{h}\int_0^h (h - y)ydy \tag{c}$$

Integrating Eq. (c) gives:

$$Q_x = \frac{b}{h}\left[\frac{hy^2}{2} - \frac{y^3}{3}\right]_0^h \qquad \text{(d)}$$

Completing the integration gives:

$$Q_x = bh^2/6 \qquad \text{(C.7)}$$

By using Eq. C.4 and following the same procedure, we find the first moment about the side of the triangle is given by:

$$Q_y = b^2\,h/6 \qquad \text{(C.8)}$$

Equation C.7 gives the first moment of the area of a right triangle about its base. This is an interesting exercise in calculus, but what does it have to do with determining the location of the centroid of the right triangle? The result presented in Eq. (C.7) is an intermediate step. We continue the solution by combining the results of Eqs. (C.7) and (C.8) with Eqs. (C.5) to obtain:

$$Q_x = bh^2/6 = A\,\bar{y} = (bh/2)\,\bar{y} \qquad \text{(e)}$$

$$Q_y = b^2h/6 = A\,\bar{x} = (bh/2)\,\bar{x} \qquad \text{(f)}$$

where $\bar{x}$ and $\bar{y}$ locate the Cx_cy_c coordinates relative to the Oxy coordinates (see Fig. C.7).

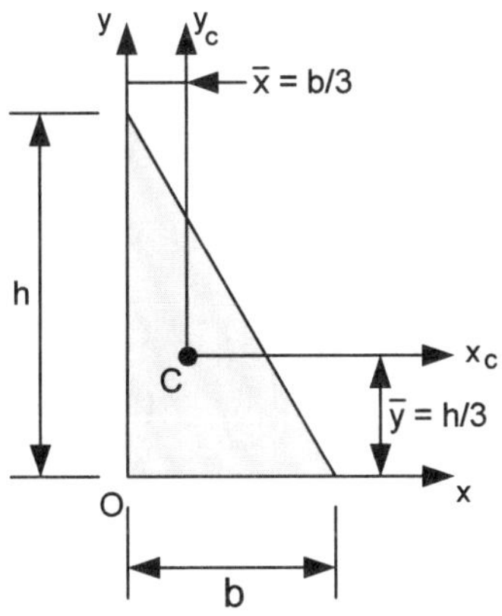

Fig. C.7 A right triangular area with a base axes Oxy and centroidal axes Cx_cy_c.

To determine the position of the centroid, let's solve Eqs. (e) and (f) for x and y to obtain:

$$\bar{y} = h/3 \qquad \bar{x} = b/3 \qquad \text{(C.9)}$$

We employ Eqs. (C.3) and (C.4) to determine the first moment of the area Q relative to either the x or y axes. The location of the centroid is then established from Eq. (C.5). The location of the centroid for common shapes has been determined, and the results are presented together with the definition of the shape of the area in Fig. C.8. This illustration is also shown inside the front cover.

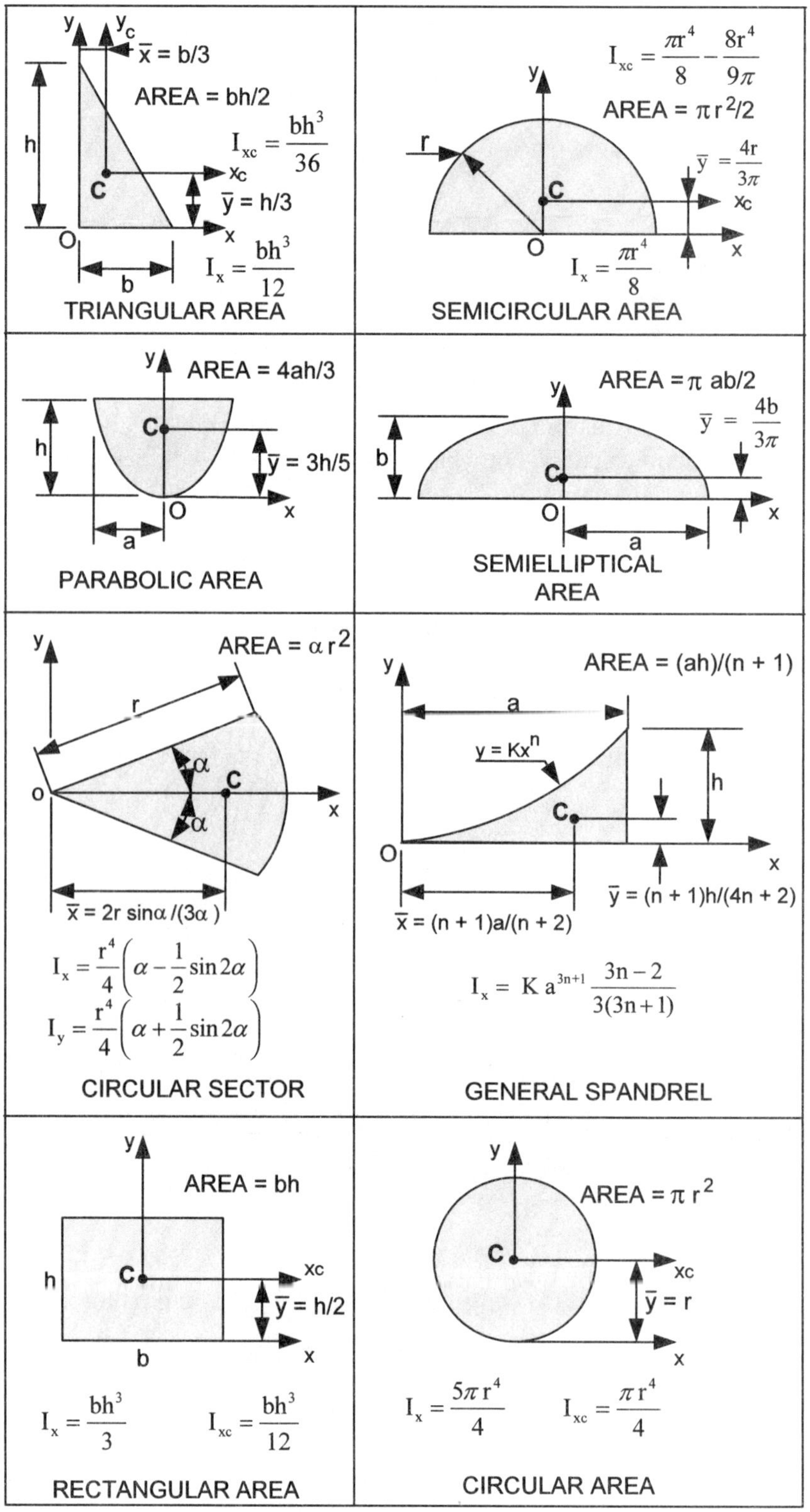

Fig. C.8 Area properties of some common shapes.

C.4 LOCATING THE CENTROID OF A COMPOSITE AREA

In many cases, the shape of a cross section is unusual and differs from the common geometries described in Fig. C.8. To analytically locate the centroid of areas with uncommon shapes, we divide its area into several different common shapes for which we have solutions for the location of the centroid. Then we combine the product of these individual areas and their centroid locations to give the location of the centroid of the composite. Let's consider the uncommon shape defined in Fig. C.9, and locate the position of its centroid by employing the composite area technique.

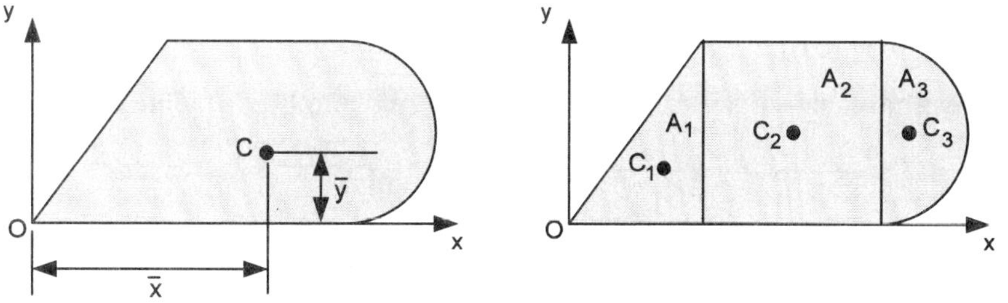

Fig. C.9 The unusual shaped area on the left is divided into common shaped areas on the right.

EXAMPLE C.3

Determine the location of the centroid of the odd shape defined in Fig. C.9.

Solution:

To begin the solution, we divide the area into three sub-regions — A_1, A_2 and A_3 as shown in Fig. C.9. Note the sub-regions are a right triangle, rectangle and semicircle. The dimensions of the three different shapes are:

- The triangle—base b = 4 units and height h = 6 units.
- The rectangle—width w = 8 units and height h = 6 units.
- The semicircle—radius R = 3 units.

We apply Eq. (C.5) to the composite area, and write:

$$\Sigma Q_x \quad \Rightarrow \quad \bar{Y}\, A_t = \Sigma\, \bar{y}_n A_n \qquad \text{(C.10)}$$

$$\Sigma Q_y \quad \Rightarrow \quad \bar{X}\, A_t = \Sigma\, \bar{x}_n A_n \qquad \text{(C.11)}$$

where A_t is the total area of the composite shape.

Let's first determine $\bar{Y}$ from Eq. (C.10):

$$\bar{Y}(A_1 + A_2 + A_3) = \bar{y}_1 A_1 + \bar{y}_2 A_2 + \bar{y}_3 A_3 \qquad \text{(a)}$$

Solving for $\bar{Y}$ yields:

$$\overline{Y} = (\overline{y}_1 A_1 + \overline{y}_2 A_2 + \overline{y}_3 A_3)/(A_1 + A_2 + A_3) \qquad \text{(b)}$$

$$\overline{Y} = \frac{\left(\frac{h}{3}\frac{bh}{2} + \frac{h}{2}wh + R\frac{\pi R^2}{2}\right)}{\left(\frac{bh}{2} + wh + \frac{\pi R^2}{2}\right)} \qquad \text{(c)}$$

Substituting results from Fig. C.8 into Eq. (b) gives:

Substituting b = 4, h = 6, w = 8 and R = 3 units into Eq. (c) yields:

$$\overline{Y} = 2.838 \text{ units}$$

This result is slightly less than h/2 as we anticipated. The presence of the triangle shifts the location of the centroid downward from the centerline of the rectangle and semi-circle.

Next, let's determine the position of the centroid in the direction of the x-axis. We begin by using Eq. (C.11), and write:

$$\overline{X}(A_1 + A_2 + A_3) = \overline{x}_1 A_1 + \overline{x}_2 A_2 + \overline{x}_3 A_3 \qquad \text{(d)}$$

Solving for $\overline{X}$ yields:

$$\overline{X} = (\overline{x}_1 A_1 + \overline{x}_2 A_2 + \overline{x}_3 A_3)/(A_1 + A_2 + A_3) \qquad \text{(e)}$$

From the information listed in Fig. C.8, we determine the centroid location for each of the shapes in the composite area as indicated below:

$$\overline{X} = \frac{\frac{2b}{3}\frac{bh}{2} + \left(b + \frac{w}{2}\right)wh + \left(b + w + \frac{4R}{3\pi}\right)\frac{\pi R^2}{2}}{\frac{bh}{2} + wh + \frac{\pi R^2}{2}} \qquad \text{(f)}$$

Substituting b = 4, h = 6, w = 8 and R = 3 units into Eq. (f) yields:

$$\overline{X} = 8.142 \text{ units}$$

We note that the location of the centroid of the unusual area is slightly to the right of the center of the rectangular area. This position is to be expected because the orientation of the right triangle with its area concentrated toward the right side tends to shift the centroid to the right.

C.5 SECOND MOMENT OF THE AREA

The second moment of the area is also know as the moment of inertia. In our discussion of beam theory in Chapter 4, we indicated the importance of the moment of inertia I_z in determining the stresses produced by internal moments. Several different second moments of the area A, illustrated in Fig. C.10, are defined in this Section.

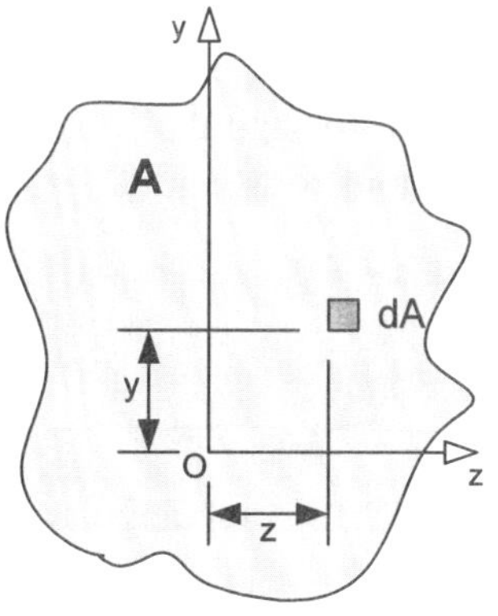

Fig. C.10 An elemental area dA is used when integrating to determine the second moment of the area A.

The second moment of the area, often called the moment of inertia, is referenced to one or both coordinate axes. The moment of inertia relative to the y and z-axes is defined by:

$$I_z = \int_A y^2 dA \qquad I_y = \int_A z^2 dA \tag{C.12}$$

We also define a polar moment of inertia of the area A relative to the origin O of the coordinate system as indicated in Fig. C.11 as:

$$J_O = \int_A r^2 dA = \int_A (z^2 + y^2) dA = \int_A z^2 dA + \int_A y^2 dA = I_y + I_z \tag{C.13}$$

The units for the second moments of the area are in.^{4} in the U. S. Customary system and m^4 or mm^4 in the SI system.

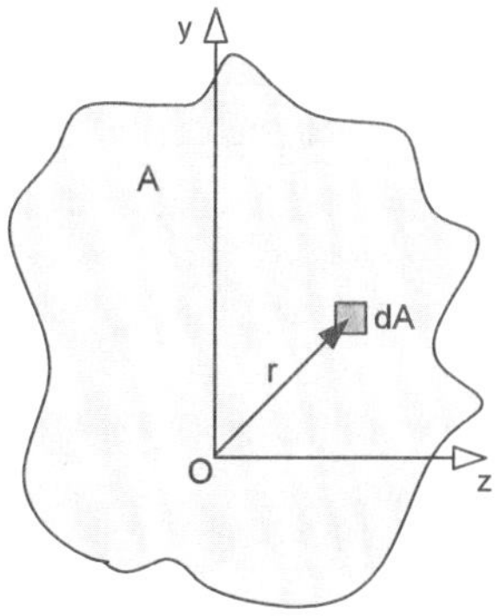

Fig. C.11 Coordinate system for the polar moment of inertia J_O.

Finally, the radius of gyration of an area A with respect to its axes is defined by:

$$I_z = r_z^2 A \qquad I_y = r_y^2 A \qquad J_o = r_o^2 A \tag{C.14}$$

The symbols r_z and r_y reference the radii of gyration relative to the z and y-axes, respectively. The radius of gyration for the polar moment of inertia is r_O.

Let's consider a few examples to demonstrate the integration of Eq. (C.12) to determine the second moment of the area.

EXAMPLE C.4

For the rectangular cross sectional area and coordinate system defined in Fig C.12, determine the equations for I_z and I_y.

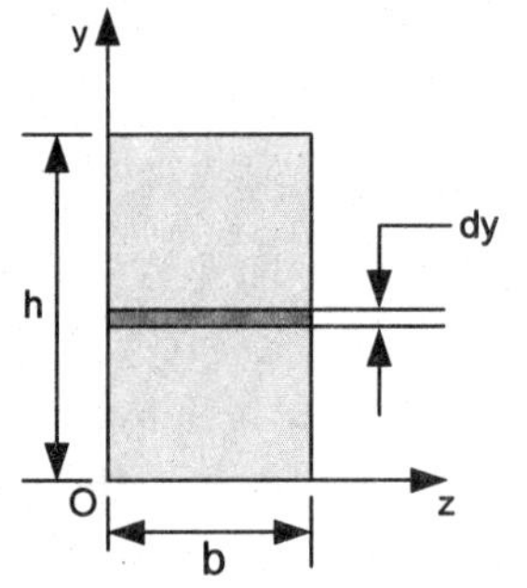

Fig. C.12 A rectangular area with a coordinate system along its edges.

Solution:

To determine I_z, we write Eq. (C.12) and observe that dA = b dy. Then:

$$I_z = \int_A y^2 dA = b\int_0^h y^2 dy = b\left[\frac{y^3}{3}\right]_0^h = \frac{bh^3}{3} \qquad \text{(C.15)}$$

Similarly for I_y, we write Eq. (C.12) and observe that dA = h dz. Then:

$$I_y = \int_A z^2 dA = h\int_0^b z^2 dz = h\left[\frac{z^3}{3}\right]_0^b = \frac{hb^3}{3} \qquad \text{(C.16)}$$

To show the importance of the location of the coordinate system in determining the second moment of the area, let's shift the origin of the coordinate system to the center of the rectangle as shown in Fig C.13.

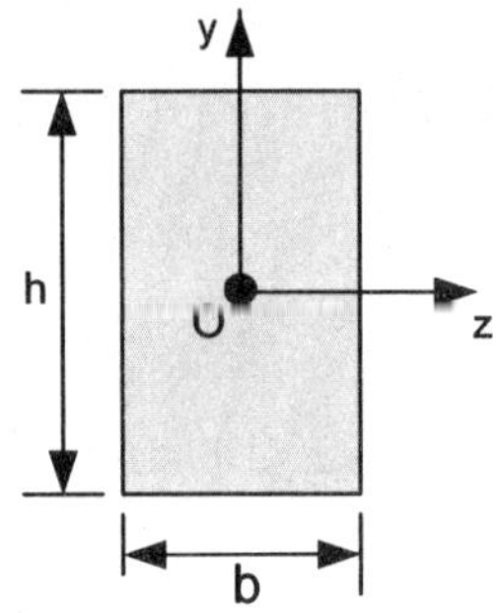

Fig. C.13 A rectangular area with a centrally located coordinate system.

EXAMPLE C.5

Determine the moment of inertia of a rectangular area relative to its centroidal axes.

Solution:

To determine the moment of inertia I_z, we write Eq. (C.12) and note that dA = b dy.

$$I_z = \int_A y^2 dA = b\int_{-h/2}^{h/2} y^2 dy = b\left[\frac{y^3}{3}\right]_{-h/2}^{h/2} = \frac{bh^3}{12} \qquad \text{(C.17)}$$

To determine the moment of inertia I_y, we write Eq. (C.12) and note that dA = h dz.

$$I_y = \int_A z^2 dA = h\int_{-b/2}^{b/2} z^2 dz = h\left[\frac{z^3}{3}\right]_{-b/2}^{b/2} = \frac{hb^3}{12} \qquad \text{(C.18)}$$

A comparison of the results for the moments of inertia for the rectangle clearly indicates the importance of the location of the coordinate system relative to the area in question. As we may be required to determine the moment of inertia about axes with arbitrary locations, a method for accounting for shifting the position of coordinates is useful.

C.6 THE PARALLEL AXIS THEOREM

Let's again consider an arbitrary area A positioned some distance from the z-axis as shown in Fig C.14. The centroidal axis of the area A is known and is identified with the z' axis. Assume that we have determined the second moment of the area with respect to the centroidal axis z'. Suppose we are required to compute the inertia I_z with respect to an axis z that is parallel to the centroidal axis. We begin again with Eq. C.12 and write:

$$I_z = \int_A y^2 dA = \int_A (y_1 + d)^2 dA$$

$$I_z = \int_A y_1^2 dA + 2d\int_A y_1 dA + d^2 \int_A dA \qquad \text{(C.19)}$$

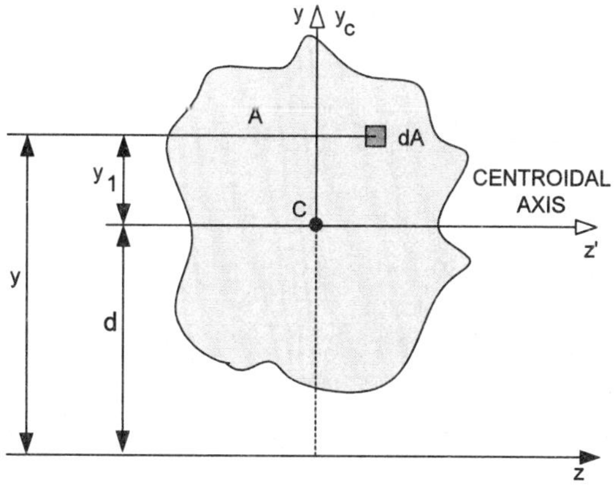

Fig. C.14 An arbitrary area A position a distance d from the z-axis.

The first term in Eq. (C.19) is the moment inertia $I_{z'}$ of the area about the centroidal axis. The second term $\int y_1$ dA is the first moment of the area about the centroidal axis, which is zero by definition of the centroid. The final term is simply Ad^2. Hence, the parallel axis theorem is given by:

$$I_z = I_{z'} + Ad^2 \qquad \text{(C.20)}$$

where $I_{z'}$ is the second moment of the area about the centroidal axis.

EXAMPLE C.6

To demonstrate the use of Eq. (C.20), let's determine the moment of inertia I_z of the rectangle shown in Fig C.15.

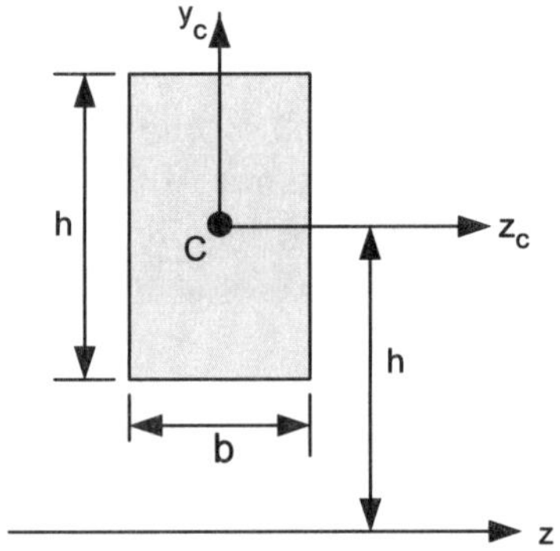

Fig. C.15 A rectangular area shifted by an amount d = h relative to the z-axis.

Solution:

To determine the moment of inertia I_z, we recall Eq. (C.20) and write:

$$I_z = I_{z'} + Ad^2 \qquad \text{(a)}$$

From Eq. (C.17) it is clear that $I_{z'} = bh^3/12$. Then we substitute into Eq. (C.20) to obtain:

$$I_z = bh^3/12 + (bh)(h^2) = (13/12)\, bh^3 \qquad \text{(b)}$$

This example illustrates two points. First, the parallel axis theorem is very helpful in determining the increase in the moment of inertia when the reference axis is some distance removed from the centroidal axis. Second, the moment of inertia is very sensitive to the movement of the reference axis relative to the centroidal axis. In this example, we moved the reference axis by an amount equal to the height h of the section and increased the inertia by a factor of 12.

C.7 MOMENTS OF INERTIA OF COMPOSITE AREAS

To determine the moment of inertia of areas with complex shapes, we divide the area into subsections to form a composite area. Each subsection is a simple shape, such as a square, rectangle, circle or semi-circle with known properties. Let's consider the structural tee with a web and a flange as illustrated in Fig. C.16 and demonstrate the procedure for determining the moment of inertia.

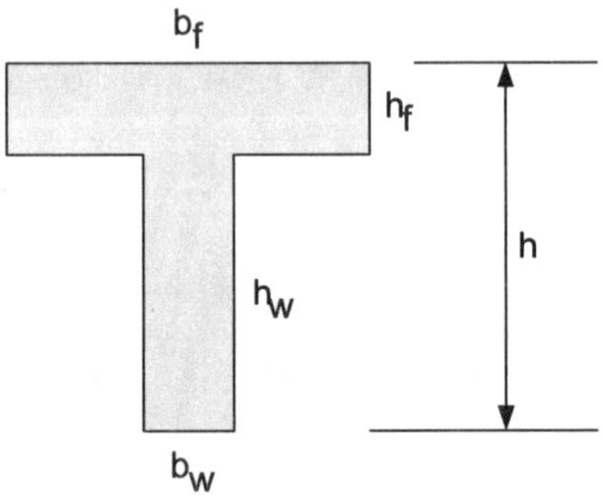

Fig. C.16 A structural tee is divided into two areas A_{web} and A_{flange}.

The procedure for determining the properties of the composite area representing the structural tee involves the three steps listed below:

- Determine the location of the centroidal axis of the composite area.
- Determine the moment of inertia of each area of the composite section about its centroidal axis.
- Employ the parallel axis theorem to determine the moment of inertia of the total section relative to the centroidal axis.

EXAMPLE C.7

Determine the moment of inertia I_z of the structural tee, shown in Fig. C.16, relative to its centroidal axis. The dimensions of the structural tee are given by:

$$h_f = 0.1\ h,\ h_w = 0.9\ h,\ b_w = 0.1\ b, \text{ and } b = 150 \text{ mm and } h = 200 \text{ mm.}$$

Solution:

To determine the location of the centroidal axis of the composite area, subdivide the structural tee into two areas, namely A_1 and A_2 as shown in Fig. C.17. Then apply Eq. (C.10) to determine the location of thc ccntroid relative to the z (reference) axis.

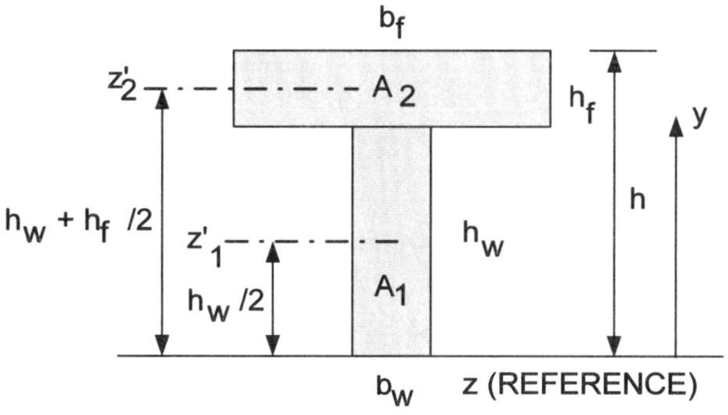

Fig. C.17 Subdivide the structural tee to form two rectangular areas and establish a convenient reference axis.

From Eq. (C.10), we write:

$$\Sigma Q_{z(REFERENCE)} = \overline{Y} A_t = \Sigma\ \overline{y}_n A_n = \overline{y}_1 A_1 + \overline{y}_2 A_2 \qquad \text{(a)}$$

Substituting the dimensional quantities from Fig. C.17 into Eq. (a) yields:

$$\overline{Y} = \frac{A_1 \dfrac{h_w}{2} + A_2 (h_w + \dfrac{h_f}{2})}{A_1 + A_2} = \frac{\dfrac{b_w h_w^2}{2} + b_f h_f h_w + \dfrac{b_f h_f^2}{2}}{b_w h_w + b_f h_f} \qquad \text{(b)}$$

Recall $h_f = 0.1$ h, $h_w = 0.9$ h, $b_w = 0.1$ b, $b_f =$ b, b = 150 mm, and h = 200 mm. Substitute these quantities into Eq. (b) to obtain:

$$\overline{Y} = 0.713 \text{ h} = 0.713 \times 200 = 142.6 \text{ mm} \qquad \text{(c)}$$

Next determine the moment for inertia of each area of the composite section about its centroidal axis. For A_1 (the web) with a width $b_w = 0.1$, b = 15 mm, and a height $h_w = 0.9$ h = 180 mm, we use Eq. (C.17) and write:

$$I_{z'1} = b_w h_w^3/12 = (15)(180)^3/12 = 7.29 \times 10^6 \text{ mm}^4 \quad \text{(d)}$$

For A_2 (the flange) with a width $b_f = 150$ mm, and a height $h_f = 0.1$ h = 20 mm, we write:

$$I_{z'2} = b_f h_f^3/12 = (150)(20)^3/12 = 0.100 \times 10^6 \text{ mm}^4 \quad \text{(e)}$$

Finally, employ the parallel axis theorem to determine the moment of inertia of the total area relative to the centroidal axis. Note for the composite area, we express the moment of inertia due to the two areas as:

$$I_z = I_{z1} + I_{z2} \quad \text{(f)}$$

We use Eq. (C.20) to expand Eq. (f) as:

$$I_z = I_{z1'} + A_1 d_1^2 + I_{z2'} + A_2 d_2^2 \quad \text{(g)}$$

The dimensions d_1 and d_2 are given by:

$$d_1 = \overline{Y} - h_w/2 = 142.6 - 90 = 52.6 \text{ mm} \quad \text{(h)}$$

$$d_2 = h_w + (h_f/2) - \overline{Y} = 180 + 10 - 142.6 = 47.4 \text{ mm} \quad \text{(i)}$$

Substituting numerical values for the terms in Eq. (g) yields the final result:

$$I_z = (7.290 \times 10^6) + (15)(180)(52.6)^2 + (0.1 \times 10^6) + (150)(20)(47.4)^2 = 21.60 \times 10^6 \text{ mm}^4$$

The determination of the moment of inertia for complex shapes is simple but tedious. Care must be exercised to avoid numerical errors in computing each of the quantities shown in Eq. (g). The moment of inertia is important in determining the bending stresses in beams because I_z occurs in the denominator of the well know flexural formula $\sigma = -My/I_z$. The procedure for establishing the position of the centroidal axis is also important because it locates the neutral axis about which bending occurs. When the position of the neutral axis is known, we can establish y_{max}, I_z and the maximum bending stress σ.

EXAMPLE C.8

Determine the following quantities for the unsymmetrical wide flanged section shown in Fig. C.18.

1. The location of the centroid relative to a defined reference axis.
2. The moment of inertia of the web, top flange, and bottom flange relative to the centroidal axis.
3. The moment of inertia of the section relative to the centroidal axis.

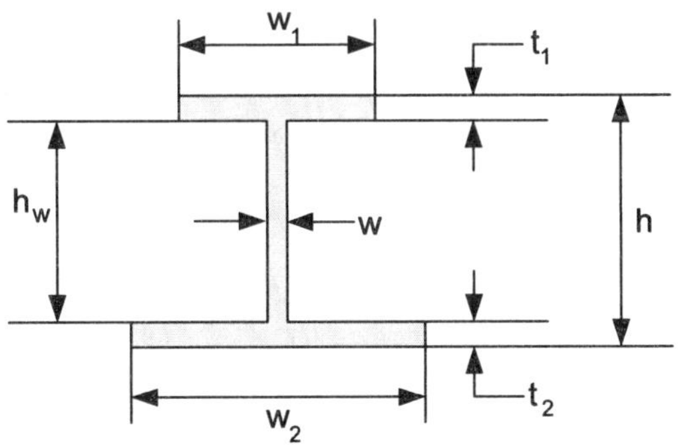

Fig. C.18 Dimensions of the unsymmetrical wide flanged section.

Solution:

To determine the location of the centroidal axis of the composite area, divide the unsymmetrical wide flanged section into three different areas consisting of the top flange, web and bottom flange as shown in Fig. C.19. Also establish a reference axis, z that is used as the datum for dimensioning the location of the centroid.

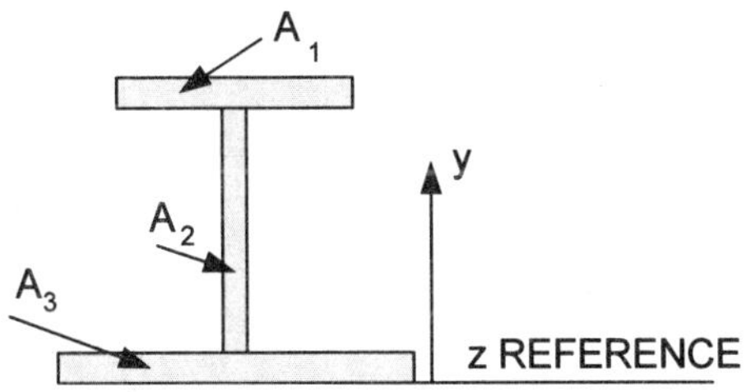

Fig. C.19 Dividing the unsymmetrical wide flanged section into three parts.

Let's apply Eq. (C.10) to determine the location of the centroid of this section relative to the z (reference) axis.

$$\Sigma Q_{z(REFERENCE)} = \overline{Y} A_t = \Sigma\ \overline{y}_n A_n = \overline{y}_1 A_1 + \overline{y}_2 A_2 + \overline{y}_3 A_3 \qquad \text{(a)}$$

Substituting the symbols for the dimensions from Fig. C.18 into Eq. (a) yields:

$$\overline{Y} = \frac{A_1(h_w + t_2 + t_1/2) + A_2(t_2 + h_w/2) + A_3(t_2/2)}{A_1 + A_2 + A_3}$$

$$\overline{Y} = \frac{1}{2}\left[\frac{t_1 w_1(2h_w + 2t_2 + t_1) + h_w w(2t_2 + h_w) + w_2 t_2^2}{w_1 t_1 + h_w w + w_2 t_2}\right]$$

Suppose we assume the proportions of the cross section as:

$$w_1 = 10\ w;\ w_2 = 16\ w;\ t_1 = 0.15\ h;\ t_2 = 0.10\ h;\ \text{and}\ h_w = 0.75\ h \qquad \text{(c)}$$

Then Eq. (b) reduces to:

$$\overline{Y} = 0.4736\ h \qquad \text{(d)}$$

Finally if the height h = 300-mm and web thickness w = 15 mm, the location of the centroidal axis is given by:

$$\overline{Y} = 142.1 \text{ mm} \qquad (e)$$

To determine the moment of inertia of each area of the composite section about its centroidal axis, apply Eq. (C.17) to each of the three rectangular areas to obtain:

$$I_{z'1} = (1/12)w_1t_1^3 = (1/12)(150)(45)^3 = 1.139 \times 10^6 \text{ mm}^4 \qquad (f)$$

$$I_{z'2} = (1/12)wh_w^3 = (1/12)(15)(225)^3 = 14.24 \times 10^6 \text{ mm}^4 \qquad (g)$$

$$I_{z'3} = (1/12)\, w_2t_2^3 = (1/12)(240)(30)^3 = 0.540 \times 10^6 \text{ mm}^4 \qquad (h)$$

Next use the parallel axis theorem [Eq. (C.20)] to determine the moment of inertia of each of the three areas relative to the centroidal axis. For the top flange (Area 1):

$$I_{z1} = I_{z'1} + A_1d_1^2 = I_{z'1} + (w_1\, t_1/4)(2h - t_1 - 2\overline{Y})^2$$

$$I_{z1} = 1.139 \times 10^6 + (150)(11.25)(600 - 45 - 284.2)^2$$

$$I_{z1} = 1.139 \times 10^6 + 123.7 \times 10^6 = 124.8 \times 10^6 \text{ mm}^4 \qquad (i)$$

For the web (Area 2):

$$I_{z2} = I_{z'2} + A_2d_2^2 = I_{z'2} + (wh_w/4)(2t_2 + h_w - 2\overline{Y})^2$$

$$I_{z2} = 14.24 \times 10^6 + (15)(56.25)(60 + 225 - 284.2)^2$$

$$I_{z2} = 14.24 \times 10^6 + 0.0005 \times 10^6 = 14.24 \times 10^6 \text{ mm}^4 \qquad (j)$$

For the bottom flange (Area 3):

$$I_{z3} = I_{z'3} + A_3d_3^2 = I_{z'3} + (w_2\, t_2/4)(2\,y - t_2)^2$$

$$I_{z3} = 0.540 \times 10^6 + (240)(7.5)(284.2 - 30)^2$$

$$I_{z3} = 0.540 \times 10^6 + 116.3 \times 10^6 = 116.8 \text{ x } 10^6 \text{ mm}^4 \qquad (k)$$

Before we complete the computation, examine the results listed in Eqs. (i – k). For both of the flanges, we note that the contribution of the $I_{z'}$ term was negligible compared to the Ad^2 term. For the web the $I_{z'}$ term was dominant and the $A_2d_2^2$ term was negligible. To complete the solution for the moment of inertia of this composite area, we sum the moments of inertia due to the three areas as:

$$I_z = I_{z1} + I_{z2} + I_{z3} \qquad (l)$$

Substituting the results for Eqs. (i – k) into Eq. (l) yields:

$$I_z = (124.8 + 14.24 + 116.8) \times 10^6 = 255.8 \times 10^6 \text{ mm}^4 \qquad (m)$$

The contribution of the web to the moment of inertia about the centroidal axis of this unsymmetrical wide flange section was a small part of the total (less than 6%). This example shows that the main purpose of the web is to move the flanges outward from the neutral (centroidal) axis.

PROBLEMS

C.1 Determine the area of a right triangle if its base is 30 mm and its height is 70 mm.

C.2 Determine the area of an isosceles triangle if its base is 30 mm and its height is 70 mm.

C.3 Determine the area of a right triangle if its base is 4in. and its height is 7 in.

C.4 Determine the area of an isosceles triangle if its base is 5 in. and its height is 9.5 in.

C.5 Determine the area of a circle with a diameter of 14 mm.

C.6 Determine the area of a circle with a diameter of 3.2 in.

C.7 Determine the area of a circle with a diameter of 88 mm.

C.8 Determine the area of a circle with a diameter of 3.6 in.

C.9 Determine the area of an ellipse if the major and minor axes are defined by a = 2b = 16 mm.

C.10 Determine the area of an ellipse if the major and minor axes are defined by a = 3b = 6 in.

C.11 Determine the area of an ellipse if the major and minor axes are defined by a = 4b = 20 mm.

C.12 Determine the area of an ellipse if the major and minor axes are defined by a = (3.5)b = 7.0 in.

C.13 Draw a right triangle with a base of 30 mm and height of 70 mm and then locate and dimension its centroid.

C.14 Draw an isosceles triangle with a base of 30 mm and height of 70 mm and then locate and dimension its centroid.

C.15 Draw a right triangle with a base of 4in. and height of 7 in. and then locate and dimension its centroid.

C.16 Draw an isosceles triangle with a base of 5 in. and height of 9.5 in. and then locate and dimension its centroid.

C.17 Verify the location of the centroid for the semicircular area defined in Fig. PC.17.

PC.17

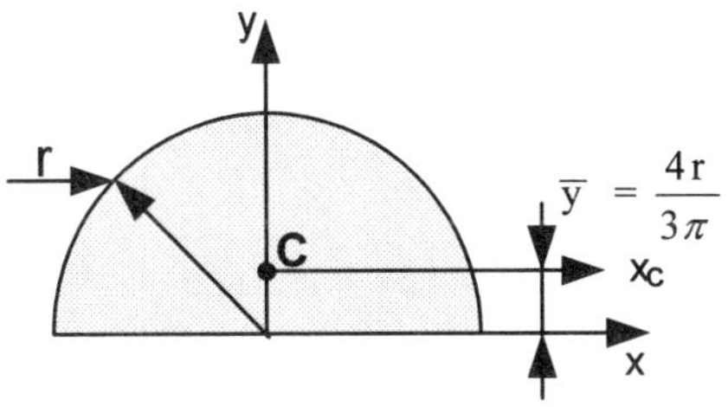

C.18 Verify the location of the centroid for the semi-elliptical area defined in Fig. PC.18.

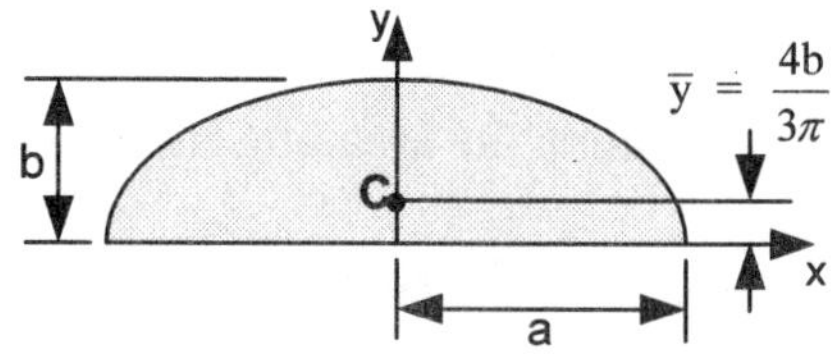

PC.18

C.19 Verify the location of the centroid for the parabolic area defined in Fig. PC.19.

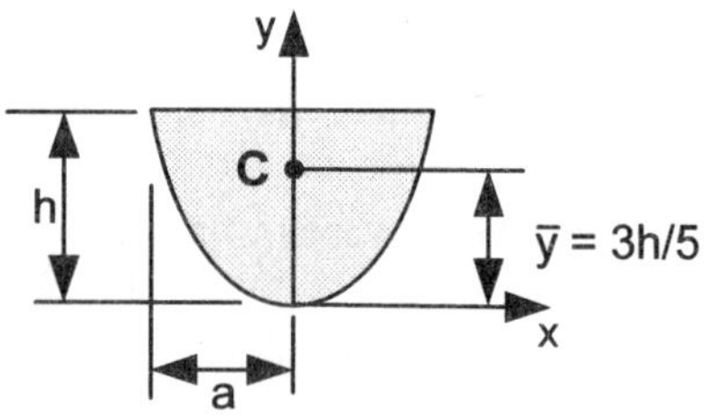

PC.19

C.20 Verify the location of the centroid for the circular sector defined in Fig. PC.20.

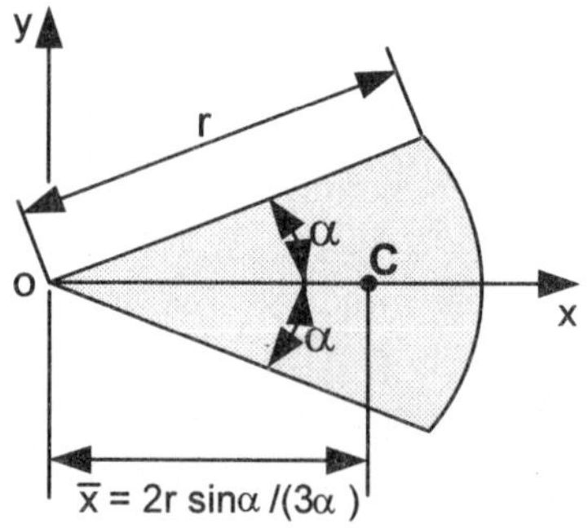

PC.20

C.21 Verify the location of the centroid for the general spandrel defined Fig. PC.21.

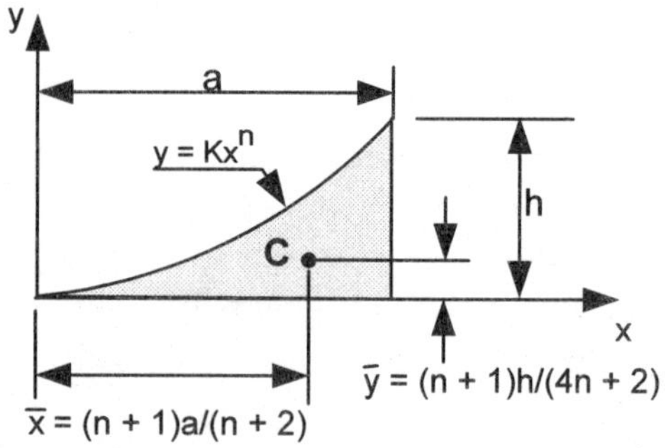

PC.21

C.22 For the unusual plate shown in Fig. PC.22, derive an equation locating the centroid relative to point A. The elliptical hole is centered in the rectangular portion of the plate.

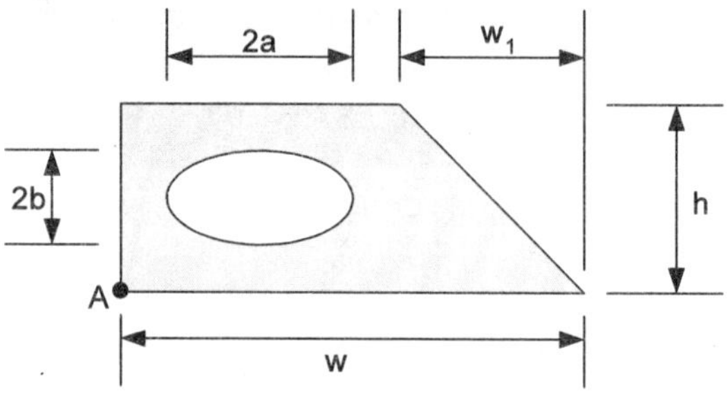

PC.22

C.23 Determine the location of the centroid relative to point A for the plate defined in Fig. PC.23. All dimensions are given in mm, and the elliptical hole is centered in the rectangular portion of the plate.

PC.23

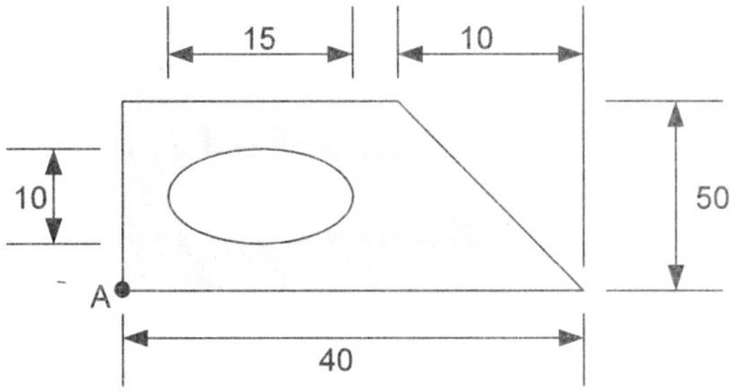

C.24 Divide the plate, illustrated in Fig. PC.23, into three areas (an ellipse, rectangle and triangle). Determine the moment of inertia for each area about its centroidal axis.

C.25 Verify that the moment of inertia of an ellipse about its centroidal axis is given by:

$I_x = \pi a b^3 /4$ and $I_y = \pi a^3 b/4$

C.26 Determine the moment of inertia for the total area of the plate, shown in Fig. PC.26, about its centroidal axis.

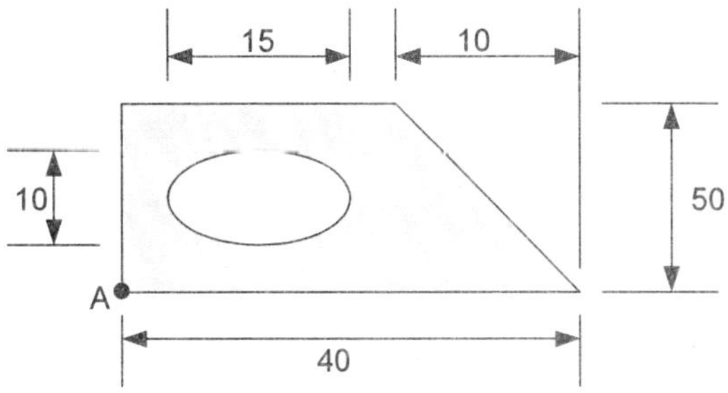

PC.26

C.27 For the U shaped section, shown in Fig. PC.27, determine the location of the centroid $\bar{y}$ relative to an axis along its base. All dimensions are in inches.

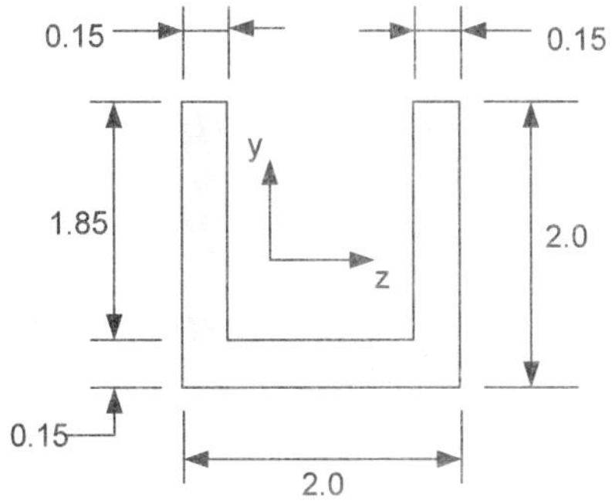

PC.27

C.28 Determine the location of the centroid $\bar{y}$, relative to an axis along its base, for the U shaped section shown in Fig. PC.28. All dimensions are in inches.

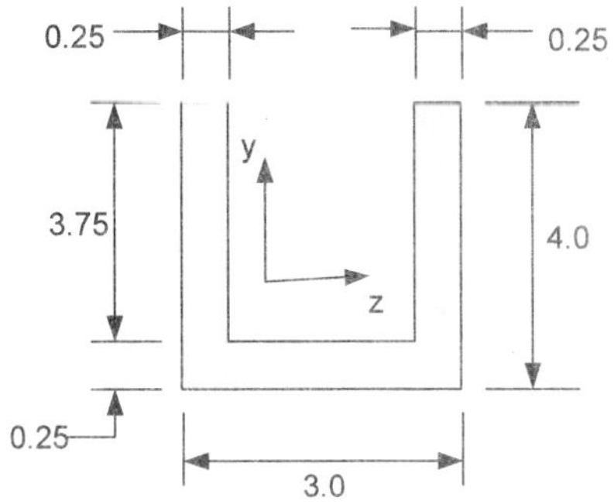

PC.28

C.29 Determine the moment of inertia I_z about the centroid of the U shaped member defined in (a) Problem C.27 and (b) Problem C.28.

C.30 Verify that the polar moment of inertia of a quarter circle area with a radius R is $J_o = \pi R^4/8$.

C.31 For the uncommon shape presented in Fig. PC.31, determine the centroid and the moment of inertia relative to the centroidal axis. The rectangular hole is centered in the elliptical area.

C.32 For the uncommon shape presented in Fig. PC.31, determine the moment of inertia relative to the z-axis.

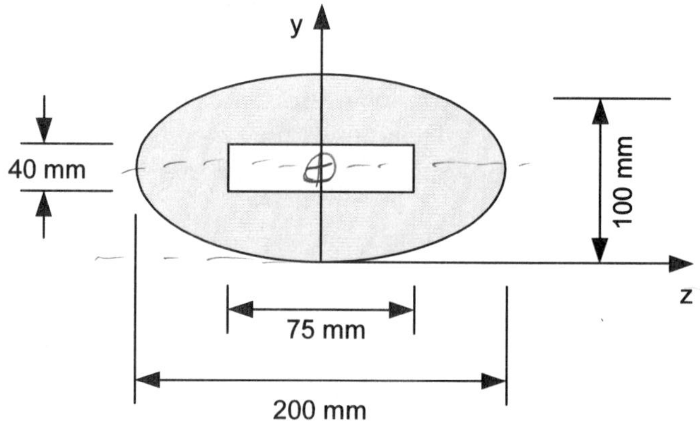

PC.31

C.33 For the uncommon shape presented in Fig. PC.31, determine the moment of inertia relative to the y-axis.

C.34 For the irregular cross sectional area, described in Fig. PC.34, locate the centroid relative to both the x and y-axes. The dimensions are given in mm.

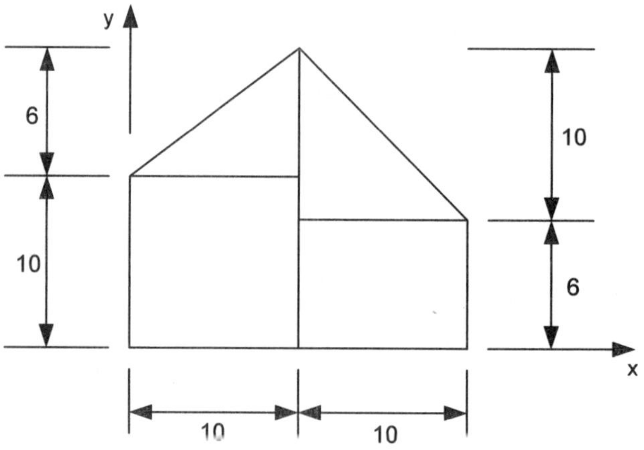

PC.34

APPENDIX D

GEOMETRIC PROPERTIES OF ROLLED STEEL SHAPES

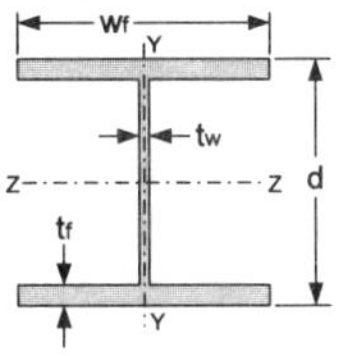

Wide-Flange Beams (U.S. Customary Units)

			Flange		Web	Axis Z-Z			Axis Y-Y		
Designation*	Area (in.^{2})	Depth (in.)	Width (in.)	Thickness (in.)	Thickness (in.)	I (in.^{4})	Z (in.^{3})	r (in.)	I (in.^{4})	Z (in.^{3})	r (in.)
W36 × 230	67.6	35.90	16.470	1.260	0.760	15000	837	14.9	940	114	3.73
× 160	47.0	36.01	12.000	1.020	0.650	9750	542	14.4	295	49.1	2.50
W33 × 201	59.1	33.68	15.745	1.150	0.715	11500	684	14.0	749	95.2	3.56
× 152	44.7	33.49	11.565	1.055	0.635	8160	487	13.5	273	47.2	2.47
× 130	38.3	33.09	11.510	0.855	0.580	6710	406	13.2	218	37.9	2.39
W30 × 132	38.9	30.31	10.545	1.000	0.615	5770	380	12.2	196	37.2	2.25
× 108	31.7	29.83	10.475	0.760	0.545	4470	299	11.9	146	27.9	2.15
W27 × 146	42.9	27.38	13.965	0.975	0.605	5630	411	11.4	443	63.5	3.21
× 94	27.7	26.92	9.990	0.745	0.490	3270	243	10.9	124	24.8	2.12
W24 × 104	30.6	24.06	12.750	0.750	0.500	3100	258	10.1	259	40.7	2.91
× 84	24.7	24.10	9.020	0.770	0.470	2370	196	9.79	94.4	20.9	1.95
× 62	18.2	23.74	7.040	0.590	0.430	1550	131	9.23	34.5	9.80	1.38
W21 × 101	29.8	21.36	12.290	0.800	0.500	2420	227	9.02	248	40.3	2.89
× 83	24.3	21.43	8.355	0.835	0.515	1830	171	8.67	81.4	19.5	1.83
× 62	18.3	20.99	8.240	0.615	0.400	1330	127	8.54	57.5	13.9	1.77
W18 × 97	28.5	18.59	11.145	0.870	0.535	1750	188	7.82	201	36.1	2.65
× 76	22.3	18.21	11.035	0.680	0.425	1330	146	7.73	152	27.6	2.61
× 60	17.6	18.24	7.555	0.695	0.415	984	108	7.47	50.1	13.3	1.69
W16 × 100	29.4	16.97	10.425	0.985	0.585	1490	175	7.10	186	35.7	2.52
× 67	19.7	16.33	10.235	0.665	0.395	954	117	6.96	119	23.2	2.46
× 40	11.8	16.01	6.995	0.505	0.305	518	64.7	6.63	28.9	8.25	1.57
× 26	7.68	15.69	5.500	0.345	0.250	301	38.4	6.26	9.59	3.49	1.12
W14 × 120	35.3	14.48	14.670	0.940	0.590	1380	190	6.24	495	67.5	3.74
× 82	24.1	14.31	10.130	0.855	0.510	882	123	6.05	148	29.3	2.48
× 43	12.6	13.66	7.995	0.530	0.305	428	62.7	5.82	45.2	11.3	1.89
× 30	8.85	13.84	6.730	0.385	0.270	291	42.0	5.73	19.6	5.82	1.49
W12 × 96	28.2	12.71	12.160	0.900	0.550	833	131	5.44	270	44.4	3.09
× 65	19.1	12.12	12.000	0.605	0.390	533	87.9	5.28	174	29.1	3.02
× 50	14.7	12.19	8.080	0.640	0.370	394	64.7	5.18	56.3	13.9	1.96
× 30	8.79	12.34	6.520	0.440	0.260	238	38.6	5.21	20.3	6.24	1.52
W10 × 60	17.6	10.22	10.080	0.680	0.420	341	66.7	4.39	116	23.0	2.57
× 45	13.3	10.10	8.020	0.620	0.350	248	49.1	4.33	53.4	13.3	2.01
× 30	8.84	10.47	5.810	0.510	0.300	170	32.4	4.38	16.7	5.75	1.37
× 22	6.49	10.17	5.750	0.360	0.240	118	23.2	4.27	11.4	3.97	1.33
W8 × 40	11.7	8.25	8.070	0.560	0.360	146	35.5	3.53	49.1	12.2	2.04
× 31	9.13	8.00	7.995	0.435	0.285	110	27.5	3.47	37.1	9.27	2.02
× 24	7.08	7.93	6.495	0.400	0.245	82.8	20.9	3.42	18.3	5.63	1.61
× 15	4.44	8.11	4.015	0.315	0.245	48.0	11.8	3.29	3.41	1.70	0.876
W6 × 25	7.34	6.38	6.080	0.455	0.320	53.4	16.7	2.70	17.1	5.61	1.52
× 16	4.74	6.28	4.030	0.405	0.260	32.1	10.2	2.60	4.43	2.20	0.967
W5 × 16	4.68	5.01	5.000	0.360	0.240	21.3	8.51	2.13	7.51	3.00	1.27
W4 × 13	3.83	4.16	4.060	0.345	0.280	11.3	5.46	1.72	3.86	1.90	1.00

Courtesy of the American Institute of Steel Construction.

*W is the symbol for a wide-flange beam, followed by the nominal depth in inches, and weight in pounds per foot of length.

GEOMETRIC PROPERTIES OF ROLLED STEEL SHAPES

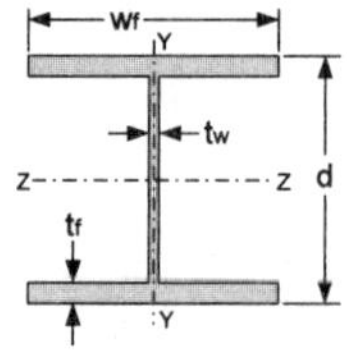

Wide-Flange Beams (SI Units)

Designation*	Area (mm^2)	Depth (mm)	Width (mm)	Flange Thickness (mm)	Web Thickness (mm)	Axis Z-Z I (10^6 mm^4)	Axis Z-Z Z (10^3 mm^3)	Axis Z-Z r (mm)	Axis Y-Y I (10^6 mm^4)	Axis Y-Y Z (10^3 mm^3)	Axis Y-Y r (mm)
W914 × 342	43610	912	418	32.0	19.3	6245	13715	378	391	1870	94.7
× 238	30325	915	305	25.9	16.5	4060	8880	366	123	805	63.5
W838 × 299	38130	855	400	29.2	18.2	4785	11210	356	312	1560	90.4
× 226	28850	851	294	26.8	16.1	3395	7980	343	114	775	62.7
× 193	24710	840	292	21.7	14.7	2795	6655	335	90.7	620	60.7
W762 × 196	25100	770	268	25.4	15.6	2400	6225	310	81.6	610	57.2
× 161	20450	758	266	19.3	13.8	1860	4900	302	60.8	457	54.6
W686 × 217	27675	695	355	24.8	15.4	2345	6735	290	184	1040	81.5
× 140	17870	684	254	18.9	12.4	1360	3980	277	51.6	406	53.8
W610 × 155	19740	611	324	19.1	12.7	1290	4230	257	108	667	73.9
× 125	15935	612	229	19.6	11.9	985	3210	249	39.3	342	49.5
× 92	11750	603	179	15.0	10.9	645	2145	234	14.4	161	35.1
W533 × 150	19225	543	312	20.3	12.7	1005	3720	229	103	660	73.4
× 124	15675	544	212	21.2	13.1	762	2800	220	33.9	320	46.5
× 92	11805	533	209	15.6	10.2	554	2080	217	23.9	228	45.0
W457 × 144	18365	472	283	22.1	13.6	728	3080	199	83.7	592	67.3
× 113	14385	463	280	17.3	10.8	554	2395	196	63.3	452	66.3
× 89	11355	463	192	17.7	10.5	410	1770	190	20.9	218	42.9
W406 × 149	18970	431	265	25.0	14.9	620	2870	180	77.4	585	64.0
× 100	12710	415	260	16.9	10.0	397	1915	177	49.5	380	62.5
× 60	7615	407	178	12.8	7.7	216	1060	168	12.0	135	39.9
× 39	4950	399	140	8.8	6.4	125	629	159	3.99	57.2	28.4
W356 × 179	22775	368	373	23.9	15.0	574	3115	158	206	1105	95.0
× 122	15550	363	257	21.7	13.0	367	2015	154	61.6	480	63.0
× 64	8130	347	203	13.5	7.7	178	1025	148	18.8	185	48.0
× 45	5710	352	171	9.8	6.9	121	688	146	8.16	95.4	37.8
W305 × 143	18195	323	309	22.9	14.0	347	2145	138	112	728	78.5
× 97	12325	308	305	15.4	9.9	222	1440	134	72.4	477	76.7
× 74	9485	310	205	16.3	9.4	164	1060	132	23.4	228	49.8
× 45	5670	313	166	11.2	6.6	99.1	633	132	8.45	102	38.6
W254 × 89	11355	260	256	17.3	10.7	142	1095	112	48.3	377	65.3
× 67	8580	257	204	15.7	8.9	103	805	110	22.2	218	51.1
× 45	5705	266	148	13.0	7.6	70.8	531	111	6.95	94.2	34.8
× 33	4185	258	146	9.1	6.1	49.1	380	108	4.75	65.1	33.8
W203 × 60	7550	210	205	14.2	9.1	60.8	582	89.7	20.4	200	51.8
× 46	5890	203	203	11.0	7.2	45.8	451	88.1	15.4	152	51.3
× 36	4570	201	165	10.2	6.2	34.5	342	86.7	7.61	92.3	40.9
× 22	2865	206	102	8.0	6.2	20.0	193	83.6	1.42	27.9	22.3
W152 × 37	4735	162	154	11.6	8.1	22.2	274	68.6	7.12	91.9	38.6
× 24	3060	160	102	10.3	6.6	13.4	167	66.0	1.84	36.1	24.6
W127 × 24	3020	127	127	9.1	6.1	8.87	139	54.1	3.13	49.2	32.3
W102 × 19	2470	106	103	8.8	7.1	4.70	89.5	43.7	1.61	31.1	25.4

Courtesy of The American Institute of Steel Construction.
*W is the symbol for a wide-flange beam, followed by the nominal depth in mm, and the mass in kg per meter of length.

GEOMETRIC PROPERTIES OF ROLLED STEEL SHAPES

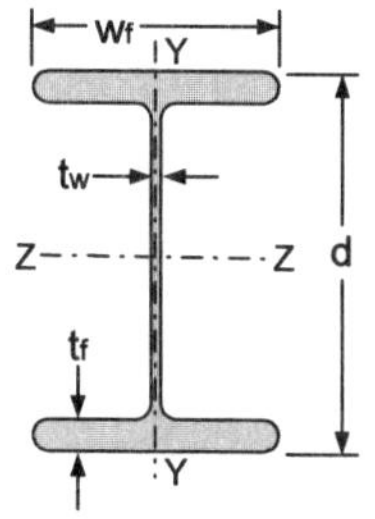

American Standard Beams (U.S. Customary Units)

Designation*	Area (in^2)	Depth (in.)	Width (in.)	Flange Thickness (in.)	Web Thickness (in.)	Axis Z-Z I ($in.^4$)	Axis Z-Z Z ($in.^3$)	Axis Z-Z r (in.)	Axis Y-Y I ($in.^4$)	Axis Y-Y Z ($in.^3$)	Axis Y-Y r (in.)
S24 × 121	35.6	24.50	8.050	1.090	0.800	3160	258	9.43	83.3	20.7	1.53
× 106	31.2	24.50	7.870	1.090	0.620	2940	240	9.71	77.1	19.6	1.57
× 100	29.3	24.00	7.245	0.870	0.745	2390	199	9.02	47.7	13.2	1.27
× 90	26.5	24.00	7.125	0.870	0.625	2250	187	9.21	44.9	12.6	1.30
× 80	23.5	24.00	7.000	0.870	0.500	2100	175	9.47	42.2	12.1	1.34
S20 × 96	28.2	20.30	7.200	0.920	0.800	1670	165	7.71	50.2	13.9	1.33
× 86	25.3	20.30	7.060	0.920	0.660	1580	155	7.89	46.8	13.3	1.36
× 75	22.0	20.00	6.385	0.795	0.635	1280	128	7.62	29.8	9.32	1.16
× 66	19.4	20.00	6.255	0.795	0.505	1190	119	7.83	27.7	8.85	1.19
S18 × 70	20.6	18.00	6.251	0.691	0.711	926	103	6.71	24.1	7.72	1.08
× 54.7	16.1	18.00	6.001	0.691	0.461	804	89.4	7.07	20.8	6.94	1.14
S15 × 50	14.7	15.00	5.640	0.622	0.550	486	64.8	5.75	15.7	5.57	1.03
× 42.9	12.6	15.00	5.501	0.622	0.411	447	59.6	5.95	14.4	5.23	1.07
S12 × 50	14.7	12.00	5.477	0.659	0.687	305	50.8	4.55	15.7	5.74	1.03
× 40.8	12.0	12.00	5.252	0.659	0.462	272	45.4	4.77	13.6	5.16	1.06
× 35	10.3	12.00	5.078	0.544	0.428	229	38.2	4.72	9.87	3.89	0.980
× 31.8	9.35	12.00	5.000	0.544	0.350	218	36.4	4.83	9.36	3.74	1.000
S10 × 35	10.3	10.00	4.944	0.491	0.594	147	29.4	3.78	8.36	3.38	0.901
× 25.4	7.46	10.00	4.661	0.491	0.311	124	24.7	4.07	6.79	2.91	0.954
S8 × 23	6.77	8.00	4.171	0.426	0.441	64.9	16.2	3.10	4.31	2.07	0.798
× 18.4	5.41	8.00	4.001	0.426	0.271	57.6	14.4	3.26	3.73	1.86	0.831
S7 × 20	5.88	7.00	3.860	0.392	0.450	42.4	12.1	2.69	3.17	1.64	0.734
× 15.3	4.50	7.00	3.662	0.392	0.252	36.7	10.5	2.86	2.64	1.44	0.766
S6 × 17.25	5.07	6.00	3.565	0.359	0.465	26.3	8.77	2.28	2.31	1.30	0.675
× 12.5	3.67	6.00	3.332	0.359	0.232	22.1	7.37	2.45	1.82	1.09	0.705
S5 × 14.75	4.34	5.00	3.284	0.326	0.494	15.2	6.09	1.87	1.67	1.01	0.620
× 10	2.94	5.00	3.004	0.326	0.214	12.3	4.92	2.05	1.22	0.809	0.643
S4 × 9.5	2.79	4.00	2.796	0.293	0.326	6.79	3.39	1.56	0.903	0.646	0.569
× 7.7	2.26	4.00	2.663	0.293	0.193	6.08	3.04	1.64	0.764	0.574	0.581
S3 × 7.5	2.21	3.00	2.509	0.260	0.349	2.93	1.95	1.15	0.586	0.468	0.516
× 5.7	1.67	3.00	2.330	0.260	0.170	2.52	1.68	1.23	0.455	0.390	0.522

Courtesy of The American Institute of Steel Construction.
*S is the symbol for a standard beam, followed by the nominal depth in inches, then the weight in pounds per foot of length.

GEOMETRIC PROPERTIES OF ROLLED STEEL SHAPES

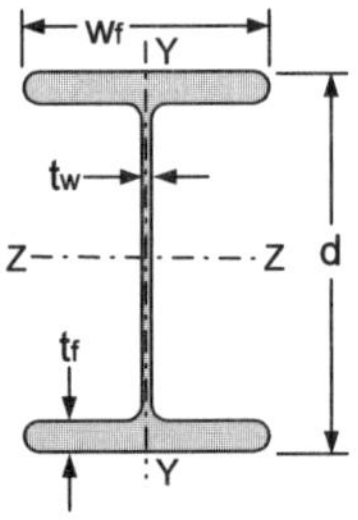

American Standard Beams (SI Units)

Designation*	Area (mm^2)	Depth (mm)	Flange Width (mm)	Flange Thickness (mm)	Web Thickness (mm)	Axis Z-Z I (10^6 mm^4)	Axis Z-Z Z (10^3 mm^3)	Axis Z-Z r (mm)	Axis Y-Y I (10^6 mm^4)	Axis Y-Y Z (10^3 mm^3)	Axis Y-Y r (mm)
S610 × 180	22970	622.3	204.5	27.7	20.3	1315	4225	240	34.7	339	38.9
× 158	20130	622.3	199.9	27.7	15.7	1225	3935	247	32.1	321	39.9
× 149	18900	609.6	184.0	22.1	18.9	995	3260	229	19.9	216	32.3
× 134	17100	609.6	181.0	22.1	15.9	937	3065	234	18.7	206	33.0
× 119	15160	609.6	177.8	22.1	12.7	874	2870	241	17.6	198	34.0
S508 × 143	18190	515.6	182.9	23.4	20.3	695	2705	196	20.9	228	33.8
× 128	16320	515.6	179.3	23.4	16.8	658	2540	200	19.5	218	34.5
× 112	14190	508.0	162.2	20.2	16.1	533	2100	194	12.4	153	29.5
× 98	12520	508.0	158.9	20.2	12.8	495	1950	199	11.5	145	30.2
S457 × 104	13290	457.2	158.8	17.6	18.1	358	1690	170	10.0	127	27.4
× 81	10390	457.2	152.4	17.6	11.7	335	1465	180	8.66	114	29.0
S381 × 74	9485	381.0	143.3	15.8	14.0	202	1060	146	6.53	91.3	26.2
× 64	8130	381.0	139.7	15.8	10.4	186	977	151	5.99	85.7	27.2
S305 × 74	9485	304.8	139.1	16.7	17.4	127	832	116	6.53	94.1	26.2
× 61	7740	304.8	133.4	16.7	11.7	113	744	121	5.66	84.6	26.9
× 52	6645	304.8	129.0	13.8	10.9	95.3	626	120	4.11	63.7	24.1
× 47	6030	304.8	127.0	13.8	8.9	90.7	596	123	3.90	61.3	25.4
S254 × 52	6645	254.0	125.6	12.5	15.1	61.2	482	96.0	3.48	55.4	22.9
× 38	4815	254.0	118.4	12.5	7.9	51.6	408	103	2.83	47.7	24.2
S203 × 34	4370	203.2	105.9	10.8	11.2	27.0	265	78.7	1.79	33.9	20.3
× 27	3490	203.2	101.6	10.8	6.9	24.0	236	82.8	1.55	30.5	21.1
S178 × 30	3795	177.8	98.0	10.0	11.4	17.6	198	68.3	1.32	26.9	18.6
× 23	2905	177.8	93.0	10.0	6.4	15.3	172	72.6	1.10	23.6	19.5
S152 × 26	3270	152.4	90.6	9.1	11.8	10.9	144	57.9	0.961	21.3	17.1
× 19	2370	152.4	84.6	9.1	5.9	9.20	121	62.2	0.758	17.9	17.9
S127 × 22	2800	127.0	83.4	8.3	12.5	6.33	99.8	47.5	0.695	16.6	15.7
× 15	1895	127.0	76.3	8.3	5.4	5.12	80.6	52.1	0.508	13.3	16.3
S102 × 14	1800	101.6	71.0	7.4	8.3	2.83	55.6	39.6	0.376	10.6	14.5
× 11	1460	101.6	67.6	7.4	4.9	2.53	49.8	41.7	0.318	9.41	14.8
S76 × 11	1425	76.2	63.7	6.6	8.9	1.22	32.0	29.2	0.244	7.67	13.1
× 8.5	1075	76.2	59.2	6.6	4.3	1.05	27.5	31.2	0.189	6.39	13.3

Courtesy of The American Institute of Steel Construction.
*S is the symbol for a standard beam, followed by the nominal depth in mm, then the mass in kg per meter of length.

GEOMETRIC PROPERTIES OF ROLLED STEEL SHAPES

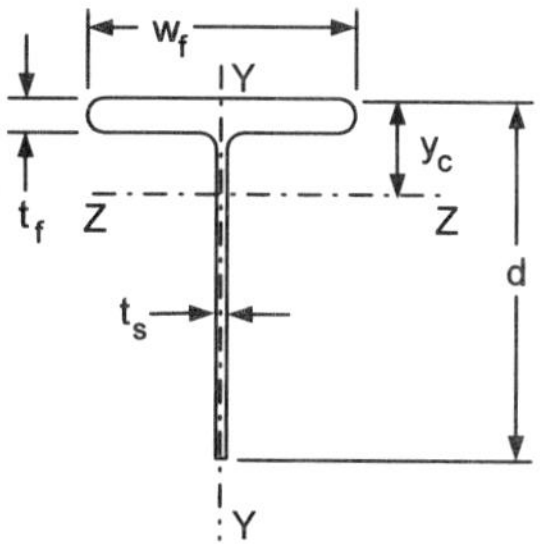

Structural Tees (U.S. Customary Units)

Designation*	Area (in.^{2})	Depth of Tee (in.)	Flange Width (in.)	Flange Thickness (in.)	Stem Thickness (in.)	Axis Z-Z I (in.^{4})	Axis Z-Z Z (in.^{3})	Axis Z-Z r (in.)	y_c (in.)	Axis Y-Y I (in.^{4})	Axis Y-Y Z (in.^{3})	Axis Y-Y r (in.)
WT18 × 115	33.8	17.950	16.470	1.260	0.760	934	67.0	5.25	4.01	470	57.1	3.73
× 80	23.5	18.005	12.000	1.020	0.650	740	55.8	5.61	4.74	147	24.6	2.50
WT15 × 66	19.4	15.155	10.545	1.000	0.615	421	37.4	4.66	3.90	98.0	18.6	2.25
× 54	15.9	14.915	10.475	0.760	0.545	349	32.0	4.69	4.01	73.0	13.9	2.15
WT12 × 52	15.3	12.030	12.750	0.750	0.500	189	20.0	3.51	2.59	130	20.3	2.91
× 47	13.8	12.155	9.065	0.875	0.515	186	20.3	3.67	2.99	54.5	12.0	1.98
× 42	12.4	12.050	9.020	0.770	0.470	166	18.3	3.67	2.97	47.2	10.5	1.95
× 31	9.11	11.870	7.040	0.590	0.430	131	15.6	3.79	3.46	17.2	4.90	1.38
WT9 × 38	11.2	9.105	11.035	0.680	0.425	71.8	9.83	2.54	1.80	76.2	13.8	2.61
× 30	8.82	9.120	7.555	0.695	0.415	64.7	9.29	2.71	2.16	25.0	6.63	1.69
× 25	7.33	8.995	7.495	0.570	0.355	53.5	7.79	2.70	2.12	20.0	5.35	1.65
× 20	5.88	8.950	6.015	0.525	0.315	44.8	6.73	2.76	2.29	9.55	3.17	1.27
WT8 × 50	14.7	8.485	10.425	0.985	0.585	76.8	11.4	2.28	1.76	93.1	17.9	2.51
× 25	7.37	8.130	7.070	0.630	0.380	42.3	6.78	2.40	1.89	18.6	5.26	1.59
× 20	5.89	8.005	6.995	0.505	0.305	33.1	5.35	2.37	1.81	14.4	4.12	1.57
× 13	3.84	7.845	5.500	0.345	0.250	23.5	4.09	2.47	2.09	4.80	1.74	1.12
WT7 × 60	17.7	7.240	14.670	0.940	0.590	51.7	8.61	1.71	1.24	247	33.7	3.74
× 41	12.0	7.155	10.130	0.855	0.510	41.2	7.14	1.85	1.39	74.2	14.6	2.48
× 34	9.99	7.020	10.035	0.720	0.415	32.6	5.69	1.81	1.29	60.7	12.1	2.46
× 24	7.07	6.985	8.030	0.595	0.340	24.9	4.48	1.87	1.35	25.7	6.40	1.91
× 15	4.42	6.920	6.730	0.385	0.270	19.0	3.55	2.07	1.58	9.79	2.91	1.49
× 11	3.25	6.870	5.000	0.335	0.230	14.8	2.91	2.14	1.76	3.50	1.40	1.04
WT6 × 60	17.6	6.560	12.320	1.105	0.710	43.4	8.22	1.57	1.28	172	28.0	3.13
× 48	14.1	6.355	12.160	0.900	0.550	32.0	6.12	1.51	1.13	135	22.2	3.09
× 36	10.6	6.125	12.040	0.670	0.430	23.2	4.54	1.48	1.02	97.5	16.2	3.04
× 25	7.34	6.095	8.080	0.640	0.370	18.7	3.79	1.60	1.17	28.2	6.97	1.96
× 15	4.40	6.170	6.520	0.440	0.260	13.5	2.75	1.75	1.27	10.2	3.12	1.52
× 8	2.36	5.995	3.990	0.265	0.220	8.70	2.04	1.92	1.74	1.41	0.706	0.773
WT5 × 56	16.5	5.680	10.415	1.250	0.755	28.6	6.40	1.32	1.21	118	22.6	2.68
× 44	12.9	5.420	10.265	0.990	0.605	20.8	4.77	1.27	1.06	89.3	17.4	2.63
× 30	8.82	5.110	10.080	0.680	0.420	12.9	3.04	1.21	0.884	58.1	11.5	2.57
× 15	4.42	5.235	5.810	0.510	0.300	9.28	2.24	1.45	1.10	8.35	2.87	1.37
× 6	1.77	4.935	3.960	0.210	0.190	4.35	1.22	1.57	1.36	1.09	0.551	0.785
WT4 × 29	8.55	4.375	8.220	0.810	0.510	9.12	2.61	1.03	0.874	37.5	9.13	2.10
× 20	5.87	4.125	8.070	0.560	0.360	5.73	1.69	0.988	0.735	24.5	6.08	2.04
× 12	3.54	3.965	6.495	0.400	0.245	3.53	1.08	0.999	0.695	9.14	2.81	1.61
× 9	2.63	4.070	5.250	0.330	0.230	3.41	1.05	1.14	0.834	3.98	1.52	1.23
× 5	1.48	3.945	3.940	0.205	0.170	2.15	0.717	1.20	0.953	1.05	0.532	0.841
WT3 × 10	2.94	3.100	6.020	0.365	0.260	1.76	0.693	0.774	0.560	6.64	2.21	1.50
× 6	1.78	3.015	4.000	0.280	0.230	1.32	0.564	0.861	0.677	1.50	0.748	0.918
WT2 × 6.5	1.91	2.080	4.060	0.345	0.280	0.526	0.321	0.524	0.440	1.93	0.950	1.00

Courtesy of The American Institute of Steel Construction.

*WT is the symbol for a structural T-section (cut from a W-section), followed by the nominal depth in inches, and the weight in pounds per foot of length.

GEOMETRIC PROPERTIES OF ROLLED STEEL SHAPES

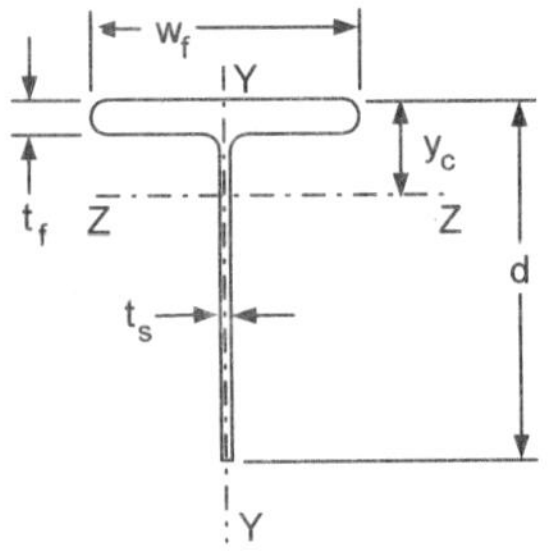

Structural Tees (SI Units)

Designation*	Area (mm^2)	Depth of Tee (mm)	Flange Width (mm)	Flange Thickness (mm)	Stem Thickness (mm)	Axis Z-Z I (10^6 mm^4)	Axis Z-Z Z (10^3 mm^3)	Axis Z-Z r (mm)	y_c (mm)	Axis Y-Y I (10^6 mm^4)	Axis Y-Y Z (10^3 mm^3)	Axis Y-Y r (mm)
WT457 × 171	21805	455.9	418.3	32.0	19.3	389	1098	133	102	196	936	94.7
× 119	15160	457.3	304.8	25.9	16.5	308	914	142	120	61.2	403	63.5
WT381 × 98	12515	384.9	267.8	25.4	15.6	175	613	118	99.1	40.8	305	57.2
× 80	10260	378.8	266.1	19.3	13.8	145	524	119	102	30.4	228	54.6
WT305 × 77	9870	305.6	323.9	19.1	12.7	78.7	328	89.2	65.8	54.1	333	73.9
× 70	8905	308.7	230.3	22.2	13.1	77.4	333	93.2	75.9	22.7	197	50.3
× 63	8000	306.1	229.1	19.6	11.9	69.1	300	93.2	75.4	19.6	172	49.5
× 46	5875	301.5	178.8	15.0	10.9	54.5	256	96.3	87.9	7.16	80.3	35.1
WT229 × 57	7225	231.3	280.3	17.3	10.8	29.9	161	64.5	45.7	31.7	226	66.3
× 45	5690	231.6	191.9	17.7	10.5	26.9	152	68.8	54.9	10.4	109	42.9
× 37	4730	228.5	190.4	14.5	9.0	22.3	128	68.6	53.8	8.32	87.7	41.9
× 30	3795	227.3	152.8	13.3	8.0	18.6	110	70.1	58.2	3.98	51.9	32.3
WT203 × 74	9485	215.5	264.8	25.0	14.9	32.0	187	57.9	44.7	38.8	293	63.8
× 37	4755	206.5	179.6	16.0	9.7	17.6	111	61.0	48.0	7.74	86.2	40.4
× 30	3800	203.3	177.7	12.8	7.7	13.8	87.7	60.2	46.0	5.99	67.5	39.9
× 19	2475	199.3	139.7	8.8	6.4	9.78	67.0	62.7	53.1	2.00	28.5	28.4
WT178 × 89	11420	183.9	372.6	23.9	15.0	21.5	141	43.4	31.5	103	552	95.0
× 61	7740	181.7	257.3	21.7	13.0	17.1	117	47.0	35.3	30.9	239	63.0
× 51	6445	178.3	254.9	18.3	10.5	13.6	93.2	46.0	32.8	25.3	198	62.5
× 36	4560	177.4	204.0	15.1	8.6	10.4	73.4	47.5	34.3	10.7	105	48.5
× 22	2850	175.8	170.9	9.8	6.9	7.91	58.2	52.6	40.1	4.07	47.7	37.8
× 16	2095	174.5	127.0	8.5	5.8	6.16	47.7	54.4	44.7	1.46	22.9	26.4
WT152 × 89	11355	166.6	312.9	28.1	18.0	18.1	135	39.9	32.5	71.6	459	79.5
× 71	9095	161.4	308.9	22.9	14.0	13.3	100	38.4	28.7	56.2	364	78.5
× 54	6840	155.6	305.8	17.0	10.9	9.66	74.4	37.6	25.9	40.6	265	77.2
× 37	4735	154.8	205.2	16.2	9.4	7.78	62.1	40.6	29.7	11.7	114	49.8
× 22	2840	156.7	165.6	11.2	6.6	5.62	45.1	44.5	32.3	4.25	51.1	38.6
× 12	1525	152.3	101.3	6.7	5.6	3.62	33.4	48.8	44.2	0.587	11.6	19.6
WT127 × 83	10645	144.3	264.5	31.8	19.2	11.9	105	33.5	30.7	49.1	370	68.1
× 65	8325	137.7	260.7	25.1	15.4	8.66	78.2	32.3	26.9	37.2	285	66.8
× 45	5690	129.8	256.0	17.3	10.7	3.37	49.0	30.7	22.5	21.2	188	65.3
× 22	2850	133.0	147.6	13.0	7.6	3.86	36.7	36.8	27.9	3.48	47.0	34.8
× 9	1140	125.3	100.6	5.3	4.8	1.81	20.0	39.9	34.5	0.454	9.03	19.9
WT102 × 43	5515	111.1	208.8	20.6	13.0	3.80	42.8	26.2	22.2	15.6	150	53.3
× 30	3785	104.8	205.0	14.2	9.1	2.39	27.7	25.1	18.7	10.2	99.6	51.8
× 18	2285	100.7	165.0	10.2	6.2	1.47	17.7	25.4	17.7	3.80	46.0	40.9
× 13	1695	103.4	133.4	8.4	5.8	1.42	17.2	29.0	21.2	1.66	24.9	31.2
× 7	955	100.2	100.1	5.2	4.3	0.895	11.7	30.5	24.2	0.437	8.72	21.4
WT76 × 15	1895	78.7	152.9	9.3	6.6	0.733	11.4	19.7	14.2	2.76	36.2	38.1
× 9	1150	76.6	101.6	7.1	5.8	0.549	9.24	21.9	17.2	0.624	12.3	23.3
WT51 × 10	1230	52.8	103.1	8.8	7.1	0.219	5.26	13.3	11.2	0.803	15.6	25.4

Courtesy of The American Institute of Steel Construction.
*WT is the symbol for a structural T-section (cut from a W-section), followed by the nominal depth in mm, and the mass in kg per meter of length.

APPENDIX E

EQUATIONS FOR DEFLECTIONS OF SIMPLY SUPPORTED BEAMS

SIMPLY SUPPORTED BEAMS LENGTH, L	SLOPE	DEFLECTION EQUATIONS
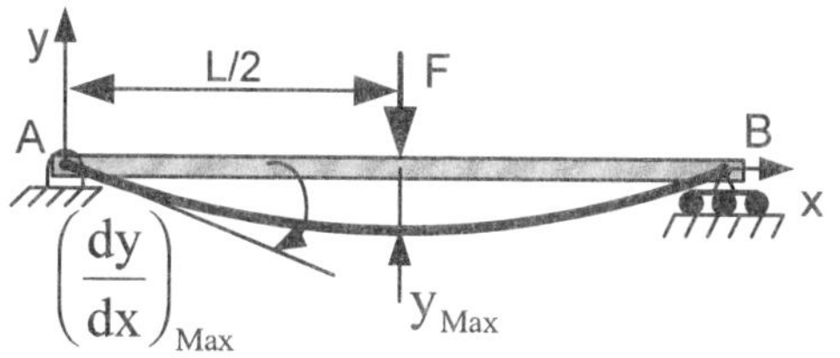	$\left(\frac{dy}{dx}\right)_{Max} = \frac{-FL^2}{16EI_z}$	$y = \frac{-Fx}{48EI_z}(3L^2 - 4x^2)$ $0 \le x \le L/2$ $y_{Max} = \frac{-FL^3}{48EI_z}$
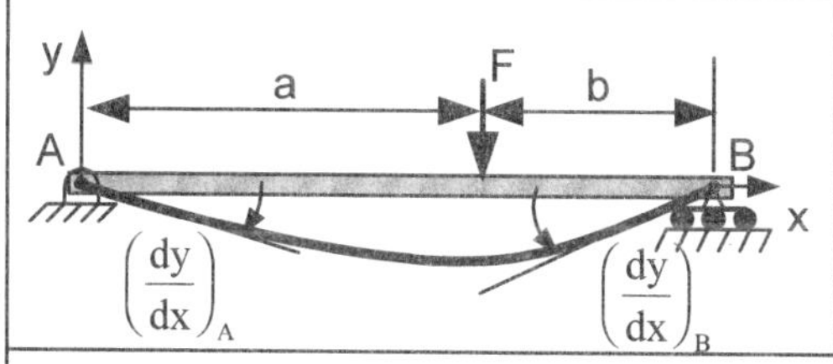	$\left(\frac{dy}{dx}\right)_A = \frac{-Fab(L+b)}{6EI_zL}$ $\left(\frac{dy}{dx}\right)_B = \frac{Fab(L+a)}{6EI_zL}$	$y = \frac{-Fbx}{6EI_zL}(L^2 - b^2 - x^2)$ $0 \le x \le a$ $y_{x=a} = \frac{-Fba}{6EI_zL}(L^2 - b^2 - a^2)$
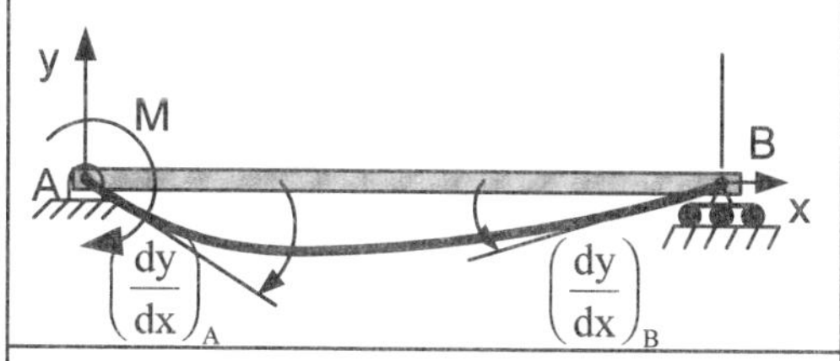	$\left(\frac{dy}{dx}\right)_A = -\frac{ML}{3EI_z}$ $\left(\frac{dy}{dx}\right)_B = \frac{ML}{6EI_z}$	$y = \frac{-Mx}{6EI_zL}(x^2 - 3Lx + 2L^2)$ $y_{Max} = \frac{-ML^2}{\sqrt{243}EI_z}$
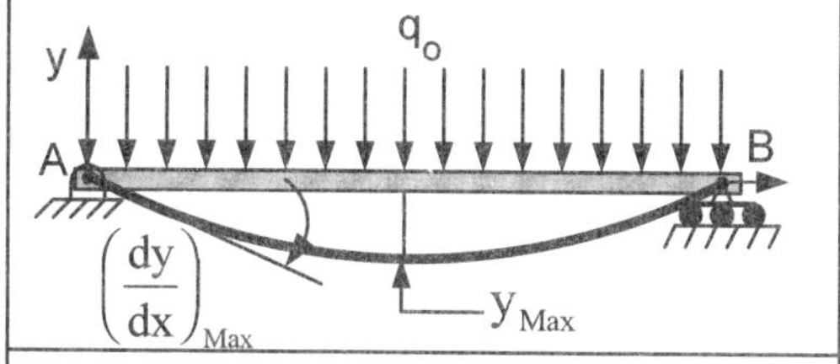	$\left(\frac{dy}{dx}\right)_{Max} = -\frac{q_0L^3}{24EI_z}$	$y = \frac{-q_0x}{24EI_z}(x^3 - 2Lx^2 + L^3)$ $y_{Max} = \frac{-5q_0L^4}{384EI_z}$
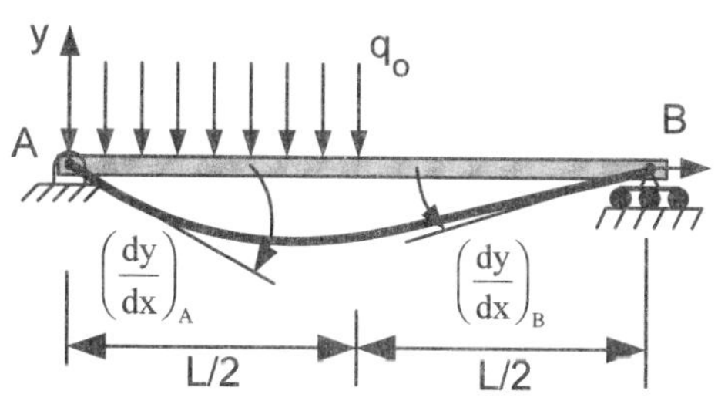	$\left(\frac{dy}{dx}\right)_A = -\frac{3q_0L^3}{128EI_z}$ $\left(\frac{dy}{dx}\right)_B = \frac{7q_0L^3}{384EI_z}$	$y = \frac{-q_0x}{384EI_z}(16x^3 - 24Lx^2 + 9L^3)$ $0 \le x \le L/2$ $y = \frac{-q_0L}{384EI_z}(8x^3 - 24Lx^2 + 17L^2x - L^3)$ $L/2 \le x \le L$ $y_{Max} = \frac{-6.563 \times 10^{-3} q_0L^4}{EI_z}$ at x = 0.4598L
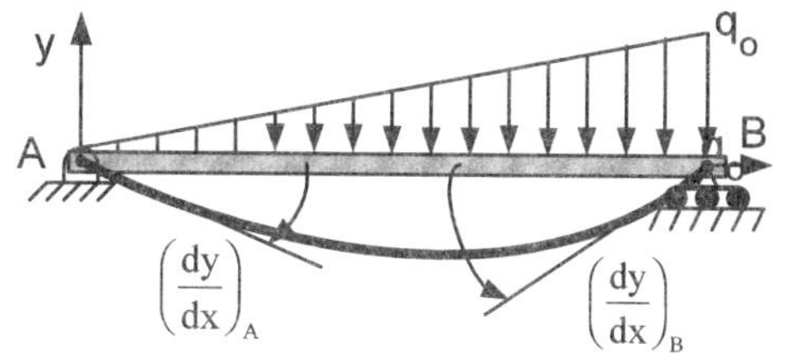	$\left(\frac{dy}{dx}\right)_A = \frac{-7q_0L^3}{360EI_z}$ $\left(\frac{dy}{dx}\right)_B = \frac{q_0L^3}{45EI_z}$	$y = \frac{-q_0x}{360EI_zL}(3x^4 - 10L^2x^2 + 7L^4)$ $y_{Max} = \frac{-6.52 \times 10^{-3} q_0L^4}{EI_z}$ at x = 0.5193

EQUATIONS FOR DEFLECTIONS OF CANTILEVER BEAMS

CANTILEVER BEAMS LENGTH, L	SLOPE	DEFLECTION EQUATIONS
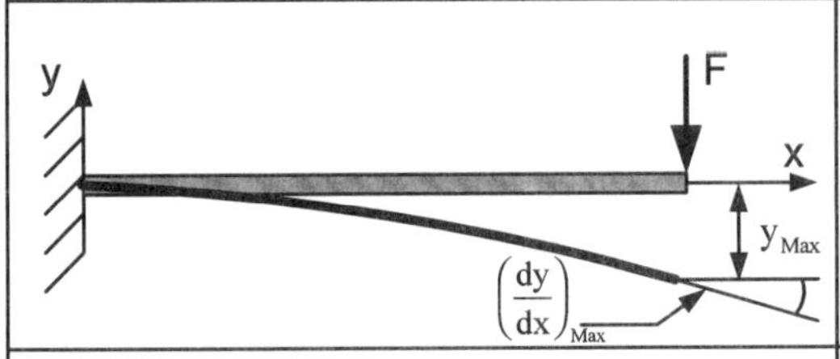	$\left(\frac{dy}{dx}\right)_{Max} = \frac{-FL^2}{2EI_z}$	$y = \frac{-Fx^2}{6EI_z}(3L - x)$ $y_{Max} = \frac{-FL^3}{3EI_z}$
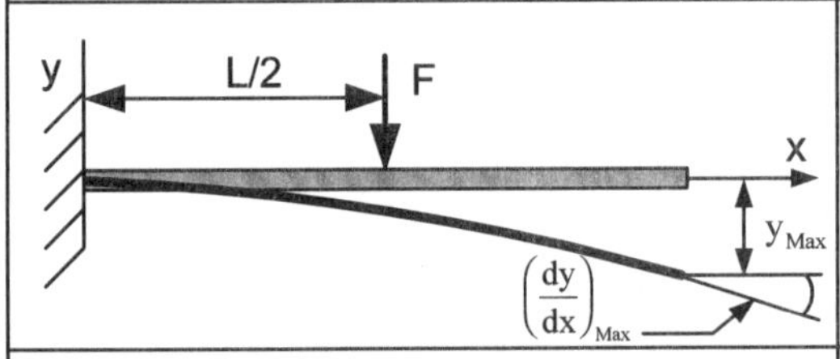	$\left(\frac{dy}{dx}\right)_{Max} = \frac{-FL^2}{8EI_z}$	$y = \frac{-Fx^2}{6EI_z}\left(\frac{3}{2}L - x\right)$ $0 \le x \le L/2$ $y = \frac{-FL^2}{24EI_z}\left(3x - \frac{1}{2}L\right)$ $L/2 \le x \le L$
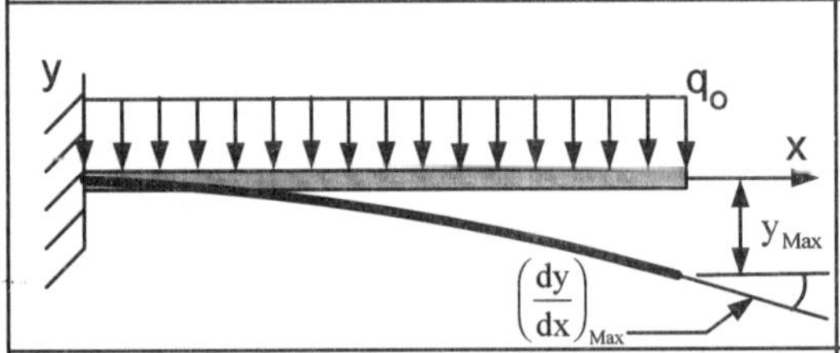	$\left(\frac{dy}{dx}\right)_{Max} = \frac{-q_0 L^3}{6EI_z}$	$y = \frac{-q_0 x^2}{24EI_z}\left(x^2 - 4Lx + 6L^2\right)$ $y_{Max} = \frac{-q_0 L^4}{8EI_z}$
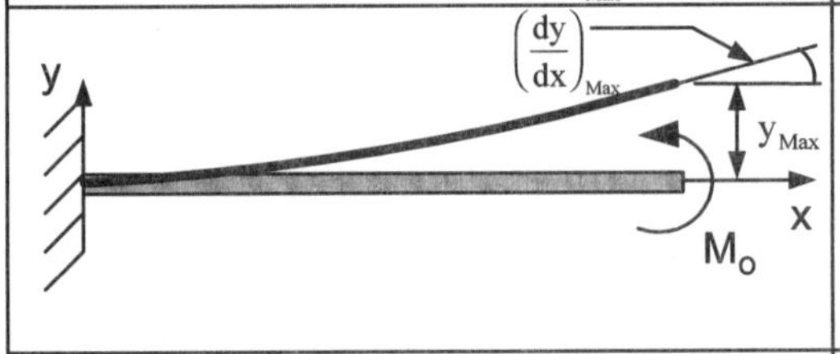	$\left(\frac{dy}{dx}\right)_{Max} = \frac{ML}{EI_z}$	$y = \frac{Mx^2}{2EI_z}$ $y_{Max} = \frac{ML^2}{2EI_z}$
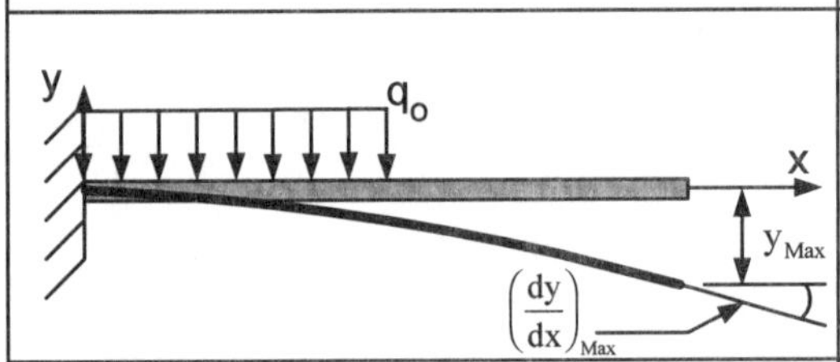	$\left(\frac{dy}{dx}\right)_{Max} = \frac{-q_0 L^3}{48EI_z}$	$y = \frac{-q_0 x^2}{24EI_z}\left(x^2 - 2Lx + \frac{3}{2}L^2\right)$ $0 \le x \le L/2$ $y = \frac{-q_0 L^3}{192EI_z}\left(4x - \frac{L}{2}\right)$ $L/2 \le x \le L$
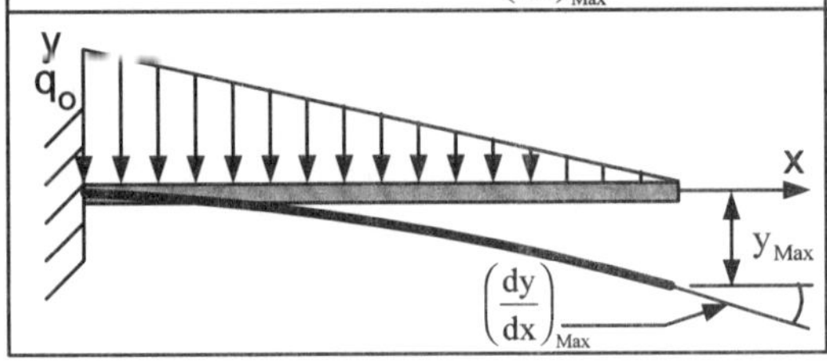	$\left(\frac{dy}{dx}\right)_{Max} = \frac{-q_0 L^3}{24EI_z}$	$y = \frac{-q_0 x^2}{120EI_z L}\left(10L^3 - 10L^2 x + 5Lx^2 - x^3\right)$ $y_{Max} = \frac{-q_0 L^4}{30EI_z}$

APPENDIX F

DESIGN PROJECTS

F.1 BRIDGES

Bridges are an essential component in the development of an effective transportation system. Bridges carry autos, trucks, railroad locomotives and cars and occasionally even an airplane across obstacles such as rivers, highways, gorges, ravines, etc. Bridges facilitate movement because they provide a relatively straight and level roadway that can be traversed at high speed. When a bridge fails or even when it is repaired, we are reminded of its importance by the long traffic delays encountered.

Bridges are exciting structures. Clearly they are structures, but why are they exciting? First, they often are unique in design with many challenging engineering problems encountered in the design, construction and operation of the bridge. Bridges often are designed with long spans to avoid the need for many intermediate supports. For example, the Akashi Kaiyo Bridge in Japan has a central span of 6,530 feet (1,990 m) to provide a roadway between the islands of Honshu and Shikoku.

Bridges are difficult to build. Foundations for piers must be set on bedrock located in deep water[1]. Materials for the support structure and roadway must often be lifted from barges located below the bridge. Other materials are shipped in special wide-body or extra-length trailers to remote bridge sites. The bridge components are sometimes difficult to handle, because they are large, heavy and require precise placement in space.

Bridges are expensive with the price per mile increasing dramatically with the span of the bridge segments. The costs are due to the quantity and the quality of the materials employed. The high quality materials, procured with rigid specifications that require extra testing to insure performance, add significantly to the costs. Also, construction of the piers, superstructure, roadway and the required approach roads is slow, and the cost of the highly skilled specialized craftsmen is extremely high.

Bridges are dangerous to build. Many of the bridge structures are located high above the water with a drop of several hundred feet to the waves below[2]. Construction workers fall to their death or are injured in handling the many thousands of tons of materials and cumbersome components in awkward places.

---

[1] For example, the deepest foundation used in constructing the Golden Gate Bridge is 115 feet below the surface at mean high water.

[2] The height of the towers on the Golden Gate Bridge is 746 feet above the surface and the clearance at the center of the roadway with the surface of the water is 215 feet.

F.1.1 Types of Bridge Designs

In the following subsections, we will describe six structural concepts most commonly employed today in bridge design, which include:

- Beam or girder bridges.
- Arch bridges.
- Cantilever bridges.
- Truss bridges.
- Suspension bridges.
- Cable stayed bridges.

Beam or Girder Bridges

The easiest way of designing a bridge is to use beams or girders to span between two piers or abutments as shown in Fig. F.1. While this method of construction is relatively easy to implement, the design is limited to relatively short spans. The beams or girders are subjected to loading due to the dead weight of the beams and roadway and additional live loads produced by vehicular traffic. The dead weight is modeled as a distributed load.

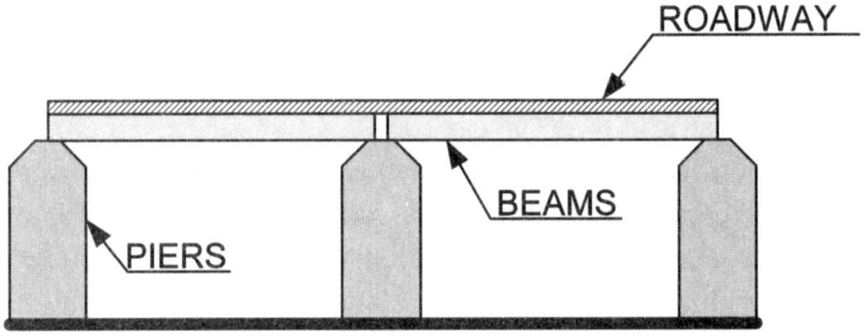

Fig. F.1 Constructing bridge spans with beams.

When we developed the theory for stress in beams, it became clear that the stresses due to the dead weight of the structure increase with the square of the length L of the span. For this reason, beam construction is used for relatively short spans. For longer spans, we seek structural designs in which the stresses increase more linearly with length of the span.

In the design of the beams, we are concerned with the cross sectional area of the structural elements. The simple rectangular area, shown in Fig. F.2, is the easiest to fabricate; however, it is inefficient in carrying stress and rarely used when a structural member is subjected to bending moments. The (I) and/or wide flange (WF) cross-section, shown in Fig. F.2, is much more efficient and cost effective in resisting bending moments. The box beam, also presented in Fig. F.2, is efficient because the lower stressed central region is removed.

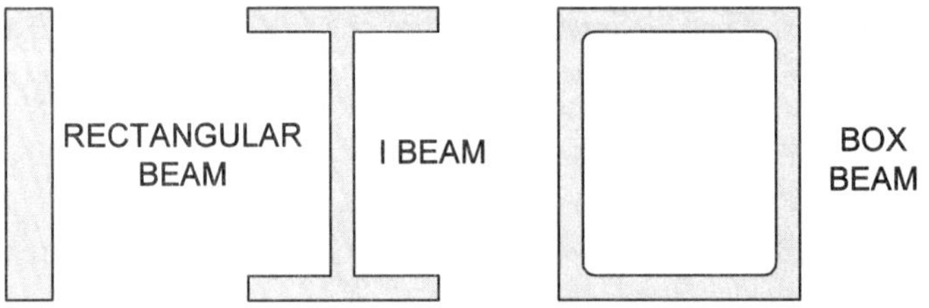

Fig. F.2 Common shapes for cross sectional areas of bars and beams.

Arch Bridges

The old bridges designed by the Roman engineers employed arches as the structural forms because the stone employed as the building material was strong in compression and very weak in tension. The Romans, lacking any of our modern materials that exhibit high tensile strength, were forced to employ the arch in constructing permanent structures. A schematic illustration of an arched bridge showing the arch, abutments, stream banks, piers and roadway is presented in Fig. F.3. The dead weight of the roadway is enormous compared to the live loads due to vehicles or people. The weight of the roadway pushes down on the arch tending to flatten and elongate it. The abutments that are fixed into the banks of the stream resist this action. Consequently, the arch is wedged into the opening between the two abutments and compression forces and stresses are induced in the arch.

The arch is still in common usage even with steel or steel reinforced concrete as the material of choice. The arch is an excellent means of raising the structure from a waterway, without the need for high piers or abutments, to provide clearance for boats. The elevation of the roadway with an arch enables ships and barges to employ the waterway for transportation of freight.

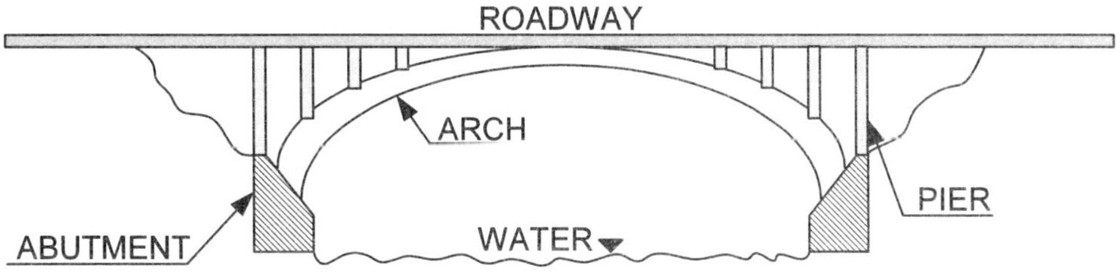

Fig. F.3 The dead weight of the structure forces the arch to flatten and elongate; thus, wedging it between the two fixed abutments creating compressive stresses in the arch.

Cantilever Bridges

A cantilever is a beam supported on one end and free on the other. This type of beam or truss structure is used in bridge construction because the design facilitates erection of large assemblies. The bridge is constructed from both sides of the river with cantilevers fixed on the two banks and each extending outward from the abutments. The two cantilever beams meet in mid-river and join to form the span. An illustration of this principle is the sketch of the Quebec Cantilever Bridge, shown in Fig. F.4 that crosses the St. Lawrence River. Note, trusses are employed instead of beams, but they are cantilevered outward in each direction from the two supports. The center section of the cantilever bridge was assembled on shore and moved by barge to the bridge site and lifted up to fill the gap between the two-cantilevered sections.

The cantilevered structures do not have to be fixed by abutments at the banks of the rivers. One cantilever arm is balanced by another oriented in the opposite direction with both segments originating from a pier. A very long bridge can be constructed by arranging several balanced cantilevered structures end to end.

Truss Bridges

We use an arch instead of a beam to avoid tension stresses due to static (dead weight of the structure) and dynamic (live) loads. We also use a truss instead of a beam to avoid inducing bending stresses in the long thin members often employed to construct bridges. We have introduced the geometry of various truss structures in Statics. The idea is to develop uniform stresses, either tension or compression, over the cross sectional area of each member of a truss. A truss is comprised of two or more triangles made by joining several straight members shown in Fig. F.5. With the loading shown, the diagonal members are subjected to compressive forces and the horizontal tie bar is subjected to tensile forces. With truss like structures, we can use simple bars and rods to build efficient, yet complex structures. The structures are efficient because each member is uniformly stressed. Also, the cross sectional area of each member can be sized to accommodate the load to which it is subjected.

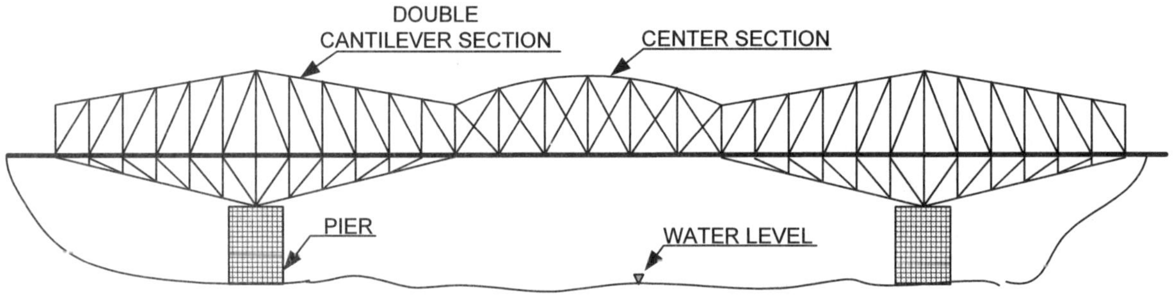

Fig. F.4 A double cantilever bridge.

Fig. F.5 A simple truss structure made with two triangles.

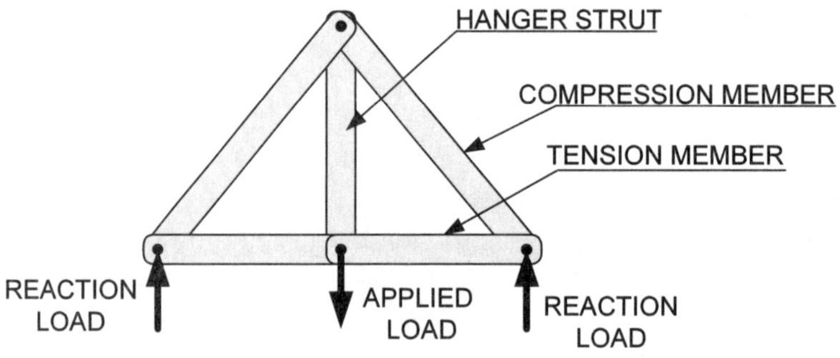

To avoid bending of the long and thin individual members, the loads must be applied at the joints where the members are connected together to form the truss. Moreover, the truss members are joined at their extremities, and members are not continuous through the joint. For a bridge intended to support a roadway, the distributed load of the roadway and the vehicular traffic is carried by an arrangement of floor beams and stringers as shown in Fig. F.6. The floor beams, connected to the truss at the joints, transmit the load of the roadway to the truss. Of course, two truss structures are employed—one on each side—for a typical bridge[3].

The joints in a truss structure are not usually connected together with pins as you might imagine after reading a typical mechanics textbook on Statics. Instead, the joints are usually welded or bolted. Often gusset plates are used to provide additional joining area and to reinforce the joint.

[3] For a four-lane bridge with traffic flow in two directions, four trusses are often used if the roadway is divided.

Joints with gusset plates are relatively rigid, particularly so when compared to the long slender members that flex under the action of any bending loads.

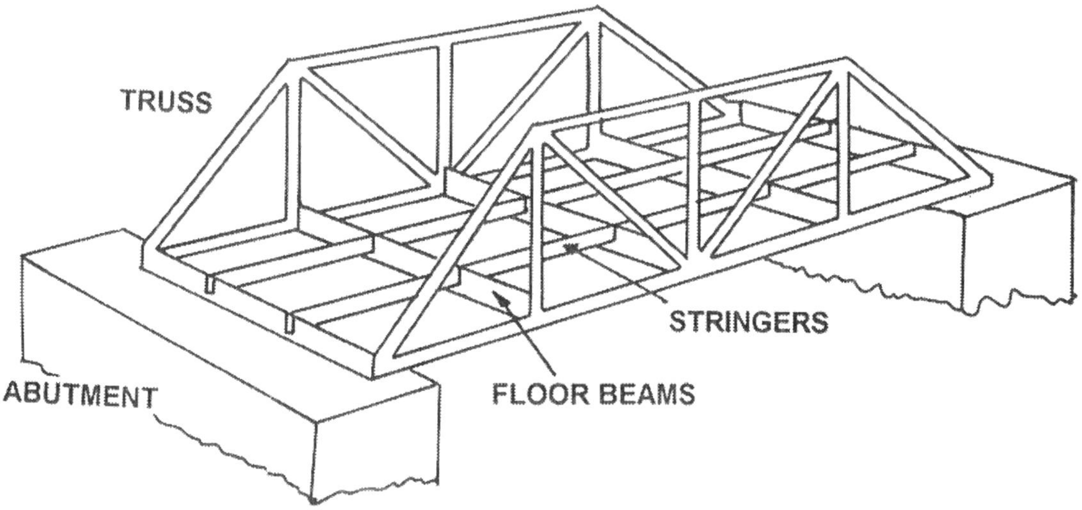

Fig. F.6 Side trusses, floor beams and stringers employed to frame a truss type bridge.

Suspension Bridges

A photograph of the Golden Gate Bridge that spans San Francisco Bay, presented in Fig. F.7, illustrates the essential design features of a suspension bridge.

Fig. F.7 The Golden Gate Bridge across San Francisco Bay

A suspension bridge is comprised of five principal components:

1. Shore based abutments for anchoring the cables and supporting the ends of the roadway.
2. High towers positioned some distance outward from the shore based abutments.
3. Main cables that are continuous from one abutment over both towers to the other abutment.
4. Smaller vertical cables (hangers) distributed over the length of the bridge that transfer the weight of the roadway to the main cables.
5. The roadway with its support structure carrying the vehicular traffic.

The suspension bridge is the most effective design for very long spans—the Akashi Kaiyo Bridge in Japan is the world's longest bridge with a central span of 6,530 feet. The design is effective because it makes extensive use of cables fabricated from many strands of very high-strength, cold-drawn wire. The wires employed exhibit a yield strength three or four times higher than the typical hot rolled steel members used in the much more common truss type bridges. Moreover, lightweight connectors have been developed for joining the hanger cables to the main cable and roadway structure. Finally, the ends of the main cable are anchored into the massive reinforced concrete abutments with no weight penalty imposed on the bridge. The efficiency of the design of a suspension bridge is apparent from its light and open appearance as evident in Fig. F.7.

Another weight saving feature of the suspension bridge is the fact that all of the cables are tension members, which are uniformly stressed. The only beams (structural elements with lower weight efficiency) employed are those used in supporting the roadway. Beams are subjected to bending and the stress distribution is not uniform. Indeed, the stress along the neutral axis of the beam is zero; thus the central regions of beam structures carry very small amounts of the bending moments while adding to the weight of the member. The geometry of the wide flange and box shaped cross sectional areas reduce the weight of the beam by removing much of the material near the neutral axis.

The interaction of the main cables, the hanger cables, and the tower of the suspension bridge is an essential concept in the transmission of the weight of the roadway to the foundations of the bridge. The force paths are shown in Fig. F.8.

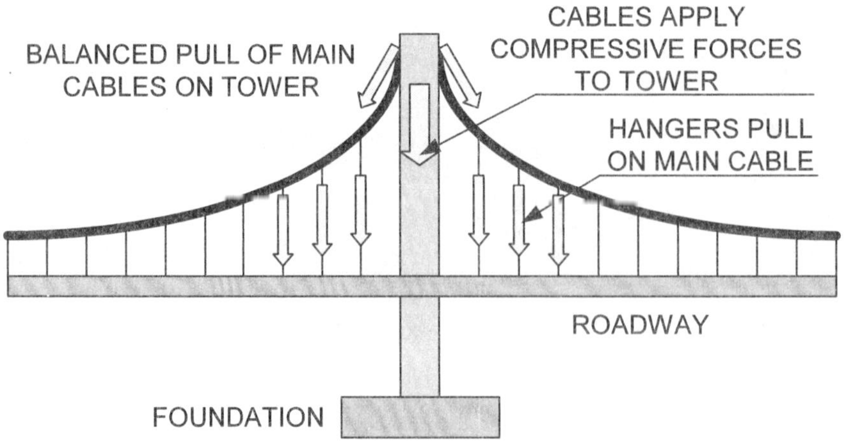

Fig. F.8 Force transmission from the roadway to the main cables to the tower of a suspension bridge.

The weight of the roadway and the vehicular traffic is supported along the length by many smaller diameter hanger cables. The forces in the hanger cables are transmitted to the main cable that is draped from the tower to the abutment. The main cable is symmetric about the tower, which implies a system of balanced forces. With symmetry-imposed balance, the horizontal components of the forces in the main cable are cancelled. The vertical components of the forces are additive and tend to press the tower into the foundation. The resulting stresses in the tower are compressive and are uniformly distributed.

Cable Stayed Bridges

Cable stayed bridges are similar in some respects to suspension bridges because cables are stretched from towers to support the roadway. However, examination of Fig. F.9 shows that the design of a cable-stayed bridge differs in many respects from a suspension bridge.

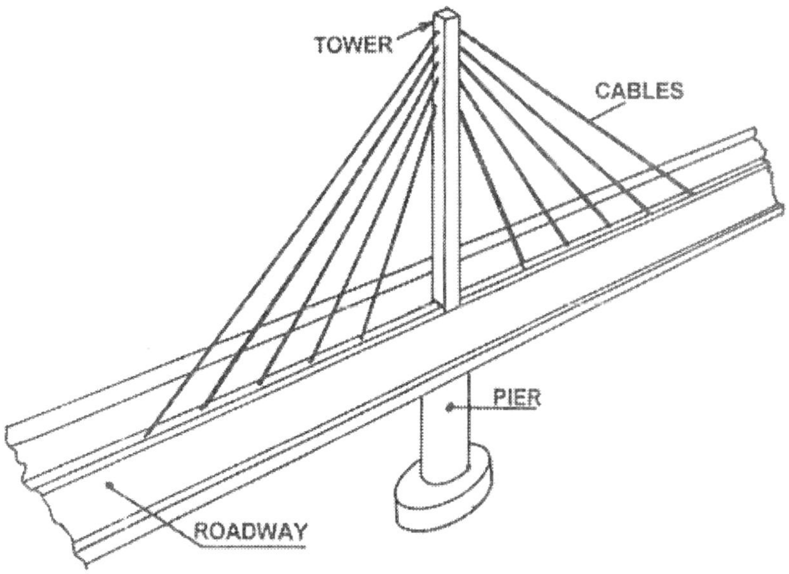

Fig. F.9 The cables supporting the roadway attach directly to the tower of a cable-stayed bridge.

In a suspension bridge, two sets of cables are employed to support the roadway—the main cables and a multitude of vertical hanger cables. However, in a cable-stayed bridge, the main cables are eliminated. Only one system of cables is employed. These cables are similar to the hanger cables on a suspension bridge, but they are attached directly to the tower and inclined downward and outward to support the roadway. Like the suspension bridge, the forces generated in the cables are balanced with the horizontal components of symmetric cables canceling each other. The vertical components of the force from each cable superimpose to produce a large compression force downward on the tower. The tower in turn transmits this compressive force to the foundation.

Many cable-stayed bridges are constructed with factory pre-cast, reinforced concrete, and box-sections. As each section is raised into position to form the deck of the bridge, a cable attached to the tower supports it. The cables, sized to support the weight of the reinforced concrete sections, are usually about 3 to 5 inches diameter.

The Pont de Normandie Bridge over the Seine River at Le Havre, France, shown in Fig. F.10 is the longest cable stayed bridge in the world with a span of 2,880 feet. The towers supporting the cables are 214-m tall and are triangular in shape. The roadway is supported with two sets of cables—one on each side of the road. The span between the two towers is 856 m, which compares to a span of 1280 m for the Golden Gate Bridge.

Fig. F.10 Pont de Normandie Bridge over the Seine River at Le Havre, France.

Fig. F.11 The Sydney Harbor Bridge

Hybrid Structural Design

Some bridges are constructed using a single design concept such as the Golden Gate Bridge, which is a classic suspension structure. Most short span highway bridges over intersections or more natural obstacles follow the classical beam design. However, in many cases two or more concepts are employed together in what may be called a hybrid design for bridges. A well-known hybrid design is the Sydney Harbor Bridge in Sydney, Australia, which is shown in Fig. F.11. Three different concepts were integrated in this design—the arch, truss and cable suspension to produce an effective structure that has become a world famous landmark. The arch was employed to produce a support structure with a long span. The arch was also elevated so that it would serve as the upper anchor point for the hanger cables that support the roadway. Finally, the arch was constructed as a truss with classical combinations of triangles.

F.1.2 Bridge Projects

Four different bridge projects are described in the subsequent subsections including:

1. A bridge spanning a river 30 m wide.
2. A bridge for a new super highway that spans a single-track railroad with a right of way 30 ft wide.
3. A bridge for a new four-lane highway that spans a wide bay with both shallow and deep water.
4. A pedestrian bridge that spans a four-lane superhighway with a median strip.

Each project entails the design of a suitable structure to meet the design specification. Following the design phase of the project, a scale model is to be constructed and tested to insure that the bridge is stable and will not fail under the specified design loads. During testing, strain and deflection will be measured and compared to predicted values for the model to verify the design analysis.

Constructing the Model

Because the model bridge structures will be relatively light, there is no need to place the foundations on bedrock. Stable soil is sufficient and pre-cast concrete blocks may be employed for the foundations if they are of suitable size and shape consistent with the design of the prototype.

Fabricating joints in the bridge may present a major problem. There are four approaches that may be followed depending on your preference and the choice of model materials.

- Adhesive bonding of lap or butt joints with a structural grade epoxy.
- Small screws and nuts for fastening members together at lap or butt joints.
- Rivets for fastening members together at lap or butt joints.
- Fastening lap or butt joints with appropriate solder.

Also, you are to develop a method for loading for your model. Your choice of the scaling factor for the load will markedly affect the approach that may be employed. Small sandbags placed at suitable intervals along the length of the model may provide a suitable distributed load. Bricks or concrete blocks may be used instead of sandbags. We suggest that the loads be applied in increments with measurements made after the application of each load increment.

We anticipate that you will measure the strain at a few critical locations on the model, and experimentally verify the stresses in the prototype. We also expect you to measure the deflection at several positions along the span of the model and verify the prediction of the deflection of the prototype.

Criteria for Assessment

In assessing performance in the design of the prototype bridge and the verification of the design with a model study, the following information developed by each design team will be considered.

1. A design report, which should include:
    - An analysis of all of the structural members.
    - Design drawings of the structure and the foundation.
    - A report describing the rationale for all of the design decisions.
2. Preliminary and final design briefings.
3. Quality of the construction of the model bridge.
4. Accuracy of the measurements of the strain and the deflection.
5. Accuracy of the predictions of strain and deflection.
6. Value of the model study in verifying the adequacy of the design of the bridge.

Bridge Project No. 1

You are to design a bridge that spans a river 30 m wide. With the embankments and the approach to the river, we anticipate the free span of the bridge to be 40 – 45 m. A view of the cross section of the stream and the embankments is illustrated in Fig. F.12. The bridge is to handle two lanes of traffic (one in each direction) with a barrier strip in the center. Also, sidewalks suitable for both bicycles and pedestrians are to be included on both sides of the bridge. The total width of the bridge is limited to 15 m.

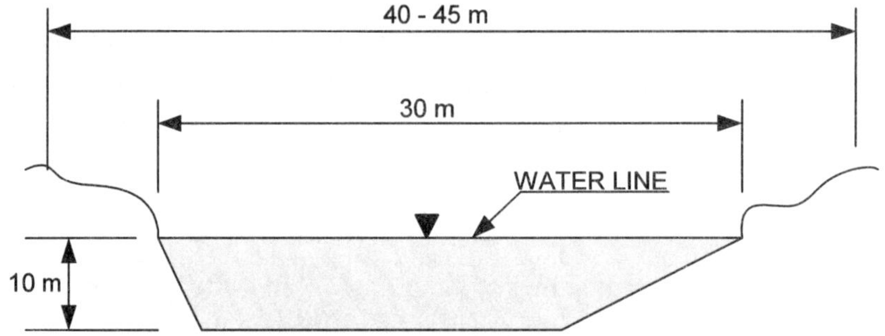

Fig. F.12 Schematic diagram of the stream and embankment.

The Design Specification

The prototype bridge is to be designed for a live load of 30 kN/m. The dead weight load per unit length will depend upon the design of the structure and roadway. The deck on the prototype bridge is 150 mm thick and fabricated from reinforced concrete. The floor beams are spaced at 4 m intervals.

The design is to include:

- The abutments.
- Piers if any are incorporated in the design.
- The approaches.
- The superstructure for the clear span.
- The roadway and supporting structures.
- Typical details for the critical joints.

After the design of the prototype bridge is complete, your team is to prepare drawings for a model bridge with a geometric scale factor $\boldsymbol{S}$ = 1/50. The structural members for the model will be fabricated in the student workshop, and this model will be erected over a simulated stream.

In designing all of the structural members, recognize their length is to be limited. We have obtained a special permit from the state highway department to ship members for the prototype up to 25 m in length and 3 m in width. Members larger than this limit pose a danger to others on the highway; consequentially, they must be fabricated at the site. Accordingly all structural members for the model are limited to 500 mm in length and 60 mm in width.

The choice of prototype materials includes carbon steel, high-strength steel, and aluminum alloy. Models are usually fabricated from either wood or plastic.

Design Approach

West Point Bridge Designer software[4] is to be employed to design the preliminary configuration and to optimize the structure. This software may be downloaded, without charge, from the following web site:

http://bridgecontest.usma.edu

You may also obtain additional information describing this software at:

http://www.bridgesite.com/funand.htm

We anticipate that you will optimize the design in terms of both strength and total cost of the prototype. Also, a factor of safety of a least two is to be employed in the specification of all of the structural components.

Bridge Project No. 2

You are to design a bridge for a new super highway that spans a single-track railroad with a right of way 30 ft wide. With the embankments and the approach to the track, we anticipate the free span of the bridge to be 40 to 45 ft. A view of the cross section of the track and the embankments is illustrated in Fig. F.13. The bridge is to handle four lanes of traffic (two in each direction) with a barrier strip in the center. Also, an emergency lane is to be included on both sides of the bridge.

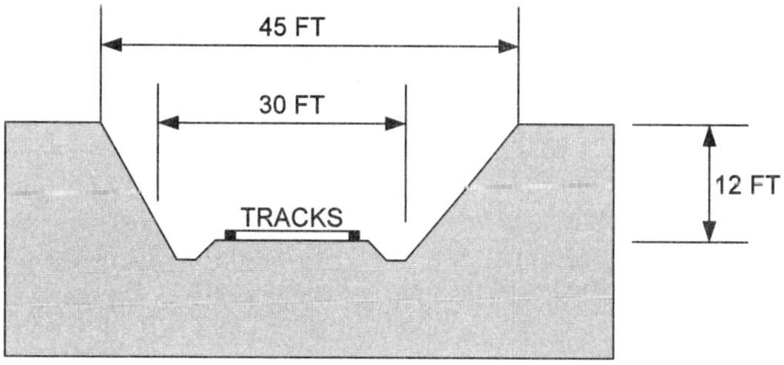

Fig. F.13 Schematic diagram of the railroad tracks and embankment.

[4] This software was developed at the U. S. Military Academy under the direction of Dr. Stephen J. Ressler, Professor and Deputy Head of the Department of Civil and Mechanical Engineering.

The Design Specification

The prototype bridge is to be designed for a live load of 6,000 lb/ft. The dead weight load per unit length will depend upon the design of the structure and roadway. The deck on the prototype bridge is 6 in. thick and fabricated from steel reinforced high-strength concrete. The State Department of Transportation has a preference for a beam type bridge. The floor beams that will cross the primary longitude support beams are to be spaced at 8 ft intervals.

The design is to include:

- The abutments.
- The approaches.
- The substructure for a clear span.
- The roadway and supporting structures.
- Typical details for the critical joints.
- Verification drawing for the railroad assuring adequate clearance.

After the design of the prototype bridge is complete, your team is to prepare drawings for a model bridge with a geometric scale factor $\mathbf{S} = 1/20$. The structural members for the model will be fabricated in the student workshop, and this model will be erected over a simulated track.

The choice of prototype materials includes carbon steel, high-strength steel, and aluminum alloy. Models are usually fabricated from either wood or plastic.

Design Approach

Because the span of the bridge is relatively short (less than its width), we are suggesting you consider a beam type bridge. However, the type of bridge design is open and your team can select another alternative. We anticipate that you will optimize the design in terms of both strength and total cost of the prototype. Also, a factor of safety of at least three is to be employed in the specification of all of the structural components.

Bridge Project No. 3

You are to design a bridge for a new highway that spans a wide bay. The bay is relatively shallow over large reaches of the span; however, there is a deep-water channel down the center of the bay as shown in the illustration in Fig. F.14. Container ships often sail up and down the bay delivering cargo to a city-port located at the mouth of the bay. The bridge is to handle four lanes of traffic (two in each direction) with a barrier strip in the center. Also, an emergency lane is to be included on both sides of the bridge if the costs are not prohibitive.

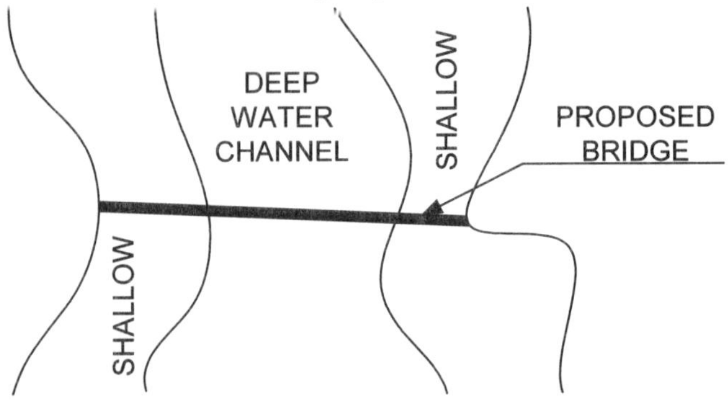

Fig. F.14 Proposed bridge route across bay.

The Design Specification

The prototype bridge is to be designed for a live load of 50kN/m. The dead weight load per unit length will depend upon the design of the structure and roadway. The deck on the prototype bridge is 150 mm thick and fabricated from steel reinforced high-strength concrete. The State Department of Transportation has a preference for a hybrid type bridge with post and beam construction across the shallows and a long high span across the deep-water channel. The deep-water channel is 520 m wide at the proposed site for the bridge. The shallow water to the left is 330 m wide and that to the right is 265 m wide.

The design is to include:

- The abutments.
- The approaches.
- The piers for the shallow water bridge structures.
- The roadway and supporting structures for the shallow water spans.
- The towers for the long span over deep water.
- The suspension or cable-stayed structure over the deep-water channel.
- The roadway and supporting structures for the deep-water spans.
- Typical details for the critical joints.

After the design of the prototype bridge is complete, your team is to prepare drawings for a model bridge with a geometric scale factor $\boldsymbol{S}$ = 1/1000. The structural members for the model will be fabricated in the student workshop, and this model will be erected over a simulated bay.

The choice of prototype materials includes carbon steel, high-strength steel, steel reinforced concrete, and aluminum alloy. Models are usually fabricated from either wood or plastic.

Design Approach

Because the span of the bridge is long—over both deep and shallow water, we are suggesting you consider a hybrid design for the bridge. You may initially wish to consider pier and beam construction for the spans over the shallow water and a suspension bridge of some type over the deep water. The length of the span over the deep water is such that either a suspension or cable stayed design is feasible. The type of bridge design is open and your team can select other alternatives. However, we anticipate that you will optimize the design in terms of both strength and total cost of the prototype. Also, a factor of safety of at least three is to be employed in the specification of all of the structural components.

Bridge Project No. 4

The Appalachian Trail extends through the Appalachian Mountains from Central Maine to Northern Georgia—a distance of 2050 miles. Many highways large and small intersect the trail and hikers, cars and trucks compete for the same space usually in remote rural areas. To minimize danger to everyone concerned, pedestrian bridges are constructed over these highways. The dual lane super highway at the site of a pedestrian bridge passes through a cut with an embankment 15 ft high on the east side of the highway and 10 ft high on the west side. The section view of the interstate highway relative to the trail is given in Fig. F.15.

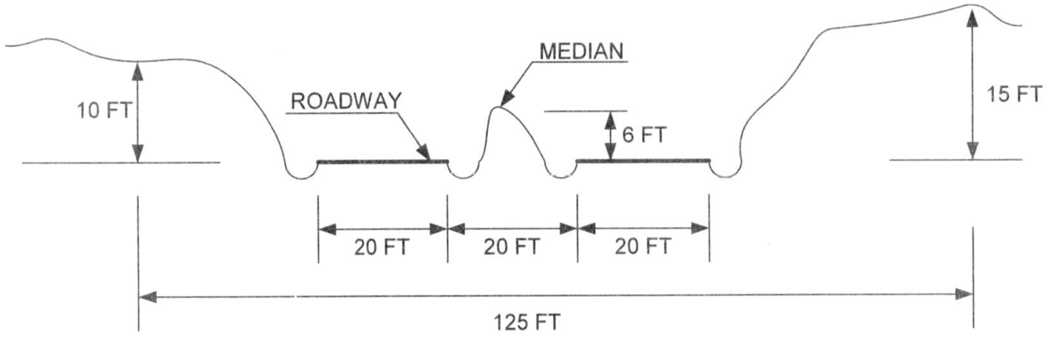

Fig. F.15 A section view of a limited access highway intersecting the Appalachian Trail.

The Design Specification

The prototype bridge is to be designed for a live load equivalent to 50 hikers with backpacks. The dead weight load per unit length will depend upon the design of the structure and pathway. The deck on the prototype bridge may also have to support all terrain vehicles but is to be too narrow to permit traffic by conventional four-wheel vehicles. The State Department of Transportation has given permission to place a support in the center of the median strip, however they require a design that will protect motorists from any debris that could be thrown from the bridge.

The design is to include:

- The abutments.
- The median pier
- The trail way.
- The supporting structures.
- The containment structure.

Design Approach

While the span of the bridge is relatively long, the loading is much lower than the typical bridge because most vehicular traffic is restricted. Also a column at the median strip effectively reduces the total span by a factor of nearly two. You may initially wish to consider beam construction for the two spans or shallow trusses. The type of bridge design is open and your team can select other alternatives. However, we anticipate that you will optimize the design in terms of both strength and total cost of the prototype. The materials to be employed are to be selected by the team. A factor of safety of at least four is to be employed in the specification of all of the structural components. Also the bridge structure must allow sufficient head room for the truck traffic that flows along this interstate highway.

F.2 STRUCTURAL SYSTEMS IN LARGE BUILDINGS

Structures have evolved from huts made from grasses and branches to skyscrapers, stadiums, high-rise apartment complexes, office towers and concert halls. High strength materials, elevators and construction machinery have played an essential role in man's ability to build larger more efficient structures and in some cases more durable buildings. The pyramids in Egypt were and are certainly durable, but they were essentially solid stone and had no purpose other than to serve as a monument and a tomb for a pharaoh. Buildings today are systems that serve a variety of purposes in a cost effective manner.

Sky scrappers are fascinating in that they enable a large number of people pursuing a common activity to work in close proximity thereby increasing the efficiency of the workplace. Large convention centers provide large lecture halls, open exhibit spaces and conference rooms that enable people to meet and exchange views or commercial goods. Concert halls provide excellent acoustics and unobstructed seating for large audiences, while providing an architectural experience for those in attendance (i.e. The Kennedy Center in Washington D. C.)

As you design the structure for a building, there are many factors to consider including:

1. The architectural experience which effects a pleasant interaction between the person and the building.
2. Space and form. Space is related to size and the three dimensions of the envelope of interior and exterior features. Form pertains to style—rectilinear or curvilinear.
3. The envelope refers to the walls, roofs, floors, windows, structure and materials. Clearly, engineers focus on the envelope.
4. Style is related to space and form and pertains to proportion, scale and composition.
5. The environment surrounding the structure markedly affects all aspects of the architectural and engineering design.
6. Structures affect society and vice versa. The new art museum in Milwaukee, Wisconsin makes a clear statement of the concern of its citizens for both art and architecture. Trailer like structures used as temporary classrooms adjacent to school buildings shows the lack of concern for education by the local population in that school district or mismanagement by the school board.
7. Design reconciles function, form, economy and time.

In the listing above, we have mixed engineering and architectural tasks and responsibilities. However, if you become a structural engineer you will usually be working with an architect. Likely, the architect will be in charge; hence, it is important that you begin to understand their values and thought processes.

F.2.1 Building Projects

In the following subsections, five different building projects will be introduced. For each project, you will be required to design a structure, analyze this design and then build a scale model of it. After the model is complete, your team will test it to verify that it meets the design specifications. The criteria used in judging the merits of your design, the model and the testing program are given below.

Constructing the Model

Because the models of the various buildings will be relatively light, they may be placed on a floor, tabletop or a level surface. Fabricating joints in the structure may present a major problem. There are four approaches that may be followed depending on your preference and the choice of model materials.

1. Adhesive bonding of lap or butt joints with a structural grade epoxy.
2. Small screws and nuts for fastening members together at lap or butt joints.
3. Rivets for fastening members together at lap or butt joints.
4. Fastening lap or butt joints in steel or brass with appropriate solder.

Also, you are to develop a method for loading your model. Your choice of the scaling factors will markedly affect the approach that may be employed to load the model. Small sandbags placed at suitable intervals along the length of the model may provide a suitable distributed load. Small metallic blocks may be used instead of sandbags. Picture hanging wire, plain wire or fishing line can be used for modeling the cables.

We anticipate that you will measure the strain at a few critical locations on the model, and experimentally verify the stresses in the prototype. We also expect you to measure the deflection at all of the critical locations on the model and verify the prediction of the deflection of the prototype.

Criteria for Assessment

In assessing the merits of the design and analysis of the building and the verification of the design with a model study, the following information developed by each design team will be considered.

1. A design report, which should include:
   - An analysis of all of the structural members.
   - Design drawings of the structure and the foundation.
   - A report describing the rationale for all of the design decisions.
2. Preliminary and final design briefings.
3. Quality of the model of the structure.
4. Accuracy of the measurements of the strain and the deflection.
5. Accuracy of the predictions of strain and deflection.
6. Value of the model study in verifying the adequacy of the design of the structure.

Building Project No. 1

An architectural firm has been retained by a city with a population of 1,200,000 to design an exhibition hall. The city council has indicated to the architects that they want a very large open space that can be configured to accommodate many different groups of exhibitors (perhaps as many as 25 different exhibits a year). Except for a row of rooms at the rear of the hall to accommodate limited office space, the rest rooms and a small medical facility, the remainder of the space is to be an open rectangle with a roof positioned high above the floor.

The Design Specification

The initial design proposed by the architect incorporates a stayed cable support structure illustrated in Fig. F.16.

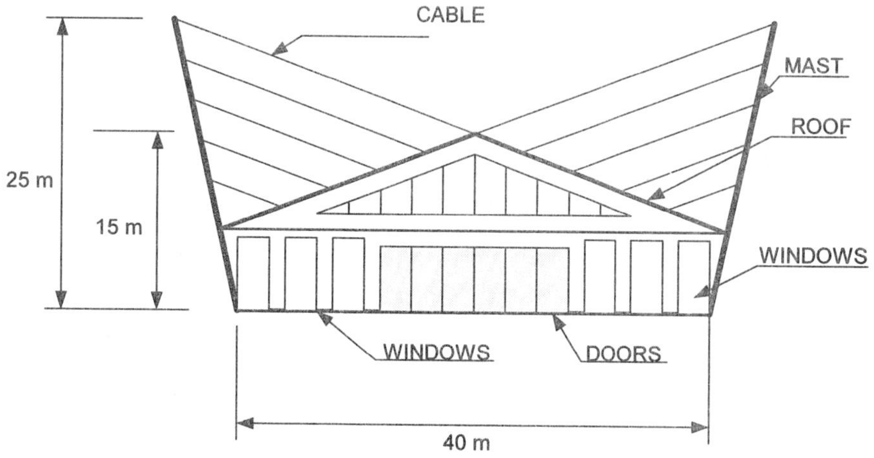

Fig. F.16 An exhibition hall with a cable stayed roof.

The architect has specified placement of a series of six masts on 20 m centers on each side of the structure. The overall length of the exhibition hall is 100 m. She retains your firm to perform the following tasks.

1. Recommend an angle of inclination for the masts.
2. Specify the size and shape of the members for the masts.
3. Specify the number of cables attached to each mast.
4. Specify the attachment points on the mast and on the roof.
5. Specify the diameter of the cables and their breaking strength.
6. Design the end connectors for both ends of the cable.
7. Design the connectors for the cables at the mast and at the roof.
8. Design the roof structure.

Design Approach

In your analysis you will be concerned with the loading on the roof, which is due primarily to three factors—dead weight of the roof structure, snow and/or ice accumulation and wind. We suggest you propose a design of a roof structure and determine its weight per unit area. For the loading due to snow and ice, consider a normally distributed load of 2.5 kN/m^2. For the load due to wind, consider a velocity of 150 km/hr. Reference a fluid mechanics textbook to establish the procedure to convert wind velocity to pressure.

Building Project No. 2

An architectural firm has been retained by the owner of a NBA basketball team to design a new sports arena for his team. While the primary purpose of the arena is to provide a basketball court and seating for spectators, it is anticipated that the arena will be used for other entertainment venues. The owner has retained an architect for the initial design of the structure. He has indicated to the architect that the space should be open and free of columns.

The Design Specification

The initial design proposed by the architect incorporates three huge space trusses that are exterior to an enclosure with a flat roof as shown in Fig. F.17. The three space trusses are triangular in shape and span a distance of 350 ft. Each end of the triangular trusses is supported by a vertical column arrangement that is also located on the exterior of the building. Suspended below and supported by the three main trusses are much smaller secondary trusses that run perpendicular to the triangular trusses to provide support for a system of tertiary trusses. The tertiary trusses, which run parallel to the triangular trusses, are placed on 10 ft centers to provide direct support for the roof deck. The roof deck measures 100 ft by 350 ft.

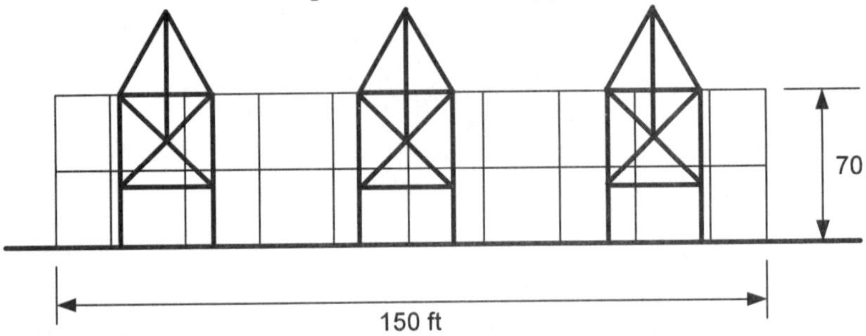

Fig. F.17 Three large triangular trusses support the roof structure for a sports arena.

The architect commissions you to perform the following tasks.

1. Specify the materials and their thickness in the design of the roof deck.
2. Design and analyze the three triangular trusses.
3. Design and analyze the columns supporting the main trusses.
4. Design and analyze the secondary trusses.
5. Design and analyze the tertiary trusses.
6. Design and analyze the column foundations.
7. Design the connections between the columns and the triangular trusses.

Design Approach

In your analysis you will be concerned with the loading on the roof, which is due primarily to two factors — dead weight of the roof structure and snow and/or ice accumulation. One of the tasks commissioned by the architect is to design a roof deck and determine its weight per unit area. For the snow and ice, consider a normally distributed load of 75 lb/ft^2.

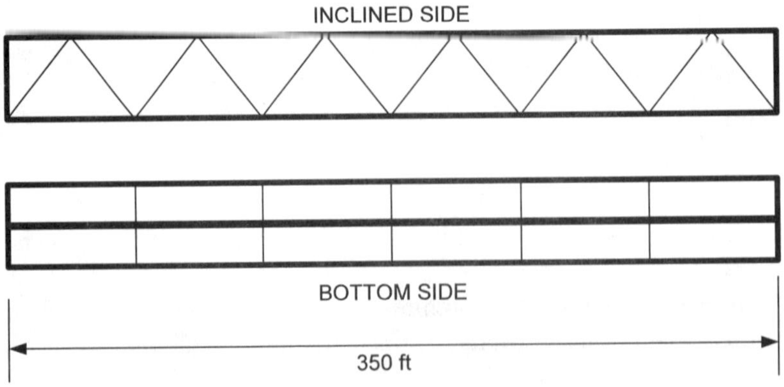

Fig. F.18 Architect's arrangement of truss members that must be maintained.

In the design of the triangular trusses, the architect insists on round tubular members for all of the members. The top longitudinal member is to be twice the diameter of the two lower longitudinal members. You are free to select the wall thickness of these tubes, although it must be a standard size. The outside diameter of the lattice members of the truss must all be same, although the wall thickness of the various members may be different.

For an example of this style of building, you may wish to examine the design details for the Crosby Kemper Arena that was constructed in 1974 in Kansas City, MO.

Building Project No. 3

In an effort to improve the attendance at a minor league baseball stadium, the team's owners have suggested a canopy over a segment of the stands that contain the more expensive seats. Because of the need to preserve a clear field of view, the architect plans to utilize cantilever beams to support the canopy. She presents you with a crude schematic diagram of the initial design as shown in Fig. F.19.

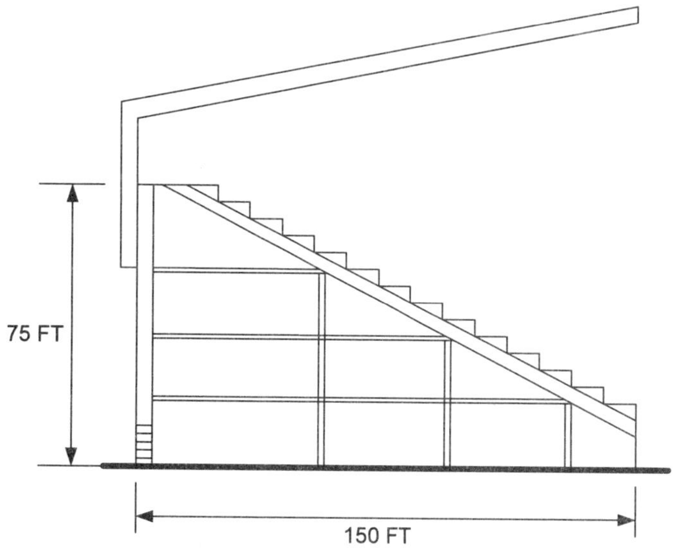

Fig. F.19 Schematic diagram of canopy over baseball stadium seats.

The Design Specification

The architect has only provided the exterior dimensions of a typical section of seats, which are to be sheltered by the installation of a canopy. She has not attempted an initial design of the structure, and retains you perform the design and to prepare the structural analysis that will be presented to the county commissioners prior to obtaining the necessary permits. Her instructions to you are minimal, but include: employ a safety factor of at least 3.0, minimize the costs and maintenance and develop an attractive structure with customer appeal.

You intend to provide the architect with the following documents upon completion of the task.

1. Specifications for the materials used in the canopy.
2. Design and analysis of the support structure.
3. Specification for the materials to be employed in the support structure.
4. Design the connections between the supports and the stadium walls.
5. Plan for construction of the complete system.

Design Approach

To begin, you will have to make several decisions regarding the canopy. Should it be:

- Permanent or removable.
- Rigid or flexible.
- Adjustable or fixed depending on the climatic conditions.
- Steel or aluminum sheeting or Dacron sailcloth.
- Flamboyant or subdued.
- The most suitable angle of inclination of the canopy to afford protection.

Regardless of your choices to these questions and others that you raise, arguments must be made to support your decisions. In your analysis you will be concerned with the loading on the canopy, which is due primarily to three factors—dead weight of the roof structure, snow and/or ice accumulation and wind loading. For the snow and ice, consider a normally distributed load of 75 lb/ft^2.

In the design of the support structure you are free to select the design approach. Trusses, beams or cable-stayed beams may be considered. Also the materials and structural form of the members is open provided that they are standard sizes and shapes.

Building Project No. 4

A new domed stadium is planned for the next Olympic games. The architect has selected an eight-segment version of the Geiger cable dome, illustrated in Fig. F.20, to cover the stadium because it is economical. The roof loads are supported by tension cables and compression struts. Loads are transferred from a center tension ring through a series of ridge cables and tension hoops to a compression ring positioned at the perimeter. The fabric used for the cover is usually a composite consisting of a high-strength waterproof fabric, a thick layer of fiberglass insulation, and a plastic sheet to serve as a vapor barrier. It has been shown that this is a very lightweight structure (2 lb/ft^2), which is essentially independent of the span.

The Design Specification

The architect has only provided the concept for the domed stadium roof, and has commissioned you to design the tension and compression rings, the cables and the struts. The compression ring is to be supported by columns arranged around the periphery. The exterior walls are light and not intended to support the rings or roof structure. The installation is to be in southern Florida; hence snow loading is not an issue. The plan to deal with possible hurricanes is to purchase insurance coverage. The sponsor for the stadium has specified its diameter as 125 m.

You plan to provide the architect with the following documents upon completion of the task.

1. Design and analysis of the ridge, valley and hoop cables.
2. Design and analysis of the vertical struts.
3. Design and analysis of the tension and compression rings.
4. Design and analysis of the supporting columns.
5. Design the connections between the cables and their attachment points.

6. Specify materials for the rings, struts and columns and the breaking strength of the cables.

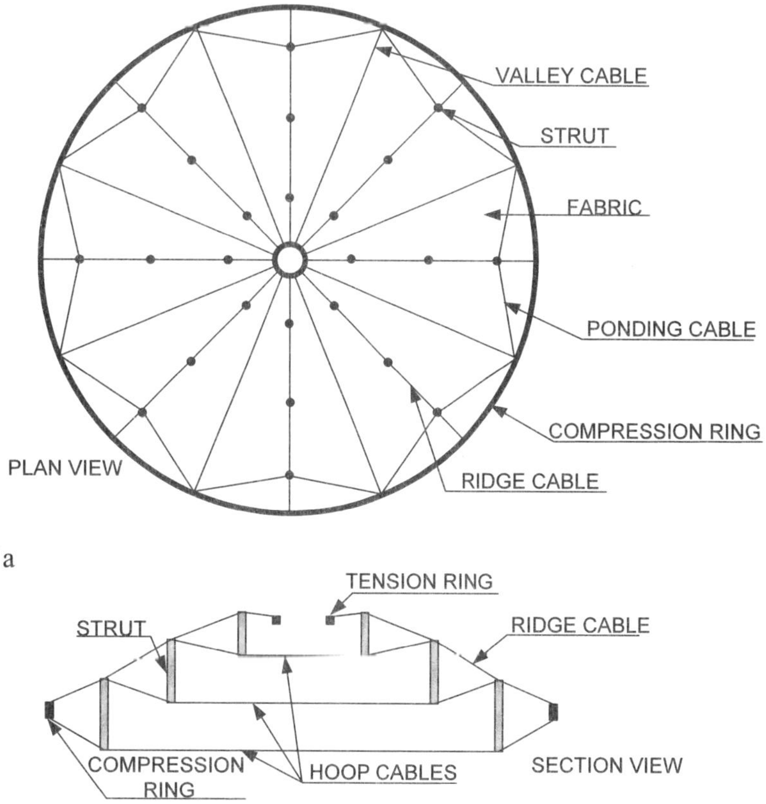

Fig. F.20 Schematic illustration of a Geiger cable dome.

Design Approach

You will establish the pitch of the dome to shed water thereby reducing the roof load that involves only dead weight and low velocity winds. Your proposal to design for a total roof load of 200 N/m^2 has been accepted by the owner, the architect and the city commissioners. Standard cables (wire ropes) are to be selected in all cases. The supplier of the roof fabric is providing loops for cable attachment at appropriate intervals. You may be required to provide guidance on the number and strength of each loop as well as their placement.

Building Project No. 5

An entrepreneur has visited your design firm to request your assistance in designing a pneumatic structure that he plans to move from city to city. His intention is to conduct auctions to sell a variety of merchandise for a few days and then move onto another small city. He cannot rent space in a commercial building at a reasonable price for short periods of time. He has considered a tent, but it does not convey the upscale image that he would like to present to his customers. He has asked your firm to design an air supported or air inflated structure that will house 100 customers with sufficient space to store a limited amount of merchandise and for a stage from which to conduct the auctions. His plan is to rent small sports facilities (football or baseball fields) and to erect the structure on a level grass covered field.

There are two types of pneumatic structures—air-inflated and air-supported as illustrated in Fig. F.21. The air-inflated structures are made up from structural elements (tubes) that are pressurized and thereby stiffened sufficiently to enable support for the structure's roof. The interior of an air-inflated structure is at atmospheric pressure. Air-supported structures consist of a membrane that is sealed about its perimeter and pressurized in order to make the enclosure relatively stiff. The interior of an air-supported structure is maintained slightly above atmospheric pressure.

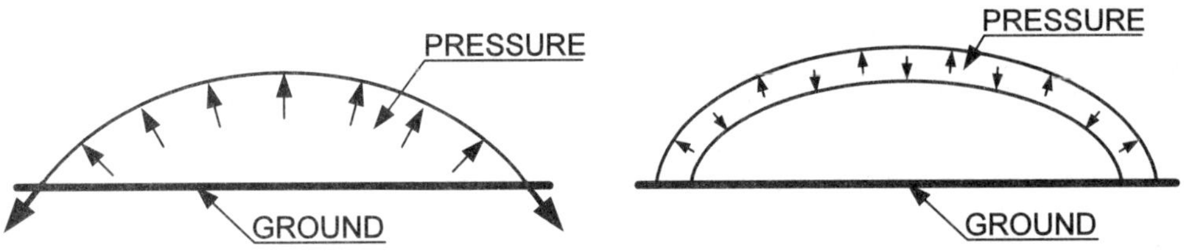

Fig. F.21 Two types of pneumatic structures.

The Design Specification

The entrepreneur has indicated that he will require doors in the front of the structure for customer access and doors in the back of the structure to permit transfer of chairs and merchandise into the interior. He has also indicated that he prefers a rectangular configuration to better seat the customers who will be bidding in the auction.

You are concerned over the possibility of snow and ice loading that will collapse the structure; however, the entrepreneur informs you that his schedule avoids cities with inclement weather in the winter months. However, he often encounters rain and wants to operate even in heavy rainstorms. After some discussion you plan to provide the entrepreneur with the following documents upon completion of the task.

1. An analysis to size the structure to accommodate 100 customers in seating that provides an excellent view of the merchandise being auctioned.
2. Design and analysis of both types of structures.
3. Design of the access openings (doors) for both types of pneumatic structures.
4. Design the seal and anchors for the air supported structure.
5. Design of the anchors for the air inflated structure.
6. Analysis of the wind loading on both structures.
7. Specification for the material used as the membrane in both types of enclosures.
8. Specification of the internal pressure in the air-supported structure.
9. Specification of the internal pressure in the air-inflated structural elements.

Design Approach

Pneumatic structures are subjected to dead loads due to the weight of the membrane and live loads due to wind, snow and ice. Because this structure will not be erected in inclement conditions, you will be concerned with only the dead weight and the external pressure distribution due to wind loads. Of course, the structure is pressurized to maintain the membrane in tension in order to support these dead weight and the wind loads.

The internal pressure required to support lightweight air-supported structures is small—10 N/m^2 or 0.3 psi. Fans are usually used to create these small pressures. The flow rate for the fans must be sufficient to overcome leakage at the access openings and at the structure-to-ground seal. To avoid large leakage at the access openings, air locks with two sets of doors are often employed. In the design of an airlock, the vestibule must be large enough to accommodate several people so that both sets of doors are rarely open at the same time. Revolving doors may also be employed; however, they are cumbersome for a structure that is likely to be erected and disassembled on a weekly basis.

Maintaining internal pressure for air-inflated structures is not a problem because the interior of the structure is not pressurized. The individual tubular members are pressurized with compressed air generated by a small compressor. The pressure levels required are much higher than with the air-supported structures. The design concept is for the pressure to produce tensile membrane stresses that are sufficiently large to compensate for compressive stresses induced by axial compression or bending of the inflated member. If load induced compression stresses overcome the tension membrane stresses, the member will buckle and fail. Another mode of failure is bursting due to over inflation or due to combined tensile stresses due to pressurization and bending.

While the air-inflated structure has the advantage of easy inflation relative to the air-supported structure, the problem of sealing the enclosure against rain requires some method for watertight connections between the inflated members.

F.3 CONSTRUCTION CRANES

When constructing new buildings it is necessary to provide for a method to lift considerable quantities of materials from trucks at ground level to some floor that is under construction. As the building grows, the height of the floor where material is delivered increases. As construction on a given floor continues, the materials must be delivered to different locations. As the building is framed and floored, construction cranes are employed to lift a wide variety of materials to the proper floor and to a specified location on that floor. After the framing and floor construction are complete, forklifts and elevators are often used to transport finishing materials within the building. Three different types of cranes are used depending upon the height of the building under construction and to some degree on construction practices in certain localities or countries. These include:

- ❑ Track cranes—x, y, z motion.
- ❑ Fixed-position column cranes—r, θ, z motion.
- ❑ Mobile cranes—x, ϕ, θ, z motion.

F.3.1 Crane Projects

In the following subsections, three different crane projects will be introduced. For each project, you will be required to design the crane and then to build a scale model of it. We encourage the design teams to employ LEGO™ components (controller, motor, gears, etc) to develop a working model of the mechanical components. After the model is complete, your team will test it to verify that it meets the design specifications. The criteria used to judge the merits of your team's design, the model and the testing program are given below.

Criteria for Assessment

In assessing performance in the design of the crane and the verification of the design with a model study, the following information developed by each design team will be considered.

1. A design report, which should include:

    - An analysis of all of the structural members in the crane.
    - Design drawings of the crane and its mechanical components.
    - A report describing the rationale for all of the design decisions.

2. Preliminary and final design briefings.
3. Quality of the construction of the model of the crane.
4. Ability of the model to lift and place simulated load.
5. Accuracy of the measurements of the strain and the deflection.
6. Accuracy of the predictions of strain and deflection.
7. Value of the model study in verifying the adequacy of the design of the crane.

Crane Project No. 1

A track crane with x, y z motion is depicted in Fig. F.22. This crane is often used in Eastern Europe to build very large apartment complexes that may be 15 to 20 stories high and 100 or more meters long. These buildings are typically much longer than they are wide; hence the track crane with steel wheels and railroad tracks is suitable for lifting and placing the materials necessary for either steel frame or reinforced concrete construction.

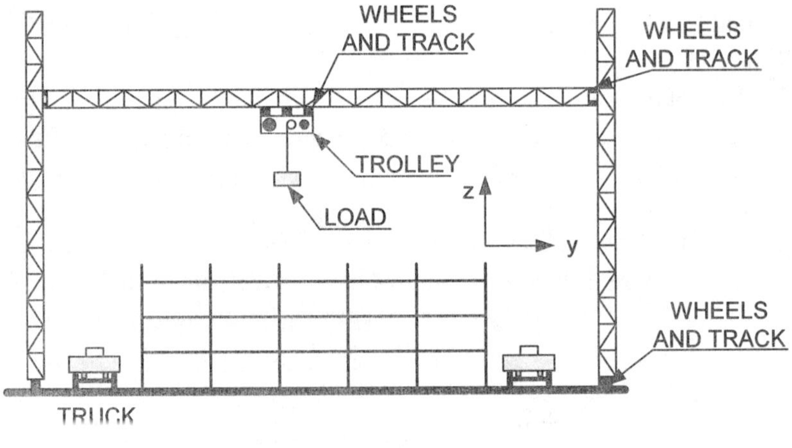

Fig. F.22 A track crane construction uses x, y ,z motion for lifting and placing payload.

The track crane incorporates two parallel tracks that run the length of the proposed building or buildings if they are in line with one another. These parallel tracks enable motion in the x direction. Two supporting columns, one on the front side and the other on the backside of the structure, are mounted on steel wheels and move along the parallel tracks in the x-direction. A cross-truss bridges the span between the two supporting columns. This truss has wheels at each end that engage tracks located on the supporting columns. The truss is moved up and down the support columns from time to time to raise the lifting mechanism above the construction site. (In some installations, the truss beam is fixed at the highest position on the support columns). A trolley moves on rails along the truss beam to provide motion in the y direction. Combining the movement of the trolley with that of the support columns enables placement at any location on the floor under construction. The loads are lifted from trucks positioned adjacent to the buildings with a hoist located on the trolley. The hoist provides the lifting power and positions the payload in the z direction.

The Design Specification

A construction firm has retained your engineering firm to design a track crane to be used in constructing a very large apartment complex consisting of 12 buildings. The buildings are to be arranged in three rows with the four buildings in line in each row. Each building is to be 12 stories high, 300 ft long and 70 ft deep. The buildings will be separated from each other and the street by green spaces each 50 ft wide. Access to the buildings will be possible with two lane streets located to the front and back of each building. The contractor plans to work on one row of buildings and to complete these structures before moving the crane to the next row. The firm plans to work on all four building sites simultaneously although the work will be sequenced to gain efficiency. The contractor has indicated that the crane capacity should be 20 ton with a maximum lifting velocity of 3 ft/s.

Your engineering design firm has been retained to:

1. Design and analyze the rail system for the traveling crane including the rail's foundation.
2. Design and analyze the support columns that provide a provision for adjusting the height of the cross-truss.
3. Design and analyze the cross-truss.
4. Design and analyze the trolley.
5. Design and analyze the hoist system including the gear train driving the hoist drum.
6. Specify the horsepower of the motor for the hoist.

Design Approach

The loads on the parallel rails include the dead weight of the structure and the 20 tons capacity of the hoist. Selection of rails and steel wheels for the support columns should support these loads with an adequate safety factor. The support columns are latticed with a rectangular or square cross section. The angles used it its fabrication should be sufficiently heavy to resist buckling again with an adequate safety factor. The cross-truss is probably the most critical component because its span is significant and it is subjected to bending stresses due to its own weight, the weight of the trolley and the hoist load. The trolley contains the motor gearing and the hoist drum. You should size the power of the electric motor and design a gear drive based on a variable motor speed that ranges from 200 to 1200 RPM. Because of the danger to personnel when cranes or elevators fail, design codes typically specify very high safety factors with 8 to 10 or more commonly required.

Crane Project No. 2

A fixed position column crane with r, θ z motion is depicted in Fig. F.23. This crane is often used in the United States to build very large office buildings that may be 15 to 20 stories high and 40 or more meters long. These buildings are usually smaller in plan view than the large apartment complexes described in the previous project but they are often higher with more floors. A fixed position crane with a long cantilevered truss is suitable for lifting and placing the materials necessary for either steel frame or reinforced concrete construction.

Fig. F.23 The top portion of a fixed column construction crane.

The fixed column crane incorporates a lattice column that is longer than the height of the building that is under construction. Its base is fixed to the ground by embedding clevises for each of its four corners into a concrete foundation. A thrust bearing is located at the top of a column, which supports a horizontal cantilevered truss while enabling it to rotate about the axis of the column. A short vertical column extends from the horizontal cantilevered truss to accommodate the stayed cables that extend in both directions and attach to the horizontal member. These cables aid in reducing the bending moment imposed on the horizontal member due to the payload and the counterweight. A trolley runs along a track that is an integral part of the longer segment of the horizontal cantilevered truss. The counterweight, motor and hoisting mechanism is located on the end of the short segment of the horizontal cantilevered truss.

Positioning the load is accomplished by rotating the horizontal cantilevered truss about the axis of the column (θ) and by running the trolley to some position (r) along the horizontal truss. The hoist positions the load in the z direction.

The Design Specification

A construction firm has retained your engineering firm to design a fixed column crane to be used in constructing a 15-story office building. The building is 40 m wide and 30 m deep. The building is only 3.5 m from a five-lane street. The city commissioners are cooperative and are willing to permit the construction firm to block one lane of the street in front of the office building. The contractor has indicated that the crane capacity should be 10 ton with a lifting velocity of 0.8 m/s. He has not specified a velocity for positioning the load in either the r or θ directions.

Your engineering design firm has been retained to:

1. Locate the position of the fixed column relative to the plan view of the office building.
2. Design the foundation for the fixed column including the connectors.
3. Design and analyze the fixed column.
4. Design and analyze the support column for the stayed cables.
5. Design and analyze the horizontal cantilevered truss.
6. Design and analyze the trolley.
7. Design and analyze the hoist system including the gear train driving the hoist drum.
8. Specify the horsepower of the motor for the hoist.
9. Prepare a plan to erect the fixed column and the horizontal cantilevered truss.

Design Approach

The loads on the fixed column include the dead weight of the structure, the 10-ton payload and the motor, drive mechanism and counter weight. The foundation must be capable of supporting these loads in addition to the bending moment imposed when a payload is lifted and moved. The fixed column is latticed with a rectangular or square cross section. The angles used it its fabrication should be sufficiently heavy to resist buckling with an adequate safety factor. The horizontal cantilevered truss is probably the most critical component because its span is significant and it is subjected to bending stresses due to its own weight, the weight of the trolley, the motor and gearing and the payload. The trolley only contains the hoist drum. You should size the power of the electric motor and design a gear drive based on a variable motor speed that ranges from 200 to 1200 RPM. Because of the danger to personnel when cranes or elevators fail, design codes typically specify very high safety factors with 8 to 10 or more commonly required.

Crane Project No. 3

A crawling crane with x, y, θ, ϕ and z motion is depicted in Fig. F.24. This crane is often used in the United States to build small commercial buildings that are up to four or five stories high. Because the crane can move in either the x or y directions, the length and width of the structure is of less significance. While this type of crane can move from one location to another at a construction site, it is not very mobile. To travel between construction sites, it is loaded on a flat bed truck for transport. A crawling crane with a long boom is suitable for lifting and placing the materials necessary for either wood or steel frame or reinforced concrete construction.

The control of the placement of the payload is accomplished with several different degrees of freedom of motion. The crane is mounted on a track driven frame, which enables it to slowly move about the construction site to positions where it is needed (x, y motion). As is evident in Fig. F.24, the crane can rotate about a central point on the frame permitting the boom to rotate in the θ direction. The boom is tilted with a cable arrangement that extends from one end of the boom to a yoke located above the rear of the cab. The pin about which the boom rotates is shown in Fig. F.25. The drive mechanism used for tilting the boom is independent of the drive for hoisting the payload. Tilting the boom enables the rotation ϕ. The final degree of freedom is the hoist for lifting the payload to a position z. The hoist drum is located in the cab with a cable extending around a pulley located at the tip of the boom. By rotating the hoist drum the payload can be raised or lowered. Placing the payload is accomplished by rotating the cab and tilting the boom.

Fig. F.24 A crawling crane with x, y, θ, ϕ and z motion.

Fig. F.25 The boom rotates about a pin located at the lower front of the cab.

The Design Specification

A rigging firm was engaged in demolishing a relatively large building. In the process, the building collapsed and damaged the boom on one of its large cranes. The firm has retained your engineering office to design a new boom to replace the damaged one. However, the rigging firm wants to increase the length and capacity of the boom. The new boom is to be 100 ft long without the extension. The capacity of the new boom at a tilt angle $\phi = 45°$ is 15-ton. The rigging firm has arranged with a different firm for the repair and upgrade of the mechanism used in hoisting.

Your engineering design firm has been retained to:

1. Design and analyze the boom.
2. Design and analyze the pinned end of the boom.
3. Design and analyze the pulley end of the boom.
4. Specify the cable employed to hoist the payload.
5. Determine the horsepower required to tilt the boom if it is loaded to capacity.
6. Specify the cable to be used in tilting the boom.

Design Approach

The loads on the boom include the dead weight of the structure and cable and the 15-ton payload. The pin and clevis must be capable of supporting these loads. Additional stresses due to a bending moment are imposed when a payload is lifted and moved. The boom is usually latticed with a rectangular or square cross section. The structural elements used in its fabrication should be sufficiently heavy to resist buckling with an adequate safety factor. In addition, the rigging firm has indicated that they would like to transport the boom in two segments each 50 ft long.

In determining the horsepower required to tilt the boom, note the five-pulley arrangement on the yoke shown in Fig. F.24. The rate of change in the angle ϕ is specified as 0.6° /s. Because of the danger to personnel when cranes or elevators fail, design codes typically specify very high safety factors with 8 to 10 or more commonly required.

F.4 COMMUNICATION TOWERS

Cell phones, pagers, television and radio transmissions, and large-scale data transmissions have resulted in the erection of large numbers of communication towers. Drive along an interstate highway and count them on your next long trip. Three designs are common depending on their purpose; however, they all tend to be placed at high elevation to reduce the effect of the terrain on signal transmission. Towers intended for radio and television tend to be very high with high-power transmitters to extend the range of the signal. A single tower may be shared with one or more stations transmitting from it. Cell phone towers are of moderate height and are not shared with competing cell phone companies. Also the transmission power for the cell phone signal is restricted to avoid interference with other signals; consequently, the distance transmitted is severely constrained. Because of these facts, there are a large number of relatively short cell phone towers sprinkled across the U. S.

F.4.1 Radio and Television Transmission Towers

The very high radio and television communication towers usually consist of a latticed column with a small cross section. The loading due to an antenna is negligible compared to the dead weight of the structure. Because the base of this type of tower is so small, cables are used to stabilize the structure. The disadvantage of this approach is that a large footprint is required to anchor the cables at locations well removed from the base of the tower. Because the distance transmitted is so important to television and radio stations these towers are located on the highest real estate near or in the city in which the stations are located. A typical communication tower is depicted in Fig. F.26.

F.4.2 Cell Phone or Short Range Transmission Towers

Because of power limitations placed on cell phone company's transmitters by the Federal Communications Commission (FCC), the distance the signal is transmitted is relatively short. For this reason, the height of the transmission tower for cell phone transmission is usually much less than for radio and television towers. The cell phone companies obtain signal coverage by building many towers distributed strategically over the geographical area, which they service. Of course, the cable stayed tower, illustrated in Fig. F.26, could be used for these shorter towers; however, cell phone towers are often erected in densely populated areas where the cost of real estate is high if it is available in sufficient size. For this reason, it is often more economical to employ a tower design that does not require a large footprint. A common design of such a tower is presented in Fig. F.27.

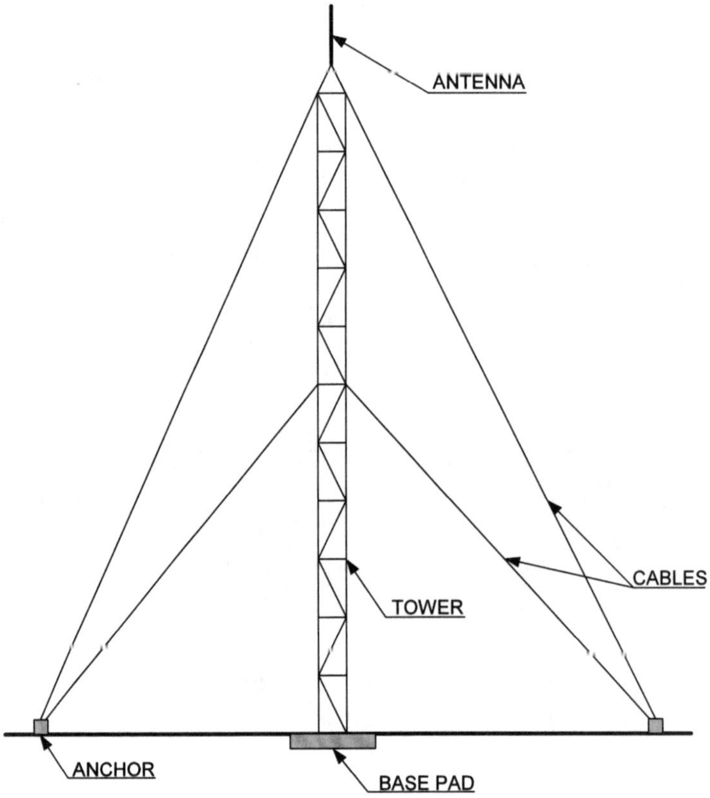

Fig. F.26 A radio or television transmission tower.

Another design of a short-range tower employs a tubular column as shown in Fig. F.28. The tube is embedded in the ground some distance to provide stability. Embedding the tube is accomplished by drilling a hole of sufficient diameter to accommodate the outside diameter of the tube. If the hole is drilled into rock, it will not be lined; however, if it is in soil the hole is usually lined. For moderate height towers, the tube is tapered or stepped, but for short towers tubes with a uniform diameter are employed. When the tube is positioned vertically in the hole, the annular ring that is necessary for clearance for erection is filled with grout.

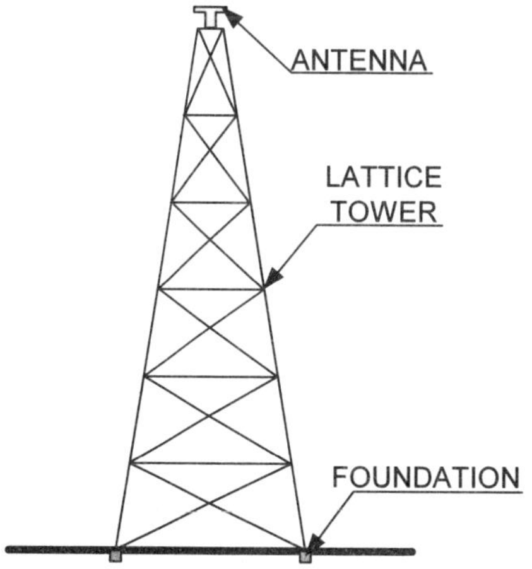

Fig. F.27 A transmission tower for short-range signal transmission in densely populated regions.

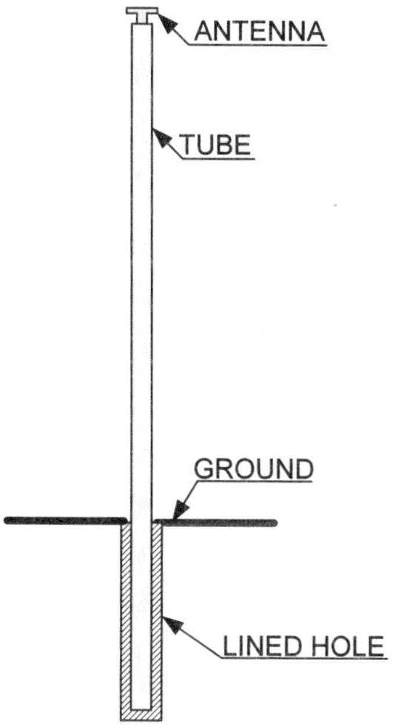

Fig. F.28 The tube tower is embedded to provide stability.

F.4.3 Tower Design Projects

Select one of the three common types of communication towers and prepare a complete design package including drawings, a parts list, material selection and specifications, a detailed analysis and a construction plan. In all cases, consider the weight of the antenna structure to be 300 N. The towers are to be designed to withstand a wind of 150 km/h from any direction. Because the installation is near Chicago, snow and ice accumulations are expected. The height of the towers is to be 120 m for the radio and television transmitter and 30 m for the cell phone transmitter.

REFERENCES

1. Whitney, C. S., Bridges their Art, Science and Evolution, Greenwich House, New York, NY, 1983.
2. Brown, A., Golden Gate: Biography of a Bridge, Doubleday and Co., Garden City, NY, 1965.
3. Spangenburg, R. and D. K. Moser, The Story of America's Bridges, Facts on File, New York, NY, 1991.
4. Salvadori, M. Building: The Fight Against Gravity, Stratford Press, Saddle Brook, NJ, 1979.
5. Billings, H. Bridges, Viking Press, New York, NY, 1966.
6. Bonanos, C., "The Father of Modern Bridges," American Heritage of Invention and Technology, V. 8, No. 1, 1992.
7. Kennon, P. Architecture and You: How to Experience and Enjoy Buildings, Whitney Library of Design, New York, NY, 1978.
8. Moore, F. Understanding Structures, WCB/McGraw-Hill, New York, NY, 1999.

INDEX

EQUATIONS FOR DEFLECTIONS OF SIMPLY SUPPORTED BEAMS

SIMPLY SUPPORTED BEAMS LENGTH, L	SLOPE	DEFLECTION EQUATIONS
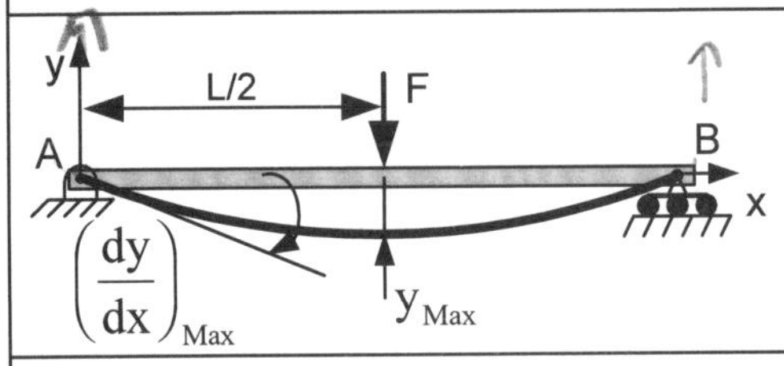	$\left(\frac{dy}{dx}\right)_{Max} = \frac{-FL^2}{16EI_z}$	$y = \frac{-Fx}{48EI_z}(3L^2 - 4x^2)$ $0 \le x \le L/2$ $y_{Max} = \frac{-FL^3}{48EI_z}$
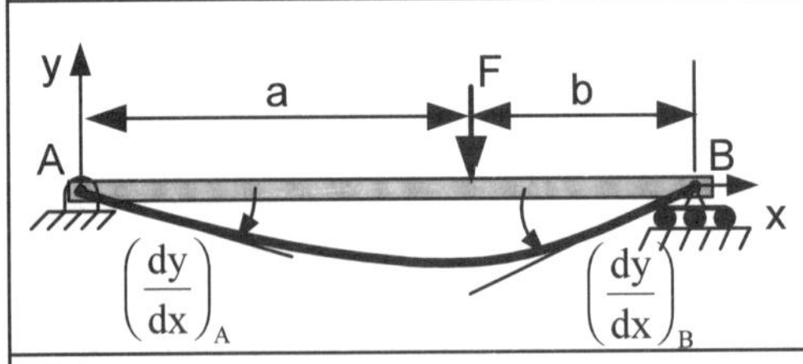	$\left(\frac{dy}{dx}\right)_A = \frac{-Fab(L+b)}{6EI_zL}$ $\left(\frac{dy}{dx}\right)_B = \frac{Fab(L+a)}{6EI_zL}$	$y = \frac{-Fbx}{6EI_zL}(L^2 - b^2 - x^2)$ $0 \le x \le a$ $y_{x=a} = \frac{-Fba}{6EI_zL}(L^2 - b^2 - a^2)$
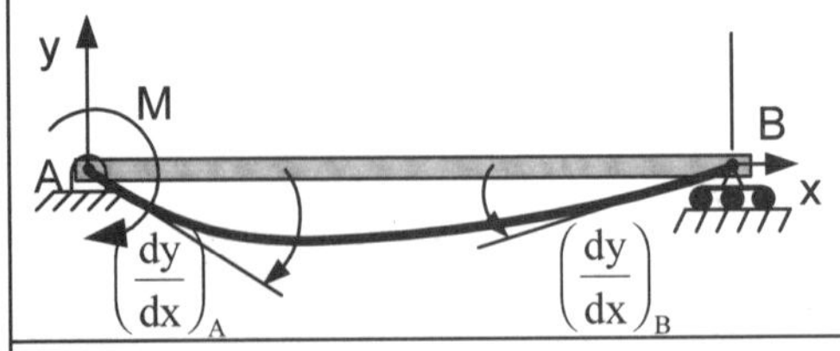	$\left(\frac{dy}{dx}\right)_A = -\frac{ML}{3EI_z}$ $\left(\frac{dy}{dx}\right)_B = \frac{ML}{6EI_z}$	$y = \frac{-Mx}{6EI_zL}(x^2 - 3Lx + 2L^2)$ $y_{Max} = \frac{-ML^2}{\sqrt{243}EI_z}$
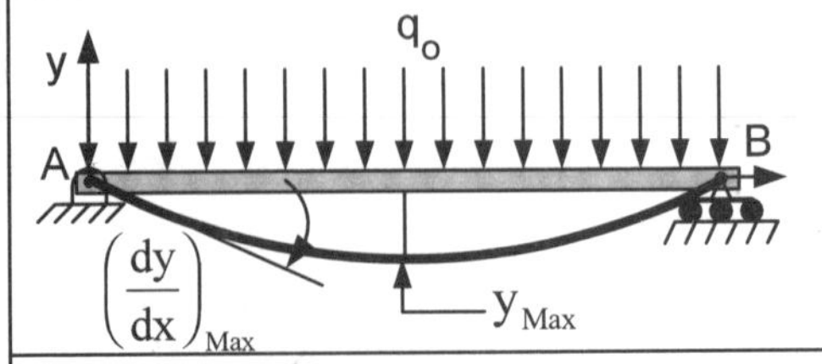	$\left(\frac{dy}{dx}\right)_{Max} = -\frac{q_0L^3}{24EI_z}$	$y = \frac{-q_0x}{24EI_z}(x^3 - 2Lx^2 + L^3)$ $y_{Max} = \frac{-5q_0L^4}{384EI_z}$
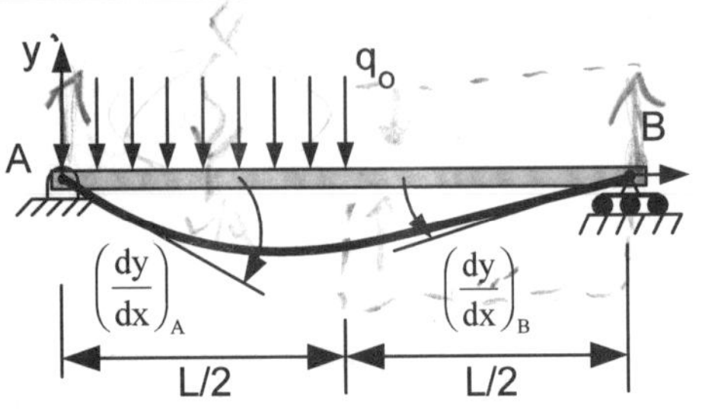	$\left(\frac{dy}{dx}\right)_A = -\frac{3q_0L^3}{128EI_z}$ $\left(\frac{dy}{dx}\right)_B = \frac{7q_0L^3}{384EI_z}$	$y = \frac{-q_0x}{384EI_z}(16x^3 - 24Lx^2 + 9L^3)$ $0 \le x \le L/2$ $y = \frac{-q_0L}{384EI_z}(8x^3 - 24Lx^2 + 17L^2x - L^3)$ $L/2 \le x \le L$ $y_{Max} = \frac{-6.563 \times 10^{-3} q_0L^4}{EI_z}$ at $x = 0.4598L$
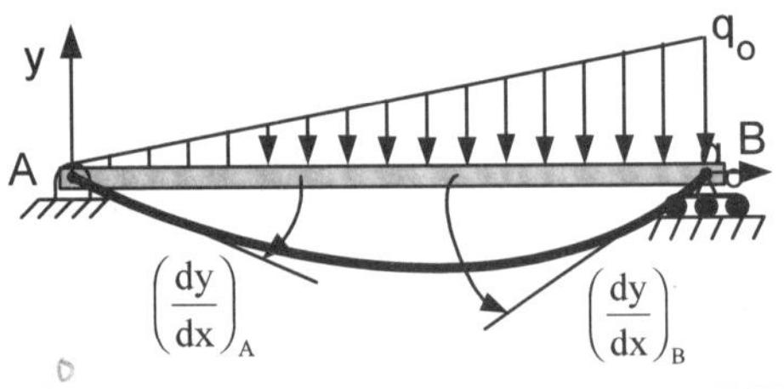	$\left(\frac{dy}{dx}\right)_A = \frac{-7q_0L^3}{360EI_z}$ $\left(\frac{dy}{dx}\right)_B = \frac{q_0L^3}{45EI_z}$	$y = \frac{-q_0x}{360EI_zL}(3x^4 - 10L^2x^2 + 7L^4)$ $y_{Max} = \frac{-6.52 \times 10^{-3} q_0L^4}{EI_z}$ at $x = 0.5193$